Do More

McGraw-Hill Connect Student Quick Tips for Blackboard Users

Use this McGraw-Hill Connect Student Quick Tips for Blackboard Users guide for a quick and easy start with your assignments within McGraw-Hill Connect or ConnectPlus. You'll get valuable tips on doing assignments, accessing resources, and support.

"Register Now" or "Sign In"

TIP: To start using Connect assignments within Blackboard, you will be asked to "Register Now" or "Sign In" the first time you click on a Connect assignment. Consider these points as you make your selection:

- If this is your first experience with a McGraw-Hill Connect assignment in Blackboard, select "Register Now" and follow the prompts to establish an account

- If this is not your first experience with a McGraw-Hill Connect assignment, simply select "Sign In" and enter the email address and password that you used for previous McGraw-Hill Connect assignments

- Enter the Connect Access Code purchased with your new textbook or choose "Buy Online" to purchase access online.

TIP: If you are creating a new account with McGraw-Hill, please choose your Security Question and Answer carefully. We will ask you for this information if you forget your password.

TIP: If you do not have an access code, or have not yet secured your tuition funds, you can click "Free Trial" during registration. This trial will provide temporary Connect access (typically three weeks) and will remind you to purchase online access before the end of your trial.

Home (Assignments)

TIP: If you are unable to begin an assignment, verify the following:

- The assignment is available (check start dates and due dates)

- You have not exceeded the maximum number of attempts for the assignment

- You have not achieved a score of 100%

NOTE: If an assignment contains questions that require manual grading, you can attempt to complete the assignment again if your instructor has enabled multiple attempts; however, you won't receive credit for the manually graded questions until the instructor reviews and enters a grade.

Continued: Home (Assignments)

TIP: If you are unable to complete your assignment in one sitting, utilize the "*Save & Exit*" button to save your work and complete it at a later time. Once you have completed your assignment, utilize the "*Submit*" button in order for your assignment to be graded.

TIP: There may be limitations on your assignment, based on your instructor's settings. You may encounter the following limitations when working on your assignment(s):

- Ability to "Print" an assignment

- Once you begin a timed assignment, the timer will not stop

Library

TIP: For shortcuts to various resources, go to the **My Connect Section** under the McGraw-Hill Higher Education link in the "Tools" area.

- If you purchased ConnectPlus, you will see an eBook link, which can also be accessed from the course section information widget of the "Home" tab

- Recorded lectures can be accessed if your instructor is using Tegrity Campus to capture lectures. You may also access recorded lectures when beginning an assignment by clicking on the projector icon in the navigation bar

- Many McGraw-Hill textbooks offer additional resources such as narrated slides and additional problem sets, which are accessible via the "Student Resources" link

Do More

Grades

TIP: Your grades and results are available in the **Grade Book** immediately.

NOTE: Your instructor has the ability to limit the amount of information (e.g. questions, answers, scores) you can view for each submitted assignment

Need More Help with Connect Assignments?

CONTACT US ONLINE:

Visit us at:

www.mcgrawhillconnect.com/support

Browse our support materials including tutorial videos and searchable knowledge base. If you cannot find an answer to your question, click on Contact Us to send us an email.

GIVE US A CALL

Call us at:

1-800-331-5094

Our live support is available:
Mon-Thurs: 8 am – 11 pm CT
Friday: 8 am – 6 pm CT
Sunday: 6 pm – 11 pm CT

Tenth Edition

Biology

Kenneth A. Mason
University of Iowa

Jonathan B. Losos
Harvard University

Susan R. Singer
Carleton College

based on the work of

Peter H. Raven
President Emeritus, Missouri Botanical Garden;
George Engelmann Professor of Botany Emeritus,
Washington University

George B. Johnson
Professor Emeritus of Biology, Washington University

Biology 121 & 122
Special Edition for Richard Daley College

2 3 4 5 6 7 8 9 0 FRD FRD 16 15 14

ISBN-13: 978-1-259-14611-4
ISBN-10: 1-259-14611-1

Learning Solutions Consultant: Bridget Hannenberg
Project Manager: Mark Bodensteiner
Cover Photo Credits: © Royalty-Free/CORBIS, © Design Pics/PunchStock, and Patrick Robinson

Brief Contents

About the Authors

Pictured left to right: Susan Rundell Singer, Jonathan Losos, Kenneth Mason

Kenneth Mason is a lecturer at the University of Iowa where he teaches introductory biology. He was formerly at Purdue University where for 6 years he was responsible for the largest introductory biology course on campus and collaborated with chemistry and physics faculty on an innovative new course supported by the National Science Foundation that combined biology, chemistry, and physics. Prior to Purdue, he was on the faculty at the University of Kansas for 11 years, where he did research on the genetics of pigmentation in amphibians, publishing both original work and reviews on the topic. While there he taught a variety of courses, was involved in curricular issues, and wrote the lab manual for an upper division genetics laboratory course. His latest move to the University of Iowa was precipitated by his wife's being named president of the University of Iowa.

Jonathan Losos is the Monique and Philip Lehner Professor for the Study of Latin America in the Department of Organismic and Evolutionary Biology and curator of herpetology at the Museum of Comparative Zoology at Harvard University. Losos's research has focused on studying patterns of adaptive radiation and evolutionary diversification in lizards. He is the recipient of several awards, including the prestigious Theodosius Dobzhansky and David Starr Jordan Prizes, the Edward Osborne Wilson Naturalist Award, and the Daniel Giraud Elliot Medal from the National Academy of Sciences. Losos has published more than 100 scientific articles.

Susan Rundell Singer is the Laurence McKinley Gould Professor of Natural Sciences in the department of biology at Carleton College in Northfield, Minnesota, where she has taught introductory biology, plant biology, genetics, and plant development for 26 years. Her research focuses on the development and evolution of flowering plants and genomics learning. Singer has authored numerous scientific publications on plant development and co-authored education reports including *Vision and Change* and "America's Lab Report." She received the American Society of Plant Biology's Excellence in Teaching Award, the Botanical Society's Bessey Award, is a AAAS fellow, served on the National Academies Board on Science Education, and chaired several National Research Council study committees including the committee that produced *Discipline-Based Education Research*.

The Learning Continues in the Digital Environment

The digital offerings for the study of biology have become a key component of both instructional and learning environments. In response to this, the author team welcomes Dr. Ian Quitadamo as Lead Digital Author for *Biology*, tenth edition. As Lead Digital Author, Ian oversaw the development of digital assessment tools in Connect. Ian's background makes him a unique and valuable addition to the tenth edition of *Biology*.

Ian Quitadamo Ian Quitadamo is an Associate Professor with a dual appointment in Biological Sciences and Science Education at Central Washington University in Ellensburg, WA. He teaches introductory and majors biology courses and cell biology, genetics, and biotechnology as well  as science teaching methods courses for future science teachers and interdisciplinary content courses in alternative energy and sustainability. Dr. Quitadamo was educated at Washington State University and holds a Bachelor's degree in biology, Master's degree in genetics and cell biology, and an interdisciplinary Ph.D. in science, education, and technology. Previously a researcher of tumor angiogenesis, he now investigates critical thinking and has published numerous studies of factors that affect student critical thinking performance. He has received the Crystal Apple award for teaching excellence, led various initiatives in critical thinking and assessment, and is active in training future and currently practicing science teachers. He served as a co-author on *Biology*, eleventh edition, by Mader and Windelspecht, copyright 2013, and is the lead digital author for *Biology*, third edition by Brooker, copyright 2014, both published by McGraw-Hill.

Committed to Excellence

With the release of the tenth edition, Raven & Johnson's *Biology* enters a new era. This edition provides an unmatched comprehensive text fully integrated with state-of-the-art digital resources. The material in the text is organized around learning outcomes keyed to major biological concepts, which provide a framework for understanding the ever-expanding universe of biological knowledge. An inquiry-based approach with robust, adaptive tools for discovery and assessment in both text and digital resources provide the intellectual challenge needed to promote student critical thinking and ensure academic success. A major strength of this hallmark tenth edition is assessment across multiple levels of Bloom's taxonomy that develops critical thinking and problem solving skill in addition to comprehensive factual knowledge. McGraw-Hill's Connect® platform offers a powerful suite of online tools including LearnSmart™ that adapts to student needs over time. The adaptive learning system helps students learn faster, study efficiently, and retain more knowledge of key concepts.

The tenth edition continues our tradition of providing the student with clear learning paths that emphasize data analysis and quantitative reasoning. Embedded eBook resources allow just-in-time exploration of major themes like evolution from directly within the eBook. Additional embedded eBook resources link to asides that delve more deeply into quantitative aspects.

The author team is experienced and fully committed to student learning and producing the best possible text for both students and faculty. Lead author Kenneth Mason (University of Iowa) has taught majors biology for more than 20 years at three major public universities. Jonathan Losos (Harvard University), a leading evolutionary biology researcher, has taught both undergraduate and graduate courses in biology for 20 years. Susan Rundell Singer (Carleton College) is a 26-year veteran science educator deeply involved in science education policy on a national level. As a team, we continually strive to improve the text by integrating the latest cognitive and best practices research with methods that are known to positively affect learning. We have multiple features that are focused on scientific inquiry, including an increased quantitative emphasis in the Scientific Thinking features. We continue to use the concise, accessible, and engaging writing style of past editions while maintaining the clear emphasis on evolution and scientific inquiry that have made this a leading textbook of choice for majors biology students. Our emphasis on evolution combined with integrated cell and molecular biology and genomics offers our readers a student-friendly text that is modern and well balanced.

The tenth edition continues to employ the aesthetically stunning art program that the Raven and Johnson *Biology* text is known for. Complex topics are represented clearly and succinctly, helping students to build the mental models needed to understanding biology.

Insights into the diversity of life that are provided by molecular tools have led to a reorganization of these topics in the tenth edition. This entire unit reflects the most current research on eukaryotic phylogenies, blending molecular, morphological, and development viewpoints. Nuclear reprogramming in stem cells, gene expression, and the importance of small RNAs in gene regulation continue to shape our treatment of these topics. These are just a few examples of the many changes in the tenth edition of *Biology* that provide students with scientifically accurate context, historical perspective, and relevant supporting details essential to a modern understanding of life science.

As the pace of scientific discovery continues to provide new insights into the foundation of life on Earth, our author team will continue to use every means possible to ensure students are as prepared as possible to engage in biological topics. Our goal now, as it has always been, is to ensure your success.

Our Consistent Themes

It is important to have consistent themes that organize and unify a text. A number of themes are used throughout the book to unify the broad-ranging material that makes up modern biology. This begins with the primary goal of this textbook to provide a comprehensive understanding of evolutionary theory and the scientific basis for this view. We use an experimental framework combining both historical and contemporary research examples to help students appreciate the progressive and integrated nature of science.

Biology Is Based on an Understanding of Evolution

When Peter Raven and George Johnson began work on *Biology* in 1982 they set out to write a text that presented biology the way they taught in their classrooms—as the product of evolution. We bear in mind always that all biology "only makes sense in the light of evolution"; so this text is enhanced by a consistent evolutionary theme that is woven throughout the text, and we have enhanced this theme in the tenth edition.

The enhanced evolutionary thread can be found in obvious examples such as the two chapters on molecular evolution, but can also be seen throughout the text. As each section considers the current state of knowledge, the "what" of biological phenomena, they also consider how each system may have arisen by evolution, the "where it came from" of biological phenomena.

We added an explicit phylogenetic perspective to the understanding of animal form and function. This is most obvious in the numerous figures containing phylogenies in the form and function chapters. The diversity material is supported by the most up-to-date approach to phylogenies of both animals and plants. Together these current approaches add even more evolutionary support to a text that set the standard for the integration of evolution in biology. Our approach allows evolution to be dealt with in the context in which it is relevant. The material throughout this book is considered not only in terms of present structure and function, but how that structure and function may have arisen via evolution by natural selection.

The emphasis on evolution is expanded in the eBook. Because a textbook limits content to a specific length, examples or additional information related to evolution cannot always be included in the printed book. The digital environment lifts these restrictions and has allowed us the opportunity to include interesting and instructional evolution material in the eBook. The topics that are supported by additional examples and information on the evolutionary aspects of a concept are highlighted with the inclusion of an "evolution" icon in the text. This icon is associated with a link in the eBook that reveals this additional material.

Biology Uses the Methods of Scientific Inquiry

Another unifying theme within the text is that knowledge arises from experimental work that moves us progressively forward. The use of historical and experimental approaches throughout allow the student not only to see where the field is now, but more importantly, how we arrived here. The incredible expansion of knowledge in biology has created challenges for authors in deciding what content to keep, and to what level an introductory text should strive. We have tried to keep as much historical context as possible and to provide this within an experimental framework consistently throughout the text.

We use a variety of approaches to expose the student to scientific inquiry. We use our Scientific Thinking figures to walk through an experiment and its implications. These figures always use material that is relevant to the story being told. Data are also provided throughout the text, and our new **Data Analysis questions** ask students to interpret these data. Students are also provided with **Inquiry questions** to stimulate critical thinking about the material throughout the book. The Data Analysis questions deal directly with data in figures or the text, while the Inquiry questions are more conceptual. This combination will allow the student experience in interpreting data, and lead the student to question the material in the text as well. Embedded eBook resources allow just-in-time exploration of quantitative aspects of the science. Quantitative Asides present in the eBook are indicated with a "quantitative" icon in the text. This icon in the eBook links to

 asides that delve more deeply into quantitative aspects of the topic under discussion.

Biology Is an Integrative Science

The explosion of molecular information has reverberated throughout all areas of biological study. Scientists are increasingly able to describe complicated processes in terms of the interaction of specific molecules, and this knowledge of life at the molecular level has illuminated relationships that were previously unknown. Using this cutting-edge information, we more strongly connect the different areas of biology in this edition.

One example of this integration concerns the structure and function of biological molecules—an emphasis of modern biology. This edition brings that focus to the entire book, using this as a theme to weave together the different aspects of content material with a modern perspective. Given the enormous amount of information that has accumulated in recent years, this emphasis on structure and function provides a necessary thread integrating these new perspectives into the fabric of the traditional biology text.

Although all current biology texts have added a genomics chapter, our text was one of the first to do so. This chapter has been updated, and we have an additional chapter on the evolution of genomes. More importantly, the results from the analysis of genomes and the proteomes they encode are presented throughout the book wherever this information is relevant. This allows a more modern perspective throughout the book rather than limiting it to a few chapters. Examples, for instance, can be found in the diversity chapters, where classification of some organisms were updated based on new findings revealed by molecular techniques.

This systems approach to biology also shows up at the level of chapter organization. We introduce genomes in the genetics section in the context of learning about DNA and genomics. We then come back to this topic with an entire chapter at the end of the evolution unit where we look at the evolution of genomes, followed by a chapter on the evolution of development, which leads into our unit on the diversity of organisms.

We're excited about the tenth edition of this quality textbook providing a learning path for a new generation of students. All of us have extensive experience teaching undergraduate biology, and we've used this knowledge as a guide in producing a text that is up to date, beautifully illustrated, and pedagogically sound for the student. We've also worked to provide clear explicit learning outcomes, and more closely integrate the text with its media support materials to provide instructors with an excellent complement to their teaching.

Ken Mason, Jonathan Losos, Susan Rundell Singer

Cutting Edge Science

Changes to the Tenth Edition

Part I: The Molecular Basis of Life

The material in this section does not change much with time. However, we have updated it to make it more friendly to the student. The Learning Outcomes have been analyzed and rewritten both for clarity and to increase linkage between Learning Outcomes and assessment in both the end-of-chapter material and online content.

In chapter 3, the material on nucleic acids has been rewritten to make it more modern. Our view of the role of RNA in particular has changed hugely in the last decade, and this introduction to these molecules has been rewritten to reflect this. Also in chapter 3 is the first Evolutionary Aside for the eBook.

Part II: Biology of the Cell

The Learning Outcomes have been analyzed and rewritten both for clarity and to increase linkage between Learning Outcomes and assessment in both end-of-chapter material and online content. Data Analysis questions were added, and some Evolutionary Aside and Quantitative Asides for the eBook were also included.

Chapter 4—New material on prokaryotic cytoskeleton was added. Material on the nuclear pore was updated and a new figure added to show our current view of this structure. The role of chromatin structure in gene expression is introduced earlier, and material on the ER and Golgi has been updated to present the most current view of these important organelles. The material on cell-to-cell connections has been updated and also given a more evolutionary perspective.

Chapter 5—Material on lipid rafts was reconsidered, and material on sphingolipids was added. These important lipids are often ignored, despite their importance in the nervous system of vertebrates. This material also includes a new figure of sphingolipids.

Chapter 7—The introduction to glycolysis was rewritten for clarity. This includes better integration of text and figures. The Krebs cycle overview figure was simplified, as was the explanatory text for greater clarity. The section on theoretical energy yield from chemiosmosis was completely rewritten to bring it up to the view of modern chemistry.

Chapter 9—The discussion of GPCR was updated to take into account new genetic data on their distribution. A new section on small ras-like G proteins was added, including a new figure showing their action. This both illustrates their importance in the control of cell division, and clarifies their connection to signaling by growth factors.

Chapter 10—Content on chromosome structure was updated and material on the behavior of chromosomes was rewritten for clarity. A figure from chapter 9 on role of growth factors was combined with a figure from chapter 10 for greater clarity and to reduce redundancy.

Part III: Genetic and Molecular Biology

The overall organization of this section remains the same. We have retained the split of transmission genetics into two chapters as it has proved successful for students.

Content changes in the molecular genetics portion of this section continue to update material that is the most rapidly changing in the entire book. We also continue to refine the idea that RNA plays a much greater role now than appreciated in the past. The more modern view of RNA continues to be under appreciated in introductory textbooks. New material continues to be put into historical context for greater student understanding. The Learning Outcomes have been analyzed and rewritten both for clarity and to increase linkage between learning outcomes and assessment in both the end-of-chapter material and online content. Data Analysis questions were added, and some Evolutionary Asides and Quantitative Asides for the eBook were also included.

Chapter 11—The behavior of chromosomes during meiosis was rewritten for clarity. This subject is one that causes great confusion for students, and two graphics—one figure and one in-text graphic—were updated to complement the new textual discussion. This section is now much easier for students to both appreciate the complex behavior of meiotic chromosomes, but also the molecular basis for this behavior.

Chapter 15—The definition of genes as one-gene/one-polypeptide was revised for clarity. The complexity of eukaryotic initiation is given greater appreciation. The idea of promoter-proximal pausing is introduced. This allows for a clearer view by students of the nature of the extensive transcription observed by whole-genome scans.

Chapter 16—Introductory material on the control of gene expression has been rewritten to reflect recent data and a more modern view of this control. Some material on DNA binding proteins was rewritten for clarity. The section on posttranscriptional control has been rewritten again as it is one of the most rapidly changing areas. This material is now on stronger conceptual ground.

Chapter 17—The chapter has been reorganized and revised to focus on biological concepts related to biotechnology, rather than using techniques as the organizational structure. Polymerase chain reaction is now clearly linked to student's prior learning about DNA replication. DNA sequencing was moved to chapter 18, which focuses on genomes so sequencing of single genes to entire genomes is explained in a coherent and cohesive way. Instead of a generic section on DNA analysis, a section on "Storing and Sorting DNA Fragments" has been introduced, followed by a section titled "Analyzing and Creating DNA Differences." We have revised the DNA fingerprinting section to include short tandem repeats. The applications sections have been updated to include, for example, sections on marker assisted breeding and transgenic salmon.

Chapter 18—A comprehensive approach to sequencing at all scales has been developed to frame the genomics chapter. A "Genes to Proteins" section also scales from individual genes and proteins to genomes and proteins. The section includes text and art explaining the yeast two-hybrid assay. A new section on comparing genomes has been added that provides the foundation for the comparative genomics in the Genome Evolution chapter placed after the principles of evolution. Text and artwork exploring genomic insights into human migration are now integrated into chapter 18.

Chapter 19—The material on nuclear reprogramming was rewritten for both clarity and to incorporate new data in this exciting area. New information on induced pluripotent stem cells is presented along with a better historical timeline of this topic. This is both of general interest to students, and is a source of controversy and misinformation. All material on plant development that was not used for direct comparisons to animals was removed or moved to chapter 41.

Part IV: Evolution

The evolution chapters were updated with new examples. A strong emphasis on the role of experimental approaches to studying evolutionary phenomena has been maintained and enhanced.

Chapter 20—This chapter has been reorganized to consolidate the discussion of selection acting on discrete and continuously distributed populations, before discussing the interaction among different evolutionary forces, which now is discussed toward the end of the chapter.

Chapter 21—The examples in chapter 21 have been updated in several important ways. First, research published in 2012 indicates that studies on selection on peppered moths by Kettlewell were completely correct in showing that bird predation favors those moths that contrasted their background. This section has been revised to clarify this previously controversial point. In addition, new data points on the decrease in the prevalence of black moths in recent years have been added, continuing to demonstrate that as air pollution has been alleviated, peppered moths are increasing in frequency. Material on dating the fossil record was moved to chapter 26. The discussion of the difference between "theory" and "hypothesis" in scientific terminology has been expanded.

Chapter 22—The discussion of hybrid inviability was expanded. The discussion of character displacement was enhanced with a detailed case study of stickleback fishes in northwestern lakes. The discussion of speciation and extinction through time has been moved to chapter 26 and chapter 59.

Chapter 23—Terminology concerning cladistic analysis and phylogenetic systematics was clarified. The example of using phylogenetic information to understand the spread of HIV from monkeys and apes to humans has been updated to reflect new discoveries.

Chapter 24—The increased number of sequenced genomes allowed us to increase the emphasis on comparative genomics informing our understanding of evolution, as represented in the new figure 24.1. The entire chapter was reorganized to present genome evolution in a conceptual rather than topical way, as reflected in the new section heads. New findings on the rapid rate of plant genome evolution are analyzed, as are the implications of additional primate sequences. A new section on how comparative genomics informs conservation biology was added.

Chapter 25—The seven sections in the previous edition have been consolidated into four sections focusing on core concepts in the evolution of development. The fully reorganized chapter now provides a more coherent and current overview of the maturing field of evolution of development. The chapter now emphasizes evolution of developmental patterns, how single-gene changes can alter form, and different ways to evolve the same structure. A new Scientific Thinking figure guides students through the research on how *Tbx4* and *Tbx 5* were co-opted for vertebrate limb development (figure 25.6). The role of *Hox* genes in digit development has been added, along with a supporting figure (figure 25.7). Our case study on the evolution of the eye has been updated, informed by new data on jellyfish and exemplified by the addition of figure 25.15.

Part V: Diversity of Life on Earth

You will notice some significant reorganization of material in Part V from the ninth edition.

Chapter 26—This is a new chapter for our tenth edition that sets the stage for the unit on Diversity of Life on Earth. This chapter focuses on the origins and diversity of life, beginning with an introduction to deep time. Understanding deep time is essential for student understanding of the origins and evidence for early life. "Earth's Changing Systems" presents our understanding of how Earth system changes have affected life and how life has affected Earth systems. The chapter then investigates the major innovations in the evolution of life, a springboard for the rest of the unit. New artwork supports student understanding of deep time and the changes that have occurred in Earth systems and life forms over geological time.

Chapter 27—New material has been added on the 2009 H1N1 pandemic. Material on bacteriophage life cycles was rewritten, and now is used as an example of a simple virus life cycle.

Chapter 28—Material on the origin of life that opened this chapter in the previous edition was moved to chapter 26 where all such material has been consolidated. A new introduction was written that looks at the history of the study of microbiology in brief.

Chapter 29—Reorganization of this chapter was guided by the newest phylogenies for the protists. The green algae presentation, including life cycles, was moved from the plant diversity chapter to the protist chapter in this edition to provide greater clarity about the algae in general for students.

Chapters 30 and 31—The Green Plant chapter in the ninth edition has been replaced with a chapter on Seedless Plants and a chapter on Seed Plants. This allowed us to move the information on the diversity of fruit and flower structure from the plant unit to the diversity unit where it is more appropriate. This approach reduces redundancy between the two units and keeps students focused on the most relevant concepts for understanding plant diversity.

Chapters 33–35—These chapters have been reorganized to reflect current understanding of phylogenetic relationships. In particular chapter 33 now discusses an overview of animal diversity and evolution, as well as the most basal members of animal phylogeny. Chapter 34 covers protostomes and chapter 35 covers deuterostomes.

Part VI: Plant Form and Function

This unit was reorganized at the chapter level in this edition. The Vegetative Plant Development chapter in the ninth edition was eliminated. Plant reproduction and development were consolidated in a single, coherent chapter 41. Information on the diversity of flowers and fruit was modified and integrated into the unit on diversity.

Chapter 37—Figure 37.2 was modified for clarity. To help students better understand mass flow, figure 37.19 was expanded to pull out details about critical events at both sources and sinks.

Chapter 41—A substantial reorganization of this chapter resulted in the incorporation of embryo development and germination into this chapter, following the section on pollination. To streamline the chapter, several figures addressing determination for flowering and the three-dimensional axes of embryo development were eliminated. The restructuring maintains student focus on what is truly core in understanding plant reproduction and development at the level of introductory biology.

Part VII: Animal Form and Function

The organizational changes made in the ninth edition have been maintained. This gives the student a system-level organization that is enhanced by the presentation of material that is both cellular and molecular in focus, and that puts this material into an evolutionary context. The Learning Outcomes have been analyzed and rewritten both for clarity and to increase linkage between Learning Outcomes and assessment in both the end-of-chapter material and online content. Data Analysis questions were added, and some Evolutionary Asides and Quantitative Asides for the eBook were also included.

Chapter 43—The material on the generation of a resting potential was rewritten for clarity. These changes emphasize membrane permeability and the role of ion channels. This provides a strong framework to understand how ion channels also function in graded and action potentials.

Chapter 50—This chapter was reorganized to make a more logical flow of topics. The section on nitrogenous wastes was moved up from section 4 to section 2. This places information on nitrogenous wastes immediately after the concept of osmoregulation, and consolidates all of the material on how various animals achieve this.

Chapter 51—The introduction and the material on innate immunity has been rewritten for clarity and to emphasize the connections between innate and adaptive immunity.

Chapter 52—The material on the development of the follicle has been updated to reflect a more accurate description of developmental timing.

Part VIII: Ecology and Behavior

This unit is rich in eBook Evolutionary Asides, for example, a number of case studies of the evolutionary significance of animal behavior are presented in chapter 54. In chapter 59, eBook Evolutionary Asides have been included exploring extinction through time, the evolutionary significance of biological "hot spots," and the evolutionary response of populations to overfishing. Befitting the nature of ecological science, the chapters are now also replete with Data Analysis questions accompanying the many graphical illustrations.

Chapter 55—The information on human population growth was updated using current statistics.

Chapter 56—The discussion of the definition of a biological community was revised.

Chapter 58—The information on human impacts on the environment and global warming was updated using the most current information available. New material discussing ocean acidification was added.

Chapter 59—Chapter 59 considers conservation biology, emphasizing the causes of species endangerment and what can be done. The information about species extinctions, including mass extinction (moved from chapter 22), was updated.

Committed to Preparing Students for the Future

Understand Biology With the Help of . . .

Integrated Learning Outcomes

Each section begins with specific Learning Outcomes that represent each major concept. At the end of each section, the Learning Outcomes Review serves as a check to help students confirm their understanding of the concepts in that section. Questions at the end of the Learning Outcomes Review ask students to think critically about what they have read.

> Any opportunity to identify "learning outcomes" is a welcome addition; we are forced more and more to identify these in learning assessments. I would use these as a guide for students to understand the minimum material they are expected to learn from each section.
>
> *Michael Lentz*
> *University of North Florida*

21.1 *The Beaks of Darwin's Finches: Evidence of Natural Selection*

Learning Outcomes

1. Describe how the species of Darwin's finches have adapted to feed in different ways.
2. Explain how climatic variation drives evolutionary change in the medium ground finch.

Upon Darwin's return to England, ornithologist John Gould informed Darwin that his collection was in fact a closely related group of distinct species, all similar to one another except for their beaks. In all, 14 species are now recognized.

Galápagos finches exhibit variation related to food gathering

The diversity of Darwin's finches is illustrated in figure 21.1. The ground finches feed on seeds that they crush in their powerful beaks; species with smaller and narrower beaks, such as the warbler finch, eat insects. Other species include fruit and bud eaters, and species that feed on cactus fruits and the insects they attract; some populations of the sharp-beaked ground finch even include "vampires" that sometimes creep up on seabirds and use their sharp beaks to pierce the seabirds' skin and drink their blood. Perhaps most remarkable are the tool users, woodpecker finches that pick up a twig, cactus spine, or leaf stalk, trim it into shape with their beaks, and then poke it into dead branches to pry out grubs.

The correspondence between the beaks of the finch species and their food source suggested to Darwin that natural selection had shaped them. In *The Voyage of the Beagle*, Darwin wrote, "Seeing this gradation and diversity of structure in one small, intimately related group of birds, one might really fancy that from an original paucity of birds in this archipelago, one species has been taken and modified for different ends."

21.3 *Artificial Selection: Human-Initiated Change*

Learning Outcomes

1. Contrast the processes of artificial and natural selection.
2. Explain what artificial selection demonstrates about the power of natural selection.

[...] eceding chapter, a variety of processes [...] change. Most evolutionary biologists, [...] win's thinking that natural selection is [...] onsible for evolution. Although we can[...] me, modern-day evidence allows us to [...] w evolution proceeds and confirms the [...] n as an agent of evolutionary change. [...] n both the field and the laboratory and [...] man-altered situations.
[...] re a classic example of evolution by [...] he visited the Galápagos Islands off [...] 1835, Darwin collected 31 specimens [...] ands. Darwin, not an expert on birds, [...] he specimens, believing by examining [...] ction contained wrens, "gross-beaks,"

Woodpecker finch (*Cactospiza pallida*)

Large ground finch (*Geospiza magnirostris*)

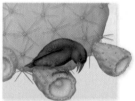
Cactus finch (*Geospiza scandens*)

Warbler finch (*Certhidea olivacea*)

Vegetarian tree finch (*Platyspiza crassirostris*)

Figure 21.1 Darwin's finches. These species show differences in beaks and feeding habits among Darwin's finches. This diversity arose when an ancestral finch colonized the islands and diversified into habitats lacking other types of small birds. The beaks of several species resemble those of different families of birds on the mainland. For example, the warbler finch has a beak very similar t[...] related.

Learning Outcomes Review 21.3

In artificial selection, humans choose which plants or animals to mate in an attempt to conserve desirable traits. Rapid and substantial results can be obtained over a very short time, often in a few generations. From this we can see that natural selection is capable of producing major evolutionary change.

■ *In what circumstances might artificial selection fail to produce a desired change?*

The Learning Continues Online

The questions in Connect are tagged to the Learning Outcomes in the text so that the online assignments and tests can be more closely correlated with the material in the textbook. The online eBook in McGraw-Hill ConnectPlus™ provides students with clear understanding of concepts through a media-rich experience. Embedded animations bring key concepts to life. Also, the eBook provides an interactive experience with the Learning Outcome Review questions.

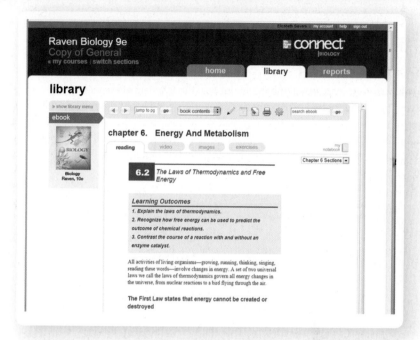

NEW! Evolutionary Asides are inserted at relevant places in the eBook. The student links to this online content with the Evolutionary Aside eBook icon found in the text. The Evolutionary Asides provide additional examples or discussions of evolutionary topics related to the textual discussion.

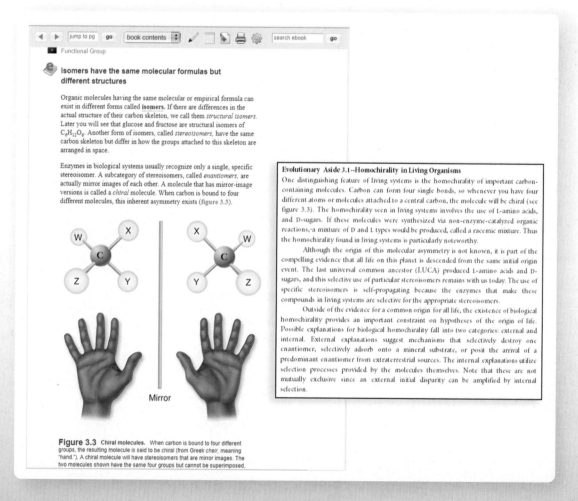

Isomers have the same molecular formulas but different structures

Organic molecules having the same molecular or empirical formula can exist in different forms called **isomers**. If there are differences in the actual structure of their carbon skeleton, we call them *structural isomers*. Later you will see that glucose and fructose are structural isomers of $C_6H_{12}O_6$. Another form of isomers, called *stereoisomers*, have the same carbon skeleton but differ in how the groups attached to this skeleton are arranged in space.

Enzymes in biological systems usually recognize only a single, specific stereoisomer. A subcategory of stereoisomers, called *enantiomers*, are actually mirror images of each other. A molecule that has mirror-image versions is called a *chiral* molecule. When carbon is bound to four different molecules, this inherent asymmetry exists (figure 3.3).

Evolutionary Aside 3.1—Homochirality in Living Organisms

One distinguishing feature of living systems is the homochirality of important carbon-containing molecules. Carbon can form four single bonds, so whenever you have four different atoms or molecules attached to a central carbon, the molecule will be chiral (see figure 3.3). The homochirality seen in living systems involves the use of L-amino acids, and D-sugars. If these molecules were synthesized via non-enzyme-catalyzed organic reactions, a mixture of D and L types would be produced, called a racemic mixture. Thus the homochirality found in living systems is particularly noteworthy.

Although the origin of this molecular asymmetry is not known, it is part of the compelling evidence that all life on this planet is descended from the same initial origin event. The last universal common ancestor (LUCA) produced L-amino acids and D-sugars, and this selective use of particular stereoisomers remains with us today. The use of specific stereoisomers is self-propagating because the enzymes that make these compounds in living systems are selective for the appropriate stereoisomers.

Outside of the evidence for a common origin for all life, the existence of biological homochirality provides an important constraint on hypotheses of the origin of life. Possible explanations for biological homochirality fall into two categories: external and internal. External explanations suggest mechanisms that selectively destroy one enantiomer, selectively adsorb onto a mineral substrate, or posit the arrival of a predominant enantiomer from extraterrestrial sources. The internal explanations utilize selection processes provided by the molecules themselves. Note that these are not mutually exclusive since an external initial disparity can be amplified by internal selection.

Figure 3.3 Chiral molecules. When carbon is bound to four different groups, the resulting molecule is said to be chiral (from Greek *cheir*, meaning "hand."). A chiral molecule will have stereoisomers that are mirror images. The two molecules shown have the same four groups but cannot be superimposed.

Apply Your Knowledge With...

Scientific Thinking Art

Key illustrations in every chapter highlight how the frontiers of knowledge are pushed forward by a combination of hypothesis and experiment. These figures begin with a hypothesis, then show how it makes explicit predictions, tests these by experiment and finally demonstrates what conclusions can be drawn, and where this leads. These provide a consistent framework to guide the student in the logic of scientific inquiry. Each illustration concludes with open-ended questions to promote scientific inquiry.

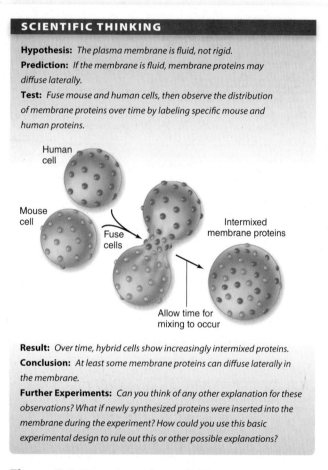

SCIENTIFIC THINKING

Hypothesis: *The plasma membrane is fluid, not rigid.*

Prediction: *If the membrane is fluid, membrane proteins may diffuse laterally.*

Test: *Fuse mouse and human cells, then observe the distribution of membrane proteins over time by labeling specific mouse and human proteins.*

Human cell

Mouse cell

Fuse cells

Allow time for mixing to occur

Intermixed membrane proteins

Result: *Over time, hybrid cells show increasingly intermixed proteins.*

Conclusion: *At least some membrane proteins can diffuse laterally in the membrane.*

Further Experiments: *Can you think of any other explanation for these observations? What if newly synthesized proteins were inserted into the membrane during the experiment? How could you use this basic experimental design to rule out this or other possible explanations?*

Figure 5.5   Test of membrane fluidity.

> Knowing how scientists solve problems, and then using this knowledge to solve a problem (as an example) drives home the concept of induction and deduction — I applaud this highly!
>
> *Marc LaBella*
> *Ocean County College*

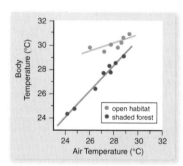

Figure 55.3   Behavioral adaptation. In open habitats, the Puerto Rican crested lizard *(Anolis cristatellus)* maintains a relatively constant temperature by seeking out and basking in patches of sunlight; as a result, it can maintain a relatively high temperature even when the air is cool. In contrast, in shaded forests, this behavior is not possible, and the lizard's body temperature conforms to that of its surroundings.

?   Inquiry question   When given the opportunity, lizards regulate their body temperature to maintain a temperature optimal for physiological functioning. Would lizards in open habitats exhibit different escape behaviors from lizards in shaded forest?

🔍   Data analysis   Can the slope of the line tell us something about the behavior of the lizard?

NEW! Data Analysis Questions

It's not enough that students learn concepts and memorize scientific facts, a biologist needs to analyze data and apply that knowledge. Data Analysis questions inserted throughout the text challenge students to analyze data and Interpret experimental results, which shows a deeper level of understanding.

Inquiry Questions

Questions that challenge students to think about and engage in what they are reading at a more sophisticated level.

NEW! Quantitative Question Bank in Connect®

Developing quantitative reasoning skills is important to the success of today's students. In addition to the Question Bank and Test Bank in Connect a separate bank of quantitative questions is readily available for seamless use in homework/practice assignments, quizzes, and exams. These algorithmic-style questions provide an opportunity for students to more deeply explore quantitative concepts and to experience repeated practice that enables quantitative skill building over time.

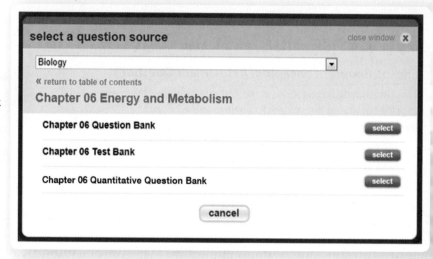

NEW! Quantitative Asides In the eBook

Quantitative Asides are inserted at relevant places in the eBook. The student links to this online content with the Quantitative Aside eBook icon found in the text. The Quantitative Asides provide additional examples or expanded discussions of a quantitative aspect of the topic under discussion.

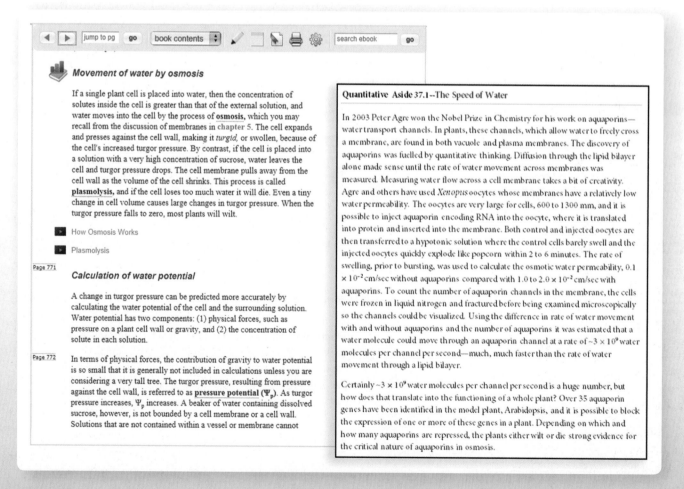

www.ravenbiology.com

Synthesize and Tie It All Together With . . .

End-of-Chapter Conceptual Assessment Questions

Thought-provoking questions at the end of each chapter tie the concepts together by asking the student to go beyond the basics to achieve a higher level of cognitive thinking.

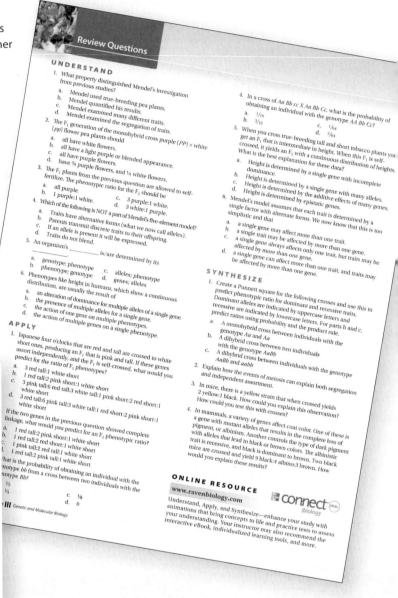

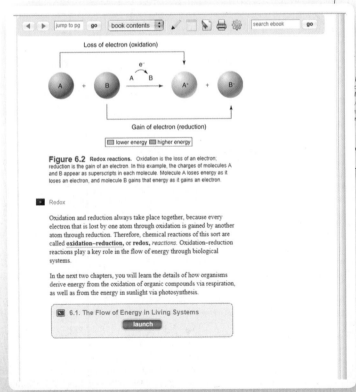

Figure 6.2 Redox reactions. Oxidation is the loss of an electron; reduction is the gain of an electron. In this example, the charges of molecules A and B appear as superscripts in each molecule. Molecule A loses energy as it loses an electron, and molecule B gains that energy as it gains an electron.

Redox

Oxidation and reduction always take place together, because every electron that is lost by one atom through oxidation is gained by another atom through reduction. Therefore, chemical reactions of this sort are called **oxidation–reduction,** or **redox,** *reactions.* Oxidation–reduction reactions play a key role in the flow of energy through biological systems.

In the next two chapters, you will learn the details of how organisms derive energy from the oxidation of organic compounds via respiration, as well as from the energy in sunlight via photosynthesis.

6.1. The Flow of Energy in Living Systems
launch

Integrated Study Quizzes

Study quizzes have been integrated into the ConnectPlus eBook for students to assess their understanding of the information presented in each section. End-of-chapter questions are linked to the answer section of the text to provide for easy study. The notebook feature allows students to collect and manage notes and highlights from the eBook to create a custom study guide.

Committed to Biology Educators

McGraw-Hill Higher Education and Blackboard Have Teamed Up

Do More

Blackboard®, the Web-based course management system, has partnered with McGraw-Hill to better allow students and faculty to use online materials and activities to complement face-to-face teaching. Blackboard features exciting social learning and teaching tools that foster more logical, visually impactful, and active learning opportunities for students. You'll transform your closed-door classrooms into communities where students remain connected to their educational experience 24 hours a day.

This partnership allows you and your students access to McGraw-Hill's Connect and McGraw-Hill Create™ right from within your Blackboard course—all with one single sign-on. Not only do you get single sign-on with Connect and Create, you also get deep integration of McGraw-Hill content and content engines right in Blackboard. Whether you're choosing a book for your course or building Connect assignments, all the tools you need are right where you want them—inside of Blackboard.

Gradebooks are now seamless. When a student completes an integrated Connect assignment, the grade for that assignment automatically (and instantly) feeds your Blackboard grade center.

McGraw-Hill and Blackboard can now offer you easy access to industry leading technology and content, whether your campus hosts it or we do. Be sure to ask your local McGraw-Hill representative for details.

McGraw-Hill Connect® Biology

McGraw-Hill Connect Biology provides online presentation, assignment, and assessment solutions. It connects your students with the tools and resources they'll need to achieve success. With Connect Biology you can deliver assignments, quizzes, and tests online. A robust set of questions and activities are presented and aligned with the textbook's Learning Outcomes. As an instructor, you can edit existing questions and author entirely new problems. Track individual student performance—by question, assignment, or in relation to the class overall—with detailed grade reports. Integrate grade reports easily with Learning Management Systems (LMS), such as WebCT and Blackboard—and much more. ConnectPlus Biology provides students with all the advantages of

Connect Biology plus 24/7 online access to an eBook. This media-rich version of the book is available through the McGraw-Hill Connect platform and allows seamless integration of text, media, and assessments.

To learn more, visit **www.mcgrawhillconnect.com**

My Lectures—Tegrity®

McGraw-Hill Tegrity records and distributes your class lecture with just a click of a button. Students can view anytime/anywhere via computer, iPod, or mobile device. It indexes as it records your PowerPoint® presentations and anything shown on your computer so students can use keywords to find exactly what they want to study. Tegrity is available as an integrated feature of McGraw-Hill Connect Biology and as a standalone.

Personalized and Adaptive Learning

McGraw-Hill LearnSmart is available as an integrated feature of McGraw-Hill Connect Biology. It is an adaptive learning system designed to help students learn faster, study more efficiently, and retain more knowledge for greater success. LearnSmart assesses a student's knowledge of course content through a series of adaptive questions. It pinpoints concepts the student does not understand and maps out a personalized study plan for success. This innovative study tool also has features that allow instructors to see exactly what students have accomplished and a built-in assessment tool for graded assignments.

Visit the following site for a demonstration:
www.mhlearnsmart.com

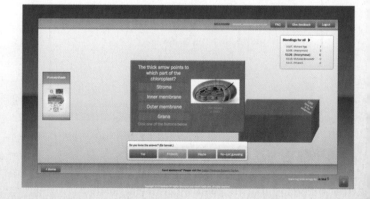

LabSmart™

Based on the same world-class super-adaptive technology as LearnSmart, McGraw-Hill LabSmart is a must-see, outcomes-based lab simulation. It assesses a student's knowledge and adaptively corrects deficiencies, allowing the student to learn faster and retain more knowledge with greater success.

First, a student's knowledge is adaptively leveled on core learning outcomes: Questioning reveals knowledge deficiencies that are corrected by the delivery of content that is conditional on a student's response. Then, a simulated lab experience requires the student to think and act like a scientist: recording, interpreting, and analyzing data using simulated equipment found in labs and clinics. The student is allowed to make mistakes—a powerful part of the learning experience! A virtual coach provides subtle hints when needed; asks questions about the student's choices; and allows the student to reflect upon and correct those mistakes. Whether your need is to overcome the logistical challenges of a traditional lab, provide better lab prep, improve student performance, or make your online experience one that rivals the real world, LabSmart accomplishes it all.

Learn more at **www.mhlabsmart.com**

An initial diagnostic establishes a student's baseline comprehension and knowledge; then the program generates a learning plan tailored to the student's academic needs and schedule. As the student works through the learning plan, the program tracks the student's progress, delivering appropriate assessment and learning resources (e.g., tutorials, figures, animations, etc.) as needed. If a student incorrectly answers questions around a particular learning objective, they are asked to review learning resources around that objective before re-assessing their mastery of the objective.

Using this program, students can identify the content they don't understand, focus their time on content they need to know but don't, and therefore improve their chances of success in the majors biology course.

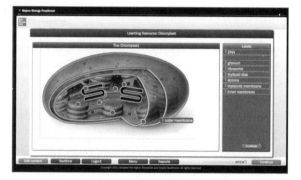

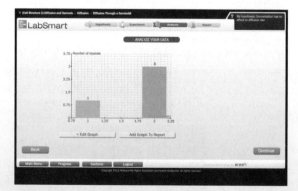

Preparing for Majors Biology

Do your majors biology students struggle the first few weeks of class, trying to get up to speed? McGraw-Hill can help.

McGraw-Hill has developed an adaptive learning tool designed to increase student success and aid retention through the first few weeks of class. Using this digital tool majors biology students can master some of the most fundamental and challenging principles of biology before they being to struggle in the first few weeks of class.

Powerful Presentation Tools

Everything you need for outstanding presentation in one place!

- FlexArt Image PowerPoints—including every piece of art that has been sized and cropped specifically for superior presentations as well as labels that you can edit, flexible art that can be picked up and moved, tables and photographs.
- Animation PowerPoints—Numerous full-color animations illustrating important processes. Harness the visual impact of concepts in motion by importing these slides into classroom presentations or online course materials.
- Lecture PowerPoints with animations fully embedded.
- Labeled and unlabeled JPEG images— Full-color digital files of all illustrations that can be readily incorporated into presentations, exams, or custom-made classroom materials.

Fully Developed Test Bank

The Digital Team (see page xviii) revised the Test Bank to fully align with the Learning Outcomes and complement questions written for the Question Bank intended for homework assignments. A thorough review process has been implemented to ensure accuracy. Provided within a computerized Test Bank powered by McGraw-Hill's flexible electronic testing program EZ Test Online, instructors can create paper and online tests or quizzes in this easy to use program! A tagging scheme allows you to sort questions by Learning Outcome, Bloom's level, topic, and section. Now, with EZ Test Online, instructors can select questions from multiple McGraw-Hill Test Banks or author their own, and then either print the test for paper distribution or give it online.

Contributors for other digital assets:

FlexArt Image PowerPoints—Carla Reinstadtler, *freelance content expert*

Lecture PowerPoints—Brian Shmaefsky, *Lone Star College*

eBook Quizzes—Amanda Rosenzweig, *Delgado Community College;* **Scott Cooper,** *University of Wisconsin–LaCrosse;* **Steven Clark,** *Lake-Sumter Community College;* **Lisa Bonneau,** *Mount Marty College*

Website—Kathleen Broomall, *University of Cincinnati–Clermont College* and **Carla Reinstadtler,** *freelance content expert*

LearnSmart—Lead: Peter Kourtev, *Central Michigan University* **Authors and reviewers: Isaac Barjis,** *New York City College of Technology;* **Anne Bullerjahn,** *Owens Community College;* **Elizabeth Drumm,** *Oakland Community College–Orchard Ridge Campus;* **Shelley Jansky,** *University of Wisconsin–Madison;* **Rita King,** *The College of New Jersey;* **Michelle Pass,** *University of North Carolina–Charlotte;* **Jennifer Warner,** *University of North Carolina, Charlotte*

Flexible Delivery Options

Raven et al. *Biology* is available in many formats in addition to the traditional textbook to give instructors and students more choices when deciding on the format of their biology text.

Foundations of Life—Chemistry, Cells, and Genetics
ISBN: 007-777580-5
Parts *1, 2, and 3*

Evolution, Diversity and Ecology
ISBN: 007-777581-3
Parts *4, 5, and 8*

Plants and Animals
ISBN: 007-777582-1
Parts 6 and 7

Also available, customized versions for all of your course needs. You're in charge of your course, so why not be in control of the content of your textbook? At McGraw-Hill Custom Publishing, we can help you create the ideal text—the one you've always imagined. Quickly. Easily. With more than 20 years of experience in custom publishing, we're experts. But at McGraw Hill we're also innovators, leading the way with new methods and means for creating simplified value-added custom textbooks.

The options are never-ending when you work with McGraw Hill. You already know what will work best for you and your students. And here, you can choose it.

McGraw-Hill Create™

With **McGraw-Hill Create,** you can easily rearrange chapters, combine material from other content sources, and quickly upload content you have written, like your course syllabus or teaching notes. Find the content you need in Create by searching through thousands of leading McGraw-Hill textbooks. Arrange your book to fit your teaching style. Create even allows you to personalize your book's appearance by selecting the cover and adding your name, school, and course information. Order a Create book and you'll receive a complimentary print review copy in 3–5 business days or a complimentary electronic review copy (eComp) via e-mail in minutes. Go to www.mcgrawhillcreate.com today and register to experience how McGraw-Hill Create empowers you to teach *your* students *your* way. **www.mcgrawhillcreate.com**

Laboratory Manuals

Biology Laboratory Manual, Tenth Edition
Vodopich/Moore ISBN: 0-07-353225-8

This laboratory manual is designed for an introductory majors biology course with a broad survey of basic laboratory techniques. The experiments and procedures are simple, safe, easy to perform, and especially appropriate for large classes. Few experiments require a second class-meeting to complete the procedure. Each exercise includes many photographs, traditional topics, and experiments that help students learn about life. Procedures within each exercise are numerous and discrete so that an exercise can be tailored to the needs of the students, the style of the instructor, and the facilities available.

Biological Investigations Lab Manual, Ninth Edition
Dolphin ISBN: 0-07-338305-8

This independent lab manual can be used for a one- or two-semester majors-level general biology lab and can be used with any majors-level general biology textbook. The labs are investigative and ask students to use more critical thinking and hands-on learning. The author emphasizes investigative, quantitative, and comparative approaches to studying the life sciences.

The Digital Story

Digital assessment is a major focus in higher education. Online tools promise anywhere, anytime access combined with the possibility of learning tailored to individual student needs. Digital assessments should span the spectrum of Bloom's taxonomy within the context of best-practice pedagogy. The increased challenge at higher Bloom's levels will help students grow intellectually and be better prepared to contribute to society.

Significant faculty demand for content at higher Bloom's levels led us to examine assessment quality and consistency of our Connect content, and to develop a scientific approach to systematically increase Bloom's levels and develop internally consistent and balanced digital assessments that promote student learning.

Our goal was to increase assessment quality of our Connect content to meet faculty and student needs. Our objective was to have 30% of all digital assessment questions in Connect at the Apply, Analyze, or Evaluate levels of Bloom's taxonomy. With thousands of existing questions, that is no small task. Consistent with best-practices research on how people learn, we took a comprehensive look at our existing digital assessments to determine Bloom's levels across our assignable content. Because this project was too extensive for a single person to accomplish, we assembled a team of faculty from research, comprehensive, liberal arts universities, and community colleges. Digital team members were selected based on commitment to student learning, biology content expertise, openness to a new vision for digital assessment and professional development, and question-writing skills.

Under the direction of lead digital author, Ian Quitadamo, team members were calibrated to a common perception of Bloom's taxonomy. The team then evaluated our existing Question Bank, Test Bank, Animation Quizzes, and Video Quizzes for appropriate level of Bloom's and compiled the results into a comprehensive database that was statistically analyzed. Results showed adequate coverage at the lower level of Bloom's taxonomy but less so at the higher levels of Bloom's. Knowing that assessment drives learning quality, we focused our efforts on "Blooming up" existing content and developing new assessments that examine students' problem-solving skills (see graphs for chapter 12). The end result of our team's scientific approach to developing digital content is a collection of engaging, diagnostic assessments that strengthen student ability to critically think, build connections across biology concepts, and develop quantitative reasoning skills that ultimately underlie student academic success and ability to contribute to society.

We would like to acknowledge our digital team and thank them for their tireless efforts:

Kerry Bohl, *University of South Florida*
David Bos, *Purdue University*
Scott Bowling, *Auburn University*
Scott Cooper, *University of Wisconsin–La Crosse*
Cynthia Dadmun, *Freelance content expert*
Jenny Dechaine, *Central Washington University*
Elizabeth Drumm, *Oakland Community College–Orchard Ridge Campus*
Susan Edwards, *Appalachian State University*

Julie Emerson, *Amherst College*
Brent Ewers, *University of Wyoming*
Chris Himes, *Massachusetts College of Liberal Arts*
Cintia Hongay, *Clarkson University*
Heather Jezorek, *University of South Florida*
Kristy Kappenman, *Central Washington University*
Jamie Kneitel, *California State University, Sacramento*
Marcy Lowenstein, *Florida International University*
Carolyn Martineau, *DePaul University*
Christin Munkittrick, *Freelance content expert*
Chris Osovitz, *University of South Florida*
Anneke Padolina, *Virginia Commonwealth University*
Marius Pfeiffer, *Tarrant County College*
Marceau Ratard, *Delgado Community College*
Nicolle Romero, *Freelance content expert*
Amanda Rosenzweig, *Delgado Community College*
Kathryn Spilios, *Boston University*
Jen Stanford, *Drexel University*
Martin St. Maurice, *Marquette University*
Salvatore Tavormina, *Austin Community College*
Sharon Thoma, *University of Wisconsin, Madison*
Gloriana Trujillo, *University of New Mexico*
Jennifer Wiatrowski, *Pasco-Hernando Community College*

Quantitative Question Bank

David Bos, *Purdue University*
Chris Osovitz, *University of South Florida*
Martin St. Maurice, *Marquette University*

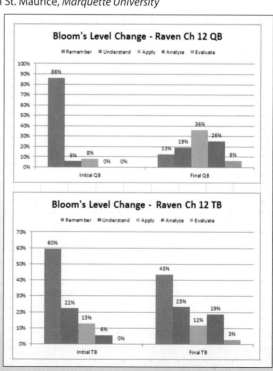

360° Development Process

McGraw-Hill's 360° Development Process is an ongoing, never-ending, education-oriented approach to building accurate and innovative print and digital products. It is dedicated to continual large-scale and incremental improvement, driven by multiple user feedback loops and checkpoints. This is initiated during the early planning stages of our new products, and intensifies during the development and production stages, then begins again upon publication in anticipation of the next edition.

This process is designed to provide a broad, comprehensive spectrum of feedback for refinement and innovation of our learning tools, for both student and instructor. The 360° Development Process includes market research, content reviews, course- and product-specific symposia, accuracy checks, and art reviews. We appreciate the expertise of the many individuals involved in this process.

General Biology Symposia

Every year McGraw-Hill conducts several General Biology Symposia, which are attended by instructors from across the country. These events are an opportunity for editors from McGraw-Hill to gather information about the needs and challenges of instructors teaching the majors biology course. It also offers a forum for the attendees to exchange ideas and experiences with colleagues they might not have otherwise met. The feedback we have received has been invaluable, and has contributed to the development of *Biology* and its supplements. A special thank you to recent attendees:

Thomas Abbott   *University of Connecticut*
Sylvester Allred   *Northern Arizona University*
Julie Anderson   *University of Wisconsin–Eau Claire*
Kim Baker   *University of Wisconsin–Green Bay*
Michael Bell   *Richland College*
Brian Berthelsen   *Iowa Western Community College*
Joe Beuchel   *Triton College*
Arlene Billock   *University of Louisiana–Lafayette*
Stephane Boissinot   *Queens College, the City University of New York*
David Bos   *Purdue University*
Scott Bowling   *Auburn University*
Jacqueline Bowman   *Arkansas Technical University*
Randy Brooks   *Florida Atlantic University*
Arthur Buikema   *Virginia Polytechnic Institute*
Anne Bullerjahn   *Owens Community College*
Helaine Burstein   *Ohio University*
Raymond Burton   *Germanna Community College*

Peter Busher   *Boston University*
Ruth Buskirk   *University of Texas–Austin*
Richard Cardullo   *University of California–Riverside*
Frank Cantelmo   *St. Johns University*
Jennifer Ciaccio   *Dixie State College*
Anne Barrett Clark   *Binghamton University*
Allison Cleveland   *University of South Florida–Tampa*
Clark Coffman   *Iowa State University*
Jennifer Coleman   *University of Massachusetts–Amherst*
Sehoya Cotner   *University of Minnesota*
Mitch Cruzan   *Portland State University*
Karen A. Curto   *University of Pittsburgh*
Rona Delay   *University of Vermont*
Mary Dettman   *Seminole State College of Florida*
Laura DiCaprio   *Ohio University*
Kathryn Dickson   *California State College–Fullerton*
Cathy Donald-Whitney   *Collin County Community College*
Moon Draper   *University of Texas–Austin*

Tod Duncan   *University of Colorado–Denver*
Brent Ewers   *University of Wyoming*
Stanley Faeth   *Arizona State University*
Michael Ferrari   *University of Missouri–Kansas City*
David Fitch   *New York University*
Donald French   *Oklahoma State University*
Douglas Gaffin   *University of Oklahoma*
John Geiser   *Western Michigan University*
Karen Gerhart   *University of California–Davis*
Julie Gibbs   *College of DuPage*
Cynthia Giffen   *University of Wisconsin–Madison*
Sharon Gill   *Western Michigan University*
William Glider   *University of Nebraska–Lincoln*
Steven Gorsich   *Central Michigan University*
Christopher Gregg   *Louisiana State University*
Stan Guffey   *The University of Tennessee*
Sally Harmych   *University of Toledo*
Bernard Hauser   *University of Florida–Gainesville*
Jean Heitz   *Unversity of Wisconsin–Madison*
Mark Hens   *University of North Carolina–Greensboro*
Albert Herrera   *University of Southern California*
Ralph James Hickey   *Miami University of Ohio–Oxford*
Jodi Huggenvik   *Southern Illinois University–Carbondale*
Brad Hyman   *University of California–Riverside*
Rick Jellen   *Brigham Young University*
Michael Kempf   *University of Tennessee–Martin*
Kyoungtae Kim   *Missouri State University*
Sherry Krayesky   *University of Louisiana–Lafayette*
Jerry Kudenov   *University of Alaska–Anchorage*
Josephine Kurdziel   *University of Michigan*
Ellen Lamb   *University of North Carolina–Greensboro*
Brenda Leady   *University of Toledo*
Graeme Lindbeck   *Valencia Community College*
David Longstreth   *Louisiana State University*
Lucile McCook   *University of Mississippi*
Susan Meiers   *Western Illinois University*
Michael Meighan   *University of California–Berkeley*
John Merrill   *Michigan State University*
John Mersfelder   *Sinclair Community College*
Melissa Michael   *University of Illinois–Urbana-Champaign*
Michelle Mynlieff   *Marquette University*
Leonore Neary   *Joliet Junior College*
Shawn Nordell   *Saint Louis University*

John Osterman   *University of Nebraska–Lincoln*
Stephanie Pandolfi   *Michigan State University*
Anneke Padolina   *Virginia Commonwealth University*
C.O. Patterson   *Texas A&M University*
Nancy Pencoe   *University of West Georgia*
Roger Persell   *Hunter College*
Marius Pfeiffer   *Tarrant County College NE*
Steve Phelps   *University of Florida*
Debra Pires   *University of California–Los Angeles*
Thomas Pitzer   *Florida International University*
Steven Pomarico   *Louisiana State University*
Jo Anne Powell-Coffman   *Iowa State University*
Lynn Preston   *Tarrant County College*
Ian Quitadamo   *Central Washington University*
Rajinder Ranu   *Colorado State University*
Marceau Ratard   *Delgado Community College–City Park*
Melanie Rathburn   *Boston University*
Robin Richardson   *Winona State University*
Mike Robinson   *University of Miami*
Amanda Rosenzweig   *Delgado Community College–City Park*
Connie Russell   *Angelo State University*
Laurie Russell   *St. Louis University*
David Scicchitano   *New York University*
Timothy Shannon   *Francis Marion University*
Brian Shmaefsky   *Lone Star College–Kingwood*
Richard Showman   *University of South Carolina*
Allison Silveus   *Tarrant County College–Trinity River Campus*
Robert Simons   *University of California–Los Angeles*
Steve Skarda   *Linn Benton Community College*
Steven D. Skopik   *University of Delaware*
Phillip Sokolove   *University of Maryland–Baltimore County*
Martin St. Maurice   *Marquette University*
Brad Swanson   *Cental Michigan University*
David Thompson   *Northern Kentucky University*
Maureen Tubbiola   *St. Cloud State University*
Ashok Upadhyaya   *University of South Florida–Tampa*
Anthony Uzwiak   *Rutgers University*
Rani Vajravelu   *University of Central Florida*
Gary Walker   *Appalachian State University*
Pat Walsh   *University of Delaware*
Elizabeth Weiss-Kuziel   *University of Texas–Austin*
Clay White   *Lone Star College–CyFair*
Leslie Whiteman   *Virginia State University*

Jennifer Wiatrowski *Pasco–Hernando Community College*
David Williams *Valencia Community College, East Campus*

Holly Williams *Seminole Community College*
Michael Windelspecht *Appalachian State University*

Robert Winning *Eastern Michigan University*
Mary Wisgirda *San Jacinto College, South Campus*

Michelle Withers *West Virginia University*
Kevin Wolbach *University of the Sciences in Philadelphia*
Jay Zimmerman *St. John's University*

Tenth Edition Reviewers

Tamarah Adair *Baylor University*
Brian P. Ashburner *University of Toledo*
Suman Batish *Temple University*
Giacomo Bernardi *University of California, Santa Cruz*
Deborah Bielser *University of Illinois*
Helen Boswell *Southern Utah University*
Carolyn J.W. Bunde *Idaho State University*
Joseph C. Bundy, Jr. *The University of North Carolina at Greensboro*
Jason Carlson *St. Cloud Technical and Community College*
Rebekah Chapman *Georgia State University*
Jennifer Ciaccio *Dixie State College*
Hudson DeYoe *University of Texas Pan American*

Elizabeth Drumm *Oakland Community College*
Arundhati Ghosh *University of Pittsburgh*
Jennifer Hatchel *College of Coastal Georgia*
Margaret Horton *University of North Carolina at Greensboro*
David W Jones *Dixie State College of Utah*
Jason Knouft *Saint Louis University*
Ellen S. Lamb *The University of North Carolina at Greensboro*
Brenda Leady *University of Toledo*
Roger Lloyd *College of Coastal Georgia*
Janet Loxterman *Idaho State University*
Susan Mazer *University of California, Santa Barbara*

Bradley G. Mehrtens *University of Illinois at Urbana—Champaign*
Jamie Moon *University of North Florida*
Rajkumar Nathaniel *Nicholls State University*
Julie Nguyen *College of the Canyons*
Judith D. Ochrietor *University of North Florida*
Joanne Odden *Metropolitan State College of Denver*
Monique Ogletree *University of Houston*
Paul Pillitteri *Southern Utah University*
Nicola Plowes *Arizona State University*
Kumkum Prabhakar *Nassau Community College*
Marceau Ratard *Delgado Community College*

Melissa Reedy *University of Illinois at Urbana—Champaign*
Laurel Roberts *University of Pittsburgh*
Amanda Rosenzweig *Delgado Community College*
Benjamin Rowley *University of Central Arkansas*
Laurie Shornick *Saint Louis University*
Sonia Suri *Valencia Community College*
John-David Swanson *University of Central Arkansas*
Maureen Walter *Florida International University*
Chad Wayne *University of Houston*
Stacey Wild *East Tennessee State University*
Rebecca Yeomans *College of Coastal Georgia*

Previous Edition Reviewers

Tamarah Adair *Baylor University*
Gladys Alexandre-Jouline *University of Tennessee at Knoxville*
Gregory Andraso *Gannon University*
Jorge E. Arriagada *St. Cloud State University*
David Asch *Youngstown State University*
Jeffrey G. Baguley *University of Nevada–Reno*
Suman Batish *Temple University*
Donald Baud *University of Memphis*
Peter Berget *Carnegie Mellon University*
Randall Bernot *Ball State University*
Deborah Bielser *University of Illinois–Champaign*
Wendy Binder *Loyola Marymount University*
Todd A. Blackledge *University of Akron*
Andrew R. Blaustein *Oregon State University*
Dennis Bogyo *Valdosta State University*
David Bos *Purdue University*
Robert Boyd *Auburn University*
Graciela Brelles-Marino *California State Polytechnic University–Pomona*
Joanna Brooke *DePaul University*
Roxanne Brown *Blinn College*
Mark Browning *Purdue University*
Cedric O. Buckley *Jackson State University*
Arthur L. Buikema, Jr. *Virginia Tech*
Sharon Bullock *UNC–Charlotte*
Lisa Burgess *Broward College*
Scott Carlson *Luther College*
John L. Carr *University of Louisiana–Monroe*
Laura Carruth *Georgia State University*
Dale Cassamatta *University of North Florida*
Peter Chabora *Queens College–CUNY*
Tien-Hsien Chang *Ohio State University*
Genevieve Chung *Broward College*

Cynthia Church *Metropolitan State College of Denver*
William Cohen *University of Kentucky*
James Collins *Kilgore College*
Joanne Conover *University of Connecticut*
Iris Cook *Westchester Community College*
Erica Corbett *Southeastern Oklahoma State University*
Robert Corin *College of Staten Island–CUNY*
William G. R. Crampton *University of Central Florida*
Scott Crousillac *Louisiana State University–Baton Rouge*
Karen A. Curto *University of Pittsburgh*
Denise Deal *Nassau Community College*
Philias Denette *Delgado Community College*
Mary Dettman *Seminole Community College–Oviedo*
Ann Marie DiLorenzo *Montclair State University*
Ernest DuBrul *University of Toledo*
Richard Duhrkopf *Baylor University*
Susan Dunford *University of Cincinnati*
Andrew R. Dyer *University of South Carolina–Aiken*
Carmen Eilertson *Georgia State University*
Richard P. Elinson *Duquesne University*
William L. Ellis *Pasco-Hernando Community College*
Seema Endley *Blinn College*
Gary Ervin *Mississippi State University*
Karl Fath *Queens College–CUNY*
Zen Faulkes *The University of Texas–Pan American*
Myriam Feldman *Lake Washington Technical College*

Melissa Fierke *State University of New York*
Gary L. Firestone *University of California–Berkeley*
Jason Flores *UNC–Charlotte*
Markus Friedrich *Wayne State University*
Deborah Garrity *Colorado State University*
Christopher Gee *University of North Carolina-Charlotte*
John R. Geiser *Western Michigan University*
J.P. Gibson *University of Oklahoma*
Matthew Gilg *University of North Florida*
Teresa Golden *Southeastern Oklahoma State University*
Venkat Gopalan *Ohio State University*
Michael Groesbeck *Brigham Young University*
Theresa Grove *Valdosta State University*
David Hanson *University of New Mexico*
Paul Hapeman *University of Florida*
Nargess Hassanzadeh-Kiabi *California State University–Los Angeles*
Stephen K. Herbert *University of Wyoming*
Hon Ho *State University of New York at New Paltz*
Barbara Hunnicutt *Seminole Community College*
Steve Huskey *Western Kentucky University*
Cynthia Jacobs *Arkansas Tech University*
Jason B. Jennings *Southwest Tennessee Community College*
Frank J. Jochem *Florida International University–Miami*
Norman Johnson *University of Massachusetts*

Gregory A. Jones *Santa Fe Community College*
Jerry Kaster *University of Wisconsin–Milwaukee*
Mary Jane Keith *Wichita State University*
Mary Kelley *Wayne State University*
Scott Kight *Montclair State University*
Wendy Kimber *Stevenson University*
Jeff Klahn *University of Iowa*
David S. Koetje *Calvin College*
Olga Kopp *Utah Valley University*
John C. Krenetsky *Metropolitan State College of Denver*
Patrick J. Krug *California State University–LA*
Robert Kurt *Lafayette College*
Marc J. LaBella *Ocean County College*
Ellen S. Lamb *University of North Carolina–Greensboro*
David Lampe *Duquesne University*
Grace Lasker *Lake Washington Technical College*
Kari Lavalli *Boston University*
Shannon Erickson Lee *California Sate University–Northridge*
Zhiming Liu *Eastern New Mexico University*
J. Mitchell Lockhart *Valdosta State University*
David Logan *Clark Atlanta University*
Thomas A. Lonergan *University of New Orleans*
Andreas Madlung *University of Puget Sound*
Lynn Mahaffy *University of Delaware*
Jennifer Marcinkiewicz *Kent State University*
Henri Maurice *University of Southern Indiana*
Deanna McCullough *University of Houston–Downtown*

Dean McCurdy *Albion College*

Richard Merritt *Houston Community College–Northwest*

Stephanie Miller *Jefferson State Community College*

Thomas Miller *University of California, Riverside*

Hector C. Miranda, Jr. *Texas Southern University*

Jasleen Mishra *Houston Community College*

Randy Mogg *Columbus State Community College*

Daniel Moon *University of North Florida*

Janice Moore *Colorado State University*

Richard C. Moore *Miami University*

Juan Morata *Miami Dade College–Wolfson*

Ellyn R. Mulcahy *Johnson County Community College*

Kimberlyn Nelson *Pennsylvania State University*

Howard Neufeld *Appalachian State University*

Jacalyn Newman *University of Pittsburgh*

Margaret N. Nsofor *Southern Illinois University–Carbondale*

Judith D. Ochrietor *University of North Florida*

Robert O'Donnell *SUNY–Geneseo*

Olumide Ogunmosin *Texas Southern University*

Nathan O. Okia *Auburn University–Montgomery*

Stephanie Pandolfi *Michigan State University*

Peter Pappas *County College of Morris*

J. Payne *Bergen Community College*

Andrew Pease *Stevenson University*

Craig Peebles *University of Pittsburgh*

David G. Pennock *Miami University*

Beverly Perry *Houston Community College*

John S. Peters *College of Charleston, SC*

Stephanie Toering Peters *Wartburg College*

Teresa Petrino-Lin *Barry University*

Susan Phillips *Brevard Community College–Palm Bay*

Paul Pillitteri *Southern Utah University*

Thomas Pitzer *Florida International University–Miami*

Uwe Pott *University of Wisconsin–Green Bay*

Nimala Prabhu *Edison State College*

Lynn Preston *Tarrant County College–NW*

Kelli Prior *Finger Lakes Community College*

Penny L. Ragland *Auburn Montgomery*

Marceau Ratard *Delgado Community College*

Michael Reagan *College of St. Benedict/St. John's University*

Nancy A. Rice *Western Kentucky University*

Linda Richardson *Blinn College*

Amanda Rosenzweig *Delgado Community College*

Cliff Ross *University of North Florida*

John Roufaiel *SUNY–Rockland Community College*

Kenneth Roux *Florida State University*

Ann E. Rushing *Baylor University*

Sangha Saha *Harold Washington College*

Eric Saliim *North Carolina Central University*

Thomas Sasek *University of Louisiana–Monroe*

Leena Sawant *Houston Community College*

Emily Schmitt *Nova Southeastern University*

Mark Schneegurt *Wichita State University*

Brenda Schoffstall *Barry University*

Scott Schuette *Southern Illinois University*

Pramila Sen *Houston Community College*

Bin Shuai *Wichita State University*

Susan Skambis *Valencia Community College*

Michael Smith *Western Kentucky University*

Ramona Smith *Brevard Community College*

Nancy G. Solomon *Miami University*

Sally K. Sommers Smith *Boston University*

Melissa Spitler *California State University–Northridge*

Ashley Spring *Brevard Community College*

Moira Van Staaden *Bowling Green State University*

Bruce Stallsmith *University of Alabama–Huntsville*

Susan Stamler *College of DuPage*

Nancy Staub *Gonzaga University*

Stanley Stevens *University of Memphis*

Ivan Still *Arkansas Tech University*

Gregory W. Stunz *Texas A&M University–Corpus Christi*

Ken D. Sumida *Chapman University*

Rema Suniga *Ohio Northern University*

Bradley Swanson *Central Michigan University*

David Tam *University of North Texas*

Franklyn Tan Te *Miami Dade College–Wolfson*

William Terzaghi *Wilkes University*

Melvin Thomson *University of Wisconsin–Parkside*

Martin Tracey *Florida International University*

James Traniello *Boston University*

Bibit Halliday Traut *City College of San Francisco*

Alexa Tullis *University of Puget Sound*

Catherine Ueckert *Northern Arizona University*

Mark VanCura *Cape Fear CC/University of NC Pembroke*

Charles J. Venglarik *Jefferson State Community College*

Diane Wagner *University of Alaska–Fairbanks*

Maureen Walter *Florida International University*

Wei Wan *Texas A&M University*

James T. Warren, Jr. *Penn State Erie*

Delon Washo-Krupps *Arizona State University*

Frederick Wasserman *Boston University*

Raymond R. White *City College of San Francisco*

Stephen W. White *Ozarks Technical Community College*

Kimberly Williams *California State University–San Bernardino*

Martha Comstock Williams *Southern Polytechnic State University*

David E. Wolfe *American River College*

Amber Wyman *Finger Lakes Community College*

Robert D. Young, Jr. *Blinn College*

A Note From the Authors

A revision of this scope relies on the talents and efforts of many people working behind the scenes and we have benefited greatly from their assistance.

Linda Davoli has been the copyeditor for each edition under this author team. She has labored many hours and always improves the clarity and consistency of the text. She has made a tremendous contribution to the quality of the final product.

We were fortunate to again work with Electronic Publishing Services to update the art program and improve the layout of the pages. Our close collaboration resulted in a text that is pedagogically effective as well as more beautiful than any other biology text on the market.

We have the continued support of an excellent team at McGraw-Hill. Rebecca Olson, the Brand Manager for *Biology* has been a steady leader during a time of change. The Director of Development, Liz Sievers, provided support in so many ways it would be impossible to name them all. Sheila Frank, lead project manager, and Tara McDermott, designer, ensured our text was on time and elegantly designed. Patrick Reidy, marketing manager, is always a sounding board for more than just marketing, and many more people behind the scenes have all contributed to the success of our text. This includes the digital team, who are also credited elsewhere, but whom we owe a great deal for their efforts to help us move toward the future.

Throughout this edition we have had the support of spouses and children, who have seen less of us than they might have liked because of the pressures of getting this revision completed. They have adapted to the many hours this book draws us away from them, and, even more than us, looked forward to its completion.

In the end, the people we owe the most are the generations of students who have used the many editions of this text. They have taught us at least as much as we have taught them, and their questions and suggestions continue to improve the text and supplementary materials.

We would like to thank Darrell Vodopich of Baylor University for providing the the flower image on the front cover (basket flower—*Centaurea americana* and the crab spider—*Misumenops* sp.) and Luke Mahler of University of California-Davis for providing the Anolis image (*Anolis gorgonae*).

Finally, we need to thank our reviewers. Instructors from across the country are continually invited to share their knowledge and experience with us through reviews and focus groups. The feedback we received shaped this edition, resulting in a reorganization of the table of contents and expanded coverage in key areas. We would especially like to thank Allison Silveus of Tarrant County College-Trinity River Campus for helping to evaluate the reviews over the animal biology chapters. All of these people took time out of their already busy lives to help us build a better edition of *Biology* for the next generation of introductory biology students, and they have our heartfelt thanks.

Contents

Biology

Chapter 1

The Science of Biology

Chapter Contents

Part | The Molecular Basis of Life

Introduction

You are about to embark on a journey—a journey of discovery about the nature of life. Nearly 180 years ago, a young English naturalist named Charles Darwin set sail on a similar journey on board H.M.S. Beagle; a replica of this ship is pictured here. What Darwin learned on his five-year voyage led directly to his development of the theory of evolution by natural selection, a theory that has become the core of the science of biology. Darwin's voyage seems a fitting place to begin our exploration of biology—the scientific study of living organisms and how they have evolved. Before we begin, however, let's take a moment to think about what biology is and why it's important.

1.1 The Science of Life

Learning Outcomes

1. Compare biology to other natural sciences.
2. Describe the characteristics of living systems.
3. Characterize the hierarchical organization of living systems.

This is the most exciting time to be studying biology in the history of the field. The amount of information available about the natural world has exploded in the last 35 years, and we are now in a position to ask and answer questions that previously were only dreamed of.

We have determined the entire sequence of the human genome and are in the process of sequencing the genomes of other species at an ever-increasing pace. We are closing in on a description of the molecular workings of the cell in unprecedented detail, and we are in the process of finally unveiling the mystery of how a single cell can give rise to the complex organization seen in multicellular organisms. With robotics, advanced imaging, and analytical techniques, we have tools available that were formerly the stuff of science fiction.

In this text, we attempt to draw a contemporary picture of the science of biology, as well as provide some history and experimental perspective on this exciting time in the discipline. In this introductory chapter, we examine the nature of biology and the foundations of science in general to put into context the information presented in the rest of the text.

Biology unifies much of natural science

The study of biology is a point of convergence for the information and tools from all of the natural sciences. Biological systems are the most complex chemical systems on Earth, and their many functions are both determined and constrained by the principles of chemistry and physics. Put another way, no new laws of nature can be gleaned from the study of biology—but that study does illuminate and illustrate the workings of those natural laws.

The intricate chemical workings of cells are based on everything we have learned from the study of chemistry. And every level of biological organization is governed by the nature of energy transactions learned from the study of thermodynamics. Biological systems do not represent any new forms of matter, and yet they are the most complex organization of matter known. The complexity of living systems is made possible by a constant source of energy—the Sun. The conversion of this energy source into organic molecules by photosynthesis is one of the most beautiful and complex reactions known in chemistry and physics.

The way we do science is changing to grapple with increasingly difficult modern problems. Science is becoming more interdisciplinary, combining the expertise from a variety of traditional disciplines and emerging fields such as nanotechnology. Biology is at the heart of this multidisciplinary approach because biological problems often require many different approaches to arrive at solutions.

Life defies simple definition

In its broadest sense, biology is the study of living things—*the science of life.* Living things come in an astounding variety of shapes and forms, and biologists study life in many different ways. They live with gorillas, collect fossils, and listen to whales. They read the messages encoded in the long molecules of heredity and count how many times a hummingbird's wings beat each second.

What makes something "alive"? Anyone could deduce that a galloping horse is alive and a car is not, but why? We cannot say, "If it moves, it's alive," because a car can move, and gelatin can wiggle in a bowl. They certainly are not alive. Although we cannot define life with a single simple sentence, we can come up with a series of seven characteristics shared by living systems:

- **Cellular organization.** All organisms consist of one or more cells. Often too tiny to see, cells carry out the basic activities of living. Each cell is bounded by a membrane that separates it from its surroundings.
- **Ordered complexity.** All living things are both complex and highly ordered. Your body is composed of many different kinds of cells, each containing many complex

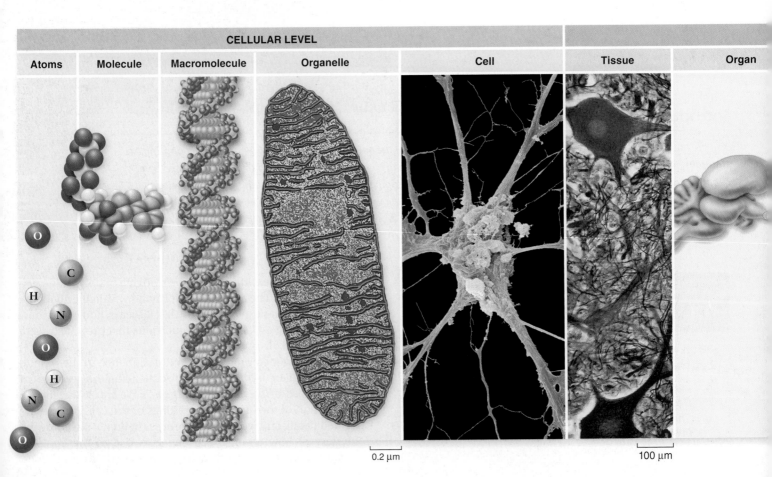

CELLULAR LEVEL						
Atoms	Molecule	Macromolecule	Organelle	Cell	Tissue	Organ

0.2 μm

100 μm

molecular structures. Many nonliving things may also be complex, but they do not exhibit this degree of ordered complexity.

- **Sensitivity.** All organisms respond to stimuli. Plants grow toward a source of light, and the pupils of your eyes dilate when you walk into a dark room.
- **Growth, development, and reproduction.** All organisms are capable of growing and reproducing, and they all possess hereditary molecules that are passed to their offspring, ensuring that the offspring are of the same species.
- **Energy utilization.** All organisms take in energy and use it to perform many kinds of work. Every muscle in your body is powered with energy you obtain from your diet.
- **Homeostasis.** All organisms maintain relatively constant internal conditions that are different from their environment, a process called **homeostasis.** For example, your body temperature remains stable despite changes in outside temperatures.
- **Evolutionary adaptation.** All organisms interact with other organisms and the nonliving environment in ways that influence their survival, and as a consequence, organisms evolve adaptations to their environments.

Living systems show hierarchical organization

The organization of the biological world is hierarchical—that is, each level builds on the level below it.

1. **The Cellular Level.** At the cellular level (figure 1.1), **atoms,** the fundamental elements of matter, are joined together into clusters called **molecules.** Complex biological molecules are assembled into tiny structures called **organelles** within membrane-bounded units we call **cells.** The cell is the basic unit of life. Many independent organisms are composed only of single cells. Bacteria are single cells, for example. All animals and plants, as well as most fungi and algae, are multicellular—composed of more than one cell.

2. **The Organismal Level.** Cells in complex multicellular organisms exhibit three levels of organization. The most basic level is that of **tissues,** which are groups of similar cells that act as a functional unit. Tissues, in turn, are grouped into **organs**—body structures composed of several different tissues that act as a structural and functional unit. Your brain is an organ composed of nerve cells and a variety of associated tissues that form protective coverings and contribute blood. At the third level of organization, organs are grouped into **organ systems.** The nervous system, for example, consists of sensory organs, the brain and spinal cord, and neurons that convey signals.

Figure 1.1 Hierarchical organization of living systems. Life is highly organized from atoms to complex multicellular organisms. Along this hierarchy of structure, atoms form molecules that are used to form organelles, which in turn form the functional subsystems within cells. Cells are organized into tissues, then into organs and organ systems such as the goose's nervous system pictured. This organization extends beyond individual organisms to populations, communities, ecosystems, and finally the biosphere.

ORGANISMAL LEVEL		POPULATIONAL LEVEL				
Organ system	Organism	Population	Species	Community	Ecosystem	Biosphere

3. **The Populational Level.** Individual organisms can be categorized into several hierarchical levels within the living world. The most basic of these is the **population**—a group of organisms of the same species living in the same place. All populations of a particular kind of organism together form a **species,** its members similar in appearance and able to interbreed. At a higher level of biological organization, a **biological community** consists of all the populations of different species living together in one place.

4. **The Ecosystem Level.** At the highest tier of biological organization, a biological community and the physical habitat within which it lives together constitute an ecological system, or **ecosystem.** For example, the soil, water, and atmosphere of a mountain ecosystem interact with the biological community of a mountain meadow in many important ways.

5. **The Biosphere.** The entire planet can be thought of as an ecosystem that we call the biosphere.

As you move up this hierarchy, novel properties emerge. These **emergent properties** result from the way in which components interact, and they often cannot be deduced just from looking at the parts themselves. Examining individual cells, for example, gives little hint about the whole animal. You, and all humans, have the same array of cell types as a giraffe. It is because the living world exhibits many emergent properties that it is difficult to define "life."

The previous descriptions of the common features and organization of living systems begins to get at the nature of what it is to be alive. The rest of this book illustrates and expands on these basic ideas to try to provide a more complete account of living systems.

Learning Outcomes Review 1.1

Biology as a science brings together other natural sciences, such as chemistry and physics, to study living systems. Life does not have a simple definition, but living systems share a number of properties that together describe life. Living systems can be organized hierarchically, from the cellular level to the entire biosphere, with emerging properties that may exceed the sum of the parts.

■ *Can you study biology without studying other sciences?*

1.2 The Nature of Science

Learning Outcomes

1. *Compare the different types of reasoning used by biologists.*
2. *Demonstrate how to formulate a hypothesis.*

Much like life itself, the nature of science defies simple description. For many years scientists have written about the "scientific method" as though there is a single way of doing science. This oversimplification has contributed to confusion on the part of nonscientists about the nature of science.

At its core, science is concerned with developing an increasingly accurate understanding of the world around us using observation and reasoning. To begin with, we assume that natural forces acting now have always acted, that the fundamental nature of the universe has not changed since its inception, and that it is not changing now. A number of complementary approaches allow understanding of natural phenomena—there is no one "scientific method."

Scientists also attempt to be as objective as possible in the interpretation of the data and observations they have collected. Because scientists themselves are human, this is not completely possible, but because science is a collective endeavor subject to scrutiny, it is self-correcting. One person's results are verified by others, and if the results cannot be repeated, they are rejected.

Much of science is descriptive

The classic vision of the scientific method is that observations lead to hypotheses that in turn make experimentally testable predictions. In this way, we dispassionately evaluate new ideas to arrive at an increasingly accurate view of nature. We discuss this way of doing science later in this chapter, but it is important to understand that much of science is purely descriptive: In order to understand anything, the first step is to describe it completely. Much of biology is concerned with arriving at an increasingly accurate description of nature.

The study of biodiversity is an example of descriptive science that has implications for other aspects of biology in addition to societal implications. Efforts are currently underway to classify all life on Earth. This ambitious project is purely descriptive, but it will lead to a much greater understanding of biodiversity as well as the effect our species has on biodiversity.

One of the most important accomplishments of molecular biology at the dawn of the 21st century was the completion of the sequence of the human genome. Many new hypotheses about human biology will be generated by this knowledge, and many experiments will be needed to test these hypotheses, but the determination of the sequence itself was descriptive science.

Science uses both deductive and inductive reasoning

The study of logic recognizes two opposite ways of arriving at logical conclusions: deductive and inductive reasoning. Science makes use of both of these methods, although induction is the primary way of reasoning in hypothesis-driven science.

Deductive reasoning

Deductive reasoning applies general principles to predict specific results. More than 2200 years ago, the Greek scientist Eratosthenes used Euclidean geometry and deductive reasoning to accurately estimate the circumference of the Earth (figure 1.2). Deductive reasoning is the reasoning of

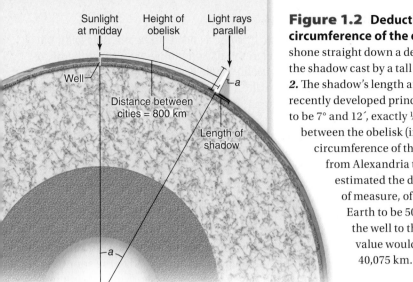

Sunlight at midday · Height of obelisk · Light rays parallel

Well

Distance between cities = 800 km

Length of shadow

a

a

Figure 1.2 **Deductive reasoning: how Eratosthenes estimated the circumference of the earth using deductive reasoning.** *1.* On a day when sunlight shone straight down a deep well at Syene in Egypt, Eratosthenes measured the length of the shadow cast by a tall obelisk in the city of Alexandria, about 800 kilometers (km) away. *2.* The shadow's length and the obelisk's height formed two sides of a triangle. Using the recently developed principles of Euclidean geometry, Eratosthenes calculated the angle, *a*, to be 7° and 12′, exactly ¹⁄₅₀ of a circle (360°). *3.* If angle *a* is ¹⁄₅₀ of a circle, then the distance between the obelisk (in Alexandria) and the well (in Syene) must be equal to ¹⁄₅₀ the circumference of the Earth. *4.* Eratosthenes had heard that it was a 50-day camel trip from Alexandria to Syene. Assuming a camel travels about 18.5 km per day, he estimated the distance between obelisk and well as 925 km (using different units of measure, of course). *5.* Eratosthenes thus deduced the circumference of the Earth to be 50 × 925 = 46,250 km. Modern measurements put the distance from the well to the obelisk at just over 800 km. Using this distance Eratosthenes's value would have been 50 × 800 = 40,000 km. The actual circumference is 40,075 km.

mathematics and philosophy, and it is used to test the validity of general ideas in all branches of knowledge. For example, if all mammals by definition have hair, and you find an animal that does not have hair, then you may conclude that this animal is not a mammal. A biologist uses deductive reasoning to infer the species of a specimen from its characteristics.

Inductive reasoning

In **inductive reasoning,** the logic flows in the opposite direction, from the specific to the general. Inductive reasoning uses specific observations to construct general scientific principles. For example, if poodles have hair, and terriers have hair, and every dog that you observe has hair, then you may conclude that all dogs have hair. Inductive reasoning leads to generalizations that can then be tested. Inductive reasoning first became important to science in the 1600s in Europe, when Francis Bacon, Isaac Newton, and others began to use the results of particular experiments to infer general principles about how the world operates.

An example from modern biology is the role of homeobox genes in development. Studies in the fruit fly, *Drosophila melanogaster,* identified genes that could cause dramatic changes in developmental fate, such as a leg appearing in the place of an antenna. When the genes themselves were isolated and their DNA sequence determined, it was found that similar genes were found in many animals, including humans. This led to the general idea that the homeobox genes act as switches to control developmental fate.

Hypothesis-driven science makes and tests predictions

Scientists establish which general principles are true from among the many that might be true through the process of systematically testing alternative proposals. If these proposals prove inconsistent with experimental observations, they are rejected as untrue. Figure 1.3 illustrates the process.

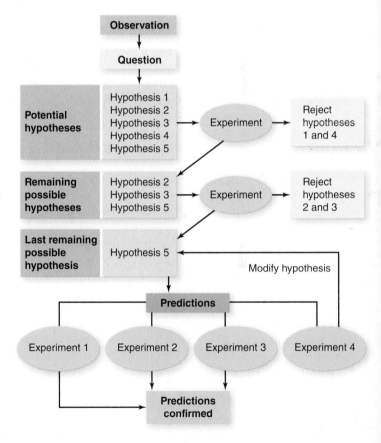

Figure 1.3 **How science is done.** This diagram illustrates how scientific investigations proceed. First, scientists make observations that raise a particular question. They develop a number of potential explanations (hypotheses) to answer the question. Next, they carry out experiments in an attempt to eliminate one or more of these hypotheses. Then, predictions are made based on the remaining hypotheses, and further experiments are carried out to test these predictions. The process can also be iterative. As experimental results are performed, the information can be used to modify the original hypothesis to fit each new observation.

After making careful observations, scientists construct a **hypothesis,** which is a suggested explanation that accounts for those observations. A hypothesis is a proposition that might be true. Those hypotheses that have not yet been disproved are retained. They are useful because they fit the known facts, but they are always subject to future rejection if, in the light of new information, they are found to be incorrect.

This process can also be *iterative,* that is, a hypothesis can be changed and refined with new data. For instance, geneticists George Beadle and Edward Tatum studied the nature of genetic information to arrive at their "one-gene/one-enzyme" hypothesis (see chapter 15). This hypothesis states that a gene represents the genetic information necessary to make a single enzyme. As investigators learned more about the molecular nature of genetic information, the hypothesis was refined to "one-gene/one-polypeptide" because enzymes can be made up of more than one polypeptide. With still more information about the nature of genetic information, other investigators found that a single gene can specify more than one polypeptide, and the hypothesis was refined again.

Testing hypotheses

We call the test of a hypothesis an **experiment.** Suppose that a room appears dark to you. To understand why it appears dark, you propose several hypotheses. The first might be, "There is no light in the room because the light switch is turned off." An alternative hypothesis might be, "There is no light in the room because the lightbulb is burned out." And yet another hypothesis might be, "I am going blind." To evaluate these hypotheses, you would conduct an experiment designed to eliminate one or more of the hypotheses.

For example, you might test your hypotheses by flipping the light switch. If you do so and the room is still dark, you have disproved the first hypothesis: Something other than the setting of the light switch must be the reason for the darkness. Note that a test such as this does not prove that any of the other hypotheses are true; it merely demonstrates that the one being tested is not. A successful experiment is one in which one or more of the alternative hypotheses is demonstrated to be inconsistent with the results and is thus rejected.

As you proceed through this text, you will encounter many hypotheses that have withstood the test of experiment. Many will continue to do so; others will be revised as new observations are made by biologists. Biology, like all science, is in a constant state of change, with new ideas appearing and replacing or refining old ones.

Establishing controls

Often scientists are interested in learning about processes that are influenced by many factors, or **variables.** To evaluate alternative hypotheses about one variable, all other variables must be kept constant. This is done by carrying out two experiments in parallel: a test experiment and a control experiment. In the **test experiment,** one variable is altered in a known way to test a particular hypothesis. In the **control experiment,** that variable is left unaltered. In all other respects the two experiments are identical, so any difference in the outcomes of the two experiments must result from the influence of the variable that was changed.

Much of the challenge of experimental science lies in designing control experiments that isolate a particular variable from other factors that might influence a process.

Using predictions

A successful scientific hypothesis needs to be not only valid but also useful—it needs to tell us something we want to know. A hypothesis is most useful when it makes predictions because those predictions provide a way to test the validity of the hypothesis. If an experiment produces results inconsistent with the predictions, the hypothesis must be rejected or modified. In contrast, if the predictions are supported by experimental testing, the hypothesis is supported. The more experimentally supported predictions a hypothesis makes, the more valid the hypothesis is.

As an example, in the early history of microbiology it was known that nutrient broth left sitting exposed to air becomes contaminated. Two hypotheses were proposed to explain this observation: spontaneous generation and the germ hypothesis. Spontaneous generation held that there was an inherent property in organic molecules that could lead to the spontaneous generation of life. The germ hypothesis proposed that preexisting microorganisms that were present in the air could contaminate the nutrient broth.

These competing hypotheses were tested by a number of experiments that involved filtering air and boiling the broth to kill any contaminating germs. The definitive experiment was performed by Louis Pasteur, who constructed flasks with curved necks that could be exposed to air, but that would trap any contaminating germs. When such flasks were boiled to sterilize them, they remained sterile, but if the curved neck was broken off, they became contaminated (figure 1.4).

SCIENTIFIC THINKING

Question: *What is the source of contamination that occurs in a flask of nutrient broth left exposed to the air?*

Germ Hypothesis: *Preexisting microorganisms present in the air contaminate nutrient broth.*

Prediction: *Sterilized broth will remain sterile if microorganisms are prevented from entering flask.*

Spontaneous Generation Hypothesis: *Living organisms will spontaneously generate from nonliving organic molecules in broth.*

Prediction: *Organisms will spontaneously generate from organic molecules in broth after sterilization.*

Test: *Use swan-necked flasks to prevent entry of microorganisms. To ensure that broth can still support life, break swan-neck after sterilization.*

Broken neck of flask

Flask is sterilized by boiling the broth.

Unbroken flask remains sterile.

Broken flask becomes contaminated after exposure to germ-laden air.

Result: *No growth occurs in sterile swan-necked flasks. When the neck is broken off, and the broth is exposed to air, growth occurs.*

Conclusion: *Growth in broth is of preexisting microorganisms.*

Figure 1.4 Experiment to test spontaneous generation versus germ hypothesis.

This result was predicted by the germ hypothesis—that when the sterile flask is exposed to air, airborne germs are deposited in the broth and grow. The spontaneous generation hypothesis predicted no difference in results with exposure to air. This experiment disproved the hypothesis of spontaneous generation and supported the hypothesis of airborne germs under the conditions tested.

Reductionism breaks larger systems into their component parts

Scientists use the philosophical approach of **reductionism** to understand a complex system by reducing it to its working parts. Reductionism has been the general approach of biochemistry, which has been enormously successful at unraveling the complexity of cellular metabolism by concentrating on individual pathways and specific enzymes. By analyzing all of the pathways and their components, scientists now have an overall picture of the metabolism of cells.

Reductionism has limits when applied to living systems, however—one of which is that enzymes do not always behave exactly the same in isolation as they do in their normal cellular context. A larger problem is that the complex interworking of many interconnected functions leads to emergent properties that cannot be predicted based on the workings of the parts. For example, an examination of all of the proteins and RNAs in a ribosome in isolation would not lead to predictions about the nature of protein synthesis. On a higher level, understanding the physiology of a single Canada goose would not lead to predictions about flocking behavior. Biologists are just beginning to come to grips with this problem and to think about ways of dealing with the whole as well as the workings of the parts. The emerging field of systems biology focuses on this different approach.

Biologists construct models to explain living systems

Biologists construct models in many different ways for a variety of uses. Geneticists construct models of interacting networks of proteins that control gene expression, often even drawing cartoon figures to represent that which we cannot see. Population biologists build models of how evolutionary change occurs. Cell biologists build models of signal transduction pathways and the events leading from an external signal to internal events. Structural biologists build actual models of the structure of proteins and macromolecular complexes in cells.

Models provide a way to organize how we think about a problem. Models can also get us closer to the larger picture and away from the extreme reductionist approach. The working parts are provided by the reductionist analysis, but the model shows how they fit together. Often these models suggest other experiments that can be performed to refine or test the model.

As researchers gain more knowledge about the actual flow of molecules in living systems, more sophisticated kinetic models can be used to apply information about isolated enzymes to their cellular context. In systems biology, this modeling is being applied on a large scale to regulatory networks during development, and even to modeling an entire bacterial cell.

The nature of scientific theories

Scientists use the word **theory** in two main ways. The first meaning of *theory* is a proposed explanation for some natural phenomenon, often based on some general principle. Thus, we speak of the principle first proposed by Newton as the "theory of gravity." Such theories often bring together concepts that were previously thought to be unrelated.

The second meaning of *theory* is the body of interconnected concepts, supported by scientific reasoning and experimental evidence, that explains the facts in some area of study. Such a theory provides an indispensable framework for organizing a body of knowledge. For example, quantum theory in physics brings together a set of ideas about the nature of the universe, explains experimental facts, and serves as a guide to further questions and experiments.

To a scientist, theories are the solid ground of science, expressing ideas of which we are most certain. In contrast, to the general public, the word *theory* usually implies the opposite—a *lack* of knowledge, or a guess. Not surprisingly, this difference often results in confusion. In this text, *theory* will always be used in its scientific sense, in reference to an accepted general principle or body of knowledge.

Some critics outside of science attempt to discredit evolution by saying it is "just a theory." The hypothesis that evolution has occurred, however, is an accepted scientific fact—it is supported by overwhelming evidence. Modern evolutionary theory is a complex body of ideas, the importance of which spreads far beyond explaining evolution. Its ramifications permeate all areas of biology, and it provides the conceptual framework that unifies biology as a science. Again, the key is how well a hypothesis fits the observations. Evolutionary theory fits the observations very well.

Research can be basic or applied

In the past it was fashionable to speak of the "scientific method" as consisting of an orderly sequence of logical, either–or steps. Each step would reject one of two mutually incompatible alternatives, as though trial-and-error testing would inevitably lead a researcher through the maze of uncertainty to the ultimate scientific answer. If this were the case, a computer would make a good scientist. But science is not done this way.

As the British philosopher Karl Popper has pointed out, successful scientists without exception design their experiments with a pretty fair idea of how the results are going to come out. They have what Popper calls an "imaginative preconception" of what the truth might be. Because insight and imagination play such a large role in scientific progress, some scientists are better at science than others—just as Bruce Springsteen stands out among songwriters or Claude Monet stands out among Impressionist painters.

Some scientists perform *basic research,* which is intended to extend the boundaries of what we know. These individuals typically work at universities, and their research is usually supported by grants from various agencies and foundations.

The information generated by basic research contributes to the growing body of scientific knowledge, and it provides the scientific foundation utilized by *applied research.* Scientists who conduct applied research are often employed in some kind of industry. Their work may involve the manufacture of food additives, the creation of new drugs, or the testing of environmental quality.

Research results are written up and submitted for publication in scientific journals, where the experiments and conclusions are reviewed by other scientists. This process of careful evaluation, called *peer review,* lies at the heart of modern science. It helps to ensure that faulty research or false claims are not given the authority of scientific fact. It also provides other scientists with a starting point for testing the reproducibility of experimental results. Results that cannot be reproduced are not taken seriously for long.

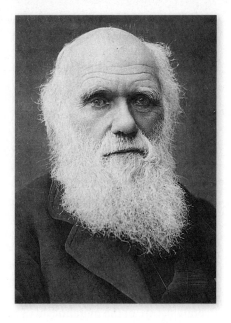

Figure 1.5 Charles Darwin. This newly rediscovered photograph taken in 1881, the year before Darwin died, appears to be the last ever taken of the great biologist.

Learning Outcomes Review 1.2

Much of science is descriptive, amassing observations to gain an accurate view. Both deductive reasoning and inductive reasoning are used in science. Scientific hypotheses are suggested explanations for observed phenomena. Hypotheses need to make predictions that can be tested by controlled experiments. Theories are coherent explanations of observed data, but they may be modified by new information.

■ *How does a scientific theory differ from a hypothesis?*

1.3 An Example of Scientific Inquiry: Darwin and Evolution

Learning Outcomes

1. *Examine Darwin's theory of evolution by natural selection as a scientific theory.*
2. *Describe the evidence that supports the theory of evolution.*

Darwin's theory of evolution explains and describes how organisms on Earth have changed over time and acquired a diversity of new forms. This famous theory provides a good example of how a scientist develops a hypothesis and how a scientific theory grows and wins acceptance.

Charles Robert Darwin (1809–1882; figure 1.5) was an English naturalist who, after 30 years of study and observation, wrote one of the most famous and influential books of all time. This book, *On the Origin of Species by Means of Natural Selection,* created a sensation when it was published, and the ideas Darwin expressed in it have played a central role in the development of human thought ever since.

The idea of evolution existed prior to Darwin

In Darwin's time, most people believed that the different kinds of organisms and their individual structures resulted from

direct actions of a Creator (many people still believe this). Species were thought to have been specially created and to be unchangeable over the course of time.

In contrast to these ideas, a number of earlier naturalists and philosophers had presented the view that living things must have changed during the history of life on Earth. That is, **evolution** has occurred, and living things are now different from how they began. Darwin's contribution was a concept he called *natural selection,* which he proposed as a coherent, logical explanation for this process, and he brought his ideas to wide public attention.

Darwin observed differences in related organisms

The story of Darwin and his theory begins in 1831, when he was 22 years old. He was part of a five-year navigational mapping expedition around the coasts of South America (figure 1.6), aboard H.M.S. *Beagle.* During this long voyage, Darwin had the chance to study a wide variety of plants and animals on continents and islands and in distant seas. Darwin observed a number of phenomena that were of central importance to his reaching his ultimate conclusion.

Repeatedly, Darwin saw that the characteristics of similar species varied somewhat from place to place. These geographical patterns suggested to him that lineages change gradually as species migrate from one area to another. On the Galápagos Islands, 960 km (600 miles) off the coast of Ecuador, Darwin encountered a variety of different finches on the various islands. The 14 species, although related, differed slightly in appearance, particularly in their beaks (figure 1.7).

Darwin thought it was reasonable to assume that all these birds had descended from a common ancestor arriving from the South American mainland several million years ago. Eating different foods on different islands, the finches' beaks had changed during their descent—"descent with modification," or evolution. (These finches are discussed in more detail in chapters 21 and 22.)

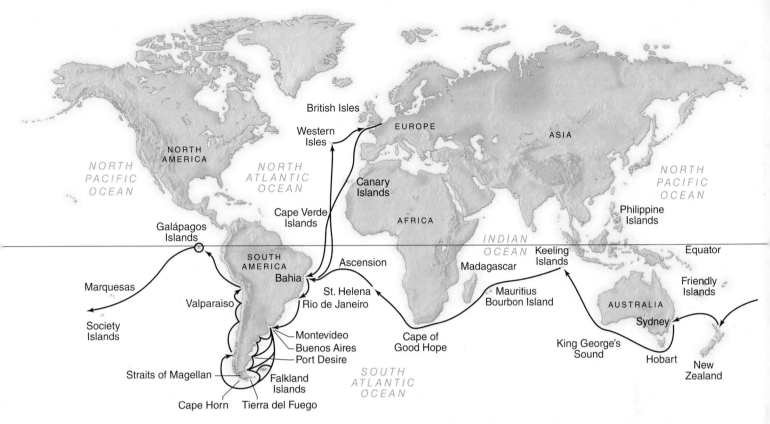

Figure 1.6 The five-year voyage of H.M.S. *Beagle*. Most of the time was spent exploring the coasts and coastal islands of South America, such as the Galápagos Islands. Darwin's studies of the animals of the Galápagos Islands played a key role in his eventual development of the concept of evolution by means of natural selection.

In a more general sense, Darwin was struck by the fact that the plants and animals on these relatively young volcanic islands resembled those on the nearby coast of South America. If each one of these plants and animals had been created independently and simply placed on the Galápagos Islands, why didn't they resemble the plants and animals of islands with similar climates—such as those off the coast of Africa, for example? Why did they resemble those of the adjacent South American coast instead?

Darwin proposed natural selection as a mechanism for evolution

It is one thing to observe the results of evolution, but quite another to understand how it happens. Darwin's great achievement lies in his ability to move beyond all the individual observations to formulate the hypothesis that evolution occurs because of natural selection.

Figure 1.7 Three Galápagos finches and what they eat. On the Galápagos Islands, Darwin observed 14 different species of finches differing mainly in their beaks and feeding habits. These three finches eat very different food items, and Darwin surmised that the different shapes of their bills represented evolutionary adaptations that improved their ability to eat the foods available in their specific habitats.

Darwin and Malthus

Of key importance to the development of Darwin's insight was his study of Thomas Malthus's *An Essay on the Principle of Population* (1798). In this book, Malthus stated that populations of plants and animals (including human beings) tend to increase geometrically, while humans are able to increase their food supply only arithmetically. Put another way, population increases by a multiplying factor—for example, in the series 2, 6, 18, 54, the starting number is multiplied by 3. Food supply increases by an additive factor—for example, the series 2, 4, 6, 8 adds 2 to each starting number. Figure 1.8 shows the difference that these two types of relationships produce over time.

Because populations increase geometrically, virtually any kind of animal or plant, if it could reproduce unchecked, would cover the entire surface of the world surprisingly quickly. Instead, populations of species remain fairly constant year after year, because death limits population numbers.

Sparked by Malthus's ideas, Darwin saw that although every organism has the potential to produce more offspring than can survive, only a limited number actually do survive and produce further offspring. Combining this observation with what he had seen on the voyage of the *Beagle,* as well as with his own experiences in breeding domestic animals, Darwin made an important association: Individuals possessing physical, behavioral, or other attributes that give them an advantage in their environment are more likely to survive and reproduce than those with less advantageous traits. By surviving, these individuals gain the opportunity to pass on their favorable characteristics to their offspring. As the frequency of these characteristics increases in the population, the nature of the population as a whole will gradually change. Darwin called this process *selection.*

Natural selection

Darwin was thoroughly familiar with variation in domesticated animals, and he began *On the Origin of Species* with a detailed discussion of pigeon breeding. He knew that animal breeders selected certain varieties of pigeons and other animals, such as dogs, to produce certain characteristics, a process Darwin called **artificial selection**.

Artificial selection often produces a great variation in traits. Domestic pigeon breeds, for example, show much greater variety than all of the wild species found throughout the world. Darwin thought that this type of change could occur in nature, too. Surely if pigeon breeders could foster variation by artificial selection, nature could do the same—a process Darwin called **natural selection.**

Darwin drafts his argument

Darwin drafted the overall argument for evolution by natural selection in a preliminary manuscript in 1842. After showing the manuscript to a few of his closest scientific friends, however, Darwin put it in a drawer, and for 16 years turned to other research. No one knows for sure why Darwin did not publish his initial manuscript—it is very thorough and outlines his ideas in detail.

The stimulus that finally brought Darwin's hypothesis into print was an essay he received in 1858. A young English naturalist named Alfred Russel Wallace (1823–1913) sent the essay to Darwin from Indonesia; it concisely set forth the hypothesis of evolution by means of natural selection, a hypothesis Wallace had developed independently of Darwin. After receiving Wallace's essay, friends of Darwin arranged for a joint presentation of their ideas at a seminar in London. Darwin then completed his own book, expanding the 1842 manuscript he had written so long ago, and submitted it for publication.

The predictions of natural selection have been tested

More than 120 years have elapsed since Darwin's death in 1882. During this period, the evidence supporting his theory has grown progressively stronger. We briefly explore some of this evidence here; in chapter 21, we will return to the theory of evolution by natural selection and examine the evidence in more detail.

The fossil record

Darwin predicted that the fossil record would yield intermediate links between the great groups of organisms—for example, between fishes and the amphibians thought to have arisen from them, and between reptiles and birds. Furthermore, natural selection predicts the relative positions in time of such transitional forms. We now know the fossil record to a degree

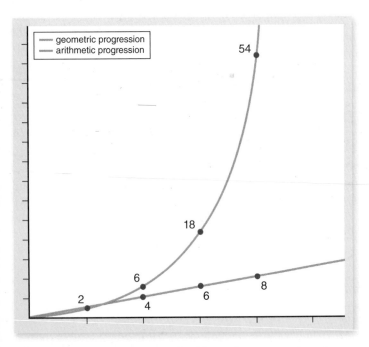

Figure 1.8 Geometric and arithmetic progressions. A geometric progression increases by a constant factor (for example, the curve shown increases ×3 for each step), whereas an arithmetic progression increases by a constant difference (for example, the line shown increases +2 for each step). Malthus contended that the human growth curve was geometric, but the human food production curve was only arithmetic.

Data analysis What is the effect of reducing the constant factor for a geometric progression? How would this change the curve in the figure?

Inquiry question Might this effect be achieved with humans? How?

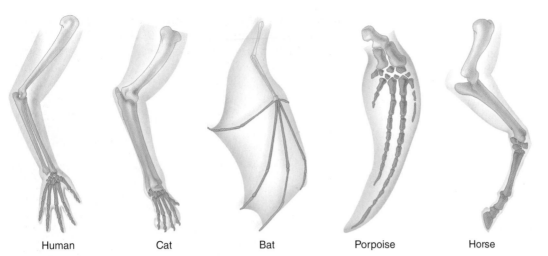

Figure 1.9 Homology among vertebrate limbs. The forelimbs of these five vertebrates show the ways in which the relative proportions of the forelimb bones have changed in relation to the particular way of life of each organism.

Human   Cat   Bat   Porpoise   Horse

that was unthinkable in the 19th century, and although truly "intermediate" organisms are hard to determine, paleontologists have found what appear to be transitional forms and found them at the predicted positions in time.

Recent discoveries of microscopic fossils have extended the known history of life on Earth back to about 3.5 billion years ago (BYA). The discovery of other fossils has supported Darwin's predictions and has shed light on how organisms have, over this enormous time span, evolved from the simple to the complex. For vertebrate animals especially, the fossil record is rich and exhibits a graded series of changes in form, with the evolutionary sequence visible for all to see.

The age of the Earth

Darwin's theory predicted the Earth must be very old, but some physicists argued that the Earth was only a few thousand years old. This bothered Darwin, because the evolution of all living things from some single original ancestor would have required a great deal more time. Using evidence obtained by studying the rates of radioactive decay, we now know that the physicists of Darwin's time were very wrong: The Earth was formed about 4.5 BYA.

The mechanism of heredity

Darwin received some of his sharpest criticism in the area of heredity. At that time, no one had any concept of genes or how heredity works, so it was not possible for Darwin to explain completely how evolution occurs.

Even though Gregor Mendel was performing his experiments with pea plants in Brünn, Austria (now Brno, the Czech Republic), during roughly the same period, genetics was established as a science only at the start of the 20th century. When scientists began to understand the laws of inheritance (discussed in chapters 12 and 13), this problem with Darwin's theory vanished.

Comparative anatomy

Comparative studies of animals have provided strong evidence for Darwin's theory. In many different types of vertebrates, for example, the same bones are present, indicating their evolutionary past. Thus, the forelimbs shown in figure 1.9 are all constructed from the same basic array of bones, modified for different purposes.

These bones are said to be **homologous** in the different vertebrates; that is, they have the same evolutionary origin, but they

now differ in structure and function. They are contrasted with **analogous** structures, such as the wings of birds and butterflies, which have similar function but different evolutionary origins.

Molecular evidence

Evolutionary patterns are also revealed at the molecular level. By comparing the genomes (that is, the sequences of all the genes) of different groups of animals or plants, we can more precisely specify the degree of relationship among the groups. A series of evolutionary changes over time should involve a continual accumulation of genetic changes in the DNA.

This difference can be seen clearly in the protein hemoglobin (figure 1.10). Rhesus monkeys, which like

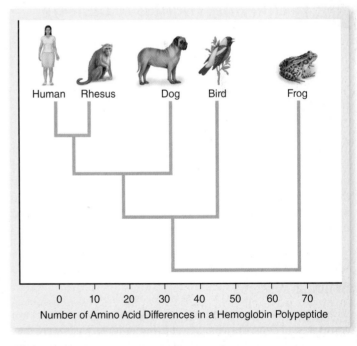

Human   Rhesus   Dog   Bird   Frog

Number of Amino Acid Differences in a Hemoglobin Polypeptide

Figure 1.10 Molecules reflect evolutionary patterns. Vertebrates that are more distantly related to humans have a greater number of amino acid differences in the hemoglobin polypeptide.

? Inquiry question Where do you imagine a snake might fall on the graph? Why?

humans are primates, have fewer differences from humans in the 146-amino-acid hemoglobin β-chain than do more distantly related mammals, such as dogs. Nonmammalian vertebrates, such as birds and frogs, differ even more.

The sequences of some genes, such as the ones specifying the hemoglobin proteins, have been determined in many organisms, and the entire time course of their evolution can be laid out with confidence by tracing the origins of particular nucleotide changes in the gene sequence. The pattern of descent obtained is called a **phylogenetic tree.** It represents the evolutionary history of the gene, its "family tree." Molecular phylogenetic trees agree well with those derived from the fossil record, which is strong direct evidence of evolution. The pattern of accumulating DNA changes represents, in a real sense, the footprints of evolutionary history.

Learning Outcomes Review 1.3

Darwin observed differences in related organisms and proposed the hypothesis of evolution by natural selection to explain these differences. The predictions generated by natural selection have been tested and continue to be tested by analysis of the fossil record, genetics, comparative anatomy, and even the DNA of living organisms.

- ■ *Does Darwin's theory of evolution by natural selection explain the origin of life?*

1.4 Unifying Themes in Biology

Learning Outcomes

1. *Discuss the unifying themes in biology.*
2. *Contrast living and nonliving systems.*

The study of biology encompasses a large number of different subdisciplines, ranging from biochemistry to ecology. In all of these, however, unifying themes can be identified. Among these are cell theory, the molecular basis of inheritance, the relationship between structure and function, evolution, and the emergence of novel properties.

Cell theory describes the organization of living systems

As was stated at the beginning of this chapter, all organisms are composed of cells, life's basic units (figure 1.11). Cells were discovered by Robert Hooke in England in 1665, using one of the first microscopes, one that magnified 30 times. Not long after that, the Dutch scientist Anton van Leeuwenhoek used microscopes capable of magnifying 300 times and discovered an amazing world of single-celled life in a drop of pond water.

In 1839, the German biologists Matthias Schleiden and Theodor Schwann, summarizing a large number of observations by themselves and others, concluded that all living

a.   60 μm

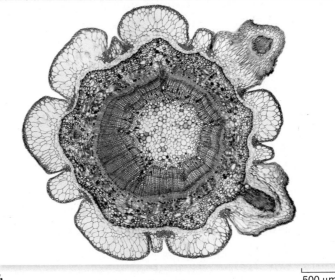

b.   500 μm

Figure 1.11 Cellular basis of life. All organisms are composed of cells. Some organisms, including the protists, shown in part (*a*) are single-celled. Others, such as the plant shown in cross section in part (*b*) consist of many cells.

organisms consist of cells. Their conclusion has come to be known as the **cell theory.** Later, biologists added the idea that all cells come from preexisting cells. The cell theory, one of the basic ideas in biology, is the foundation for understanding the reproduction and growth of all organisms.

The molecular basis of inheritance explains the continuity of life

Even the simplest cell is incredibly complex—more intricate than any computer. The information that specifies what a cell is like—its detailed plan—is encoded in **deoxyribonucleic acid (DNA),** a long, cablelike molecule. Each DNA molecule is formed from two long chains of building blocks, called nucleotides, wound around each other (see chapter 14). Four different nucleotides are found in DNA, and the sequence in which they occur encodes the cell's information. Specific sequences of several hundred to many thousand nucleotides make up a **gene,** a discrete unit of information.

The continuity of life from one generation to the next—heredity—depends on the faithful copying of a cell's DNA into daughter cells. The entire set of DNA instructions that specifies a cell is called its *genome*. The sequence of the human genome, 3 billion nucleotides long, was decoded in rough draft form in 2001, a triumph of scientific investigation.

The relationship between structure and function underlies living systems

One of the unifying themes of molecular biology is the relationship between structure and function. Function in molecules, and larger macromolecular complexes, is dependent on their structure.

Although this observation may seem trivial, it has far-reaching implications. We study the structure of molecules and macromolecular complexes to learn about their function. When we know the function of a particular structure, we can infer the function of similar structures found in different contexts, such as in different organisms.

Biologists study both aspects, looking for the relationships between structure and function. On the one hand, this allows similar structures to be used to infer possible similar functions. On the other hand, this knowledge also gives clues as to what kinds of structures may be involved in a process if we know about the functionality.

For example, suppose that we know the structure of a human cell's surface receptor for insulin, the hormone that controls uptake of glucose. We then find a similar molecule in the membrane of a cell from a different species—perhaps even a very different organism, such as a worm. We might conclude that this membrane molecule acts as a receptor for an insulin-like molecule produced by the worm. In this way, we might be able to discern the evolutionary relationship between glucose uptake in worms and in humans.

The diversity of life arises by evolutionary change

The unity of life that we see in certain key characteristics shared by many related life-forms contrasts with the incredible diversity of living things in the varied environments of Earth. The underlying unity of biochemistry and genetics argues that all life has evolved from the same origin event. The diversity of life arises by evolutionary change leading to the present biodiversity we see.

Biologists divide life's great diversity into three great groups, called domains: Bacteria, Archaea, and Eukarya (figure 1.12). The domains Bacteria and Archaea are composed of single-celled organisms (*prokaryotes*) with little internal structure, and the domain Eukarya is made up of organisms (*eukaryotes*) composed of a complex, organized cell or multiple complex cells.

Within Eukarya are four main groups called kingdoms (see figure 1.12). Kingdom Protista consists of all the unicellular eukaryotes except yeasts (which are fungi), as well as the multicellular algae. Because of the great diversity among the protists, many biologists feel kingdom Protista should be split into several kingdoms.

Kingdom Plantae consists of organisms that have cell walls of cellulose and obtain energy by photosynthesis. Organisms in the kingdom Fungi have cell walls of chitin and obtain energy by secreting digestive enzymes and then absorbing the products they release from the external environment. Kingdom Animalia contains organisms that lack cell walls and obtain energy by first ingesting other organisms and then digesting them internally.

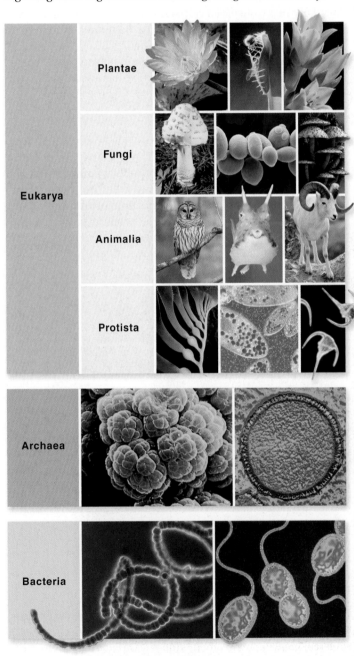

Figure 1.12 The diversity of life. Biologists categorize all living things into three overarching groups called domains: Bacteria, Archaea, and Eukarya. Domain Eukarya is composed of four kingdoms: Plantae, Fungi, Animalia, and Protista.

Evolutionary conservation explains the unity of living systems

Biologists agree that all organisms alive today have descended from some simple cellular creature that arose about 3.5 BYA. Some of the characteristics of that earliest organism have been preserved. The storage of hereditary information in DNA, for example, is common to all living things.

The retention of these conserved characteristics in a long line of descent usually reflects that they have a fundamental role in the biology of the organism—one not easily changed once adopted. A good example is provided by the homeodomain proteins, which play critical roles in early development in eukaryotes. Conserved characteristics can be seen in approximately 1850 homeodomain proteins, distributed among three different kingdoms of organisms (figure 1.13). The homeodomain proteins are powerful developmental tools that evolved early, and for which no better alternative has arisen.

Cells are information-processing systems

One way to think about cells is as highly complex nanomachines that process information. The information stored in DNA is used to direct the synthesis of cellular components, and the particular set of components can differ from cell to cell. The way that proteins fold in space is a form of information that is three-dimensional, and interesting properties emerge from the interaction of these shapes in macromolecular complexes. The control of gene expression allows differentiation of cell

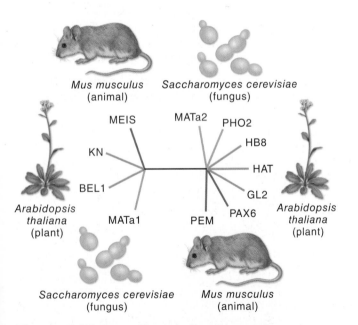

Figure 1.13 Tree of homeodomain proteins.
Homeodomain proteins are found in fungi *(brown)*, plants *(green)*, and animals *(blue)*. Based on their sequence similarities, these 11 different homeodomain proteins (uppercase letters at the ends of branches) fall into two groups, with representatives from each kingdom in each group. That means, for example, the mouse homeodomain protein PAX6 is more closely related to fungal and flowering plant proteins, such as PHO2 and GL2, than it is to the mouse protein MEIS.

types in time and space, leading to changes over developmental time into different tissue types—even though all cells in an organism carry the same genetic information.

Cells also process information that they receive about the environment. Cells sense their environment through proteins in their membranes, and this information is transmitted across the membrane to elaborate signal-transduction chemical pathways that can change the functioning of a cell.

This ability of cells to sense and respond to their environment is critical to the function of tissues and organs in multicellular organisms. A multicellular organism can regulate its internal environment, maintaining constant temperature, pH, and concentrations of vital ions. This homeostasis is possible because of elaborate signaling networks that coordinate the activities of different cells in different tissues.

Living systems exist in a nonequilibrium state

A key feature of living systems is that they are open systems that function far from thermodynamic equilibrium. This has a number of implications for their behavior. A constant supply of energy is necessary to maintain a stable nonequilibrium state. Consider the state of the nucleic acids, and proteins in all of your cells: at equilibrium they are not polymers, they would all be hydrolyzed to monomer nucleotides and amino acids. Second, nonequilibrium systems exhibit self-organizing properties not seen in equilibrium systems.

These self-organizing properties of living systems show up at different levels of the hierarchical organization. At the cellular level, macromolecular complexes such as the spindle necessary for chromosome separation can self-organize. At the population level, a flock of birds, a school of fish, or the bacteria in a biofilm are all also self-organizing. This kind of interacting behavior of individual units leads to emergent properties that are not predictable from the nature of the units themselves.

Emergent properties are properties of collections of molecules, cells, individuals, that are distinct from the categorical properties that can be described by such statistics as mean and standard deviation. The mathematics necessary to describe these kind of interacting systems is nonlinear dynamics. The emerging field of systems biology is beginning to model biological systems in this way. The kinds of feedback and feedforward loops that exist between molecules in cells, or neurons in a nervous system, lead to emergent behaviors like human consciousness.

Learning Outcomes Review 1.4

Biology is a broad and complex field, but we can identify unifying themes in this complexity. Cells are the basic unit of life, and they are information-processing machines. The structures of molecules, macromolecular complexes, cells, and even higher levels of organization are related to their functions. The diversity of life can be classified and organized based on similar features; biologists identify three large domains that encompass six kingdoms. Living organisms are able to use energy to construct complex molecules from simple ones, and are thus not in a state of thermodynamic equilibrium.

■ *How do viruses fit into our definitions of living systems?*

1.1 The Science of Life

Biology unifies much of natural science.

The study of biological systems is interdisciplinary because solutions require many different approaches to solve a problem.

Life defies simple definition.

Although life is difficult to define, living systems have seven characteristics in common. They are composed of one or more cells; are complex and highly ordered; can respond to stimuli; can grow, reproduce, and transmit genetic information to their offspring; need energy to accomplish work; can maintain relatively constant internal conditions (homeostasis); and are capable of evolutionary adaptation to the environment.

Living systems show hierarchical organization.

The hierarchical organization of living systems progresses from atoms to the biosphere. At each higher level, emergent properties arise that are greater than the sum of the parts.

1.2 The Nature of Science

At its core, science is concerned with understanding the nature of the world by using observation and reasoning.

Much of science is descriptive.

Science is concerned with developing an increasingly accurate description of nature through observation and experimentation.

Science uses both deductive and inductive reasoning.

Deductive reasoning applies general principles to predict specific results. Inductive reasoning uses specific observations to construct general scientific principles.

Hypothesis-driven science makes and tests predictions.

A hypothesis is constructed based on observations, and it must generate experimentally testable predictions. Experiments involve a test in which a variable is manipulated, and a control in which the variable is not manipulated. Hypotheses are rejected if their predictions cannot be verified by observation or experiment.

Reductionism breaks larger systems into their component parts.

Reductionism attempts to understand a complex system by breaking it down into its component parts. It is limited because parts may act differently when isolated from the larger system.

Biologists construct models to explain living systems.

A model provides a way of organizing our thinking about a problem; models may also suggest experimental approaches.

The nature of scientific theories.

Scientists use the word *theory* in two main ways: as a proposed explanation for some natural phenomenon and as a body of concepts that explains facts in an area of study.

Research can be basic or applied.

Basic research extends the boundaries of what we know; applied research seeks to use scientific findings in practical areas such as agriculture, medicine, and industry.

1.3 An Example of Scientific Inquiry: Darwin and Evolution

Darwin's theory of evolution shows how a scientist develops a hypothesis and sets forth evidence, as well as how a scientific theory grows and gains acceptance.

The idea of evolution existed prior to Darwin.

A number of naturalists and philosophers had suggested living things had changed during Earth's history. Darwin's contribution was the concept of natural selection as a mechanism for evolutionary change.

Darwin observed differences in related organisms.

During the voyage of the H.M.S. *Beagle,* Darwin had an opportunity to observe worldwide patterns of diversity.

Darwin proposed natural selection as a mechanism for evolution.

Darwin noted that species produce many offspring, but only a limited number survive and reproduce. He observed that the traits of offspring can be changed by artificial selection. Darwin proposed that individuals possessing traits that increase survival and reproductive success become more numerous in populations over time. This is the essence of descent with modification (natural selection). Alfred Russel Wallace independently came to the same conclusions from his own studies.

The predictions of natural selection have been tested.

Natural selection has been tested using data from many fields. Among these are the fossil record; the age of the Earth, determined by rates of radioactive decay to be 4.5 billion years; genetic experiments such as those of Gregor Mendel, showing that traits can be inherited as discrete units; comparative anatomy and the study of homologous structures; and molecular data that provides evidence for changes in DNA and proteins over time.

Taken together, these findings strongly support evolution by natural selection. No data to conclusively disprove evolution has been found.

1.4 Unifying Themes in Biology

Cell theory describes the organization of living systems.

The cell is the basic unit of life and is the foundation for understanding growth and reproduction in all organisms.

The molecular basis of inheritance explains the continuity of life.

Hereditary information, encoded in genes found in the DNA molecule, is passed on from one generation to the next.

The relationship between structure and function underlies living systems.

The function of macromolecules and their complexes is dictated by and dependent on their structure. Similarity of structure and function from one life-form to another may indicate an evolutionary relationship.

The diversity of life arises by evolutionary change.

Living organisms appear to have had a common origin from which a diversity of life arose by evolutionary change. They can be grouped into three domains comprising six kingdoms based on their differences.

Evolutionary conservation explains the unity of living systems.

The underlying similarities in biochemistry and genetics support the contention that all life evolved from a single source.

Cells are information-processing systems.

Cells can sense and respond to environmental changes through proteins located on their cell membranes. Differential expression of stored genetic information is the basis for different cell types.

Living systems exist in a nonequilibrium state.

Organisms are open systems that need a constant supply of energy to maintain their stable nonequilibrium state. Living things are able to self-organize, creating levels of complexity that may exhibit emergent properties.

UNDERSTAND

1. Which of the following is NOT a property of life?

   a. Energy utilization   c. Order
   b. Movement   d. Homeostasis

2. The process of inductive reasoning involves

   a. the use of general principles to predict a specific result.
   b. the generation of specific predictions based on a belief system.
   c. the use of specific observations to develop general principles.
   d. the use of general principles to support a hypothesis.

3. A hypothesis in biology is best described as

   a. a possible explanation of an observation.
   b. an observation that supports a theory.
   c. a general principle that explains some aspect of life.
   d. an unchanging statement that correctly predicts some aspect of life.

4. A scientific theory is

   a. a guess about how things work in the world.
   b. a statement of how the world works that is supported by experimental data.
   c. a belief held by many scientists.
   d. Both a and c are correct.

5. The cell theory states that

   a. cells are small.
   b. cells are highly organized.
   c. there is only one basic type of cell.
   d. all living things are made up of cells.

6. The molecule DNA is important to biological systems because

   a. it can be replicated.
   b. it encodes the information for making a new individual.
   c. it forms a complex, double-helical structure.
   d. nucleotides form genes.

7. The organization of living systems is

   a. linear with cells at one end and the biosphere at the other.
   b. circular with cells in the center.
   c. hierarchical with cells at the base, and the biosphere at the top.
   d. chaotic and beyond description.

8. The idea of evolution

   a. was original to Darwin.
   b. was original to Wallace.
   c. predated Darwin and Wallace.
   d. Both a and b are correct.

APPLY

1. What is the significance of Pasteur's experiment to test the germ hypothesis?

   a. It proved that heat can sterilize a broth.
   b. It demonstrated that cells can arise spontaneously.
   c. It demonstrated that some cells are germs.
   d. It demonstrated that cells can only arise from other cells.

2. Which of the following is NOT an example of reductionism?

   a. Analysis of an isolated enzyme's function in an experimental assay
   b. Investigation of the effect of a hormone on cell growth in a Petri dish
   c. Observation of the change in gene expression in response to specific stimulus
   d. An evaluation of the overall behavior of a cell

3. How is the process of natural selection different from that of artificial selection?

   a. Natural selection produces more variation.
   b. Natural selection makes an individual better adapted.
   c. Artificial selection is a result of human intervention.
   d. Artificial selection results in better adaptations.

4. If you found a fossil for a modern organism next to the fossil of a dinosaur, this would

   a. argue against evolution by natural selection.
   b. have no bearing on evolution by natural selection.
   c. indicate that dinosaurs may still exist.
   d. Both b and c are correct.

5. The theory of evolution by natural selection is a good example of how science proceeds because

   a. it rationalizes a large body of observations.
   b. it makes predictions that have been tested by a variety of approaches.
   c. it represents Darwin's belief of how life has changed over time.
   d. Both b and c are correct.

6. In which domain of life would you find only single-celled organisms?

   a. Eukarya   c. Archaea
   b. Bacteria   d. Both b and c are correct.

7. Evolutionary conservation occurs when a characteristic is

   a. important to the life of the organism.
   b. not influenced by evolution.
   c. no longer functionally important.
   d. found in more primitive organisms.

SYNTHESIZE

1. Exobiology is the study of life on other planets. In recent years, scientists have sent various spacecraft out into the galaxy in search for extraterrestrial life. Assuming that all life shares common properties, what should exobiologists be looking for as they explore other worlds?

2. The classic experiment by Pasteur (figure 1.4) tested the hypothesis that cells arise from other cells. In this experiment cell growth was measured following sterilization of broth in a swan-necked flask or in a flask with a broken neck.

   a. Which variables were kept the same in these two experiments?
   b. How does the shape of the flask affect the experiment?
   c. Predict the outcome of each experiment based on the two hypotheses.
   d. Some bacteria (germs) are capable of producing heat-resistant spores that protect the cell and allow it to continue to grow after the environment cools. How would the outcome of this experiment have been affected if spore-forming bacteria were present in the broth?

Chapter 2

The Nature of Molecules and the Properties of Water

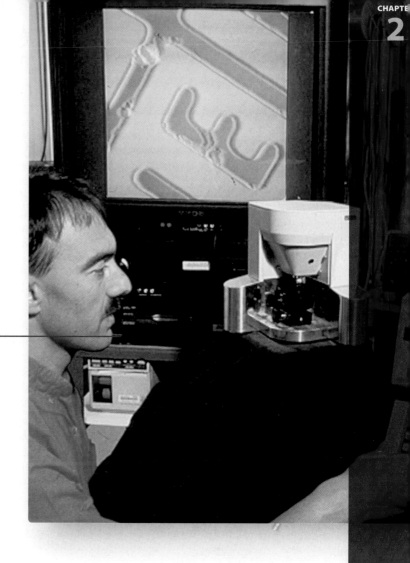

Chapter Contents

Introduction

About 12.5 billion years ago (BYA), an enormous explosion probably signaled the beginning of the universe. This explosion started a process of star building and planetary formation that eventually led to the formation of Earth, about 4.5 BYA. Around 3.5 BYA, life began on Earth and started to diversify. To understand the nature of life on Earth, we first need to understand the nature of the matter that forms the building blocks of all life.

The earliest speculations about the world around us included this most basic question, "What is it made of?" The ancient Greeks recognized that larger things may be built of smaller parts. This concept was formed into a solid experimental scientific idea in the early 20th century, when physicists began trying to break atoms apart. From those humble beginnings to the huge particle accelerators used by the modern physicists of today, the picture of the atomic world emerges as fundamentally different from the tangible, macroscopic world around us.

To understand how living systems are assembled, we must first understand a little about atomic structure, about how atoms can be linked together by chemical bonds to make molecules, and about the ways in which these small molecules are joined together to make larger molecules, until finally we arrive at the structures of cells and then of organisms. Our study of life on Earth therefore begins with physics and chemistry. For many of you, this chapter will be a review of material encountered in other courses.

The Nature of Atoms

Learning Outcomes

1. *Define an element based on its composition.*
2. *Describe how atomic structure produces chemical properties.*
3. *Explain where electrons are found in an atom.*

Any substance in the universe that has mass and occupies space is defined as *matter*. All matter is composed of extremely small particles called **atoms.** Because of their size, atoms are difficult to study. Not until early in the 20th century did scientists carry out the first experiments revealing the physical nature of atoms (figure 2.1).

SCIENTIFIC THINKING

Hypothesis: *Atoms are composed of diffuse positive charge with embedded negative charge (electrons).*

Prediction: *If alpha particles (α), which are helium nuclei, are shot at a thin foil of gold, the α-particles will not be deflected much by the diffuse positive charge or by the light electrons.*

Test: *α-Particles are shot at a thin sheet of gold foil surrounded by a detector screen, which shows flashes of light when hit by the particles.*

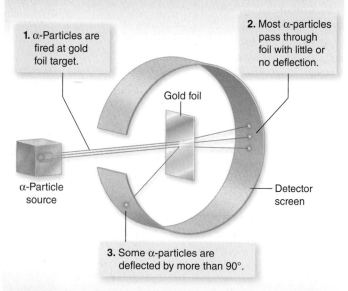

1. α-Particles are fired at gold foil target.

2. Most α-particles pass through foil with little or no deflection.

Gold foil

α-Particle source

Detector screen

3. Some α-particles are deflected by more than 90°.

Result: *Most particles are not deflected at all, but a small percentage of particles are deflected at angles of 90° or more.*

Conclusion: *The hypothesis is not supported. The large deflections observed led to a view of the atom as composed of a very small central region containing positive charge (the nucleus) surrounded by electrons.*

Further Experiments: *How does the Bohr atom with its quantized energy for electrons extend this model?*

Figure 2.1 Rutherford scattering experiment.
Large-angle scattering of α-particles led Rutherford to propose the existence of the nucleus.

Atomic structure includes a central nucleus and orbiting electrons

Objects as small as atoms can be "seen" only indirectly, by using complex technology such as tunneling microscopy (figure 2.2). We now know a great deal about the complexities of atomic structure, but the simple view put forth in 1913 by the Danish physicist Niels Bohr provides a good starting point for understanding atomic theory. Bohr proposed that every atom possesses an orbiting cloud of tiny subatomic particles called *electrons* whizzing around a core, like the planets of a miniature solar system. At the center of each atom is a small, very dense nucleus formed of two other kinds of subatomic particles: *protons* and *neutrons* (figure 2.3).

Atomic number and the elements

Within the nucleus, the cluster of protons and neutrons is held together by a force that works only over short, subatomic distances. Each proton carries a positive (+) charge, and each neutron has no charge. Each electron carries a negative (–) charge. Typically, an atom has one electron for each proton and is, thus, electrically neutral. Different atoms are defined by the number of protons, a quantity called the *atomic number*. The chemical behavior of an atom is due to the number and configuration of electrons, as we will see later in this chapter. Atoms with the same atomic number (that is, the same number of protons) have the same chemical properties and are said to belong to the same element. Formally speaking, an *element* is any substance that cannot be broken down to any other substance by ordinary chemical means.

Atomic mass

The terms *mass* and *weight* are often used interchangeably, but they have slightly different meanings. *Mass* refers to the amount of a substance, but *weight* refers to the force gravity exerts on a substance. An object has the same mass whether it is on the Earth or the Moon, but its weight will be greater on the Earth because the Earth's gravitational force is greater than the Moon's. The *atomic mass* of an atom is equal to the sum of the masses of its protons and neutrons. Atoms that occur naturally on Earth contain from 1 to 92 protons and up to 146 neutrons.

Figure 2.2 Scanning-tunneling microscope image. The scanning-tunneling microscope is a nonoptical way of imaging that allows atoms to be visualized. This image shows a lattice of oxygen atoms (dark blue) on a rhodium crystal (light blue).

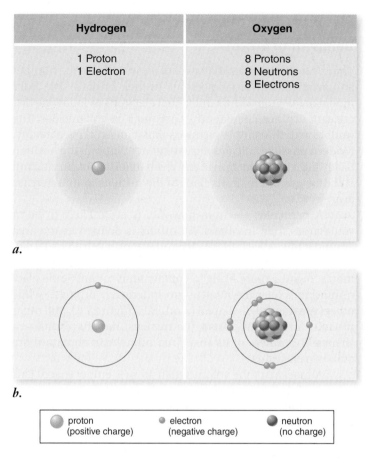

Hydrogen	Oxygen
1 Proton 1 Electron	8 Protons 8 Neutrons 8 Electrons

a.

b.

● proton (positive charge)	● electron (negative charge)	● neutron (no charge)

Figure 2.3 Basic structure of atoms. All atoms have a nucleus consisting of protons and neutrons, except hydrogen, the smallest atom, which usually has only one proton and no neutrons in its nucleus. Oxygen typically has eight protons and eight neutrons in its nucleus. In the simple "Bohr model" of atoms pictured here, electrons spin around the nucleus at a relatively far distance. *a.* Atoms are depicted as a nucleus with a cloud of electrons (not shown to scale). *b.* The electrons are shown in discrete energy levels. These are described in greater detail in the text.

The mass of atoms and subatomic particles is measured in units called *daltons.* To give you an idea of just how small these units are, note that it takes 602 million million billion (6.02×10^{23}) daltons to make 1 gram (g). A proton weighs approximately 1 dalton (actually 1.007 daltons), as does a neutron (1.009 daltons). In contrast, electrons weigh only 1/1840 of

a dalton, so they contribute almost nothing to the overall mass of an atom.

Electrons

The positive charges in the nucleus of an atom are neutralized, or counterbalanced, by negatively charged electrons, which are located in regions called **orbitals** that lie at varying distances around the nucleus. Atoms with the same number of protons and electrons are electrically neutral; that is, they have no net charge, and are therefore called *neutral atoms.*

Electrons are maintained in their orbitals by their attraction to the positively charged nucleus. Sometimes other forces overcome this attraction, and an atom loses one or more electrons. In other cases, atoms gain additional electrons. Atoms in which the number of electrons does not equal the number of protons are known as *ions,* and they are charged particles. An atom having more protons than electrons has a net positive charge and is called a **cation.** For example, an atom of sodium (Na) that has lost one electron becomes a sodium ion (Na^+), with a charge of +1. An atom having fewer protons than electrons carries a net negative charge and is called an **anion.** A chlorine atom (Cl) that has gained one electron becomes a chloride ion (Cl^-), with a charge of –1.

Isotopes

Although all atoms of an element have the same number of protons, they may not all have the same number of neutrons. Atoms of a single element that possess different numbers of neutrons are called **isotopes** of that element.

Most elements in nature exist as mixtures of different isotopes. Carbon (C), for example, has three isotopes, all containing six protons (figure 2.4). Over 99% of the carbon found in nature exists as an isotope that also contains six neutrons. Because the total mass of this isotope is 12 daltons (6 from protons plus 6 from neutrons), it is referred to as carbon-12 and is symbolized ^{12}C. Most of the rest of the naturally occurring carbon is carbon-13, an isotope with seven neutrons. The rarest carbon isotope is carbon-14, with eight neutrons. Unlike the other two isotopes, carbon-14 is unstable: This means that its nucleus tends to break up into elements with lower atomic numbers. This nuclear breakup, which emits a significant amount of energy, is called *radioactive decay,* and isotopes that decay in this fashion are **radioactive isotopes.**

Some radioactive isotopes are more unstable than others, and therefore they decay more readily. For any given isotope, however, the rate of decay is constant. The decay time is usually expressed as the *half-life,* the time it takes for one-half

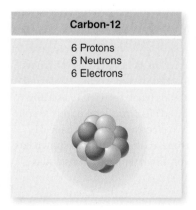

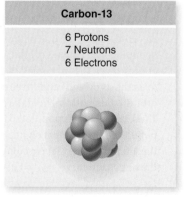

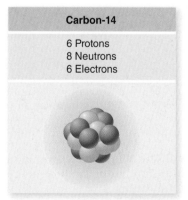

Carbon-12	Carbon-13	Carbon-14
6 Protons 6 Neutrons 6 Electrons	6 Protons 7 Neutrons 6 Electrons	6 Protons 8 Neutrons 6 Electrons

Figure 2.4 The three most abundant isotopes of carbon. Isotopes of a particular element have different numbers of neutrons.

of the atoms in a sample to decay. Carbon-14, for example, often used in the carbon dating of fossils and other materials, has a half-life of 5730 years. A sample of carbon containing 1 g of carbon-14 today would contain 0.5 g of carbon-14 after 5730 years, 0.25 g 11,460 years from now, 0.125 g 17,190 years from now, and so on. By determining the ratios of the different isotopes of carbon and other elements in biological samples and in rocks, scientists are able to accurately determine when these materials formed.

Radioactivity has many useful applications in modern biology. Radioactive isotopes are one way to label, or "tag," a specific molecule and then follow its progress, either in a chemical reaction or in living cells and tissue. The downside, however, is that the energetic subatomic particles emitted by radioactive substances have the potential to severely damage living cells, producing genetic mutations and, at high doses, cell death. Consequently, exposure to radiation is carefully controlled and regulated. Scientists who work with radio-activity follow strict handling protocols and wear radiation-sensitive badges to monitor their exposure over time to help ensure a safe level of exposure.

Electrons determine the chemical behavior of atoms

The key to the chemical behavior of an atom lies in the number and arrangement of its electrons in their orbitals. The Bohr model of the atom shows individual electrons as following discrete, or distinct, circular orbits around a central nucleus. The trouble with this simple picture is that it doesn't reflect reality. Modern physics indicates that we cannot pinpoint the position of any individual electron at any given time. In fact, an electron could be anywhere, from close to the nucleus to infinitely far away from it.

A particular electron, however, is more likely to be in some areas than in others. An orbital is defined as the area around a nucleus where an electron is most likely to be found. These orbitals represent probability distributions for electrons, that is, regions more likely to contain an electron. Some electron orbitals near the nucleus are spherical (*s* orbitals), while others are dumbbell-shaped (*p* orbitals) (figure 2.5). Still other orbitals, farther away from the nucleus, may have different shapes. Regardless of its shape, no orbital can contain more than two electrons.

Almost all of the volume of an atom is empty space. This is because the electrons are usually far away from the nucleus, relative to its size. If the nucleus of an atom were the size of a golf ball, the orbit of the nearest electron would be a mile away. Consequently, the nuclei of two atoms never come close enough in nature to interact with each other. It is for this reason that an atom's electrons, not its protons or neutrons, determine its chemical behavior, and it also explains why the isotopes of an element, all of which have the same arrangement of electrons, behave the same way chemically.

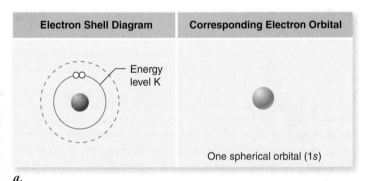

a.

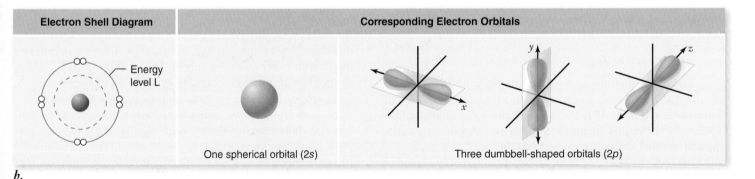

b.

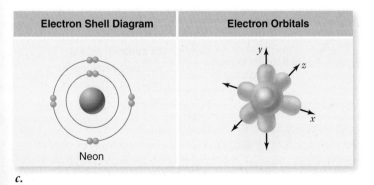

c.

Figure 2.5 Electron orbitals. *a.* The lowest energy level, or electron shell—the one nearest the nucleus—is level K. It is occupied by a single *s* orbital, referred to as 1*s*. ***b.*** The next highest energy level, L, is occupied by four orbitals: one *s* orbital (referred to as the 2*s* orbital) and three *p* orbitals (each referred to as a 2*p* orbital). Each orbital holds two paired electrons with opposite spin. Thus, the K level is populated by two electrons, and the L level is populated by a total of eight electrons. ***c.*** The neon atom shown has the L and K energy levels completely filled with electrons and is thus unreactive.

Atoms contain discrete energy levels

Because electrons are attracted to the positively charged nucleus, it takes work to keep them in their orbitals, just as it takes work to hold a grapefruit in your hand against the pull of gravity. The formal definition of energy is the ability to do work.

The grapefruit held above the ground is said to possess *potential energy* because of its position. If you release it, the grapefruit falls, and its potential energy is reduced. On the other hand, if you carried the grapefruit to the top of a building, you would increase its potential energy. Electrons also have a potential energy that is related to their position. To oppose the attraction of the nucleus and move the electron to a more distant orbital requires an input of energy, which results in an electron with greater potential energy. The chlorophyll that makes plants green captures energy from light during photosynthesis in this way. As you'll see in chapter 8—light energy excites electrons in the chlorophyll molecule. Moving an electron closer to the nucleus has the opposite effect: Energy is released, usually as radiant energy (heat or light), and the electron ends up with less potential energy (figure 2.6).

One of the initially surprising aspects of atomic structure is that electrons within the atom have discrete **energy levels.** These discrete levels correspond to quanta (sing., quantum), which means specific amount of energy. To use the grapefruit analogy again, it is as though a grapefruit could only be raised to particular floors of a building. Every atom exhibits a ladder of potential energy values, a discrete set of orbitals at particular energetic "distances" from the nucleus.

Because the amount of energy an electron possesses is related to its distance from the nucleus, electrons that are the same distance from the nucleus have the same energy, even if they occupy different orbitals. Such electrons are said to occupy the same energy level. The energy levels are denoted with letters K, L, M, and so on (see figure 2.6). Be careful not to confuse energy levels, which are drawn as rings to indicate an electron's *energy,* with orbitals, which have a variety of three-dimensional shapes and indicate an electron's most likely *location.* Electron orbitals are arranged so that as they are filled, this fills each energy level in successive order. This filling of orbitals and energy levels is what is responsible for the chemical reactivity of elements.

During some chemical reactions, electrons are transferred from one atom to another. In such reactions, the loss of an electron is called **oxidation,** and the gain of an electron is called *reduction.*

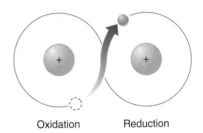

Oxidation   Reduction

Notice that when an electron is transferred in this way, it keeps its energy of position. In organisms, chemical energy is stored in high-energy electrons that are transferred from one atom to another in reactions involving oxidation and reduction (described in chapter 7). When the processes of oxidation and reduction are coupled, which often happens, one atom or molecule is oxidized while another is reduced in the same reaction. We call these combinations *redox reactions.*

Learning Outcomes Review 2.1

An atom consists of a nucleus of protons and neutrons surrounded by a cloud of electrons. For each atom, the number of protons is the atomic number; atoms with the same atomic number constitute an element. Atoms of a single element that have different numbers of neutrons are called isotopes. Electrons, which determine the chemical behavior of an element, are located about a nucleus in orbitals representing discrete energy levels. No orbital can contain more than two electrons, but each energy level consists of multiple orbitals, and thus contains many electrons with the same energy.

- **If the number of protons exceeds the number of neutrons, is the charge on the atom positive or negative?**
- **If the number of protons exceeds electrons?**

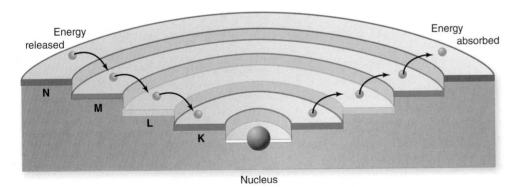

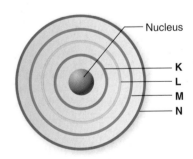

Figure 2.6 Atomic energy levels. Electrons have energy of position. When an atom absorbs energy, an electron moves to a higher energy level, farther from the nucleus. When an electron falls to lower energy levels, closer to the nucleus, energy is released. The first two energy levels are the same as shown in the previous figure.

Elements Found in Living Systems

Ninety elements occur naturally, each with a different number of protons and a different arrangement of electrons. When the 19th-century Russian chemist Dmitri Mendeleev arranged the known elements in a table according to their atomic number, he discovered one of the great generalizations of science: The elements exhibit a pattern of chemical properties that repeats itself in groups of eight. This periodically repeating pattern lent the table its name: the periodic table of elements (figure 2.7).

The periodic table displays elements according to atomic number and properties

The eight-element periodicity that Mendeleev found is based on the interactions of the electrons in the outermost energy level of the different elements. These electrons are called **valence electrons,** and their interactions are the basis for the elements' differing chemical properties. For most of the atoms important to life, the outermost energy level can contain no more than eight electrons; the chemical behavior of an element reflects how many of the eight positions are filled.

Elements possessing all eight electrons in their outer energy level (two for helium) are *inert,* or nonreactive. These elements, which include helium (He), neon (Ne), argon (Ar), and so on, are termed the *noble gases.* In sharp contrast, elements with seven electrons (one fewer than the maximum number of eight) in their outer energy level, such as fluorine (F), chlorine (Cl), and bromine (Br), are highly reactive. They tend to gain the extra electron needed to fill the energy level. Elements with only one electron in their outer energy level, such as lithium (Li), sodium (Na), and potassium (K), are also very reactive. They tend to lose the single electron in their outer level.

Mendeleev's periodic table leads to a useful generalization, the **octet rule,** or *rule of eight* (Latin *octo,* "eight"): Atoms tend to establish completely full outer energy levels. For the main group elements of the periodic table, the rule of eight is accomplished by one filled *s* orbital and three filled *p* orbitals (figure 2.8). The exception to this is He, in the first row, which needs only two electrons to fill the 1*s* orbital. Most chemical behavior of biological interest can be predicted quite accurately from this simple rule, combined with the tendency of atoms to balance positive and negative charges. For instance, you read earlier that sodium ion (Na$^+$) has lost an electron, and chloride ion (Cl$^-$) has gained an electron. In the following section, we describe how these ions react to form table salt.

Of the 90 naturally occurring elements on Earth, only 12 (C, H, O, N, P, S, Na, K, Ca, Mg, Fe, Cl) are found in living systems in more than trace amounts (0.01% or higher). These elements all have atomic numbers less than 21, and thus, have low atomic masses. Of these 12, the first 4 elements (carbon, hydrogen, oxygen, and nitrogen) constitute 96.3% of the weight of your body. The majority of molecules that make up your body (other than water) are compounds of carbon, which we call

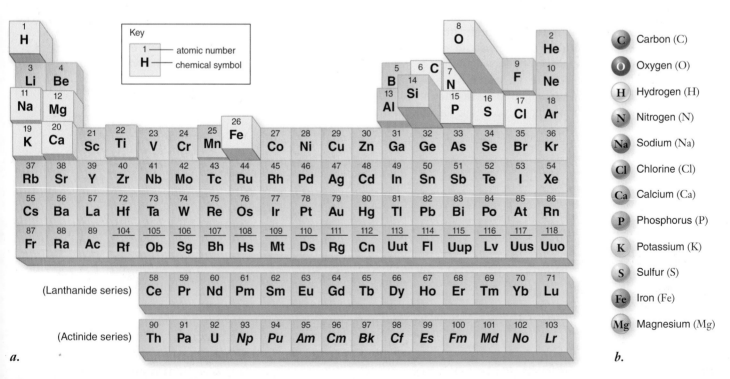

Figure 2.7 Periodic table of the elements. *a.* In this representation, the frequency of elements that occur in the Earth's crust is indicated by the height of the block. Elements shaded in green are found in living systems in more than trace amounts. *b.* Common elements found in living systems are shown in colors that will be used throughout the text.

Nonreactive	Reactive
2 protons 2 neutrons 2 electrons	7 protons 7 neutrons 7 electrons

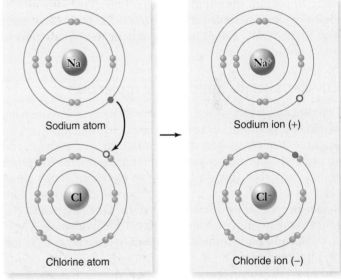

Figure 2.8 Electron energy levels for helium and nitrogen. Green balls represent electrons, blue ball represents the nucleus with number of protons indicated by number of (+) charges. Note that the helium atom has a filled K shell and is thus unreactive, whereas the nitrogen atom has five electrons in the L shell, three of which are unpaired, making it reactive.

organic compounds. These organic compounds contain primarily these four elements (CHON), explaining their prevalence in living systems. Some trace elements, such as zinc (Zn) and iodine (I), play crucial roles in living processes even though they are present in tiny amounts. Iodine deficiency, for example, can lead to enlargement of the thyroid gland, causing a bulge at the neck called a goiter.

Learning Outcomes Review 2.2

The periodic table shows the elements in terms of atomic number and repeating chemical properties. Only 12 elements are found in significant amounts in living organisms: C, H, O, N, P, S, Na, K, Ca, Mg, Fe, and Cl.

- *Why are the noble gases more stable than other elements in the periodic table?*

2.3 The Nature of Chemical Bonds

Learning Outcomes

1. *Predict which elements are likely to form ions.*
2. *Explain how molecules can be built from atoms joined by covalent bonds.*
3. *Contrast polar and nonpolar covalent bonds.*

A group of atoms held together by energy in a stable association is called a *molecule.* When a molecule contains atoms of more than one element, it is called a *compound.* The atoms in a molecule are joined by *chemical bonds;* these bonds can result when atoms with opposite charges attract each other (ionic bonds), when two atoms share one or more pairs of electrons

TABLE 2.1	Bonds and Interactions	
Name	**Basis of Interaction**	**Strength**
Covalent bond	Sharing of electron pairs	Strong
Ionic bond	Attraction of opposite charges	
Hydrogen bond	Sharing of H atom	
Hydrophobic interaction	Forcing of hydrophobic portions of molecules together in presence of polar substances	
van der Waals attraction	Weak attractions between atoms due to oppositely polarized electron clouds	Weak

(covalent bonds), or when atoms interact in other ways (table 2.1). We will start by examining *ionic bonds,* which form when atoms with opposite electrical charges (ions) attract.

Ionic bonds form crystals

Common table salt, the molecule sodium chloride (NaCl), is a lattice of ions in which the atoms are held together by ionic bonds (figure 2.9). Sodium has 11 electrons: 2 in the inner

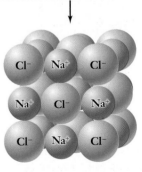

Figure 2.9 The formation of ionic bonds by sodium chloride.
a. When a sodium atom donates an electron to a chlorine atom, the sodium atom becomes a positively charged sodium ion, and the chlorine atom becomes a negatively charged chloride ion. *b.* The electrostatic attraction of oppositely charged ions leads to the formation of a lattice of Na^+ and Cl^-.

b. NaCl crystal

chapter **2** *The Nature of Molecules and the Properties of Water* **23**

energy level (K), 8 in the next level (L), and 1 in the outer (valence) level (M). The single, unpaired valence electron has a strong tendency to join with another unpaired electron in another atom. A stable configuration can be achieved if the valence electron is lost to another atom that also has an unpaired electron. The loss of this electron results in the formation of a positively charged sodium ion, Na^+.

The chlorine atom has 17 electrons: 2 in the K level, 8 in the L level, and 7 in the M level. As you can see in the figure, one of the orbitals in the outer energy level has an unpaired electron (red circle). The addition of another electron fills that level and causes a negatively charged chloride ion, Cl^-, to form.

When placed together, metallic sodium and gaseous chlorine react swiftly and explosively, as the sodium atoms donate electrons to chlorine to form Na^+ and Cl^- ions. Because opposite charges attract, the Na^+ and Cl^- remain associated in an *ionic compound,* NaCl, which is electrically neutral. The electrical attractive force holding NaCl together, however, is not directed specifically between individual Na^+ and Cl^- ions, and no individual sodium chloride molecules form. Instead, the force exists between any one ion and *all* neighboring ions of the opposite charge. The ions aggregate in a crystal matrix with a precise geometry. Such aggregations are what we know as salt crystals. If a salt such as NaCl is placed in water, the electrical attraction of the water molecules, for reasons we will point out later in this chapter, disrupts the forces holding the ions in their crystal matrix, causing the salt to dissolve into a roughly equal mixture of free Na^+ and Cl^- ions.

Because living systems always include water, ions are more important than ionic crystals. Important ions in biological systems include Ca^{2+}, which is involved in cell signaling, K^+ and Na^+, which are involved in the conduction of nerve impulses.

Covalent bonds build stable molecules

Covalent bonds form when two atoms share one or more pairs of valence electrons. Consider gaseous hydrogen (H_2) as an example. Each hydrogen atom has an unpaired electron and an unfilled outer energy level; for these reasons, the hydrogen atom is unstable. However, when two hydrogen atoms are in close association, each atom's electron is attracted to both nuclei. In effect, the nuclei are able to share their electrons. The result is a diatomic (two-atom) molecule of hydrogen gas.

The molecule formed by the two hydrogen atoms is stable for three reasons:

1. **It has no net charge.** The diatomic molecule formed as a result of this sharing of electrons is not charged because it still contains two protons and two electrons.
2. **The octet rule is satisfied.** Each of the two hydrogen atoms can be considered to have two orbiting electrons in its outer energy level. This state satisfies the octet rule, because each shared electron orbits both nuclei and is included in the outer energy level of both atoms.
3. **It has no unpaired electrons.** The bond between the two atoms also pairs the two free electrons.

Unlike ionic bonds, covalent bonds are formed between two individual atoms, giving rise to true, discrete molecules.

The strength of covalent bonds

The strength of a covalent bond depends on the number of shared electrons. Thus *double bonds,* which satisfy the octet rule by allowing two atoms to share two pairs of electrons, are stronger than *single bonds,* in which only one electron pair is shared. In practical terms, more energy is required to break a double bond than a single bond. The strongest covalent bonds are *triple bonds,* such as those that link the two nitrogen atoms of nitrogen gas molecules (N_2).

Covalent bonds are represented in chemical formulas as lines connecting atomic symbols. Each line between two bonded atoms represents the sharing of one pair of electrons. The *structural formulas* of hydrogen gas and oxygen gas are H—H and O=O, respectively, and their *molecular formulas* are H_2 and O_2. The structural formula for N_2 is N≡N.

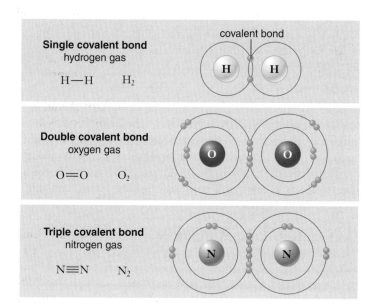

Molecules with several covalent bonds

A vast number of biological compounds are composed of more than two atoms. An atom that requires two, three, or four additional electrons to fill its outer energy level completely may acquire them by sharing its electrons with two or more other atoms.

For example, the carbon atom (C) contains six electrons, four of which are in its outer energy level and are unpaired. To satisfy the octet rule, a carbon atom must form four covalent bonds. Because four covalent bonds may form in many ways, carbon atoms are found in many different kinds of molecules. CO_2 (carbon dioxide), CH_4 (methane), and C_2H_5OH (ethanol) are just a few examples.

Polar and nonpolar covalent bonds

Atoms differ in their affinity for electrons, a property called **electronegativity.** In general, electronegativity increases left to right across a row of the periodic table and decreases down the column. Thus the elements in the upper-right corner have the highest electronegativity.

For bonds between identical atoms, for example, between two hydrogen or two oxygen atoms, the affinity for electrons is obviously the same, and the electrons are equally shared. Such bonds are termed **nonpolar.** The resulting compounds (H_2 or O_2) are also referred to as nonpolar.

For atoms that differ greatly in electronegativity, electrons are not shared equally. The shared electrons are more likely to be closer to the atom with greater electronegativity, and less likely to be near the atom of lower electronegativity. In this case, although the molecule is still electrically neutral (same number of protons as electrons), the distribution of charge is not uniform. This unequal distribution results in regions of partial negative charge near the more electronegative atom, and regions of partial positive charge near the less electronegative atom. Such bonds are termed **polar covalent bonds,** and the molecules polar molecules. When drawing polar molecules, these partial charges are usually symbolized by the lowercase Greek letter delta (δ). The partial charge seen in a polar covalent bond is relatively small—far less than the unit charge of an ion. For biological molecules, we can predict polarity of bonds by knowing the relative electronegativity of a small number of important atoms (table 2.2). Notice that although C and H differ slightly in electronegativity, this small difference is negligible, and C—H bonds are considered nonpolar.

Because of its importance in the chemistry of water, we will explore the nature of polar and nonpolar molecules in the following section on water. Water (H_2O) is a polar molecule with electrons more concentrated around the oxygen atom.

Chemical reactions alter bonds

The formation and breaking of chemical bonds, which is the essence of chemistry, is termed a *chemical reaction.* All chemical reactions involve the shifting of atoms from one molecule or ionic compound to another, without any change in the number or identity of the atoms. For convenience, we refer to the original molecules before the reaction starts as *reactants,* and the molecules resulting from the chemical reaction as *products.* For example:

$$6H_2O + 6CO_2 \longrightarrow C_6H_{12}O_6 + 6O_2$$
$$\text{\textit{reactants}} \quad \longrightarrow \quad \text{\textit{products}}$$

You may recognize this reaction as a simplified form of the photosynthesis reaction, in which water and carbon dioxide are combined to produce glucose and oxygen. Most animal life ultimately depends on this reaction, which takes place in plants. (Photosynthetic reactions will be discussed in detail in chapter 8.)

TABLE 2.2	Relative Electronegativities of Some Important Atoms
Atom	**Electronegativity**
O	3.5
N	3.0
C	2.5
H	2.1

The extent to which chemical reactions occur is influenced by three important factors:

1. **Temperature.** Heating the reactants increases the rate of a reaction because the reactants collide with one another more often. (Care must be taken that the temperature is not so high that it destroys the molecules.)
2. **Concentration of reactants and products.** Reactions proceed more quickly when more reactants are available, allowing more frequent collisions. An accumulation of products typically slows the reaction and, in reversible reactions, may speed the reaction in the reverse direction.
3. **Catalysts.** A catalyst is a substance that increases the rate of a reaction. It doesn't alter the reaction's equilibrium between reactants and products, but it does shorten the time needed to reach equilibrium, often dramatically. In living systems, proteins called enzymes catalyze almost every chemical reaction.

Many reactions in nature are reversible. This means that the products may themselves be reactants, allowing the reaction to proceed in reverse. We can write the preceding reaction in the reverse order:

$$C_6H_{12}O_6 + 6O_2 \longrightarrow 6H_2O + 6CO_2$$
$$\text{\textit{reactants}} \quad \longrightarrow \quad \text{\textit{products}}$$

This reaction is a simplified version of the oxidation of glucose by cellular respiration, in which glucose is broken down into water and carbon dioxide in the presence of oxygen. Virtually all organisms carry out forms of glucose oxidation; details are covered later, in chapter 7.

Learning Outcomes Review 2.3

An ionic bond is an attraction between ions of opposite charge in an ionic compound. A covalent bond is formed when two atoms share one or more pairs of electrons. Complex biological compounds are formed in large part by atoms that can form one or more covalent bonds: C, H, O, and N. A polar covalent bond is formed by unequal sharing of electrons. Nonpolar bonds exhibit equal sharing of electrons.

■ *How is a polar covalent bond different from an ionic bond?*

2.4 *Water: A Vital Compound*

Learning Outcomes

1. *Relate how the structure of water leads to hydrogen bonds.*
2. *Describe water's cohesive and adhesive properties.*

Of all the common molecules, only water exists as a liquid at the relatively low temperatures that prevail on the Earth's surface. Three-fourths of the Earth is covered by liquid water

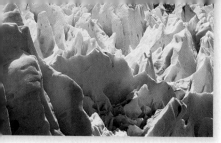
a. Solid

b. Liquid

c. Gas

Figure 2.10 Water takes many forms. *a.* When water cools below 0°C, it forms beautiful crystals, familiar to us as snow and ice. *b.* Ice turns to liquid when the temperature is above 0°C. *c.* Liquid water becomes steam when the temperature rises above 100°C, as seen in this hot spring at Yellowstone National Park.

(figure 2.10). When life was beginning, water provided a medium in which other molecules could move around and interact, without being held in place by strong covalent or ionic bonds. Life evolved in water for 2 billion years before spreading to land. And even today, life is inextricably tied to water. About two-thirds of any organism's body is composed of water, and all organisms require a water-rich environment, either inside or outside it, for growth and reproduction. It is no accident that tropical rain forests are bursting with life, while dry deserts appear almost lifeless except when water becomes temporarily plentiful, such as after a rainstorm.

Water's structure facilitates hydrogen bonding

Water has a simple molecular structure, consisting of an oxygen atom bound to two hydrogen atoms by two single covalent bonds (figure 2.11). The resulting molecule is stable: It satisfies the octet rule, has no unpaired electrons, and carries no net electrical charge.

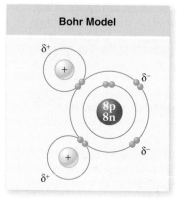

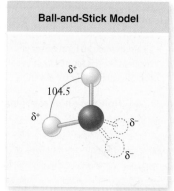

a.

b.

Figure 2.11 Water has a simple molecular structure. *a.* Each water molecule is composed of one oxygen atom and two hydrogen atoms. The oxygen atom shares one electron with each hydrogen atom. *b.* The greater electronegativity of the oxygen atom makes the water molecule polar: Water carries two partial negative charges (δ^-) near the oxygen atom and two partial positive charges (δ^+), one on each hydrogen atom. *c.* Space-filling model shows what the molecule would look like if it were visible.

The single most outstanding chemical property of water is its ability to form weak chemical associations, called **hydrogen bonds.** These bonds form between the partially negative O atoms and the partially positive H atoms of two water molecules. Although these bonds have only 5–10% of the strength of covalent bonds, they are important to DNA and protein structure, and thus responsible for much of the chemical organization of living systems.

The electronegativity of O is much greater than that of H (see table 2.2), and so the bonds between these atoms are highly polar. *The polarity of water underlies water's chemistry and the chemistry of life.*

If we consider the shape of a water molecule, we see that its two covalent bonds have a partial charge at each end: δ^- at the oxygen end and δ^+ at the hydrogen end. The most stable arrangement of these charges is a *tetrahedron (a pyramid with a triangle as its base),* in which the two negative and two positive charges are approximately equidistant from one another. The oxygen atom lies at the center of the tetrahedron, the hydrogen atoms occupy two of the apexes (corners), and the partial negative charges occupy the other two apexes (figure 2.11*b*). The bond angle between the two covalent oxygen–hydrogen bonds is 104.5°. This value is slightly less than the bond angle of a regular tetrahedron, which would be 109.5°. In water, the partial negative charges occupy more space than the partial positive regions, so the oxygen–hydrogen bond angle is slightly compressed.

Water molecules are cohesive

The polarity of water allows water molecules to be attracted to one another: that is, water is *cohesive.* The oxygen end of each water molecule, which is δ^-, is attracted to the hydrogen end, which is δ^+, of other molecules. The attraction produces hydrogen bonds among water molecules (figure 2.12). Each hydrogen bond is individually very weak and transient, lasting on average only a hundred-billionth (10^{-11}) of a second. The cumulative effects of large numbers of these bonds, however, can be enormous. Water forms an abundance of hydrogen bonds, which are responsible for many of its important physical properties (table 2.3).

Water's cohesion is responsible for its being a liquid, not a gas, at moderate temperatures. The cohesion of liquid water is also responsible for its **surface tension.** Small insects can walk on water (figure 2.13) because at the air–water interface, all the surface water molecules are hydrogen-bonded to molecules below them.

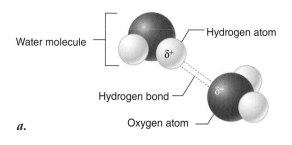

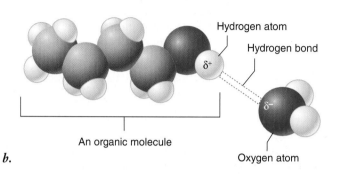

Figure 2.12 **Structure of a hydrogen bond.** *a.* Hydrogen bond between two water molecules. *b.* Hydrogen bond between an organic molecule (*n*-butanol) and water. H in *n*-butanol forms a hydrogen bond with oxygen in water. This kind of hydrogen bond is possible any time H is bound to a more electronegative atom (see table 2.2).

Water molecules are adhesive

The polarity of water causes it to be attracted to other polar molecules as well. This attraction for other polar substances is called *adhesion*. Water adheres to any substance with which it can form hydrogen bonds. This property explains why substances containing polar molecules get "wet" when they are immersed in water, but those that are composed of nonpolar molecules (such as oils) do not.

The attraction of water to substances that have electrical charges on their surface is responsible for capillary action. If a glass tube with a narrow diameter is lowered into a beaker of water, the water will rise in the tube above the level of the water in

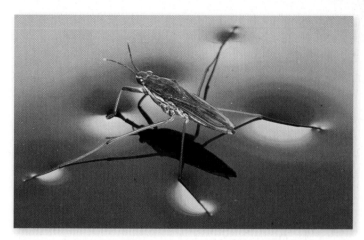

Figure 2.13 **Cohesion.** Some insects, such as this water strider, literally walk on water. Because the surface tension of the water is greater than the force of one foot, the strider glides atop the surface of the water rather than sinking. The high surface tension of water is due to hydrogen bonding between water molecules.

the beaker, because the adhesion of water to the glass surface, drawing it upward, is stronger than the force of gravity, pulling it downward. The narrower the tube, the greater the electrostatic forces between the water and the glass, and the higher the water rises (figure 2.14).

Figure 2.14 **Adhesion.** Capillary action causes the water within a narrow tube to rise above the surrounding water level; the adhesion of the water to the glass surface, which draws water upward, is stronger than the force of gravity, which tends to pull it down. The narrower the tube, the greater the surface area available for adhesion for a given volume of water, and the higher the water rises in the tube.

TABLE 2.3	The Properties of Water	
Property	**Explanation**	**Example of Benefit to Life**
Cohesion	Hydrogen bonds hold water molecules together.	Leaves pull water upward from the roots; seeds swell and germinate.
High specific heat	Hydrogen bonds absorb heat when they break and release heat when they form, minimizing temperature changes.	Water stabilizes the temperature of organisms and the environment.
High heat of vaporization	Many hydrogen bonds must be broken for water to evaporate.	Evaporation of water cools body surfaces.
Lower density of ice	Water molecules in an ice crystal are spaced relatively far apart because of hydrogen bonding.	Because ice is less dense than water, lakes do not freeze solid, allowing fish and other life in lakes to survive the winter.
Solubility	Polar water molecules are attracted to ions and polar compounds, making these compounds soluble.	Many kinds of molecules can move freely in cells, permitting a diverse array of chemical reactions.

2.5 Properties of Water

Water moderates temperature through two properties: its high specific heat and its high heat of vaporization. Water also has the unusual property of being less dense in its solid form, ice, than as a liquid. Water acts as a solvent for polar molecules and exerts an organizing effect on nonpolar molecules. All these properties result from its polar nature.

Water's high specific heat helps maintain temperature

The temperature of any substance is a measure of how rapidly its individual molecules are moving. In the case of water, a large input of thermal energy is required to break the many hydrogen bonds that keep individual water molecules from moving about. Therefore, water is said to have a high **specific heat,** which is defined as the amount of heat 1 g of a substance must absorb or lose to change its temperature by 1 degree Celsius (°C). Specific heat measures the extent to which a substance resists changing its temperature when it absorbs or loses heat. Because polar substances tend to form hydrogen bonds, the more polar it is, the higher is its specific heat. The specific heat of water (1 calorie/g/°C) is twice that of most carbon compounds and nine times that of iron. Only ammonia, which is more polar than water and forms very strong hydrogen bonds, has a higher specific heat than water (1.23 cal/g/°C). Still, only 20% of the hydrogen bonds are broken as water heats from 0° to 100°C.

Because of its high specific heat, water heats up more slowly than almost any other compound and holds its temperature longer. Because organisms have a high water content, water's high specific heat allows them to maintain a relatively constant internal temperature. The heat generated by the chemical reactions inside cells would destroy the cells if not for the absorption of this heat by the water within them.

Water's high heat of vaporization facilitates cooling

The **heat of vaporization** is defined as the amount of energy required to change 1 g of a substance from a liquid to a gas. A considerable amount of heat energy (586 cal) is required to accomplish this change in water. As water changes from a liquid to a gas it requires energy (in the form of heat) to break its many hydrogen bonds. The evaporation of water from a surface cools that surface. Many organisms dispose of excess body heat by evaporative cooling, for example, through sweating in humans and many other vertebrates.

Solid water is less dense than liquid water

At low temperatures, water molecules are locked into a crystal-like lattice of hydrogen bonds, forming solid ice (see figure 2.10*a*). Interestingly, ice is less dense than liquid water because the hydrogen bonds in ice space the water molecules relatively far apart. This unusual feature enables icebergs to float. If water did not have this property, nearly all bodies of water would be ice, with only the shallow surface melting every year. The buoyancy of ice is important ecologically because it means bodies of water freeze from the top down and not the bottom up. Because ice floats on the surface of lakes in the winter and the water beneath the ice remains liquid, fish and other animals keep from freezing.

The solvent properties of water help move ions and polar molecules

Water molecules gather closely around any substance that bears an electrical charge, whether that substance carries a full charge (ion) or a charge separation (polar molecule). For example, sucrose (table sugar) is composed of molecules that contain polar hydroxyl (OH) groups. A sugar crystal dissolves rapidly in water because water molecules can form hydrogen bonds with individual hydroxyl groups of the sucrose molecules. Therefore, sucrose is said to be *soluble* in water. Water is termed the *solvent,* and sugar is called the *solute.* Every time a sucrose molecule dissociates, or breaks away, from a solid sugar crystal, water molecules surround it in a cloud, forming a *hydration shell* that prevents it from associating with other sucrose molecules. Hydration shells also form around ions such as Na^+ and Cl^- (figure 2.15).

Water organizes nonpolar molecules

Water molecules always tend to form the maximum possible number of hydrogen bonds. When nonpolar molecules such as oils, which do not form hydrogen bonds, are placed in water, the water molecules act to exclude them. The nonpolar molecules aggregate, or clump together, thus minimizing their disruption of the hydrogen bonding of water. In effect, they shrink from contact with water, and for this reason they are referred to as **hydrophobic** (Greek *hydros,* "water," and *phobos,* "fearing"). In contrast, polar molecules, which readily form hydrogen bonds with water, are said to be **hydrophilic** ("water-loving").

The tendency of nonpolar molecules to aggregate in water is known as **hydrophobic exclusion.** By forcing the hydrophobic portions of molecules together, water causes these molecules to

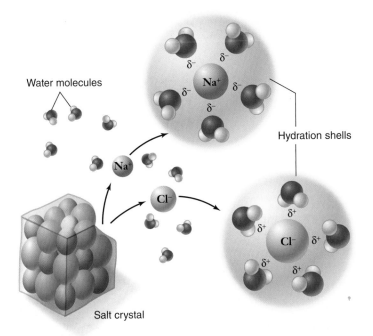

Figure 2.15 Why salt dissolves in water. When a crystal of table salt dissolves in water, individual Na$^+$ and Cl$^-$ ions break away from the salt lattice and become surrounded by water molecules. Water molecules orient around Na$^+$ so that their partial negative poles face toward the positive Na$^+$; water molecules surrounding Cl$^-$ orient in the opposite way, with their partial positive poles facing the negative Cl$^-$. Surrounded by hydration shells, Na$^+$ and Cl$^-$ never reenter the salt lattice.

assume particular shapes. This property can also affect the structure of proteins, DNA, and biological membranes. In fact, the interaction of nonpolar molecules and water is critical to living systems.

Water can form ions

The covalent bonds of a water molecule sometimes break spontaneously. In pure water at 25°C, only 1 out of every 550 million water molecules undergoes this process. When it happens, a proton (hydrogen atom nucleus) dissociates from the molecule. Because the dissociated proton lacks the negatively charged electron it was sharing, its positive charge is no longer counterbalanced, and it becomes a hydrogen ion, H$^+$. The rest of the dissociated water molecule, which has retained the shared electron from the covalent bond, is negatively charged and forms a hydroxide ion, OH$^-$. This process of spontaneous ion formation is called *ionization*:

$$H_2O \longrightarrow OH^- + H^+$$
water   *hydroxide ion*   *hydrogen ion (proton)*

At 25°C, 1 liter (L) of water contains one ten-millionth (or 10^{-7}) mole of H$^+$ ions. A **mole** (mol) is defined as the weight of a substance in grams that corresponds to the atomic masses of all of the atoms in a molecule of that substance. In the case of H$^+$, the atomic mass is 1, and a mole of H$^+$ ions would weigh 1 g. One mole of any substance always contains 6.02×10^{23} molecules of the substance. Therefore, the **molar concentration** of hydrogen ions in pure water, represented as [H$^+$], is 10^{-7} mol/L. (In reality, the H$^+$ usually associates with another water molecule to form a hydronium ion, H_3O^+.)

2.6 Acids and Bases

The concentration of hydrogen ions, and concurrently of hydroxide ions, in a solution is described by the terms *acidity* and *basicity,* respectively. Pure water, having an [H$^+$] of 10^{-7} mol/L, is considered to be neutral, that is, neither acidic nor basic. Recall that for every H$^+$ ion formed when water dissociates, an OH$^-$ ion is also formed, meaning that the dissociation of water produces H$^+$ and OH$^-$ in equal amounts.

The pH scale measures hydrogen ion concentration

The *pH scale* (figure 2.16) is a more convenient way to express the hydrogen ion concentration of a solution. This scale defines *pH,* which stands for "partial hydrogen," as the negative logarithm of the hydrogen ion concentration in the solution:

$$pH = -\log [H^+]$$

Because the logarithm of the hydrogen ion concentration is simply the exponent of the molar concentration of H$^+$, the pH equals the exponent times –1. For water, therefore, an [H$^+$] of 10^{-7} mol/L corresponds to a pH value of 7. This is the neutral point—a balance between H$^+$ and OH$^-$—on the pH scale. This balance occurs because the dissociation of water produces equal amounts of H$^+$ and OH$^-$.

Note that, because the pH scale is *logarithmic,* a difference of 1 on the scale represents a 10-fold change in [H$^+$]. A solution with a pH of 4 therefore has 10 times the [H$^+$] of a solution with a pH of 5 and 100 times the [H$^+$] of a solution with a pH of 6.

Acids

Any substance that dissociates in water to increase the [H$^+$] (and lower the pH) is called an **acid.** The stronger an acid is, the more hydrogen ions it produces and the lower its pH. For example, hydrochloric acid (HCl), which is abundant in your stomach, ionizes completely in water. A dilution of 10^{-1} mol/L of HCl dissociates to form 10^{-1} mol/L of H$^+$, giving the solution

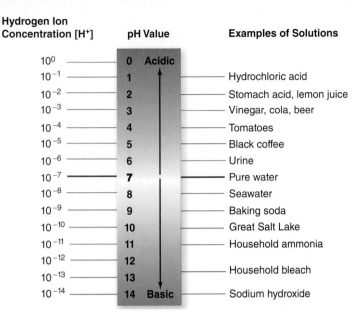

Figure 2.16 The pH scale. The pH value of a solution indicates its concentration of hydrogen ions. Solutions with a pH less than 7 are acidic, whereas those with a pH greater than 7 are basic. The scale is logarithmic, which means that a pH change of 1 represents a 10-fold change in the concentration of hydrogen ions. Thus, lemon juice is 100 times more acidic than tomato juice, and seawater is 10 times more basic than pure water, which has a pH of 7.

a pH of 1. The pH of champagne, which bubbles because of the carbonic acid dissolved in it, is about 2.

Bases

A substance that combines with H⁺ when dissolved in water, and thus lowers the [H⁺], is called a **base.** Therefore, basic (or alkaline) solutions have pH values above 7. Very strong bases, such as sodium hydroxide (NaOH), have pH values of 12 or more. Many common cleaning substances, such as ammonia and bleach, accomplish their action because of their high pH.

Buffers help stabilize pH

The pH inside almost all living cells, and in the fluid surrounding cells in multicellular organisms, is fairly close to neutral, 7. Most of the enzymes in living systems are extremely sensitive to pH. Often even a small change in pH will alter their shape, thereby disrupting their activities. For this reason, it is important that a cell maintain a constant pH level.

But the chemical reactions of life constantly produce acids and bases within cells. Furthermore, many animals eat substances that are acidic or basic. Cola drinks, for example, are moderately strong (although dilute) acidic solutions. Despite such variations in the concentrations of H⁺ and OH⁻, the pH of an organism is kept at a relatively constant level by buffers (figure 2.17).

A **buffer** is a substance that resists changes in pH. Buffers act by releasing hydrogen ions when a base is added and absorbing hydrogen ions when acid is added, with the overall effect of keeping [H⁺] relatively constant.

Within organisms, most buffers consist of pairs of substances, one an acid and the other a base. The key buffer in human blood is an acid–base pair consisting of carbonic acid

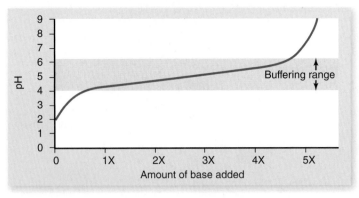

Figure 2.17 Buffers minimize changes in pH. Adding a base to a solution neutralizes some of the acid present, and so raises the pH. Thus, as the curve moves to the right, reflecting more and more base, it also rises to higher pH values. A buffer makes the curve rise or fall very slowly over a portion of the pH scale, called the "buffering range" of that buffer.

Data analysis If we call each step on the *x*-axis one volume of base, how many volumes of base must be added to change the pH from 4 to 6?

(acid) and bicarbonate (base). These two substances interact in a pair of reversible reactions. First, carbon dioxide (CO_2) and H_2O join to form carbonic acid (H_2CO_3), which in a second reaction dissociates to yield bicarbonate ion (HCO_3^-) and H⁺.

If some acid or other substance adds H⁺ to the blood, the HCO_3^- acts as a base and removes the excess H⁺ by forming H_2CO_3. Similarly, if a basic substance removes H⁺ from the blood, H_2CO_3 dissociates, releasing more H⁺ into the blood. The forward and reverse reactions that interconvert H_2CO_3 and HCO_3^- thus stabilize the blood's pH.

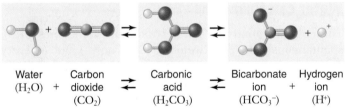

| Water (H_2O) | + | Carbon dioxide (CO_2) | ⇌ | Carbonic acid (H_2CO_3) | ⇌ | Bicarbonate ion (HCO_3^-) | + | Hydrogen ion (H⁺) |

The reaction of carbon dioxide and water to form carbonic acid is a crucial one because it permits carbon, essential to life, to enter water from the air. The Earth's oceans are rich in carbon because of the reaction of carbon dioxide with water.

In a condition called blood acidosis, human blood, which normally has a pH of about 7.4, drops to a pH of about 7.1. This condition is fatal if not treated immediately. The reverse condition, blood alkalosis, involves an increase in blood pH of a similar magnitude and is just as serious.

Learning Outcomes Review 2.6

Acid solutions have a high [H⁺], and basic solutions have a low [H⁺] (and therefore a high [OH⁻]). The pH of a solution is the negative logarithm of its [H⁺]. Low pH values indicate acids, and high pH values indicate bases. Even small changes in pH can be harmful to life. Buffer systems in organisms help to maintain pH within a narrow range.

■ *A change of 2 pH units indicates what change in [H⁺]?*

2.1 The Nature of Atoms

All matter is composed of atoms (figure 2.3).

Atomic structure includes a central nucleus and orbiting electrons.

Electrically neutral atoms have the same number of protons as electrons. Atoms that gain or lose electrons are called ions.

Each element is defined by its atomic number, the number of protons in the nucleus. Atomic mass is the sum of the mass of protons and neutrons in an atom. Isotopes are forms of a single element with different numbers of neutrons, and thus different atomic mass. Radioactive isotopes are unstable.

Electrons determine the chemical behavior of atoms.

The potential energy of electrons increases as distance from the nucleus increases. Electron orbitals are probability distributions. s-Orbitals are spherical; other orbitals have different shapes, such as the dumbbell-shaped p-orbitals.

Atoms contain discrete energy levels.

Energy levels correspond to quanta (sing. quantum) of energy, a "ladder" of energy levels that an electron may have.

The loss of electrons from an atom is called oxidation. The gain of electrons is called reduction. Electrons can be transferred from one atom to another in coupled redox reactions.

2.2 Elements Found in Living Systems

The periodic table displays elements according to atomic number and properties.

Atoms tend to establish completely full outer energy levels (the octet rule). Elements with filled outermost orbitals are inert.

Ninety elements occur naturally in the Earth's crust. Twelve of these elements are found in living organisms in greater than trace amounts: C, H, O, N, P, S, Na, K, Ca, Mg, Fe, and Cl.

Compounds of carbon are called organic compounds. The majority of molecules in living systems are composed of C bound to H, O, and N.

2.3 The Nature of Chemical Bonds

Molecules contain two or more atoms joined by chemical bonds. Compounds contain two or more different elements.

Ionic bonds form crystals.

Ions with opposite electrical charges form ionic bonds, such as NaCl (figure 2.9b).

Covalent bonds build stable molecules.

A molecule formed by a covalent bond is stable because it has no net charge, the octet rule is satisfied, and it has no unpaired electrons. Covalent bonds may be single, double, or triple, depending on the number of pairs of electrons shared. Nonpolar covalent bonds involve equal sharing of electrons between atoms. Polar covalent bonds involve unequal sharing of electrons.

Chemical reactions alter bonds.

Temperature, reactant concentration, and the presence of catalysts affect reaction rates. Most biological reactions are reversible, such as the conversion of carbon dioxide and water into carbohydrates.

2.4 Water: A Vital Compound

Water's structure facilitates hydrogen bonding.

Hydrogen bonds are weak interactions between a partially positive H in one molecule and a partially negative O in another molecule (figure 2.11).

Water molecules are cohesive.

Cohesion is the tendency of water molecules to adhere to one another due to hydrogen bonding. The cohesion of water is responsible for its surface tension.

Water molecules are adhesive.

Adhesion occurs when water molecules adhere to other polar molecules. Capillary action results from water's adhesion to the sides of narrow tubes, combined with its cohesion.

2.5 Properties of Water

Water's high specific heat helps maintain temperature.

The specific heat of water is high because it takes a considerable amount of energy to disrupt hydrogen bonds.

Water's high heat of vaporization facilitates cooling.

Breaking hydrogen bonds to turn liquid water into vapor takes a lot of energy. Many organisms lose excess heat through evaporative cooling, such as sweating.

Solid water is less dense than liquid water.

Hydrogen bonds are spaced farther apart in the solid phase of water than in the liquid phase. As a result, ice floats.

The solvent properties of water help move ions and polar molecules.

Water's polarity makes it a good solvent for polar substances and ions. Polar molecules or portions of molecules are attracted to water (hydrophilic). Molecules that are nonpolar are repelled by water (hydrophobic). Water makes nonpolar molecules clump together.

Water organizes nonpolar molecules.

Nonpolar molecules will aggregate to avoid water. This maximizes the hydrogen bonds that water can make. This hydrophobic exclusion can affect the structure of DNA, proteins and biological membranes.

Water can form ions.

Water dissociates into H^+ and OH^-. The concentration of H^+, shown as $[H^+]$, in pure water is 10^{-7} mol/L.

2.6 Acids and Bases (figure 2.16)

The pH scale measures hydrogen ion concentration.

pH is defined as the negative logarithm of $[H^+]$. Pure water has a pH of 7. A difference of 1 pH unit means a 10-fold change in $[H^+]$.

Acids have a greater $[H^+]$ and therefore a lower pH; bases have a lower $[H^+]$ and therefore a higher pH.

Buffers help stabilize pH.

Carbon dioxide and water react reversibly to form carbonic acid. A buffer resists changes in pH by absorbing or releasing H^+. The key buffer in the human blood is the carbonic acid/bicarbonate pair.

UNDERSTAND

1. The property that distinguishes an atom of one element (carbon, for example) from an atom of another element (oxygen, for example) is
   a. the number of electrons.
   b. the number of protons.
   c. the number of neutrons.
   d. the combined number of protons and neutrons.

2. If an atom has one valence electron, that is, a single electron in its outer energy level, it will most likely form
   a. one polar, covalent bond.
   b. two nonpolar, covalent bonds.
   c. two covalent bonds.
   d. an ionic bond.

3. An atom with a net positive charge must have more
   a. protons than neutrons.
   b. protons than electrons.
   c. electrons than neutrons.
   d. electrons than protons.

4. The isotopes carbon-12 and carbon-14 differ in
   a. the number of neutrons.
   b. the number of protons.
   c. the number of electrons.
   d. Both b and c are correct.

5. Which of the following is NOT a property of the elements most commonly found in living organisms?
   a. The elements have a low atomic mass.
   b. The elements have an atomic number less than 21.
   c. The elements possess eight electrons in their outer energy level.
   d. The elements are lacking one or more electrons from their outer energy level.

6. Ionic bonds arise from
   a. shared valence electrons.
   b. attractions between valence electrons.
   c. charge attractions between valence electrons.
   d. attractions between ions of opposite charge.

7. A solution with a high concentration of hydrogen ions
   a. is called a base.
   b. is called an acid.
   c. has a high pH.
   d. Both b and c are correct.

APPLY

1. Using the periodic table on page 22, which of the following atoms would you predict should form a positively charged ion (cation)?
   a. Fluorine (F)
   b. Neon (Ne)
   c. Potassium (K)
   d. Sulfur (S)

2. Refer to the element pictured. How many covalent bonds could this atom form?
   a. Two
   b. Three
   c. Four
   d. None

3. A molecule with polar covalent bonds would
   a. be soluble in water.
   b. not be soluble in water.
   c. contain atoms with very similar electronegativity.
   d. Both b and c are correct.

4. Hydrogen bonds are formed
   a. between any molecules that contain hydrogen.
   b. only between water molecules.
   c. when hydrogen is part of a polar bond.
   d. when two atoms of hydrogen share an electron.

5. If you shake a bottle of oil and vinegar then let it sit, it will separate into two phases because
   a. the nonpolar oil is soluble in water.
   b. water can form hydrogen bonds with the oil.
   c. polar oil is not soluble in water.
   d. nonpolar oil is not soluble in water.

6. The decay of radioactive isotopes involves changes to the nucleus of atoms. Explain how this differs from the changes in atoms that occur during chemical reactions.

SYNTHESIZE

1. Elements that form ions are important for a range of biological processes. You have learned something about the cations sodium (Na^+), calcium (Ca^{2+}) and potassium (K^+) in this chapter. Use your knowledge of the definition of a cation to identify other examples from the periodic table.

2. A popular theme in science fiction literature has been the idea of silicon-based life-forms in contrast to our carbon-based life. Evaluate the possibility of silicon-based life based on the chemical structure and potential for chemical bonding of a silicon atom.

3. Recent efforts by NASA to search for signs of life on Mars have focused on the search for evidence of liquid water rather than looking directly for biological organisms (living or fossilized). Use your knowledge of the influence of water on life on Earth to construct an argument justifying this approach.

ONLINE RESOURCE

www.ravenbiology.com

Understand, Apply, and Synthesize—enhance your study with animations that bring concepts to life and practice tests to assess your understanding. Your instructor may also recommend the interactive eBook, individualized learning tools, and more.

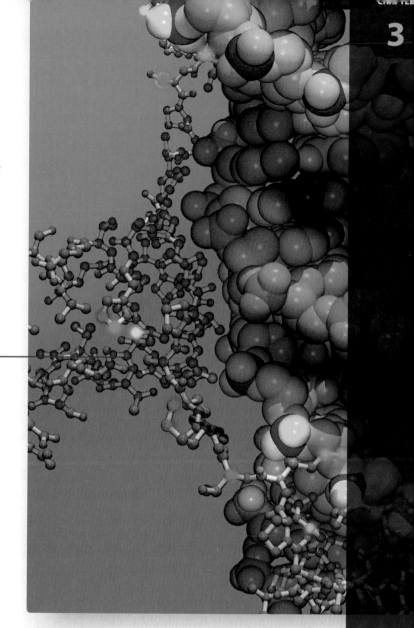

Chapter 3

The Chemical Building Blocks of Life

Chapter Contents

Introduction

A cup of water contains more molecules than there are stars in the sky. But many molecules are much larger than water molecules. Many thousands of distinct biological molecules are long chains made of thousands or even billions of atoms. These enormous assemblages, which are almost always synthesized by living things, are macromolecules. *As you may know, biological macromolecules can be divided into four categories: carbohydrates, nucleic acids, proteins, and lipids, and they are the basic chemical building blocks from which all organisms are composed.*

We take the existence of these classes of macromolecules for granted now, but as late as the 19th century many theories of "vital forces" were associated with living systems. One such theory held that cells contained a substance, protoplasm, that was responsible for the chemical reactions in living systems. Any disruption of cells was thought to disturb the protoplasm. Such a view makes studying the chemical reactions of cells in the lab (in vitro) impossible. The demonstration of fermentation in a cell-free system marked the beginning of modern biochemistry (figure 3.1). This approach involves studying biological molecules outside of cells to infer their role inside cells. Because these biological macromolecules all involve carbon-containing compounds, we begin with a brief summary of carbon and its chemistry.

Hypothesis: *Chemical reactions, such as the fermentation reaction in yeast, are controlled by enzymes and do not require living cells.*

Prediction: *If yeast cells are broken open, these enzymes should function outside of the cell.*

Test: *Yeast is mixed with quartz sand and diatomaceous earth and then ground in a mortar and pestle. The resulting paste is wrapped in canvas and subjected to 400–500 atm pressure in a press. Fermentable and nonfermentable substrates are added to the resulting fluid, with fermentation being measured by the production of CO_2.*

Yeast   Quartz sand   Diatomaceous earth   400–500 atm pressure   Cane sugar   Glucose   Lactose, mannose

Grind in mortar/pestle.   Wrap in canvas and apply pressure in a press.

Result: *When a fermentable substrate (cane sugar, glucose) is used, CO_2 is produced; when a nonfermentable substrate (lactose, mannose) is used, no CO_2 is produced. In addition, visual inspection of the fluid shows no visible yeast cells.*

Conclusion: *The hypothesis is supported. The fermentation reaction can occur in the absence of live yeast.*

Historical Significance: *Although this is not precisely the intent of the original experiment, it represents the first use of a cell-free system. Such systems allow for the study of biochemical reactions in vitro and the purification of proteins involved. We now know that the "fermentation reaction" is actually a complex series of reactions. Would such a series of reactions be your first choice for this kind of demonstration?*

Figure 3.1   The demonstration of cell-free fermentation. The German chemist Eduard Buchner's (1860–1917) demonstration of fermentation by fluid produced from yeast, but not containing any live cells, both argued against the protoplasm theory and provided a method for future biochemists to examine the chemistry of life outside of cells.

3.1 Carbon: The Framework of Biological Molecules

Learning Outcomes

1. *Describe the relationship between functional groups and macromolecules.*
2. *Recognize the different kinds of isomers.*
3. *List the different kinds of biological macromolecules.*

In chapter 2, we reviewed the basics of chemistry. Biological systems obey all the laws of chemistry. Thus, chemistry forms the basis of living systems.

The framework of biological molecules consists predominantly of carbon atoms bonded to other carbon atoms or to atoms of oxygen, nitrogen, sulfur, phosphorus, or hydrogen. Because carbon atoms can form up to four covalent bonds, molecules containing carbon can form straight chains, branches, or even rings, balls, tubes, and coils.

Molecules consisting only of carbon and hydrogen are called *hydrocarbons*. Because carbon–hydrogen covalent bonds store considerable energy, hydrocarbons make good fuels. Gasoline, for example, is rich in hydrocarbons, and propane gas,

another hydrocarbon, consists of a chain of three carbon atoms, with eight hydrogen atoms bound to it. The chemical formula for propane is C_3H_8. Its structural formula is

$$
\begin{array}{c}
\text{H} \quad \text{H} \quad \text{H} \\
| \quad\quad | \quad\quad | \\
\text{H—C—C—C—H} \\
| \quad\quad | \quad\quad | \\
\text{H} \quad \text{H} \quad \text{H}
\end{array}
$$
Propane structural formula

Theoretically speaking, the length of a chain of carbon atoms is unlimited. As described in the rest of this chapter, the four main types of biological molecules often consist of huge chains of carbon-containing compounds.

Functional groups account for differences in molecular properties

Carbon and hydrogen atoms both have very similar electronegativities. Electrons in C—C and C—H bonds are therefore evenly distributed, with no significant differences in charge over the molecular surface. For this reason, hydrocarbons are nonpolar. Most biological molecules produced by cells, however, also contain other atoms. Because these other atoms frequently have different electronegativities, molecules containing them exhibit regions of partial positive or negative charge. They are polar. These molecules can be thought of as a

C—H core to which specific molecular groups, called **functional groups,** are attached. One such common functional group is —OH, called a *hydroxyl group.*

Functional groups have definite chemical properties that they retain no matter where they occur. Both the hydroxyl and carbonyl (C=O) groups, for example, are polar because of the electronegativity of the oxygen atoms (see chapter 2). Other common functional groups are the acidic carboxyl (COOH), phosphate (PO_4^-), and the basic amino (NH_2) group. Many of these functional groups can also participate in hydrogen bonding. Hydrogen bond donors and acceptors can be predicted based on their electronegativities shown in table 2.2. Figure 3.2 illustrates these biologically important functional groups and lists the macromolecules in which they are found.

 ## Isomers have the same molecular formulas but different structures

Organic molecules having the same molecular or empirical formula can exist in different forms called **isomers.** If there are differences in the actual structure of their carbon skeleton, we call them *structural isomers.* Later you will see that glucose and fructose are structural isomers of $C_6H_{12}O_6$. Another form of isomers, called *stereoisomers,* have the same carbon skeleton but differ in how the groups attached to this skeleton are arranged in space.

Enzymes in biological systems usually recognize only a single, specific stereoisomer. A subcategory of stereoisomers, called *enantiomers,* are actually mirror images of each other. A molecule that has mirror-image versions is called a *chiral* molecule. When carbon is bound to four different molecules, this inherent asymmetry exists (figure 3.3).

Chiral compounds are characterized by their effect on polarized light. Polarized light has a single plane, and chiral molecules rotate this plane either to the right (Latin, *dextro*) or left (Latin, *levo*). We therefore call the two chiral forms *D* for *dextrorotatory* and *L* for *levorotatory.* Living systems tend to produce only a single enantiomer of the two possible forms; for example, in most organisms we find primarily D-sugars and L-amino acids.

Functional Group	Structural Formula	Example	Found In
Hydroxyl	—OH	Ethanol	carbohydrates, proteins, nucleic acids, lipids
Carbonyl	$\overset{O}{\underset{}{\|\|}}$ —C—	Acetaldehyde	carbohydrates, nucleic acids
Carboxyl	—C with =O and OH	Acetic acid	proteins, lipids
Amino	—N with two H	Alanine	proteins, nucleic acids
Sulfhydryl	—S—H	Cysteine	proteins
Phosphate	—O—P—O⁻ with O⁻ and O	Glycerol phosphate	nucleic acids
Methyl	—C—H with two H	Alanine	proteins

Figure 3.2 The primary functional chemical groups. These groups tend to act as units during chemical reactions and give specific chemical properties to the molecules that possess them. Amino groups, for example, make a molecule more basic, and carboxyl groups make a molecule more acidic. These functional groups are also not limited to the examples in the "Found In" column but are widely distributed in biological molecules.

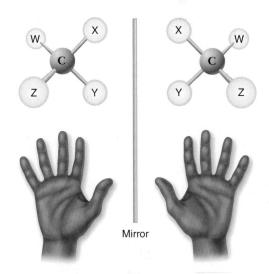

Figure 3.3 Chiral molecules. When carbon is bound to four different groups, the resulting molecule is said to be chiral (from Greek *cheir,* meaning "hand"). A chiral molecule will have stereoisomers that are mirror images. The two molecules shown have the same four groups but cannot be superimposed, much like your two hands cannot be superimposed but must be flipped to match. These types of stereoisomers are called *enantiomers.*

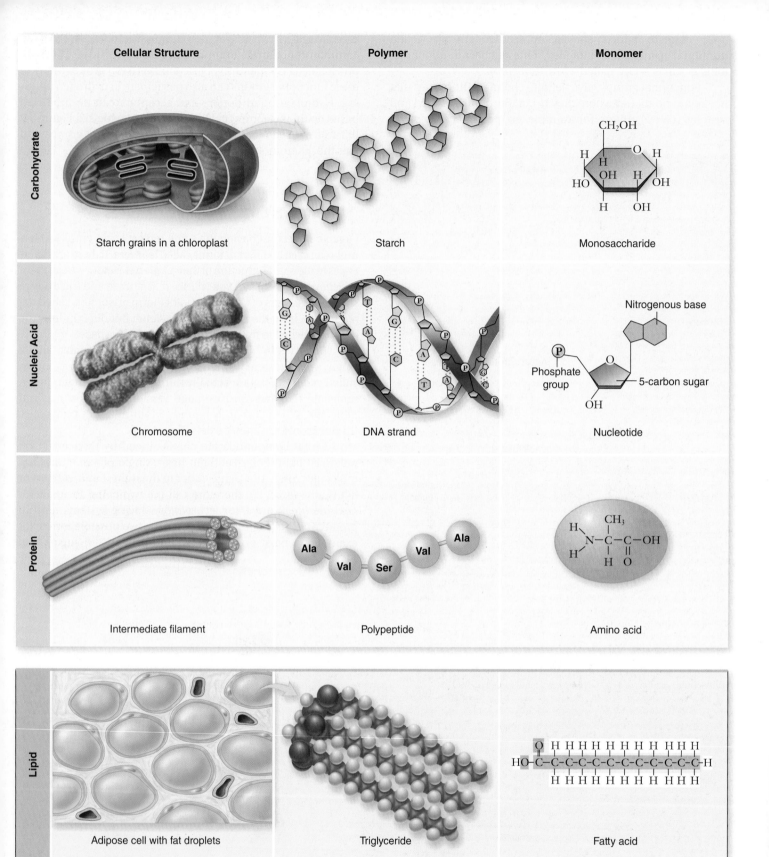

Cellular Structure	Polymer	Monomer
Carbohydrate Starch grains in a chloroplast	Starch	Monosaccharide
Nucleic Acid Chromosome	DNA strand	Nucleotide
Protein Intermediate filament	Polypeptide	Amino acid
Lipid Adipose cell with fat droplets	Triglyceride	Fatty acid

Figure 3.4 Polymer macromolecules. The four major biological macromolecules are shown. Carbohydrates, nucleic acids, and proteins all form polymers and are shown with the monomers used to make them. Lipids do not fit this simple monomer–polymer relationship, however, because they are constructed from glycerol and fatty acids. All four types of macromolecules are also shown in their cellular context.

TABLE 3.1	Macromolecules		
Macromolecule	**Subunit**	**Function**	**Example**
CARBOHYDRATES			
Starch, glycogen	Glucose	Energy storage	Potatoes
Cellulose	Glucose	Structural support in plant cell walls	Paper; strings of celery
Chitin	Modified glucose	Structural support	Crab shells
NUCLEIC ACIDS			
DNA	Nucleotides	Encodes genes	Chromosomes
RNA	Nucleotides	Needed for gene expression	Messenger RNA
PROTEINS			
Functional	Amino acids	Catalysis; transport	Hemoglobin
Structural	Amino acids	Support	Hair; silk
LIPIDS			
Fats	Glycerol and three fatty acids	Energy storage	Butter; corn oil; soap
Phospholipids	Glycerol, two fatty acids, phosphate, and polar R groups	Cell membranes	Phosphatidylcholine
Prostaglandins	Five-carbon rings with two nonpolar tails	Chemical messengers	Prostaglandin E (PGE)
Steroids	Four fused carbon rings	Membranes; hormones	Cholesterol; estrogen
Terpenes	Long carbon chains	Pigments; structural support	Carotene; rubber

Biological macromolecules include carbohydrates, nucleic acids, proteins, and lipids

Remember that biological macromolecules are traditionally grouped into carbohydrates, nucleic acids, proteins, and lipids (table 3.1). In many cases, these macromolecules are polymers. A **polymer** is a long molecule built by linking together a large number of small, similar chemical subunits called **monomers.** They are like railroad cars coupled to form a train. The nature of a polymer is determined by the monomers used to build the polymer. Here are some examples. Complex carbohydrates such as starch are polymers composed of simple ring-shaped sugars. Nucleic acids (DNA and RNA) are polymers of nucleotides, and proteins are polymers of amino acids (figure 3.4). These long chains are built via chemical reactions termed *dehydration reactions* and are broken down by *hydrolysis reactions.* Lipids are macromolecules, but they really don't follow the monomer–polymer relationship. However, lipids are formed through dehydration reactions, which link the fatty acids to glycerol.

The dehydration reaction

Despite the differences between monomers of these major polymers, the basic chemistry of their synthesis is similar: To form a covalent bond between two monomers, an —OH group is removed from one monomer, and a hydrogen atom (H) is removed from the other (figure 3.5*a*). For example, this simple chemistry is the same for linking amino acids together to make a protein or assembling glucose units together to make starch. This reaction is also used to link fatty acids to glycerol in lipids. This chemical reaction is called condensation, or a **dehydration reaction,** because the removal of —OH and —H is the same as

the removal of a molecule of water (H_2O). For every subunit added to a macromolecule, one water molecule is removed. These and other biochemical reactions require that the reacting substances are held close together and that the correct chemical bonds are stressed and broken. This process of positioning and stressing, termed *catalysis,* is carried out within cells by enzymes.

The hydrolysis reaction

Cells disassemble macromolecules into their constituent subunits through reactions that are the reverse of dehydration—a molecule of water is added instead of removed (figure 3.5*b*). In this process, called **hydrolysis,** a hydrogen atom is attached to one subunit and a hydroxyl group to the other, breaking a specific covalent bond in the macromolecule. When you eat a potato, which contains starch (discussed later), your body breaks the starch down into glucose units by hydrolysis. The potato plant built the starch molecules originally by dehydration reactions.

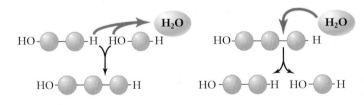

a. Dehydration reaction   *b.* Hydrolysis reaction

Figure 3.5 Making and breaking macromolecules.
a. Biological macromolecules are polymers formed by linking monomers together through dehydration reactions. This process releases a water molecule for every bond formed. *b.* Breaking the bond between subunits involves hydrolysis, which reverses the loss of a water molecule by dehydration.

3.2 Carbohydrates: Energy Storage and Structural Molecules

Monosaccharides are simple sugars

Carbohydrates are a loosely defined group of molecules that all contain carbon, hydrogen, and oxygen in the molar ratio 1:2:1. Their empirical formula (which lists the number of atoms in the molecule with subscripts) is $(CH_2O)_n$, where n is the number of carbon atoms. Because they contain many carbon–hydrogen (C—H) bonds, which release energy when oxidation occurs, carbohydrates are well suited for energy storage. Sugars are among the most important energy-storage molecules, and they exist in several different forms.

The simplest of the carbohydrates are the **monosaccharides** (Greek *mono,* "single," and Latin *saccharum,* "sugar"). Simple sugars contain as few as three carbon atoms, but those that play the central role in energy storage have six (figure 3.6). The empirical formula of six-carbon sugars is:

$$C_6H_{12}O_6 \qquad or \qquad (CH_2O)_6$$

Six-carbon sugars can exist in a straight-chain form, but dissolved in water (an aqueous environment) they almost always form rings.

The most important of the six-carbon monosaccharides for energy storage is glucose, which you first encountered in the examples of chemical reactions in chapter 2. Glucose has seven energy-storing C—H bonds (figure 3.7). Depending on the orientation of the carbonyl group (C=O) when the ring is closed, glucose can exist in two different forms: alpha (α) or beta (β).

Sugar isomers have structural differences

Glucose is not the only sugar with the formula $C_6H_{12}O_6$. Both structural isomers and stereoisomers of this simple six-carbon skeleton exist in nature. Fructose is a structural isomer that differs in the position of the carbonyl carbon (C=O); galactose is a stereoisomer that differs in the position of —OH and —H groups relative to the ring (figure 3.8). These differences often account for substantial functional differences between the isomers. Your taste buds can discern them: Fructose tastes much sweeter than glucose, despite the fact that both sugars have identical chemical composition. Enzymes that act on different sugars can distinguish both the structural and stereoisomers of this basic six-carbon skeleton. The different stereoisomers of glucose are also important in the polymers that can be made using glucose as a monomer, as you will see later in this chapter.

Disaccharides serve as transport molecules in plants and provide nutrition in animals

Most organisms transport sugars within their bodies. In humans, the glucose that circulates in the blood does so as a simple monosaccharide. In plants and many other organisms, however, glucose is converted into a transport form before it is moved from place to place within the organism. In such a form, it is less readily metabolized during transport.

Transport forms of sugars are commonly made by linking two monosaccharides together to form a **disaccharide** (Greek *di,* "two"). Disaccharides serve as effective reservoirs of glucose because the enzymes that normally use glucose in the organism cannot break the bond linking the two monosaccharide subunits. Enzymes that can do so are typically present only in the tissue that uses glucose.

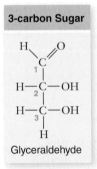

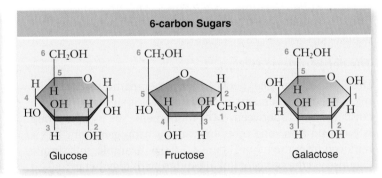

3-carbon Sugar	5-carbon Sugars	6-carbon Sugars
Glyceraldehyde	Ribose / Deoxyribose	Glucose / Fructose / Galactose

Figure 3.6 Monosaccharides. Monosaccharides, or simple sugars, can contain as few as three carbon atoms and are often used as building blocks to form larger molecules. The five-carbon sugars ribose and deoxyribose are components of nucleic acids (see figure 3.15). The carbons are conventionally numbered (in *blue*) from the more oxidized end.

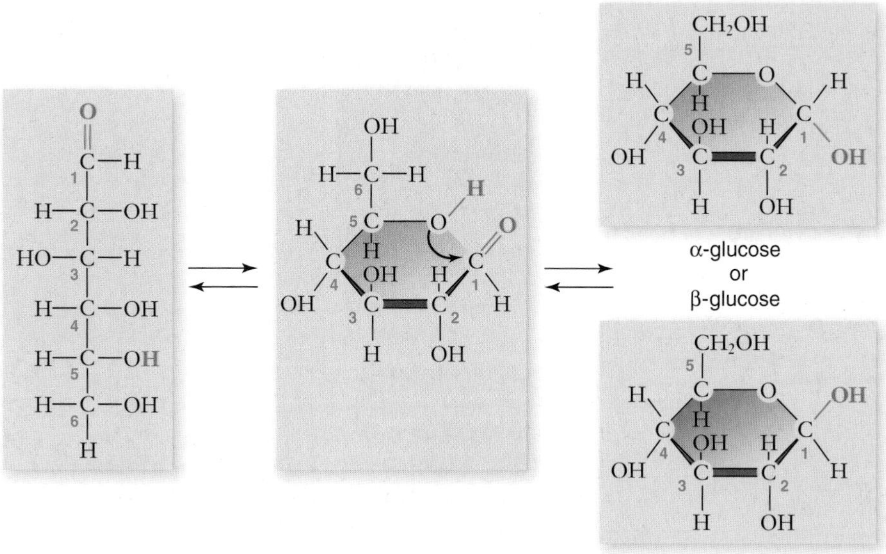

Figure 3.7 **Structure of the glucose molecule.** Glucose is a linear, six-carbon molecule that forms a six-membered ring in solution. Ring closure occurs such that two forms can result: α-glucose and β-glucose. These structures differ only in the position of the —OH bound to carbon 1. The structure of the ring can be represented in many ways; shown here are the most common, with the carbons conventionally numbered so that the forms can be compared easily. The heavy lines in the ring structures represent portions of the molecule that are projecting out of the page toward you.

Transport forms differ depending on which monosaccharides are linked to form the disaccharide. Glucose forms transport disaccharides with itself and with many other monosaccharides, including fructose and galactose. When glucose forms a disaccharide with the structural isomer fructose, the resulting disaccharide is *sucrose,* or table sugar (figure 3.9a). Sucrose is the form most plants use to transport glucose and is the sugar that most humans and other animals eat. Sugarcane and sugar beets are rich in sucrose.

When glucose is linked to the stereoisomer galactose, the resulting disaccharide is *lactose,* or milk sugar. Many mammals supply energy to their young in the form of lactose. Adults often have greatly reduced levels of lactase, the enzyme required to cleave lactose into its two monosaccharide components, and thus they cannot metabolize lactose efficiently. This can result in lactose intolerance in humans. Most of the energy that is channeled into lactose production is therefore reserved for offspring. For this reason, lactose as an energy source is primarily for offspring in mammals.

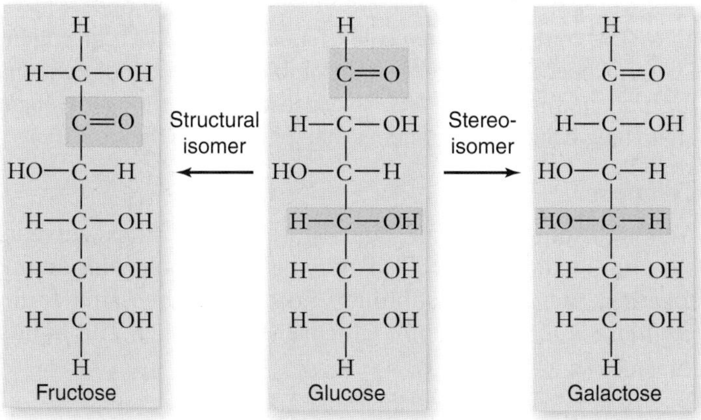

Polysaccharides provide energy storage and structural components

Polysaccharides are longer polymers made up of monosaccharides that have been joined through dehydration reactions. **Starch,** a storage polysaccharide, consists entirely of α-glucose molecules linked in long chains. **Cellulose,** a structural polysaccharide, also consists of glucose molecules linked in chains, but these molecules are β-glucose. Because starch is built from α-glucose we call the linkages α linkages; cellulose has β linkages.

Starches and glycogen

Organisms store the metabolic energy contained in monosaccharides by converting them into disaccharides, such as *maltose* (figure 3.9b). These are then linked together into the insoluble polysaccharides called *starches.* These polysaccharides differ mainly in how the polymers branch.

The starch with the simplest structure is *amylose.* It is composed of many hundreds of α-glucose molecules linked together in long, unbranched chains. Each linkage occurs between the

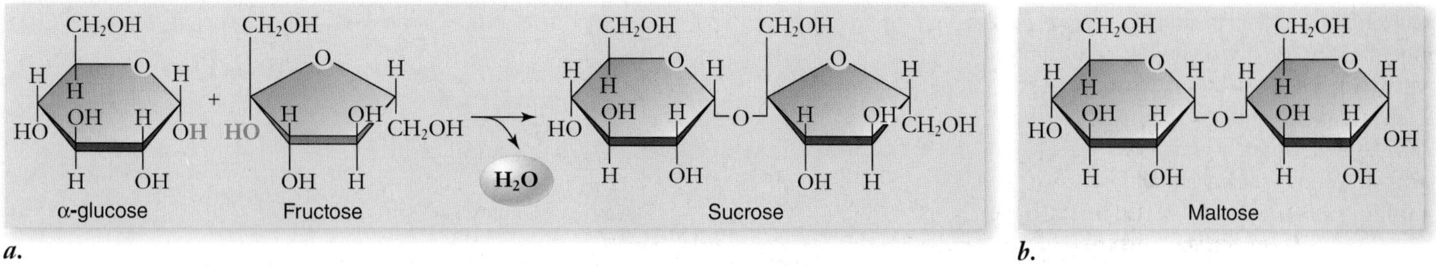

Figure 3.8 **Isomers and stereoisomers.** Glucose, fructose, and galactose are isomers with the empirical formula $C_6H_{12}O_6$. A structural isomer of glucose, such as fructose, has identical chemical groups bonded to different carbon atoms. Notice that this results in a five-membered ring in solution (see figure 3.6). A stereoisomer of glucose, such as galactose, has identical chemical groups bonded to the same carbon atoms but in different orientations (the —OH at carbon 4).

a.

b.

Figure 3.9 **How disaccharides form.** Some disaccharides are used to transport glucose from one part of an organism's body to another; one example is sucrose (*a*), which is found in sugarcane. Other disaccharides, such as maltose (*b*), are used in grain for storage.

chapter **3** *The Chemical Building Blocks of Life*

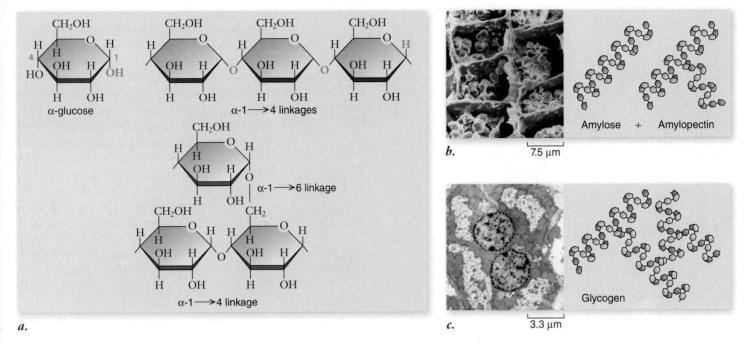

Figure 3.10 Polymers of glucose: Starch and glycogen. *a.* Starch chains consist of polymers of α-glucose subunits joined by α-(1⟶4) glycosidic linkages. These chains can be branched by forming similar α-(1⟶6) glycosidic bonds. These storage polymers then differ primarily in their degree of branching. *b.* Starch is found in plants and is composed of amylose and amylopectin, which are unbranched and branched, respectively. The branched form is insoluble and forms starch granules in plant cells. *c.* Glycogen is found in animal cells and is highly branched and also insoluble, forming glycogen granules.

carbon 1 (C-1) of one glucose molecule and the C-4 of another, making them α-(1⟶4) linkages (figure 3.10*a*). The long chains of amylose tend to coil up in water, a property that renders amylose insoluble. Potato starch is about 20% amylose (figure 3.10*b*).

Most plant starch, including the remaining 80% of potato starch, is a somewhat more complicated variant of amylose called *amylopectin*. Pectins are branched polysaccharides with the branches occurring due to bonds between the C-1 of one molecule and the C-6 of another [α-(1⟶6) linkages]. These short amylose branches consist of 20 to 30 glucose subunits (figure 3.10*b*).

The comparable molecule to starch in animals is **glycogen.** Like amylopectin, glycogen is an insoluble polysaccharide containing branched amylose chains. Glycogen has a much longer average chain length and more branches than plant starch (figure 3.10*c*).

Cellulose

Although some chains of sugars store energy, others serve as structural material for cells. For two glucose molecules to link together, the glucose subunits must be of the same form. *Cellulose* is a polymer of β-glucose (figure 3.11). The bonds

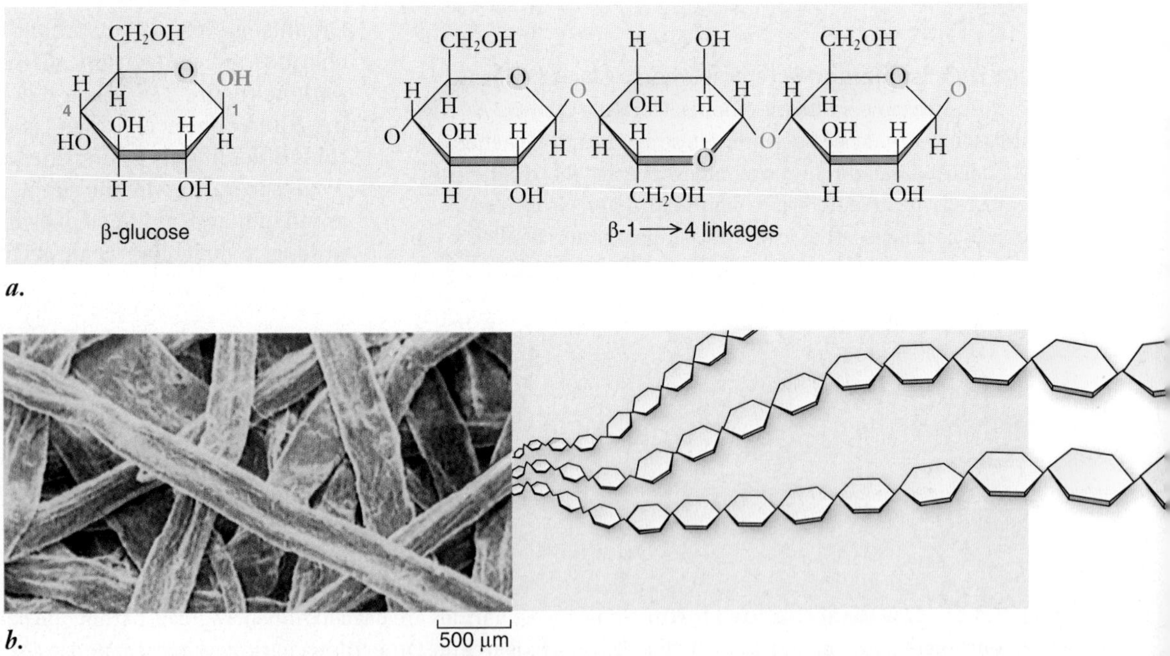

Figure 3.11 Polymers of glucose: Cellulose. Starch chains consist of α-glucose subunits, and cellulose chains consist of β-glucose subunits. *a.* Thus the bonds between adjacent glucose molecules in cellulose are β-(1⟶4) glycosidic linkages. *b.* Cellulose is unbranched and forms long fibers. Cellulose fibers can be very strong and are quite resistant to metabolic breakdown, which is one reason wood is such a good building material.

between adjacent glucose molecules still exist between the C-1 of the first glucose and the C-4 of the next glucose, but these are β-(1⟶4) linkages.

The properties of a chain of glucose molecules consisting of all β-glucose are very different from those of starch. These long, unbranched β-linked chains make tough fibers. Cellulose is the chief component of plant cell walls (see figure 3.11b). It is chemically similar to amylose, with one important difference: The starch-hydrolyzing enzymes that occur in most organisms cannot break the bond between two β-glucose units because they only recognize α linkages.

Because cellulose cannot be broken down readily by most creatures, it works well as a biological structural material. But some animals, such as cows, are able to break down cellulose by means of symbiotic bacteria and protists in their digestive tracts. These organisms provide the necessary enzymes for cleaving the β-(1⟶4) linkages, thus enabling access to a rich source of energy.

Chitin

Chitin, the structural material found in arthropods and many fungi, is a polymer of *N*-acetylglucosamine, a substituted version of glucose. When cross-linked by proteins, it forms a tough, resistant surface material that serves as the hard exoskeleton of insects and crustaceans (figure 3.12; see chapter 34). Few organisms are able to digest chitin, but most possess a chitinase enzyme, probably to protect against fungi.

Learning Outcomes Review 3.2

Monosaccharides have three to six or more carbon atoms typically arranged in a ring form. Disaccharides consist of two linked monosaccharides; polysaccharides are long chains of monosaccharides. Structural differences between sugar isomers can lead to functional differences. Starches are branched polymers of α-glucose used for energy storage. Cellulose in plants consists of unbranched chains of β-glucose that are not easily digested.

■ *How do the structures of starch, glycogen, and cellulose affect their function?*

Figure 3.12 Chitin. Chitin is the principal structural element in the external skeletons of many invertebrates, such as this lobster.

3.3 Nucleic Acids: Information Molecules

Learning Outcomes

1. Describe the structure of nucleotides.
2. Contrast the structures of DNA and RNA.
3. Discuss the functions of DNA and RNA.
4. Recognize other nucleotides involved in energy metabolism.

The biochemical activity of a cell depends on production of a large number of proteins, each with a specific sequence. The information necessary to produce the correct proteins is passed through generations of organisms, even though the proteins themselves are not inherited.

Nucleic acids carry information inside cells, just as disks contain the information in a computer or road maps display information needed by travelers. Two main varieties of nucleic acids are **deoxyribonucleic acid** (**DNA;** figure 3.13) and **ribonucleic acid (RNA).**

Genetic information is stored in DNA, and short-lived copies of this are made in the form of RNA, which is then used to direct the synthesis of proteins during the process of gene expression (as discussed in detail in chapter 15). Unique among macromolecules, nucleic acids are able to serve as templates for producing precise copies of themselves. This characteristic allows genetic information to be preserved during cell division and during the reproduction of organisms.

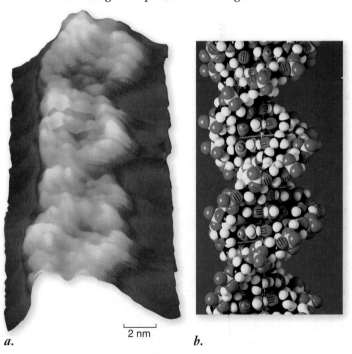

a. 2 nm *b.*

Figure 3.13 Images of DNA. *a.* A scanning-tunneling micrograph of DNA (false color; 2,000,000×) showing approximately three turns of the DNA double helix. *b.* A space-filling model for comparison to the image of actual DNA in *(a).*

The role of RNA in cells is much more complicated: RNA carries information, is part of the organelle responsible for protein synthesis, and recent work indicates it is also involved in the control of gene expression. As a carrier of information, the form of RNA called **messenger RNA (mRNA)** consists of transcribed single-stranded copies of portions of the DNA. These transcripts serve as blueprints specifying the amino acid sequences of proteins. This process will be described in detail in chapter 15.

Nucleic acids are nucleotide polymers

Nucleic acids are long polymers of repeating subunits called **nucleotides.** Each nucleotide consists of three components: a pentose, or five-carbon sugar (ribose in RNA and deoxyribose in DNA); a phosphate ($-PO_4^-$) group; and an organic nitrogenous (nitrogen-containing) base (figure 3.14). When a nucleic acid polymer forms, the phosphate group of one nucleotide binds to the hydroxyl group from the pentose sugar of another, releasing water and forming a *phosphodiester bond* by a dehydration reaction. A **nucleic acid,** then, is simply a chain of five-carbon sugars linked together by phosphodiester bonds with a nitrogenous base protruding from each sugar (see figure 3.15a). These chains of nucleotides, *polynucleotides,* have different ends: a phosphate on one end and an —OH from a sugar on the other end. We conventionally refer to these ends as 5′ ("five-prime," $-PO_4^-$) and 3′ ("three-prime," —OH) taken from the carbon numbering of the sugar (figure 3.15a).

Nucleotides have five types of nitrogenous bases (figure 3.15b). Two of these are large, double-ring molecules called *purines* that are each found in both DNA and RNA; the two purines are adenine (A) and guanine (G). The other three bases are single-ring molecules called *pyrimidines* that include

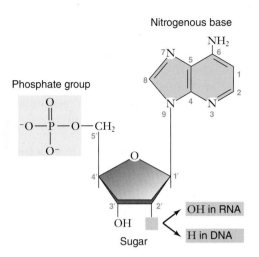

Figure 3.14 Structure of a nucleotide. The nucleotide subunits of DNA and RNA are made up of three elements: a five-carbon sugar (ribose or deoxyribose), an organic nitrogenous base (adenine is shown here), and a phosphate group. Notice that all the numbers on the sugar are given as "primes" (1′, 2′, etc.) to distinguish them from the numbering on the rings of the bases.

cytosine (C, in both DNA and RNA), thymine (T, in DNA only), and uracil (U, in RNA only).

DNA stores genetic information

Organisms use sequences of nucleotides in DNA to encode the information specifying the amino acid sequences of their proteins. This method of encoding information is very similar to the way in which sequences of letters encode information in a

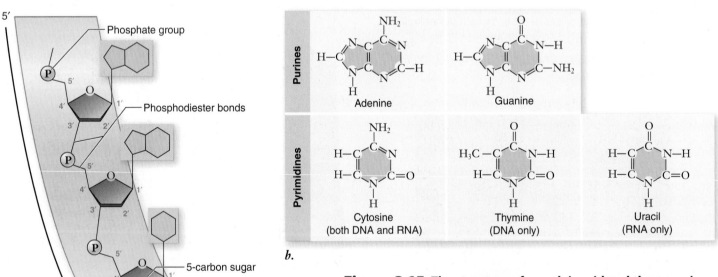

b.

Figure 3.15 The structure of a nucleic acid and the organic nitrogenous bases. *a.* In a nucleic acid, nucleotides are linked to one another via phosphodiester bonds formed between the phosphate of one nucleotide and the sugar of the next nucleotide. We call this the sugar-phosphate backbone, and the organic bases protrude from this chain. The backbone also has different ends: a 5′ phosphate end and a 3′ hydroxyl end (the blue numbers come from the numbers in the sugars). *b.* The organic nitrogenous bases can be either purines or pyrimidines. The base thymine is found in DNA. The base uracil is found in RNA.

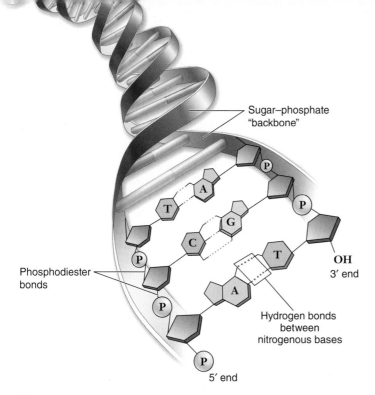

Figure 3.16 The structure of DNA. DNA consists of two polynucleotide chains running in opposite directions wrapped about a single helical axis. Hydrogen bond formation (dashed lines) between the nitrogenous bases, called base-pairing, causes the two chains of DNA to bind to each other and form a double helix.

sentence. A sentence written in English consists of a combination of the 26 different letters of the alphabet in a certain order; the code of a DNA molecule consists of different combinations of the four types of nucleotides in specific sequences, such as CGCTTACG.

DNA molecules in organisms exist as two chains wrapped about each other in a long linear molecule in eukaryotes, and a circular molecule in most prokaryotes. The two strands of a DNA polymer wind around each other like the outside and inside rails of a spiral staircase. Such a spiral shape is called a helix, and a helix composed of two chains is called a **double helix.** Each step of DNA's helical staircase is composed of a base-pair. The pair consists of a base in one chain attracted by hydrogen bonds to a base opposite it on the other chain (figure 3.16).

The base-pairing rules arise from the most stable hydrogen bonding configurations between the bases: Adenine pairs with thymine (in DNA) or with uracil (in RNA), and cytosine pairs with guanine. The bases that participate in base-pairing are said to be **complementary** to each other. Additional details of the structure of DNA and how it interacts with RNA in the production of proteins are presented in chapters 14 and 15.

In eukaryotic organisms, the DNA is further complexed with protein to form structures we call chromosomes. This actually forms a higher order structure that affects the function of DNA as it is involved in the control of gene expression (see chapter 16).

RNA has many roles in a cell

RNA is similar to DNA, but with two major chemical differences. First, RNA molecules contain ribose sugars, in which the C-2 is bonded to a hydroxyl group. (In DNA, a hydrogen atom replaces this hydroxyl group.) Second, RNA molecules use uracil in place of thymine. Uracil has a similar structure to thymine, except that one of its carbons lacks a methyl ($—CH_3$) group.

RNA is produced by transcription (copying) from DNA, and is usually single-stranded (figure 3.17). The role of RNA in cells is quite varied: it carries information in the form of **mRNA**, it is part of the ribosome, in the form of **ribosomal RNA (rRNA),** and it carries amino acids in the form of **transfer RNA (tRNA).** There has been a revolution of late in how we view RNA since it has been found to function as an enzyme, and newly discovered forms of RNA are involved in regulating gene expression (explored in more detail in chapter 16).

Other nucleotides are vital components of energy reactions

In addition to serving as subunits of DNA and RNA, nucleotide bases play other critical roles in the life of a cell. For example,

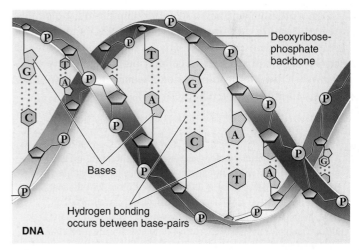

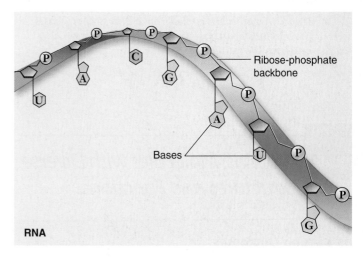

Figure 3.17 DNA versus RNA. DNA forms a double helix, uses deoxyribose as the sugar in its sugar–phosphate backbone, and uses thymine among its nitrogenous bases. RNA is usually single-stranded, uses ribose as the sugar in its sugar–phosphate backbone, and uses uracil in place of thymine.

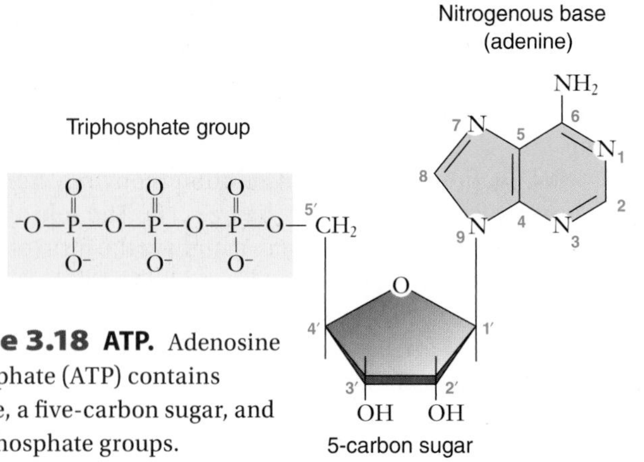

Figure 3.18 ATP. Adenosine triphosphate (ATP) contains adenine, a five-carbon sugar, and three phosphate groups.

adenine is a key component of the molecule **adenosine triphosphate (ATP;** figure 3.18)—the energy currency of the cell. Cells use ATP as energy in a variety of transactions, the way we use money in society. ATP is used to drive energetically unfavorable chemical reactions, to power transport across membranes, and to power the movement of cells.

Two other important nucleotide-containing molecules are **nicotinamide adenine dinucleotide (NAD⁺)** and **flavin adenine dinucleotide (FAD).** These molecules function as electron carriers in a variety of cellular processes. You will see the action of these molecules in detail when we discuss photosynthesis and respiration (chapters 7–8).

Learning Outcomes Review 3.3

A nucleic acid is a polymer composed of alternating phosphate and five-carbon sugar groups with a nitrogenous base protruding from each sugar. In DNA, this sugar is deoxyribose. In RNA, the sugar is ribose. RNA also contains the base uracil instead of thymine. DNA is a double-stranded helix that stores hereditary information as a specific sequence of nucleotide bases. RNA has multiple roles in a cell, including carrying information from DNA and forming part of the ribosome.

■ *If an RNA molecule is copied from a DNA strand, what is the relationship between the sequence of bases in RNA and each DNA strand?*

3.4 Proteins: Molecules with Diverse Structures and Functions

Learning Outcomes

1. Describe the possible levels of protein structure.
2. Explain how motifs and domains contribute to protein structure.
3. Understand the relationship between amino acid sequence and their three-dimensional structure.

Proteins are the most diverse group of biological macromolecules, both chemically and functionally. Because proteins have so many different functions in cells we could not begin to list them all. We can, however, group these functions into the following seven categories. This list is a summary only, however; details are covered in later chapters.

1. **Enzyme catalysis.** Enzymes are biological catalysts that facilitate specific chemical reactions. Because of this property, the appearance of enzymes was one of the most important events in the evolution of life. Enzymes are three-dimensional globular proteins that fit snugly around the molecules they act on. This fit facilitates chemical reactions by stressing particular chemical bonds.

2. **Defense.** Other globular proteins use their shapes to "recognize" foreign microbes and cancer cells. These cell-surface receptors form the core of the body's endocrine and immune systems.

3. **Transport.** A variety of globular proteins transport small molecules and ions. The transport protein hemoglobin, for example, transports oxygen in the blood. Membrane transport proteins help move ions and molecules across the membrane.

4. **Support.** Protein fibers play structural roles. These fibers include keratin in hair, fibrin in blood clots, and collagen. The last one, collagen, forms the matrix of skin, ligaments, tendons, and bones and is the most abundant protein in a vertebrate body.

5. **Motion.** Muscles contract through the sliding motion of two kinds of protein filaments: actin and myosin. Contractile proteins also play key roles in the cell's cytoskeleton and in moving materials within cells.

6. **Regulation.** Small proteins called hormones serve as intercellular messengers in animals. Proteins also play many regulatory roles within the cell—turning on and shutting off genes during development, for example. In addition, proteins receive information, acting as cell-surface receptors.

7. **Storage.** Calcium and iron are stored in the body by binding as ions to storage proteins.

Table 3.2 summarizes these functions and includes examples of the proteins that carry them out in the human body.

Proteins are polymers of amino acids

Proteins are linear polymers made with 20 different amino acids. **Amino acids,** as their name suggests, contain an amino group ($—NH_2$) and an acidic carboxyl group ($—COOH$). The specific order of amino acids determines the protein's structure and function. Many scientists believe amino acids were among the first molecules formed on the early Earth. It seems highly likely that the oceans that existed early in the history of the Earth contained a wide variety of amino acids.

Amino acid structure

The generalized structure of an amino acid is shown as amino and carboxyl groups bonded to a central carbon atom, with an additional hydrogen and a functional side group indicated

TABLE 3.2	The Many Functions of Protein		
Function	**Class of Protein**	**Examples**	**Examples of Use**
Enzyme catalysis	Enzymes	Glycosidases	Cleave polysaccharides
		Proteases	Break down proteins
		Polymerases	Synthesize nucleic acids
		Kinases	Phosphorylate sugars and proteins
Defense	Immunoglobulins	Antibodies	Mark foreign proteins for elimination
	Toxins	Snake venom	Blocks nerve function
	Cell-surface antigens	MHC* proteins	"Self" recognition
Transport	Circulating transporters	Hemoglobin	Carries O_2 and CO_2 in blood
		Myoglobin	Carries O_2 and CO_2 in muscle
		Cytochromes	Electron transport
	Membrane transporters	Sodium–potassium pump	Excitable membranes
		Proton pump	Chemiosmosis
		Glucose transporter	Transports glucose into cells
Support	Fibers	Collagen	Forms cartilage
		Keratin	Forms hair, nails
		Fibrin	Forms blood clots
Motion	Muscle	Actin	Contraction of muscle fibers
		Myosin	Contraction of muscle fibers
Regulation	Osmotic proteins	Serum albumin	Maintains osmotic concentration of blood
	Gene regulators	*lac* Repressor	Regulates transcription
	Hormones	Insulin	Controls blood glucose levels
		Vasopressin	Increases water retention by kidneys
		Oxytocin	Regulates uterine contractions and milk production
Storage	Ion-binding	Ferritin	Stores iron, especially in spleen
		Casein	Stores ions in milk
		Calmodulin	Binds calcium ions

*MHC, major histocompatibility complex.

by R. These components completely fill the bonds of the central carbon:

$$H_2N - \underset{\underset{H}{|}}{\overset{\overset{R}{|}}{C}} - COOH$$

The unique character of each amino acid is determined by the nature of the R group. Notice that unless the R group is an H atom, as in glycine, amino acids are chiral and can exist as two enantiomeric forms: D or L. In living systems, only the L-amino acids are found in proteins, and D-amino acids are rare.

The R group also determines the chemistry of amino acids. Serine, in which the R group is —CH₂OH, is a polar molecule. Alanine, which has —CH₃ as its R group, is nonpolar. The 20 common amino acids are grouped into five chemical classes, based on their R group:

1. Nonpolar amino acids, such as leucine, often have R groups that contain —CH₂ or —CH₃.
2. Polar uncharged amino acids, such as threonine, have R groups that contain oxygen (or —OH).
3. Charged amino acids, such as glutamic acid, have R groups that contain acids or bases that can ionize.
4. Aromatic amino acids, such as phenylalanine, have R groups that contain an organic (carbon) ring with alternating single and double bonds. These are also nonpolar.
5. Amino acids that have special functions have unique properties. Some examples are methionine, which is often the first amino acid in a chain of amino acids; proline, which causes kinks in chains; and cysteine, which links chains together.

Each amino acid affects the shape of a protein differently, depending on the chemical nature of its side group. For example, portions of a protein chain with numerous nonpolar amino acids tend to fold into the interior of the protein by hydrophobic exclusion.

Peptide bonds

In addition to its R group, each amino acid, when ionized, has a positive amino (NH_3^+) group at one end and a negative carboxyl (COO^-) group at the other. The amino and carboxyl groups on a pair of amino acids can undergo a dehydration reaction to form a covalent bond. The covalent bond that links two amino acids is called a **peptide bond** (figure 3.19). The two amino acids linked by such a bond are not free to rotate around the N—C linkage because the peptide bond has a partial double-bond character. This is different from the N—C and C—C bonds to the central carbon of the amino acid. This lack of rotation about the peptide bond is one factor that determines the structural character of the coils and other regular shapes formed by chains of amino acids.

A protein is composed of one or more long unbranched chains. Each chain is called a **polypeptide** and is composed of amino acids linked by peptide bonds. The terms *protein* and *polypeptide* tend to be used loosely and may be confusing. For proteins that include only a single polypeptide chain, the two terms are synonymous.

The pioneering work of Frederick Sanger in the early 1950s provided the evidence that each kind of protein has a specific amino acid sequence. Using chemical methods to remove successive amino acids and then identify them, Sanger succeeded in determining the amino acid sequence of insulin. In so doing he demonstrated clearly that this protein had a defined sequence, which was the same for all insulin molecules in the solution. Although many different amino acids occur in nature, only 20 commonly occur in proteins. Of these 20, 8 are called essential amino acids because humans cannot synthesize them and thus must get them from their diets. Figure 3.20 illustrates these 20 amino acids and their side groups.

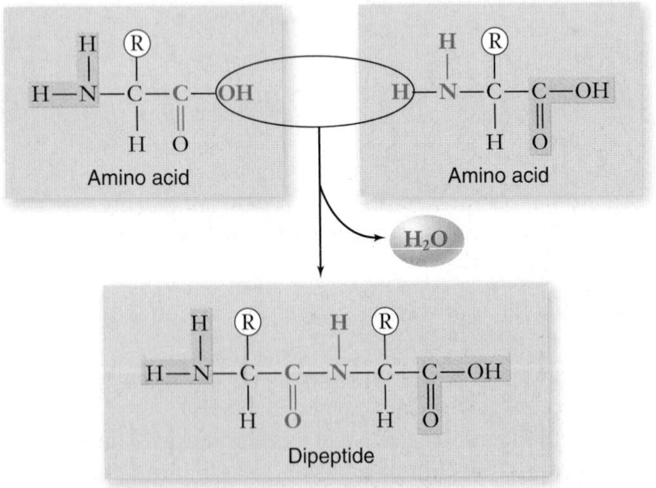

Proteins have levels of structure

The shape of a protein determines its function. One way to study the shape of something as small as a protein is to look at it with very short wavelength energy—in other words, with X-rays. X-rays can be passed through a crystal of protein to produce a diffraction pattern. This pattern can then be analyzed by a painstaking procedure that allows the investigator to build up a three-dimensional picture of the position of each atom. The first protein to be analyzed in this way was myoglobin, and the related protein hemoglobin was analyzed soon thereafter.

As more and more proteins were studied, a general principle became evident: In every protein studied, essentially all the internal amino acids are nonpolar ones—amino acids such as leucine, valine, and phenylalanine. Water's tendency to hydrophobically exclude nonpolar molecules literally shoves the nonpolar portions of the amino acid chain into the protein's interior (figure 3.21). This tendency forces the nonpolar amino acids into close contact with one another, leaving little empty space inside. Polar and charged amino acids are restricted to the surface of the protein, except for the few that play key functional roles.

The structure of proteins is usually discussed in terms of a hierarchy of four levels: *primary, secondary, tertiary,* and *quaternary* (figure 3.22). We will examine this view and then integrate it with a more modern approach arising from our increasing knowledge of protein structure.

Primary structure: amino acid sequence

The **primary structure** of a protein is its amino acid sequence. Because the R groups that distinguish the amino acids play no role in the peptide backbone of proteins, a protein can consist of any sequence of amino acids. Thus, because any of 20 different amino acids might appear at any position, a protein containing 100 amino acids could form any of 20^{100} different amino acid sequences (that's the same as 10^{130}, or 1 followed by 130 zeros—more than the number of atoms known in the universe). This important property of proteins permits great diversity.

Consider the protein hemoglobin, the protein your blood uses to transport oxygen. Hemoglobin is composed of two α-globin peptide chains and two β-globin peptide chains. The α-globin chains differ from the β-globin ones in the sequence of amino acids. Furthermore, any alteration in the normal sequence of either of the types of globin proteins, even by a single amino acid, can have drastic effects on how the protein functions.

Secondary structure: Hydrogen bonding patterns

The amino acid side groups are not the only portions of proteins that form hydrogen bonds. The peptide groups of the main chain can also do so. These hydrogen bonds can be with water or with other peptide groups. If the peptide groups formed too many hydrogen bonds with water, the proteins would tend to behave like a random coil and wouldn't produce

Figure 3.19 The peptide bond. A peptide bond forms when the amino end of one amino acid joins to the carboxyl end of another. Reacting amino and carboxyl groups are shown in red and nonreacting groups are highlighted in green. Notice that the resulting dipeptide still has an amino end and a carboxyl end. Because of the partial double-bond nature of peptide bonds, the resulting peptide chain cannot rotate freely around these bonds.

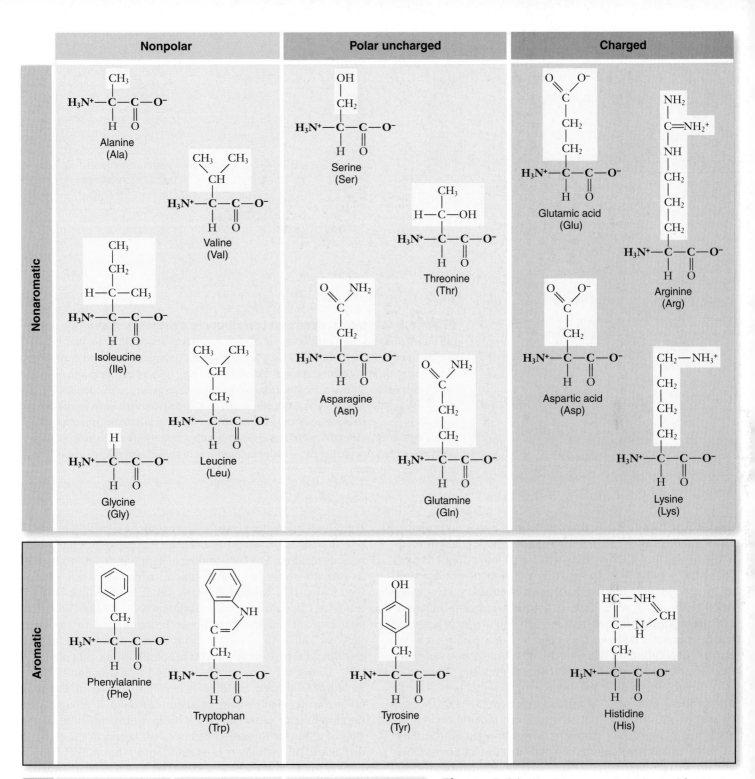

Nonpolar

Alanine (Ala)

Valine (Val)

Isoleucine (Ile)

Leucine (Leu)

Glycine (Gly)

Polar uncharged

Serine (Ser)

Threonine (Thr)

Asparagine (Asn)

Glutamine (Gln)

Charged

Glutamic acid (Glu)

Arginine (Arg)

Aspartic acid (Asp)

Lysine (Lys)

Nonaromatic

Aromatic

Phenylalanine (Phe)

Tryptophan (Trp)

Tyrosine (Tyr)

Histidine (His)

Special function

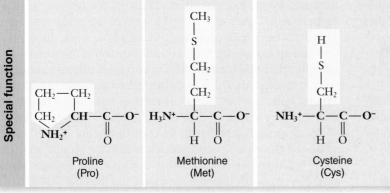

Proline (Pro)

Methionine (Met)

Cysteine (Cys)

Figure 3.20 The 20 common amino acids. Each amino acid has the same chemical backbone, but differs in the side, or R, group. Seven of the amino acids are nonpolar because they have —CH₂ or —CH₃ in their R groups. Two of the seven contain ring structures with alternating double and single bonds, which classifies them also as aromatic. Another five are polar because they have oxygen or a hydroxyl group in their R groups. Five others are capable of ionizing to a charged form. The remaining three special-function amino acids have chemical properties that allow them to help form links between protein chains or kinks in proteins.

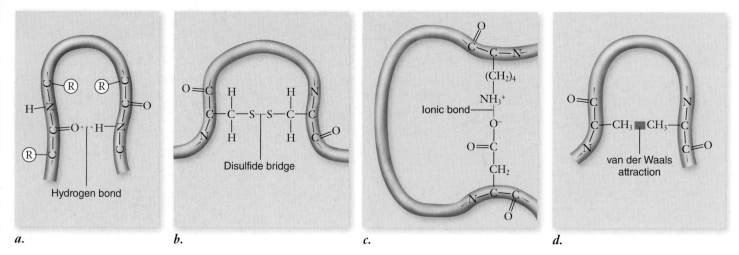

a.　　　　　　　　　b.　　　　　　　　　c.　　　　　　　　　d.

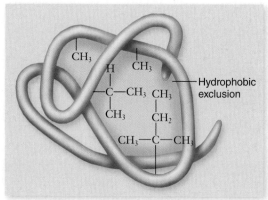

Hydrophobic exclusion

e.

Figure 3.21 Interactions that contribute to a protein's shape. Aside from the bonds that link together the amino acids in a protein, several other weaker forces and interactions determine how a protein will fold. *a.* Hydrogen bonds can form between the different amino acids. *b.* Covalent disulfide bridges can form between two cysteine side chains. *c.* Ionic bonds can form between groups with opposite charge. *d.* van der Waals attractions, which are weak attractions between atoms due to oppositely polarized electron clouds, can occur. *e.* Polar portions of the protein tend to gather on the outside of the protein and interact with water, whereas the hydrophobic portions of the protein, including nonpolar amino acid chains, are shoved toward the interior of the protein.

the kinds of globular structures that are common in proteins. Linus Pauling suggested that the peptide groups could interact with one another if the peptide was coiled into a spiral that he called the **α helix.** We now call this sort of regular interaction of groups in the peptide backbone **secondary structure.** Another form of secondary structure can occur between regions of peptide aligned next to each other to form a planar structure called a **β sheet.** These can be either parallel or antiparallel depending on whether the adjacent sections of peptide are oriented in the same direction, or opposite direction.

These two kinds of secondary structure create regions of the protein that are cylindrical (α helices) and planar (β sheets). A protein's final structure can include regions of each type of secondary structure. For example, DNA-binding proteins usually have regions of α helix that can lay across DNA and interact directly with the bases of DNA. Porin proteins that form holes in membranes are composed of β sheets arranged to form a pore in the membrane. Finally in hemoglobin, the α- and β-globin peptide chains that make up the final molecule each have characteristic regions of secondary structure.

Tertiary structure: Folds and links

The final folded shape of a globular protein is called its **tertiary structure.** This tertiary structure contains regions that have secondary structure and determines how these are further arranged in space to produce the overall structure. A protein is initially driven into its tertiary structure by hydrophobic exclusion from water. Ionic bonds between oppositely charged

R groups bring regions into close proximity, and disulfide bonds (covalent links between two cysteine R groups) lock particular regions together. The final folding of a protein is determined by its primary structure—the chemical nature of its side groups (see figures 3.21 and 3.22). Many small proteins can be fully unfolded ("denatured") and will spontaneously refold into their characteristic shape. Other larger proteins tend to associate together and form insoluble clumps when denatured, such as the film that can form when you heat milk for hot chocolate.

The tertiary structure is stabilized by a number of forces including hydrogen bonding between R groups of different amino acids, electrostatic attraction between R groups with opposite charge (also called salt bridges), hydrophobic exclusion of nonpolar R groups, and covalent bonds in the form of disulfides. The stability of a protein, once it has folded into its tertiary shape, is strongly influenced by how well its interior fits together. When two nonpolar chains in the interior are very close together, they experience a form of molecular attraction called van der Waals forces. Individually quite weak, these forces can add up to a strong attraction when many of them come into play, like the combined strength of hundreds of hooks and loops on a strip of Velcro. These forces are effective only over short distances, however. No "holes" or cavities exist in the interior of proteins. The variety of different nonpolar amino acids, with a different-sized R group with its own distinctive shape, allows nonpolar chains to fit very precisely within the protein interior.

It is therefore not surprising that changing a single amino acid can drastically alter the structure, and thus the function of a

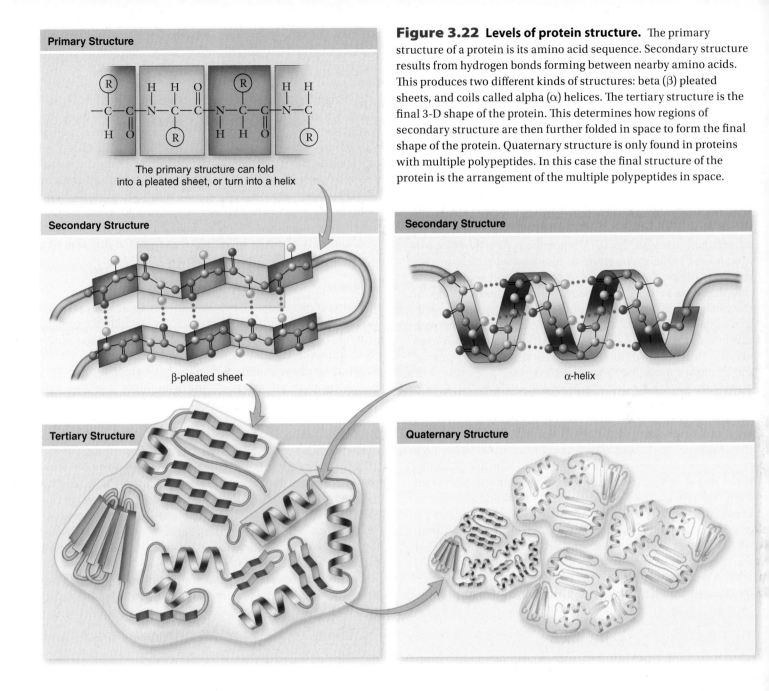

Primary Structure

The primary structure can fold into a pleated sheet, or turn into a helix

Secondary Structure

β-pleated sheet

Secondary Structure

α-helix

Tertiary Structure

Quaternary Structure

Figure 3.22 Levels of protein structure. The primary structure of a protein is its amino acid sequence. Secondary structure results from hydrogen bonds forming between nearby amino acids. This produces two different kinds of structures: beta (β) pleated sheets, and coils called alpha (α) helices. The tertiary structure is the final 3-D shape of the protein. This determines how regions of secondary structure are then further folded in space to form the final shape of the protein. Quaternary structure is only found in proteins with multiple polypeptides. In this case the final structure of the protein is the arrangement of the multiple polypeptides in space.

protein. The sickle cell version of hemoglobin (HbS), for example, is a change of a single glutamic acid for a valine in the β-globin chain. This change substitutes a charged amino acid for a nonpolar one on the surface of the protein, leading the protein to become sticky and form clumps. Another variant of hemoglobin called HbE, actually the most common in human populations, causes a change from glutamic acid to lysine at a different site in the β-globin chain. In this case the structural change is not as dramatic, but it still impairs function, resulting in blood disorders called anemia and thalassemia. More than 700 structural variants of hemoglobin are known, with up to 7% of the world's population being carriers of forms that are medically important.

Quaternary structure: Subunit arrangements

When two or more polypeptide chains associate to form a functional protein, the individual chains are referred to as subunits

of the protein. The arrangement of these subunits is termed its **quaternary structure**. In proteins composed of subunits, the interfaces where the subunits touch one another are often nonpolar, and they play a key role in transmitting information between the subunits about individual subunit activities.

Remember that the protein hemoglobin is composed of two α-chain subunits and two β-chain subunits. Each α- and β-globin chain has a primary structure consisting of a specific sequence of amino acids. This then assumes a characteristic secondary structure consisting of α helices and β sheets that are then arranged into a specific tertiary structure for each α- and β-globin subunit. Lastly, these subunits are then arranged into their final quaternary structure. This is the final structure of the protein. For proteins that consist of only a single peptide chain, the enzyme lysozyme for example, the tertiary structure is the final structure of the protein.

Motifs and domains are additional structural characteristics

To directly determine the sequence of amino acids in a protein is a laborious task. Although the process has been automated, it remains slow and difficult.

The ability to sequence DNA changed this situation rather suddenly. Sequencing DNA was a much simpler process, and even before it was automated, the number of known sequences rose quickly. With the advent of automation, the known sequences increased even more dramatically. Today the entire sequence of hundreds of bacterial genomes and more than a dozen animal genomes, including that of humans, has been determined. Because the DNA sequence is directly related to amino acid sequence in proteins, biologists now have a large database of protein sequences to compare and analyze. This new information has also stimulated thought about the logic of the genetic code and whether underlying patterns exist in protein structure. Our view of protein structure has evolved with this new information. Researchers still view the four-part hierarchical structure as important, but two new terms have entered the biologist's vocabulary: motif and domain.

Motifs

As biologists discovered the 3-D structure of proteins (an even more laborious task than determining the sequence), they noticed similarities between otherwise dissimilar proteins. These similar structures are called **motifs,** or sometimes "supersecondary structure." The term *motif* is borrowed from the arts and refers to a recurring thematic element in music or design.

One very common protein motif is the β-α-β motif, which creates a fold or crease; the so-called "Rossmann fold" at the core of nucleotide-binding sites in a wide variety of proteins. A second motif that occurs in many proteins is the β barrel, which is a β sheet folded around to form a tube. A third type of motif, the helix-turn-helix, consists of two α helices separated by a bend. This motif is important because many proteins use it to bind to the DNA double helix (figure 3.23; see also chapter 16).

Motifs indicate a logic to structure that investigators still do not understand. Do they simply represent a reuse by evolution of something that already works, or are they an optimal solution to a problem, such as how to bind a nucleotide? One way to think about it is that if amino acids are letters in the language of proteins, then motifs represent repeated words or phrases. Motifs have been useful in determining the function of unknown proteins. Databases of protein motifs are used to search new unknown proteins. Finding motifs with known functions may allow an investigator to infer the function of a new protein.

Domains

Domains of proteins are functional units within a larger structure. They can be thought of as substructure within the tertiary structure of a protein (see figure 3.23). To continue the metaphor: Amino acids are letters in the protein language, motifs are words or phrases, and domains are paragraphs.

Most proteins are made up of multiple domains that perform different parts of the protein's function. In many cases, these domains can be physically separated. For example, transcription factors (discussed in chapter 16) are proteins that bind to DNA and initiate its transcription. If the DNA-binding region is exchanged with a different transcription factor, then the specificity of the factor for DNA can be changed without changing its ability to stimulate transcription. Such "domain-swapping" experiments have been performed with many transcription factors, and they indicate, among other things, that the DNA-binding and activation domains are functionally separate.

These functional domains of proteins may also help the protein to fold into its proper shape. As a polypeptide chain

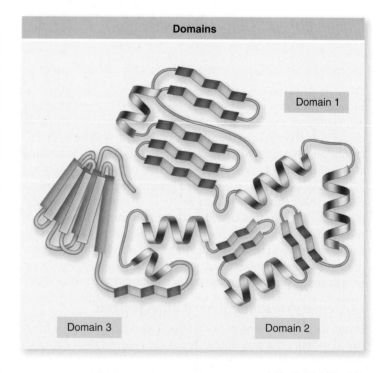

Figure 3.23 Motifs and domains. The elements of secondary structure can combine, fold, or crease to form motifs. These motifs are found in different proteins and can be used to predict function. Proteins also are made of larger domains, which are functionally distinct parts of a protein. The arrangement of these domains in space is the tertiary structure of a protein.

folds, the domains take their proper shape, each more or less independently of the others. This action can be demonstrated experimentally by artificially producing the fragment of a polypeptide that forms the domain in the intact protein, and showing that the fragment folds to form the same structure as it exhibits in the intact protein. A single polypeptide chain connects the domains of a protein, like a rope tied into several adjacent knots.

Domains can also correspond to the structure of the genes that encode them. Later, in chapter 15, you will see that genes in eukaryotes are often in pieces within the genome, and these pieces, called *exons,* sometimes encode the functional domains of a protein. This finding led to the idea of evolution acting by shuffling protein-encoding domains.

The process of folding relies on chaperone proteins

Until recently, scientific investigators thought that newly made proteins fold spontaneously, randomly trying out different configurations as hydrophobic interactions with water shoved nonpolar amino acids into the protein's interior until the final structure was arrived at. We now know this view is too simple. Protein chains can fold in so many different ways that trial and error would simply take too long. In addition, as the open chain folds its way toward its final form, nonpolar "sticky" interior portions are exposed during intermediate stages. If these intermediate forms are placed in a test tube in an environment identical to that inside a cell, they stick to other, unwanted protein partners, forming a gluey mess.

How do cells avoid having their proteins clump into a mass? A vital clue came in studies of unusual mutations that prevent viruses from replicating in bacterial cells. It turns out that the virus proteins produced inside the cells could not fold properly. Further study revealed that normal cells contain **chaperone proteins,** which help other proteins to fold correctly.

Molecular biologists have now identified many proteins that act as molecular chaperones. This class of proteins has multiple subclasses, and representatives have been found in essentially every organism that has been examined. Furthermore, these proteins seem to be essential for viability as well, illustrating their fundamental importance. Many are heat shock proteins, produced in greatly increased amounts when cells are exposed to elevated temperature. High temperatures cause proteins to unfold, and heat shock chaperone proteins help the cell's proteins to refold properly.

One class of these proteins, called chaperonins, has been extensively studied. In the bacterium *Escherichia coli* (*E. coli*), one example is the essential protein GroE chaperonin. In mutants in which the GroE chaperonin is inactivated, fully 30% of the bacterial proteins fail to fold properly. Chaperonins associate to form a large macromolecular complex that resembles a cylindrical container. Proteins can move into the container, and the container itself can change its shape considerably (figure 3.24). Experiments have shown that an improperly folded protein can enter the chaperonin and be refolded. Although we don't know exactly how this happens, it seems to involve changes in the hydrophobicity of the interior of the chamber.

The flexibility of the structure of chaperonins is amazing. We tend to think of proteins as being fixed structures, but this is clearly not the case for chaperonins and this flexibility is necessary for their function. It also illustrates that even domains that may be very widely separated in a very large protein are still functionally connected. The folding process within a chaperonin harnesses the hydrolysis of ATP to power these changes in structure necessary for function. This entire process can occur in a cyclic manner until the appropriate structure is achieved. Cells use these chaperonins both to accomplish the original folding of some proteins and to restore the structure of incorrectly folded ones.

Some diseases may result from improper folding

Chaperone protein deficiencies may be implicated in certain diseases in which key proteins are improperly folded. Cystic fibrosis is

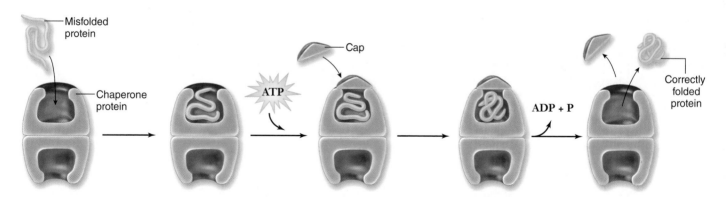

Chance for protein to refold

Figure 3.24 How one type of chaperone protein works. This barrel-shaped chaperonin is from the GroE family of chaperone proteins. It is composed of two identical rings each with seven identical subunits, each of which has three distinct domains. An incorrectly folded protein enters one chamber of the barrel, and a cap seals the chamber. Energy from the hydrolysis of ATP fuels structural alterations to the chamber, changing it from hydrophobic to hydrophilic. This change allows the protein to refold. After a short time, the protein is ejected, either folded or unfolded, and the cycle can repeat itself.

a hereditary disorder in which a mutation disables a vital protein that moves ions across cell membranes. As a result, people with cystic fibrosis have thicker than normal mucus. This results in breathing problems, lung disease, and digestive difficulties, among other things. One interesting feature of the molecular analysis of this disease has been the number of different mutations found in human populations. One diverse class of mutations all result in problems with protein folding. The number of different mutations that can result in improperly folded proteins may be related to the fact that the native protein often fails to fold properly.

Denaturation inactivates proteins

If a protein's environment is altered, the protein may change its shape or even unfold completely. This process is called **denaturation** (figure 3.25). Proteins can be denatured when the pH, temperature, or ionic concentration of the surrounding solution changes.

Denatured proteins are usually biologically inactive. This action is particularly significant in the case of enzymes. Because practically every chemical reaction in a living organism is catalyzed by a specific enzyme, it is vital that a cell's enzymes work properly.

The traditional methods of food preservation, salt curing and pickling, involve denaturation of proteins. Prior to the general availability of refrigerators and freezers, the only practical

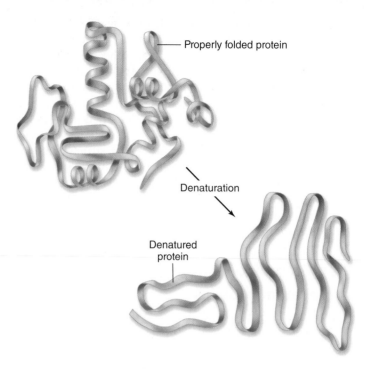

Figure 3.25 Protein denaturation. Changes in a protein's environment, such as variations in temperature or pH, can cause a protein to unfold and lose its shape in a process called denaturation. In this denatured state, proteins are biologically inactive.

SCIENTIFIC THINKING

Hypothesis: *The 3-D structure of a protein is the thermodynamically stable structure. It depends only on the primary structure of the protein and the solution conditions.*

Prediction: *If a protein is denatured and allowed to renature under native conditions, it will refold into the native structure.*

Test: *Ribonuclease is treated with a reducing agent to break disulfide bonds and is then treated with urea to completely unfold the protein. The disulfide bonds are reformed under nondenaturing conditions to see if the protein refolds properly.*

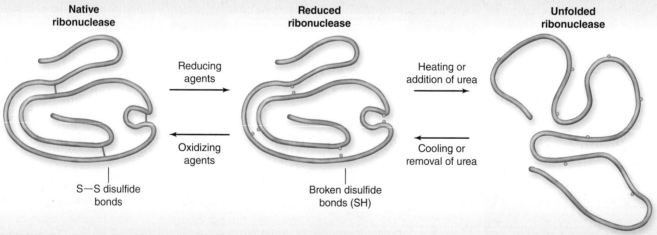

Result: *Denatured Ribonuclease refolds properly under nondenaturing conditions.*

Conclusion: *The hypothesis is supported. The information in the primary structure (amino acid sequence) is sufficient for refolding to occur. This implies that protein folding results in the thermodynamically stable structure.*

Further Experiments: *If the disulfide bonds were allowed to reform under denaturing conditions, would we get the same result? How can we rule out that the protein had not been completely denatured and therefore retained some structure?*

Figure 3.26 Primary structure determines tertiary structure.

way to keep microorganisms from growing in food was to keep the food in a solution containing a high concentration of salt or vinegar, which denatured the enzymes of most microorganisms and prevented them from growing on the food.

Most enzymes function within a very narrow range of environmental conditions. Blood-borne enzymes that course through a human body at a pH of about 7.4 would rapidly become denatured in the highly acidic environment of the stomach. Conversely, the protein-degrading enzymes that function at a pH of 2 or less in the stomach would be denatured in the relatively basic pH of the blood. Similarly, organisms that live near oceanic hydrothermal vents have enzymes that work well at these extremes of temperature (over 100°C). They cannot survive in cooler waters, because their enzymes do not function properly at lower temperatures. Any given organism usually has a tolerance range of pH, temperature, and salt concentration. Within that range, its enzymes maintain the proper shape to carry out their biological functions.

When a protein's normal environment is reestablished after denaturation, a small protein may spontaneously refold into its natural shape, driven by the interactions between its nonpolar amino acids and water (figure 3.26). This process is termed *renaturation,* and it was first established for the enzyme ribonuclease (RNase). The renaturation of RNase led to the doctrine that primary structure determines tertiary structure. Larger proteins can rarely refold spontaneously, however, because of the complex nature of their final shape, so this simple idea needs to be qualified.

The fact that some proteins can spontaneously renature implies that tertiary structure is strongly influenced by primary structure. In an extreme example, the *E. coli* ribosome can be taken apart and put back together experimentally. Although this process requires temperature and ion concentration shifts, it indicates an amazing degree of self-assembly. That complex structures can arise by self-assembly is a key idea in the study of modern biology.

It is important to distinguish denaturation from **dissociation.** For proteins with quaternary structure, the subunits may be dissociated without losing their individual tertiary structure. For example, the four subunits of hemoglobin may dissociate into four individual molecules (two α-globins and two β-globins) without denaturation of the folded globin proteins. They readily reassume their four-subunit quaternary structure.

Learning Outcomes Review 3.4

Proteins are molecules with diverse functions. They are constructed from 20 different kinds of amino acids. Protein structure can be viewed at four levels: (1) the amino acid sequence, or primary structure; (2) coils and sheets, called secondary structure; (3) the three-dimensional shape, called tertiary structure; and (4) individual polypeptide subunits associated in a quaternary structure. Different proteins often have similar substructures called motifs and can be broken down into functional domains. Proteins have a narrow range of conditions in which they fold properly; outside that range, proteins tend to unfold (denaturation). Under some conditions, denatured proteins can refold and become functional again (renaturation).

■ *How does our knowledge of protein structure help us to predict the function of unknown proteins?*

Learning Outcomes

1. *Describe the structure of triglycerides.*
2. *Explain how fats function as energy-storage molecules.*
3. *Apply knowledge of the structure of phospholipids to the formation of membranes.*

Lipids are a somewhat loosely defined group of molecules with one main chemical characteristic: They are insoluble in water. Storage fats such as animal fat are one kind of lipid. Oils such as those from olives, corn, and coconut are also lipids, as are waxes such as beeswax and earwax. Even some vitamins are lipids!

Lipids have a very high proportion of nonpolar carbon–hydrogen (C—H) bonds, and so long-chain lipids cannot fold up like a protein to confine their nonpolar portions away from the surrounding aqueous environment. Instead, when they are placed in water, many lipid molecules spontaneously cluster together and expose what polar (hydrophilic) groups they have to the surrounding water, while confining the nonpolar (hydrophobic) parts of the molecules together within the cluster. You may have noticed this effect when you add oil to a pan containing water, and the oil beads up into cohesive drops on the water's surface. This spontaneous assembly of lipids is of paramount importance to cells, as it underlies the structure of cellular membranes.

Fats consist of complex polymers of fatty acids attached to glycerol

Many lipids are built from a simple skeleton made up of two main kinds of molecules: fatty acids and glycerol. Fatty acids are long-chain hydrocarbons with a carboxylic acid (COOH) at one end. Glycerol is a three-carbon polyalcohol (three —OH groups). Many lipid molecules consist of a glycerol molecule with three fatty acids attached, one to each carbon of the glycerol backbone. Because it contains three fatty acids, a fat molecule is commonly called a **triglyceride** (the more accurate chemical name is *triacylglycerol*). This basic structure is depicted in figure 3.27. The three fatty acids of a triglyceride need not be identical, and often they are very different from one another. The hydrocarbon chains of fatty acids vary in length. The most common are even-numbered chains of 14 to 20 carbons. The many C—H bonds of fats serve as a form of long-term energy storage.

If all of the internal carbon atoms in the fatty acid chains are bonded to at least two hydrogen atoms, the fatty acid is said to be **saturated,** which refers to its having all the hydrogen atoms possible (see figure 3.27). A fatty acid that has double bonds between one or more pairs of successive carbon atoms is said to be **unsaturated.** Fatty acids with one double bond are called monounsaturated, and those with more than one double bond are termed **polyunsaturated.** Most naturally occurring unsaturated fatty acids have double bonds with a cis configuration where the carbon chain is on the same side before and after the double bond (double bonds in fatty acids in 3.27*b* are all cis).

Structural Formula	Structural Formula

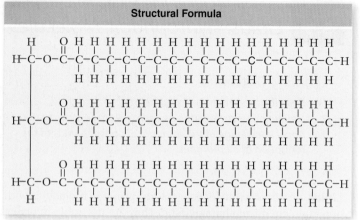

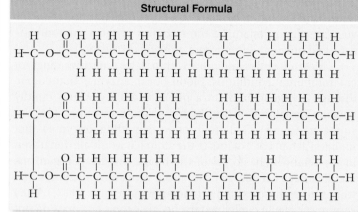

Space-Filling Model	Space-Filling Model

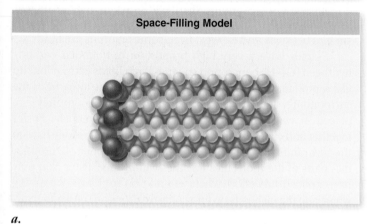

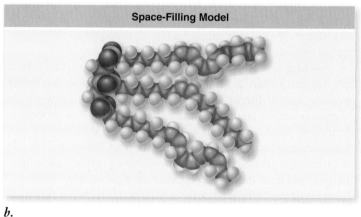

a.   *b.*

Figure 3.27 Saturated and unsaturated fats. *a.* A saturated fat is composed of triglycerides that contain three saturated fatty acids (the kind that have no double bonds). A saturated fat therefore has the maximum number of hydrogen atoms bonded to its carbon chain. Most animal fats are saturated. *b.* Unsaturated fat is composed of triglycerides that contain three unsaturated fatty acids (the kind that have one or more double bonds). These have fewer than the maximum number of hydrogen atoms bonded to the carbon chain. This example includes both a monounsaturated and two polyunsaturated fatty acids. Plant fats are typically unsaturated. The many kinks of the double bonds prevent the triglyceride from closely aligning, which makes them liquid oils at room temperature.

When fats are partially hydrogenated industrially, this can produce double bonds with a trans configuration where the carbon chain is on opposite sides before and after the double bond. These are the so called trans fats. These have been linked to elevated levels of low-density lipoprotein (LDL) "bad cholesterol" and lowered levels of high-density lipoprotein (HDL) "good cholesterol." This condition is thought to be associated with an increased risk for coronary heart disease.

Having double bonds changes the behavior of the molecule because free rotation cannot occur about a C=C double bond as it can with a C—C single bond. This characteristic mainly affects melting point: that is, whether the fatty acid is a solid fat or a liquid oil at room temperature. Fats containing polyunsaturated fatty acids have low melting points because their fatty acid chains bend at the double bonds, preventing the fat molecules from aligning closely with one another. Most saturated fats, such as animal fat or those in butter, are solid at room temperature.

Placed in water, triglycerides spontaneously associate together, forming fat globules that can be very large relative to the size of the individual molecules. Because fats are insoluble in water, they can be deposited at specific locations within an organism, such as in vesicles of adipose tissue.

Organisms contain many other kinds of lipids besides fats (figure 3.28). *Terpenes* are long-chain lipids that are components of many biologically important pigments, such as chlorophyll and the visual pigment retinal. Rubber is also a terpene. *Steroids,* another class of lipid, are composed of four carbon rings. Most animal cell membranes contain the steroid cholesterol. Other steroids, such as testosterone and estrogen, function as hormones in multicellular animals. *Prostaglandins* are a group of about 20 lipids that are modified fatty acids, with two nonpolar "tails" attached to a five-carbon ring. Prostaglandins act as local chemical messengers in many vertebrate tissues. Later chapters explore the effects of some of these complex fatty acids.

Fats are excellent energy-storage molecules

Most fats contain over 40 carbon atoms. The ratio of energy-storing C—H bonds in fats is more than twice that of carbohydrates (see section 3.2), making fats much more efficient molecules for storing chemical energy. On average, fats yield about 9 kilocalories (kcal) of chemical energy per gram, as compared with about 4 kcal/g for carbohydrates.

Most fats produced by animals are saturated (except some fish oils), whereas most plant fats are unsaturated (see

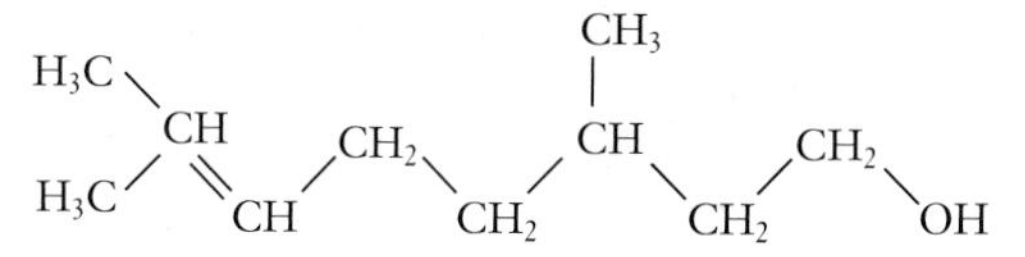

a. Terpene (citronellol)

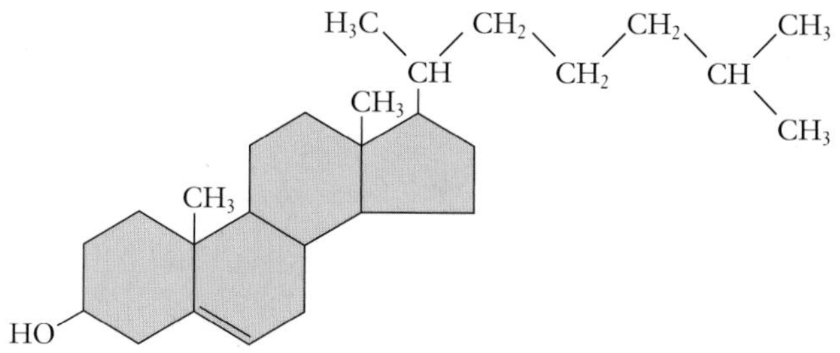

b. Steroid (cholesterol)

Figure 3.28 Other kinds of lipids. ***a.*** Terpenes are found in biological pigments, such as chlorophyll and retinal, and **(b)** steroids play important roles in membranes and as the basis for a class of hormones involved in chemical signaling.

figure 3.27). The exceptions are the tropical plant oils (palm oil and coconut oil), which are saturated even though they are liquid at room temperature. An oil may be converted into a solid fat by chemically adding hydrogen. Most peanut butter is usually artificially hydrogenated to make the peanut fats solidify, preventing them from separating out as oils while the jar sits on the store shelf. However, artificially hydrogenating unsaturated fats produces the *trans*-fatty acids described above.

When an organism consumes excess carbohydrate, it is converted into starch, glycogen, or fats reserved for future use. The reason that many humans in developed countries gain weight as they grow older is that the amount of energy they need decreases with age, but their intake of food does not. Thus, an increasing proportion of the carbohydrates they ingest is converted into fat.

A diet heavy in fats is one of several factors thought to contribute to heart disease, particularly atherosclerosis. In atherosclerosis, sometimes referred to as "hardening of the arteries," fatty substances called plaque adhere to the lining of blood vessels, blocking the flow of blood. Fragments of a plaque can break off from a deposit and clog arteries to the brain, causing a stroke.

Phospholipids form membranes

Complex lipid molecules called **phospholipids** are among the most important molecules of the cell because they form the core of all biological membranes. An individual phospholipid can be thought of as a substituted triglyceride, that is, a triglyceride with a phosphate replacing one of the fatty acids. The basic structure of a phospholipid includes three kinds of subunits:

1. *Glycerol,* a three-carbon alcohol, in which each carbon bears a hydroxyl group. Glycerol forms the backbone of the phospholipid molecule.
2. *Fatty acids,* long chains of —CH_2 groups (hydrocarbon chains) ending in a carboxyl (—COOH) group. Two fatty acids are attached to the glycerol backbone in a phospholipid molecule.
3. *A phosphate group* (—PO_4^{2-}) attached to one end of the glycerol. The charged phosphate group usually has a charged organic molecule linked to it, such as choline, ethanolamine, or the amino acid serine.

The phospholipid molecule can be thought of as having a polar "head" at one end (the phosphate group) and two long, very nonpolar "tails" at the other (figure 3.29). This structure is essential for how these molecules function, although it first

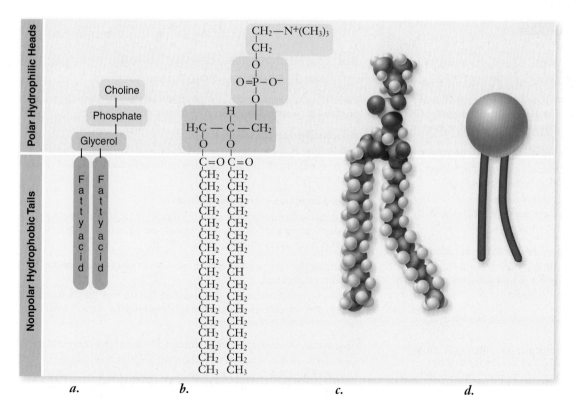

a. **b.** **c.** **d.**

Figure 3.29 Phospholipids. The phospholipid phosphatidylcholine is shown as **(a)** a schematic, **(b)** a formula, **(c)** a space-filling model, and **(d)** an icon used in depictions of biological membranes.

appears paradoxical. Why would a molecule need to be soluble in water, but also not soluble in water? The formation of a membrane shows the unique properties of such a structure.

In water, the nonpolar tails of nearby lipid molecules aggregate away from the water, forming spherical *micelles,* with the tails facing inward (figure 3.30*a*). This is actually how detergent molecules work to make grease soluble in water. The grease is soluble within the nonpolar interior of the micelle and the polar surface of the micelle is soluble in water. With phospholipids, a more complex structure forms in which two layers of molecules line up, with the hydrophobic tails of each layer pointing toward one another, or inward, leaving the hydrophilic heads oriented outward, forming a bilayer (figure 3.30*b*). Lipid bilayers are the basic framework of biological membranes, discussed in detail in chapter 5.

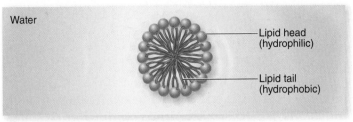
a.

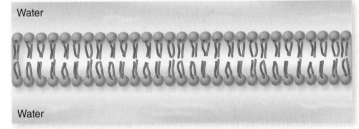
b.

Figure 3.30 Lipids spontaneously form micelles or lipid bilayers in water. In an aqueous environment, lipid molecules orient so that their polar (hydrophilic) heads are in the polar medium, water, and their nonpolar (hydrophobic) tails are held away from the water. *a.* Droplets called micelles can form, or *(b)* phospholipid molecules can arrange themselves into two layers; in both structures, the hydrophilic heads extend outward and the hydrophobic tails inward. This second example is called a phospholipid bilayer.

Learning Outcomes Review 3.5

Triglycerides are made of fatty acids linked to glycerol. Fats can contain twice as many C—H bonds as carbohydrates and thus they store energy efficiently. Because the C—H bonds in lipids are nonpolar, they are not water-soluble and aggregate together in water. Phospholipids replace one fatty acid with a hydrophilic phosphate group. This allows them to spontaneously form bilayers, which are the basis of biological membranes.

■ *Why do phospholipids form membranes while triglycerides form insoluble droplets?*

Chapter Review

3.1 Carbon: The Framework of Biological Molecules

Carbon, the backbone of all biological molecules, can form four covalent bonds and make long chains. Hydrocarbons consist of carbon and hydrogen, and their bonds store considerable energy.

Functional groups account for differences in molecular properties.

Functional groups are small molecular entities that confer specific chemical characteristics when attached to a hydrocarbon.

Carbon and hydrogen have similar electronegativity so C—H bonds are not polar. Oxygen and nitrogen have greater electronegativity, leading to polar bonds.

Isomers have the same molecular formulas but different structures.

Structural isomers are molecules with the same formula but different structures; stereoisomers differ in how groups are attached. Enantiomers are mirror-image stereoisomers.

Biological macromolecules include carbohydrates, nucleic acids, proteins, and lipids.

Most important biological macromolecules are polymers—long chains of monomer units. Biological polymers are formed by elimination of water (H and OH) from two monomers (dehydration reaction). They are broken down by adding water (hydrolysis).

3.2 Carbohydrates: Energy Storage and Structural Molecules

The empirical formula of a carbohydrate is $(CH_2O)_n$. Carbohydrates are used for energy storage and as structural molecules.

Monosaccharides are simple sugars.

Simple sugars contain three to six or more carbon atoms. Examples are glyceraldehyde (3 carbons), deoxyribose (5 carbons), and glucose (6 carbons).

Sugar isomers have structural differences.

The general formula for six-carbon sugars is $C_6H_{12}O_6$, and many isomeric forms are possible. Living systems often have enzymes for converting isomers from one to the other.

Disaccharides serve as transport molecules in plants and provide nutrition in animals.

Plants convert glucose into the disaccharide sucrose for transport within their bodies. Female mammals produce the disaccharide lactose to nourish their young.

Polysaccharides provide energy storage and structural components.

Glucose is used to make three important polymers: glycogen (in animals), and starch and cellulose (in plants). Chitin is a related structural material found in arthropods and many fungi.

3.3 Nucleic Acids: Information Molecules

Deoxyribonucleic acid (DNA) and ribonucleic acid (RNA) are polymers composed of nucleotide monomers. Cells use nucleic acids for information storage and transfer.

Nucleic acids are nucleotide polymers.

Nucleic acids contain four different nucleotide bases. In DNA these are adenine, guanine, cytosine, and thymine. In RNA, thymine is replaced by uracil.

DNA stores genetic information.

DNA exists as a double helix held together by specific base pairs: adenine with thymine and guanine with cytosine. The nucleic acid sequence constitutes the genetic code.

RNA has many roles in a cell.

RNA is made by copying DNA. RNA carries information from DNA and forms part of the ribosome. RNA can also be an enzyme and affect gene expression.

Other nucleotides are vital components of energy reactions.

Adenosine triphosphate (ATP) provides energy in cells; NAD^+ and FAD transport electrons in cellular processes.

3.4 Proteins: Molecules with Diverse Structures and Functions

Most enzymes are proteins. Proteins also provide defense, transport, motion, and regulation, among many other roles.

Proteins are polymers of amino acids.

Amino acids are joined by peptide bonds to make polypeptides. The 20 common amino acids are characterized by R groups that determine their properties.

Proteins have levels of structure.

Protein structure is defined by the following hierarchy: primary (amino acid sequence), secondary (hydrogen bonding patterns), tertiary (three-dimensional folding), and quaternary (associations between two or more polypeptides).

Motifs and domains are additional structural characteristics.

Motifs are similar structural elements found in dissimilar proteins. They can create folds, creases, or barrel shapes. Domains are functional subunits or sites within a tertiary structure.

The process of folding relies on chaperone proteins.

Chaperone proteins assist in the folding of proteins. Heat shock proteins are an example of chaperone proteins.

Some diseases may result from improper folding.

Some forms of cystic fibrosis and Alzheimer disease are associated with misfolded proteins.

Denaturation inactivates proteins.

Denaturation refers to an unfolding of tertiary structure, which usually destroys function. Some denatured proteins may recover function when conditions are returned to normal. This implies that primary structure strongly influences tertiary structure.

Disassociation refers to separation of quaternary subunits with no changes to their tertiary structure.

3.5 Lipids: Hydrophobic Molecules

Lipids are insoluble in water because they have a high proportion of nonpolar C—H bonds.

Fats consist of complex polymers of fatty acids attached to glycerol.

Many lipids exist as triglycerides, three fatty acids connected to a glycerol molecule. Saturated fatty acids contain the maximum number of hydrogen atoms. Unsaturated fatty acids contain one or more double bonds between carbon atoms.

Fats are excellent energy-storage molecules.

The energy stored in the C—H bonds of fats is more than twice that of carbohydrates: 9 kcal/g compared with 4 kcal/g. For this reason, excess carbohydrate is converted to fat for storage.

Phospholipids form membranes.

Phospholipids contain two fatty acids and one phosphate attached to glycerol. In phospholipid-bilayer membranes, the phosphate heads are hydrophilic and cluster on the two faces of the membrane, and the hydrophobic tails are in the center.

Review Questions

UNDERSTAND

1. How is a polymer formed from multiple monomers?
   a. From the growth of the chain of carbon atoms
   b. By the removal of an —OH group and a hydrogen atom
   c. By the addition of an —OH group and a hydrogen atom
   d. Through hydrogen bonding

2. Why are carbohydrates important molecules for energy storage?
   a. The C—H bonds found in carbohydrates store energy.
   b. The double bonds between carbon and oxygen are very strong.
   c. The electronegativity of the oxygen atoms means that a carbohydrate is made up of many polar bonds.
   d. They can form ring structures in the aqueous environment of a cell.

3. Plant cells store energy in the form of _____, and animal cells store energy in the form of _____.
   a. fructose; glucose
   b. disaccharides; monosaccharides
   c. cellulose; chitin
   d. starch; glycogen

4. Which carbohydrate would you find as part of a molecule of RNA?
   a. Galactose
   b. Deoxyribose
   c. Ribose
   d. Glucose

5. A molecule of DNA or RNA is a polymer of
   a. monosaccharides.   c. amino acids.
   b. nucleotides.   d. fatty acids.

6. What makes cellulose different from starch?

    a. Starch is produced by plant cells, and cellulose is produced by animal cells.
    b. Cellulose forms long filaments, and starch is highly branched.
    c. Starch is insoluble, and cellulose is soluble.
    d. All of the choices are correct.

7. What monomers make up a protein?

    a. Monosaccharides   c. Amino acids
    b. Nucleotides   d. Fatty acids

8. A triglyceride is a form of _____ composed of _____.

    a. lipid; fatty acids and glucose
    b. lipid; fatty acids and glycerol
    c. carbohydrate; fatty acids
    d. lipid; cholesterol

APPLY

1. You can use starch or glycogen as an energy source, but not cellulose because

    a. starch and cellulose have similar structures.
    b. cellulose and glycogen have similar structures.
    c. starch and glycogen have similar structures.
    d. your body makes starch but not cellulose.

2. Which of the following is NOT a difference between DNA and RNA?

    a. Deoxyribose sugar versus ribose sugar
    b. Thymine versus uracil
    c. Double-stranded versus single-stranded
    d. Phosphodiester versus hydrogen bonds

3. Which part of an amino acid has the greatest influence on the overall structure of a protein?

    a. The $(-NH_2)$ amino group
    b. The R group
    c. The $(-COOH)$ carboxyl group
    d. Both a and c are correct.

4. A mutation that alters a single amino acid within a protein can alter

    a. the primary level of protein structure.
    b. the secondary level of protein structure.
    c. the tertiary level of protein structure.
    d. All of the choices are correct.

5. Two different proteins have the same domain in their structure. From this we can infer that they have

    a. the same primary structure.
    b. similar function.
    c. very different functions.
    d. the same primary structure but different function.

6. What aspect of triglyceride structure accounts for their insolubility in water?

    a. The COOH group of fatty acids
    b. The nonpolar C—H bonds in fatty acids
    c. The OH groups in glycerol
    d. The C=C bonds found in unsaturated fatty acids

7. The spontaneous formation of a lipid bilayer in an aqueous environment occurs because

    a. the polar head groups of the phospholipids can interact with water.
    b. the long fatty acid tails of the phospholipids can interact with water.
    c. the fatty acid tails of the phospholipids are hydrophobic.
    d. Both a and c are correct.

SYNTHESIZE

1. How do the four biological macromolecules differ from one another? How does the structure of each relate to its function?

2. Hydrogen bonds and hydrophobic interactions each play an important role in stabilizing and organizing biological macromolecules. Consider the four macromolecules discussed in this chapter. Describe how these affect the form and function of each type of macromolecule. Would a disruption in the hydrogen bonds affect form and function? Hydrophobic interactions?

3. Plants make both starch and cellulose. Would you predict that the enzymes involved in starch synthesis could also be used by the plant for cellulose synthesis? Construct an argument to explain this based on the structure and function of the enzymes and the polymers synthesized.

ONLINE RESOURCE

www.ravenbiology.com

Understand, Apply, and Synthesize—enhance your study with animations that bring concepts to life and practice tests to assess your understanding. Your instructor may also recommend the interactive eBook, individualized learning tools, and more.

Chapter 4

Cell Structure

Chapter Contents

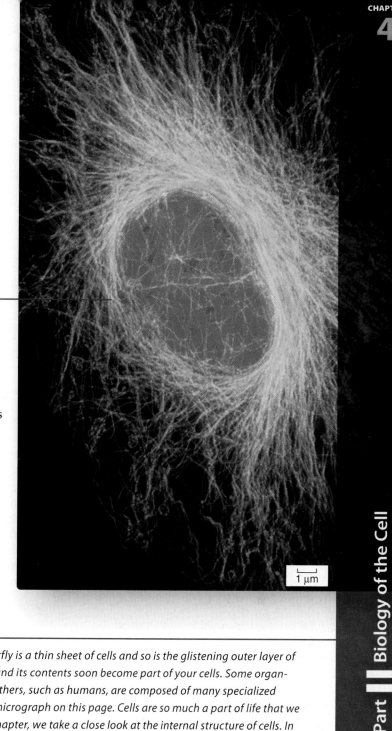

1 μm

Part II   Biology of the Cell

Introduction

All organisms are composed of cells. The gossamer wing of a butterfly is a thin sheet of cells and so is the glistening outer layer of your eyes. The hamburger or tomato you eat is composed of cells, and its contents soon become part of your cells. Some organisms consist of a single cell too small to see with the unaided eye. Others, such as humans, are composed of many specialized cells, such as the fibroblast cell shown in the striking fluorescence micrograph on this page. Cells are so much a part of life that we cannot imagine an organism that is not cellular in nature. In this chapter, we take a close look at the internal structure of cells. In chapters 5 to 10, we will focus on cells in action—how they communicate with their environment, grow, and reproduce.

4.1   Cell Theory

Learning Outcomes

1. *Discuss the cell theory.*
2. *Describe the factors that limit cell size.*
3. *Categorize structural and functional similarities in cells.*

Cells are characteristically microscopic in size. Although there are exceptions, a typical eukaryotic cell is 10 to 100 micrometers (μm) (10–100 millionths of a meter) in diameter, although most prokaryotic cells are only 1 to 10 μm in diameter.

Because cells are so small, they were not discovered until the invention of the microscope in the 17th century. English natural philosopher Robert Hooke was the first to observe cells in 1665, naming the shapes he saw in cork *cellulae* (Latin, "small rooms"). This is known to us as *cells.* Another early microscopist, Dutch Anton van Leeuwenhoek, first observed living cells, which he termed "animalcules," or little animals.

After these early efforts, a century and a half passed before biologists fully recognized the importance of cells. In 1838, German botanist Matthias Schleiden stated that all plants "are aggregates of fully individualized, independent, separate beings, namely the cells themselves." In 1839, German physiologist Theodor Schwann reported that all animal tissues also consist of individual cells. Thus, the cell theory was born.

Cell theory is the unifying foundation of cell biology

The cell theory was proposed to explain the observation that all organisms are composed of cells. It sounds simple, but it is a far-reaching statement about the organization of life.

In its modern form, the *cell theory* includes the following three principles:

1. All organisms are composed of one or more cells, and the life processes of metabolism and heredity occur within these cells.
2. Cells are the smallest living things, the basic units of organization of all organisms.
3. Cells arise only by division of a previously existing cell.

Although life likely evolved spontaneously in the environment of early Earth, biologists have concluded that no additional cells are originating spontaneously at present. Rather, life on Earth represents a continuous line of descent from those early cells.

Cell size is limited

Most cells are relatively small for reasons related to the diffusion of substances into and out of them. The rate of diffusion is affected by a number of variables, including (1) surface area available for diffusion, (2) temperature, (3) concentration gradient of diffusing substance, and (4) the distance over which diffusion must occur. As the size of a cell increases, the length of time for diffusion from the outside membrane to the interior of the cell increases as well. Larger cells need to synthesize more macromolecules, have correspondingly higher energy requirements, and produce a greater quantity of waste. Molecules used for energy and biosynthesis must be transported through the membrane. Any metabolic waste produced must be removed, also passing through the membrane. The rate at which this transport occurs depends on both the distance to the membrane and the area of membrane available. For this reason, an organism made up of many relatively small cells has an advantage over one composed of fewer, larger cells.

The advantage of small cell size is readily apparent in terms of the **surface area-to-volume ratio.** As a cell's size increases, its volume increases much more rapidly than its surface area. For a spherical cell, the surface area is proportional to the square of the radius, whereas the volume is proportional to the cube of the radius. Thus, if the radii of two cells differ by a factor of 10, the larger cell will have 10^2, or 100 times, the surface area, but 10^3, or 1000 times, the volume of the smaller cell (figure 4.1).

The cell surface provides the only opportunity for interaction with the environment, because all substances enter and

Figure 4.1 Surface area-to-volume ratio. As a cell gets larger, its volume increases at a faster rate than its surface area. If the cell radius increases by 10 times, the surface area increases by 100 times, but the volume increases by 1000 times. A cell's surface area must be large enough to meet the metabolic needs of its volume.

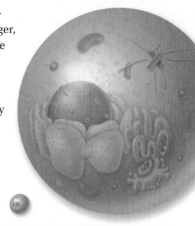

Cell radius (*r*)	1 unit	10 unit
Surface area ($4\pi r^2$)	12.57 unit^2	1257 unit^2
Volume ($\frac{4}{3}\pi r^3$)	4.189 unit^3	4189 unit^3
Surface Area / Volume	3	0.3

exit a cell via this surface. The membrane surrounding the cell plays a key role in controlling cell function. Because small cells have more surface area per unit of volume than large ones, control over cell contents is more effective when cells are relatively small.

Although most cells are small, some quite large cells do exist. These cells have apparently overcome the surface area-to-volume problem by one or more adaptive mechanisms. For example, some cells, such as skeletal muscle cells, have more than one nucleus, allowing genetic information to be spread around a large cell. Some other large cells, such as neurons, are long and skinny, so that any given point within the cell is close to the plasma membrane. This permits diffusion between the inside and outside of the cell to still be rapid.

Microscopes allow visualization of cells and components

Other than egg cells, not many cells are visible to the naked eye (figure 4.2). Most are less than 50 μm in diameter, far smaller than the period at the end of this sentence. So, to visualize cells we need the aid of technology. The development of microscopes and their refinement over the centuries has allowed us to continually explore cells in greater detail.

The resolution problem

How do we study cells if they are too small to see? The key is to understand why we can't see them. The reason we can't see such small objects is the limited resolution of the human eye. *Resolution* is the minimum distance two points can be apart and still be distinguished as two separate points. When two objects are closer together than about 100 μm, the light reflected from each strikes the same photoreceptor cell at the rear of the eye. Only when the objects are farther than 100 μm apart can the light from each strike different cells, allowing your eye to resolve them as two distinct objects rather than one.

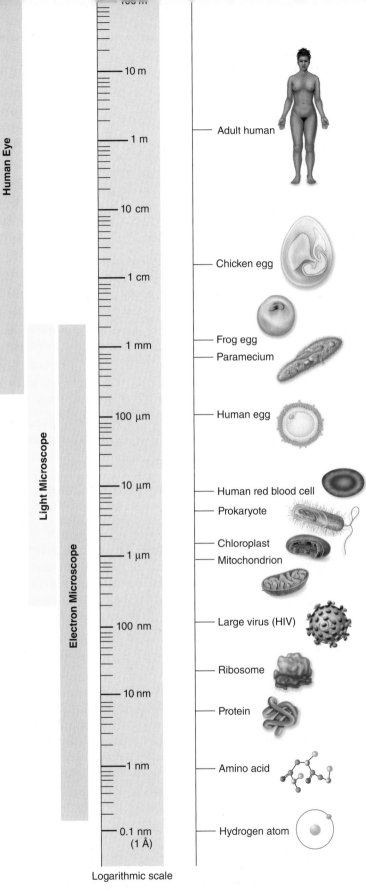

Light Microscope

Electron Microscope

- 10 m — Adult human
- 1 m
- 10 cm
- 1 cm — Chicken egg
- 1 mm — Frog egg
- Paramecium
- 100 μm — Human egg
- 10 μm — Human red blood cell
- Prokaryote
- 1 μm — Chloroplast
- Mitochondrion
- 100 nm — Large virus (HIV)
- 10 nm — Ribosome
- Protein
- 1 nm — Amino acid
- 0.1 nm (1 Å) — Hydrogen atom

Logarithmic scale

Figure 4.2 The size of cells and their contents. Except for vertebrate eggs, which can typically be seen with the unaided eye, most cells are microscopic in size. Prokaryotic cells are generally 1 to 10 μm across.

$1 \text{ m} = 10^2 \text{ cm} = 10^3 \text{ mm} = 10^6 \text{ μm} = 10^9 \text{ nm}$

Types of microscopes

One way to overcome the limitations of our eyes is to increase magnification so that small objects appear larger. The first microscopists used glass lenses to magnify small cells and cause them to appear larger than the 100-μm limit imposed by the human eye. The glass lens increases focusing power. Because the glass lens makes the object appear closer, the image on the back of the eye is bigger than it would be without the lens.

Modern *light microscopes,* which operate with visible light, use two magnifying lenses (and a variety of correcting lenses) to achieve very high magnification and clarity (table 4.1). The first lens focuses the image of the object on the second lens, which magnifies it again and focuses it on the back of the eye. Microscopes that magnify in stages using several lenses are called *compound microscopes.* They can resolve structures that are separated by at least 200 nanometers (nm).

Light microscopes, even compound ones, are not powerful enough to resolve many of the structures within cells. For example, a cell membrane is only 5 nm thick. Why not just add another magnifying stage to the microscope to increase its resolving power? This doesn't work because when two objects are closer than a few hundred nanometers, the light beams reflecting from the two images start to overlap each other. The only way two light beams can get closer together and still be resolved is if their wavelengths are shorter. One way to avoid overlap is by using a beam of electrons rather than a beam of light. Electrons have a much shorter wavelength, and an *electron microscope,* employing electron beams, has 1000 times the resolving power of a light microscope. *Transmission electron microscopes,* so called because the electrons used to visualize the specimens are transmitted through the material, are capable of resolving objects only 0.2 nm apart—which is only twice the diameter of a hydrogen atom!

A second kind of electron microscope, the *scanning electron microscope,* beams electrons onto the surface of the specimen. The electrons reflected back from the surface, together with other electrons that the specimen itself emits as a result of the bombardment, are amplified and transmitted to a screen, where the image can be viewed and photographed. Scanning electron microscopy yields striking three-dimensional images. This technique has improved our understanding of many biological and physical phenomena (see table 4.1).

Using stains to view cell structure

Although resolution remains a physical limit, we can improve the images we see by altering the sample. Certain chemical stains increase the contrast between different cellular components. Structures within the cell absorb or exclude the stain differentially, producing contrast that aids resolution.

Stains that bind to specific types of molecules have made these techniques even more powerful. This method uses antibodies that bind, for example, to a particular protein. This process, called *immunohistochemistry,* uses antibodies generated in animals such as rabbits or mice. When these animals are injected with specific proteins, they produce antibodies that bind to the injected protein. The antibodies are then purified and chemically bonded to enzymes, to stains, or to fluorescent molecules. When cells are incubated in a solution containing

TABLE 4.1	Microscopes

LIGHT MICROSCOPES

Bright-field microscope:
Light is transmitted through a specimen, giving little contrast. Staining specimens improves contrast but requires that cells be fixed (not alive), which can distort or alter components.

28 μm

Dark-field microscope:
Light is directed at an angle toward the specimen. A condenser lens transmits only light reflected off the specimen. The field is dark, and the specimen is light against this dark background.

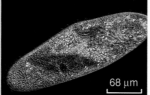
68 μm

Phase-contrast microscope:
Components of the microscope bring light waves out of phase, which produces differences in contrast and brightness when the light waves recombine.

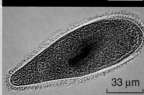
33 μm

Differential-interference–contrast microscope:
Polarized light is split into two beams that have slightly different paths through the sample. Combining these two beams produces greater contrast, especially at the edges of structures.

27 μm

Fluorescence microscope:
Fluorescent stains absorb light at one wavelength, then emit it at another. Filters transmit only the emitted light.

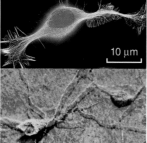
10 μm

Confocal microscope:
Light from a laser is focused to a point and scanned across the fluorescently stained specimen in two directions. This produces clear images of one plane of the specimen. Other planes of the specimen are excluded to prevent the blurring of the image. Multiple planes can be used to reconstruct a 3-D image.

25 μm

ELECTRON MICROSCOPES

Transmission electron microscope:
A beam of electrons is passed through the specimen. Electrons that pass through are used to expose film. Areas of the specimen that scatter electrons appear dark. False coloring enhances the image.

3 μm

Scanning electron microscope:
An electron beam is scanned across the surface of the specimen, and electrons are knocked off the surface. Thus, the topography of the specimen determines the contrast and the content of the image. False coloring enhances the image.

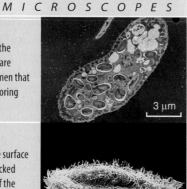
7 μm

the antibodies, the antibodies bind to cellular structures that contain the target molecule and can be seen with light microscopy. This approach has been used extensively in the analysis of cell structure and function.

All cells exhibit basic structural similarities

The general plan of cellular organization varies between different organisms, but despite these modifications, all cells resemble one another in certain fundamental ways. Before we begin a detailed examination of cell structure, let's first summarize four major features all cells have in common: (1) a nucleoid or nucleus where genetic material is located, (2) cytoplasm, (3) *ribosomes* to synthesize proteins, and (4) a plasma membrane.

Centrally located genetic material

Every cell contains DNA, the hereditary molecule. In **prokaryotes,** the simplest organisms, most of the genetic material lies in a single circular molecule of DNA. It typically resides near the center of the cell in an area called the **nucleoid.** This area is not segregated, however, from the rest of the cell's interior by membranes.

By contrast, the DNA of eukaryotes, which are more complex organisms, is contained in the nucleus, which is surrounded by a double-membrane structure called the **nuclear envelope.** In both types of organisms, the DNA contains the genes that code for the proteins synthesized by the cell. (Details of nucleus structure are described later in the chapter.)

The cytoplasm

A semifluid matrix called the **cytoplasm** fills the interior of the cell. The cytoplasm contains all of the sugars, amino acids, and proteins the cell uses to carry out its everyday activities. Although it is an aqueous medium, cytoplasm is more like jello than water due to the high concentration of proteins and other macromolecules. We call any discrete macromolecular structure in the cytoplasm specialized for a particular function an **organelle.** The part of the cytoplasm that contains organic molecules and ions in solution is called the **cytosol** to distinguish it from the larger organelles suspended in this fluid.

The plasma membrane

The **plasma membrane** encloses a cell and separates its contents from its surroundings. The plasma membrane is a phospholipid bilayer about 5 to 10 nm (5–10 billionths of a meter) thick, with proteins embedded in it. Viewed in cross section with the electron microscope, such membranes appear as two dark lines separated by a lighter area. This distinctive appearance arises from the tail-to-tail packing of the phospholipid molecules that make up the membrane (see chapter 5).

Plasma membrane

Protein

Cell interior

20 nm

The proteins of the plasma membrane are generally responsible for a cell's ability to interact with the environment. *Transport proteins* help molecules and ions move across the plasma membrane, either from the environment to the interior of the cell or vice versa. *Receptor proteins* induce changes within the cell when they come in contact with specific molecules in the environment, such as hormones, or with molecules on the surface of neighboring cells. These molecules can function as *markers* that identify the cell as a particular type. This interaction between cell surface molecules is especially important in multicellular organisms, whose cells must be able to recognize one another as they form tissues.

We'll examine the structure and function of cell membranes more thoroughly in chapter 5.

Learning Outcomes Review 4.1

All organisms are single cells or aggregates of cells, and all cells arise from preexisting cells. Cell size is limited primarily by the efficiency of diffusion across the plasma membrane. As a cell becomes larger, its volume increases more quickly than its surface area. Past a certain point, diffusion cannot support the cell's needs. All cells are bounded by a plasma membrane and filled with cytoplasm. The genetic material is found in the central portion of the cell; and in eukaryotic cells, it is contained in a membrane-bounded nucleus.

■ *Would finding life on Mars change our view of cell theory?*

4.2 Prokaryotic Cells

Learning Outcomes

1. *Describe the organization of prokaryotic cells.*
2. *Distinguish between bacterial and archaeal cell types.*

When cells were visualized with microscopes, two basic cellular architectures were recognized: eukaryotic and prokaryotic. These terms refer to the presence or absence, respectively, of a membrane-bounded nucleus that contains genetic material. We have already mentioned that in addition to lacking a nucleus, prokaryotic cells do not have an internal membrane system or numerous membrane-bounded organelles.

Prokaryotic cells have relatively simple organization

Prokaryotes are the simplest organisms. Prokaryotic cells are small. They consist of cytoplasm surrounded by a plasma membrane and are encased within a

rigid **cell wall.** They have no distinct interior compartments (figure 4.3). A prokaryotic cell is like a one-room cabin in which eating, sleeping, and watching TV all occur.

Prokaryotes are very important in the ecology of living organisms. Some harvest light by photosynthesis, others break down dead organisms and recycle their components. Still others cause disease or have uses in many important industrial processes. Prokaryotes have two main domains: archaea and bacteria. Chapter 28 covers prokaryotic diversity in more detail.

> **? Inquiry question** What modifications would you include if you wanted to make a cell as large as possible?

Although prokaryotic cells do contain organelles like **ribosomes,** which carry out protein synthesis, most lack the membrane-bounded organelles characteristic of eukaryotic cells. It was long thought that prokaryotes also lack the elaborate cytoskeleton found in eukaryotes, but we have now found they have molecules related to both actin and tubulin, which form two of the cytoskeletal elements described later in the chapter. The strength and shape of the cell is determined by the cell wall and not these cytoskeletal elements (see figure 4.3). However, cell wall structure is influenced by the cytoskeleton. For instance, the presence of actin-like MreB fibers running the length of the cell lead to perpendicular cell-wall fibers that produce a rod-shaped cell. This can be seen when MreB protein is removed, cells become spherical rather than rod-shaped. During cell division, cell-wall deposition is influenced by the tubulin-like FtsZ protein (see chapter 10).

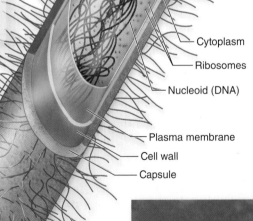

Pilus
Cytoplasm
Ribosomes
Nucleoid (DNA)
Plasma membrane
Cell wall
Capsule
Pili
Flagellum

Figure 4.3 Structure of a prokaryotic cell. Generalized cell organization of a prokaryote. The nucleoid is visible as a dense central region segregated from the cytoplasm. Some prokaryotes have hairlike growths (called pili [singular, pilus]) on the outside of the cell.

0.3 μm

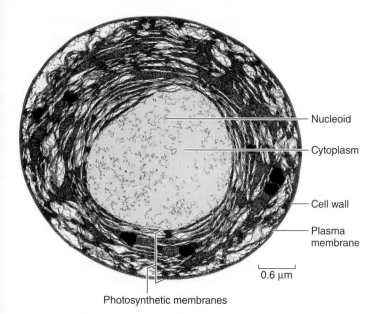

Figure 4.4 **Electron micrograph of a photosynthetic bacterial cell.** Extensive folded photosynthetic membranes are shown in green in this false colored electron micrograph of a *Prochloron* cell.

The plasma membrane of a prokaryotic cell carries out some of the functions organelles perform in eukaryotic cells. For example, some photosynthetic bacteria, such as the cyanobacterium *Prochloron* (figure 4.4), have an extensively folded plasma membrane, with the folds extending into the cell's interior. These membrane folds contain the bacterial pigments connected with photosynthesis. In eukaryotic plant cells, photosynthetic pigments are found in the inner membrane of the chloroplast.

Because a prokaryotic cell contains no membrane-bounded organelles, the DNA, enzymes, and other cytoplasmic constituents have access to all parts of the cell. Reactions are not compartmentalized as they are in eukaryotic cells, and the whole prokaryote operates as a single unit.

Bacterial cell walls consist of peptidoglycan

Most bacterial cells are encased by a strong **cell wall.** This cell wall is composed of *peptidoglycan,* which consists of a carbohydrate matrix (polymers of sugars) that is cross-linked by short polypeptide units. Details about the structure of this cell wall are discussed in chapter 28. Cell walls protect the cell, maintain its shape, and prevent excessive uptake or loss of water. The exception is the class Mollicutes, which includes the common genus *Mycoplasma,* which lack a cell wall. Plants, fungi, and most protists also have cell walls but with a chemical structure different from peptidoglycan.

The susceptibility of bacteria to antibiotics often depends on the structure of their cell walls. The drugs penicillin and vancomycin, for example, interfere with the ability of bacteria to cross-link the peptides in their peptidoglycan cell wall. Like removing all the nails from a wooden house, this destroys the integrity of the structural matrix, which can no longer prevent water from rushing in and swelling the cell to bursting.

Some bacteria also secrete a jelly-like protective capsule of polysaccharide around the cell. Many disease-causing bacteria have such a capsule, which enables them to adhere to teeth, skin, food—or to practically any surface that can support their growth.

Archaea lack peptidoglycan

We are still learning about the physiology and structure of archaea. Many of these organisms are difficult to culture in the laboratory, and so this group has not yet been studied in detail. More is known about their genetic makeup than about any other feature.

The cell walls of archaea are composed of various chemical compounds, including polysaccharides and proteins, and possibly even inorganic components. A common feature distinguishing archaea from bacteria is the nature of their membrane lipids. The chemical structure of archaeal lipids is distinctly different from that of lipids in bacteria and can include saturated hydrocarbons that are covalently attached to

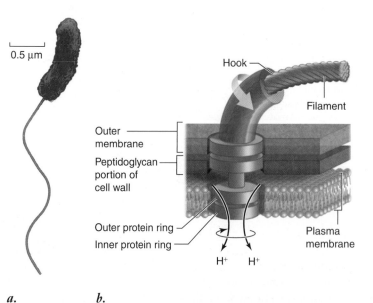

Figure 4.5 **Some prokaryotes move by rotating their flagella.** *a.* The photograph shows *Vibrio cholerae,* the microbe that causes the serious disease cholera. *b.* The bacterial flagellum is a complex structure. The motor proteins, powered by a proton gradient, are anchored in the plasma membrane. Two rings are found in the cell wall. The motor proteins cause the entire structure to rotate. *c.* As the flagellum rotates it creates a spiral wave down the structure. This powers the cell forward.

glycerol at both ends, such that their membrane is a mono-layer. These features seem to confer greater thermal stability to archaeal membranes, although the trade-off seems to be an inability to alter the degree of saturation of the hydrocarbons—meaning that archaea with this characteristic cannot adapt to changing environmental temperatures.

The cellular machinery that replicates DNA and synthesized proteins in archaea is more closely related to eukaryotic systems than to bacterial systems. Even though they share a similar overall cellular architecture with prokaryotes, archaea appear to be more closely related on a molecular basis to eukaryotes.

Some prokaryotes move by means of rotating flagella

Flagella (singular, *flagellum*) are long, threadlike structures protruding from the surface of a cell that are used in locomotion. Prokaryotic flagella are protein fibers that extend out from the cell. There may be one or more per cell, or none, depending on the species. Bacteria can swim at speeds of up to 70 cell lengths per second by rotating their flagella like screws (figure 4.5). The rotary motor uses the energy stored in a gradient that transfers protons across the plasma membrane to power the movement of the flagellum. Interestingly, the same principle, in which a proton gradient powers the rotation of a molecule, is used in eukaryotic mitochondria and chloroplasts by an enzyme that synthesizes ATP (see chapters 7 and 8).

Learning Outcomes Review 4.2

Prokaryotes are small cells that lack complex interior organization. The two domains of prokaryotes are archaea and bacteria. The cell wall of bacteria is composed of peptidoglycan, which is not found in archaea. Archaea have cell walls made from a variety of polysaccharides and peptides, as well as membranes containing unusual lipids. Some bacteria move using a rotating flagellum.

■ *What features do bacteria and archaea share?*

4.3 Eukaryotic Cells

Learning Outcomes

1. *Compare the organization of eukaryotic and prokaryotic cells.*
2. *Discuss the role of the nucleus in eukaryotic cells.*
3. *Describe the role of ribosomes in protein synthesis.*

Eukaryotic cells (figures 4.6 and 4.7) are far more complex than prokaryotic cells. The hallmark of the eukaryotic cell is compartmentalization. This is achieved through a combination of an extensive **endomembrane system** that weaves through the cell interior and by numerous *organelles.* These organelles include membrane-bounded structures that form compartments within which multiple biochemical processes can proceed simultaneously and independently.

Plant cells often have a large, membrane-bounded sac called a **central vacuole,** which stores proteins, pigments, and waste materials. Both plant and animal cells contain **vesicles—**smaller sacs that store and transport a variety of materials. Inside the nucleus, the DNA is wound tightly around proteins and packaged into compact units called **chromosomes.**

All eukaryotic cells are supported by an internal protein scaffold, the **cytoskeleton.** Although the cells of animals and some protists lack cell walls, the cells of fungi, plants, and many protists have strong cell walls composed of cellulose or chitin fibers embedded in a matrix of other polysaccharides and proteins. Through the rest of this chapter, we will examine the internal components of eukaryotic cells in more detail.

The nucleus acts as the information center

The largest and most easily seen organelle within a eukaryotic cell is the **nucleus** (Latin, "kernel" or "nut"), first described by the Scottish botanist Robert Brown in 1831. Nuclei are roughly spherical in shape, and in animal cells, they are typically located in the central region of the cell (figure 4.8*a*). In some cells, a network of fine cytoplasmic filaments seems to cradle the nucleus in this position.

The nucleus is the repository of the genetic information that enables the synthesis of nearly all proteins of a living eukaryotic cell. Most eukaryotic cells possess a single nucleus, although the cells of fungi and some other groups may have from several to many nuclei. Mammalian erythrocytes (red blood cells) lose their nuclei when they mature. Many nuclei exhibit a dark-staining zone called the **nucleolus,** which is a region where intensive synthesis of ribosomal RNA is taking place.

The nuclear envelope

The surface of the nucleus is bounded by *two* phospholipid bilayer membranes, which together make up the **nuclear envelope** (see figure 4.8). The outer membrane of the nuclear envelope is continuous with the cytoplasm's interior membrane system, called the *endoplasmic reticulum* (described later).

Scattered over the surface of the nuclear envelope are what appear as shallow depressions in the electron micrograph but are in fact structures called **nuclear pores** (see figure 4.8*b, c*). These pores form 50 to 80 nm apart at locations where the two membrane layers of the nuclear envelope come together. The structure consists of a central framework with eightfold symmetry that is embedded in the nuclear envelope. This is bounded by a cytoplasmic face with eight fibers, and a nuclear face with a complex ring that forms a basket beneath the central ring. The pore allows ions and small molecules to diffuse freely between nucleoplasm and cytoplasm while controlling the passage of proteins and RNA–protein complexes. Transport across the pore is controlled and consists mainly of the import of proteins that function in the nucleus, and the export to the cytoplasm of RNA and RNA–protein complexes formed in the nucleus.

Figure 4.6 Structure of an animal cell. In this generalized diagram of an animal cell, the plasma membrane encases the cell, which contains the cytoskeleton and various cell organelles and interior structures suspended in a semifluid matrix called the cytoplasm. Some kinds of animal cells possess finger-like projections called microvilli. Other types of eukaryotic cells—for example, many protist cells—may possess flagella, which aid in movement, or cilia, which can have many different functions.

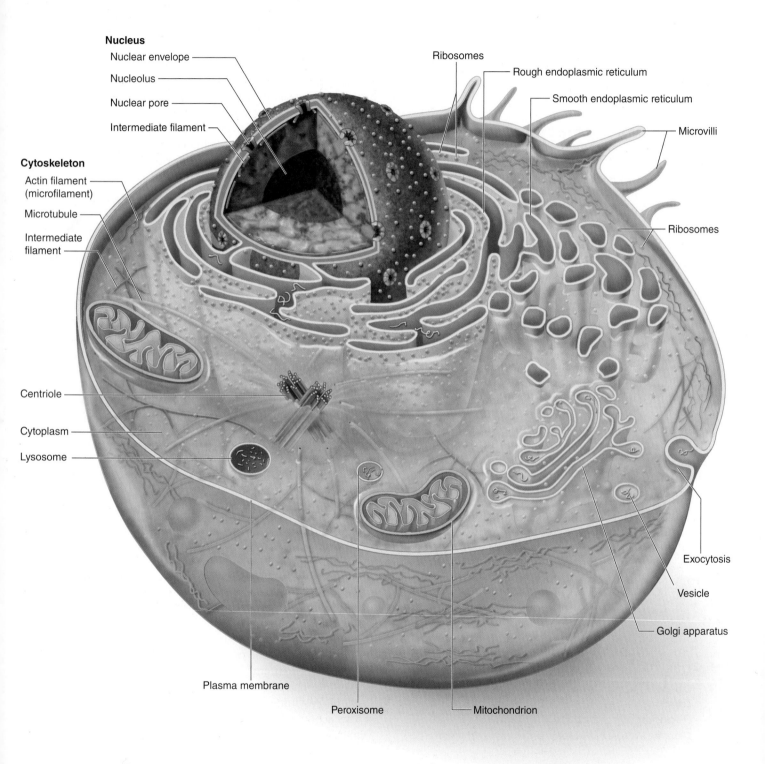

Figure 4.7 Structure of a plant cell. Most mature plant cells contain a large central vacuole, which occupies a major portion of the internal volume of the cell, and organelles called chloroplasts, within which photosynthesis takes place. The cells of plants, fungi, and some protists have cell walls, although the composition of the walls varies among the groups. Plant cells have cytoplasmic connections to one another through openings in the cell wall called plasmodesmata. Flagella occur in sperm of a few plant species, but are otherwise absent from plant and fungal cells. Centrioles are also usually absent.

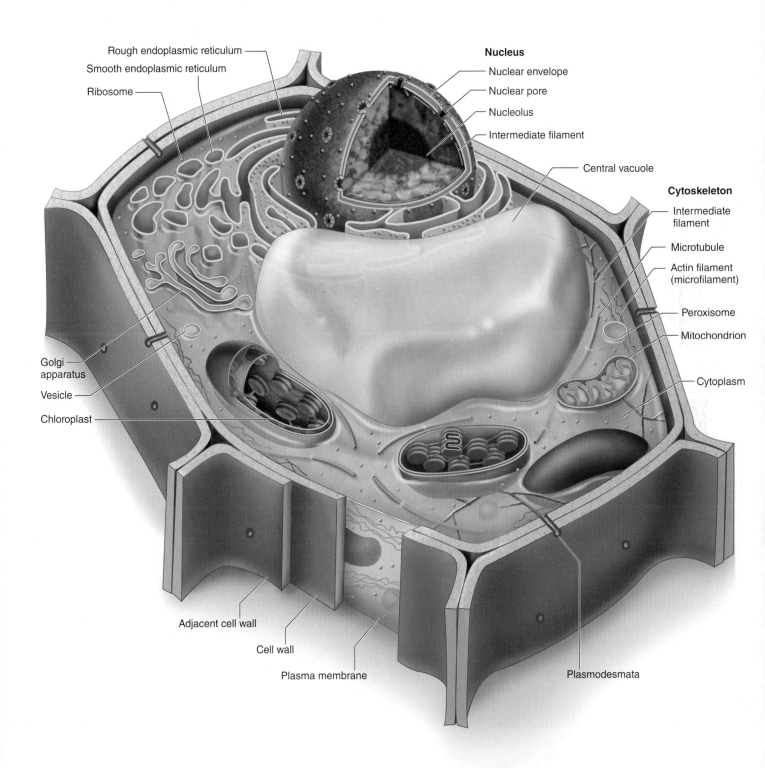

Rough endoplasmic reticulum
Smooth endoplasmic reticulum
Ribosome

Nucleus
Nuclear envelope
Nuclear pore
Nucleolus
Intermediate filament

Central vacuole

Cytoskeleton
Intermediate filament
Microtubule
Actin filament (microfilament)
Peroxisome
Mitochondrion
Cytoplasm

Golgi apparatus
Vesicle
Chloroplast

Adjacent cell wall
Cell wall
Plasma membrane
Plasmodesmata

Figure 4.8 The nucleus. *a.* The nucleus is composed of a double membrane called the nuclear envelope, enclosing a fluid-filled interior containing chromatin. The individual nuclear pores extend through the two membrane layers of the envelope. The close-up of the nuclear pore shows the central hub, cytoplasmic ring with fibers, and nuclear ring with basket. *b.* A freeze-fracture electron micrograph (see figure 5.4) of a cell nucleus, showing many nuclear pores. *c.* A transmission electron micrograph of the nuclear membrane showing a single nuclear pore. The dark material within the pore is protein, which acts to control access through the pore. *d.* The nuclear lamina is visible as a dense network of fibers made of intermediate filaments. The nucleus has been colored purple in the micrographs.

(b): © Dr. Richard Kessel & Dr. Gene Shih/Visuals Unlimited

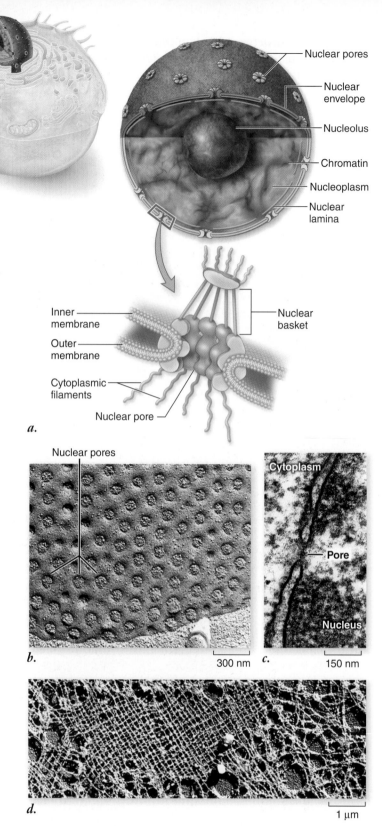

The inner surface of the nuclear envelope is covered with a network of fibers that make up the nuclear lamina (see figure 4.8*d*). This is composed of intermediate filament fibers called *nuclear lamins.* This structure gives the nucleus its shape and is also involved in the deconstruction and reconstruction of the nuclear envelope that accompanies cell division.

Chromatin: DNA packaging

In both prokaryotes and eukaryotes, DNA is the molecule that stores genetic information. In eukaryotes, the DNA is divided into multiple linear chromosomes, which are organized with proteins into a complex structure called **chromatin.** It is becoming clear that the very structure of chromatin affects the function of DNA. Changes in gene expression that do not involve changes in DNA sequence, so-called epigenetic changes, involve alterations in chromatin structure (see chapter 16). Although still not fully understood, this offers an exciting new view of many old ideas.

Chromatin is usually in a more extended form that is organized in the nucleus, although we still do not fully understand this organization. When cells divide, the chromatin must be further compacted into a more highly condensed state that forms the X-shaped chromosomes visible in the light microscope.

The nucleolus: Ribosomal subunit manufacturing

Before cells can synthesize proteins in large quantity, they must first construct a large number of ribosomes to carry out this synthesis. Hundreds of copies of the genes encoding the ribosomal RNAs are clustered together on the chromosome, facilitating ribosome construction. By transcribing RNA molecules from this cluster, the cell rapidly generates large numbers of the molecules needed to produce ribosomes.

The clusters of ribosomal RNA genes, the RNAs they produce, and the ribosomal proteins all come together within the nucleus during ribosome production. These ribosomal assembly areas are easily visible within the nucleus as one or more dark-staining regions called nucleoli (singular, *nucleolus*). Nucleoli can be seen under the light microscope even when the chromosomes are uncoiled.

Ribosomes are the cell's protein synthesis machinery

Although the DNA in a cell's nucleus encodes the amino acid sequence of each protein in the cell, the proteins are not assembled there. A simple experiment demonstrates this: If a brief pulse of radioactive amino acid is administered to a cell, the radioactivity shows up associated with newly made protein

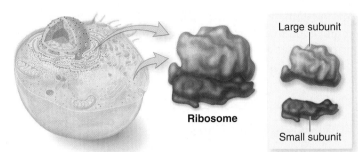

Figure 4.9 A ribosome. Ribosomes consist of a large and a small subunit composed of rRNA and protein. The individual subunits are synthesized in the nucleolus and then move through the nuclear pores to the cytoplasm, where they assemble to translate mRNA. Ribosomes serve as sites of protein synthesis.

in the cytoplasm, not in the nucleus. When investigators first carried out these experiments, they found that protein synthesis is associated with large RNA–protein complexes (called ribosomes) outside the nucleus.

Ribosomes are among the most complex molecular assemblies found in cells. Each ribosome is composed of two subunits (figure 4.9), each of which is composed of a combination of RNA, called **ribosomal RNA (rRNA),** and proteins. The subunits join to form a functional ribosome only when they are actively synthesizing proteins. This complicated process requires the two other main forms of RNA: **messenger RNA (mRNA),** which carries coding information from DNA, and **transfer RNA (tRNA),** which carries amino acids. Ribosomes use the information in mRNA to direct the synthesis of a protein. This process will be described in more detail in chapter 15.

Ribosomes are found either free in the cytoplasm or associated with internal membranes, as described in the following section. Free ribosomes synthesize proteins that are found in the cytoplasm, nuclear proteins, mitochondrial proteins, and proteins found in other organelles not derived from the endomembrane system. Membrane-associated ribosomes synthesize membrane proteins, proteins found in the endomembrane system, and proteins destined for export from the cell.

Ribosomes can be thought of as "universal organelles" because they are found in all cell types from all three domains of life. As we build a picture of the minimal essential functions for cellular life, ribosomes will be on the short list. Life is protein-based, and ribosomes are the factories that make proteins.

Learning Outcomes Review 4.3

In contrast to prokaryotic cells, eukaryotic cells exhibit compartmentalization. Eukaryotic cells contain an endomembrane system and organelles that carry out specialized functions. The nucleus, composed of a double membrane connected to the endomembrane system, contains the cell's genetic information. Material moves between the nucleus and cytoplasm through nuclear pores. Ribosomes translate mRNA, which is transcribed from DNA in the nucleus, into polypeptides that make up proteins. Ribosomes are a universal organelle found in all known cells.

■ **Would you expect cells in different organs in complex animals to have the same structure?**

4.4 The Endomembrane System

Learning Outcomes

1. Identify the different parts of the endomembrane system.
2. Contrast the different functions of internal membranes and compartments.
3. Evaluate the importance of each step in the protein-processing pathway.

The interior of a eukaryotic cell is packed with membranes so thin that they are invisible under the low resolving power of light microscopes. This endomembrane system fills the cell, dividing it into compartments, channeling the passage of molecules through the interior of the cell, and providing surfaces for the synthesis of lipids and some proteins. The presence of these membranes in eukaryotic cells marks one of the fundamental distinctions between eukaryotes and prokaryotes.

The largest of the internal membranes is called the **endoplasmic reticulum (ER).** *Endoplasmic* means "within the cytoplasm," and *reticulum* is Latin for "a little net." The ER is composed of a phospholipid bilayer embedded with proteins. The ER has functional subdivisions, described below, and forms a variety of structures from folded sheets to complex tubular networks (figure 4.10). The two largest compartments in eukaryotic cells are the inner region of the ER, called the

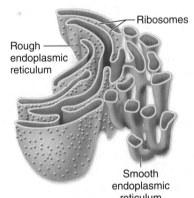

Figure 4.10 The endoplasmic reticulum. Rough ER (RER), blue in the drawing, is composed more of flattened sacs and forms a compartment throughout the cytoplasm. Ribosomes associated with the cytoplasmic face of the RER extrude newly made proteins into the interior, or lumen. The smooth ER (SER), green in the drawing, is a more tubelike structure connected to the RER. The micrograph has been colored to match the drawing.

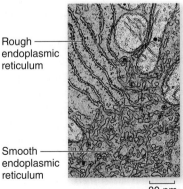

80 nm

cisternal space, or lumen, and the region exterior to it, the cytosol, which is the fluid component of the cytoplasm containing dissolved organic molecules such as proteins and ions.

The rough ER is a site of protein synthesis

The **rough ER (RER)** gets its name from its pebbly surface appearance. The RER is not easily visible with a light microscope, but it can be seen using the electron microscope. It appears to be composed primarily of flattened sacs, the surfaces of which are bumpy with ribosomes (see figure 4.10).

The proteins synthesized on the surface of the RER are destined to be exported from the cell, sent to lysosomes or vacuoles (described in a later section), or embedded in the plasma membrane. These proteins enter the cisternal space as a first step in the pathway that will sort proteins to their eventual destinations. This pathway also involves vesicles and the Golgi apparatus, described later. The sequence of the protein being synthesized determines whether the ribosome will become associated with the ER or remain a cytoplasmic ribosome.

In the ER, newly synthesized proteins can be modified by the addition of short-chain carbohydrates to form **glycoproteins.** Those proteins destined for secretion are separated from other products and later packaged into vesicles that move to the Golgi for further modification and packaging for transport to other cellular locations.

The smooth ER has multiple roles

Regions of the ER with relatively few bound ribosomes are referred to as **smooth ER (SER).** The SER has a variety of structures ranging from a network of tubules, to flattened sacs, to higher order tubular arrays. The membranes of the SER contain many embedded enzymes. Enzymes anchored within the ER are involved in the synthesis of a variety of carbohydrates and lipids. Steroid hormones are synthesized in the SER as well. The majority of membrane lipids are assembled in the SER and then sent to whatever parts of the cell need membrane components. Membrane proteins in the plasma membrane and other cellular membrane are inserted by ribosomes on the RER.

An important function of the SER is to store intracellular Ca^{2+}. This keeps the cytoplasmic level low, allowing Ca^{2+} to be used as a signaling molecule. In muscle cells, for example, Ca^{2+} is used to trigger muscle contraction. In other cells, Ca^{2+} release from SER stores is involved in diverse signaling pathways.

The ratio of SER to RER is not fixed but depends on a cell's function. In multicellular animals such as ourselves, great variation exists in this ratio. Cells that carry out extensive lipid synthesis, such as those in the testes, intestine, and brain, have abundant SER. Cells that synthesize proteins that are secreted, such as antibodies, have much more extensive RER.

Another role of the SER is the modification of foreign substances to make them less toxic. In the liver, the enzymes of the SER carry out this detoxification. This action can include neutralizing substances that we have taken for a therapeutic reason, such as penicillin. Thus, relatively high doses are prescribed for some drugs to offset our body's efforts to remove them. Liver cells have extensive SER as well as enzymes that can process a variety of substances by chemically modifying them.

The Golgi apparatus sorts and packages proteins

Flattened stacks of membranes form a complex called the **Golgi body,** or **Golgi apparatus** (figure 4.11)**.** These structures are named for Camillo Golgi, the 19th-century Italian physician who first identified them. The individual stacks of membrane are called **cisternae** (Latin, "collecting vessels"), and they vary in number within the Golgi body from 1 or a few in protists, to 20 or more in animal cells and to several hundred in plant cells. In vertebrates individual Golgi are linked to form a Golgi ribbon. They are especially abundant in glandular cells, which manufacture and secrete substances.

The Golgi apparatus functions in the collection, packaging, and distribution of molecules synthesized at one location and used at another within the cell or even outside of it. A Golgi body has a front and a back, with distinctly different membrane compositions at these opposite ends. The front, or receiving end, is called the *cis* face and is usually located near the ER. Materials arrive at the *cis* face in transport vesicles that bud off the ER and exit the *trans* face, where they are discharged in

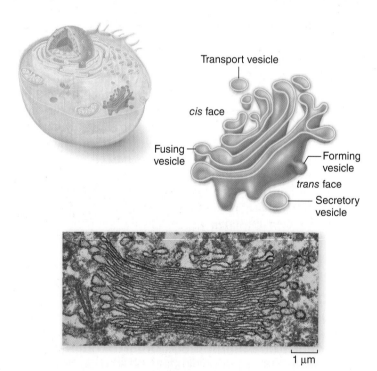

1 μm

Figure 4.11 The Golgi apparatus. The Golgi apparatus is a smooth, concave, membranous structure. It receives material for processing in transport vesicles on the *cis* face and sends the material packaged in transport or secretory vesicles off the *trans* face. The substance in a vesicle could be for export out of the cell or for distribution to another region within the same cell.

secretory vesicles (figure 4.12). How material transits through the Golgi has been a source of much contention. Models include maturation of the individual cisternae from *cis* to *trans*, transport between cisternae by vesicles, and direct tubular connections. Although there is probably transport of material by all of these, it now appears that the primary mechanism is cisternal maturation.

Proteins and lipids manufactured on the rough and smooth ER membranes are transported into the Golgi apparatus and modified as they pass through it. The most common alteration is the addition or modification of short sugar chains, forming glycoproteins and glycolipids. In many instances, enzymes in the Golgi apparatus modify existing glycoproteins and glycolipids made in the ER by cleaving a sugar from a chain or by modifying one or more of the sugars. These are then packaged into small, membrane-bounded vesicles that pinch off from the *trans* face of the Golgi. These vesicles then diffuse to other locations in the cell, distributing the newly synthesized molecules to their appropriate destinations.

Another function of the Golgi apparatus is the synthesis of cell-wall components. Noncellulose polysaccharides that form part of the cell wall of plants are synthesized in the Golgi apparatus and sent to the plasma membrane, where they can be added to the cellulose that is assembled on the exterior of the cell. Other polysaccharides secreted by plants are also synthesized in the Golgi apparatus.

Lysosomes contain digestive enzymes

Membrane-bounded digestive vesicles, called **lysosomes,** are also components of the endomembrane system. They arise from the Golgi apparatus. They contain high levels of degrading enzymes, which catalyze the rapid breakdown of proteins, nucleic acids, lipids, and carbohydrates. Throughout the lives of eukaryotic cells, lysosomal enzymes break down old organelles and recycle their component molecules. This makes room for newly formed organelles. For example, mitochondria are replaced in some tissues every 10 days.

The digestive enzymes in the lysosome are optimally active at acid pH. Lysosomes are activated by fusing with a food vesicle produced by *phagocytosis* (a specific type of endocytosis; see chapter 5) or by fusing with an old or worn-out organelle. The fusion event activates proton pumps in the lysosomal membrane, resulting in a lower internal pH. As the interior pH falls, the arsenal of digestive enzymes contained in the lysosome is activated. This leads to the degradation of macromolecules in the food vesicle or the destruction of the old organelle.

A number of human genetic disorders, collectively called lysosomal storage disorders, affect lysosomes. For example, the genetic abnormality called Tay–Sachs disease is caused by the loss of function of a single lysosomal enzyme (hexosaminidase). This enzyme is necessary to break down a membrane glycolipid found in nerve cells. Accumulation of glycolipid in lysosomes affects nerve cell function, leading to a variety of clinical symptoms such as seizures and muscle rigidity.

In addition to breaking down organelles and other structures within cells, lysosomes eliminate other cells that the cell

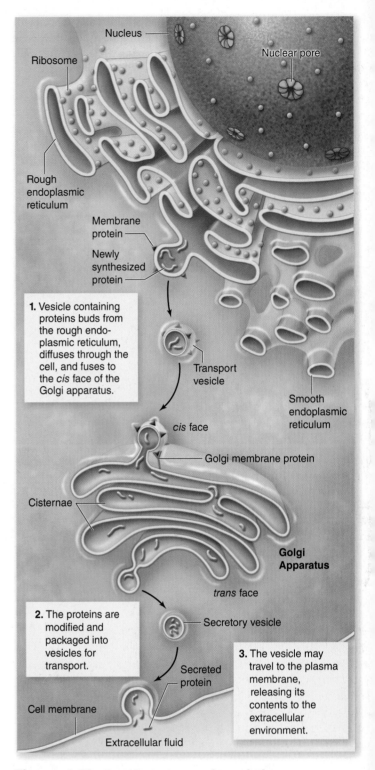

Figure 4.12 Protein transport through the endomembrane system. Proteins synthesized by ribosomes on the RER are translocated into the internal compartment of the ER. These proteins may be used at a distant location within the cell or secreted from the cell. They are transported within vesicles that bud off the RER. These transport vesicles travel to the *cis* face of the Golgi apparatus. There they can be modified and packaged into vesicles that bud off the *trans* face of the Golgi apparatus. Vesicles leaving the *trans* face transport proteins to other locations in the cell, or fuse with the plasma membrane, releasing their contents to the extracellular environment.

has engulfed by phagocytosis. When a white blood cell, for example, phagocytizes a passing pathogen, lysosomes fuse with the resulting "food vesicle," releasing their enzymes into the vesicle and degrading the material within (figure 4.13).

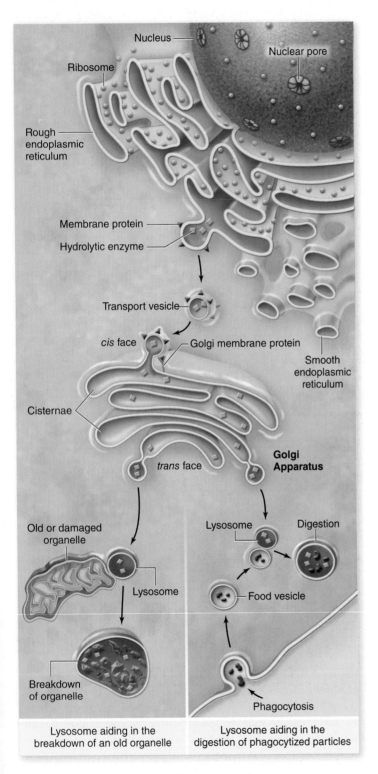

Figure 4.13 Lysosomes. Lysosomes are formed from vesicles budding off the Golgi. They contain hydrolytic enzymes that digest particles or cells taken into the cell by phagocytosis, and break down old organelles.

Microbodies are a diverse category of organelles

Eukaryotic cells contain a variety of enzyme-bearing, membrane-enclosed vesicles called **microbodies.** These are found in the cells of plants, animals, fungi, and protists. The distribution of enzymes into microbodies is one of the principal ways eukaryotic cells organize their metabolism.

Peroxisomes: Peroxide utilization

An important type of microbody is the **peroxisome** (figure 4.14)**,** which contains enzymes involved in the oxidation of fatty acids. If these oxidative enzymes were not isolated within microbodies, they would tend to short-circuit the metabolism of the cytoplasm, which often involves adding hydrogen atoms to oxygen. Because many peroxisomal proteins are synthesized by cytoplasmic ribosomes, the organelles themselves were long thought to form by the addition of lipids and proteins, leading to growth. As they grow larger, they divide to produce new peroxisomes. Although division of peroxisomes still appears to occur, it is now clear that peroxisomes can form from the fusion of ER-derived vesicles. These vesicles then import peroxisomal proteins to form a mature peroxisome. Genetic screens have isolated some 32 genes that encode proteins involved in biogenesis and maintenance of peroxisomes. The human genetic diseases called peroxisome biogenesis disorders (PBDs) can be caused by mutations in some of these genes.

Peroxisomes get their name from the hydrogen peroxide produced as a by-product of the activities of oxidative enzymes.

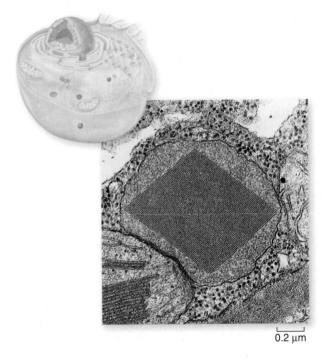

0.2 μm

Figure 4.14 A peroxisome. Peroxisomes are spherical organelles that may contain a large crystal structure composed of protein. Peroxisomes contain digestive and detoxifying enzymes that produce hydrogen peroxide as a by-product. A peroxisome has been colored green in the electron micrograph.

Hydrogen peroxide is dangerous to cells because of its violent chemical reactivity. However, peroxisomes also contain the enzyme catalase, which breaks down hydrogen peroxide into its harmless constituents—water and oxygen.

Plants use vacuoles for storage and water balance

Plant cells have specialized membrane-bounded structures called **vacuoles.** The most conspicuous example is the large central vacuole seen in most plant cells (figure 4.15). In fact, *vacuole* actually means blank space, referring to its appearance in the light microscope. The membrane surrounding this vacuole is called the **tonoplast** because it contains channels for water that are used to help the cell maintain its tonicity, or osmotic balance (see osmosis in chapter 5).

For many years biologists assumed that only one type of vacuole existed and that it served multiple functions. The functions assigned to this vacuole included water balance and storage of both useful molecules (such as sugars, ions, and pigments) and waste products. The vacuole was also thought to store enzymes involved in the breakdown of macromolecules and those used in detoxifying foreign substances. Old textbooks of plant physiology referred to vacuoles as the attic of the cell for the variety of substances thought to be stored there.

Studies of tonoplast transporters and the isolation of vacuoles from a variety of cell types have led to a more complex view of vacuoles. These studies have made it clear that different vacuolar types can be found in different cells. These vacuoles are specialized, depending on the function of the cell.

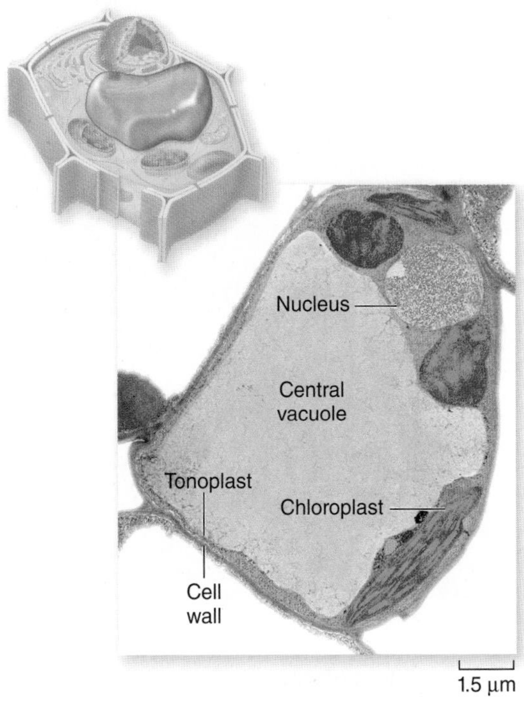

The central vacuole is clearly important for a number of roles in all plant cells. The central vacuole and the water channels of the tonoplast maintain the tonicity of the cell, allowing the cell to expand and contract, depending on conditions. The central vacuole is also involved in cell growth by occupying most of the volume of the cell. Plant cells grow by expanding the vacuole, rather than by increasing cytoplasmic volume.

Vacuoles with a variety of functions are also found in some types of fungi and protists. One form is the contractile vacuole, found in some protists, which can pump water and is used to maintain water balance in the cell. Other vacuoles are used for storage or to segregate toxic materials from the rest of the cytoplasm. The number and kind of vacuoles found in a cell depends on the needs of the particular cell type.

Learning Outcomes Review 4.4

The endoplasmic reticulum (ER) is an extensive system of folded membranes that spatially organize the cell's biosynthetic activities. Smooth ER (SER) is the site of lipid and membrane synthesis and is used to store Ca^{2+}. Rough ER (RER) is covered with ribosomes and is a site of protein synthesis. Proteins from the RER are transported by vesicles to the Golgi apparatus where they are modified, packaged, and distributed to their final location. Lysosomes are vesicles that contain digestive enzymes used to degrade materials such as invaders or worn-out components. Peroxisomes carry out oxidative metabolism that generates peroxides. Vacuoles are membrane-bounded structures with roles ranging from storage to cell growth in plants. They are also found in some fungi and protists.

■ *How do ribosomes on the RER differ from cytoplasmic ribosomes?*

Figure 4.15 The central vacuole. A plant's central vacuole stores dissolved substances and can expand in size to increase the tonicity of a plant cell. Micrograph shown with false color.

4.5 Mitochondria and Chloroplasts: Cellular Generators

Learning Outcomes

1. Describe the structure of mitochondria and chloroplasts.
2. Compare the function of mitochondria and chloroplasts.
3. Explain the probable origin of mitochondria and chloroplasts.

Mitochondria and chloroplasts share structural and functional similarities. Structurally, they are both surrounded by a double membrane, and both contain their own DNA and protein synthesis machinery. Functionally, they are both involved in energy metabolism, as we will explore in detail in later chapters on energy metabolism and photosynthesis.

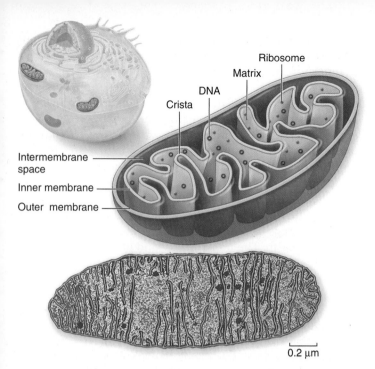

Figure 4.16 Mitochondria. The inner membrane of a mitochondrion is shaped into folds called cristae that greatly increase the surface area for oxidative metabolism. A mitochondrion in cross section and cut lengthwise is shown colored red in the micrograph.

Mitochondria metabolize sugar to generate ATP

Mitochondria (singular, *mitochondrion*) are typically tubular or sausage-shaped organelles about the size of bacteria that are found in all types of eukaryotic cells (figure 4.16). Mitochondria are bounded by two membranes: a smooth outer membrane, and an inner folded membrane with numerous contiguous layers called **cristae** (singular, *crista*).

The cristae partition the mitochondrion into two compartments: a **matrix,** lying inside the inner membrane; and an outer compartment, or **intermembrane space,** lying between the two mitochondrial membranes. On the surface of the inner membrane, and also embedded within it, are proteins that carry out oxidative metabolism, the oxygen-requiring process by which energy in macromolecules is used to produce ATP (chapter 7).

Mitochondria have their own DNA; this DNA contains several genes that produce proteins essential to the mitochondrion's role in oxidative metabolism. Thus, the mitochondrion, in many respects, acts as a cell within a cell, containing its own genetic information specifying proteins for its unique functions. The mitochondria are not fully autonomous, however, because most of the genes that encode the enzymes used in oxidative metabolism are located in the cell nucleus.

A eukaryotic cell does not produce brand-new mitochondria each time the cell divides. Instead, the mitochondria themselves divide in two, doubling in number, and these are partitioned between the new cells. Most of the components required for mitochondrial division are encoded by genes in the nucleus and are translated into proteins by cytoplasmic ribosomes. Mitochondrial replication is, therefore, impossible without nuclear participation, and mitochondria thus cannot be grown in a cell-free culture.

Chloroplasts use light to generate ATP and sugars

Plant cells and cells of other eukaryotic organisms that carry out photosynthesis typically contain from one to several hundred **chloroplasts.** Chloroplasts bestow an obvious advantage on the organisms that possess them: They can manufacture their own food. Chloroplasts contain the photosynthetic pigment chlorophyll that gives most plants their green color.

The chloroplast, like the mitochondrion, is surrounded by two membranes (figure 4.17). However, chloroplasts are larger and more complex than mitochondria. In addition to the outer and inner membranes, which lie in close association with each other, chloroplasts have closed compartments of stacked membranes called **grana** (singular, *granum*), which lie inside the inner membrane.

A chloroplast may contain a hundred or more grana, and each granum may contain from a few to several dozen disk-shaped structures called **thylakoids.** On the surface of the thylakoids are the light-capturing photosynthetic pigments, to be discussed in depth in chapter 8. Surrounding the thylakoid is a fluid matrix called the *stroma*. The enzymes used to synthesize glucose during photosynthesis are found in the stroma.

Like mitochondria, chloroplasts contain DNA, but many of the genes that specify chloroplast components are also located in the nucleus. Some of the elements used in photosynthesis, including the specific protein components

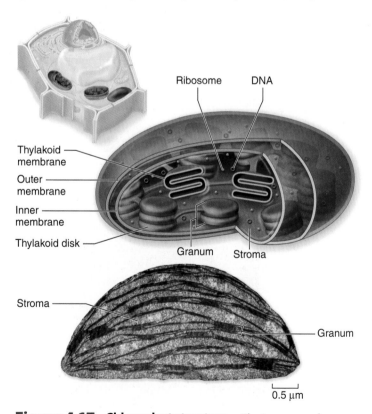

Figure 4.17 Chloroplast structure. The inner membrane of a chloroplast surrounds a membrane system of stacks of closed chlorophyll-containing vesicles called thylakoids, within which photosynthesis occurs. Thylakoids are typically stacked one on top of the other in columns called grana. The chloroplast has been colored green in the micrograph.

necessary to accomplish the reaction, are synthesized entirely within the chloroplast.

Other DNA-containing organelles in plants, called *leucoplasts,* lack pigment and a complex internal structure. In root cells and some other plant cells, leucoplasts may serve as starch-storage sites. A leucoplast that stores starch (amylose) is sometimes termed an **amyloplast.** These organelles—chloroplasts, leucoplasts, and amyloplasts—are collectively called **plastids.** All plastids are produced by the division of existing plastids.

> **?** **Inquiry question** Mitochondria and chloroplasts both generate ATP. What structural features do they share?

Mitochondria and chloroplasts arose by endosymbiosis

Symbiosis is a close relationship between organisms of different species that live together. As noted in chapter 29, the theory of **endosymbiosis** proposes that some of today's eukaryotic organelles evolved by a symbiosis arising between two cells that were each free-living. One cell, a prokaryote, was engulfed by and became part of another cell, which was the precursor of modern eukaryotes (figure 4.18).

According to the endosymbiont theory, the engulfed prokaryotes provided their hosts with certain advantages associated with their special metabolic abilities. Two key eukaryotic organelles are believed to be the descendants of these endosymbiotic prokaryotes: mitochondria, which are thought to have originated as bacteria capable of carrying out oxidative metabolism, and chloroplasts, which apparently arose from photosynthetic bacteria. This is discussed in detail in chapter 29.

> **Learning Outcomes Review 4.5**
>
> Mitochondria and chloroplasts have similar structures, with an outer membrane and an extensive inner membrane compartment. Both mitochondria and chloroplasts have their own DNA, but both also depend on nuclear genes for some functions. Mitochondria and chloroplasts are both involved in energy conversion: Mitochondria metabolize sugar to produce ATP, whereas chloroplasts harness light energy to produce ATP and synthesize sugars. Endosymbiosis theory proposes that both mitochondria and chloroplasts arose as prokaryotic cells were engulfed by a eukaryotic precursor.
>
> ■ *Many proteins in mitochondria and chloroplasts are encoded by nuclear genes. In light of the endosymbiont hypothesis, how might this come about?*

4.6 *The Cytoskeleton*

> **Learning Outcomes**
>
> 1. *Contrast the structure and function of different fibers in the cytoskeleton.*
> 2. *Illustrate the role of microtubules in intracellular transport.*

The cytoplasm of all eukaryotic cells is crisscrossed by a network of protein fibers that supports the shape of the cell and anchors organelles to fixed locations. This network, called the cytoskeleton, is a dynamic system, constantly assembling and disassembling. Individual fibers consist of polymers of identical protein subunits that attract one another and spontaneously assemble into long chains. Fibers disassemble in the same way, as one subunit after another breaks away from one end of the chain.

Three types of fibers compose the cytoskeleton

Eukaryotic cells may contain the following three types of cytoskeletal fibers, each formed from a different kind of subunit: (1) actin filaments, sometimes called microfilaments, (2) microtubules, and (3) intermediate filaments.

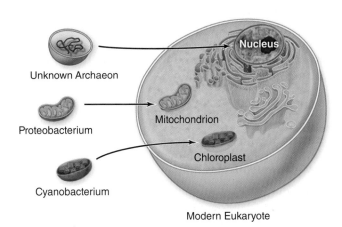

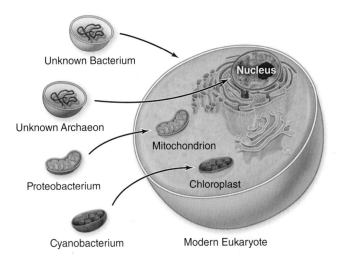

Figure 4.18 Possible origins of eukaryotic cells. Both mitochondria and chloroplasts are thought to have arisen by endosymbiosis when a free-living cell is taken up but not digested. The nature of the engulfing cell is unknown. Two possibilities are (1) the engulfing cell (top) is an archaeon that gave rise to the nuclear genome and cytoplasmic contents. (2) The engulfing cell (bottom) consists of a nucleus derived from an archaeon in a bacterial cell. This could arise by a fusion event or by engulfment of the archaeon by the bacterium.

Actin filaments (microfilaments)

Actin filaments are long fibers about 7 nm in diameter. Each filament is composed of two protein chains loosely twined together like two strands of pearls (figure 4.19). Each "pearl," or subunit, on the chain is the globular protein **actin.** Actin filaments exhibit polarity, that is, they have plus (+) and minus (–) ends. These designate the direction of growth of the filaments.

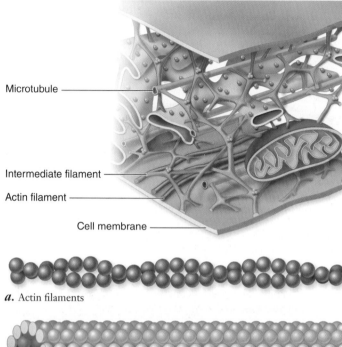

Microtubule

Intermediate filament

Actin filament

Cell membrane

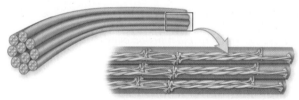

a. Actin filaments

b. Microtubules

c. Intermediate filament

Figure 4.19 Molecules that make up the cytoskeleton.
a. Actin filaments: Actin filaments, also called *microfilaments,* are made of two strands of the globular protein actin twisted together. They are often found in bundles or in a branching network. Actin filaments in many cells are concentrated below the plasma membrane in bundles known as stress fibers, which may have a contractile function. *b. Microtubules:* Microtubules are composed of α- and β-tubulin protein subunits arranged side by side to form a tube. Microtubules are comparatively stiff cytoskeletal elements and have many functions in the cell including intracellular transport and the separation of chromosomes during mitosis. *c. Intermediate filaments:* Intermediate filaments are composed of overlapping staggered tetramers of protein. These tetramers are then bundled into cables. This molecular arrangement allows for a ropelike structure that imparts tremendous mechanical strength to the cell.

Actin molecules spontaneously form these filaments, even in a test tube.

Cells regulate the rate of actin polymerization through other proteins that act as switches, turning on polymerization when appropriate. Actin filaments are responsible for cellular movements such as contraction, crawling, "pinching" during division, and formation of cellular extensions.

Microtubules

Microtubules, the largest of the cytoskeletal elements, are hollow tubes about 25 nm in diameter, each composed of a ring of 13 protein protofilaments (see figure 4.19). Globular proteins consisting of dimers of α- and β-*tubulin* subunits polymerize to form the 13 protofilaments. The protofilaments are arrayed side by side around a central core, giving the microtubule its characteristic tube shape.

In many cells, microtubules form from nucleation centers near the center of the cell and radiate toward the periphery. They are in a constant state of flux, continually polymerizing and depolymerizing. The average half-life of a microtubule ranges from as long as 10 minutes in a nondividing animal cell to as short as 20 seconds in a dividing animal cell. The ends of the microtubule are designated as plus (+) (away from the nucleation center) or minus (–) (toward the nucleation center).

Along with facilitating cellular movement, microtubules organize the cytoplasm and are responsible for moving materials within the cell itself, as described shortly.

Intermediate filaments

The most durable element of the cytoskeleton in animal cells is a system of tough, fibrous protein molecules twined together in an overlapping arrangement (see figure 4.19). These *intermediate filaments* are characteristically 8 to 10 nm in diameter—between the size of actin filaments and microtubules. Once formed, intermediate filaments are stable and usually do not break down.

Intermediate filaments constitute a mixed group of cytoskeletal fibers. The most common type, composed of protein subunits called *vimentin,* provides structural stability for many kinds of cells. *Keratin,* another class of intermediate filament, is found in epithelial cells (cells that line organs and body cavities) and associated structures such as hair and fingernails. The intermediate filaments of nerve cells are called *neurofilaments.*

Centrosomes are microtubule-organizing centers

Centrioles are barrel-shaped organelles found in the cells of animals and most protists. They occur in pairs, usually located at right angles to each other near the nuclear membranes (figure 4.20). The region surrounding the pair in almost all animal cells is referred to as a *centrosome.* Surrounding the centrioles in the centrosome is the **pericentriolar material,** which contains ring-shaped structures composed of tubulin. The pericentriolar material can nucleate the assembly of microtubules in animal cells. Structures with this function are called

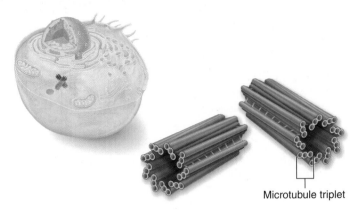

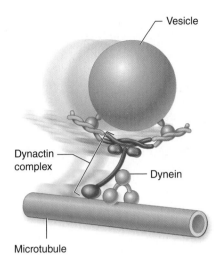

Figure 4.21
Molecular motors.
Vesicles can be transported along microtubules using motor proteins that use ATP to generate force. The vesicles are attached to motor proteins by connector molecules, such as the dynactin complex shown here. The motor protein dynein moves the connected vesicle along microtubules.

Figure 4.20 Centrioles. Each centriole is composed of nine triplets of microtubules. Centrioles are usually not found in plant cells. In animal cells they help to organize microtubules.

microtubule-organizing centers. The centrosome is also responsible for the reorganization of microtubules that occurs during cell division. The centrosomes of plants and fungi lack centrioles, but still contain microtubule-organizing centers. You will learn more about the actions of the centrosomes when we describe the process of cell division in chapter 10.

The cytoskeleton helps move materials within cells

Actin filaments and microtubules often orchestrate their activities to affect cellular processes. For example, during cell reproduction (see chapter 10), newly replicated chromosomes move to opposite sides of a dividing cell because they are attached to shortening microtubules. Then, in animal cells, a belt of actin pinches the cell in two by contracting like a purse string.

Muscle cells also use actin filaments, which slide along filaments of the motor protein myosin when a muscle contracts. The fluttering of an eyelash, the flight of an eagle, and the awkward crawling of a baby all depend on these cytoskeletal movements within muscle cells.

Not only is the cytoskeleton responsible for the cell's shape and movement, but it also provides a scaffold that holds certain enzymes and other macromolecules in defined areas of the cytoplasm. For example, many of the enzymes involved in cell metabolism bind to actin filaments, as do ribosomes. By moving and anchoring particular enzymes near one another, the cytoskeleton, like the endoplasmic reticulum, helps organize the cell's activities.

Molecular motors

All eukaryotic cells must move materials from one place to another in the cytoplasm. One way cells do this is by using the channels of the endoplasmic reticulum as an intracellular highway. Material can also be moved using vesicles loaded with cargo that can move along the cytoskeleton like a railroad track. For example, in a nerve cell with an axon that may extend far from the cell body, vesicles can be moved along tracks of microtubules from the cell body to the end of the axon.

Four components are required to move material along microtubules: (1) a vesicle or organelle that is to be transported, (2) a motor protein that provides the energy-driven motion, (3) a connector molecule that connects the vesicle to the motor molecule, and (4) microtubules on which the vesicle will ride like a train on a rail (figure 4.21).

The direction a vesicle is moved depends on the type of motor protein involved and the fact that microtubules are organized with their plus ends toward the periphery of the cell. In one case, a protein called kinectin binds vesicles to the motor protein *kinesin*. Kinesin uses ATP to power its movement toward the cell periphery, dragging the vesicle with it as it travels along the microtubule toward the plus end (figure 4.22). As nature's tiniest motors, these proteins pull the transport

---

SCIENTIFIC THINKING

Hypothesis: *Kinesin molecules can act as molecular motors and move along microtubules using energy from ATP.*

Test: *A microscope slide is covered with purified kinesin. Purified microtubules are added in a buffer containing ATP. The microtubules are monitored under a microscope using a video recorder to capture any movement.*

Frame 1   Frame 2   Frame 3

Result: *Over time, the movement of individual microtubules can be observed in the microscope. This is shown schematically in the figure by the movement of specific microtubules shown in color.*

Conclusion: *Kinesin acts as a molecular motor moving along (in this case actually moving) microtubules.*

Further Experiments: *Are there any further controls that are not shown in this experiment? What additional conclusions could be drawn by varying the amount of kinesin sticking to the slide?*

Figure 4.22 Demonstration of kinesin as molecular motor. Microtubules can be observed moving over a slide coated with kinesin.

TABLE 4.2

Eukaryotic Cell Structures and their Functions

Structure		Description	Function
Plasma membrane		Phospholipid bilayer with embedded proteins	Regulates what passes into and out of cell; cell-to-cell recognition; connection and adhesion; cell communication
Nucleus		Structure (usually spherical) that contains chromosomes and is surrounded by double membrane	Instructions for protein synthesis and cell reproduction; contains genetic information
Chromosomes		Long threads of DNA that form a complex with protein	Contain hereditary information used to direct synthesis of proteins
Nucleolus		Site of genes for rRNA synthesis	Synthesis of rRNA and ribosome assembly
Ribosomes		Small, complex assemblies of protein and RNA, often bound to ER	Sites of protein synthesis
Endoplasmic reticulum (ER)		Network of internal membranes	Intracellular compartment forms transport vesicles; participates in lipid synthesis and synthesis of membrane or secreted proteins
Golgi apparatus		Stacks of flattened vesicles	Packages proteins for export from cell; forms secretory vesicles
Lysosomes		Vesicles derived from Golgi apparatus that contain hydrolytic digestive enzymes	Digest worn-out organelles and cell debris; digest material taken up by endocytosis
Microbodies		Vesicles that are formed from incorporation of lipids and proteins and that contain oxidative and other enzymes	Isolate particular chemical activities from rest of cell
Mitochondria		Bacteria-like elements with double membrane	"Power plants" of the cell; sites of oxidative metabolism
Chloroplasts		Bacteria-like elements with double membrane surrounding a third, thylakoid membrane containing chlorophyll, a photosynthetic pigment	Sites of photosynthesis
Cytoskeleton		Network of protein filaments	Structural support; cell movement; movement of vesicles within cells
Flagella (cilia)		Cellular extensions with 9 + 2 arrangement of pairs of microtubules	Motility or moving fluids over surfaces
Cell wall		Outer layer of cellulose or chitin; or absent	Protection; support

vesicles along the microtubular tracks. Another set of vesicle proteins, called the dynactin complex, binds vesicles to the motor protein *dynein* (see figure 4.22), which directs movement in the opposite direction along microtubules toward the minus end, inward toward the cell's center. (Dynein is also involved in the movement of eukaryotic flagella, as discussed later.) The destination of a particular transport vesicle and its content is thus determined by the nature of the linking protein embedded within the vesicle's membrane.

The major eukaryotic cell structures and their respective functions are summarized in table 4.2.

Learning Outcomes Review 4.6

The three principal fibers of the cytoskeleton are actin filaments (microfilaments), microtubules, and intermediate filaments. These fibers interact to modulate cell shape and permit cell movement. They also act to move materials within the cytoplasm. Material is also moved in large cells using vesicles and molecular motors. The motor proteins move vesicles along tracks of microtubules.

■ *What advantage does the cytoskeleton give to large eukaryotic cells?*

4.7 Extracellular Structures and Cell Movement

Learning Outcomes

1. *Describe how cells move.*
2. *Identify the different cytoskeletal elements involved in cell movement.*
3. *Classify the elements of extracellular matrix in animal cells.*

Essentially all cell motion is tied to the movement of actin filaments, microtubules, or both. Intermediate filaments act as intracellular tendons, preventing excessive stretching of cells. Actin filaments play a major role in determining the shape of cells. Because actin filaments can form and dissolve so readily, they enable some cells to change shape quickly.

Some cells crawl

The arrangement of actin filaments within the cell cytoplasm allows cells to crawl, literally! Crawling is a significant cellular phenomenon, essential to such diverse processes as inflammation, clotting, wound healing, and the spread of cancer. White blood cells in particular exhibit this ability. Produced in the bone marrow, these cells are released into the circulatory system and then eventually crawl out of venules and into the tissues to destroy potential pathogens.

At the leading edge of a crawling cell, actin filaments rapidly polymerize, and their extension forces the edge of the cell forward. This extended region is stabilized when microtubules polymerize into the newly formed region. Overall forward

movement of the cell is then achieved through the action of the protein **myosin,** which is best known for its role in muscle contraction. Myosin motors along the actin filaments contract, pulling the contents of the cell toward the newly extended front edge.

Cells crawl when these steps occur continuously, with a leading edge extending and stabilizing, and then motors contracting to pull the remaining cell contents along. Receptors on the cell surface can detect molecules outside the cell and stimulate extension in specific directions, allowing cells to move toward particular targets.

Flagella and cilia aid movement

Earlier in this chapter, we described the structure of prokaryotic flagella. Eukaryotic cells have a completely different kind of flagellum, consisting of a circle of nine microtubule pairs surrounding two central microtubules. This arrangement is referred to as the *9 + 2 structure* (figure 4.23).

As pairs of microtubules move past each other using arms composed of the motor protein dynein, the eukaryotic flagellum *undulates,* or waves up and down, rather than rotates. When examined carefully, each flagellum proves to be an outward projection of the cell's interior, containing cytoplasm and enclosed by the plasma membrane. The microtubules of the flagellum are derived from a **basal body,** situated just below the point where the flagellum protrudes from the surface of the cell.

The flagellum's complex microtubular apparatus evolved early in the history of eukaryotes. Today the cells of many multicellular and some unicellular eukaryotes no longer possess flagella and are nonmotile. Other structures, called

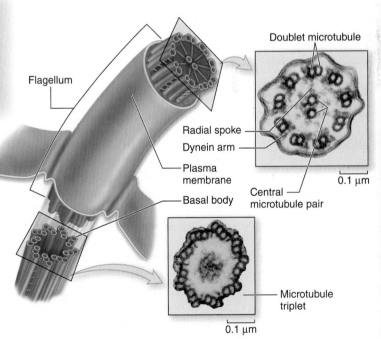

Figure 4.23 Flagella and cilia. A eukaryotic flagellum originates directly from a basal body. The flagellum has two microtubules in its core connected by radial spokes to an outer ring of nine paired microtubules with dynein arms (9 + 2 structure). The basal body consists of nine microtubule triplets connected by short protein segments. The structure of cilia is similar to that of flagella, but cilia are usually shorter.

a.

40 μm

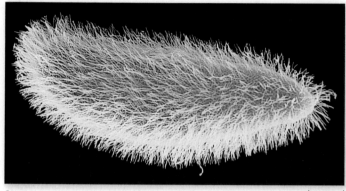

b.

67 μm

Figure 4.24 Flagella and cilia. *a.* A green alga with numerous flagella that allow it to move through the water. *b.* Paramecia are covered with many cilia, which beat in unison to move the cell. The cilia can also be used to move fluid into the paramecium's mouth to ingest material.

cilia (singular, *cilium*), with an organization similar to the 9 + 2 arrangement of microtubules can still be found within them. Cilia are short cellular projections that are often organized in rows. They are more numerous than flagella on the cell surface, but have the same internal structure.

In many multicellular organisms, cilia carry out tasks far removed from their original function of propelling cells through water. In several kinds of vertebrate tissues, for example, the beating of rows of cilia move water over the tissue surface. The sensory cells of the vertebrate ear also contain conventional cilia surrounded by actin-based stereocilia; sound waves bend these structures and provide the initial sensory input for hearing. Thus, the 9 + 2 structure of flagella and cilia appears to be a fundamental component of eukaryotic cells (figure 4.24).

Plant cell walls provide protection and support

The cells of plants, fungi, and many types of protists have cell walls, which protect and support the cells. The cell walls of these eukaryotes are chemically and structurally different from prokaryotic cell walls. In plants and protists, the cell walls are composed of fibers of the polysaccharide cellulose, whereas in fungi, the cell walls are composed of chitin.

In plants, **primary walls** are laid down when the cell is still growing. Between the walls of adjacent cells a sticky substance, called the **middle lamella,** glues the cells together (figure 4.25).

Some plant cells produce strong **secondary walls,** which are deposited inside the primary walls of fully expanded cells.

Animal cells secrete an extracellular matrix

Animal cells lack the cell walls that encase plants, fungi, and most protists. Instead, animal cells secrete an elaborate mixture of glycoproteins into the space around them, forming the *extracellular matrix (ECM)* (figure 4.26). The fibrous protein collagen, the same protein found in cartilage, tendons, and ligaments may be abundant in the ECM. Strong fibers of collagen and another fibrous protein, elastin, are embedded within a complex web of other glycoproteins, called proteoglycans, that form a protective layer over the cell surface.

> **? Inquiry question** The passageways of the human trachea (the path of airflow into and out of the lungs) are known to be lined with ciliated cells. What function could these cilia perform?

The ECM of some cells is attached to the plasma membrane by a third kind of glycoprotein, *fibronectin*. Fibronectin molecules bind not only to ECM glycoproteins but also to proteins called **integrins.** Integrins are an integral part of the

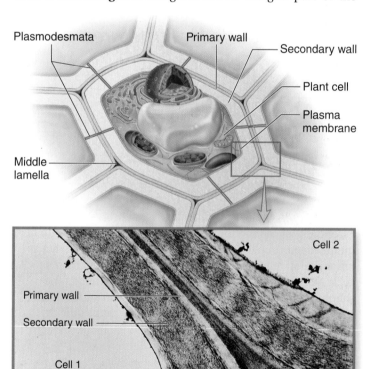

Figure 4.25 Cell walls in plants. Plant cell walls are thick, strong, and rigid. Primary cell walls are laid down when the cell is young. Thicker secondary cell walls may be added later when the cell is fully grown.

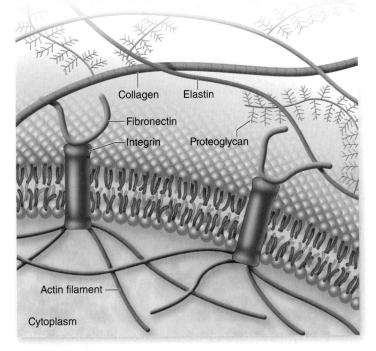

Collagen   Elastin
Fibronectin
Integrin   Proteoglycan

Actin filament

Cytoplasm

Figure 4.26 The extracellular matrix. Animal cells are surrounded by an extracellular matrix composed of various glycoproteins that give the cells support, strength, and resilience.

plasma membrane, extending into the cytoplasm, where they are attached to the microfilaments and intermediate filaments of the cytoskeleton. Linking ECM and cytoskeleton, integrins allow the ECM to influence cell behavior in important ways. They can alter gene expression and cell migration patterns by a combination of mechanical and chemical signaling pathways. In this way, the ECM can help coordinate the behavior of all the cells in a particular tissue.

Table 4.3 compares and reviews the features of three types of cells.

Learning Outcomes Review 4.7

Cell movement involves proteins. These can either be internal in the case of crawling cells that use actin and myosin, or external in the case of cells powered by cilia or flagella. Eukaryotic cilia and flagella are different from prokaryotic flagella because they are composed of bundles of microtubules in a 9 + 2 array. They undulate rather than rotate.

Plant cells have a cellulose-based cell wall. Animal cells lack a cell wall. In animal cells, the cytoskeleton is linked to a web of glycoproteins called the extracellular matrix.

■ *What cellular roles are performed by microtubules and microfilaments and not intermediate filaments?*

TABLE 4.3	A Comparison of Prokaryotic, Animal, and Plant Cells		
	Prokaryote	**Animal**	**Plant**
EXTERIOR STRUCTURES			
Cell wall	Present (protein-polysaccharide)	Absent	Present (cellulose)
Cell membrane	Present	Present	Present
Flagella/cilia	Flagella may be present	May be present (9 + 2 structure)	Absent except in sperm of a few species (9 + 2 structure)
INTERIOR STRUCTURES			
Endoplasmic reticulum	Absent	Usually present	Usually present
Ribosomes	Present	Present	Present
Microtubules	Absent	Present	Present
Centrioles	Absent	Present	Absent
Golgi apparatus	Absent	Present	Present
Nucleus	Absent	Present	Present
Mitochondria	Absent	Present	Present
Chloroplasts	Absent	Absent	Present
Chromosomes	Single; circle of DNA	Multiple; DNA–protein complex	Multiple; DNA–protein complex
Lysosomes	Absent	Usually present	Present
Vacuoles	Absent	Absent or small	Usually a large single vacuole

4.8 Cell-to-Cell Interactions

Learning Outcomes

1. *Differentiate between types of cell junctions.*
2. *Describe the roles of surface proteins.*

A basic feature of multicellular animals is the formation of diverse kinds of *tissue*, such as skin, blood, or muscle, where cells are organized in specific ways. Cells must also be able to communicate with each other and have markers of individual identity. All of these functions—connections between cells, markers of cellular identity, and cell communication—involve membrane proteins and proteins secreted by cells. As an organism develops, the cells acquire their identities by carefully controlling the *expression* of those genes, turning on the specific set of genes that encode the functions of each cell type. Table 4.4 provides a summary of the kinds of connections seen between cells that are explored in the following sections.

Surface proteins give cells identity

One key set of genes functions to mark the surfaces of cells, identifying them as being of a particular type. When cells make contact, they "read" each other's cell-surface markers and react accordingly. Cells that are part of the same tissue type recognize each other, and they frequently respond by forming connections between their surfaces to better coordinate their functions.

Glycolipids

Most tissue-specific cell-surface markers are glycolipids, that is, lipids with carbohydrate heads. The glycolipids on the surface of red blood cells are also responsible for the A, B, and O blood types.

MHC proteins

One example of the function of cell-surface markers is the recognition of "self" and "nonself" cells by the immune system. This function is vital for multicellular organisms, which need to defend themselves against invading or malignant cells. The immune system of vertebrates uses a particular set of markers to distinguish self from nonself cells, encoded by genes of the *major histocompatibility complex* (*MHC*). Cell recognition in the immune system is covered in chapter 51.

 ### Cell connections mediate cell-to-cell adhesion

The evolution of multicellularity required the acquisition of molecules that can connect cells to each other. It appears that multicellularity arose independently in different lineages, but the types of connections between cells are remarkably conserved, and many of the proteins involved are ancient.

The nature of the physical connections between the cells of a tissue in large measure determines what the tissue is like. Indeed, a tissue's proper functioning often depends critically on how the individual cells are arranged within it. Just as a house cannot maintain its structure without nails and cement, so a tissue cannot maintain its characteristic architecture without the appropriate cell junctions. Cell junctions can be

TABLE 4.4	Cell-to-Cell Connections and Cell Identity		
Type of Connection	**Structure**	**Function**	**Example**
Surface markers	Variable, integral proteins or glycolipids in plasma membrane	Identify the cell	MHC complexes, blood groups, antibodies
Septate junctions Tight junctions	Tightly bound, leakproof, fibrous claudin protein seal that surrounds cell	Holds cells together such that materials pass through but not between the cells	Junctions between epithelial cells in the gut
Adhesive junction (desmosome)	Variant cadherins, desmocollins, bind to intermediate filaments of cytoskeleton	Creates strong flexible connections between cells. Found in vertebrates	Epithelium
Adhesive junction (adherens junction)	Classical cadherins, bind to microfilaments of cytoskeleton	Connects cells together. Oldest form of cell junction, found in all multicellular organisms	Tissues with high mechanical stress, such as the skin
Adhesive junction (Hemidesmosome, focal adhesion)	Integrin proteins bind cell to extracellular matrix	Provide attachment to a substrate	Involved in cell movement and important during development
Communicating junction (gap junction)	Six transmembrane connexon/pannexin proteins creating a pore that connects cells	Allows passage of small molecules from cell to cell in a tissue	Excitable tissue such as heart muscle
Communicating junction (plasmodesmata)	Cytoplasmic connections between gaps in adjoining plant cell walls	Communicating junction between plant cells	Plant tissues

characterized by both their visible structure in the microscope, and the proteins involved in the junction.

Adhesive junctions

Adhesive junctions appear to have been the first to evolve. Primitive forms can even be found in sponges, and they are found in all animal species. They mechanically attach the cytoskeleton of a cell to the cytoskeletons of other cells or to the extracellular matrix. These junctions are found in tissues subject to mechanical stress, such as muscle and skin epithelium.

Adherens junctions are based on the protein **cadherin,** which is a Ca^{2+}-dependent adhesion molecule with very wide phylogenetic distribution. Cadherin is a single-pass transmembrane protein with an extracellular domain that can interact with the extracellular domain of a cadherin in an adjacent cell to join the cells together (figure 4.27). Adherens junctions are found in animals ranging from jellyfish to vertebrates. Cadherins found in these junctions are called classical cadherins and are broken down into types I and II. When cells bearing either type I or type II cadherins are mixed, they sort into populations joined by I to I or by II to II interactions. There is some evidence for interactions between type I and type II cadherins, but they are not as strong. On the cytoplasmic side, the cadherins interact indirectly through other proteins with actin to form flexible connections between cells (see figure 4.27).

Desmosomes are a cadherin-based junction unique to vertebrates. They contain the cadherins desmocollin and desmoglein, which interact with intermediate filaments of cytoskeletons instead of actin. Desmosomes join adjacent cells (figure 4.28b). These connections support tissues against mechanical stress.

Hemidesmosomes and focal adhesions connect cells to the basal lamina or other ECM. In this case the proteins that interact with the ECM are called integrins. The integrins are members of a large superfamily of cell-surface receptors that bind to a protein component of the extracellular matrix. At least 20 different integrins exist, each with a differently shaped binding domain. These junctions also connect to the cytoskeleton of cells: actin filaments at focal adhesions and intermediate filaments at hemidesmosomes.

Septate, or Tight, junctions

Septate junctions are found in both invertebrates and vertebrates and form a barrier that can seal off a sheet of cells. The proteins found at these junctions have been given different names in different systems; in *Drosophila*, the proteins include Discs Large and Neurexin. Their wide distribution indicates that they probably evolved soon after or with adherens junctions.

Tight junctions are unique to vertebrates and contain proteins called Claudins because of their ability to occlude or block substances from passing between cells. This form of junction between cells acts as a wall within the tissue, keeping molecules on one side or the other (see figure 4.28a).

Creating sheets of cells. The cells that line an animal's digestive tract are organized in a sheet only one cell thick. One surface of the sheet faces the inside of the tract, and the other faces the extracellular space, where blood vessels are located. Tight junctions encircle each cell in the sheet, like a belt cinched around a person's waist. The junctions between neighboring cells are so securely attached that there is no space between them for leakage. Hence, nutrients absorbed from the food in the digestive tract must pass directly through the cells in the sheet to enter the bloodstream because they cannot pass through spaces between cells.

The tight junctions between the cells lining the digestive tract also partition the plasma membranes of these cells into separate compartments. Transport proteins in the membrane facing the inside of the tract carry nutrients from that side to the cytoplasm of the cells. Other proteins, located in the membrane on the opposite side of the cells, transport those nutrients from the cytoplasm to the extracellular fluid, where they can enter the bloodstream. Tight junctions effectively segregate the proteins on opposite sides of the sheet, preventing them from drifting within the membrane from one side of the sheet to the other. When tight junctions are experimentally disrupted, just this sort of migration occurs.

Communicating junctions

The proteins involved in the junctions previously described can be found in some single-celled organisms as well. The evolution of multicellularity also led to a new form of cellular connection: the *communicating junctions*. These junctions allow communication between cells by diffusion through small openings. Communicating junctions permit small molecules or ions to pass from one cell to the other. In animals, these direct communication channels between cells are called *gap junctions,* and in plants, *plasmodesmata.*

Gap junctions in animals. Gap junctions are found in both invertebrates and vertebrates. In invertebrates they are formed by proteins known as pannexins. In vertebrates pannexin-base gap junctions exist, but there is an additional

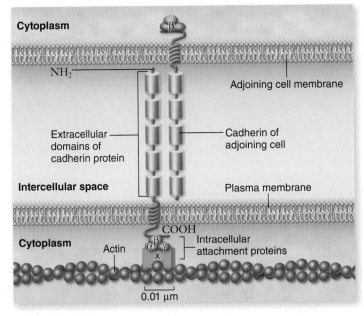

Figure 4.27 A cadherin-mediated junction. The cadherin molecule is anchored to actin in the cytoskeleton and passes through the membrane to interact with the cadherin of an adjoining cell.

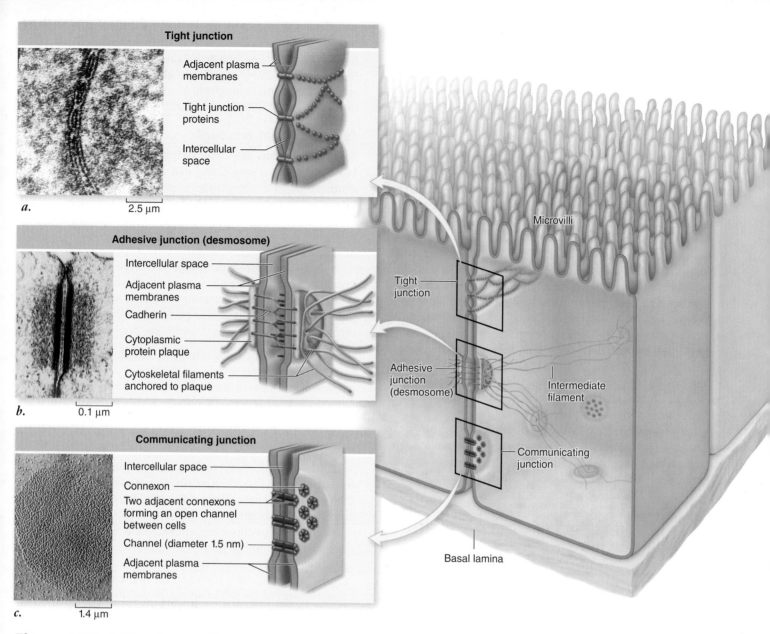

Figure 4.28 Cell junction types in animal epithelium. Here, the diagram of gut epithelial cells on the right illustrates the comparative structures and locations of common cell junctions. The detailed models on the left show the structures of the three major types of cell junctions: *(a)* tight junction; *(b)* adhesive junction, the example shown is a desmosome; *(c)* communicating junction, the example shown is a gap junction.

Tight junction
Adjacent plasma membranes
Tight junction proteins
Intercellular space

a. 2.5 μm

Adhesive junction (desmosome)
Intercellular space
Adjacent plasma membranes
Cadherin
Cytoplasmic protein plaque
Cytoskeletal filaments anchored to plaque

b. 0.1 μm

Communicating junction
Intercellular space
Connexon
Two adjacent connexons forming an open channel between cells
Channel (diameter 1.5 nm)
Adjacent plasma membranes

c. 1.4 μm

Microvilli
Tight junction
Adhesive junction (desmosome)
Intermediate filament
Communicating junction
Basal lamina

type based on similar proteins called connexons. In each case, a structure is formed by complexes of six identical transmembrane proteins (see figure 4.28c). The proteins are arranged in a circle to create a channel through the plasma membrane that protrudes several nanometers from the cell surface. A gap junction forms when the connexons/pannexins of two cells align perfectly, creating an open channel that spans the plasma membranes of both cells.

Gap junctions provide passageways large enough to permit small substances, such as simple sugars and amino acids, to pass from one cell to the next. Yet the passages are small enough to prevent the passage of larger molecules, such as proteins.

Gap junction channels are dynamic structures that can open or close in response to a variety of factors, including Ca^{2+}

and H^+ ions. This gating serves at least one important function. When a cell is damaged, its plasma membrane often becomes leaky. Ions in high concentrations outside the cell, such as Ca^{2+}, flow into the damaged cell and close its gap junction channels. This isolates the cell and prevents the damage from spreading.

Plasmodesmata in plants. In plants, cell walls separate every cell from all others. Cell–cell junctions occur only at holes or gaps in the walls, where the plasma membranes of adjacent cells can come into contact with one another. Cytoplasmic connections that form across the touching plasma membranes are called **plasmodesmata** (singular, *plasmodesma*) (figure 4.29). The majority of living cells within a

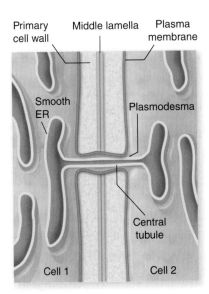

Primary cell wall   Middle lamella   Plasma membrane

Smooth ER

Plasmodesma

Central tubule

Cell 1   Cell 2

Figure 4.29 Plasmodesmata. Plant cells can communicate through specialized openings in their cell walls, called plasmodesmata, where the cytoplasm of adjoining cells are connected.

higher plant are connected to their neighbors by these junctions.

Plasmodesmata function much like gap junctions in animal cells, although their structure is more complex. Unlike gap junctions, plasmodesmata are lined with plasma membrane and contain a central tubule that connects the endoplasmic reticulum of the two cells.

Learning Outcomes Review 4.8

The evolution of multicellularity required the acquisition of cell adhesion molecules to connect cells together. Cell connections fall into three basic categories: (1) adhesive junctions provide strength and flexibility; (2) tight, or septate, junctions help to make sheets of cells that form watertight seals; and (3) communicating junctions, including gap junctions in animals and plasmodesmata in plants, allow passage of some materials between cells. Cells in multicellular organisms have distinct identity and connections. Cell identity is conferred by surface glycoproteins, which include the MHC proteins that are important in the immune system.

■ *How do cell junctions help to form tissues?*

Chapter Review

4.1 Cell Theory

Cell theory is the unifying foundation of cell biology.
All organisms are composed of one or more cells. Cells arise only by division of preexisting cells.

Cell size is limited.
Cell size is constrained by the diffusion distance. As cell size increases, diffusion becomes inefficient.

Microscopes allow visualization of cells and components.
Magnification gives better resolution than is possible with the naked eye. Staining with chemicals enhances contrast of structures.

All cells exhibit basic structural similarities.
All cells have centrally located DNA, a semifluid cytoplasm, and an enclosing plasma membrane.

4.2 Prokaryotic Cells (figure 4.3)

Prokaryotic cells have relatively simple organization.
Prokaryotic cells contain DNA and ribosomes, but they lack a nucleus, an internal membrane system, and membrane-bounded organelles. A rigid cell wall surrounds the plasma membrane.

Bacterial cell walls consist of peptidoglycan.
Peptidoglycan is composed of carbohydrate cross-linked with short peptides.

Archaea lack peptidoglycan.
Archaeal cell walls do not contain peptidoglycan, and they have unique plasma membranes.

Some prokaryotes move by means of rotating flagella.
Prokaryotic flagella rotate because of proton transfer across the plasma membrane.

4.3 Eukaryotic Cells (figures 4.6 and 4.7)

Eukaryotic cells have a membrane-bounded nucleus, an endomembrane system, and many different organelles.

The nucleus acts as the information center.
The nucleus is surrounded by an envelope of two phospholipid bilayers; the outer layer is contiguous with the ER. Pores allow exchange of small molecules. The nucleolus is a region of the nucleoplasm where rRNA is transcribed and ribosomes are assembled.

In most prokaryotes, DNA is organized into a single circular chromosome. In eukaryotes, numerous chromosomes are present.

Ribosomes are the cell's protein synthesis machinery.
Ribosomes translate mRNA to produce polypeptides. They are found in all cell types.

4.4 The Endomembrane System

The endoplasmic reticulum (ER) creates channels and passages within the cytoplasm (figure 4.10).

The rough ER is a site of protein synthesis.
The rough ER (RER), studded with ribosomes, synthesizes and modifies proteins and manufactures membranes.

The smooth ER has multiple roles.
The smooth endoplasmic reticulum (SER) lacks ribosomes; it is involved in carbohydrate and lipid synthesis and detoxification.

The Golgi apparatus sorts and packages proteins.
The Golgi apparatus receives vesicles from the ER, modifies and packages macromolecules, and transports them (figure 4.11).

Lysosomes contain digestive enzymes.
Lysosomes break down macromolecules and recycle the components of old organelles (figure 4.13).

Microbodies are a diverse category of organelles.

Plants use vacuoles for storage and water balance.

4.5 Mitochondria and Chloroplasts: Cellular Generators

Mitochondria and chloroplasts have a double-membrane structure, contain their own DNA, and can divide independently.

Mitochondria metabolize sugar to generate ATP.
The inner membrane of mitochondria is extensively folded into layers called cristae. Proteins on the surface and in the inner membrane carry out metabolism to produce ATP (figure 4.16).

Chloroplasts use light to generate ATP and sugars.
Chloroplasts capture light energy via thylakoid membranes arranged in stacks called grana, and use it to synthesize glucose (figure 4.17).

Mitochondria and chloroplasts arose by endosymbiosis.
The endosymbiont theory proposes that mitochondria and chloroplasts were once prokaryotes engulfed by another cell.

4.6 The Cytoskeleton

The cytoskeleton consists of crisscrossed protein fibers that support the shape of the cell and anchor organelles (figure 4.19).

Three types of fibers compose the cytoskeleton.
Actin filaments, or microfilaments, are long, thin polymers involved in cellular movement. Microtubules are hollow structures that move materials within a cell. Intermediate filaments serve a wide variety of functions.

Centrosomes are microtubule-organizing centers.
Centrosomes help assemble the nuclear division apparatus of animal cells (figure 4.20).

The cytoskeleton helps move materials within cells.
Molecular motors move vesicles along microtubules, like a train on a railroad track. Kinesin and dynein are two motor proteins.

4.7 Extracellular Structures and Cell Movement

Some cells crawl.
Cell crawling occurs as actin polymerization forces the cell membrane forward, while myosin pulls the cell body forward.

Flagella and cilia aid movement.
Eukaryotic flagella have a 9 + 2 structure and arise from a basal body. Cilia are shorter and more numerous than flagella.

Plant cell walls provide protection and support.
Plants have cell walls composed of cellulose fibers. The middle lamella, between cell walls, holds adjacent cells together.

Animal cells secrete an extracellular matrix.
Glycoproteins are the main component of the extracellular matrix (ECM) of animal cells.

4.8 Cell-to-Cell Interactions (figure 4.27)

Surface proteins give cells identity.
Glycolipids and MHC proteins on cell surfaces help distinguish self from nonself.

Cell connections mediate cell-to-cell adhesion.
Cell junctions include tight junctions, adhesive junctions, and communicating junctions. In animals, gap junctions allow the passage of small molecules between cells. In plants, plasmodesmata penetrate the cell wall and connect cells.

Review Questions

UNDERSTAND

1. Which of the following statements is NOT part of the cell theory?
   a. All organisms are composed of one or more cells.
   b. Cells come from other cells by division.
   c. Cells are the smallest living things.
   d. Eukaryotic cells have evolved from prokaryotic cells.

2. All cells have all of the following except
   a. plasma membrane.   c. cytoplasm.
   b. genetic material.   d. cell wall.

3. Eukaryotic cells are more complex than prokaryotic cells. Which of the following are found only in a eukaryotic cell?
   a. Cell wall
   b. Plasma membrane
   c. Endoplasmic reticulum
   d. Ribosomes

4. Which of the following are differences between bacteria and archaea?
   a. The molecular architecture of their cell walls
   b. The type of ribosomes found in each
   c. Archaea have an internal membrane system that bacteria lack.
   d. Both a and b are correct.

5. The cytoskeleton includes
   a. microtubules made of actin filaments.
   b. microfilaments made of tubulin.
   c. intermediate filaments made of twisted fibers of vimentin and keratin.
   d. smooth endoplasmic reticulum.

6. The smooth endoplasmic reticulum is
   a. involved in protein synthesis.
   b. a site of protein glycosylation.
   c. used to store a variety of ions.
   d. the site of lipid and membrane synthesis.

7. Plasmodesmata in plants and gap junctions in animals are functionally similar in that
   a. each is used to anchor layers of cells.
   b. they form channels between cells that allow diffusion of small molecules.
   c. they form tight junctions between cells.
   d. they are anchored to the extracellular matrix.

APPLY

1. The most important factor that limits the size of a cell is the
   a. quantity of proteins and organelles a cell can make.
   b. rate of diffusion of small molecules.
   c. surface area-to-volume ratio of the cell.
   d. amount of DNA in the cell.

2. All eukaryotic cells possess each of the following except
   a. mitochondria.
   b. cell wall.
   c. cytoskeleton.
   d. nucleus.

3. Adherens junctions, which contain cadherin, are found in all animals. Given this, which of the following predictions is most likely?
   a. Cadherins would not be found in the ancestor to all animals.
   b. Cadherins would be found in prokaryotes.
   c. Cadherins would be found in the ancestor to all animals.
   d. Cadherins would be found in vertebrates but not invertebrates.

4. Different motor proteins like kinesin and myosin are similar in that they can
   a. interact with microtubules.
   b. use energy from ATP to produce movement.
   c. interact with actin.
   d. do both a and b.

5. The protein sorting pathway involves the following organelles/compartments in order:
   a. SER, RER, transport vesicle, Golgi.
   b. RER, lysosome, Golgi.
   c. RER, transport vesicle, Golgi, final destination.
   d. Golgi, transport vesicle, RER, final destination.

6. Chloroplasts and mitochondria have many common features because both
   a. are present in plant cells.
   b. arose by endosymbiosis.
   c. function to oxidize glucose.
   d. function to produce glucose.

7. Eukaryotic cells are composed of three types of cytoskeletal filaments. How are these three filaments similar?
   a. They contribute to the shape of the cell.
   b. They are all made of the same type of protein.
   c. They are all the same size and shape.
   d. They are all equally dynamic and flexible.

SYNTHESIZE

1. The smooth endoplasmic reticulum is the site of synthesis of the phospholipids that make up all the membranes of a cell—especially the plasma membrane. Use the diagram of an animal cell (figure 4.6) to trace a pathway that would carry a phospholipid molecule from the SER to the plasma membrane. What endomembrane compartments would the phospholipids travel through? How can a phospholipid molecule move between membrane compartments?

2. Use the information provided in table 4.3 to develop a set of predictions about the properties of mitochondria and chloroplasts if these organelles were once free-living prokaryotic cells. How do your predictions match with the evidence for endosymbiosis?

3. In evolutionary theory, homologous traits are those with a similar structure and function derived from a common ancestor. Analogous traits represent adaptations to a similar environment, but from distantly related organisms. Consider the structure and function of the flagella found on eukaryotic and prokaryotic cells. Are the flagella an example of a homologous or analogous trait? Defend your answer.

4. The protist, *Giardia intestinalis,* is the organism associated with water-borne diarrheal diseases. *Giardia* is an unusual eukaryote because it seems to lack mitochondria. Provide two possible evolutionary scenarios for this in the context of the endosymbiotic theory.

ONLINE RESOURCE

www.ravenbiology.com

Understand, Apply, and Synthesize—enhance your study with animations that bring concepts to life and practice tests to assess your understanding. Your instructor may also recommend the interactive eBook, individualized learning tools, and more.

100 nm

Membranes

Chapter Contents

Introduction

A cell's interactions with the environment are critical, a give-and-take that never ceases. Without it, life could not exist. Living cells are encased within a lipid membrane through which few water-soluble substances can pass. The membrane also contains protein passageways that permit specific substances to move into and out of the cell and allow the cell to exchange information with its environment. Eukaryotic cells also contain internal membranes like those of the mitochondrion and endoplasmic reticulum pictured here. We call the delicate skin of lipids with embedded protein molecules that encase the cell a plasma membrane. This chapter examines the structure and function of this remarkable membrane.

5.1 The Structure of Membranes

Learning Outcomes

1. *Describe the components of biological membranes.*
2. *Explain the fluid mosaic model of membrane structure.*

The membranes that encase all living cells are two phospholipid sheets that are only 5–10 nm thick; more than 10,000 of these sheets piled on one another would just equal the thickness of this sheet of paper. Biologists established the components of membranes—not only lipids, but also proteins and other molecules—through biochemical assays, but the organization of the membrane components remained elusive.

We begin by considering the theories that have been advanced about membrane structure. We then look at the individual components of membranes more closely.

The fluid mosaic model shows proteins embedded in a fluid lipid bilayer

The lipid layer that forms the foundation of a cell's membranes is a bilayer formed of **phospholipids.** These phospholipids include primarily the glycerol phospholipids (figure 5.1), and the sphingolipids such as sphingomyelin (figure 5.2). Note that although these look superficially similar, they are built on a different carbon skeleton. For many years, biologists thought that the protein components of the cell membrane covered the inner and outer surfaces of the phospholipid bilayer like a coat of paint. An early model portrayed the membrane as a sandwich; a phospholipid bilayer between two layers of globular protein.

In 1972, S. Jonathan Singer and Garth J. Nicolson revised the model in a simple but profound way: They proposed that the globular proteins are *inserted* into the lipid bilayer, with their nonpolar segments in contact with the nonpolar interior of the bilayer and their polar portions protruding out from the membrane surface. In this model, called the *fluid mosaic model,* a mosaic of proteins floats in or on the fluid lipid bilayer like boats on a pond (figure 5.3).

We now recognize two categories of membrane proteins based on their association with the membrane. *Integral membrane proteins* are embedded in the membrane, and *peripheral proteins* are associated with the surface of the membrane.

Cellular membranes consist of four component groups

A eukaryotic cell contains many membranes. Although they are not all identical, they share the same fundamental architecture. Cell membranes are assembled from four components (table 5.1):

1. **Phospholipid bilayer.** Every cell membrane is composed of phospholipids in a bilayer. The other components of the membrane are embedded within the bilayer, which provides a flexible matrix and, at the same time, imposes a barrier to permeability. Animal cell membranes also contain cholesterol, a steroid with a polar hydroxyl group (—OH). Plant cells have other sterols, but little or no cholesterol.
2. **Transmembrane proteins.** A major component of every membrane is a collection of proteins that float in the lipid bilayer. These proteins have a variety of functions, including transport and communication across the membrane. Many integral membrane proteins are not fixed in position. They can move about, just as the phospholipid molecules do. Some membranes are crowded with proteins, but in others, the proteins are more sparsely distributed.
3. **Interior protein network.** Membranes are structurally supported by intracellular proteins that reinforce the membrane's shape. For example, a red blood cell has a characteristic biconcave shape because a scaffold made

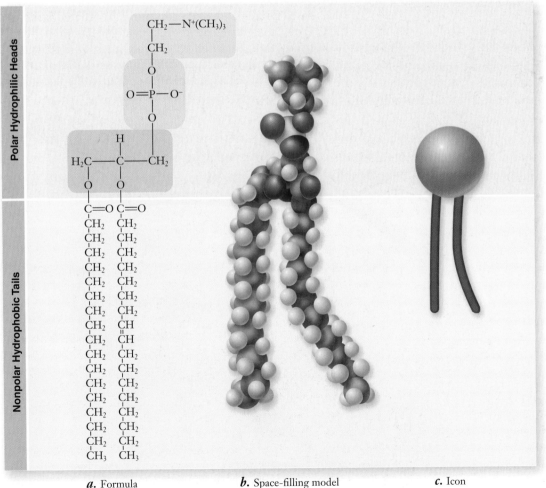

a. Formula *b.* Space-filling model *c.* Icon

Figure 5.1 Different views of phospholipid structure. Phospholipids are composed of glycerol (*pink*) linked to two fatty acids and a phosphate group. The phosphate group (*yellow*) can have additional molecules attached, such as the positively charged choline (*green*) shown. Phosphatidylcholine is a common component of membranes. It is shown in (*a*) with its chemical formula, (*b*) as a space-filling model, and (*c*) as the icon that is used in most of the figures in this chapter.

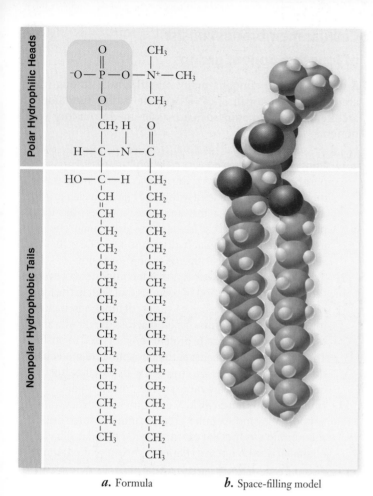

Polar Hydrophilic Heads

Nonpolar Hydrophobic Tails

a. Formula   *b.* Space-filling model

Figure 5.2 Sphingomyelin. Sphingomyelin is a sphingolipid found in animal cells. *a.* Formula. *b.* Space-filling model.

of a protein called spectrin links proteins in the plasma membrane with actin filaments in the cell's cytoskeleton.

Membranes use networks of other proteins to control the lateral movements of some key membrane proteins, anchoring them to specific sites.

4. **Cell-surface markers.** As you learned in the preceding chapter, membrane sections assemble in the endoplasmic reticulum, transfer to the Golgi apparatus, and then are transported to the plasma membrane. The ER adds chains of sugar molecules to membrane proteins and lipids, converting them into **glycoproteins** and **glycolipids.** Different cell types exhibit different varieties of these glycoproteins and glycolipids on their surfaces, which act as cell identity markers.

Cellular membranes have an organized substructure

Originally, it was believed that because of its fluidity, the plasma membrane was uniform, with lipids and proteins free to diffuse rapidly in the plane of the membrane. However, in the last decade evidence has accumulated suggesting the plasma membrane is not homogeneous and contains microdomains with distinct lipid and protein composition. This was first observed in epithelial cells in which the lipid composition of the apical and basal membranes was shown to be distinctly different. Theoretical work also showed that lipids can exist in either a disordered or an ordered phase within a bilayer.

This led to the idea of lipid microdomains called *lipid rafts* that are heavily enriched in cholesterol and sphingolipids. These lipids appear to interact with each other, and with raft-associated proteins—together forming an ordered structure. This is now technically defined as "dynamic nanometer-sized, sterol and sphingolipid-enriched protein assemblies." There is evidence that signaling molecules, such as the B- and T-cell receptors discussed in chapter 51, associate with lipid rafts and that this association affects their function.

Figure 5.3 The fluid mosaic model of cell membranes.
Integral proteins protrude through the plasma membrane, with nonpolar regions that tether them to the membrane's hydrophobic interior. Carbohydrate chains are often bound to the extracellular portion of these proteins, forming glycoproteins. Peripheral membrane proteins are associated with the surface of the membrane. Membrane phospholipids can be modified by the addition of carbohydrates to form glycolipids. Inside the cell, actin filaments and intermediate filaments interact with membrane proteins. Outside the cell, many animal cells have an elaborate extracellular matrix composed primarily of glycoproteins.

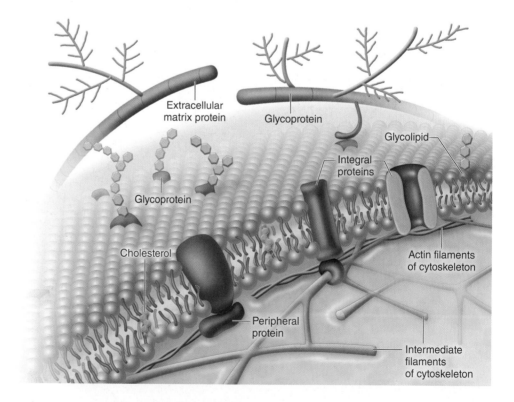

Extracellular matrix protein

Glycoprotein

Glycolipid

Glycoprotein

Integral proteins

Glycoprotein

Cholesterol

Actin filaments of cytoskeleton

Peripheral protein

Intermediate filaments of cytoskeleton

TABLE 5.1 Components of the Cell Membrane

Component	Composition	Function	How It Works	Example
Phospholipid bilayer	Phospholipid molecules	Provides permeability barrier, matrix for proteins	Excludes water-soluble molecules from nonpolar interior of bilayer and cell	Bilayer of cell is impermeable to large water-soluble molecules, such as glucose
Transmembrane proteins	Carriers	Actively or passively transport molecules across membrane	Move specific molecules through the membrane in a series of conformational changes	Glycophorin carrier for sugar transport; sodium–potassium pump
	Channels	Passively transport molecules across membrane	Create a selective tunnel that acts as a passage through membrane	Sodium and potassium channels in nerve, heart, and muscle cells
	Receptors	Transmit information into cell	Signal molecules bind to cell-surface portion of the receptor protein. This alters the portion of the receptor protein within the cell, inducing activity	Specific receptors bind peptide hormones and neurotransmitters
Interior protein network	Spectrins	Determine shape of cell	Form supporting scaffold beneath membrane, anchored to both membrane and cytoskeleton	Red blood cell
	Clathrins	Anchor certain proteins to specific sites, especially on the exterior plasma membrane in receptor-mediated endocytosis	Proteins line coated pits and facilitate binding to specific molecules	Localization of low-density lipoprotein receptor within coated pits
Cell-surface markers	Glycoproteins	"Self" recognition	Create a protein/carbohydrate chain shape characteristic of individual	Major histocompatibility complex protein recognized by immune system
	Glycolipid	Tissue recognition	Create a lipid/carbohydrate chain shape characteristic of tissue	A, B, O blood group markers

In addition to these horizontal structures there is also vertical structure to the plasma membrane. That is, the distribution of membrane lipids in the plasma membrane is asymmetrical, with the outer leaflet enriched in the glycerol phospholipid phosphatidylcholine and in sphingolipids. This is despite being symmetrically distributed in the ER where they are synthesized. Some of this sorting occurs in the Golgi and is also affected by enzymes that transport lipids across the bilayer from one face to the other.

Electron microscopy has provided structural evidence

Electron microscopy allows biologists to examine the delicate, filmy structure of a cell membrane. We discussed two types of electron microscopes in chapter 4: the transmission electron microscope (TEM) and the scanning electron microscope (SEM). Both provide illuminating views of membrane structure.

When examining cell membranes with electron microscopy, specimens must be prepared for viewing. In one method of preparing a specimen, the tissue of choice is embedded in a hard epoxy matrix. The epoxy block is then cut with a microtome, a machine with a very sharp blade that makes incredibly thin, transparent "epoxy shavings" less than 1 μm thick that peel away from the block of tissue.

These shavings are placed on a grid, and a beam of electrons is directed through the grid with the TEM. At the high magnification an electron microscope provides, resolution is good enough to reveal the double layers of a membrane. False color can be added to the micrograph to enhance detail.

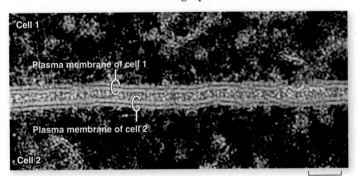

Freeze-fracturing a specimen is another way to visualize the inside of the membrane (figure 5.4). The tissue is embedded in a medium and quick frozen with liquid nitrogen. The frozen tissue is then "tapped" with a knife, causing a crack between the phospholipid layers of membranes. Proteins, carbohydrates, pits, pores, channels, or any other structure affiliated with the membrane will pull apart (whole, usually) and stick with one or the other side of the split membrane.

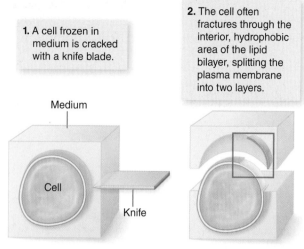

1. A cell frozen in medium is cracked with a knife blade.

2. The cell often fractures through the interior, hydrophobic area of the lipid bilayer, splitting the plasma membrane into two layers.

Medium

Cell

Knife

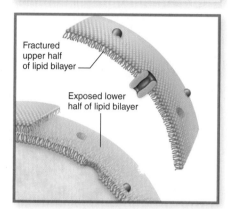

3. The plasma membrane separates such that proteins and other embedded membrane structures remain within one or the other layers of the membrane.

Fractured upper half of lipid bilayer

Exposed lower half of lipid bilayer

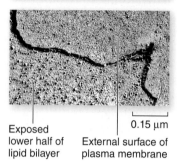

4. The exposed membrane is coated with platinum, which forms a replica of the membrane. The underlying membrane is dissolved away, and the replica is then viewed with electron microscopy.

Exposed lower half of lipid bilayer

External surface of plasma membrane

0.15 μm

Figure 5.4 Viewing a plasma membrane with freeze-fracture microscopy.

Next, a very thin coating of platinum is evaporated onto the fractured surface, forming a replica or "cast" of the surface. After the topography of the membrane has been preserved in the cast, the actual tissue is dissolved away, and the cast is examined with electron microscopy, creating a textured and three-dimensional view of the membrane.

Learning Outcomes Review 5.1

Cellular membranes contain four components: (1) a phospholipid bilayer, (2) transmembrane proteins, (3) an internal protein network providing structural support, and (4) cell-surface markers composed of glycoproteins and glycolipids. The fluid mosaic model of membrane structure includes both the fluid nature of the membrane and the mosaic composition of proteins floating in the phospholipid bilayer. Transmission electron microscopy (TEM) and scanning electron microscopy (SEM) have provided evidence supporting the fluid mosaic model.

■ *If the plasma membrane were just a phospholipid bilayer, how would this affect its function?*

5.2 Phospholipids: The Membrane's Foundation

Learning Outcomes

1. List the different components of phospholipids.
2. Explain how membranes form spontaneously.
3. Describe the factors involved in membrane fluidity.

Like the fat molecules (triglycerides) described in chapter 3, glycerol phospholipids have a backbone derived from the three-carbon polyalcohol *glycerol*. Attached to this backbone are one to three fatty acids, long chains of carbon atoms ending in a carboxyl (—COOH) group. A triglyceride molecule has three such chains, one attached to each carbon in the backbone. Because these chains are nonpolar, they do not form hydrogen bonds with water, and triglycerides are not water-soluble.

A phospholipid, by contrast, has only two fatty acid chains attached to its backbone. The third carbon of the glycerol carries a phosphate group, thus the name *phospho*lipid. An additional polar organic molecule is often added to the phosphate group as well. By varying the polar organic group, and the fatty acid chains, a large variety of lipids can be constructed on this simple molecular framework.

In addition to the glycerol phospholipids, eukaryotic cell membranes have sphingolipids, which usually have saturated fatty acid chains that may aid in organizing the membrane into lipid rafts and other microstructures.

Phospholipids spontaneously form bilayers

The phosphate groups are charged, and other molecules attached to them are polar or charged. This creates a huge change in the molecule's physical properties compared with a triglyceride. The strongly polar phosphate end is hydrophilic, or "water-loving," while the fatty acid end is strongly nonpolar and hydrophobic, or "water-fearing." The two nonpolar fatty acids extend in one direction, roughly parallel to each other, and the polar phosphate group points in the other direction. To represent this structure, phospholipids are often diagrammed as a polar head with two dangling nonpolar tails, as in figure 5.1c.

What happens when a collection of phospholipid molecules is placed in water? The polar water molecules repel the long, nonpolar tails of the phospholipids while seeking partners for hydrogen bonding. Because of the polar nature of the water molecules, the nonpolar tails of the phospholipids end up packed closely together, sequestered as far as possible from water. Every phospholipid molecule is oriented with its polar head toward water and its nonpolar tails away. When *two* layers form with the tails facing each other, no tails ever come in contact with water. The resulting structure is the phospholipid bilayer. Phospholipid bilayers form spontaneously, driven by the tendency of water molecules to form the maximum number of hydrogen bonds.

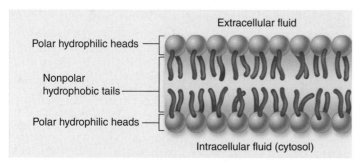

Extracellular fluid

Polar hydrophilic heads

Nonpolar hydrophobic tails

Polar hydrophilic heads

Intracellular fluid (cytosol)

The nonpolar interior of a lipid bilayer impedes the passage of any water-soluble substances through the bilayer, just as a layer of oil impedes the passage of a drop of water. This barrier to water-soluble substances is the key biological property of the lipid bilayer.

The phospholipid bilayer is fluid

A lipid bilayer is stable because water's affinity for hydrogen bonding never stops. Just as surface tension holds a soap bubble together, even though it is made of a liquid, so the hydrogen bonding of water holds a membrane together. Although water drives phospholipids into a bilayer configuration, it does not have any effect on the mobility of phospholipids and their nonlipid neighbors in the bilayer. Because phospholipids interact relatively weakly with one another, individual phospholipids

SCIENTIFIC THINKING

Hypothesis: *The plasma membrane is fluid, not rigid.*

Prediction: *If the membrane is fluid, membrane proteins may diffuse laterally.*

Test: *Fuse mouse and human cells, then observe the distribution of membrane proteins over time by labeling specific mouse and human proteins.*

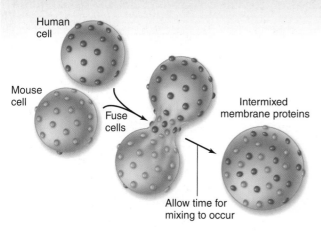

Human cell

Mouse cell

Fuse cells

Intermixed membrane proteins

Allow time for mixing to occur

Result: *Over time, hybrid cells show increasingly intermixed proteins.*

Conclusion: *At least some membrane proteins can diffuse laterally in the membrane.*

Further Experiments: *Can you think of any other explanation for these observations? What if newly synthesized proteins were inserted into the membrane during the experiment? How could you use this basic experimental design to rule out this or other possible explanations?*

Figure 5.5 **Test of membrane fluidity.**

and unanchored proteins are comparatively free to move about within the membrane. This can be demonstrated vividly by fusing cells and watching their proteins intermix with time (figure 5.5).

Membrane fluidity can change

The degree of membrane fluidity changes with the composition of the membrane itself. Much like triglycerides can be solid or liquid at room temperature, depending on their fatty acid composition, membrane fluidity can be altered by changing the membrane's fatty acid composition.

Saturated fats tend to make the membrane less fluid because they pack together well. Unsaturated fats make the membrane more fluid—the "kinks" introduced by the double bonds keep them from packing tightly. You saw this effect on fats and oils earlier in chapter 3.

In animal cells cholesterol may make up as much as 50% of membrane lipids in the outer leaflet. The cholesterol can fill gaps left by unsaturated fatty acids. This has the effect of decreasing membrane fluidity, but it increases the strength of the membrane. Overall this leads to a membrane with intermediate fluidity that is more durable and also less permeable.

Changes in the environment can have drastic effects on the membranes of single-celled organisms such as bacteria. Increasing temperature makes a membrane more fluid, and decreasing temperature makes it less fluid. Bacteria have evolved mechanisms to maintain a constant membrane fluidity despite fluctuating temperatures. Some bacteria contain enzymes called *fatty acid desaturases* that can introduce double bonds into fatty acids in membranes. Genetic studies, involving either the inactivation of these enzymes or the introduction of them into cells that normally lack them, indicate that the action of these enzymes confers cold tolerance. At colder temperatures, the double bonds introduced by fatty acid desaturase make the membrane more fluid, counteracting the environmental effect of reduced temperature.

Learning Outcomes Review 5.2

Biological membranes consist of a phospholipid bilayer. Each phospholipid has a hydrophilic (phosphate) head and a hydrophobic (lipid) tail. In water, phospholipid molecules spontaneously form a bilayer, with phosphate groups facing out toward the water and lipid tails facing in, where they are sequestered from water. Membrane fluidity varies with composition and conditions: unsaturated fats disturb packing of the lipid tails and make the membrane more fluid, as do higher temperatures.

■ *Would a phospholipid bilayer form in a nonpolar solvent?*

5.3 Proteins: Multifunctional Components

Learning Outcomes

1. Illustrate the functions of membrane proteins.
2. Illustrate how proteins can associate with the membrane.
3. Identify a transmembrane domain.

Cell membranes contain a complex assembly of proteins enmeshed in the fluid soup of phospholipid molecules. This very flexible organization permits a broad range of interactions with the environment, some directly involving membrane proteins.

Proteins and protein complexes perform key functions

Although cells interact with their environment through their plasma membranes in many ways, we will focus on six key classes of membrane protein in this chapter and in chapter 9 (figure 5.6).

1. **Transporters.** Membranes are very selective, allowing only certain solutes to enter or leave the cell, either through channels or carriers composed of proteins.
2. **Enzymes.** Cells carry out many chemical reactions on the interior surface of the plasma membrane, using enzymes attached to the membrane.
3. **Cell-surface receptors.** Membranes are exquisitely sensitive to chemical messages, which are detected by receptor proteins on their surfaces.
4. **Cell-surface identity markers.** Membranes carry cell-surface markers that identify them to other cells. Most cell types carry their own ID tags, specific combinations of cell-surface proteins and protein complexes such as glycoproteins that are characteristic of that cell type.
5. **Cell-to-cell adhesion proteins.** Cells use specific proteins to glue themselves to one another. Some act by forming temporary interactions, and others form a more permanent bond. (See chapter 4.)
6. **Attachments to the cytoskeleton.** Surface proteins that interact with other cells are often anchored to the cytoskeleton by linking proteins.

Structural features of membrane proteins relate to function

As we've just detailed, membrane proteins can serve a variety of functions. These diverse functions arise from the diverse structures of these proteins, yet they also have common structural features related to their role as membrane proteins.

The anchoring of proteins in the bilayer

Some membrane proteins are attached to the surface of the membrane by special molecules that associate strongly with phospholipids. Like a ship tied to a floating dock, these anchored proteins are free to move about on the surface of the membrane tethered to a phospholipid. The anchoring molecules are modified lipids that have (1) nonpolar regions that insert into the internal portion of the lipid bilayer and (2) chemical bonding domains that link directly to proteins.

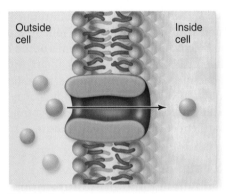
Transporter

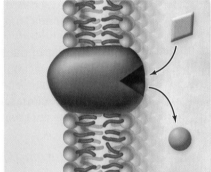
Enzyme

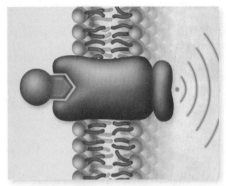
Cell-surface receptor

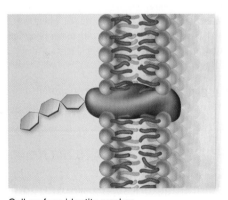
Cell-surface identity marker

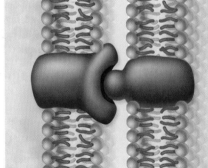
Cell-to-cell adhesion

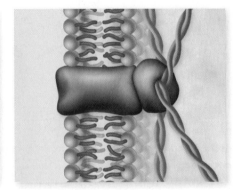
Attachment to the cytoskeleton

Figure 5.6 Functions of plasma membrane proteins. Membrane proteins act as transporters, enzymes, cell-surface receptors, and cell-surface identity markers, as well as aiding in cell-to-cell adhesion and securing the cytoskeleton.

? Inquiry question According to the fluid mosaic model, membranes are held together by hydrophobic interactions. Considering the forces that some cells may experience, why do membranes not break apart every time an animal moves?

In the first image labeled "Transporter", the labels "Outside cell" and "Inside cell" appear.

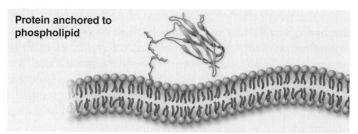
Protein anchored to phospholipid

In contrast, other proteins actually span the lipid bilayer (transmembrane proteins). The part of the protein that extends through the lipid bilayer and that is in contact with the nonpolar interior are α helices or β-pleated sheets (see chapter 3) that consist of nonpolar amino acids. Because water avoids nonpolar amino acids, these portions of the protein are held within the interior of the lipid bilayer. The polar ends protrude from both sides of the membrane. Any movement of the protein out of the membrane, in either direction, brings the nonpolar regions of the protein into contact with water, which "shoves" the protein back into the interior. These forces prevent the transmembrane proteins from simply popping out of the membrane and floating away.

Transmembrane domains

Cell membranes contain a variety of different transmembrane proteins, which differ in the way they traverse the lipid bilayer. The primary difference lies in the number of times that the protein crosses the membrane. Each membrane-spanning region is called a **transmembrane domain.** These domains are composed of hydrophobic amino acids usually arranged into α helices (figure 5.7).

Proteins need only a single transmembrane domain to be anchored in the membrane, but they often have more than one such domain. An example of a protein with a single transmembrane domain is the linking protein that attaches the spectrin network of the cytoskeleton to the interior of the plasma membrane.

Biologists classify some types of receptors based on the number of transmembrane domains they have, such as G protein–coupled receptors with seven membrane-spanning domains (chapter 9). These receptors respond to external molecules, such as epinephrine, and initiate a cascade of events inside the cell.

Another example is bacteriorhodopsin, one of the key transmembrane proteins that carries out photosynthesis in halophilic (salt-loving) archaea. It contains seven nonpolar helical segments that traverse the membrane, forming a structure within the membrane through which protons pass during the light-driven pumping of protons.

Pores

Some transmembrane proteins have extensive nonpolar regions with secondary configurations of β-pleated sheets instead of α helices (chapter 3). The β sheets form a characteristic motif, folding back and forth in a cylinder so the sheets arrange themselves like a pipe through the membrane. This forms a polar environment in the interior of the β sheets spanning the membrane. This so-called *β barrel,* open on both ends, is a common feature of the porin class of proteins that are found within the outer membrane of some bacteria. The openings allow molecules to pass through the membrane (figure 5.8).

Learning Outcomes Review 5.3

Proteins in the membrane confer the main differences between membranes of different cells. Their functions include transport, enzymatic action, reception of extracellular signals, cell-to-cell interactions, and cell identity markers. Peripheral proteins can be anchored in the membrane by modified lipids. Integral membrane proteins span the membrane and have one or more hydrophobic regions, called transmembrane domains, that anchor them.

■ *Why are transmembrane domains hydrophobic?*

? Inquiry question Based only on amino acid sequence, how would you recognize an integral membrane protein?

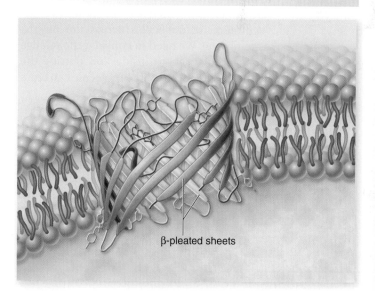

β-pleated sheets

Figure 5.8 A pore protein. The bacterial transmembrane protein porin creates large open tunnels called pores in the outer membrane of a bacterium. Sixteen strands of β-pleated sheets run antiparallel to one another, creating a so-called β barrel in the bacterial outer cell membrane. The tunnel allows water and other materials to pass through the membrane.

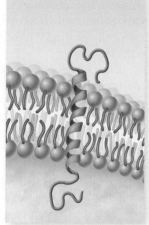

a.   *b.*

Figure 5.7 Transmembrane domains. Integral membrane proteins have at least one hydrophobic transmembrane domain (shown in blue) to anchor them in the membrane. *a.* Receptor protein with seven transmembrane domains. *b.* Protein with single transmembrane domain.

Learning Outcomes

1. Compare simple diffusion and facilitated diffusion.
2. Differentiate between channel proteins and carrier proteins.
3. Predict the direction of water movement by osmosis.

Many substances can move in and out of the cell without the cell's having to expend energy. This type of movement is termed **passive transport.** Some ions and molecules can pass through the membrane fairly easily and do so because of a *concentration gradient*—a difference between the concentration on the inside of the membrane and that on the outside. Some substances also move in response to a gradient, but do so through specific channels formed by proteins in the membrane.

Transport can occur by simple diffusion

Molecules and ions dissolved in water are in constant random motion. This random motion causes a net movement of these substances from regions of high concentration to regions of lower concentration, a process called **diffusion** (figure 5.9).

Net movement driven by diffusion will continue until the concentration is the same in all regions. Consider what happens when you add a drop of colored ink to a bowl of water. Over time the ink becomes dispersed throughout the solution. This is due to diffusion of the ink molecules. In the context of cells, we are usually concerned with differences in concentration of molecules across the plasma membrane. We need to consider the relative concentrations both inside and outside the cell, as well as how readily a molecule can cross the membrane.

Figure 5.9 Diffusion. If a drop of colored ink is dropped into a beaker of water (*a*) its molecules dissolve (*b*) and diffuse (*c*). Eventually, diffusion results in an even distribution of ink molecules throughout the water (*d*).

The major barrier to crossing a biological membrane is the hydrophobic interior that repels polar molecules but not nonpolar molecules. If a concentration difference exists for a nonpolar molecule, it will move across the membrane until the concentration is equal on both sides. At this point, movement in both directions still occurs, but there is no net change in either direction. This includes molecules like O_2 and nonpolar organic molecules such as steroid hormones.

The plasma membrane has limited permeability to small polar molecules and very limited permeability to larger polar molecules and ions. The movement of water, one of the most important polar molecules, is discussed in its own section later on.

Proteins allow membrane diffusion to be selective

Many important molecules required by cells cannot easily cross the plasma membrane. These molecules can still enter the cell by diffusion through specific channel proteins or carrier proteins embedded in the plasma membrane, provided there is a higher concentration of the molecule outside the cell than inside. We call this process of diffusion mediated by a membrane protein **facilitated diffusion. Channel proteins** have a hydrophilic interior that provides an aqueous channel through which polar molecules can pass when the channel is open. **Carrier proteins,** in contrast to channels, bind specifically to the molecule they assist, much like an enzyme binds to its substrate. These channels and carriers are usually selective for one type of molecule, and thus the cell membrane is said to be **selectively permeable.**

Facilitated diffusion of ions through channels

You saw in chapter 2 that atoms with an unequal number of protons and electrons have an electric charge and are called ions. Those that carry a positive charge are called *cations* and those that carry a negative charge are called *anions*.

Because of their charge, ions interact well with polar molecules such as water, but are repelled by nonpolar molecules such as the interior of the plasma membrane. Therefore, ions cannot move between the cytoplasm of a cell and the extracellular fluid without the assistance of membrane transport proteins.

Ion channels possess a hydrated interior that spans the membrane. Ions can diffuse through the channel in either direction, depending on their relative concentration across the membrane (figure 5.10). Some channel proteins can be opened or closed in response to a stimulus. These channels are called *gated channels,* and depending on the nature of the channel, the stimulus can be either chemical or electrical.

Three conditions determine the direction of net movement of the ions: (1) their relative concentrations on either side of the membrane, (2) the voltage difference across the membrane and for the gated channels, and (3) the state of the gate (open or

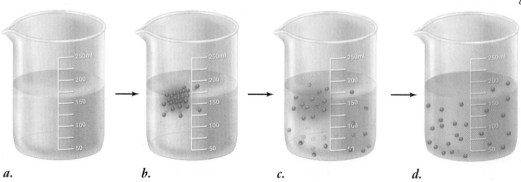

a.   b.   c.   d.

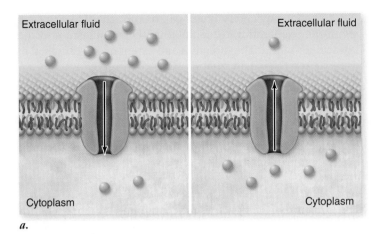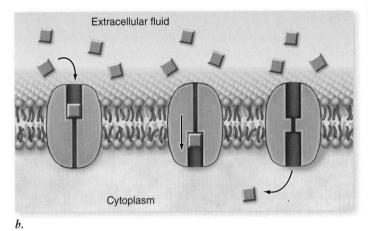

a.   *b.*

Figure 5.10 Facilitated diffusion. Diffusion can be facilitated by membrane proteins. *a.* The movement of ions through a channel is shown. On the left the concentration is higher outside the cell, so the ions move into the cell. On the right the situation is reversed. In both cases, transport continues until the concentration is equal on both sides of the membrane. At this point, ions continue to cross the membrane in both directions, but there is no net movement in either direction. *b.* Carrier proteins bind specifically to the molecules they transport. In this case, the concentration is higher outside the cell, so molecules bind to the carrier on the outside. The carrier's shape changes, allowing the molecule to cross the membrane. This is reversible, so net movement continues until the concentration is equal on both sides of the membrane.

closed). A voltage difference is an electrical potential difference across the membrane called a *membrane potential.* Changes in membrane potential form the basis for transmission of signals in the nervous system and some other tissues. (We discuss this topic in detail in chapter 43.) Each type of channel is specific for a particular ion, such as calcium (Ca^{2+}), sodium (Na^+), potassium (K^+), or chloride (Cl^-), or in some cases, for more than one cation or anion. Ion channels play an essential role in signaling by the nervous system.

Facilitated diffusion by carrier proteins

Carrier proteins can help transport both ions and other solutes, such as some sugars and amino acids, across the membrane. Transport through a carrier is still a form of diffusion and therefore requires a concentration difference across the membrane.

Carriers must bind to the molecule they transport, so the relationship between concentration and rate of transport differs from that due to simple diffusion. As concentration increases, transport by simple diffusion shows a linear increase in rate of transport. But when a carrier protein is involved, a concentration increase means that more of the carriers are bound to the transported molecule. At high enough concentrations all carriers will be occupied, and the rate of transport will be constant. This means that the carrier exhibits *saturation.*

This situation is somewhat like that of a stadium (the cell) where a crowd must pass through turnstiles to enter. If there are unoccupied turnstiles, you can go right through, but when all are occupied, you must wait. When ticket holders are passing through the gates at maximum speed, the rate at which they enter cannot increase, no matter how many are waiting outside.

Facilitated diffusion in red blood cells

Several examples of facilitated diffusion can be found in the plasma membrane of vertebrate red blood cells (RBCs). One RBC carrier protein, for example, transports a different molecule in each direction: chloride ion (Cl^-) in one direction and bicarbonate ion (HCO_3^-) in the opposite direction. As you will

learn in chapter 48, this carrier is important in the uptake and release of carbon dioxide.

The glucose transporter is a second vital facilitated diffusion carrier in RBCs. Red blood cells keep their internal concentration of glucose low through a chemical trick: They immediately add a phosphate group to any entering glucose molecule, converting it to a highly charged glucose phosphate that can no longer bind to the glucose transporter, and therefore cannot pass back across the membrane. This maintains a steep concentration gradient for unphosphorylated glucose, favoring its entry into the cell.

The glucose transporter that assists the entry of glucose into the cell does not appear to form a channel in the membrane. Instead, this transmembrane protein appears to bind to a glucose molecule and then to flip its shape, dragging the glucose through the bilayer and releasing it on the inside of the plasma membrane. After it releases the glucose, the transporter reverts to its original shape and is then available to bind the next glucose molecule that comes along outside the cell.

Osmosis is the movement of water across membranes

The cytoplasm of a cell contains ions and molecules, such as sugars and amino acids, dissolved in water. The mixture of these substances and water is called an *aqueous solution.* Water is termed the **solvent,** and the substances dissolved in the water are **solutes.** Both water and solutes tend to diffuse from regions of high concentration to ones of low concentration; that is, they diffuse down their concentration gradients.

When two regions are separated by a membrane, what happens depends on whether the solutes can pass freely through that membrane. Most solutes, including ions and sugars, are not lipid-soluble and, therefore, are unable to cross the lipid bilayer. The concentration gradient of these solutes can lead to the movement of water.

Osmosis

Water molecules interact with dissolved solutes by forming hydration shells around the charged solute molecules. When a membrane separates two solutions with different concentrations of solutes, the concentrations of *free* water molecules on the two sides of the membrane also differ. The side with higher solute concentration has tied up more water molecules in hydration shells and thus has fewer free water molecules.

As a consequence of this difference, free water molecules move down their concentration gradient, toward the higher solute concentration. This net diffusion of water across a membrane toward a higher solute concentration is called **osmosis** (figure 5.11).

The concentration of *all* solutes in a solution determines the **osmotic concentration** of the solution. If two solutions have unequal osmotic concentrations, the solution with the higher concentration is **hypertonic** (Greek *hyper,* "more than"), and the solution with the lower concentration is **hypotonic** (Greek *hypo,* "less than"). When two solutions have the same osmotic concentration, the solutions are **isotonic** (Greek *iso,* "equal"). The terms *hyperosmotic, hypoosmotic,* and *isosmotic* are also used to describe these conditions.

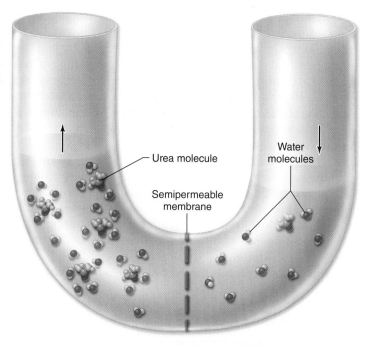

Figure 5.11 Osmosis. Concentration differences in charged or polar molecules that cannot cross a semipermeable membrane result in movement of water, which can cross the membrane. Water molecules form hydrogen bonds with charged or polar molecules creating a hydration shell around them in solution. A higher concentration of polar molecules (urea) shown on the left side of the membrane leads to water molecules gathering around each urea molecule. These water molecules are no longer free to diffuse across the membrane. The polar solute has reduced the concentration of free water molecules, creating a gradient. This causes a net movement of water by diffusion from right to left in the U-tube, raising the level on the left and lowering the level on the right.

A cell in any environment can be thought of as a plasma membrane separating two solutions: the cytoplasm and the extracellular fluid. The direction and extent of any diffusion of water across the plasma membrane is determined by comparing the osmotic strength of these solutions. Put another way, water diffuses out of a cell in a hypertonic solution (that is, the cytoplasm of the cell is hypotonic, compared with the extracellular fluid). This loss of water causes the cell to shrink until the osmotic concentrations of the cytoplasm and the extracellular fluid become equal.

Aquaporins: Water channels

The transport of water across the membrane is complex. Studies on artificial membranes show that water, despite its polarity, can cross the membrane, but this flow is limited. Water flow in living cells is facilitated by **aquaporins,** which are specialized channels for water.

A simple experiment demonstrates this. If an amphibian egg is placed in hypotonic spring water (the solute concentration in the cell is higher than that of the surrounding water), it does not swell. If aquaporin mRNA is then injected into the egg, the channel proteins are expressed and appear in the egg's plasma membrane. Water can now diffuse into the egg, causing it to swell.

More than 11 different kinds of aquaporins have been found in mammals. These fall into two general classes: those that are specific for only water, and those that allow other small hydrophilic molecules, such as glycerol or urea, to cross the membrane as well. This latter class explains how some membranes allow the easy passage of small hydrophilic substances.

The human genetic disease, hereditary (nephrogenic) diabetes insipidus (NDI), has been shown to be caused by a nonfunctional aquaporin protein. This disease causes the excretion of large volumes of dilute urine, illustrating the importance of aquaporins to our physiology.

Osmotic pressure

What happens to a cell in a hypotonic solution? (That is, the cell's cytoplasm is hypertonic relative to the extracellular fluid.) In this situation, water diffuses into the cell from the extracellular fluid, causing the cell to swell. The pressure of the cytoplasm pushing out against the cell membrane, or hydrostatic pressure, increases. The amount of water that enters the cell depends on the difference in solute concentration between the cell and the extracellular fluid. This is measured as **osmotic pressure,** defined as the force needed to stop osmotic flow.

If the membrane is strong enough, the cell reaches an equilibrium, at which the osmotic pressure, which tends to drive water into the cell, is exactly counterbalanced by the hydrostatic pressure, which tends to drive water back out of the cell. However, a plasma membrane by itself cannot withstand large internal pressures, and an isolated cell under such conditions would burst like an overinflated balloon (figure 5.12).

Accordingly, it is important for animal cells, which only have plasma membranes, to maintain osmotic balance. In contrast, the cells of prokaryotes, fungi, plants, and many protists are surrounded by strong cell walls, which can withstand high internal pressures without bursting.

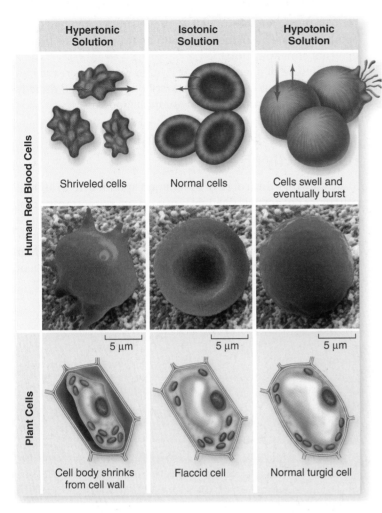

Hypertonic Solution	Isotonic Solution	Hypotonic Solution

Human Red Blood Cells

Shriveled cells | Normal cells | Cells swell and eventually burst

5 µm | 5 µm | 5 µm

Plant Cells

Cell body shrinks from cell wall | Flaccid cell | Normal turgid cell

Figure 5.12 How solutes create osmotic pressure. In a hypertonic solution, water moves out of the cell, causing the cell to shrivel. In an isotonic solution, water diffuses into and out of the cell at the same rate, with no change in cell size. In a hypotonic solution, water moves into the cell. Direction and amount of water movement is shown with blue arrows *(top)*. As water enters the cell from a hypotonic solution, pressure is applied to the plasma membrane until the cell ruptures. Water enters the cell due to osmotic pressure from the higher solute concentration in the cell. Osmotic pressure is measured as the force needed to stop osmosis. The strong cell wall of plant cells can withstand the hydrostatic pressure to keep the cell from rupturing. This is not the case with animal cells.

Maintaining osmotic balance

Organisms have developed many strategies for solving the dilemma posed by being hypertonic to their environment and therefore having a steady influx of water by osmosis.

Extrusion. Some single-celled eukaryotes, such as the protist *Paramecium,* use organelles called contractile vacuoles to remove water. Each vacuole collects water from various parts of the cytoplasm and transports it to the central part of the vacuole, near the cell surface. The vacuole possesses a small pore that opens to the outside of the cell. By contracting rhythmically, the vacuole pumps out

(extrudes) through this pore the water that is continuously drawn into the cell by osmotic forces.

Isosmotic Regulation. Some organisms that live in the ocean adjust their internal concentration of solutes to match that of the surrounding seawater. Because they are isosmotic with respect to their environment, no net flow of water occurs into or out of these cells.

Many terrestrial animals solve the problem in a similar way, by circulating a fluid through their bodies that bathes cells in an isotonic solution. The blood in your body, for example, contains a high concentration of the protein albumin, which elevates the solute concentration of the blood to match that of your cells' cytoplasm.

Turgor. Most plant cells are hypertonic to their immediate environment, containing a high concentration of solutes in their central vacuoles. The resulting internal hydrostatic pressure, known as **turgor pressure,** presses the plasma membrane firmly against the interior of the cell wall, making the cell rigid. Most green plants depend on turgor pressure to maintain their shape, and thus they wilt when they lack sufficient water.

Learning Outcomes Review 5.4

Passive transport involves diffusion, which requires a concentration gradient. Hydrophobic molecules can diffuse directly through the membrane (simple diffusion). Polar molecules and ions can also diffuse through the membrane, but only with the aid of a channel or carrier protein (facilitated diffusion). Channel proteins assist by forming a hydrophilic passageway through the membrane, whereas carrier proteins bind to the molecule they assist. Water passes through the membrane and through aquaporins in response to solute concentration differences inside and outside the cell. This process is called osmosis.

- *If you require intravenous (IV) medication in the hospital, what should the concentration of solutes in the IV solution be relative to your blood cells?*

5.5 Active Transport Across Membranes

Learning Outcomes

1. *Differentiate between active transport and diffusion.*
2. *Describe the function of the Na⁺/K⁺ pump.*
3. *Explain the energetics of coupled transport.*

Diffusion, facilitated diffusion, and osmosis are passive transport processes that move materials down their concentration gradients, but cells can also actively move substances across a cell membrane *up* their concentration gradients. This process requires the expenditure of energy, typically from ATP, and is therefore called **active transport.**

Active transport uses energy to move materials against a concentration gradient

Like facilitated diffusion, active transport involves highly selective protein carriers within the membrane that bind to the transported substance, which could be an ion or a simple molecule, such as a sugar, an amino acid, or a nucleotide. These carrier proteins are called **uniporters** if they transport a single type of molecule and symporters or antiporters if they transport two different molecules together. **Symporters** transport two molecules in the same direction, and **antiporters** transport two molecules in opposite directions. These terms can also be used to describe facilitated diffusion carriers.

Active transport is one of the most important functions of any cell. It enables a cell to take up additional molecules of a substance that is already present in its cytoplasm in concentrations higher than in the extracellular fluid. Active transport also enables a cell to move substances out of its cytoplasm and into the extracellular fluid, despite higher external concentrations.

The use of energy from ATP in active transport may be direct or indirect. Let's first consider how ATP is used directly to move ions against their concentration gradients.

The sodium–potassium pump runs directly on ATP

More than one-third of all of the energy expended by an animal cell that is not actively dividing is used in the active transport of sodium (Na^+) and potassium (K^+) ions. Most animal cells have a low internal concentration of Na^+, relative to their surroundings, and a high internal concentration of K^+. They maintain these concentration differences by actively pumping Na^+ out of the cell and K^+ in.

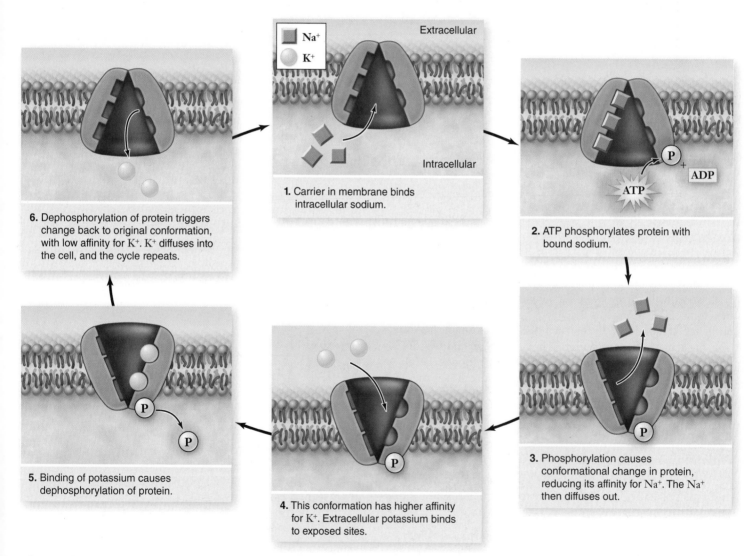

Figure 5.13 The sodium–potassium pump. The protein carrier known as the sodium–potassium pump transports sodium (Na^+) and potassium (K^+) across the plasma membrane. For every three Na^+ transported out of the cell, two K^+ are transported into it. The sodium–potassium pump is fueled by ATP hydrolysis. The affinity of the pump for Na^+ and K^+ is changed by adding or removing phosphate (P), which changes the conformation of the protein.

The remarkable protein that transports these two ions across the cell membrane is known as the **sodium–potassium pump** (Na+/K+ pump) (figure 5.13). This carrier protein uses the energy stored in ATP to move these two ions. In this case, the energy is used to change the conformation of the carrier protein, which changes its affinity for either Na+ ions or K+ ions. This is an excellent illustration of how subtle changes in the structure of a protein affect its function.

The important characteristic of the Na+/K+ pump is that it is an active transport mechanism, transporting Na+ and K+ from areas of low concentration to areas of high concentration. This transport is the opposite of passive transport by diffusion; it is achieved only by the constant expenditure of metabolic energy. The Na+/K+ pump works through the following series of conformational changes in the transmembrane protein (summarized in figure 5.13):

Step 1. Three Na+ bind to the cytoplasmic side of the protein, causing the protein to change its conformation.

Step 2. In its new conformation, the protein binds a molecule of ATP and cleaves it into adenosine diphosphate (ADP) and phosphate (P$_i$). ADP is released, but the phosphate group is covalently linked to the protein. The protein is now phosphorylated.

Step 3. The phosphorylation of the protein induces a second conformational change in the protein. This change translocates the three Na+ across the membrane, so they now face the exterior. In this new conformation, the protein has a low affinity for Na+, and the three bound Na+ break away from the protein and diffuse into the extracellular fluid.

Step 4. The new conformation has a high affinity for K+, two of which bind to the extracellular side of the protein as soon as it is free of the Na+.

Step 5. The binding of the K+ causes another conformational change in the protein, this time resulting in the hydrolysis of the bound phosphate group.

Step 6. Freed of the phosphate group, the protein reverts to its original shape, exposing the two K+ to the cytoplasm. This conformation has a low affinity for K+, so the two bound K+ dissociate from the protein and diffuse into the interior of the cell. The original conformation has a high affinity for Na+. When these ions bind, they initiate another cycle.

In every cycle, three Na+ leave the cell and two K+ enter. The changes in protein conformation that occur during the cycle are rapid, enabling each carrier to transport as many as 300 Na+ per second. The Na+/K+ pump appears to exist in all animal cells, although cells vary widely in the number of pump proteins they contain.

Coupled transport uses ATP indirectly

Some molecules are moved against their concentration gradient by using the energy stored in a gradient of a different molecule. In this process, called *coupled transport,* the energy released as one molecule moves down its concentration gradient is captured and used to move a different molecule against its gradient. As you just saw, the energy stored in ATP molecules can be used to create a gradient of Na+ and K+ across the membrane. These gradients can then be used to power the transport of other molecules across the membrane.

As one example, let's consider the active transport of glucose across the membrane in animal cells. Glucose is such an important molecule that there are a variety of transporters for it, one of which was discussed earlier under passive transport. In a multicellular organism, intestinal epithelial cells can have a higher concentration of glucose inside the cell than outside, so these cells need to be able to transport glucose against its concentration gradient. This requires energy and a different transporter than the one involved in facilitated diffusion of glucose.

The active glucose transporter uses the Na+ gradient produced by the Na+/K+ pump as a source of energy to power the movement of glucose into the cell. In this system, both glucose and Na+ bind to the transport protein, which allows Na+ to pass into the cell down its concentration gradient, capturing the energy and using it to move glucose into the cell. In this kind of cotransport, both molecules are moving in the same direction across the membrane; therefore the transporter is a symporter (figure 5.14).

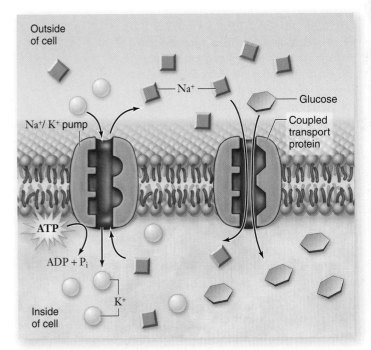

Figure 5.14 Coupled transport. A membrane protein transports Na+ into the cell, down its concentration gradient, at the same time it transports a glucose molecule into the cell. The gradient driving the Na+ entry allows sugar molecules to be transported against their concentration gradient. The Na+ gradient is maintained by the Na+/K+ pump. ADP = adenosine diphosphate; ATP = adenosine triphosphate; P$_i$ = inorganic phosphate

In a related process, called *countertransport,* the inward movement of Na⁺ is coupled with the outward movement of another substance, such as Ca²⁺ or H⁺. As in cotransport, both Na⁺ and the other substance bind to the same transport protein, which in this case is an antiporter, as the substances bind on opposite sides of the membrane and are moved in opposite directions. In countertransport, the cell uses the energy released as Na⁺ moves down its concentration gradient into the cell to eject a substance against its concentration gradient. In both cotransport and countertransport, the potential energy in the concentration gradient of one molecule is used to transport another molecule against its concentration gradient. They differ only in the direction that the second molecule moves relative to the first.

Learning Outcomes Review 5.5

Active transport requires both a carrier protein and energy, usually in the form of ATP, to move molecules against a concentration gradient. The Na⁺/K⁺ pump uses ATP to moved Na⁺ in one direction and K⁺ in the other to create and maintain concentration differences of these ions. In coupled transport, a favorable concentration gradient of one molecule is used to move a different molecule against its gradient, such as in the transport of glucose by Na⁺.

■ *Can active transport involve a channel protein? Why or why not?*

Bulk Transport by Endocytosis and Exocytosis

Learning Outcomes

1. Distinguish between endocytosis and exocytosis.
2. Illustrate how endocytosis can be specific.

The lipid nature of cell plasma membranes raises a second problem. The substances cells require for growth are mostly large, polar molecules that cannot cross the hydrophobic barrier a lipid bilayer creates. How do these substances get into cells? Two processes are involved in this **bulk transport:** *endocytosis* and *exocytosis.*

Bulk material enters the cell in vesicles

In **endocytosis,** the plasma membrane envelops food particles and fluids. Cells use three major types of endocytosis: phagocytosis, pinocytosis, and receptor-mediated endocytosis (figure 5.15). Like active transport, these processes also require energy expenditure.

Figure 5.15 Endocytosis. Both *(a)* phagocytosis and *(b)* pinocytosis are forms of endocytosis. *c.* In receptor-mediated endocytosis, cells have pits coated with the protein clathrin that initiate endocytosis when target molecules bind to receptor proteins in the plasma membrane. Photo inserts (false color has been added to enhance distinction of structures): *(a)* A TEM of phagocytosis of a bacterium, *Rickettsia tsutsugamushi,* by a mouse peritoneal mesothelial cell. The bacterium enters the host cell by phagocytosis and replicates in the cytoplasm. *(b)* A TEM of pinocytosis in a smooth muscle cell. *(c)* A coated pit appears in the plasma membrane of a developing egg cell, covered with a layer of proteins. When an appropriate collection of molecules gathers in the coated pit, the pit deepens and will eventually seal off to form a vesicle.

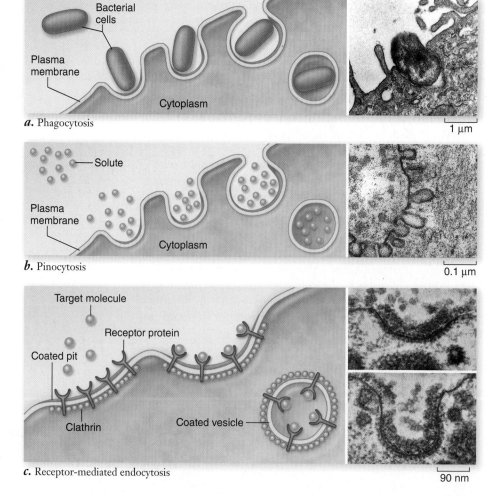

a. Phagocytosis — 1 μm

b. Pinocytosis — 0.1 μm

c. Receptor-mediated endocytosis — 90 nm

Phagocytosis and pinocytosis

If the material the cell takes in is particulate (made up of discrete particles), such as an organism or some other fragment of organic matter (figure 5.15*a*), the process is called **phagocytosis** (Greek *phagein,* "to eat," + *cytos,* "cell"). If the material the cell takes in is liquid (figure 5.15*b*), the process is called **pinocytosis** (Greek *pinein,* "to drink"). Pinocytosis is common among animal cells. Mammalian egg cells, for example, "nurse" from surrounding cells; the nearby cells secrete nutrients that the maturing egg cell takes up by pinocytosis.

Virtually all eukaryotic cells constantly carry out these kinds of endocytotic processes, trapping particles and extracellular fluid in vesicles and ingesting them. Endocytosis rates vary from one cell type to another. They can be surprisingly high; some types of white blood cells ingest up to 25% of their cell volume each hour.

Receptor-mediated endocytosis

Molecules are often transported into eukaryotic cells through **receptor-mediated endocytosis.** These molecules first bind to specific receptors in the plasma membrane—they have a conformation that fits snugly into the receptor. Different cell types contain a characteristic battery of receptor types, each for a different kind of molecule in their membranes.

The portion of the receptor molecule that lies inside the membrane is trapped in an indented pit coated on the cytoplasmic side with the protein *clathrin.* Each pit acts like a molecular mousetrap, closing over to form an internal vesicle when the right molecule enters the pit (figure 5.15*c*). The trigger that releases the trap is the binding of the properly fitted target molecule to the embedded receptor. When binding occurs, the cell reacts by initiating endocytosis; the process is highly specific and very fast. The vesicle is now inside the cell carrying its cargo.

One type of molecule that is taken up by receptor-mediated endocytosis is low-density lipoprotein (LDL). LDL molecules bring cholesterol into the cell where it can be incorporated into membranes. Cholesterol plays a key role in determining the stiffness of the body's membranes. In the human genetic disease familial hypercholesterolemia, the LDL receptors lack tails, so they are never fastened in the clathrin-coated pits and as a result, do not trigger vesicle formation. The cholesterol stays in the bloodstream of affected individuals, accumulating as plaques inside arteries and leading to heart attacks.

It is important to understand that endocytosis in itself does not bring substances directly into the cytoplasm of a cell. The material taken in is still separated from the cytoplasm by the membrane of the vesicle.

Material can leave the cell by exocytosis

The reverse of endocytosis is **exocytosis**, the discharge of material from vesicles at the cell surface (figure 5.16). In plant cells, exocytosis is an important means of exporting the materials needed to construct the cell wall through the plasma membrane. Among protists, contractile vacuole discharge is considered a form of exocytosis. In animal cells, exocytosis provides a mechanism for secreting many hormones, neurotransmitters, digestive enzymes, and other substances.

The mechanisms for transport across cell membranes are summarized in table 5.2.

Learning Outcomes Review 5.6

Large molecules and other bulky materials can enter a cell by endocytosis and leave the cell by exocytosis. These processes require energy. Endocytosis may be mediated by specific receptor proteins in the membrane that trigger the formation of vesicles.

■ *What feature unites transport by receptor-mediated endocytosis, transport by a carrier, and catalysis by an enzyme?*

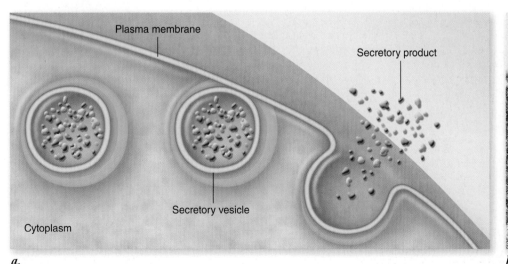
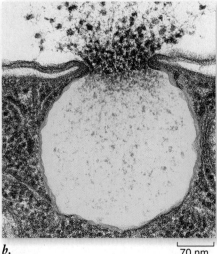

Figure 5.16 Exocytosis. *a.* Proteins and other molecules are secreted from cells in small packets called vesicles, whose membranes fuse with the plasma membrane, releasing their contents outside the cell. *b.* A false-colored transmission electron micrograph showing exocytosis.

TABLE 5.2   Mechanisms for Transport Across Cell Membranes

Process		How It Works	Example
PASSIVE PROCESSES			
Diffusion			
Direct		Random molecular motion produces net migration of nonpolar molecules toward region of lower concentration	Movement of oxygen into cells
Facilitated Diffusion			
Protein channel		Polar molecules or ions move through a protein channel; net movement is toward region of lower concentration	Movement of ions in or out of cell
Protein carrier		Molecule binds to carrier protein in membrane and is transported across; net movement is toward region of lower concentration	Movement of glucose into cells
Osmosis			
Aquaporins		Diffusion of water across the membrane via osmosis; requires osmotic gradient	Movement of water into cells placed in a hypotonic solution
ACTIVE PROCESSES			
Active Transport			
Protein carrier			
Na^+/K^+ pump		Carrier uses energy to move a substance across a membrane against its concentration gradient	Na^+ and K^+ against their concentration gradients
Coupled transport		Molecules are transported across a membrane against their concentration gradients by the cotransport of sodium ions or protons down their concentration gradients	Coupled uptake of glucose into cells against its concentration gradient using a Na^+ gradient
Endocytosis			
Membrane vesicle			
Phagocytosis		Particle is engulfed by membrane, which folds around it and forms a vesicle	Ingestion of bacteria by white blood cells
Pinocytosis		Fluid droplets are engulfed by membrane, which forms vesicles around them	"Nursing" of human egg cells
Receptor-mediated endocytosis		Endocytosis triggered by a specific receptor, forming clathrin-coated vesicles	Cholesterol uptake
Exocytosis			
Membrane vesicle		Vesicles fuse with plasma membrane and eject contents	Secretion of mucus; release of neurotransmitters

5.1 The Structure of Membranes

The fluid mosaic model shows proteins embedded in a fluid lipid bilayer.

Membranes are sheets of phospholipid bilayers with associated proteins (figure 5.3). Hydrophobic regions of a membrane are oriented inward and hydrophilic regions oriented outward. In the fluid mosaic model, proteins float on or in the lipid bilayer.

Cellular membranes consist of four component groups.

In eukaryotic cells, membranes have four components: a phospholipid bilayer, transmembrane proteins (integral membrane proteins), an interior protein network, and cell-surface markers. The interior protein network is composed of cytoskeletal filaments and peripheral membrane proteins, which are associated with the membrane but are not an integral part. Membranes contain glycoproteins and glycolipids on the surface that act as cell identity markers.

Cellular membranes have an organized substructure

Cholesterol and sphingolipid can associate to form microdomains. The two leaflets of the plasma membrane are also not identical.

Electron microscopy has provided structural evidence.

Transmission electron microscopy (TEM) and scanning electron microscopy (SEM) have confirmed the structure predicted by the fluid mosaic model.

5.2 Phospholipids: The Membrane's Foundation

Phospholipids are composed of two fatty acids and a phosphate group linked to a three-carbon glycerol molecule.

Phospholipids spontaneously form bilayers.

The phosphate group of a phospholipid is polar and hydrophilic; the fatty acids are nonpolar and hydrophobic, and they orient away from the polar head of the phospholipids. The nonpolar interior of the lipid bilayer impedes the passage of water and water-soluble substances.

The phospholipid bilayer is fluid.

Hydrogen bonding of water keeps the membrane in its bilayer configuration; however, phospholipids and unanchored proteins in the membrane are loosely associated and can diffuse laterally.

Membrane fluidity can change.

Membrane fluidity depends on the fatty acid composition of the membrane. Unsaturated fats tend to make the membrane more fluid because of the "kinks" of double bonds in the fatty acid tails. Temperature also affects fluidity. Some bacteria have enzymes that alter the fatty acids of the membrane to compensate for temperature changes.

5.3 Proteins: Multifunctional Components

Proteins and protein complexes perform key functions.

Transporters are integral membrane proteins that carry specific substances through the membrane. Enzymes often occur on the interior surface of the membrane. Cell-surface receptors respond to external chemical messages and change conditions inside the cell; cell identity markers on the surface allow recognition of the body's cells as "self." Cell-to-cell adhesion proteins glue cells together; surface proteins that interact with other cells anchor to the cytoskeleton.

Structural features of membrane proteins relate to function.

Surface proteins are attached to the surface by nonpolar regions that associate with polar regions of phospholipids. Transmembrane proteins may cross the bilayer a number of times, and each membrane-spanning region is called a transmembrane domain. Such a domain is composed of hydrophobic amino acids usually arranged in α helices. In certain proteins, β-pleated sheets in the nonpolar region form a pipelike passageway having a polar environment. An example is the porin class of proteins.

5.4 Passive Transport Across Membranes

Transport can occur by simple diffusion.

Simple diffusion is the passive movement of a substance along a chemical or electrical gradient. Biological membranes pose a barrier to hydrophilic polar molecules, while they allow hydrophobic substances to diffuse freely.

Proteins allow membrane diffusion to be selective.

Ions and large hydrophilic molecules cannot cross the phospholipid bilayer. Diffusion can still occur with the help of proteins, thus we call this facilitated diffusion. These proteins can be either channels, or carriers. Channels allow the diffusion of ions based on concentration and charge across the membrane. They are specific for different ions, but form an aqueous pore in the membrane. Carrier proteins bind to the molecules they transport, much like an enzyme. The rate of transport by a carrier is limited by the number of carriers in the membrane.

Osmosis is the movement of water across membranes.

The direction of movement due to osmosis depends on the solute concentration on either side of the membrane (figure 5.12). Solutions can be isotonic, hypotonic, or hypertonic. Cells in an isotonic solution are in osmotic balance; cells in a hypotonic solution will gain water; and cells in a hypertonic solution will lose water. Aquaporins are water channels that facilitate the diffusion of water.

5.5 Active Transport Across Membranes

Active transport uses energy to move materials against a concentration gradient.

Active transport uses specialized protein carriers that couple a source of energy to transport. They are classified based on the number of molecules and direction of transport. Uniporters transport a specific molecule in one direction; symporters transport two molecules in the same direction; and antiporters transport two molecules in opposite directions.

The sodium–potassium pump runs directly on ATP.

The sodium–potassium pump moves Na^+ out of the cell and K^+ into the cell against their concentration gradients using ATP. In every cycle of the pump, three Na^+ leave the cell and two K^+ enter it. This pump appears to be almost universal in animal cells.

Coupled transport uses ATP indirectly.

Coupled transport occurs when the energy released by a diffusing molecule is used to transport a different molecule against its concentration gradient in the same direction. Countertransport is similar to coupled transport, but the two molecules move in opposite directions.

5.6 Bulk Transport by Endocytosis and Exocytosis

Bulk transport moves large quantities of substances that cannot pass through the cell membrane.

Bulk material enters the cell in vesicles.

In endocytosis, the cell membrane surrounds material and pinches off to form a vesicle. In receptor-mediated endocytosis, specific molecules bind to receptors on the cell membrane.

Material can leave the cell by exocytosis.

In exocytosis, material in a vesicle is discharged when the vesicle fuses with the membrane.

UNDERSTAND

1. The fluid mosaic model of the membrane describes the membrane as
   a. containing a significant quantity of water in the interior.
   b. composed of fluid phospholipids on the outside and protein on the inside.
   c. composed of protein on the outside and fluid phospholipids on the inside.
   d. made of proteins and lipids that can freely move.

2. What chemical property characterizes the interior of the phospholipid bilayer?
   a. It is hydrophobic.
   b. It is hydrophilic.
   c. It is polar.
   d. It is saturated.

3. The transmembrane domain of an integral membrane protein
   a. is composed of hydrophobic amino acids.
   b. often forms an α-helical structure.
   c. can cross the membrane multiple times.
   d. All of the choices are correct.

4. The specific function of a membrane within a cell is determined by the
   a. degree of saturation of the fatty acids within the phospholipid bilayer.
   b. location of the membrane within the cell.
   c. presence of lipid rafts and cholesterol.
   d. type and number of membrane proteins.

5. The movement of water across a membrane is dependent on
   a. the solvent concentration.
   b. the solute concentration.
   c. the presence of carrier proteins.
   d. membrane potential.

6. If a cell is in an isotonic environment, then
   a. the cell will gain water and burst.
   b. no water will move across the membrane.
   c. the cell will lose water and shrink.
   d. osmosis still occurs, but there is no net gain or loss of cell volume.

7. Which of the following is NOT a mechanism for bringing material into a cell?
   a. Exocytosis
   b. Endocytosis
   c. Pinocytosis
   d. Phagocytosis

APPLY

1. A bacterial cell that can alter the composition of saturated and unsaturated fatty acids in its membrane lipids is adapted to a cold environment. If this cell is shifted to a warmer environment, it will react by
   a. increasing the amount of cholesterol in its membrane.
   b. altering the amount of protein present in the membrane.
   c. increasing the degree of saturated fatty acids in its membrane.
   d. increasing the percentage of unsaturated fatty acids in its membrane.

2. What variable(s) influence(s) whether a nonpolar molecule can move across a membrane by passive diffusion?
   a. The structure of the phospholipids bilayer
   b. The difference in concentration of the molecule across the membrane

c. The presence of transport proteins in the membrane
   d. All of the choices are correct.

3. Which of the following does NOT contribute to the selective permeability of a biological membrane?
   a. Specificity of the carrier proteins in the membrane
   b. Selectivity of channel proteins in the membrane
   c. Hydrophobic barrier of the phospholipid bilayer
   d. Hydrogen bond formation between water and phosphate groups

4. How are *active* transport and *coupled* transport related?
   a. They both use ATP to move molecules.
   b. Active transport establishes a concentration gradient, but coupled transport doesn't.
   c. Coupled transport uses the concentration gradient established by active transport.
   d. Active transport moves one molecule, but coupled transport moves two.

5. A cell can use the process of facilitated diffusion to
   a. concentrate a molecule such as glucose inside a cell.
   b. remove all of a toxic molecule from a cell.
   c. move ions or large polar molecules across the membrane regardless of concentration.
   d. move ions or large polar molecules from a region of high concentration to a region of low concentration.

SYNTHESIZE

1. Figure 5.5 describes a classic experiment demonstrating the ability of proteins to move within the plane of the cell's plasma membrane. The following table outlines three different experiments using the fusion of labeled mouse and human cells.

Experiment	Conditions	Temperature (°C)	Result
1	Fuse human and mouse cells	37	Intermixed membrane proteins
2	Fuse human and mouse cells in presence of ATP inhibitors	37	Intermixed membrane proteins
3	Fuse human and mouse cells	4	No intermixing of membrane proteins

What conclusions can you reach about the movement of these proteins?

2. Each compartment of the endomembrane system of a cell is connected to the plasma membrane. Create a simple diagram of a cell including the RER, Golgi apparatus, vesicle, and the plasma membrane. Starting with the RER, use two different colors to represent the inner and outer halves of the bilayer for each of these membranes. What do you observe?

3. The distribution of lipids in the ER membrane is symmetric, that is, it is the same in both leaflets of the membrane. The Golgi apparatus and plasma membrane do not have symmetric distribution of membrane lipids. What kinds of processes could achieve this outcome?

ONLINE RESOURCE

www.ravenbiology.com

Understand, Apply, and Synthesize—enhance your study with animations that bring concepts to life and practice tests to assess your understanding. Your instructor may also recommend the interactive eBook, individualized learning tools, and more.

Chapter 6

Energy and Metabolism

Chapter Contents

Introduction

Life can be viewed as a constant flow of energy, channeled by organisms to do the work of living. Each of the significant properties by which we define life—order, growth, reproduction, responsiveness, and internal regulation—requires a constant supply of energy. Both the lion and the giraffe need to eat to provide energy for a wide variety of cellular functions. Deprived of a source of energy, life stops. Therefore, a comprehensive study of life would be impossible without discussing bioenergetics, *the analysis of how energy powers the activities of living systems. In this chapter, we focus on energy—what it is and how it changes during chemical reactions.*

6.1 The Flow of Energy in Living Systems

Learning Outcomes

1. Differentiate between kinetic and potential energy.
2. Identify the source of energy for the biosphere.
3. Contrast oxidation and reduction reactions.

Thermodynamics is the branch of chemistry concerned with energy changes. Cells are governed by the laws of physics and chemistry, so we must understand these laws in order to understand how cells function.

Energy can take many forms

Energy is defined as the capacity to do work. We think of energy as existing in two states: kinetic energy and potential energy (figure 6.1). **Kinetic energy** is the energy of motion. Moving objects perform work by causing other matter to move. **Potential energy** is stored energy. Objects that are not actively moving but have the capacity to do so possess potential energy. A boulder perched on a hilltop has gravitational potential energy. As it begins to roll downhill, some of its potential energy is converted into kinetic energy. Much of the work that living organisms carry out involves transforming potential energy into kinetic energy.

Energy can take many forms: mechanical energy, heat, sound, electric current, light, or radioactivity. Because it can exist in so many forms, energy can be measured in many ways. Heat is the most convenient way of measuring energy because all other forms of energy can be converted into heat. In fact, the term *thermodynamics* means "heat changes."

The unit of heat most commonly employed in biology is the kilocalorie (kcal). One kilocalorie is equal to 1000 calories (cal). One calorie is the heat required to raise the temperature of one gram of water one degree Celsius (°C). (You are probably more used to seeing the term *Calorie* with a capital C. This is used on food labels and is actually the same as kilocalorie.) Another energy unit, often used in physics, is the *joule;* one joule equals 0.239 cal.

The Sun provides energy for living systems

Energy flows into the biological world from the Sun. It is estimated that sunlight provides the Earth with more than 13×10^{23} calories per year, or 40 million billion calories per second! Plants, algae, and certain kinds of bacteria capture a fraction of this energy through photosynthesis.

In photosynthesis, energy absorbed from sunlight is used to combine small molecules (water and carbon dioxide) into more complex ones (sugars). This process converts carbon from an inorganic to an organic form. In the process, energy from sunlight is stored as potential energy in the covalent bonds between atoms in the sugar molecules.

Breaking the bonds between atoms requires energy. In fact, the strength of a covalent bond is measured by the amount of energy required to break it. For example, it takes 98.8 kcal to break one mole (6.023×10^{23}) of the carbon–hydrogen (C—H) bonds found in organic molecules. Fat molecules have many C—H bonds, and breaking those bonds provides lots of energy.

a. Potential energy

b. Kinetic energy

Figure 6.1 Potential and kinetic energy. *a.* Objects that have the capacity to move but are not moving have potential energy. The energy required for the girl to climb to the top of the slide is stored as potential energy. ***b.*** Objects that are in motion have kinetic energy. The stored potential energy is released as kinetic energy as the girl slides down.

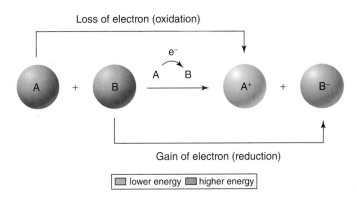

Loss of electron (oxidation)

Gain of electron (reduction)

☐ lower energy ☐ higher energy

Figure 6.2 Redox reactions. Oxidation is the loss of an electron; reduction is the gain of an electron. In this example, the charges of molecules A and B appear as superscripts in each molecule. Molecule A loses energy as it loses an electron, and molecule B gains that energy as it gains an electron.

This is one reason animals store fat. The oxidation of one mole of a 16-carbon fatty acid that is completely saturated with hydrogens yields 2340 kcal.

Oxidation–reduction reactions transfer electrons while bonds are made or broken

During a chemical reaction, the energy stored in chemical bonds may be used to make new bonds. In some of these reactions, electrons actually pass from one atom or molecule to another. An atom or molecule that loses an electron is said to be oxidized, and the process by which this occurs is called **oxidation.** The name comes from the fact that oxygen is the most common electron acceptor in biological systems. Conversely, an atom or molecule that gains an electron is said to be reduced, and the process is called *reduction.* The reduced form of a molecule has a higher level of energy than the oxidized form (figure 6.2).

Oxidation and reduction always take place together, because every electron that is lost by one atom through oxidation is gained by another atom through reduction. Therefore, chemical reactions of this sort are called **oxidation–reduction,** or **redox,** *reactions.* Oxidation–reduction reactions play a key role in the flow of energy through biological systems.

In the next two chapters, you will learn the details of how organisms derive energy from the oxidation of organic compounds via respiration, as well as from the energy in sunlight via photosynthesis.

Learning Outcomes Review 6.1

Energy is defined as the capacity to do work. The two forms of energy are kinetic energy, or energy of motion, and potential energy, or stored energy. The ultimate source of energy for living systems is the Sun. Organisms derive their energy from oxidation–reduction reactions. In oxidation, a molecule loses an electron; in reduction, a molecule gains an electron.

■ *What energy source might ecosystems at the bottom of the ocean use?*

6.2 The Laws of Thermodynamics and Free Energy

Learning Outcomes

1. *Explain the laws of thermodynamics.*
2. *Relate free energy changes to the outcome of chemical reactions.*
3. *Contrast the course of a reaction with and without an enzyme catalyst.*

All activities of living organisms—growing, running, thinking, singing, reading these words—involve changes in energy. A set of two universal laws we call the laws of thermodynamics govern all energy changes in the universe, from nuclear reactions to a bird flying through the air.

The First Law states that energy cannot be created or destroyed

The **First Law of Thermodynamics** concerns the amount of energy in the universe. Energy cannot be created or destroyed; it can only change from one form to another (from potential to kinetic, for example). The total amount of energy in the universe remains constant.

The lion eating a giraffe at the beginning of this chapter is acquiring energy. Rather than creating new energy or capturing the energy in sunlight, the lion is merely transferring some of the potential energy stored in the giraffe's tissues to its own body, just as the giraffe obtained the potential energy stored in the plants it ate while it was alive.

Within any living organism, chemical potential energy stored in some molecules can be shifted to other molecules and stored in different chemical bonds. It can also be converted into other forms, such as kinetic energy, light, or electricity. During each conversion, some of the energy dissipates into the environment as **heat,** which is a measure of the random motion of molecules (and therefore a measure of one form of kinetic energy). Energy continuously flows through the biological world in one direction, with new energy from the Sun constantly entering the system to replace the energy dissipated as heat.

Heat can be harnessed to do work only when there is a heat gradient—that is, a temperature difference between two areas. Cells are too small to maintain significant internal temperature differences, so heat energy is incapable of doing the work of cells. Instead, cells must rely on chemical reactions for energy.

Although the total amount of energy in the universe remains constant, the energy available to do work decreases as more of it is progressively lost as heat.

The Second Law states that some energy is lost as disorder increases

The **Second Law of Thermodynamics** concerns the transformation of potential energy into heat, or random molecular motion during any energy transaction. It states that the disorder in the universe, more formally called **entropy,** is continuously increasing. Put simply, disorder is more likely than order. For example, it is much more likely that a column of bricks will tumble over than that a pile of bricks will arrange themselves spontaneously to form a column.

In general, energy transformations proceed spontaneously to convert matter from a more ordered, less stable form to a less ordered, but more stable form. For this reason, the second law is sometimes called "time's arrow." Looking at the photographs in figure 6.3, you could put the pictures into correct sequence using the information that time had elapsed with only natural processes occurring. Although it might be great if our rooms would straighten themselves up, we know from experience how much work it takes to do so.

The Second Law of Thermodynamics can also be stated simply as "entropy increases." When the universe formed, it held all the potential energy it will ever have. It has become progressively more disordered ever since, with every energy exchange increasing the amount of entropy.

Chemical reactions can be predicted based on changes in free energy

It takes energy to break the chemical bonds that hold the atoms in a molecule together. Heat energy, because it increases atomic motion, makes it easier for the atoms to pull apart. Both chemical bonding and heat have a significant influence on a molecule. Chemical bonding reduces disorder; heat increases it. The net effect, the amount of energy actually available to break and subsequently form other chemical bonds, is called the *free energy* of that molecule. In a more general sense, **free energy** is defined as the energy available to do work in any system.

For a molecule within a cell, where pressure and volume usually do not change, the free energy is denoted by the symbol G (for "Gibbs free energy"). G is equal to the energy contained in a molecule's chemical bonds (called **enthalpy** and designated H) together with the energy term (TS) related to the degree of disorder in the system, where S is the symbol for *entropy* and T is the absolute temperature expressed in the Kelvin scale ($K = {}^{\circ}C + 273$):

$$G = H - TS$$

Chemical reactions break some bonds in the reactants and form new ones in the products. Consequently, reactions can produce changes in free energy. When a chemical reaction occurs under conditions of constant temperature, pressure, and volume—as do most biological reactions—the change symbolized by the Greek capital letter delta, Δ, in free energy (ΔG) is simply:

$$\Delta G = \Delta H - T\Delta S$$

We can use the change in free energy, or ΔG, to predict whether a chemical reaction is spontaneous or not. For some reactions, the ΔG is positive, which means that the products of the reaction contain *more* free energy than the reactants; the bond energy *(H)* is higher, or the disorder *(S)* in the system is lower. Such reactions do not proceed spontaneously because they require an input of energy. Any reaction that requires an input of energy is said to be **endergonic** ("inward energy").

For other reactions, the ΔG is negative. In this case, the products of the reaction contain less free energy than the reactants; either the bond energy is lower, or the disorder is higher, or both. Such reactions tend to proceed spontaneously. These reactions release the excess free energy as heat and are thus said to be **exergonic** ("outward energy"). Any chemical reaction tends to proceed spontaneously if the difference in disorder *(T∆S)* is *greater* than the difference in bond energies between reactants and products *(∆H)*.

Note that *spontaneous* does not mean the same thing as *instantaneous*. A spontaneous reaction may proceed very slowly. Figure 6.4 sums up endergonic and exergonic reactions.

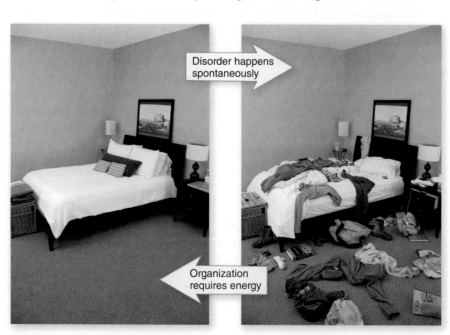

Figure 6.3 Entropy in action. As time elapses, the room shown at right becomes more disorganized. Entropy has increased in this room. It takes energy to restore it to the ordered state shown at left.

Disorder happens spontaneously

Organization requires energy

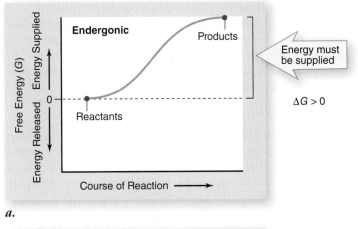

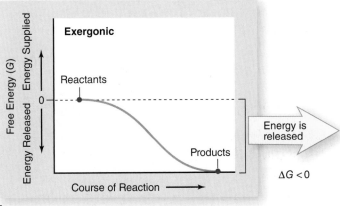

Figure 6.4 Energy in chemical reactions. *a.* In an endergonic reaction, the products of the reaction contain more energy than the reactants, and the extra energy must be supplied for the reaction to proceed. *b.* In an exergonic reaction, the products contain less energy than the reactants, and the excess energy is released.

Because chemical reactions are reversible, a reaction that is exergonic in the forward direction will be endergonic in the reverse direction. For each reaction, an equilibrium exists at some point between the relative amounts of reactants and products. This equilibrium has a numeric value and is called the *equilibrium constant.* This characteristic of reactions provides us with another way to think about free energy changes: an exergonic reaction has an equilibrium favoring the products, and an endergonic reaction has an equilibrium favoring the reactants.

Spontaneous chemical reactions require activation energy

If all chemical reactions that release free energy tend to occur spontaneously, why haven't all such reactions already occurred? Consider the gasoline tank of your car: The oxidation of the hydrocarbons in gasoline is an exergonic reaction, but your gas tank does not spontaneously explode. One reason is that most reactions require an input of energy to get started. In the case of your car, this input consists of the electrical sparks in the engine's cylinders, producing a controlled explosion.

Activation energy

Before new chemical bonds can form, even bonds that contain less energy, existing bonds must first be broken, and that requires energy input. The extra energy needed to destabilize existing chemical bonds and initiate a chemical reaction is called **activation energy** (figure 6.5).

The rate of an exergonic reaction depends on the activation energy required for the reaction to begin. Reactions with larger activation energies tend to proceed more slowly because fewer molecules succeed in getting over the initial energy hurdle. The rate of reactions can be increased in two ways: (1) by increasing the energy of reacting molecules or (2) by lowering activation energy. Chemists often drive important industrial reactions by increasing the energy of the reacting molecules, which is frequently accomplished simply by heating up the reactants. The other strategy is to use a catalyst to lower the activation energy.

How catalysts work

Stressing particular chemical bonds can make them easier to break. The process of influencing chemical bonds in a way that lowers the activation energy needed to initiate a reaction is called **catalysis,** and substances that accomplish this are known as *catalysts* (see figure 6.5).

Catalysts exert their action by affecting an intermediate stage in a reaction—the transition state. The energy needed to reach this transition state is the activation energy. Catalysts stabilize this transition state, thus lowering activation energy.

Catalysts cannot violate the basic laws of thermodynamics; they cannot make an endergonic reaction proceed spontaneously. By reducing the activation energy, a catalyst accelerates both the forward and the reverse reactions by exactly the same amount. Therefore, a catalyst does not alter the proportion of reactant ultimately converted into product.

To understand this, imagine a bowling ball resting in a shallow depression on the side of a hill. Only a narrow rim of dirt below the ball prevents it from rolling down the hill. Now imagine digging away that rim of dirt. If you remove enough

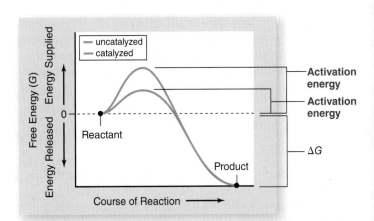

Figure 6.5 Activation energy and catalysis. Exergonic reactions do not necessarily proceed rapidly because activation energy must be supplied to destabilize existing chemical bonds. Catalysts accelerate particular reactions by lowering the amount of activation energy required to initiate the reaction. Catalysts do not alter the free-energy change produced by the reaction.

chapter **6** *Energy and Metabolism*

dirt from below the ball, it will start to roll down the hill—but removing dirt from below the ball will *never* cause the ball to roll up the hill. Removing the lip of dirt simply allows the ball to move freely; gravity determines the direction it then travels.

Similarly, the direction in which a chemical reaction proceeds is determined solely by the difference in free energy between reactants and products. Like digging away the soil below the bowling ball on the hill, catalysts reduce the energy barrier that is preventing the reaction from proceeding. Only exergonic reactions can proceed spontaneously, and catalysts cannot change that. What catalysts *can* do is make a reaction proceed much faster. In living systems, enzymes act as catalysts.

Learning Outcomes Review 6.2

The First Law of Thermodynamics states that energy cannot be created or destroyed. The Second Law states that disorder, or entropy, is increasing. Free-energy changes (ΔG) can predict whether chemical reactions take place. Reactions with a negative ΔG occur spontaneously, and those with a positive ΔG do not. Energy needed to initiate a reaction is termed activation energy. Catalysts stabilize an intermediate transition state, lowering activation energy and accelerating reactions.

■ *Can an enzyme make an endergonic reaction exergonic?*

6.3 ATP: The Energy Currency of Cells

Learning Outcomes

1. *Describe the role of ATP in short-term energy storage.*
2. *Distinguish which bonds in ATP are "high energy."*

The chief "currency" all cells use for their energy transactions is the nucleotide *adenosine triphosphate (ATP)*. ATP powers almost every energy-requiring process in cells, from making sugars, to supplying activation energy for chemical reactions, to actively transporting substances across membranes, to moving through the environment and growing.

Cells store and release energy in the bonds of ATP

You saw in chapter 3 that nucleotides serve as the building blocks for nucleic acids, but they play other cellular roles as well. ATP is used as a building block for RNA molecules, and it also has a critical function as a portable source of energy on demand for endergonic cellular processes.

The structure of ATP

ATP is composed of three smaller components (figure 6.6). The first component is a five-carbon sugar, ribose, which serves as the framework to which the other two subunits are attached.

The second component is adenine, an organic molecule composed of two carbon–nitrogen rings. Each of the nitrogen atoms in the ring has an unshared pair of electrons and weakly attracts hydrogen ions, making adenine chemically a weak base. The third component of ATP is a chain of three phosphates, thus adenosine *tri*phosphate.

How ATP stores energy

The key to how ATP stores energy lies in its triphosphate group. Phosphate groups are highly negatively charged, and thus they strongly repel one another. This electrostatic repulsion makes the covalent bonds joining the phosphates unstable. The molecule is often referred to as a "coiled spring," with the phosphates straining away from one another.

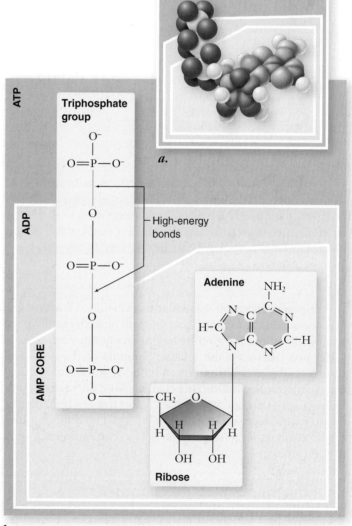

Figure 6.6 The ATP molecule. The model (*a*) and the structural diagram (*b*) both show that ATP has a core of AMP. Addition of one phosphate to AMP yields ADP, and addition of a second phosphate yields ATP. These two terminal phosphates are attached by high-energy bonds so that removing either by hydrolysis is an exergonic reaction that releases energy. ADP, adenosine diphosphate; AMP, adenosine monophosphate; ATP, adenosine triphosphate

The unstable bonds holding the phosphates together in the ATP molecule have a low activation energy and are easily broken by hydrolysis. When they break, they can transfer a considerable amount of energy. In other words, the hydrolysis of ATP has a negative ΔG, and the energy it releases can be used to perform work.

In most reactions involving ATP, only the outermost high-energy phosphate bond is hydrolyzed, cleaving off the phosphate group on the end. When this happens, ATP becomes *adenosine diphosphate (ADP)* plus an **inorganic phosphate (P_i),** and energy equal to 7.3 kcal/mol is released under standard conditions. The liberated phosphate group usually attaches temporarily to some intermediate molecule. When that molecule is dephosphorylated, the phosphate group is released as P_i.

Both of the two terminal phosphates can be hydrolyzed to release energy, leaving *adenosine monophosphate (AMP)*, but the third phosphate is not attached by a high-energy bond. With only one phosphate group, AMP has no other phosphates to provide the electrostatic repulsion that makes the bonds holding the two terminal phosphate groups high-energy bonds.

ATP hydrolysis drives endergonic reactions

Cells use ATP to drive endergonic reactions. These reactions do not proceed spontaneously because their products possess more free energy than their reactants. However, if the cleavage of ATP's terminal high-energy bond releases more energy than the other reaction consumes, the two reactions can be coupled so that the energy released by the hydrolysis of ATP can be used to supply the endergonic reaction with the energy it needs. Coupled together, these reactions result in a net release of energy ($-\Delta G$) and are therefore exergonic and proceed spontaneously. Because almost all the endergonic reactions in cells require less energy than is released by the cleavage of ATP, ATP can provide most of the energy a cell needs.

 Data analysis Consider the reaction: glutamate + $NH_3 \longrightarrow$ glutamine ($\Delta G = +3.4$ kcal/mol). If this reaction is coupled to ATP hydrolysis ($\Delta G = -7.3$ kcal/mol), what would be the overall ΔG? Would this process be endergonic or exergonic?

ATP cycles continuously

The same feature that makes ATP an effective energy donor—the instability of its phosphate bonds—prevents it from being a good long-term energy-storage molecule. Fats and carbohydrates serve that function better.

The use of ATP can be thought of as a cycle: Cells use exergonic reactions to provide the energy needed to synthesize ATP from ADP + P_i; they then use the hydrolysis of ATP to provide energy to drive the endergonic reactions they need (figure 6.7).

Most cells do not maintain large stockpiles of ATP. Instead, they typically have only a few seconds' supply of ATP at any given time, and they continually produce more from ADP and P_i. It is estimated that even a sedentary individual turns over an amount of ATP in one day roughly equal to his or her body weight. This statistic makes clear the importance of ATP synthesis. In the next two chapters we will explore in detail the cellular mechanisms for synthesizing ATP.

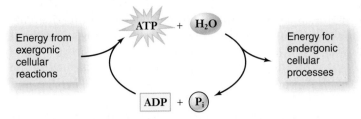

Figure 6.7 The ATP cycle. ATP is synthesized and hydrolyzed in a cyclic fashion. The synthesis of ATP from ADP + P_i is endergonic and is powered by exergonic cellular reactions. The hydrolysis of ATP to ADP + P_i is exergonic, and the energy released is used to power endergonic cellular functions such as muscle contraction. ADP, adenosine diphosphate; ATP, adenosine triphosphate; P_i, inorganic phosphate

Learning Outcomes Review 6.3

ATP is a nucleotide with three phosphate groups. Endergonic cellular processes can be driven by coupling to the exergonic hydrolysis of the two terminal phosphates. The bonds holding the terminal phosphate groups together are easily broken, releasing energy like a coiled spring. The cell is constantly building ATP using exergonic reactions and breaking it down to drive endergonic reactions.

■ *If the molecular weight of ATP is 507.18 g/mol, and the ΔG for hydrolysis is –7.3 kcal/mol, how much energy is released over the course of the day by a 100-kg man?*

6.4 Enzymes: Biological Catalysts

Learning Outcomes

1. *Discuss the specificity of enzymes.*
2. *Explain how enzymes bind to their substrates.*
3. *List the factors that influence the rate of enzyme-catalyzed reactions.*

The chemical reactions within living organisms are regulated by controlling the points at which catalysis takes place. Life itself, therefore, can be seen as regulated by catalysts. The agents that carry out most of the catalysis in living organisms are called enzymes. Most enzymes are proteins, although increasing evidence indicates that some enzymes are actually RNA molecules, as discussed later in this chapter.

An enzyme alters the activation energy of a reaction

The unique three-dimensional shape of an enzyme enables it to stabilize a temporary association between **substrates**—the molecules that will undergo the reaction. By bringing two substrates together in the correct orientation or by stressing particular chemical bonds of a substrate, an enzyme lowers the activation energy required for new bonds to form. The reaction thus proceeds much more quickly than it would without the enzyme.

The enzyme itself is not changed or consumed in the reaction, so only a small amount of an enzyme is needed, and it can be used over and over.

As an example of how an enzyme works, let's consider the reaction of carbon dioxide and water to form carbonic acid. This important enzyme-catalyzed reaction occurs in vertebrate red blood cells:

$$CO_2 + H_2O \rightleftharpoons H_2CO_3$$

carbon dioxide | water | carbonic acid

This reaction may proceed in either direction, but because it has a large activation energy, the reaction is very slow in the absence of an enzyme: Perhaps 200 molecules of carbonic acid form in an hour in a cell in the absence of any enzyme. Reactions that proceed this slowly are of little use to a cell. Vertebrate red blood cells overcome this problem by employing an enzyme within their cytoplasm called *carbonic anhydrase* (enzyme names usually end in "–ase"). Under the same conditions, but in the presence of carbonic anhydrase, an estimated 600,000 molecules of carbonic acid form every *second!* Thus, the enzyme increases the reaction rate by more than one million times.

Thousands of different kinds of enzymes are known, each catalyzing one or a few specific chemical reactions. By facilitating particular chemical reactions, the enzymes in a cell determine the course of metabolism—the collection of all chemical reactions—in that cell.

Different types of cells contain different sets of enzymes, and this difference contributes to structural and functional variations among cell types. For example, the chemical reactions taking place within a red blood cell differ from those that occur within a nerve cell, in part because different cell types contain different arrays of enzymes.

Active sites of enzymes conform to fit the shape of substrates

Most enzymes are globular proteins with one or more pockets or clefts, called **active sites,** on their surface (figure 6.8). Substrates bind to the enzyme at these active sites, forming an **enzyme-substrate complex** (see figure 6.10). For catalysis to occur within the complex, a substrate molecule must fit precisely into an active site. When that happens, amino acid side groups of the enzyme end up very close to certain bonds of the substrate. These side groups interact chemically with the substrate, usually stressing or distorting a particular bond and consequently lowering the activation energy needed to break the bond. After the bonds of the substrates are broken, or new bonds are formed, the substrates have been converted to products. These products then dissociate from the enzyme, leaving the enzyme ready to bind its next substrate and begin the cycle again.

Proteins are not rigid. The binding of a substrate induces the enzyme to adjust its shape slightly, leading to a better *induced fit* between enzyme and substrate (figure 6.9). This

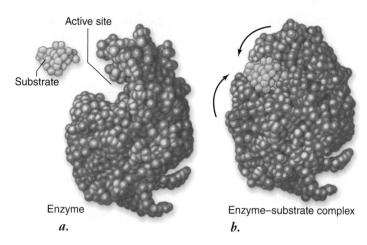

Active site
Substrate
Enzyme
a.
Enzyme–substrate complex
b.

Figure 6.8 Enzyme binding its substrate. *a.* The active site of the enzyme lysozyme fits the shape of its substrate, a peptidoglycan that makes up bacterial cell walls. *b.* When the substrate, indicated in yellow, slides into the groove of the active site, the protein is induced to alter its shape slightly and bind the substrate more tightly. This alteration of the shape of the enzyme to better fit the substrate is called induced fit.

interaction may also facilitate the binding of other substrates; in such cases, one substrate "activates" the enzyme to receive other substrates.

Enzymes occur in many forms

Although many enzymes are suspended in the cytoplasm of cells, not attached to any structure, other enzymes function

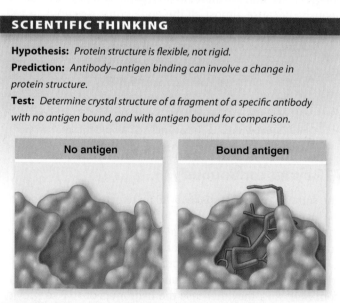

SCIENTIFIC THINKING

Hypothesis: *Protein structure is flexible, not rigid.*

Prediction: *Antibody–antigen binding can involve a change in protein structure.*

Test: *Determine crystal structure of a fragment of a specific antibody with no antigen bound, and with antigen bound for comparison.*

No antigen | Bound antigen

Result: *After binding, the antibody folds around the antigen forming a pocket.*

Conclusion: *In this case, binding involves an induced-fit kind of change in conformation.*

Further Experiments: *Why is this experiment easier to do with an antibody than with an enzyme? Can this experiment be done with an enzyme?*

Figure 6.9 Induced-fit binding of antibody to antigen.

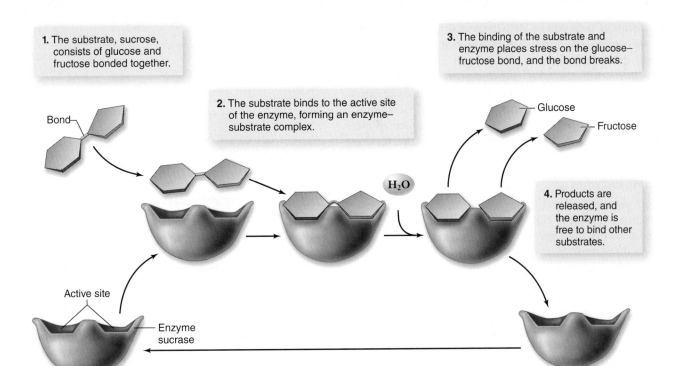

1. The substrate, sucrose, consists of glucose and fructose bonded together.

2. The substrate binds to the active site of the enzyme, forming an enzyme–substrate complex.

3. The binding of the substrate and enzyme places stress on the glucose–fructose bond, and the bond breaks.

4. Products are released, and the enzyme is free to bind other substrates.

Bond

Glucose

Fructose

H_2O

Active site

Enzyme sucrase

Figure 6.10 The catalytic cycle of an enzyme. Enzymes increase the speed at which chemical reactions occur, but they are not altered permanently themselves as they do so. In the reaction illustrated here, the enzyme sucrase is splitting the sugar sucrose into two simpler sugars: glucose and fructose.

as integral parts of cell membranes and organelles. Enzymes may also form associations called *multienzyme complexes* to carry out reaction sequences. And, as mentioned earlier, evidence exists that some enzymes may consist of RNA rather than being only protein.

Multienzyme complexes

Often several enzymes catalyzing different steps of a sequence of reactions are associated with one another in noncovalently bonded assemblies called **multienzyme complexes.** The bacterial pyruvate dehydrogenase multienzyme complex, shown in figure 6.11, contains enzymes that carry out three sequential reactions in oxidative metabolism. Each complex has multiple copies of each of the three enzymes—60 protein subunits in all. The many subunits work together to form a molecular machine that performs multiple functions.

Multienzyme complexes offer the following significant advantages in catalytic efficiency:

1. The rate of any enzyme reaction is limited by how often the enzyme collides with its substrate. If a series of sequential reactions occurs within a multienzyme complex, the product of one reaction can be delivered to the next enzyme without releasing it to diffuse away.
2. Because the reacting substrate doesn't leave the complex while it goes through the series of reactions, unwanted side reactions are prevented.
3. All of the reactions that take place within the multienzyme complex can be controlled as a unit.

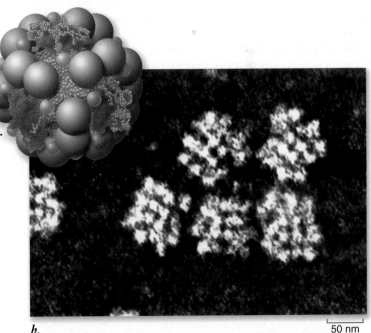

a.

b.

50 nm

Figure 6.11 A complex enzyme: pyruvate dehydrogenase. Pyruvate dehydrogenase, which catalyzes the oxidation of pyruvate, is one of the most complex enzymes known. *a.* A model of the enzyme showing the arrangement of the 60 protein subunits. *b.* Many of the protein subunits are clearly visible in the electron micrograph.

In addition to pyruvate dehydrogenase, which controls entry to the Krebs cycle during aerobic respiration (see chapter 7), several other key processes in the cell are catalyzed by multienzyme complexes. One well-studied system is the fatty acid synthetase complex that catalyzes the synthesis of fatty acids from two-carbon precursors. Seven different enzymes make up this multienzyme complex, and the intermediate reaction products remain associated with the complex for the entire series of reactions.

Nonprotein enzymes

Until a few years ago, most biology textbooks contained statements such as "Proteins called enzymes are the catalysts of biological systems." We can no longer make that statement without qualification.

Thomas R. Cech and colleagues at the University of Colorado reported in 1981 that certain reactions involving RNA molecules appear to be catalyzed in cells by RNA itself, rather than by enzymes. This initial observation has been corroborated by additional examples of RNA catalysis. Like enzymes, these RNA catalysts, which are loosely called "ribozymes," greatly accelerate the rate of particular biochemical reactions and show extraordinary substrate specificity.

Research has revealed at least two sorts of ribozymes. Some ribozymes have folded structures and catalyze reactions on themselves, a process called *intra*molecular catalysis. Other ribozymes act on other molecules without being changed themselves, a process called *inter*molecular catalysis.

The most striking example of the role of RNA as enzyme is emerging from recent work on the structure and function of the ribosome. For many years it was thought that RNA was a structural framework for this vital organelle, but it is now clear that ribosomal RNA plays a key role in ribosome function. The ribosome itself is a ribozyme.

The ability of RNA, an informational molecule, to act as a catalyst has stirred great excitement because it seems to answer the question—Which came first, the protein or the nucleic acid? It now seems at least possible that RNA evolved first and may have catalyzed the formation of the first proteins.

Environmental and other factors affect enzyme function

The rate of an enzyme-catalyzed reaction is affected by the concentrations of both the substrate and the enzyme that works on it. In addition, any chemical or physical factor that alters the enzyme's three-dimensional shape—such as temperature, pH, and the binding of regulatory molecules—can affect the enzyme's ability to catalyze the reaction.

Temperature

Increasing the temperature of an uncatalyzed reaction increases its rate because the additional heat increases random molecular movement. This motion can add stress to molecular bonds and affect the activation energy of a reaction.

The rate of an enzyme-catalyzed reaction also increases with temperature, but only up to a point called the *optimum*

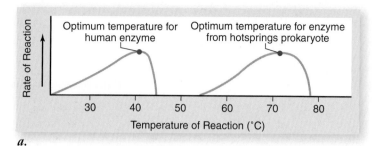
a.

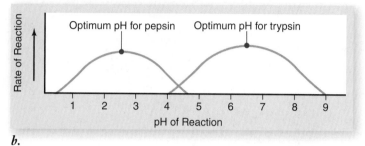
b.

Figure 6.12 Enzyme sensitivity to the environment. The activity of an enzyme is influenced by both (a) temperature and (b) pH. Most human enzymes, such as the protein-degrading enzyme trypsin, work best at temperatures of about 40°C and within a pH range of 6 to 8. The hot springs prokaryote tolerates a higher environmental temperature and a correspondingly higher temperature optimum for enzymes. Pepsin works in the acidic environment of the stomach and has a lower optimum pH.

temperature (figure 6.12a). Below this temperature, the hydrogen bonds and hydrophobic interactions that determine the enzyme's shape are not flexible enough to permit the induced fit that is optimum for catalysis. Above the optimum temperature, these forces are too weak to maintain the enzyme's shape against the increased random movement of the atoms in the enzyme. At higher temperatures, the enzyme denatures, as described in chapter 3.

Most human enzymes have an optimum temperature between 35°C and 40°C—a range that includes normal body temperature. Prokaryotes that live in hot springs have more stable enzymes (that is, enzymes held together more strongly), so the optimum temperature for those enzymes can be 70°C or higher. In each case the optimal temperature for the enzyme corresponds to the "normal" temperature usually encountered in the body or the environment, depending on the type of organism.

pH

Ionic interactions between oppositely charged amino acid residues, such as glutamic acid (–) and lysine (+), also hold enzymes together. These interactions are sensitive to the hydrogen ion concentration of the fluid in which the enzyme is dissolved, because changing that concentration shifts the balance between positively and negatively charged amino acid residues. For this reason, most enzymes have an *optimum pH* that usually ranges from pH 6 to 8.

Enzymes able to function in very acidic environments are proteins that maintain their three-dimensional shape even in the presence of high hydrogen ion concentrations. The enzyme pepsin, for example, digests proteins in the stomach at pH 2, a very acidic level (figure 6.12b).

Inhibitors and activators

Enzyme activity is also sensitive to the presence of specific substances that can bind to the enzyme and cause changes in its shape. Through these substances, a cell is able to regulate which of its enzymes are active and which are inactive at a particular time. This ability allows the cell to increase its efficiency and to control changes in its characteristics during development. A substance that binds to an enzyme and *decreases* its activity is called an **inhibitor.** Very often, the end product of a biochemical pathway acts as an inhibitor of an early reaction in the pathway, a process called *feedback inhibition* (discussed later in this chapter).

Enzyme inhibition occurs in two ways: **Competitive inhibitors** compete with the substrate for the same active site, occupying the active site and thus preventing substrates from binding; **noncompetitive inhibitors** bind to the enzyme in a location other than the active site, changing the shape of the enzyme and making it unable to bind to the substrate (figure 6.13).

Many enzymes can exist in either an active or inactive conformation; such enzymes are called *allosteric enzymes.* Most noncompetitive inhibitors bind to a specific portion of the enzyme called an **allosteric site.** These sites serve as chemical on/off switches; the binding of a substance to the site can switch the enzyme between its active and inactive configurations. A substance that binds to an allosteric site and reduces enzyme activity is called an **allosteric inhibitor** (figure 6.13b).

This kind of control is also used to activate enzymes. An **allosteric activator** binds to allosteric sites to keep an enzyme in its active configuration, thereby *increasing* enzyme activity.

Enzyme cofactors

Enzyme function is often assisted by additional chemical components known as **cofactors.** These can be metal ions that are often found in the active site participating directly in catalysis. For example, the metallic ion zinc is used by some enzymes, such as protein-digesting carboxypeptidase, to draw electrons away from their position in covalent bonds, making the bonds less stable and easier to break. Other metallic elements, such as molybdenum and manganese, are also used as cofactors. Like zinc, these substances are required in the diet in small amounts.

When the cofactor is a nonprotein organic molecule, it is called a **coenzyme.** Many of the small organic molecules essential in our diets that we call vitamins function as coenzymes. For example, the B vitamins B_6 and B_{12} both function as coenzymes for a number of different enzymes. Modified nucleotides are also used as coenzymes.

In numerous oxidation–reduction reactions that are catalyzed by enzymes, the electrons pass in pairs from the active site of the enzyme to a coenzyme that serves as the electron acceptor. The coenzyme then transfers the electrons to a different enzyme, which releases them (and the energy they bear) to the substrates in another reaction. Often, the electrons combine with protons (H^+) to form hydrogen atoms. In this way, coenzymes shuttle energy in the form of hydrogen atoms from one enzyme to another in a cell. The role of coenzymes and the specifics of their action will be explored in detail in the following two chapters.

Learning Outcomes Review 6.4

Enzymes are biological catalysts that accelerate chemical reactions inside the cell. Enzymes bind to their substrates based on molecular shape, which allows them to be highly specific. Enzyme activity is affected by conditions such as temperature and pH and the presence of inhibitors or activators. Some enzymes also require an inorganic cofactor or an organic coenzyme.

■ *Why do proteins and RNA function as enzymes but DNA does not?*

6.5 Metabolism: The Chemical Description of Cell Function

Learning Outcomes

1. *Explain the kinds of reactions that make up metabolism.*
2. *Discuss what is meant by a metabolic pathway.*
3. *Recognize that metabolism is a product of evolution.*

Living chemistry, the total of all chemical reactions carried out by an organism, is called **metabolism.** Those chemical reactions that expend energy to build up molecules are called *anabolic* reactions, or **anabolism.** Reactions that harvest energy by breaking down molecules are called *catabolic* reactions, or **catabolism.** This section presents a general overview of metabolic processes that will be described in much greater detail in later chapters.

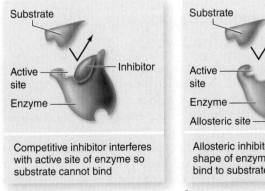
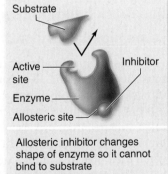

Competitive inhibitor interferes with active site of enzyme so substrate cannot bind

Allosteric inhibitor changes shape of enzyme so it cannot bind to substrate

a. Competitive inhibition   *b.* Noncompetitive inhibition

Figure 6.13 How enzymes can be inhibited. *a.* In competitive inhibition, the inhibitor has a shape similar to the substrate and competes for the active site of the enzyme. *b.* In noncompetitive inhibition, the inhibitor binds to the enzyme at the allosteric site, a place away from the active site, effecting a conformational change in the enzyme, making it unable to bind to its substrate.

Biochemical pathways organize chemical reactions in cells

Organisms contain thousands of different kinds of enzymes that catalyze a bewildering variety of reactions. Many of these reactions in a cell occur in sequences called **biochemical pathways.** In such pathways, the product of one reaction becomes the substrate for the next (figure 6.14). Biochemical pathways are the organizational units of metabolism—the elements an organism controls to achieve coherent metabolic activity.

Many sequential enzyme steps in biochemical pathways take place in specific compartments of the cell; for example, the steps of the Krebs cycle (see chapter 7) occur in the matrix inside mitochondria in eukaryotes. By determining where many of the enzymes that catalyze these steps are located, we can "map out" a model of metabolic processes in the cell.

Biochemical pathways may have evolved in stepwise fashion

In the earliest cells, the first biochemical processes probably involved energy-rich molecules scavenged from the environment. Most of the molecules necessary for these processes are thought to have existed independently in the "organic soup" of the early oceans.

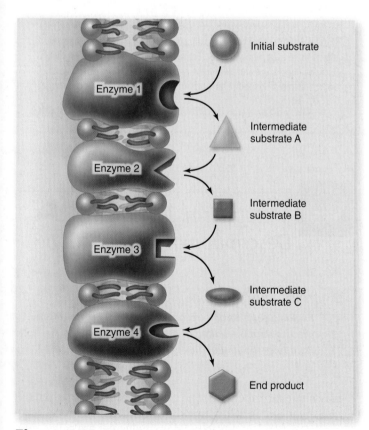

Figure 6.14 A biochemical pathway. The original substrate is acted on by enzyme 1, changing the substrate to a new intermediate, substrate A, recognized as a substrate by enzyme 2. Each enzyme in the pathway acts on the product of the previous stage. These enzymes may be either soluble or arranged in a membrane as shown.

The first catalyzed reactions were probably simple, one-step reactions that brought these molecules together in various combinations. Eventually, the energy-rich molecules became depleted in the external environment, and only organisms that had evolved some means of making those molecules from other substances could survive. Thus, a hypothetical reaction,

$$\begin{array}{c} F \\ + \\ G \end{array} \longrightarrow H$$

where two energy-rich molecules (F and G) react to produce compound H and release energy, became more complex when the supply of F in the environment ran out.

A new reaction was added in which the depleted molecule, F, is made from another molecule, E, which was also present in the environment:

$$E \longrightarrow \begin{array}{c} F \\ + \\ G \end{array} \longrightarrow H$$

When the supply of E was in turn exhausted, organisms that were able to make E from some other available precursor, D, survived. When D was depleted, those organisms in turn were replaced by ones able to synthesize D from another molecule, C:

$$C \longrightarrow D \longrightarrow E \longrightarrow \begin{array}{c} F \\ + \\ G \end{array} \longrightarrow H$$

This hypothetical biochemical pathway would have evolved slowly through time, with the final reactions in the pathway evolving first and earlier reactions evolving later.

Looking at the pathway now, we would say that the "advanced" organism, starting with compound C, is able to synthesize H by means of a series of steps. This is how the biochemical pathways within organisms are thought to have evolved—not all at once, but one step at a time, backward.

Feedback inhibition regulates some biochemical pathways

For a biochemical pathway to operate efficiently, its activity must be coordinated and regulated by the cell. Not only is it unnecessary to synthesize a compound when plenty is already present, but doing so would waste energy and raw materials that could be put to use elsewhere. It is to the cell's advantage, therefore, to temporarily shut down biochemical pathways when their products are not needed.

The regulation of simple biochemical pathways often depends on an elegant feedback mechanism: The end-product of the pathway binds to an allosteric site on the enzyme that catalyzes the first reaction in the pathway. This mode of regulation is called **feedback inhibition** (figure 6.15).

In the hypothetical pathway we just described, the enzyme catalyzing the reaction $C \longrightarrow D$ would possess an allosteric site for H, the end-product of the pathway. As the pathway churned out its product and the amount of H in the cell increased, it would become more likely that an H molecule would encounter

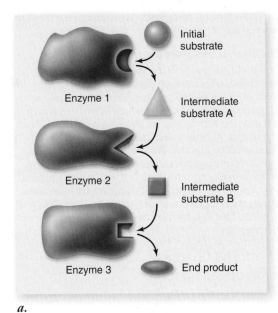

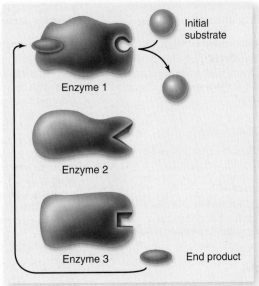

a.   *b.*

the allosteric site on the C ⟶ D enzyme. Binding to the allosteric site would essentially shut down the reaction C ⟶ D and in turn effectively shut down the whole pathway.

In this chapter we have reviewed the basics of energy and its transformations as carried out in living systems. Chemical bonds are the primary location of energy storage and release, and cells have developed elegant methods of making and breaking chemical bonds to create the molecules they need. Enzymes facilitate these reactions by serving as catalysts. In the following chapters you will learn the details of the mechanisms by which organisms harvest, store, and utilize energy.

Learning Outcomes Review 6.5

Metabolism is the sum of all chemical reactions in a cell. Anabolic reactions use energy to build up molecules. Catabolic reactions release energy by breaking down molecules. In a metabolic pathway, the end-product of one reaction is the substrate for the next reaction. Evolution may have favored organisms that could use precursor molecules to synthesize a nutrient. Over time, more reactions would be linked together as novel enzymes arose by mutation.

■ **Is a catabolic pathway likely to be subject to feedback inhibition?**

Chapter Review

6.1 The Flow of Energy in Living Systems

Thermodynamics is the study of energy changes.

Energy can take many forms.

Energy is the capacity to do work. Potential energy is stored energy, and kinetic energy is the energy of motion. Energy can take many forms: mechanical, heat, sound, electric current, light, or radioactive radiation. Energy is measured in units of heat known as kilocalories.

The Sun provides energy for living systems.

Photosynthesis stores light energy from the Sun as potential energy in the covalent bonds of sugar molecules. Breaking these bonds in living cells releases energy for use in other reactions.

Oxidation–reduction reactions transfer electrons while bonds are made or broken.

Oxidation is a reaction involving the loss of electrons. Reduction is the gain of electrons (figure 6.2). These two reactions take place together and are therefore termed redox reactions.

6.2 The Laws of Thermodynamics and Free Energy

The First Law states that energy cannot be created or destroyed.

Virtually all activities of living organisms require energy. Energy changes form as it moves through organisms and their biochemical systems, but it is not created or destroyed.

The Second Law states that some energy is lost as disorder increases.

The disorder, or entropy, of the universe is continuously increasing. In an open system like the Earth, which is receiving energy from the Sun, this may not be the case. To increase order, however, energy must be expended. In energy conversions, some energy is always lost as heat.

Chemical reactions can be predicted based on changes in free energy.

Free energy (G) is the energy available to do work in any system. Changes in free energy (ΔG) predict the direction of reactions. Reactions with a negative ΔG are spontaneous (exergonic) reactions, and reactions with a positive ΔG are not spontaneous (endergonic).

Endergonic chemical reactions absorb energy from the surroundings, whereas exergonic reactions release energy to the surroundings.

Spontaneous chemical reactions require activation energy.

Activation energy is the energy required to destabilize chemical bonds and initiate chemical reactions (figure 6.5). Even exergonic reactions require this activation energy. Catalysts speed up chemical reactions by lowering the activation energy.

6.3 ATP: The Energy Currency of Cells

Adenosine triphosphate (ATP) is the molecular currency used for cellular energy transactions.

Cells store and release energy in the bonds of ATP.

The energy of ATP is stored in the bonds between its terminal phosphate groups. These groups repel each other due to their negative charge and therefore the covalent bonds joining these phosphates are unstable.

ATP hydrolysis drives endergonic reactions.

Enzymes hydrolyze the terminal phosphate group of ATP to release energy for reactions. If ATP hydrolysis is coupled to an endergonic reaction with a positive ΔG with magnitude less than that for ATP hydrolysis, the two reactions together will be exergonic.

ATP cycles continuously.

ATP hydrolysis releases energy to drive endergonic reactions, and it is synthesized with energy from exergonic reactions (figure 6.7).

6.4 Enzymes: Biological Catalysts

An enzyme alters the activation energy of a reaction.

Enzymes lower the activation energy needed to initiate a chemical reaction.

Active sites of enzymes conform to fit the shape of substrates.

Substrates bind to the active site of an enzyme. Enzymes adjust their shape to the substrate so there is a better fit (figure 6.8).

Enzymes occur in many forms.

Enzymes can be free in the cytosol or exist as components bound to membranes and organelles. Enzymes involved in a biochemical pathway can form multienzyme complexes. While most enzymes are proteins, some are actually RNA molecules, called ribozymes.

Environmental and other factors affect enzyme function.

An enzyme's functionality depends on its ability to maintain its three-dimensional shape, which can be affected by temperature and pH. The activity of enzymes can be affected by inhibitors. Competitive inhibitors compete for the enzyme's active site, which leads to decreased enzyme activity (figure 6.13). Enzyme activity can be controlled by effectors. Allosteric enzymes have a second site, located away from the active site, that binds effectors to activate or inhibit the enzyme. Noncompetitive inhibitors and activators bind to the allosteric site, changing the structure of the enzyme to inhibit or activate it. Cofactors are nonorganic metals necessary for enzyme function. Coenzymes are nonprotein organic molecules, such as certain vitamins, needed for enzyme function. Often coenzymes serve as electron acceptors.

6.5 Metabolism: The Chemical Description of Cell Function

Metabolism is the sum of all biochemical reactions in a cell. Anabolic reactions require energy to build up molecules, and catabolic reactions break down molecules and release energy.

Biochemical pathways organize chemical reactions in cells.

Chemical reactions in biochemical pathways use the product of one reaction as the substrate for the next.

Biochemical pathways may have evolved in stepwise fashion.

In the primordial "soup" of the early oceans, many reactions were probably single-step reactions combining two molecules. As one of the substrate molecules was depleted, organisms having an enzyme that could synthesize the substrate would have a selective advantage. In this manner, biochemical pathways are thought to have evolved "backward" with new reactions producing limiting substrates for existing reactions.

Feedback inhibition regulates some biochemical pathways.

Biosynthetic pathways are often regulated by the end product of the pathway. Feedback inhibition occurs when the end-product of a reaction combines with an enzyme's allosteric site to shut down the enzyme's activity (figure 6.15).

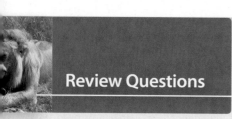

Review Questions

UNDERSTAND

1. A covalent bond between two atoms represents what kind of energy?
   a. Kinetic energy
   b. Potential energy
   c. Mechanical energy
   d. Solar energy

2. During a redox reaction the molecule that gains an electron has been
   a. reduced and now has a higher energy level.
   b. oxidized and now has a lower energy level.
   c. reduced and now has a lower energy level.
   d. oxidized and now has a higher energy level.

3. An endergonic reaction has the following properties
   a. $+\Delta G$ and the reaction is spontaneous.
   b. $+\Delta G$ and the reaction is not spontaneous.
   c. $-\Delta G$ and the reaction is spontaneous.
   d. $-\Delta G$ and the reaction is not spontaneous.

4. A spontaneous reaction is one in which
   a. the reactants have a higher free energy than the products.
   b. the products have a higher free energy than the reactants.
   c. an input of energy is required.
   d. entropy is decreased.

5. What is *activation energy*?

 a. The thermal energy associated with random movements of molecules
 b. The energy released through breaking chemical bonds
 c. The difference in free energy between reactants and products
 d. The energy required to initiate a chemical reaction

6. Which of the following is NOT a property of a catalyst?

 a. A catalyst reduces the activation energy of a reaction.
 b. A catalyst lowers the free energy of the reactants.
 c. A catalyst does not change as a result of the reaction.
 d. A catalyst works in both the forward and reverse directions of a reaction.

7. Where is the energy stored in a molecule of ATP?

 a. Within the bonds between nitrogen and carbon
 b. In the carbon-to-carbon bonds found in the ribose
 c. In the phosphorus-to-oxygen double bond
 d. In the bonds connecting the two terminal phosphate groups

APPLY

1. Cells use ATP to drive endergonic reactions because

 a. ATP is the universal catalyst.
 b. energy released by ATP hydrolysis makes ΔG for coupled reactions more negative.
 c. energy released by ATP hydrolysis makes ΔG for coupled reactions more positive.
 d. the conversion of ATP to ADP is also endergonic.

2. Which of the following statements is NOT true about enzymes?

 a. Enzymes use the three-dimensional shape of their active site to bind reactants.
 b. Enzymes lower the activation energy for a reaction.
 c. Enzymes make ΔG for a reaction more negative.
 d. Enzymes can catalyze the forward and reverse directions of a reaction.

3. ATP hydrolysis has a ΔG of –7.4 kcal/mol. Can an endergonic reaction with a ΔG of 12 kcal/mol be "driven" by ATP hydrolysis?

 a. No, the overall ΔG is still positive.
 b. Yes, the overall ΔG would now be negative.
 c. Yes, but only if an enzyme is used to lower ΔG.
 d. No, overall ΔG is now negative.

4. An online auction site offers a perpetual-motion machine. You decide not to bid on this because

 a. there is not enough energy in the universe to power this machine.
 b. the First Law says you cannot create energy.
 c. the Second Law says that energy loss due to entropy will not allow for perpetual motion.
 d. it could work, but would require a strong catalyst.

5. Enzymes have similar responses to both changes in temperature and pH. The effect of both is on the

 a. rate of movement of the substrate molecules.
 b. strength of the chemical bonds within the substrate.
 c. three-dimensional shape of the enzyme.
 d. rate of movement of the enzyme.

6. Feedback inhibition is an efficient way to control a metabolic pathway because the

 a. first enzyme in a pathway is inhibited by its own product.
 b. last enzyme in a pathway is inhibited by its own product.
 c. first enzyme in a pathway is inhibited by the end-product of the pathway.
 d. last enzyme in a pathway is inhibited by the end-product of the pathway.

SYNTHESIZE

1. Examine the graph showing the rate of reaction versus temperature for an enzyme–catalyzed reaction in a human.

 a. Describe what is happening to the enzyme at around 40°C.
 b. Explain why the line touches the *x*-axis at approximately 20°C and 45°C.
 c. Average body temperature for humans is 37°C. Suggest a reason why the temperature optimum of this enzyme is greater than 37°C.

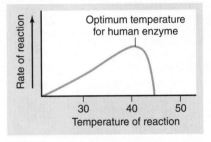

2. Phosphofructokinase functions to add a phosphate group to a molecule of fructose 6-phosphate. This enzyme functions early in glycolysis, an energy-yielding biochemical pathway discussed in chapter 7. The enzyme has an active site that binds fructose and ATP. An allosteric inhibitory site also binds ATP when cellular levels of ATP are very high.

 a. Predict the rate of the reaction if the levels of cellular ATP are low.
 b. Predict the rate of the reaction if levels of cellular ATP are very high.
 c. Describe what is happening to the enzyme when levels of ATP are very high.

ONLINE RESOURCE

www.ravenbiology.com

Understand, Apply, and Synthesize—enhance your study with animations that bring concepts to life and practice tests to assess your understanding. Your instructor may also recommend the interactive eBook, individualized learning tools, and more.

Chapter 7

How Cells Harvest Energy

Chapter Contents

Introduction

Life is driven by energy. All the activities organisms carry out—the swimming of bacteria, the purring of a cat, your thinking about these words—use energy. In this chapter, we discuss the processes all cells use to derive chemical energy from organic molecules and to convert that energy to ATP. Then, in chapter 8, we will examine photosynthesis, which uses light energy to make chemical energy. We consider the conversion of chemical energy to ATP first because all organisms, both the plant, a photosynthesizer, and the caterpillar feeding on the plant, pictured in the photo are capable of harvesting energy from chemical bonds. Energy harvest via respiration is a universal process.

Overview of Respiration

Plants, algae, and some bacteria harvest the energy of sunlight through photosynthesis, converting radiant energy into chemical energy. These organisms, along with a few others that use chemical energy in a similar way, are called **autotrophs** ("self-feeders"). All other organisms live on the organic compounds autotrophs produce, using them as food, and are called **heterotrophs** ("fed by others"). At least 95% of the kinds of organisms on Earth—all animals and fungi, and most protists and prokaryotes—are heterotrophs. Autotrophs also extract energy from organic compounds—they just have the additional capacity to use the energy from sunlight to synthesize these compounds. The process by which energy is harvested is **cellular respiration**—the oxidation of organic compounds to extract energy from chemical bonds.

Cells oxidize organic compounds to drive metabolism

Most foods contain a variety of carbohydrates, proteins, and fats, all rich in energy-laden chemical bonds. Carbohydrates and fats, as you recall from chapter 3, possess many carbon–hydrogen (C—H) bonds, as well as carbon-oxygen (C—O) bonds.

The job of extracting energy from the complex organic mixture in most foods is tackled in stages. First, enzymes break down the large molecules into smaller ones, a process called digestion (see chapter 47). Then, other enzymes dismantle these fragments a bit at a time, harvesting energy from C—H and other chemical bonds at each stage.

The reactions that break down these molecules share a common feature: They are oxidations. Energy metabolism is therefore concerned with redox reactions, and to understand the process we must follow the fate of the electrons lost from the food molecules.

These reactions are not the simple transfer of electrons, however; they are also **dehydrogenations.** That is, the electrons lost are accompanied by protons, so that what is really lost is a hydrogen atom, not just an electron.

Cellular respiration is the complete oxidation of glucose

In chapter 6, you learned that an atom that loses electrons is said to be *oxidized,* and an atom accepting electrons is said to be *reduced.* Oxidation reactions are often coupled with reduction reactions in living systems, and these paired reactions are called *redox reactions.* Cells utilize enzyme-facilitated redox reactions to take energy from food sources and convert it to ATP.

Redox reactions

Oxidation–reduction reactions play a key role in the flow of energy through biological systems because the electrons that pass from one atom to another carry energy with them. The amount of energy an electron possesses depends on its orbital position, or energy level, around the atom's nucleus. When this electron departs from one atom and moves to another in a redox reaction, the electron's energy is transferred with it.

Figure 7.1 shows how an enzyme catalyzes a redox reaction involving an energy-rich substrate molecule, with the help of a cofactor, **nicotinamide adenosine dinucleotide (NAD⁺).** In this reaction, NAD^+ accepts a pair of electrons from the substrate, along with a proton, to form **NADH** (this process is described in more detail shortly). The oxidized product is now released from the enzyme's active site, as is NADH.

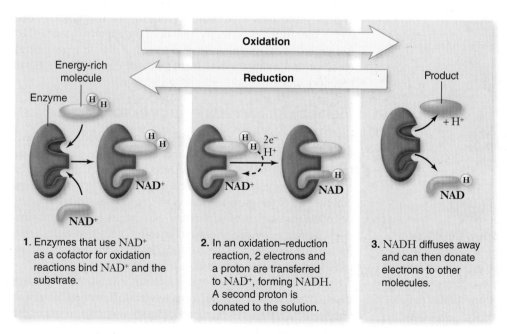

1. Enzymes that use NAD^+ as a cofactor for oxidation reactions bind NAD^+ and the substrate.

2. In an oxidation–reduction reaction, 2 electrons and a proton are transferred to NAD^+, forming NADH. A second proton is donated to the solution.

3. NADH diffuses away and can then donate electrons to other molecules.

Figure 7.1 Oxidation–reduction reactions often employ cofactors. Cells use a chemical cofactor called nicotinamide adenosine dinucleotide (NAD^+) to carry out many oxidation-reduction reactions. Two electrons and a proton are transferred to NAD^+ with another proton donated to the solution. Molecules that gain electrons are said to be reduced, and ones that lose energetic electrons are said to be oxidized. NAD^+ oxidizes energy-rich molecules by acquiring their electrons (in the figure, this proceeds 1 ⟶ 2 ⟶ 3) and then reduces other molecules by giving the electrons to them (in the figure, this proceeds 3 ⟶ 2 ⟶ 1). NADH is the reduced form of NAD^+.

In the overall process of cellular energy harvest dozens of redox reactions take place, and a number of molecules, including NAD$^+$, act as electron acceptors. During each transfer of electrons energy is released. This energy may be captured and used to make ATP or to form other chemical bonds; the rest is lost as heat.

At the end of this process, high-energy electrons from the initial chemical bonds have lost much of their energy, and these depleted electrons are transferred to a final electron acceptor (figure 7.2). When this acceptor is oxygen, the process is called **aerobic respiration.** When the final electron acceptor is an inorganic molecule other than oxygen, the process is called **anaerobic respiration,** and when it is an organic molecule, the process is called **fermentation.**

"Burning" carbohydrates

Chemically, there is little difference between the catabolism of carbohydrates in a cell and the burning of wood in a fireplace. In both instances, the reactants are carbohydrates and oxygen, and the products are carbon dioxide, water, and energy:

$$\underset{\text{glucose}}{C_6H_{12}O_6} + \underset{\text{oxygen}}{6O_2} \longrightarrow \underset{\substack{\text{carbon}\\\text{dioxide}}}{6CO_2} + \underset{\text{water}}{6H_2O} + \text{energy (heat and ATP)}$$

The change in free energy in this reaction is −686 kcal/mol (or −2870 kJ/mol) under standard conditions (that is, at room temperature, 1 atm pressure, and so forth). In the conditions that exist inside a cell, the energy released can be as high as −720 kcal/mol (−3012 kJ/mol) of glucose. This means that under actual cellular conditions, more energy is released than under standard conditions.

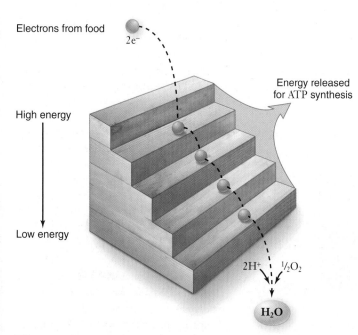

Electrons from food
2e$^-$

High energy

Low energy

Energy released for ATP synthesis

2H$^+$ ½O$_2$

H$_2$O

Figure 7.2 How electron transport works. This diagram shows how ATP is generated when electrons transfer from one energy level to another. Rather than releasing a single explosive burst of energy, electrons "fall" to lower and lower energy levels in steps, releasing stored energy with each fall as they tumble to the lowest (most electronegative) electron acceptor, O$_2$.

The same amount of energy is released whether glucose is catabolized or burned, but when it is burned, most of the energy is released as heat. Cells harvest useful energy from the catabolism of glucose by using a portion of the energy to drive the production of ATP.

Electron carriers play a critical role in energy metabolism

During respiration, glucose is oxidized to CO$_2$. If the electrons were given directly to O$_2$, the reaction would be combustion, and cells would burst into flames. Instead, as you have just seen, the cell transfers the electrons to intermediate electron carriers, then eventually to O$_2$.

Many forms of electron carriers are used in this process: (1) soluble carriers that move electrons from one molecule to another, (2) membrane-bound carriers that form a redox chain, and (3) carriers that move within the membrane. The common feature of all of these carriers is that they can be reversibly oxidized and reduced. Some of these carriers, such as the iron-containing cytochromes, can carry just electrons, and some carry both electrons and protons.

NAD$^+$ is one of the most important electron (and proton) carriers. As shown on the left in figure 7.3, the NAD$^+$ molecule is composed of two nucleotides bound together. The two nucleotides that make up NAD$^+$, nicotinamide monophosphate (NMP) and adenosine monophosphate (AMP), are joined head-to-head by their phosphate groups. The two nucleotides serve different functions in the NAD$^+$ molecule: AMP acts as the core, providing a shape recognized by many enzymes; NMP is the active part of the molecule, because it is readily reduced, that is, it easily accepts electrons.

When NAD$^+$ acquires two electrons and a proton from the active site of an enzyme, it is reduced to NADH, shown on the right in figure 7.3. The NADH molecule now carries the two energetic electrons and can supply them to other molecules and reduce them.

This ability to supply high-energy electrons is critical to both energy metabolism and to the biosynthesis of many organic molecules, including fats and sugars. In animals, when ATP is plentiful, the reducing power of the accumulated NADH is diverted to supplying fatty acid precursors with high-energy electrons, reducing them to form fats and storing the energy of the electrons.

Metabolism harvests energy in stages

It is generally true that the larger the release of energy in any single step, the more of that energy is released as heat, and the less is available to be channeled into more useful paths. In the combustion of gasoline, the same amount of energy is released whether all of the gasoline in a car's gas tank explodes at once, or burns in a series of very small explosions inside the cylinders. By releasing the energy in gasoline a little at a time, the harvesting efficiency is greater, and more of the energy can be used to push the pistons and move the car.

The same principle applies to the oxidation of glucose inside a cell. If all of the electrons were transferred to oxygen in one explosive step, releasing all of the free energy at once, the

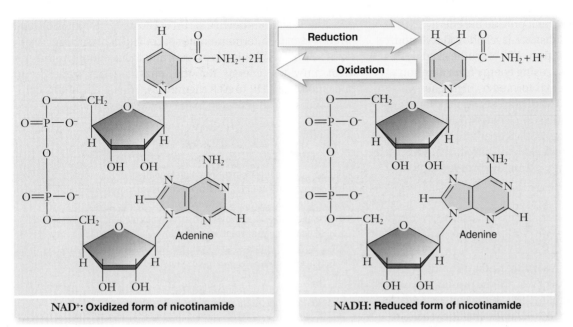

Figure 7.3 NAD⁺ and NADH. This dinucleotide serves as an "electron shuttle" during cellular respiration. NAD⁺ accepts a pair of electrons and a proton from catabolized macromolecules and is reduced to NADH.

Figure 7.3 NAD⁺ and NADH. This dinucleotide serves as an "electron shuttle" during cellular respiration. NAD⁺ accepts a pair of electrons and a proton from catabolized macromolecules and is reduced to NADH.

NAD⁺: Oxidized form of nicotinamide

NADH: Reduced form of nicotinamide

cell would recover very little of that energy in a useful form. Instead, cells burn their fuel much as a car does, a little at a time.

The electrons in the C—H bonds of glucose are stripped off in stages in the series of enzyme-catalyzed reactions collectively referred to as glycolysis and the Krebs cycle. The electrons are removed by transferring them to NAD⁺, as described earlier, or to other electron carriers.

The energy released by all of these oxidation reactions is also not all released at once (see figure 7.2). The electrons are passed to another set of electron carriers called the **electron transport chain,** which is located in the mitochondrial inner membrane. Movement of electrons through this chain produces potential energy in the form of an electrochemical gradient. We examine this process in more detail later in this chapter.

ATP plays a central role in metabolism

The previous chapter introduced ATP as the energy currency of the cell. Cells use ATP to power most of those activities that require work—one of the most obvious of which is movement. Tiny fibers within muscle cells pull against one another when muscles contract. Mitochondria can move a meter or more along the narrow nerve cells that extend from your spine to your feet. Chromosomes are pulled apart by microtubules during cell division. All of these movements require the expenditure of energy by ATP hydrolysis. Cells also use ATP to drive endergonic reactions that would otherwise not occur spontaneously (see chapter 6).

How does ATP drive an endergonic reaction? The enzyme that catalyzes a particular reaction has two binding sites on its surface: one for the reactant and another for ATP. The ATP site splits the ATP molecule, liberating over 7 kcal ($\Delta G = -7.3$ kcal/mol) of chemical energy. This energy pushes the reactant at the second site "uphill," reaching the activation energy and driving the endergonic reaction. Thus endergonic reactions coupled to ATP hydrolysis become favorable.

The many steps of cellular respiration have as their ultimate goal the production of ATP. ATP synthesis is itself an endergonic reaction, which requires energy from cellular exergonic reactions to drive this synthesis.

Cells make ATP by two fundamentally different mechanisms

The synthesis of ATP can be accomplished by two distinct mechanisms: one that involves chemical coupling with an intermediate bound to phosphate, and another that relies on an electrochemical gradient of protons for the potential energy to phosphorylate ADP.

1. In *substrate-level phosphorylation,* ATP is formed by transferring a phosphate group directly to ADP from a phosphate-bearing intermediate, or substrate (figure 7.4). During **glycolysis,** the initial breakdown of glucose (discussed later), the chemical bonds of glucose are

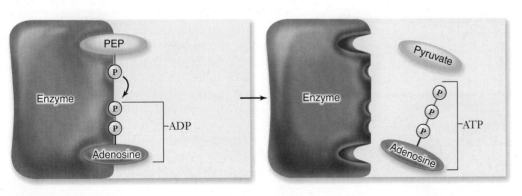

Figure 7.4 Substrate-level phosphorylation. Some molecules, such as phosphoenolpyruvate (PEP), possess a high-energy phosphate (P) bond similar to the bonds in ATP. When PEP's phosphate group is transferred enzymatically to ADP, the energy in the bond is conserved, and ATP is created.

shifted around in reactions that provide the energy required to form ATP by substrate-level phosphorylation.

2. In **oxidative phosphorylation,** ATP is synthesized by the enzyme **ATP synthase,** using energy from a proton (H^+) gradient. This gradient is formed by high-energy electrons from the oxidation of glucose passing down an electron transport chain (described later). These electrons, with their energy depleted, are then donated to oxygen, hence the term *oxidative phosphorylation.* ATP synthase uses the energy from the proton gradient to catalyze the reaction:

$$ADP + P_i \longrightarrow ATP$$

Eukaryotes and aerobic prokaryotes produce the vast majority of their ATP this way.

In most organisms, these two processes are combined. To harvest energy to make ATP from glucose in the presence of oxygen, the cell carries out a complex series of enzyme-catalyzed reactions that remove energetic electrons via oxidation reactions. These electrons are then used in an electron transport chain that passes the electrons down a series of carriers while translocating protons into the intermembrane space. The final electron acceptor in aerobic respiration is oxygen, and the resulting proton gradient provides energy for the enzyme ATP synthase to phosphorylate ADP to ATP (figure 7.5). The details of this complex process will be covered in the remainder of this chapter.

Learning Outcomes Review 7.1

Cells acquire energy from the complete oxidation of glucose. In these redox reactions, protons as well as electrons are transferred, and thus they are dehydrogenation reactions. Electron carriers aid in the gradual, stepwise release of the energy from oxidation, rather than rapid combustion. The result is the synthesis of ATP, a portable source of energy. ATP synthesis can occur by two mechanisms: substrate-level phosphorylation and oxidative phosphorylation.

■ *Why don't cells just link the oxidation of glucose directly to cellular functions that require the energy?*

Figure 7.5 An overview of aerobic respiration.

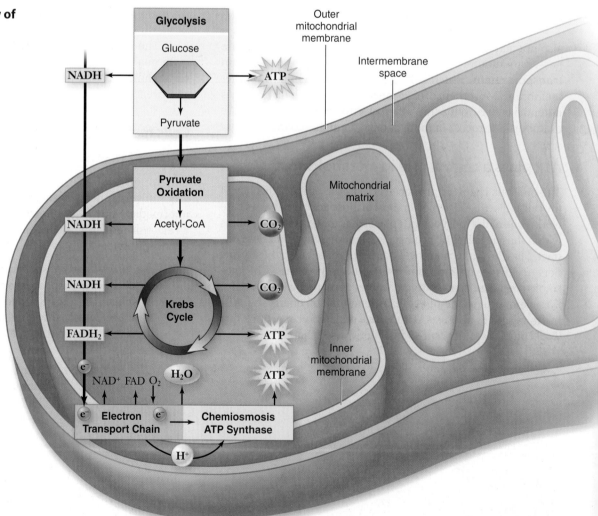

Learning Outcomes

1. *Describe the process of glycolysis.*
2. *Calculate the energy yield from glycolysis.*
3. *Distinguish between aerobic respiration and fermentation.*

Glucose molecules can be dismantled in many ways, but primitive organisms evolved a glucose-catabolizing process that releases enough free energy to drive the synthesis of ATP in enzyme-coupled reactions. Glycolysis occurs in the cytoplasm and converts glucose into two 3-carbon molecules of pyruvate (figure 7.6). For each molecule of glucose that passes through this transformation, the cell nets two ATP molecules.

Glycolysis converts glucose into two pyruvate and yields two ATP and two NADH in the process

The first half of glycolysis consists of five sequential reactions that convert one molecule of glucose into two molecules of the 3-carbon compound **glyceraldehyde 3-phosphate (G3P).** These reactions require the expenditure of ATP, so they constitute an endergonic process. In the second half of glycolysis, five more reactions convert G3P into pyruvate in an energy-yielding process that generates ATP.

Priming reactions The first three reactions "prime" glucose by changing it into a compound that can be readily cleaved into two 3-carbon phosphorylated molecules. Two of these reactions transfer a phosphate from ATP, so this step requires the cell to use two ATP molecules.

Cleavage This 6-carbon diphosphate sugar is then split into two 3-carbon monophosphate sugars. One of these is G3P, and the other is converted into G3P. The G3P then undergoes a series of reactions that eventually yields more energy than was spent priming (figure 7.7).

Oxidation and ATP formation Each G3P is oxidized, transferring two electrons (and one proton) to NAD$^+$, thus forming NADH. A molecule of P$_i$ is also added to G3P to produce 1,3-bisphosphoglycerate (BPG). The phosphate incorporated can be transferred to ADP by substrate-level phosphorylation (see figure 7.4) to allow a positive yield of ATP at the end of the process.

Another four reactions convert BPG into pyruvate. In the process, the phosphates are transferred to ADP to yield two ATP per G3P. The entire process is shown in detail in figure 7.7.

Each glucose molecule is split into two G3P molecules, so the overall reaction sequence has a net yield of two molecules of ATP, as well as two molecules of NADH and two of pyruvate:

4 ATP (2 ATP for each of the 2 G3P molecules)
– 2 ATP (used in the two reactions in the first step)

2 ATP (net yield for entire process)

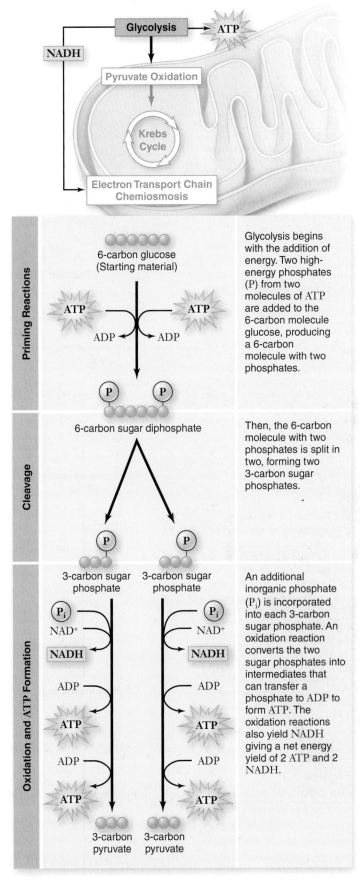

Figure 7.6 An overview of glycolysis.

Glycolysis begins with the addition of energy. Two high-energy phosphates (P) from two molecules of ATP are added to the 6-carbon molecule glucose, producing a 6-carbon molecule with two phosphates.

Then, the 6-carbon molecule with two phosphates is split in two, forming two 3-carbon sugar phosphates.

An additional inorganic phosphate (P$_i$) is incorporated into each 3-carbon sugar phosphate. An oxidation reaction converts the two sugar phosphates into intermediates that can transfer a phosphate to ADP to form ATP. The oxidation reactions also yield NADH giving a net energy yield of 2 ATP and 2 NADH.

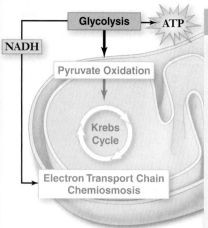

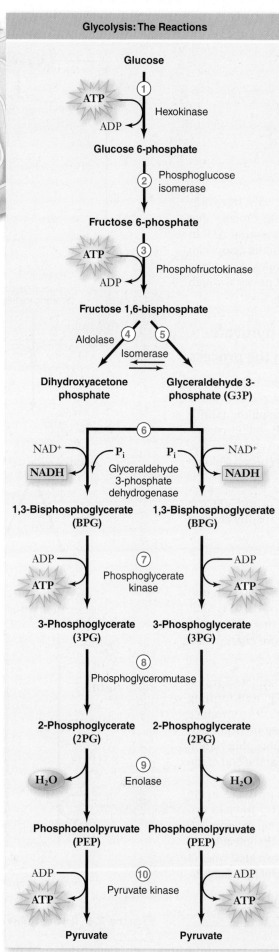

Glycolysis: The Reactions

Glucose

① Hexokinase
ATP → ADP

Glucose 6-phosphate

② Phosphoglucose isomerase

Fructose 6-phosphate

③ Phosphofructokinase
ATP → ADP

Fructose 1,6-bisphosphate

④ Aldolase ⑤ Isomerase

Dihydroxyacetone phosphate   **Glyceraldehyde 3-phosphate (G3P)**

⑥ Glyceraldehyde 3-phosphate dehydrogenase
NAD^+ P_i P_i NAD^+
NADH   **NADH**

1,3-Bisphosphoglycerate (BPG)   **1,3-Bisphosphoglycerate (BPG)**

⑦ Phosphoglycerate kinase
ADP → **ATP**   ADP → **ATP**

3-Phosphoglycerate (3PG)   **3-Phosphoglycerate (3PG)**

⑧ Phosphoglyceromutase

2-Phosphoglycerate (2PG)   **2-Phosphoglycerate (2PG)**

⑨ Enolase
H_2O H_2O

Phosphoenolpyruvate (PEP)   **Phosphoenolpyruvate (PEP)**

⑩ Pyruvate kinase
ADP → **ATP**   ADP → **ATP**

Pyruvate   **Pyruvate**

---

1. Phosphorylation of glucose by ATP.

2–3. Rearrangement, followed by a second ATP phosphorylation.

4–5. The 6-carbon molecule is split into two 3-carbon molecules—one G3P, another that is converted into G3P in another reaction.

6. Oxidation followed by phosphorylation produces two NADH molecules and two molecules of BPG, each with one high-energy phosphate bond.

7. Removal of high-energy phosphate by two ADP molecules produces two ATP molecules and leaves two 3PG molecules.

8–9. Removal of water yields two PEP molecules, each with a high-energy phosphate bond.

10. Removal of high-energy phosphate by two ADP molecules produces two ATP molecules and two pyruvate molecules.

Figure 7.7
The glycolytic pathway.

The first five reactions convert a molecule of glucose into two molecules of G3P. The second five reactions convert G3P into pyruvate.

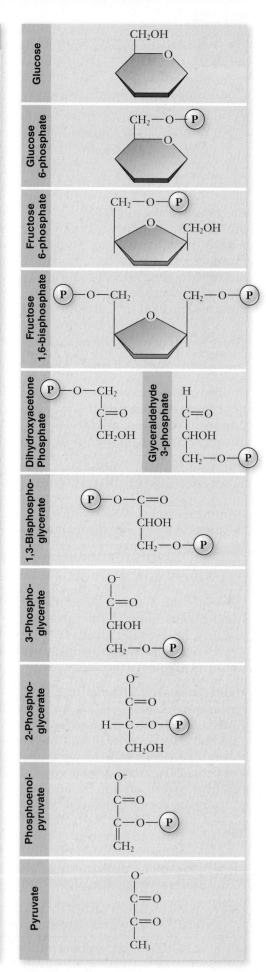

The hydrolysis of one molecule of ATP yields a ΔG of –7.3 kcal/mol under standard conditions. Thus cells harvest a maximum of 14.6 kcal of energy per mole of glucose from glycolysis.

A brief history of glycolysis

Although the ATP yield from glycolysis is low, it is actually quite efficient, with just under 40% of the energy released being trapped as ATP. For more than a billion years during the anaerobic first stages of life on Earth, glycolysis was the primary way heterotrophic organisms generated ATP from organic molecules.

Like many biochemical pathways, glycolysis is believed to have evolved backward—the last steps in the process being the most ancient. Thus, the second half of glycolysis, the ATP-yielding breakdown of G3P, may have been the original process. The synthesis of G3P from glucose would have appeared later, perhaps when alternative sources of G3P were depleted.

Why does glycolysis take place in modern organisms, since its energy yield in the absence of oxygen is comparatively little? There are several possible answers. First, the process is energetically efficient, and better than the alternative—no ATP. Second, evolution is an incremental process: Change occurs by improving on past successes. In catabolic metabolism, glycolysis satisfied the one essential evolutionary criterion—it was an improvement. Cells that could not carry out glycolysis were at a competitive disadvantage, and only cells capable of glycolysis survived. Later improvements in catabolic metabolism built on this framework to increase the yield of ATP as oxygen became available as an oxidizing agent. Metabolism evolved as one layer of reactions added to another. Nearly every present-day organism carries out glycolysis, as a metabolic memory of its evolutionary past.

The last section of this chapter discusses the evolution of metabolism in more detail.

NADH must be recycled to continue respiration

Inspect for a moment the net reaction of the glycolytic sequence:

$$\text{glucose} + 2\,\text{ADP} + 2\,\text{P}_i + 2\,\text{NAD}^+ \longrightarrow 2\,\text{pyruvate} + 2\,\text{ATP} + 2\,\text{NADH} + 2\text{H}^+ + 2\text{H}_2\text{O}$$

You can see that three changes occur in glycolysis: (1) glucose is converted into two molecules of pyruvate; (2) two molecules of ADP are converted into ATP via substrate-level phosphorylation; and (3) two molecules of NAD^+ are reduced to NADH. This leaves the cell with two problems: extracting the energy that remains in the two pyruvate molecules, and regenerating NAD^+ to be able to continue glycolysis.

Recycling NADH

As long as food molecules that can be converted into glucose are available, a cell can continually churn out ATP to drive its activities. In doing so, however, it accumulates NADH and depletes the pool of NAD^+ molecules. A cell does not contain a large amount of NAD^+, and for glycolysis to continue, NADH must be recycled into NAD^+. Some molecule other than NAD^+ must ultimately accept the electrons taken from G3P and be reduced. Two processes can carry out this key task (figure 7.8):

1. **Aerobic respiration.** Oxygen is an excellent electron acceptor. Through a series of electron transfers, electrons taken from G3P can be donated to oxygen, forming water. This process occurs in the mitochondria of eukaryotic cells in the presence of oxygen. Because air is rich in oxygen, this process is also referred to as *aerobic metabolism*. A significant amount of ATP is also produced.
2. **Fermentation.** When oxygen is unavailable, an organic molecule can accept electrons. The organic molecules used are quite varied and include acetaldehyde in ethanolic fermentation or pyruvate itself in lactic acid fermentation. This reaction plays an important role in the metabolism of most organisms, even those capable of aerobic respiration.

The fate of pyruvate

The fate of the pyruvate that is produced by glycolysis depends on which of these two processes takes place. The aerobic

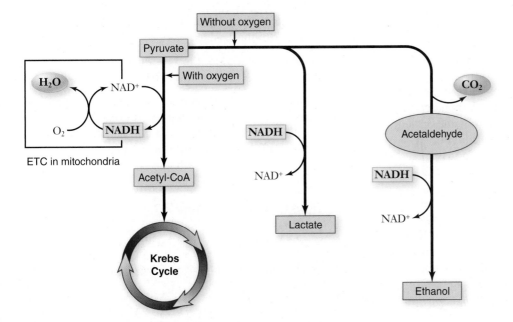

Figure 7.8 The fate of pyruvate and NADH produced by glycolysis. In the presence of oxygen, NADH is oxidized by the electron transport chain (ETC) in mitochondria using oxygen as the final electron acceptor. This regenerates NAD^+, allowing glycolysis to continue. The pyruvate produced by glycolysis is oxidized to acetyl-CoA, which enters the Krebs cycle. In the absence of oxygen, pyruvate is instead reduced, oxidizing NADH and regenerating NAD^+ thus allowing glycolysis to continue. Direct reduction of pyruvate, as in muscle cells, produces lactate. In yeast, carbon dioxide is first removed from pyruvate, producing acetaldehyde, which is then reduced to ethanol.

respiration path starts with the oxidation of pyruvate to produce acetyl coenzyme A (acetyl-CoA), which is then further oxidized in a series of reactions called the Krebs cycle. The fermentation path, by contrast, uses the reduction of all or part of pyruvate to oxidize NADH back to NAD$^+$. We examine aerobic respiration next; fermentation is described in detail in a later section.

Learning Outcomes Review 7.2

Glycolysis splits the 6-carbon molecule glucose into two 3-carbon molecules of pyruvate. This process uses two ATP molecules in "priming" reactions and eventually produces four molecules of ATP per glucose for a net yield of two ATP. The oxidation reactions of glycolysis require NAD$^+$ and produce NADH. When oxygen is abundant, NAD$^+$ is regenerated in the electron transport chain, using O$_2$ as an acceptor. When oxygen is absent, NAD$^+$ is regenerated in a fermentation reaction using an organic molecule as an electron receptor.

■ *Does glycolysis taking place in the cytoplasm argue for or against the endosymbiotic origin of mitochondria?*

7.3 The Oxidation of Pyruvate to Produce Acetyl-CoA

Learning Outcome

1. *Diagram how the oxidation of pyruvate links glycolysis with the Krebs cycle.*

In the presence of oxygen, the oxidation of glucose that begins in glycolysis continues where glycolysis leaves off—with pyruvate. In eukaryotic organisms, the extraction of additional energy from pyruvate takes place exclusively inside mitochondria. In prokaryotes similar reactions take place in the cytoplasm and at the plasma membrane.

The cell harvests pyruvate's considerable energy in two steps. First, pyruvate is oxidized to produce a 2-carbon compound and CO$_2$, with the electrons transferred to NAD$^+$ to produce NADH. Next, the 2-carbon compound is oxidized to CO$_2$ by the reactions of the Krebs cycle.

Pyruvate is oxidized in a "decarboxylation" reaction that cleaves off one of pyruvate's three carbons. This carbon departs as CO$_2$ (figure 7.9). The remaining 2-carbon compound, called an acetyl group, is then attached to coenzyme A; this entire molecule is called *acetyl-CoA*. A pair of electrons and one associated proton is transferred to the electron carrier NAD$^+$, reducing it to NADH, with a second proton donated to the solution.

The reaction involves three intermediate stages, and it is catalyzed within mitochondria by a *multienzyme complex*. As chapter 6 noted, a multienzyme complex organizes a series of enzymatic steps so that the chemical intermediates do not diffuse away or undergo other reactions. Within the complex, component polypeptides pass the substrates from one enzyme to the next without releasing them. *Pyruvate dehydrogenase*,

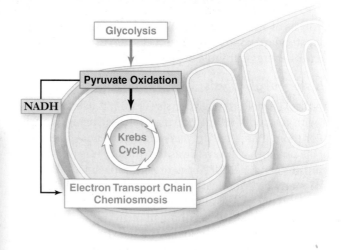

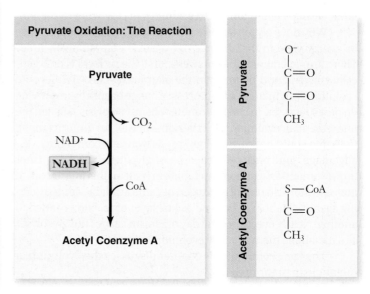

Figure 7.9 The oxidation of pyruvate. This complex reaction uses NAD$^+$ to accept electrons, reducing it to NADH. The product, acetyl coenzyme A (acetyl-CoA), feeds the acetyl unit into the Krebs cycle, and the CoA is recycled for another oxidation of pyruvate. NADH provides energetic electrons for the electron transport chain.

the complex of enzymes that removes CO$_2$ from pyruvate, is one of the largest enzymes known; it contains 60 subunits! The reaction can be summarized as:

$$\text{pyruvate} + \text{NAD}^+ + \text{CoA} \longrightarrow \text{acetyl-CoA} + \text{NADH} + \text{CO}_2 + \text{H}^+$$

The molecule of NADH produced is used later to produce ATP. The acetyl group is fed into the Krebs cycle, with the CoA being recycled for another oxidation of pyruvate. The Krebs cycle then completes the oxidation of the original carbons from glucose.

Learning Outcome Review 7.3

Pyruvate is oxidized in the mitochondria to produce acetyl-CoA and CO$_2$. Acetyl-CoA is the molecule that links glycolysis and the reactions of the Krebs cycle.

■ *What are the advantages and disadvantages of a multienzyme complex?*

The Krebs Cycle

are transferred to electron carriers. These electrons are then used by the electron transport chain to drive *proton pumps* that generate ATP.

Learning Outcomes

1. *Relate the nine reactions of the Krebs cycle to the flow of carbon and electrons in the cycle.*
2. *Diagram the oxidation reactions in the Krebs cycle.*

In this third stage, the acetyl group from pyruvate is oxidized in a series of nine reactions called the *Krebs cycle.* These reactions occur in the matrix of mitochondria.

In this cycle, the 2-carbon acetyl group of acetyl-CoA combines with a 4-carbon molecule called oxaloacetate. The resulting 6-carbon molecule, citrate, then goes through a several-step sequence of electron-yielding oxidation reactions, during which two CO_2 molecules split off, restoring oxaloacetate. The regenerated oxaloacetate is used to bind to another acetyl group for the next round of the cycle.

In each turn of the cycle, a new acetyl group is added and two carbons are lost, as two CO_2 molecules and more electrons

An overview of the Krebs cycle

The nine reactions of the Krebs cycle take in 2-carbon units in the form of acetyl-CoA and oxidize them, transferring electrons and protons to NADH and $FADH_2$ (figure 7.10).

The first reaction combines the 4-carbon oxaloacetate with the acetyl group to produce the 6-carbon citrate molecule. Five more steps, which have been simplified in figure 7.10, convert citrate to a 5-carbon intermediate and then to the 4-carbon succinate. During these reactions, two NADH and one ATP are produced.

Succinate undergoes three additional reactions, also simplified in the figure, to become oxaloacetate. During these reactions, one more NADH is produced; in addition, a molecule of flavin adenine dinucleotide (FAD), another cofactor, becomes reduced to $FADH_2$.

The specifics of each reaction are described next.

Figure 7.10 **An overview of the Krebs cycle.**

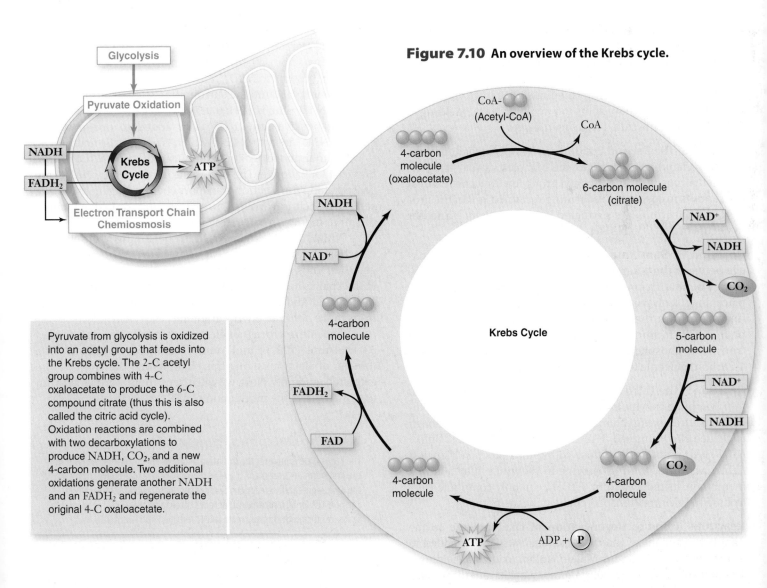

Pyruvate from glycolysis is oxidized into an acetyl group that feeds into the Krebs cycle. The 2-C acetyl group combines with 4-C oxaloacetate to produce the 6-C compound citrate (thus this is also called the citric acid cycle). Oxidation reactions are combined with two decarboxylations to produce NADH, CO_2, and a new 4-carbon molecule. Two additional oxidations generate another NADH and an $FADH_2$ and regenerate the original 4-C oxaloacetate.

The Krebs cycle extracts electrons and synthesizes one ATP

Figure 7.11 summarizes the sequence of the Krebs cycle reactions. A 2-carbon group from acetyl-CoA enters the cycle at the beginning, and two CO_2 molecules, one ATP, and four pairs of electrons are produced.

Reaction 1: Condensation Citrate is formed from acetyl-CoA and oxaloacetate. This condensation reaction is irreversible, committing the 2-carbon acetyl group to the Krebs cycle. The reaction is inhibited when the cell's ATP concentration is high and stimulated when it is low. The result is that when the cell possesses ample amounts of ATP, the Krebs cycle shuts down, and acetyl-CoA is channeled into fat synthesis.

Reactions 2 and 3: Isomerization Before the oxidation reactions can begin, the hydroxyl (—OH) group of citrate must be repositioned. This rearrangement is done in two steps: First, a water molecule is removed from one carbon; then water is added to a different carbon. As a result, an —H group and an —OH group change positions. The product is an isomer of citrate called *isocitrate*. This rearrangement facilitates the subsequent reactions.

Reaction 4: The First Oxidation In the first energy-yielding step of the cycle, isocitrate undergoes an oxidative decarboxylation reaction. First, isocitrate is oxidized, yielding a pair of electrons that reduce a molecule of NAD^+ to NADH. Then the oxidized intermediate is decarboxylated; the central carboxyl group splits off to form CO_2, yielding a 5-carbon molecule called α-*ketoglutarate*.

Reaction 5: The Second Oxidation Next, α-ketoglutarate is decarboxylated by a multienzyme complex similar to pyruvate dehydrogenase. The succinyl group left after the removal of CO_2 joins to coenzyme A, forming *succinyl-CoA*. In the process, two electrons are extracted, and they reduce another molecule of NAD^+ to NADH.

Reaction 6: Substrate-Level Phosphorylation The linkage between the 4-carbon succinyl group and CoA is a high-energy bond. In a coupled reaction similar to those that take place in glycolysis, this bond is cleaved, and the energy released drives the phosphorylation of guanosine diphosphate (GDP), forming guanosine triphosphate (GTP). GTP can transfer a phosphate to ADP converting it into ATP. The 4-carbon molecule that remains is called *succinate*.

Reaction 7: The Third Oxidation Next, succinate is oxidized to *fumarate* by an enzyme located in the inner mitochondrial membrane. The free-energy change in this reaction is not large enough to reduce NAD^+. Instead, FAD is the electron acceptor. Unlike NAD^+, FAD is not free to diffuse within the mitochondrion; it is tightly associated with its enzyme in the inner mitochondrial membrane. Its reduced form, $FADH_2$, can only contribute electrons to the electron transport chain in the membrane.

Reactions 8 and 9: Regeneration of Oxaloacetate In the final two reactions of the cycle, a water molecule is added to fumarate, forming *malate*. Malate is then oxidized, yielding a 4-carbon molecule of *oxaloacetate* and two electrons that reduce a molecule of NAD^+ to NADH. Oxaloacetate, the molecule that began the cycle, is now free to combine with another 2-carbon acetyl group from acetyl-CoA and begin the cycle again.

Glucose becomes CO_2 and potential energy

In the process of aerobic respiration, glucose is entirely consumed. The 6-carbon glucose molecule is cleaved into two 3-carbon pyruvate molecules during glycolysis. One of the carbons of each pyruvate is then lost as CO_2 in the conversion of pyruvate to acetyl-CoA. The two other carbons from acetyl-CoA are lost as CO_2 during the oxidations of the Krebs cycle.

All that is left to mark the passing of a glucose molecule into six CO_2 molecules is its energy, some of which is preserved in four ATP molecules and in the reduced state of 12 electron carriers. Ten of these carriers are NADH molecules; the other two are $FADH_2$.

Following the electrons in the reactions reveals the direction of transfer

As you examine the changes in electrical charge in the reactions that oxidize glucose, a good strategy for keeping the transfers clear is always to *follow the electrons*. For example, in glycolysis, an enzyme extracts two hydrogens—that is, two electrons and two protons—from glucose and transfers both electrons and one of the protons to NAD^+. The other proton is released as a hydrogen ion, H^+, into the surrounding solution. This transfer converts NAD^+ into NADH; that is, two negative electrons ($2e^-$) and one positive proton (H^+) are added to one positively charged NAD^+ to form NADH, which is electrically neutral.

As mentioned earlier, energy captured by NADH is not harvested all at once. The two electrons carried by NADH are passed along the electron transport chain, which consists of a series of electron carriers, mostly proteins, embedded within the inner membranes of mitochondria.

NADH delivers electrons to the beginning of the electron transport chain, and oxygen captures them at the end. The oxygen then joins with hydrogen ions to form water. At each step in the chain, the electrons move to a slightly more electronegative carrier, and their positions shift slightly. Thus, the electrons move *down* an energy gradient.

The entire process of electron transfer releases a total of 53 kcal/mol (222 kJ/mol) under standard conditions. The transfer of electrons along this chain allows the energy to be extracted gradually. Next, we will discuss how this energy is put to work to drive the production of ATP.

Learning Outcomes Review 7.4

The Krebs cycle completes the oxidation of glucose begun with glycolysis. In the first segment, acetyl-CoA is added to oxaloacetate to produce citrate. In the next segment, five reactions produce succinate, two NADH from NAD^+, and one ATP. Finally, succinate undergoes three more reactions to regenerate oxaloacetate, producing one more NADH and one $FADH_2$ from FAD.

■ *What happens to the electrons removed from glucose at this point?*

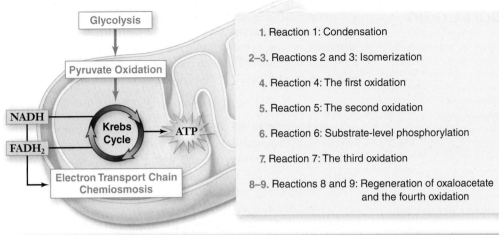

Figure 7.11 The Krebs cycle. This series of reactions takes place within the matrix of the mitochondrion. For the complete breakdown of a molecule of glucose, the two molecules of acetyl-CoA produced by glycolysis and pyruvate oxidation each have to make a trip around the Krebs cycle. Follow the different carbons through the cycle, and notice the changes that occur in the carbon skeletons of the molecules and where oxidation reactions take place as they proceed through the cycle.

1. Reaction 1: Condensation

2–3. Reactions 2 and 3: Isomerization

4. Reaction 4: The first oxidation

5. Reaction 5: The second oxidation

6. Reaction 6: Substrate-level phosphorylation

7. Reaction 7: The third oxidation

8–9. Reactions 8 and 9: Regeneration of oxaloacetate and the fourth oxidation

Krebs Cycle: The Reactions

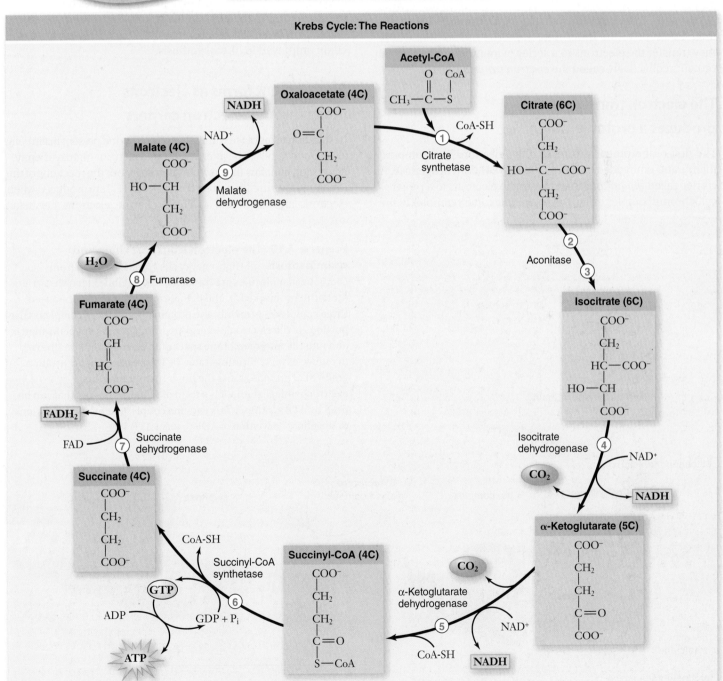

The Electron Transport Chain and Chemiosmosis

The NADH and FADH$_2$ molecules formed during aerobic respiration each contain a pair of electrons that were gained when NAD$^+$ and FAD were reduced. The NADH and FADH$_2$ carry their electrons to the inner mitochondrial membrane, where they transfer the electrons to a series of membrane-associated proteins collectively called the *electron transport chain.*

The electron transport chain produces a proton gradient

The first of the proteins to receive the electrons is a complex, membrane-embedded enzyme called **NADH dehydrogenase.** A carrier called *ubiquinone* then passes the electrons to a protein–cytochrome complex called the *bc₁ complex.* Each complex in the chain operates as a proton pump, driving a proton out across the membrane into the intermembrane space (figure 7.12*a*).

The electrons are then carried by another carrier, *cytochrome c,* to the cytochrome oxidase complex. This complex uses four electrons to reduce a molecule of oxygen. Each oxygen then combines with two protons to form water:

$$O_2 + 4H^+ + 4e^- \longrightarrow 2H_2O$$

In contrast to NADH, which contributes its electrons to NADH dehydrogenase, FADH$_2$, which is located in the inner mitochondrial membrane, feeds its electrons to ubiquinone, which is also in the membrane. Electrons from FADH$_2$ thus "skip" the first step in the electron transport chain.

The plentiful availability of a strong electron acceptor, oxygen, is what makes oxidative respiration possible. As you'll see in chapter 8, the electron transport chain used in aerobic respiration is similar to, and may well have evolved from, the chain employed in photosynthesis.

The gradient forms as electrons move through electron carriers

Respiration takes place within the mitochondria present in virtually all eukaryotic cells. The internal compartment, or matrix, of a mitochondrion contains the enzymes that carry out the reactions of the Krebs cycle. As mentioned earlier, protons (H$^+$) are produced when electrons are transferred to NAD$^+$. As the electrons harvested

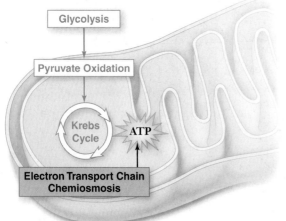

Figure 7.12 The electron transport chain and chemiosmosis. *a.* High-energy electrons harvested from catabolized molecules are transported by mobile electron carriers (ubiquinone, marked Q, and cytochrome c, marked C) between three complexes of membrane proteins. These three complexes use portions of the electrons' energy to pump protons out of the matrix and into the intermembrane space. The electrons are finally used to reduce oxygen, forming water. ***b.*** This creates a concentration gradient of protons across the inner membrane. This electrochemical gradient is a form of potential energy that can be used by ATP synthase. This enzyme couples the reentry of protons to the phosphorylation of ADP to form ATP.

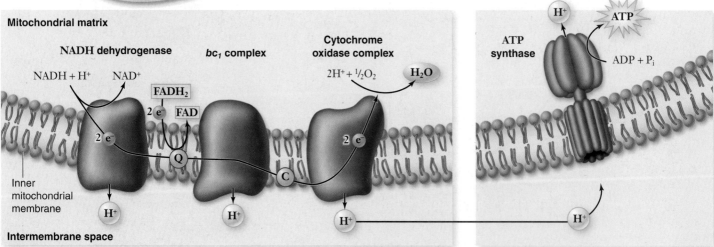

a. The electron transport chain

b. Chemiosmosis

by oxidative respiration are passed along the electron transport chain, the energy they release transports protons out of the matrix and into the outer compartment called the intermembrane space.

Three transmembrane complexes of the electron transport chain in the inner mitochondrial membrane actually accomplish the proton transport (see figure 7.12a). The flow of highly energetic electrons induces a change in the shape of pump proteins, which causes them to transport protons across the membrane. The electrons contributed by NADH activate all three of these proton pumps, whereas those contributed by FADH$_2$ activate only two because of where they enter the chain. In this way a proton gradient is formed between the intermembrane space and the matrix.

Chemiosmosis utilizes the electrochemical gradient to produce ATP

Because the mitochondrial matrix is negative compared with the intermembrane space, positively charged protons are attracted to the matrix. The higher outer concentration of protons also tends to drive protons back in by diffusion, but because membranes are relatively impermeable to ions, this process occurs only very slowly. Most of the protons that reenter the matrix instead pass through ATP synthase, an enzyme that uses the energy of the gradient to catalyze the synthesis of ATP from ADP and P$_i$. Because the chemical formation of ATP is driven by a diffusion force similar to osmosis, this process is referred to as *chemiosmosis* (figure 7.12b). The newly formed ATP is transported by facilitated diffusion to the many places in the cell where enzymes require energy to drive endergonic reactions. This chemiosmotic mechanism for the coupling of electron transport and ATP synthesis was controversial when it was proposed. Over the years, experimental evidence accumulated to support this hypothesis (figure 7.13).

The energy released by the reactions of cellular respiration ultimately drives the proton pumps that produce the

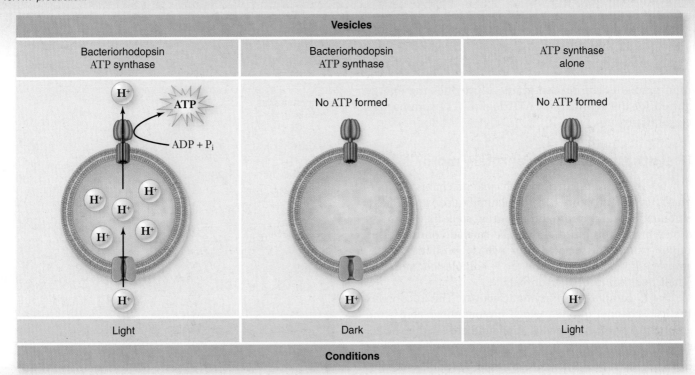

SCIENTIFIC THINKING

Hypothesis: *ATP synthase enzyme uses a proton gradient to provide energy for phosphorylation reaction.*

Prediction: *The source of the proton gradient should not matter. A proton gradient formed by the light-driven pump bacteriorhodopsin should power phosphorylation in the light but not in the dark.*

Test: *Artificial vesicles are made with bacteriorhodopsin and ATP synthase, and ATP synthase alone. These are illuminated with light and assessed for ATP production.*

Result: *The vesicle with both bacteriorhodopsin and ATP synthase can form ATP in the light but not in the dark. The vesicle with ATP synthase alone cannot form ATP in the light.*

Conclusion: *ATP synthase is able to utilize a proton gradient for energy to form ATP.*

Further Experiments: *What other controls would be appropriate for this type of experiment? Why is this experiment a better test of the chemiosmotic hypothesis than the acid bath experiment in Jangendorf/chapter 8 (see figure 8.16)?*

Figure 7.13 Evidence for the chemiosmotic synthesis of ATP by ATP synthase.

Figure 7.14 Aerobic respiration in the mitochondria. The entire process of aerobic respiration is shown in cellular context. Glycolysis occurs in the cytoplasm with the pyruvate and NADH produced entering the mitochondria. Here, pyruvate is oxidized and fed into the Krebs cycle to complete the oxidation process. All the energetic electrons harvested by oxidations in the overall process are transferred by NADH and FADH$_2$ to the electron transport chain. The electron transport chain uses the energy released during electron transport to pump protons across the inner membrane. This creates an electrochemical gradient that contains potential energy. The enzyme ATP synthase uses this gradient to phosphorylate ADP to form ATP.

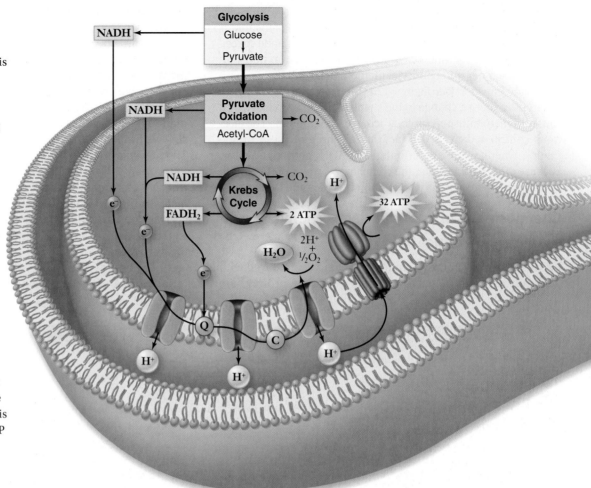

proton gradient. The proton gradient provides the energy required for the synthesis of ATP. Figure 7.14 summarizes the overall process.

ATP synthase is a molecular rotary motor

ATP synthase uses a fascinating molecular mechanism to perform ATP synthesis (figure 7.15). Structurally, the enzyme has a membrane-bound portion and a narrow stalk that connects the membrane portion to a knoblike catalytic portion. This complex can be dissociated into two subportions: the F$_0$ membrane-bound complex, and the F$_1$ complex composed of the stalk and a knob, or head domain.

The F$_1$ complex has enzymatic activity. The F$_0$ complex contains a channel through which protons move across the membrane down their concentration gradient. As they do so, their movement causes part of the F$_0$ complex and the stalk to rotate relative to the knob. The mechanical energy of this rotation is used to change the conformation of the catalytic domain in the F$_1$ complex.

Thus, the synthesis of ATP is achieved by a tiny rotary motor, the rotation of which is driven directly by a gradient of protons. The flow of protons is like that of water in a hydroelectric power plant. Like the flow of water driven by gravity causes a turbine to rotate and generate electrical current, the proton gradient produces the energy that drives the rotation of the ATP synthase generator.

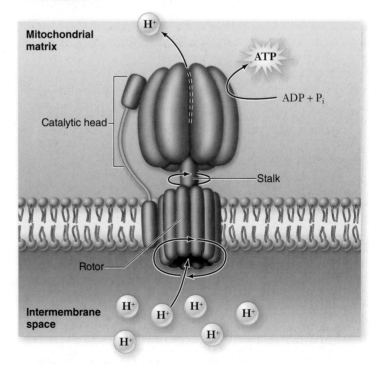

Figure 7.15 The ATP rotary engine. Protons move across the membrane down their concentration gradient. The energy released causes the rotor and stalk structures to rotate. This mechanical energy alters the conformation of the ATP synthase enzyme to catalyze the formation of ATP.

7.6 Energy Yield of Aerobic Respiration

Learning Outcome

1. *Calculate the number of ATP molecules produced by aerobic respiration.*

How much metabolic energy (in the form of ATP) does a cell gain from aerobic breakdown of glucose? This simple question has actually been a source of some controversy in biochemistry.

The theoretical yield for eukaryotes is 30 molecules of ATP per glucose molecule

The number of molecules of ATP produced by ATP synthase per molecules of glucose depends on the number of protons transported across the inner membrane, and the number of protons needed per ATP synthesized. The number of protons transported per NADH and FADH₂ is 10 and 6 H⁺, respectively.

Each ATP synthesized requires 4 H⁺, leading to $10/4 = 2.5$ ATP/NADH, and $6/4 = 1.5$ ATP/FADH₂.

To finish the bookkeeping: oxidizing glucose to pyruvate via glycolysis yields 2 ATP directly, and $2 \times 2.5 = 5$ ATP from NADH. The oxidation of pyruvate to acetyl-CoA yields another $2 \times 2.5 = 5$ ATP from NADH. Lastly, the Krebs cycle produces 2 ATP directly, $6 \times 2.5 = 15$ ATP from NADH, and $2 \times 1.5 = 3$ ATP from FADH₂. Summing all of these leads to 32 ATP for respiration (figure 7.16).

This number is accurate for bacteria, but it does not hold for eukaryotes because the NADH produced in the cytoplasm by glycolysis needs to be transported into the mitochondria by active transport, which costs one ATP per NADH transported. This reduces the predicted yield for eukaryotes to 30 ATP.

Calculation of P/O ratios has changed over time

The value for the amount of ATP synthesized per O₂ molecule reduced is called the phosphate-to-oxygen ratio (P/O ratio). Both theoretical calculations, and direct measurement of this value, have been contentious issues. When theoretical calculations were first made, we lacked detailed knowledge of the respiratory chain, and the mechanism for coupling electron transport to ATP synthesis. Since redox reactions occur at three sites for NADH and two sites for FADH₂, it was assumed that three molecules of ATP were produced per NADH and two per FADH₂. We now know that assumption was overly simplistic.

Understanding that a proton gradient is the link between electron transport and ATP synthesis changed the nature of the calculations. We need to know the number of protons pumped during electron transport: 10 H⁺ per NADH, and 6 H⁺ per FADH₂. Then we need to know the number of protons needed per ATP. Since ATP synthase is a rotary motor, this calculation depends on the number of binding sites for ATP, and the number of protons required for rotation. We know that ATP synthase has three binding sites for ATP. If 12 protons are used per rotation, you get the value of 4 H⁺ per ATP used in the previous

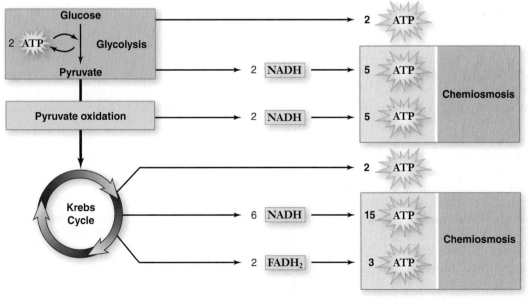

Total net ATP yield = 32
(30 in eukaryotes)

Figure 7.16 Theoretical ATP yield. The theoretical yield of ATP harvested from glucose by aerobic respiration totals 32 molecules. In eukaryotes this is reduced to 30 because it takes 1 ATP to transport each molecule of NADH that is generated by glycolysis in the cytoplasm into the mitochondria.

calculation. Actual measurements of the P/O ratio have been problematic, but now appear to be at most 2.5.

We can also calculate how efficiently respiration captures the free energy released by the oxidation of glucose in the form of ATP. The amount of free energy released by the oxidation of glucose is 686 kcal/mol, and the free energy stored in each ATP is 7.3 kcal/mol. Therefore, a eukaryotic cell harvests about $(7.3 \times 30)/686 = 32\%$ of the energy available in glucose. (By comparison, a typical car converts only about 25% of the energy in gasoline into useful energy.)

The higher energy yield of aerobic respiration was one of the key factors that fostered the evolution of heterotrophs. As this mechanism for producing ATP evolved, nonphotosynthetic organisms became more effective at using respiration to extract energy from molecules derived from other organisms. As long as some organisms captured energy by photosynthesis, others could exist solely by feeding on them.

Learning Outcome Review 7.6

Passage of electrons down the electron transport chain produces roughly 2.5 molecules of ATP per molecule of NADH (1.5 ATP per FADH$_2$). This process plus the ATP from substrate-level phosphorylation can yield a maximum of 32 ATP for the complete oxidation of glucose. NADH generated in the cytoplasm of eukaryotes yields only two ATP/NADH due to the cost of transport into the mitochondria, lowering the yield to 30 ATP.

■ *How does chemiosmosis allow for noninteger numbers of ATP/NADH?*

7.7 Regulation of Aerobic Respiration

Learning Outcome

1. *Understand the control points for cellular respiration.*

When cells possess plentiful amounts of ATP, the key reactions of glycolysis, the Krebs cycle, and fatty acid breakdown are inhibited, slowing ATP production. The regulation of these biochemical pathways by the level of ATP is an example of feedback inhibition. Conversely, when ATP levels in the cell are low, ADP levels are high, and ADP activates enzymes in the pathways of carbohydrate catabolism to stimulate the production of more ATP.

Control of glucose catabolism occurs at two key points in the catabolic pathway, namely at a point in glycolysis and at the beginning of the Krebs cycle (figure 7.17). The control point in glycolysis is the enzyme phosphofructokinase, which catalyzes the conversion of fructose phosphate to fructose bisphosphate. This is the first reaction of glycolysis that is not readily reversible, committing the substrate to the glycolytic sequence. ATP itself is an allosteric inhibitor (see chapter 6) of phosphofructokinase, as is the Krebs cycle intermediate citrate. High levels of both ATP and citrate inhibit phosphofructokinase. Thus, under conditions

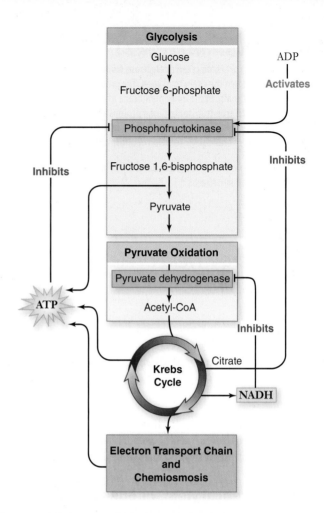

Figure 7.17 Control of glucose catabolism. The relative levels of ADP and ATP and key intermediates NADH and citrate control the catabolic pathway at two key points: the committing reactions of glycolysis and the Krebs cycle.

when ATP is in excess, or when the Krebs cycle is producing citrate faster than it is being consumed, glycolysis is slowed.

The main control point in the oxidation of pyruvate occurs at the committing step in the Krebs cycle with the enzyme pyruvate dehydrogenase, which converts pyruvate to acetyl-CoA. This enzyme is inhibited by high levels of NADH, a key product of the Krebs cycle.

Another control point in the Krebs cycle is the enzyme citrate synthetase, which catalyzes the first reaction, the conversion of oxaloacetate and acetyl-CoA into citrate. High levels of ATP inhibit citrate synthetase (as well as phosphofructokinase, pyruvate dehydrogenase, and two other Krebs cycle enzymes), slowing down the entire catabolic pathway.

Learning Outcome Review 7.7

Respiration is controlled by levels of ATP in the cell and levels of key intermediates in the process. The control point for glycolysis is the enzyme phosphofructokinase, which is inhibited by ATP or citrate (or both). The main control point in oxidation of pyruvate is the enzyme pyruvate dehydrogenase, inhibited by NADH.

■ *How does feedback inhibition ensure economic production of ATP?*

Oxidation Without O$_2$

In the presence of oxygen, cells can use oxygen to produce a large amount of ATP. But even when no oxygen is present to accept electrons, some organisms can still respire *anaerobically,* using inorganic molecules as final electron acceptors for an electron transport chain.

For example, many prokaryotes use sulfur, nitrate, carbon dioxide, or even inorganic metals as the final electron acceptor in place of oxygen (figure 7.18). The free energy released by using these other molecules as final electron acceptors is not as great as that using oxygen because they have a lower affinity for electrons. The amount of ATP produced is less, but the process is still respiration and not fermentation.

Methanogens use carbon dioxide

Among the heterotrophs that practice anaerobic respiration are Archaea such as thermophiles and methanogens. Methanogens use carbon dioxide (CO_2) as the electron acceptor, reducing CO_2 to CH_4 (methane). The hydrogens are derived from organic molecules produced by other organisms. Methanogens are found in diverse environments, including soil and the digestive systems of ruminants like cows.

Sulfur bacteria use sulfate

Evidence of a second anaerobic respiratory process among primitive bacteria is seen in a group of rocks about 2.7 BYA, known as the Woman River iron formation. Organic material in these rocks is enriched for the light isotope of sulfur, ^{32}S, relative to the heavier isotope, ^{34}S. No known geochemical process produces such enrichment, but biological sulfur reduction does, in a process still carried out today by certain prokaryotes.

In this sulfate respiration, the prokaryotes derive energy from the reduction of inorganic sulfates (SO_4) to hydrogen sulfide (H_2S). The hydrogen atoms are obtained from organic molecules other organisms produce. These prokaryotes thus are similar to methanogens, but they use SO_4 as the oxidizing (that is, electron-accepting) agent in place of CO_2.

The early sulfate reducers set the stage for the evolution of photosynthesis, creating an environment rich in H_2S. As discussed in chapter 8, the first form of photosynthesis obtained hydrogens from H_2S using the energy of sunlight.

Fermentation uses organic compounds as electron acceptors

In the absence of oxygen, cells that cannot utilize an alternative electron acceptor for respiration must rely exclusively on

a.

0.625 μm

b.

Figure 7.18 Sulfur-respiring prokaryote. *a.* The micrograph shows the archaeal species *Thermoproteus tenax*. This organism can use elemental sulfur as a final electron acceptor for anaerobic respiration. *b. Thermoproteus* is often found in sulfur-containing hot springs such as the Norris Geyser Basin in Yellowstone National Park shown here.

glycolysis to produce ATP. Under these conditions, the electrons generated by glycolysis are donated to organic molecules in a process called *fermentation*. This process recycles NAD^+, the electron acceptor that allows glycolysis to proceed.

Bacteria carry out more than a dozen kinds of fermentation reactions, often using pyruvate or a derivative of pyruvate to accept the electrons from NADH. Organic molecules other than pyruvate and its derivatives can be used as well; the important point is that the process regenerates NAD^+:

$$\text{organic molecule} + \text{NADH} \longrightarrow \text{reduced organic molecule} + NAD^+$$

Often the reduced organic compound is an organic acid— such as acetic acid, butyric acid, propionic acid, or lactic acid—or an alcohol.

Ethanol fermentation

Eukaryotic cells are capable of only a few types of fermentation. In one type, which occurs in yeast, the molecule that accepts electrons from NADH is derived from pyruvate, the end-product of glycolysis.

Yeast enzymes remove a terminal CO_2 group from pyruvate through decarboxylation, producing a 2-carbon molecule called acetaldehyde. The CO_2 released causes bread made with yeast to rise. The acetaldehyde accepts a pair of electrons from NADH, producing NAD^+ and ethanol (ethyl alcohol) (figure 7.19).

This particular type of fermentation is of great interest to humans, because it is the source of the ethanol in wine and beer. Ethanol is a by-product of fermentation that is actually toxic to yeast; as it approaches a concentration of about 12%, it begins to kill the yeast. That explains why naturally fermented wine contains only about 12% ethanol.

Lactic acid fermentation

Most animal cells regenerate NAD^+ without decarboxylation. Muscle cells, for example, use the enzyme lactate dehydrogenase to transfer electrons from NADH back to the pyruvate that is produced by glycolysis. This reaction converts pyruvate into lactic acid and regenerates NAD^+ from NADH (see figure 7.19). It therefore closes the metabolic circle, allowing glycolysis to continue as long as glucose is available.

Circulating blood removes excess lactate, the ionized form of lactic acid, from muscles, but when removal cannot keep pace with production, the accumulating lactic acid interferes with muscle function and contributes to muscle fatigue.

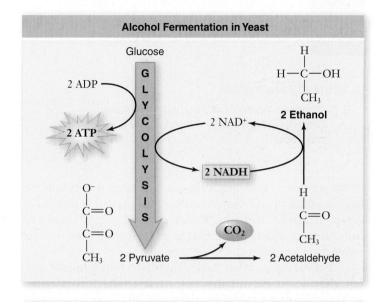

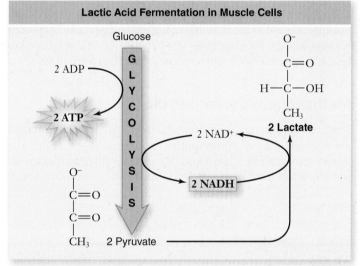

Figure 7.19 Fermentation. Yeasts carry out the conversion of pyruvate to ethanol. Muscle cells convert pyruvate into lactate, which is less toxic than ethanol. In each case, the reduction of a metabolite of glucose has oxidized NADH back to NAD^+ to allow glycolysis to continue under anaerobic conditions.

Learning Outcomes Review 7.8

Nitrate, sulfur, and CO_2 are all used as terminal electron acceptors in anaerobic respiration of different organisms. Organic molecules can also accept electrons in fermentation reactions that regenerate NAD^+. Fermentation reactions produce a variety of compounds, including ethanol in yeast and lactic acid in humans.

■ *In what kinds of ecosystems would you expect to find anaerobic respiration?*

7.9 Catabolism of Proteins and Fats

Learning Outcomes

1. *Identify the entry points for proteins and fats in energy metabolism.*
2. *Recognize the importance of key intermediates in metabolism.*

Thus far we have focused on the aerobic respiration of glucose, which organisms obtain from the digestion of carbohydrates or from photosynthesis. Organic molecules other than glucose,

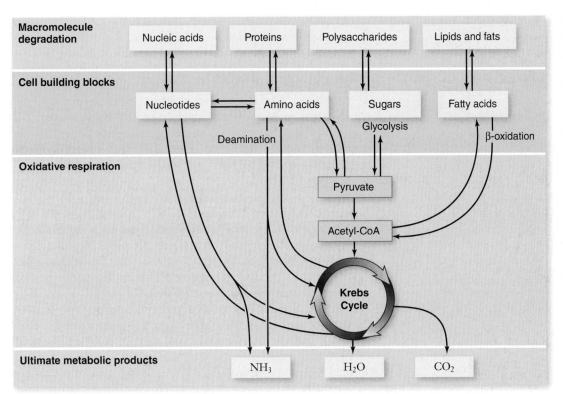

| Macromolecule degradation | Nucleic acids | Proteins | Polysaccharides | Lipids and fats |

Figure 7.20 How cells extract chemical energy.

All eukaryotes and many prokaryotes extract energy from organic molecules by oxidizing them. The first stage of this process, breaking down macromolecules into their constituent parts, yields little energy. The second stage, oxidative or aerobic respiration, extracts energy, primarily in the form of high-energy electrons, and produces water and carbon dioxide. Key intermediates in these energy pathways are also used for biosynthetic pathways, shown by reverse arrows.

particularly proteins and fats, are also important sources of energy (figure 7.20).

Catabolism of proteins removes amino groups

Proteins are first broken down into their individual amino acids. The nitrogen-containing side group (the amino group) is then removed from each amino acid in a process called **deamination.** A series of reactions converts the carbon chain that remains into a molecule that enters glycolysis or the Krebs cycle. For example, alanine is converted into pyruvate, glutamate into α-ketoglutarate (figure 7.21), and aspartate into oxaloacetate. The reactions of glycolysis and the Krebs cycle then extract the high-energy electrons from these molecules and put them to work making ATP.

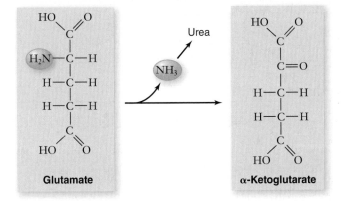

Figure 7.21 Deamination. After proteins are broken down into their amino acid constituents, the amino groups are removed from the amino acids to form molecules that participate in glycolysis and the Krebs cycle. For example, the amino acid glutamate becomes α-ketoglutarate, a Krebs cycle intermediate, when it loses its amino group.

Catabolism of fatty acids produces acetyl groups

Fats are broken down into fatty acids plus glycerol. Long-chain fatty acids typically have an even number of carbons, and the many C—H bonds provide a rich harvest of energy. Fatty acids are oxidized in the matrix of the mitochondrion. Enzymes remove the 2-carbon acetyl groups from the end of each fatty acid until the entire fatty acid is converted into acetyl groups (figure 7.22). Each acetyl group is combined with coenzyme A to form acetyl-CoA. This process is known as **β oxidation.** This process is oxygen-dependent, which explains why aerobic exercise burns fat, but anaerobic exercise does not.

How much ATP does the catabolism of fatty acids produce? Let's compare a hypothetical 6-carbon fatty acid with the 6-carbon glucose molecule, which we've said yields about 30 molecules of ATP in a eukaryotic cell. Two rounds of β oxidation would convert the fatty acid into three molecules of acetyl-CoA. Each round requires one molecule of ATP to prime the process, but it also produces one molecule of NADH and one of FADH$_2$. These molecules together yield four molecules of ATP (assuming 2.5 ATP per NADH, and 1.5 ATP per FADH$_2$).

The oxidation of each acetyl-CoA in the Krebs cycle ultimately produces an additional 10 molecules of ATP. Overall, then, the ATP yield of a 6-carbon fatty acid is approximately: 8 (from two rounds of β oxidation) − 2 (for priming those two rounds) + 30 (from oxidizing the three acetyl-CoAs) = 36 molecules of ATP. Therefore, the respiration of a 6-carbon fatty acid yields 20% more ATP than the respiration of glucose.

Moreover, a fatty acid of that size would weigh less than two thirds as much as glucose, so a gram of fatty acid contains more than twice as many kilocalories as a gram of glucose. You can see from this fact why fat is a storage molecule for excess

Figure 7.22

β oxidation. Through a series of reactions known as β oxidation, the last two carbons in a fatty acid combine with coenzyme A to form acetyl-CoA, which enters the Krebs cycle. The fatty acid, now two carbons shorter, enters the pathway again and keeps reentering until all its carbons have been used to form acetyl-CoA molecules. Each round of β oxidation uses one molecule of ATP and generates one molecule each of $FADH_2$ and NADH.

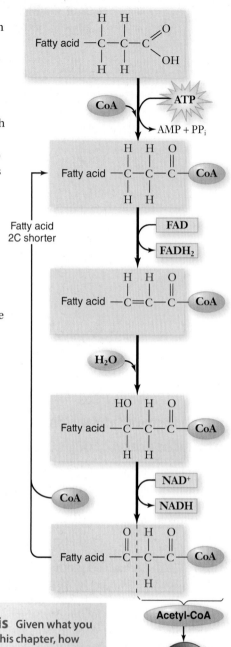

Data analysis Given what you have learned in this chapter, how many ATP would be produced by the oxidation of a fatty acid that has 16 carbons?

Cells can make glucose, amino acids, and fats, as well as getting them from external sources. They use reactions similar to those that break down these substances. In many cases, the reverse pathways even share enzymes if the free-energy changes are small. For example, gluconeogenesis, the process of making new glucose, uses all but three enzymes of the glycolytic pathway. Thus, much of glycolysis runs forward or backward, depending on the concentrations of the intermediates—with only three key steps having different enzymes for forward and reverse directions.

Acetyl-CoA has many roles

Many different metabolic processes generate acetyl-CoA. Not only does the oxidation of pyruvate produce it, but the metabolic breakdown of proteins, fats, and other lipids also generates acetyl-CoA. Indeed, almost all molecules catabolized for energy are converted into acetyl-CoA.

Acetyl-CoA has a role in anabolic metabolism as well. Units of two carbons derived from acetyl-CoA are used to build up the hydrocarbon chains in fatty acids. Acetyl-CoA produced from a variety of sources can therefore be channeled into fatty acid synthesis or into ATP production, depending on the organism's energy requirements. Which of these two options is taken depends on the level of ATP in the cell.

When ATP levels are high, the oxidative pathway is inhibited, and acetyl-CoA is channeled into fatty acid synthesis. This explains why many animals (humans included) develop fat reserves when they consume more food than their activities require. Alternatively, when ATP levels are low, the oxidative pathway is stimulated, and acetyl-CoA flows into energy-producing oxidative metabolism.

Learning Outcomes Review 7.9

Proteins can be broken into their constituent amino acids, which are then deaminated and can enter metabolism at glycolysis or different steps of the Krebs cycle. Fats can be broken into units of acetyl-CoA by β oxidation and then fed into the Krebs cycle. Many metabolic processes can be used reversibly, to either build up (anabolism) or break down (catabolism) the major biological macromolecules. Key intermediates, such as pyruvate and acetyl-CoA, connect these processes.

■ *Can fats be oxidized in the absence of O_2?*

energy in many types of animals. If excess energy were stored instead as carbohydrate, as it is in plants, animal bodies would have to be much bulkier.

A small number of key intermediates connect metabolic pathways

Oxidation pathways of food molecules are interrelated in that a small number of key intermediates, such as pyruvate and acetyl-CoA, link the breakdown from different starting points. These key intermediates allow the interconversion of different types of molecules, such as sugars and amino acids (see figure 7.20).

7.10 Evolution of Metabolism

Learning Outcome

1. *Describe one possible hypothesis for the evolution of metabolism.*

We talk about cellular respiration as a continuous series of stages, but it is important to note that these stages evolved over time, and metabolism has changed a great deal in that time.

Both anabolic processes and catabolic processes evolved in concert with each other. We do not know the details of this biochemical evolution, or the order of appearance of these processes. Therefore the following timeline is based on the available geochemical evidence and represents a hypothesis rather than a strict timeline.

The earliest life-forms degraded carbon-based molecules present in the environment

The most primitive forms of life are thought to have obtained chemical energy by degrading, or breaking down, organic molecules that were abiotically produced, that is, carbon-containing molecules formed by inorganic processes on the early Earth.

The first major event in the evolution of metabolism was the origin of the ability to harness chemical bond energy. At an early stage, organisms began to store this energy in the bonds of ATP.

The evolution of glycolysis also occurred early

The second major event in the evolution of metabolism was glycolysis, the initial breakdown of glucose. As proteins evolved diverse catalytic functions, it became possible to capture a larger fraction of the chemical bond energy in organic molecules by breaking chemical bonds in a series of steps.

Glycolysis undoubtedly evolved early in the history of life on Earth, because this biochemical pathway has been retained by all living organisms. It is a chemical process that does not appear to have changed for more than 2 billion years.

Anoxygenic photosynthesis allowed the capture of light energy

The third major event in the evolution of metabolism was anoxygenic photosynthesis. Early in the history of life, a different way of generating ATP evolved in some organisms. Instead of obtaining energy for ATP synthesis by reshuffling chemical bonds, as in glycolysis, these organisms developed the ability to use light to pump protons out of their cells and to use the resulting proton gradient to power the production of ATP through chemiosmosis.

Photosynthesis evolved in the absence of oxygen and works well without it. Dissolved H_2S, present in the oceans of the early Earth beneath an atmosphere free of oxygen gas, served as a ready source of hydrogen atoms for building organic molecules. Free sulfur was produced as a by-product of this reaction.

Oxygen-forming photosynthesis used a different source of hydrogen

The substitution of H_2O for H_2S in photosynthesis was the fourth major event in the history of metabolism. Oxygen-forming photosynthesis employs H_2O rather than H_2S as a source of hydrogen atoms and their associated electrons. Because it garners its electrons from reduced oxygen rather than from reduced sulfur, it generates oxygen gas rather than free sulfur.

More than 2 BYA, small cells capable of carrying out this oxygen-forming photosynthesis, such as cyanobacteria,

became the dominant forms of life on Earth. Oxygen gas began to accumulate in the atmosphere. This was the beginning of a great transition that changed conditions on Earth permanently. Our atmosphere is now 20.9% oxygen, every molecule of which is derived from an oxygen-forming photosynthetic reaction.

Nitrogen fixation provided new organic nitrogen

Nitrogen is available from dead organic matter, and from chemical reactions that generated the original organic molecules. For life to expand, a new source of nitrogen was needed. Nitrogen fixation was the fifth major step in the evolution of metabolism. Proteins and nucleic acids cannot be synthesized from the products of photosynthesis because both of these biologically critical molecules contain nitrogen. Obtaining nitrogen atoms from N_2 gas, a process called *nitrogen fixation,* requires breaking an $N\equiv N$ triple bond.

This important reaction evolved in the hydrogen-rich atmosphere of the early Earth, where no oxygen was present. Oxygen acts as a poison to nitrogen fixation, which today occurs only in oxygen-free environments or in oxygen-free compartments within certain prokaryotes.

Aerobic respiration utilized oxygen

Respiration is the sixth and final event in the history of metabolism. Aerobic respiration employs the same kind of proton pumps as photosynthesis and is thought to have evolved as a modification of the basic photosynthetic machinery.

Biologists think that the ability to carry out photosynthesis without H_2S first evolved among purple nonsulfur bacteria, which obtain their hydrogens from organic compounds instead. It was perhaps inevitable that among the descendants of these respiring photosynthetic bacteria, some would eventually do without photosynthesis entirely, subsisting only on the energy and electrons derived from the breakdown of organic molecules. The mitochondria within all eukaryotic cells are thought to be descendants of these bacteria.

The complex process of aerobic metabolism developed over geological time, as natural selection favored organisms with more efficient methods of obtaining energy from organic molecules. The process of photosynthesis, as you have seen in this concluding section, has also developed over time, and the rise of photosynthesis changed life on Earth forever. The next chapter explores photosynthesis in detail.

Learning Outcome Review 7.10

Major milestones in the evolution of metabolism include the evolution of pathways to extract energy from organic compounds, the pathways of photosynthesis, and those of nitrogen fixation. Photosynthesis began as an anoxygenic process that later evolved to produce free oxygen, thus allowing the evolution of aerobic metabolism.

■ *What evidence can you cite for this hypothesis of the evolution of metabolism?*

7.1 Overview of Respiration (figure 7.5)

Cells oxidize organic compounds to drive metabolism.

Cellular respiration is the complete oxidation of glucose.

Aerobic respiration uses oxygen as the final electron acceptor for redox reactions. Anaerobic respiration utilizes inorganic molecules as acceptors, and fermentation uses organic molecules.

Electron carriers play a critical role in energy metabolism.

Electron carriers can be reversibly oxidized and reduced. For example, NAD^+ is reduced to NADH by acquiring two electrons; NADH supplies these electrons to other molecules to reduce them.

Metabolism harvests energy in stages.

Mitochondria of eukaryotic cells move electrons in steps via the electron transport chain to capture energy efficiently.

ATP plays a central role in metabolism.

The ultimate goal of cellular respiration is synthesis of ATP, which is used to power most of the cell's activities.

Cells make ATP by two fundamentally different mechanisms.

Substrate-level phosphorylation transfers a phosphate directly to ADP (figure 7.4). Oxidative phosphorylation generates ATP via the enzyme ATP synthase, powered by a proton gradient.

7.2 Glycolysis: Splitting Glucose (figures 7.6 & 7.7)

Glycolysis converts glucose into two pyruvate and yields two ATP and two NADH in the process.

Priming reactions add two phosphates to glucose; this is cleaved into two 3-carbon molecules of glyceraldehyde 3-phosphate (G3P). Oxidation of G3P transfers electrons to NAD^+, yielding NADH. After four more reactions, the final product is two molecules of pyruvate. Glycolysis produces 2 net ATP, 2 NADH, and 2 pyruvate.

Glycolysis is an ancient process with a low energy yield, but it can be efficient with up to 40% of available energy trapped as ATP. Glycolysis was probably the first catabolic reaction to evolve.

NADH must be recycled into NAD^+ to continue respiration.

In the presence of oxygen, pyruvate is oxidized to acetyl-CoA, which can be oxidized by the Krebs cycle. This process leads to a large amount of ATP. In the absence of oxygen, a fermentation reaction uses all or part of pyruvate to oxidize NADH.

In the presence of oxygen, NADH passes electrons to the electron transport chain. In the absence of oxygen, NADH passes the electrons to an organic molecule such as acetaldehyde (fermentation).

7.3 The Oxidation of Pyruvate to Produce Acetyl-CoA (figure 7.9)

Pyruvate is oxidized to yield 1 CO_2, 1 NADH, and 1 acetyl-CoA. Acetyl-CoA enters the Krebs cycle as 2-carbon acetyl units.

7.4 The Krebs Cycle (figures 7.10 & 7.11)

An overview of the Krebs cycle.

The Krebs cycle extracts electrons and synthesizes one ATP.

The first reaction is an irreversible condensation that produces citrate; it is inhibited when ATP is plentiful. The second and third reactions rearrange citrate to isocitrate. The fourth and fifth reactions are oxidations; in each reaction, one NAD^+ is reduced to NADH. The sixth reaction is a substrate-level phosphorylation producing

GTP, and from that ATP. The seventh reaction is another oxidation that reduces FAD to $FADH_2$. Reactions eight and nine regenerate oxaloacetate, including one final oxidation that reduces NAD^+ to NADH.

Glucose becomes CO_2 and potential energy.

As a glucose molecule is broken down to CO_2, some of its energy is preserved in 4 ATP, 10 NADH, and 2 $FADH_2$.

Following the electrons in the reactions reveals the direction of transfer.

7.5 The Electron Transport Chain and Chemiosmosis (figure 7.12)

The electron transport chain produces a proton gradient.

In the inner mitochondrial membrane, NADH is oxidized to NAD^+ by NADH dehydrogenase. Electrons move through ubiquinone and the bc_1 complex to cytochrome oxidase, where they join with H^+ and O_2 to form H_2O. This results in three protons being pumped into the intermembrane space. For $FADH_2$, electrons are passed directly to ubiquinone. Thus only two protons are pumped into the intermembrane space.

The gradient forms as electrons move through electron carriers.

Chemiosmosis utilizes the electrochemical gradient to produce ATP.

ATP synthase is a molecular rotary motor.

Protons diffuse back into the mitochondrial matrix via the ATP synthase channel. The enzyme uses this energy to synthesize ATP (figure 7.15).

7.6 Energy Yield of Aerobic Respiration

The theoretical yield for eukaryotes is 30 molecules of ATP per glucose molecule (figure 7.16).

Calculation of P/O ratios has changed over time.

7.7 Regulation of Aerobic Respiration

Glucose catabolism is controlled by the concentration of ATP molecules and intermediates in the Krebs cycle (figure 7.17).

7.8 Oxidation Without O_2 (figure 7.8)

In the absence of oxygen other final electron acceptors can be used for respiration.

Methanogens use carbon dioxide.

Sulfur bacteria use sulfate.

Fermentation uses organic compounds as electron acceptors (figure 7.19).

Fermentation is the regeneration of NAD^+ by oxidation of NADH and reduction of an organic molecule. In yeast, pyruvate is decarboxylated, then reduced to ethanol. In animals, pyruvate is reduced directly to lactate.

7.9 Catabolism of Proteins and Fats

Catabolism of proteins removes amino groups (figure 7.20).

Catabolism of fatty acids produces acetyl groups.

Fatty acids are converted to acetyl groups by successive rounds of β oxidation (figure 7.22). These acetyl groups feed into the Krebs cycle to be oxidized and generate NADH for electron transport.

A small number of key intermediates connect metabolic pathways.

Acetyl-CoA has many roles.

With high ATP, acetyl-CoA is converted into fatty acids.

7.10 Evolution of Metabolism

Major milestones are recognized in the evolution of metabolism; the order of events is hypothetical.

The earliest life-forms degraded carbon-based molecules present in the environment.

The evolution of glycolysis also occurred early.

Anoxygenic photosynthesis allowed the capture of light energy.

Oxygen-forming photosynthesis used a different source of hydrogen.

Nitrogen fixation provided new organic nitrogen.

Aerobic respiration utilized oxygen.

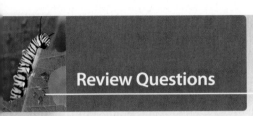

Review Questions

UNDERSTAND

1. An *autotroph* is an organism that
   a. extracts energy from organic sources.
   b. converts energy from sunlight into chemical energy.
   c. relies on the energy produced by other organisms as an energy source.
   d. does both a and b.

2. Which of the following processes is (are) required for the complete oxidation of glucose?
   a. The Krebs cycle
   b. Glycolysis
   c. Pyruvate oxidation
   d. All of the choices are correct.

3. Which of the following is NOT a product of glycolysis?
   a. ATP   c. CO_2
   b. Pyruvate   d. NADH

4. Glycolysis produces ATP by
   a. phosphorylating organic molecules in the priming reactions.
   b. the production of glyceraldehyde 3-phosphate.
   c. substrate-level phosphorylation.
   d. the reduction of NAD^+ to NADH.

5. What is the role of NAD^+ in the process of cellular respiration?
   a. It functions as an electron carrier.
   b. It functions as an enzyme.
   c. It is the final electron acceptor for anaerobic respiration.
   d. It is a nucleotide source for the synthesis of ATP.

6. The reactions of the Krebs cycle occur in the
   a. inner membrane of the mitochondria.
   b. intermembrane space of the mitochondria.
   c. cytoplasm.
   d. matrix of the mitochondria.

7. The electrons carried by NADH and $FADH_2$ can be
   a. pumped into the intermembrane space.
   b. transferred to the ATP synthase.
   c. moved between proteins in the inner membrane of the mitochondrion.
   d. transported into the matrix of the mitochondrion.

APPLY

1. Which of the following is NOT a true statement regarding cellular respiration?
   a. Enzymes catalyze reactions that transfer electrons.
   b. Electrons have a higher potential energy at the end of the process.
   c. Carbon dioxide gas is a by-product.
   d. The process involves multiple redox reactions.

2. The direct source of energy for the ATP produced by ATP synthase comes from
   a. the electron transport chain.
   b. a proton gradient.
   c. substrate-level phosphorylation.
   d. the oxidation reactions occurring during respiration.

3. Anaerobic respiration
   a. occurs in humans in the absence of O_2.
   b. occurs in yeast and is how we make beer and wine.
   c. yields less energy than aerobic respiration because other final electron acceptors have lower affinity for electrons than O_2.
   d. yields more energy than aerobic respiration because other final electron acceptors have higher affinity for electrons than O_2.

4. What is the importance of fermentation to cellular metabolism?
   a. It generates glucose for the cell in the absence of O_2.
   b. It oxidizes NADH to NAD^+ during electron transport.
   c. It oxidizes NADH to NAD^+ in the absence of O_2.
   d. It reduces NADH to NAD^+ in the absence of O_2.

5. The link between electron transport and ATP synthesis
   a. is a high-energy intermediate like phosphoenol pyruvate.
   b. is the transfer of electrons to ATP synthase.
   c. is a proton gradient.
   d. depends on the absence of oxygen.

6. A chemical agent that makes holes in the inner membrane of the mitochondria would
   a. stop the movement of electrons down the electron transport chain.
   b. stop ATP synthesis.
   c. stop the Krebs cycle.
   d. All of the choices are correct.

7. Yeast cells that have mutations in genes that encode enzymes in glycolysis can still grow on glycerol. They are able to utilize glycerol because it

   a. enters glycolysis after the step affected by the mutation.
   b. can feed into the Krebs cycle and generate ATP via electron transport and chemiosmosis.
   c. can be utilized by fermentation.
   d. can donate electrons directly to the electron transport chain.

SYNTHESIZE

1. Use the following table to outline the relationship between the molecules and the metabolic reactions.

Molecules	Glycolysis	Cellular Respiration
Glucose		
Pyruvate		
Oxygen		
ATP		
CO_2		

2. Human babies and hibernating or cold-adapted animals are able to maintain body temperature (a process called *thermogenesis*) due to the presence of brown fat. Brown fat is characterized by a high concentration of mitochondria. These brown fat mitochondria have a special protein located within their inner membranes. *Thermogenin* is a protein that functions as a passive proton transporter. Propose a likely explanation for the role of brown fat in thermogenesis based on your knowledge of metabolism, transport, and the structure and function of mitochondria.

3. Recent data indicate a link between colder temperatures and weight loss. If adults retain brown fat, how could this be explained?

ONLINE RESOURCE

Understand, Apply, and Synthesize—enhance your study with animations that bring concepts to life and practice tests to assess your understanding. Your instructor may also recommend the interactive eBook, individualized learning tools, and more.

Chapter 8

Photosynthesis

Chapter Contents

Introduction

The rich diversity of life that covers our Earth would be impossible without photosynthesis. Almost every oxygen atom in the air we breathe was once part of a water molecule, liberated by photosynthesis. All the energy released by the burning of coal, firewood, gasoline, and natural gas, and by our bodies' burning of all the food we eat—directly or indirectly—has been captured from sunlight by photosynthesis. It is vitally important, then, that we understand photosynthesis. Research may enable us to improve crop yields and land use, important goals in an increasingly crowded world. In chapter 7, we described how cells extract chemical energy from food molecules and use that energy to power their activities. In this chapter, we examine photosynthesis, the process by which organisms such as the aptly named sunflowers in the picture capture energy from sunlight and use it to build food molecules that are rich in chemical energy.

8.1 Overview of Photosynthesis

Learning Outcomes

1. *Explain the reaction for photosynthesis.*
2. *Describe the structure of the chloroplast.*

Life is powered by sunshine. The energy used by most living cells comes ultimately from the Sun and is captured by plants, algae, and bacteria through the process of photosynthesis.

The diversity of life is only possible because our planet is awash in energy streaming Earthward from the Sun. Each day, the radiant energy that reaches Earth equals the power from about 1 million Hiroshima-sized atomic bombs. Photosynthesis captures about 1% of this huge supply of energy (an amount equal to 10,000 Hiroshima bombs) and uses it to provide the energy that drives all life.

Photosynthesis combines CO_2 and H_2O, producing glucose and O_2

Photosynthesis occurs in a wide variety of organisms, and it comes in different forms. These include a form of photosynthesis that does not produce oxygen (anoxygenic) and a form that does (oxygenic). Anoxygenic photosynthesis is found in four different bacterial groups: purple bacteria, green sulfur bacteria, green nonsulfur bacteria, and heliobacteria. Oxygenic photosynthesis is found in cyanobacteria, seven groups of algae, and essentially all land plants. These two types of photosynthesis share similarities in the types of pigments they use to trap light energy, but they differ in the arrangement and action of these pigments.

In the case of plants, photosynthesis takes place primarily in the leaves. Figure 8.1 illustrates the levels of organization in a plant leaf. As you learned in chapter 4, the cells of plant leaves contain organelles called chloroplasts, which carry out the photosynthetic process. No other structure in a plant cell is able to carry out photosynthesis (figure 8.2). Photosynthesis takes place in three stages:

1. capturing energy from sunlight;
2. using the energy to make ATP and to reduce the compound $NADP^+$, an electron carrier, to NADPH; and
3. using the ATP and NADPH to power the synthesis of organic molecules from CO_2 in the air.

The first two stages require light and are commonly called the **light-dependent reactions.**

The third stage, the formation of organic molecules from CO_2, is called **carbon fixation.** This process takes place via a cyclic series of reactions. As long as ATP and NADPH are available, the carbon fixation reactions can occur either in the presence or in the absence of light, and so these reactions are also called the **light-independent reactions.**

The following simple equation summarizes the overall process of photosynthesis:

$$6CO_2 + 12H_2O + light \longrightarrow C_6H_{12}O_6 + 6H_2O + 6O_2$$

carbon dioxide — water — glucose — water — oxygen

You may notice that this equation is the reverse of the reaction for respiration. In respiration, glucose is oxidized to CO_2 using O_2 as an electron acceptor. In photosynthesis, CO_2 is reduced to glucose using electrons gained from the oxidation of water. The oxidation of H_2O and the reduction of CO_2 requires energy that is provided by light. Although this statement is an oversimplification, it provides a useful "global perspective."

In plants, photosynthesis takes place in chloroplasts

In the preceding chapter, you saw that a mitochondrion's complex structure of internal and external membranes contribute to its function. The same is true for the structure of the chloroplast.

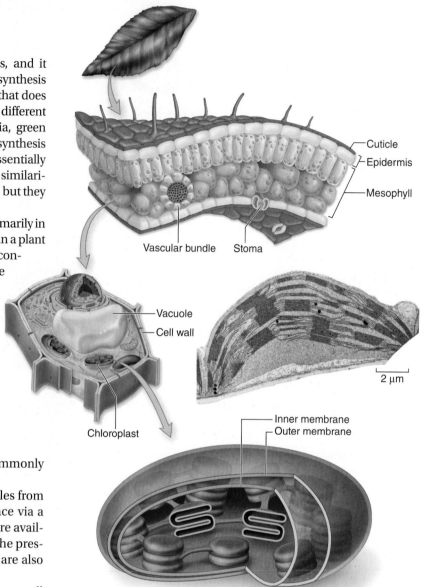

Figure 8.1 Journey into a leaf. A plant leaf possesses a thick layer of cells (the mesophyll) rich in chloroplasts. The inner membrane of the chloroplast is organized into flattened structures called thylakoid disks, which are stacked into columns called grana. The rest of the interior is filled with a semifluid substance called stroma.

The internal membrane of chloroplasts, called the *thylakoid membrane,* is a continuous phospholipid bilayer organized into flattened sacs that are found stacked on one another in columns called *grana* (singular, *granum*). The thylakoid membrane contains **chlorophyll** and other photosynthetic pigments for capturing light energy along with the machinery to make ATP. Connections between grana are termed *stroma lamella.*

Surrounding the thylakoid membrane system is a semi-liquid substance called **stroma.** The stroma houses the enzymes needed to assemble organic molecules from CO_2 using energy from ATP coupled with reduction via NADPH. In the thylakoid membrane, photosynthetic pigments are clustered together to form **photosystems,** which show distinct organization within the thylakoid.

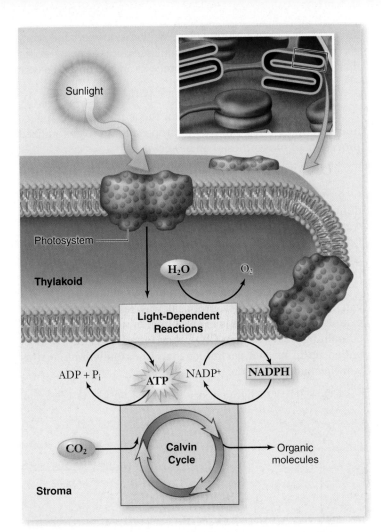

Figure 8.2 Overview of photosynthesis. In the light-dependent reactions, photosystems in the thylakoid absorb photons of light and use this energy to generate ATP and NADPH. Electrons lost from the photosystems are replaced by the oxidation of water, producing O_2 as a by-product. The ATP and NADPH produced by the light reactions is used during carbon fixation via the Calvin cycle in the stroma.

Each pigment molecule within the photosystem is capable of capturing photons, which are packets of energy. When light of a proper wavelength strikes a pigment molecule in the photosystem, the resulting excitation passes from one pigment molecule to another.

The excited electron is not transferred physically—rather, its *energy* passes from one molecule to another. The passage is similar to the transfer of kinetic energy along a row of upright dominoes. If you push the first one over, it falls against the next, and that one against the next, and so on, until all of the dominoes have fallen down.

Eventually, the energy arrives at a key chlorophyll molecule in contact with a membrane-bound protein that can accept an electron. The energy is transferred as an excited electron to that protein, which passes it on to a series of other membrane proteins that put the energy to work making ATP and NADPH.

These compounds are then used to build organic molecules. The photosystem thus acts as a large antenna, gathering the light energy harvested by many individual pigment molecules.

Learning Outcomes Review 8.1

Photosynthesis consists of light-dependent reactions that require sunlight, and others that convert CO_2 into organic molecules. The overall reaction is essentially the reverse of respiration and produces O_2 as a by-product. The chloroplast's inner membrane, the thylakoid, is the site in which photosynthetic pigments are clustered, allowing passage of energy from one molecule to the next. The thylakoid membrane is organized into flattened sacs stacked in columns called grana.

■ **How is the structure of the chloroplast similar to the mitochondria?**

8.2 The Discovery of Photosynthetic Processes

Learning Outcomes

1. *Describe experiments that support our understanding of photosynthesis.*
2. *Differentiate between the light-dependent and light-independent reactions.*

The story of how we learned about photosynthesis begins over 300 years ago, and it continues to this day. It starts with curiosity about how plants manage to grow, often increasing their organic mass considerably.

Plants do not increase mass from soil and water alone

From the time of the Greeks, plants were thought to obtain their food from the soil, literally sucking it up with their roots. A Belgian doctor, Jan Baptista van Helmont (1580–1644) thought of a simple way to test this idea.

He planted a small willow tree in a pot of soil, after first weighing the tree and the soil. The tree grew in the pot for several years, during which time van Helmont added only water. At the end of five years, the tree was much larger, its weight having increased by 74.4 kg. However, the soil in the pot weighed only 57 g less than it had five years earlier. With this experiment, van Helmont demonstrated that the substance of the plant was not produced only from the soil. He incorrectly concluded, however, that the water he had been adding mainly accounted for the plant's increased biomass.

A hundred years passed before the story became clearer. The key clue was provided by the English scientist Joseph Priestly (1733–1804). On the 17th of August, 1771, Priestly put a living sprig of mint into air in which a wax candle had burnt out.

On the 27th of the same month, Priestly found that another candle could be burned in this same air. Somehow, the vegetation seemed to have restored the air. Priestly found that while a mouse could not breathe candle-exhausted air, air "restored" by vegetation was not "at all inconvenient to a mouse." The key clue was that *living vegetation adds something to the air*.

How does vegetation "restore" air? Twenty-five years later, the Dutch physician Jan Ingenhousz (1730–1799) solved the puzzle. He demonstrated that air was restored only in the presence of sunlight and only by a plant's green leaves, not by its roots. He proposed that the green parts of the plant carry out a process that uses sunlight to split carbon dioxide into carbon and oxygen. He suggested that the oxygen was released as O_2 gas into the air, while the carbon atom combined with water to form carbohydrates. Other research refined his conclusions, and by the end of the nineteenth century, the overall reaction for photosynthesis could be written as:

$$CO_2 + H_2O + \text{light energy} \longrightarrow (CH_2O) + O_2$$

It turns out, however, that there's more to it than that. When researchers began to examine the process in more detail in the twentieth century, the role of light proved to be unexpectedly complex.

Photosynthesis includes both light-dependent and light-independent reactions

At the beginning of the twentieth century, the English plant physiologist F. F. Blackman (1866–1947) came to the surprising conclusion that photosynthesis is in fact a multistage process, only one portion of which uses light directly.

Blackman measured the effects of different light intensities, CO_2 concentrations, and temperatures on photosynthesis. As long as light intensity was relatively low, he found photosynthesis could be accelerated by increasing the amount of light, but not by increasing the temperature or CO_2 concentration (figure 8.3). At high light intensities, however, an increase in temperature or CO_2 concentration greatly accelerated photosynthesis.

Blackman concluded that photosynthesis consists of an initial set of what he called "light" reactions, that are largely independent of temperature but depend on light, and a second set of "dark" reactions (more properly called light-independent reactions), that seemed to be independent of light but limited by CO_2.

Do not be confused by Blackman's labels—the so-called "dark" reactions occur in the light (in fact, they require the products of the light-dependent reactions); his use of the word *dark* simply indicates that light is not *directly* involved in those reactions.

Blackman found that increased temperature increased the rate of the light-independent reactions, but only up to about 35°C. Higher temperatures caused the rate to fall off rapidly. Because many plant enzymes begin to be denatured at 35°C, Blackman concluded that enzymes must carry out the light-independent reactions.

O_2 comes from water, not from CO_2

In the 1930s, C. B. van Niel (1897–1985) working at the Hopkins Marine Station at Stanford, discovered that purple sulfur bacteria do not release oxygen during photosynthesis; instead, they convert hydrogen sulfide (H_2S) into globules of pure elemental sulfur that accumulate inside them. The process van Niel observed was:

$$CO_2 + 2H_2S + \text{light energy} \longrightarrow (CH_2O) + H_2O + 2S$$

The striking parallel between this equation and Ingenhousz's equation led van Niel to propose that the generalized process of photosynthesis can be shown as:

$$CO_2 + 2H_2A + \text{light energy} \longrightarrow (CH_2O) + H_2O + 2A$$

In this equation, the substance H_2A serves as an electron donor. In photosynthesis performed by green plants, H_2A is water, whereas in purple sulfur bacteria, H_2A is hydrogen sulfide. The product, A, comes from the splitting of H_2A. Therefore, the O_2 produced during green plant photosynthesis results from splitting water, not carbon dioxide.

When isotopes came into common use in the early 1950s, van Niel's revolutionary proposal was tested. Investigators examined photosynthesis in green plants supplied with water containing heavy oxygen (^{18}O); they found that the ^{18}O label ended up in oxygen gas rather than in carbohydrate, just as van Niel had predicted:

$$CO_2 + 2H_2{}^{18}O + \text{light energy} \longrightarrow (CH_2O) + H_2O + {}^{18}O_2$$

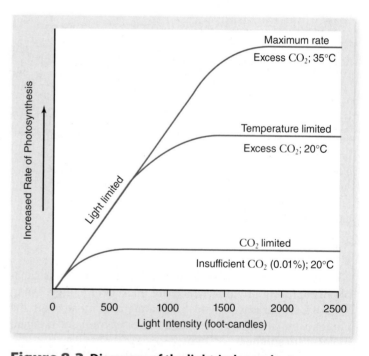

Figure 8.3 Discovery of the light-independent reactions. Blackman measured photosynthesis rates under differing light intensities, CO_2 concentrations, and temperatures. As this graph shows, light is the limiting factor at low light intensities, but temperature and CO_2 concentration are the limiting factors at higher light intensities. This implies the existence of reactions using CO_2 that involve enzymes.

Data analysis Blackman found that increasing light intensity above 2000 foot-candles did not lead to any further increase in the rate of photosynthesis. Can you suggest a hypothesis that would explain this?

In algae and green plants, the carbohydrate typically produced by photosynthesis is glucose. The complete balanced equation for photosynthesis in these organisms thus becomes:

$$6CO_2 + 12H_2O + \text{light energy} \longrightarrow C_6H_{12}O_6 + 6H_2O + 6O_2$$

ATP and NADPH from light-dependent reactions reduce CO₂ to make sugars

In his pioneering work on the light-dependent reactions, van Niel proposed that the H^+ ions and electrons generated by the splitting of water were used to convert CO_2 into organic matter in a process he called *carbon fixation.* In the 1950s, Robin Hill (1899–1991) demonstrated that van Niel was right, light energy could be harvested and used in a reduction reaction. Chloroplasts isolated from leaf cells were able to reduce a dye and release oxygen in response to light. Later experiments showed that the electrons released from water were transferred to $NADP^+$ and that illuminated chloroplasts deprived of CO_2 accumulate ATP. If CO_2 is introduced, neither ATP nor NADPH accumulate, and the CO_2 is assimilated into organic molecules.

These experiments are important for three reasons: First, they firmly demonstrate that photosynthesis in plants occurs within chloroplasts. Second, they show that the light-dependent reactions use light energy to reduce $NADP^+$ and to manufacture ATP. Third, they confirm that the ATP and NADPH from this early stage of photosynthesis are then used in the subsequent reactions to reduce carbon dioxide, forming simple sugars.

Learning Outcomes Review 8.2

Early experiments indicated that plants "restore" air to usable form, that is, produce oxygen—but only in the presence of sunlight. Further experiments showed that there are both light-dependent and independent reactions. The light-dependent reactions produce O_2 from H_2O, and generate ATP and NADPH. The light-independent reactions synthesize organic compounds through carbon fixation.

■ *Where does the carbon in your body come from?*

Learning Outcomes

1. *Discuss how pigments are important to photosynthesis.*
2. *Relate the absorption spectrum of a pigment to its color.*

For plants to make use of the energy of sunlight, some biochemical structure must be present in chloroplasts and the thylakoids that can absorb this energy. Molecules that absorb light energy in the visible range are termed **pigments.** We are most familiar with them as dyes that impart a certain color to clothing or other materials. The color that we see is the color that is not absorbed—that is, it is reflected. To understand how plants use pigments to capture light energy, we must first review current knowledge about the nature of light.

Light is a form of energy

The wave nature of light produces an electromagnetic spectrum that differentiates light based on its wavelength (figure 8.4). We are most familiar with the visible range of this spectrum because we can actually see it, but visible light is only a small part of the entire spectrum. Visible light can be divided into its separate colors by the use of a prism, which separates light based on wavelength.

A particle of light, termed a **photon,** acts like a discrete bundle of energy. We use the wave concept of light to understand different colors of light and the particle nature of light to understand the energy transfers that occur during photosynthesis. Thus, we will refer both to wavelengths of light and to photons of light throughout the chapter.

The energy in photons

The energy content of a photon is inversely proportional to the wavelength of the light: Short-wavelength light contains photons of higher energy than long-wavelength light (see figure 8.4). X-rays, which contain a great deal of energy, have very short wavelengths—much shorter than those of visible light.

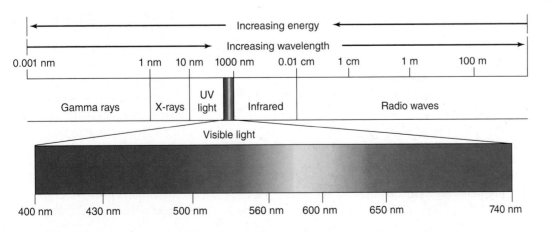

Figure 8.4 The electromagnetic spectrum. Light is a form of electromagnetic energy conveniently thought of as a wave. The shorter the wavelength of light, the greater its energy. Visible light represents only a small part of the electromagnetic spectrum between 400 and 740 nm.

A beam of light is able to remove electrons from certain molecules, creating an electrical current. This phenomenon is called the **photoelectric effect,** and it occurs when photons transfer energy to electrons. The strength of the photoelectric effect depends on the wavelength of light; that is, short wavelengths are much more effective than long ones in producing the photoelectric effect because they have more energy.

In photosynthesis, chloroplasts are acting as photoelectric devices: They absorb sunlight and transfer the excited electrons to a carrier. As we unravel the details of this process, it will become clear how this process traps energy and uses it to synthesize organic compounds.

Each pigment has a characteristic absorption spectrum

When a photon strikes a molecule with the amount of energy needed to excite an electron, then the molecule will absorb the photon raising the electron to a higher energy level. Whether the photon's energy is absorbed depends on how much energy it carries (defined by its wavelength), and also on the chemical nature of the molecule it hits.

As described in chapter 2, electrons occupy discrete energy levels in their orbits around atomic nuclei. To boost an electron into a different energy level requires just the right amount of energy, just as reaching the next rung on a ladder requires you to raise your foot just the right distance. A specific atom, therefore, can absorb only certain photons of light—namely, those that correspond to the atom's available energy levels. As a result, each molecule has a characteristic **absorption spectrum,** the range and efficiency of photons it is capable of absorbing.

As mentioned earlier, pigments are good absorbers of light in the visible range. Organisms have evolved a variety of different pigments, but only two general types are used in green plant photosynthesis: chlorophylls and carotenoids. In some organisms, other molecules also absorb light energy.

Chlorophyll absorption spectra

Chlorophylls absorb photons within narrow energy ranges. Two kinds of chlorophyll in plants, chlorophyll *a* and chlorophyll *b,* preferentially absorb violet-blue and red light (figure 8.5). Neither of these pigments absorbs photons with wavelengths between about 500 and 600 nm; light of these wavelengths is reflected. When these reflected photons are subsequently absorbed by the retinal pigment in our eyes, we perceive them as green.

Chlorophyll *a* is the main photosynthetic pigment in plants and cyanobacteria and is the only pigment that can act directly to convert light energy to chemical energy. **Chlorophyll *b*,** acting as an **accessory pigment,** or secondary light-absorbing pigment, complements and adds to the light absorption of chlorophyll *a.*

Chlorophyll *b* has an absorption spectrum shifted toward the green wavelengths. Therefore, chlorophyll *b* can absorb photons that chlorophyll *a* cannot, greatly increasing the proportion of the photons in sunlight that plants can harvest. In addition, a variety of different accessory pigments are found in plants, bacteria, and algae.

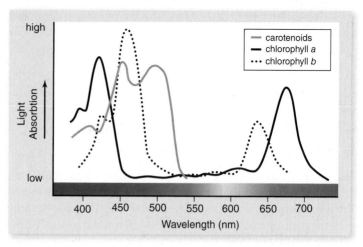

Figure 8.5 **Absorption spectra for chlorophyll and carotenoids.** The peaks represent wavelengths of light of sunlight absorbed by the two common forms of photosynthetic pigment, chlorophylls *a* and *b,* and the carotenoids. Chlorophylls absorb predominantly violet-blue and red light in two narrow bands of the spectrum and reflect green light in the middle of the spectrum. Carotenoids absorb mostly blue and green light and reflect orange and yellow light.

Structure of chlorophylls

Chlorophylls absorb photons by means of an excitation process analogous to the photoelectric effect. These pigments contain a complex ring structure, called a *porphyrin ring,* with alternating single and double bonds. At the center of the ring is a magnesium atom (figure 8.6).

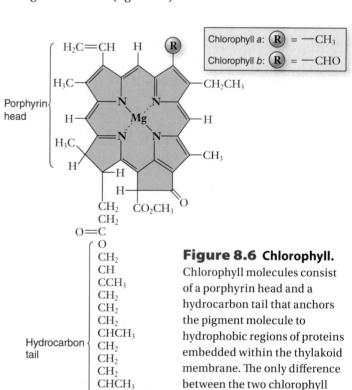

Figure 8.6 **Chlorophyll.** Chlorophyll molecules consist of a porphyrin head and a hydrocarbon tail that anchors the pigment molecule to hydrophobic regions of proteins embedded within the thylakoid membrane. The only difference between the two chlorophyll molecules is the substitution of a —CHO (aldehyde) group in chlorophyll *b* for a —CH$_3$ (methyl) group in chlorophyll *a.*

Hypothesis: *All wavelengths of light are equally effective in promoting photosynthesis.*

Prediction: *Illuminating plant cells with light broken into different wavelengths by a prism will produce the same amount of O_2 for all wavelengths.*

Test: *A filament of algae immobilized on a slide is illuminated by light that has passed through a prism. Motile bacteria that require O_2 for growth are added to the slide.*

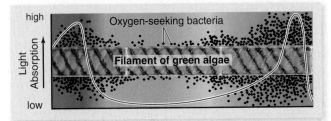

Result: *The bacteria move to regions of high O_2, or regions of most active photosynthesis. This is in the purple/blue and red regions of the spectrum.*

Conclusion: *All wavelengths are not equally effective at promoting photosynthesis. The most effective constitute the action spectrum for photosynthesis.*

Further Experiments: *How does the action spectrum relate to the various absorption spectra in figure 8.5?*

Figure 8.7 Determination of an action spectrum for photosynthesis.

Photons excite electrons in the porphyrin ring, which are then channeled away through the alternating carbon single- and double-bond system. Different small side groups attached to the outside of the ring alter the absorption properties of the molecule in the different kinds of chlorophyll (see figure 8.6). The precise absorption spectrum is also influenced by the local microenvironment created by the association of chlorophyll with different proteins.

The **action spectrum** of photosynthesis—that is, the relative effectiveness of different wavelengths of light in promoting photosynthesis—corresponds to the absorption spectrum for chlorophylls. This is demonstrated in the experiment in figure 8.7. All plants, algae, and cyanobacteria use chlorophyll *a* as their primary pigments.

It is reasonable to ask why these photosynthetic organisms do not use a pigment like retinal (the pigment in our eyes), which has a broad absorption spectrum that covers the range of 500 to 600 nm. The most likely hypothesis involves *photoefficiency.* Although retinal absorbs a broad range of wavelengths, it does so with relatively low efficiency. Chlorophyll, in contrast, absorbs in only two narrow bands, but does so with high efficiency. Therefore, plants and most other photosynthetic organisms achieve far higher overall energy capture rates with chlorophyll than with other pigments.

Carotenoids and other accessory pigments

Carotenoids consist of carbon rings linked to chains with alternating single and double bonds. They can absorb photons with a wide range of energies, although they are not always highly efficient in transferring this energy. Carotenoids assist in photosynthesis by capturing energy from light composed of wavelengths that are not efficiently absorbed by chlorophylls (figure 8.5; see also figure 8.8).

Carotenoids also perform a valuable role in scavenging free radicals. The oxidation–reduction reactions that occur in the chloroplast can generate destructive free radicals. Carotenoids can act as general-purpose antioxidants to lessen damage. Thus carotenoids have a protective role in addition to their role as light-absorbing molecules. This protective role is not surprising, because unlike the chlorophylls, carotenoids are found in many different kinds of organisms, including members of all three domains of life.

You may have heard that eating carrots can enhance vision. If this effect is real, it is probably due to the high content of β-carotene in carrots. This carotenoid consists of two molecules of vitamin A joined together. The oxidation of vitamin A produces retinal, the pigment used in vertebrate vision.

Oak leaf in summer

Oak leaf in autumn

Figure 8.8 Fall colors are produced by carotenoids and other accessory pigments. During the spring and summer, chlorophyll in leaves masks the presence of carotenoids and other accessory pigments. When cool fall temperatures cause leaves to cease manufacturing chlorophyll, the chlorophyll is no longer present to reflect green light, and the leaves reflect the orange and yellow light that carotenoids and other pigments do not absorb.

Phycobiliproteins are accessory pigments found in cyanobacteria and some algae. These pigments contain a system of alternating double bonds similar to those found in other pigments and molecules that transfer electrons. Phycobiliproteins can be organized to form another light-harvesting complex that can absorb green light, which is reflected by chlorophyll. These complexes are probably ecologically important to cyanobacteria, helping them to exist in low-light situations in oceans. In this habitat, green light remains because red and blue light has been absorbed by green algae closer to the surface.

Learning Outcomes Review 8.3

A pigment is a molecule that can absorb light energy; its absorption spectrum shows the wavelengths at which it absorbs energy most efficiently. A pigment's color results from the wavelengths it does not absorb, which we then see. The main photosynthetic pigment is chlorophyll, which exists in several forms with slightly different absorption spectra. Many photosynthetic organisms have accessory pigments with absorption spectra different from chlorophyll; these increase light capture.

■ *What is the difference between an action spectrum and an absorption spectrum?*

8.4 *Photosystem Organization*

Learning Outcomes

1. *Describe the nature of photosystems.*
2. *Contrast the function of reaction center and antenna chlorophyll molecules.*

One way to study the role that pigments play in photosynthesis is to measure the correlation between the output of photosynthesis and the intensity of illumination—that is, how much photosynthesis is produced by how much light. Experiments on plants show that the output of photosynthesis increases linearly at low light intensities, but finally becomes saturated (no further increase) at high-intensity light. Saturation occurs because all of the light-absorbing capacity of the plant is in use.

Production of one O₂ molecule requires many chlorophyll molecules

Given the saturation observed with increasing light intensity, the next question is how many chlorophyll molecules have actually absorbed a photon. The question can be phrased this way: "Does saturation occur when all chlorophyll molecules have absorbed photons?" Finding an answer required being able to measure both photosynthetic output (on the basis of O₂ production) and the number of chlorophyll molecules present.

Using the unicellular algae *Chlorella,* investigators could obtain these values. Illuminating a *Chlorella* culture with pulses of light with increasing intensity should increase the

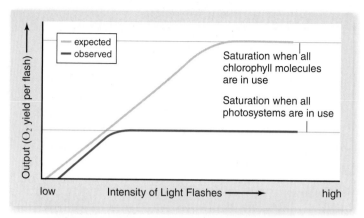

Figure 8.9 Saturation of photosynthesis. When photosynthetic saturation is achieved, further increases in intensity cause no increase in output. This saturation occurs far below the level expected for the number of individual chlorophyll molecules present. This led to the idea of organized photosystems, each containing many chlorophyll molecules. These photosystems saturate at a lower O_2 yield than that expected for the number of individual chlorophyll molecules.

 Data analysis Draw the curves for photosystems that have a greater or lesser number of chlorophyll molecules than the curve shown.

yield of O_2 per pulse until the system becomes saturated. Then O_2 production can be compared with the number of chlorophyll molecules present in the culture.

The observed level of O_2 per chlorophyll molecule at saturation, however, turned out to be only one molecule of O_2 per 2500 chlorophyll molecules (figure 8.9). This result was very different from what was expected, and it led to the idea that light is absorbed not by independent pigment molecules, but rather by clusters of chlorophyll and accessory pigment molecules (photosystems). Light is absorbed by any one of hundreds of pigment molecules in a photosystem, and each pigment molecule transfers its excitation energy to a single molecule with a lower energy level than the others.

A generalized photosystem contains an antenna complex and a reaction center

In chloroplasts and all but one class of photosynthetic prokaryotes, light is captured by photosystems. Each photosystem is a network of chlorophyll *a* molecules, accessory pigments, and associated proteins held within a protein matrix on the surface of the photosynthetic membrane. Like a magnifying glass focusing light on a precise point, a photosystem channels the excitation energy gathered by any one of its pigment molecules to a specific molecule, the reaction center chlorophyll. This molecule then passes the energy out of the photosystem as excited electrons that are put to work driving the synthesis of ATP and organic molecules.

A photosystem thus consists of two closely linked components: (1) an *antenna complex* of hundreds of pigment molecules that gather photons and feed the captured light energy to the reaction center; and (2) a *reaction center* consisting of one or more chlorophyll *a* molecules in a matrix of protein, that passes excited electrons out of the photosystem.

The antenna complex

The **antenna complex** is also called a light-harvesting complex, which accurately describes its role. This light-harvesting complex captures photons from sunlight (figure 8.10) and channels them to the reaction center chlorophylls.

In chloroplasts, light-harvesting complexes consist of a web of chlorophyll molecules linked together and held tightly in the thylakoid membrane by a matrix of proteins. Varying amounts of carotenoid accessory pigments may also be present. The protein matrix holds individual pigment molecules in orientations that are optimal for energy transfer.

The excitation energy resulting from the absorption of a photon passes from one pigment molecule to an adjacent molecule on its way to the reaction center. After the transfer, the excited electron in each molecule returns to the low-energy level it had before the photon was absorbed. Consequently, it is energy, not the excited electrons themselves, that passes from one pigment molecule to the next. The antenna complex funnels the energy from many electrons to the reaction center.

The reaction center

The **reaction center** is a transmembrane protein–pigment complex. The reaction center of purple photosynthetic bacteria is simpler than the one in chloroplasts but better understood. A pair of bacteriochlorophyll *a* molecules acts as a trap for photon energy, passing an excited electron to an acceptor precisely positioned as its neighbor. Note that here in the reaction center, the excited electron itself is transferred, and not just the energy, as was the case in the pigment–pigment transfers of the antenna complex. This difference allows the energy absorbed from

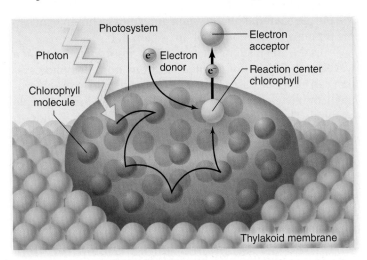

Figure 8.10 How the antenna complex works. When light of the proper wavelength strikes any pigment molecule within a photosystem, the light is absorbed by that pigment molecule. The excitation energy is then transferred from one molecule to another within the cluster of pigment molecules until it encounters the reaction center chlorophyll *a*. When excitation energy reaches the reaction center chlorophyll, electron transfer is initiated.

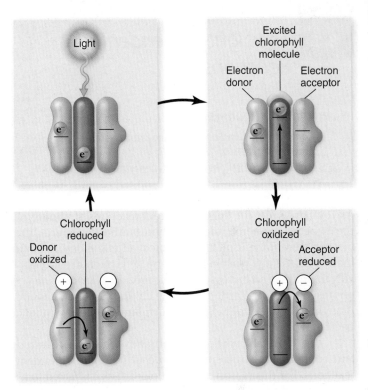

Figure 8.11 Converting light to chemical energy. When a chlorophyll in the reaction center absorbs a photon of light, an electron is excited to a higher energy level. This light-energized electron can be transferred to the primary electron acceptor, reducing it. The oxidized chlorophyll then fills its electron "hole" by oxidizing a donor molecule. The source of this donor varies with the photosystem as discussed in the text.

photons to move away from the chlorophylls, and it is the key conversion of light into chemical energy.

Figure 8.11 shows the transfer of excited electrons from the reaction center to the primary electron acceptor. By energizing an electron of the reaction center chlorophyll, light creates a strong electron donor where none existed before. The chlorophyll transfers the energized electron to the primary acceptor (a molecule of quinone), reducing the quinone and converting it to a strong electron donor. A nearby weak electron donor then passes a low-energy electron to the chlorophyll, restoring it to its original condition. The quinone transfers its electrons to another acceptor, and the process is repeated.

In plant chloroplasts, water serves as this weak electron donor. When water is oxidized in this way, oxygen is released along with two protons (H^+).

Learning Outcomes Review 8.4

Chlorophylls and accessory pigments are organized into photosystems found in the thylakoid membrane. The photosystem can be subdivided into an antenna complex, which is involved in light harvesting, and a reaction center, where the photochemical reactions occur. In the reaction center, an excited electron is passed to an acceptor; this transfers energy away from the chlorophylls and is key to the conversion of light into chemical energy.

■ *Why were photosystems an unexpected finding?*

The Light-Dependent Reactions

As you have seen, the light-dependent reactions of photosynthesis occur in membranes. In photosynthetic bacteria, the plasma membrane itself is the photosynthetic membrane. In many bacteria, the plasma membrane folds in on itself repeatedly to produce an increased surface area. In plants and algae, photosynthesis is carried out by chloroplasts, which are thought to be the evolutionary descendants of photosynthetic bacteria.

The internal thylakoid membrane is highly organized and contains the structures involved in the light-dependent reactions. For this reason, the reactions are also referred to as the thylakoid reactions. The thylakoid reactions take place in four stages:

1. **Primary photoevent.** A photon of light is captured by a pigment. This primary photoevent excites an electron within the pigment.
2. **Charge separation.** This excitation energy is transferred to the reaction center, which transfers an energetic electron to an acceptor molecule, initiating electron transport.
3. **Electron transport.** The excited electrons are shuttled along a series of electron carrier molecules embedded within the photosynthetic membrane. Several of them react by transporting protons across the membrane, generating a proton gradient. Eventually the electrons are used to reduce a final acceptor, NADPH.
4. **Chemiosmosis.** The protons that accumulate on one side of the membrane now flow back across the membrane through ATP synthase where chemiosmotic synthesis of ATP takes place, just as it does in aerobic respiration (see chapter 7).

These four processes make up the two stages of the light-dependent reactions mentioned at the beginning of this chapter. Steps 1 through 3 represent the stage of capturing energy from light; step 4 is the stage of producing ATP (and, as you'll see, NADPH). In the rest of this section we discuss the evolution of photosystems and the details of photosystem function in the light-dependent reactions.

Some bacteria use a single photosystem

Photosynthetic pigment arrays are thought to have evolved more than 2 BYA in bacteria similar to the purple and green bacteria alive today. In these bacteria, a single photosystem is used that generates ATP via electron transport. This process returns the electrons back to the reaction center. For this

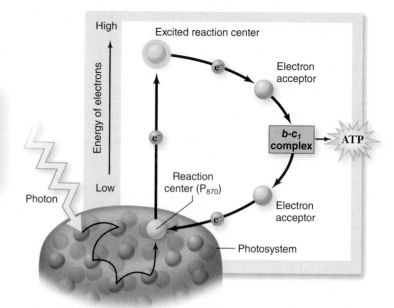

Figure 8.12 The path of an electron in purple nonsulfur bacteria. When a light-energized electron is ejected from the photosystem reaction center (P_{870}) it returns to the photosystem via a cyclic path that produces ATP but not NADPH.

reason, it is called cyclic photophosphorylation. These systems do not produce oxygen and so are also anoxygenic.

In the purple nonsulfur bacteria, peak absorption occurs at a wavelength of 870 nm (near infrared, not visible to the human eye), and thus the reaction center pigment is called P_{870}. Absorption of a photon by chlorophyll P_{870} does not raise an electron to a high enough level to be passed to NADP, so they must generate reducing power in a different way.

When the P_{870} reaction center absorbs a photon, the excited electron is passed to an electron transport chain that passes the electrons back to the reaction center, generating a proton gradient for ATP synthesis (figure 8.12). The proteins in the purple bacterial photosystem appear to be homologous to the proteins in the modern photosystem II.

In the green sulfur bacteria, peak absorption occurs at a wavelength of 840 nm. Excited electrons from this photosystem can either be passed to NADPH, or returned to the chlorophyll by an electron transport chain similar to the purple bacteria. They then use electrons from hydrogen sulfide to replace those passed to NADPH. The proteins in the green sulfur bacterial photosystem appear to be homologous to the proteins in the modern photosystem I.

Neither of these systems generates sufficient oxidizing power to oxidize H_2O. They are both anoxygenic and anaerobic. The linked photosystems of cyanobacteria and plant chloroplasts generate the oxidizing power necessary to oxidize H_2O, allowing it to serve as a source of both electrons and protons. This production of O_2 by oxygenic photosynthesis literally changed the atmosphere of the world.

Chloroplasts have two connected photosystems

In contrast to the sulfur bacteria, plants have two linked photosystems. This overcomes the limitations of cyclic photophosphorylation by providing an alternative source of electrons from the oxidation of water. The oxidation of water also generates O_2, thus oxygenic photosynthesis. The noncyclic transfer of electrons also produces NADPH, which can be used in the biosynthesis of carbohydrates.

One photosystem, called **photosystem I,** has an absorption peak of 700 nm, so its reaction center pigment is called P_{700}. This photosystem can pass electrons to NADPH similarly to the photosystem found in the sulfur bacteria discussed earlier. The other photosystem, called **photosystem II,** has an absorption peak of 680 nm, so its reaction center pigment is called P_{680}. This photosystem can generate an oxidation potential high enough to oxidize water. Working together, the two photosystems carry out a noncyclic transfer of electrons that generate both ATP and NADPH.

The photosystems were named I and II in the order of their discovery, and not in the order in which they operate in the light-dependent reactions. In plants and algae, the two photosystems are specialized for different roles in the overall process of oxygenic photosynthesis. Photosystem I transfers electrons ultimately to $NADP^+$, producing NADPH. The electrons lost from photosystem I are replaced by electrons from photosystem II. Photosystem II with its high oxidation potential can oxidize water to replace the electrons transferred to photosystem I. Thus there is an overall flow of electrons from water to NADPH.

These two photosystems are connected by a complex of electron carriers called the **cytochrome/b_6-f complex** (explained shortly). This complex can use the energy from the passage of electrons to move protons across the thylakoid membrane to generate the proton gradient used by an ATP synthase enzyme.

The two photosystems work together in noncyclic photophosphorylation

Evidence for the action of two photosystems came from experiments that measured the rate of photosynthesis using two light beams of different wavelengths: one red and the other far-red. Using both beams produced a rate greater than the sum of the rates using individual beams of these wavelengths (figure 8.13). This surprising result, called the *enhancement effect,* can be explained by a mechanism involving two photosystems acting in series (that is, one after the other), one photosystem absorbs preferentially in the red, the other in the far-red.

Plants use photosystems II and I in series, first one and then the other, to produce both ATP and NADPH. This two-stage process is called **noncyclic photophosphorylation** because the path of the electrons is not a circle—the electrons ejected from the photosystems do not return to them, but rather end up in NADPH. The photosystems are replenished with electrons obtained by splitting water.

The scheme shown in figure 8.14, called a *Z diagram,* illustrates the two electron-energizing steps, one catalyzed by each photosystem. The horizontal axis shows the progress of the light reactions and the relative positions of the complexes, and the vertical axis shows relative energy levels of electrons. The electrons originate from water, which holds onto its electrons very tightly (redox potential = +820 mV), and end up in NADPH, which holds its electrons much more loosely (redox potential = –320 mV).

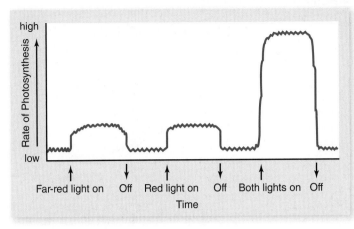

Figure 8.13 The enhancement effect. The rate of photosynthesis when red and far-red light are provided together is greater than the sum of the rates when each wavelength is provided individually. This result baffled researchers in the 1950s. Today, it provides key evidence that photosynthesis is carried out by two photochemical systems that act in series. One absorbs maximally in the far red, the other in the red portion of the spectrum.

Data analysis If "both lights on" showed a rate equal to the sum of each light, what would you conclude?

Photosystem II acts first. High-energy electrons generated by photosystem II are used to synthesize ATP and are then passed to photosystem I to drive the production of NADPH. For every pair of electrons obtained from a molecule of water, one molecule of NADPH and slightly more than one molecule of ATP are produced.

Photosystem II

The reaction center of photosystem II closely resembles the reaction center of purple bacteria. It consists of a core of 10 transmembrane protein subunits with electron transfer components and two P_{680} chlorophyll molecules arranged around this core. The light-harvesting antenna complex consists of molecules of chlorophyll *a* and accessory pigments bound to several protein chains. The reaction center of photosystem II differs from the reaction center of the purple bacteria in that it also contains four manganese atoms. These manganese atoms are essential for the oxidation of water.

Although the chemical details of the oxidation of water are not entirely clear, the outline is emerging. Four manganese atoms are bound in a cluster to reaction center proteins. Two water molecules are also bound to this cluster of manganese atoms. When the reaction center of photosystem II absorbs a photon, an electron in a P_{680} chlorophyll molecule is excited, which transfers this electron to an acceptor. The oxidized P_{680} then removes an electron from a manganese atom. The oxidized manganese atoms, with the aid of reaction center proteins, remove electrons from oxygen atoms in the two water molecules. This process requires the reaction center to absorb four photons to complete the oxidation of two water molecules, producing one O_2 in the process.

chapter **8** *Photosynthesis*

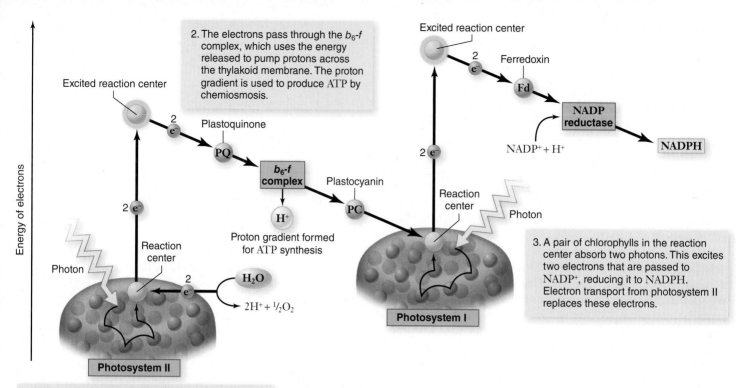

2. The electrons pass through the b_6-f complex, which uses the energy released to pump protons across the thylakoid membrane. The proton gradient is used to produce ATP by chemiosmosis.

3. A pair of chlorophylls in the reaction center absorb two photons. This excites two electrons that are passed to NADP+, reducing it to NADPH. Electron transport from photosystem II replaces these electrons.

1. A pair of chlorophylls in the reaction center absorb two photons of light. This excites two electrons that are transferred to plastoquinone (PQ). Loss of electrons from the reaction center produces an oxidation potential capable of oxidizing water.

Figure 8.14 Z diagram of photosystems I and II. Two photosystems work sequentially and have different roles. Photosystem II passes energetic electrons to photosystem I via an electron transport chain. The electrons lost are replaced by oxidizing water. Photosystem I uses energetic electrons to reduce NADP+ to NADPH.

The role of the b_6-f complex

The primary electron acceptor for the light-energized electrons leaving photosystem II is a quinone molecule. The reduced quinone that results from accepting a pair of electrons (*plastoquinone*) is a strong electron donor; it passes the excited electron pair to a proton pump called the **b_6-f complex** embedded within the thylakoid membrane (figure 8.15). This complex closely resembles the bc_1 complex in the respiratory electron transport chain of mitochondria, discussed in chapter 7.

Arrival of the energetic electron pair causes the b_6-f complex to pump a proton into the thylakoid space. A small, copper-containing protein called *plastocyanin* then carries the electron pair to photosystem I.

Photosystem I

The reaction center of photosystem I consists of a core transmembrane complex consisting of 12 to 14 protein subunits with two bound P_{700} chlorophyll molecules. Energy is fed to it by an antenna complex consisting of chlorophyll *a* and accessory pigment molecules.

Photosystem I accepts an electron from plastocyanin into the "hole" created by the exit of a light-energized electron. The absorption of a photon by photosystem I boosts the electron leaving the reaction center to a very high energy level. The electrons are passed to an iron–sulfur protein called *ferredoxin*. Unlike photosystem II and the bacterial photosystem, the plant photosystem I does not rely on quinones as electron acceptors.

Making NADPH

Photosystem I passes electrons to ferredoxin on the stromal side of the membrane (outside the thylakoid). The reduced ferredoxin carries an electron with very high potential. Two of them, from two molecules of reduced ferredoxin, are then donated to a molecule of NADP+ to form NADPH. The reaction is catalyzed by the membrane-bound enzyme *NADP reductase*.

Because the reaction occurs on the stromal side of the membrane and involves the uptake of a proton in forming NADPH, it contributes further to the proton gradient established during photosynthetic electron transport. The function of the two photosystems is summarized in figure 8.15.

ATP is generated by chemiosmosis

Protons are pumped from the stroma into the thylakoid compartment by the b_6-f complex. The splitting of water also produces added protons that contribute to the gradient. The thylakoid membrane is impermeable to protons, so this creates an electrochemical gradient that can be used to synthesize ATP.

ATP synthase

The chloroplast has ATP synthase enzymes in the thylakoid membrane that form a channel, allowing protons to cross back out into the stroma. These channels protrude like knobs on the external surface of the thylakoid membrane. As protons pass out of the thylakoid through the ATP synthase channel, ADP is phosphorylated to ATP and released into the stroma (see figure 8.15). The stroma contains the enzymes that catalyze the reactions of carbon fixation—the Calvin cycle reactions.

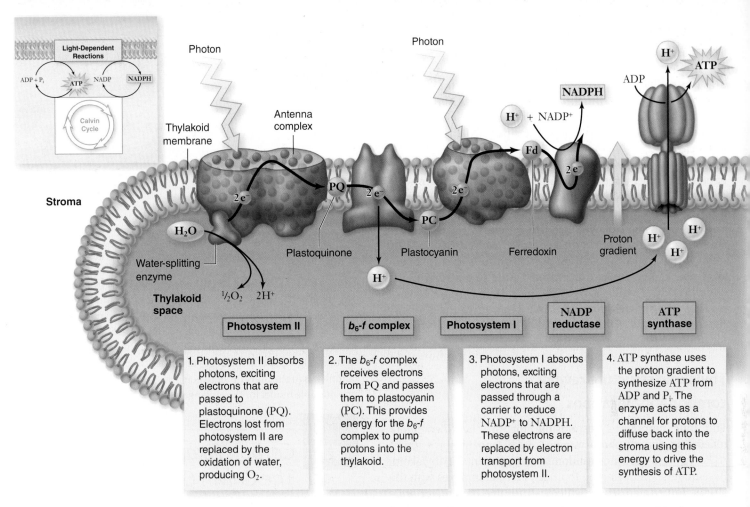

Figure 8.15 The photosynthetic electron transport system and ATP synthase. The two photosystems are arranged in the thylakoid membrane joined by an electron transport system that includes the b_6-f complex. These function together to create a proton gradient that is used by ATP synthase to synthesize ATP.

1. Photosystem II absorbs photons, exciting electrons that are passed to plastoquinone (PQ). Electrons lost from photosystem II are replaced by the oxidation of water, producing O_2.

2. The b_6-f complex receives electrons from PQ and passes them to plastocyanin (PC). This provides energy for the b_6-f complex to pump protons into the thylakoid.

3. Photosystem I absorbs photons, exciting electrons that are passed through a carrier to reduce $NADP^+$ to NADPH. These electrons are replaced by electron transport from photosystem II.

4. ATP synthase uses the proton gradient to synthesize ATP from ADP and P_i. The enzyme acts as a channel for protons to diffuse back into the stroma using this energy to drive the synthesis of ATP.

This mechanism is the same as that seen in the mitochondrial ATP synthase, and, in fact, the two enzymes are evolutionarily related. This similarity in generating a proton gradient by electron transport and ATP by chemiosmosis illustrates the similarities in structure and function in mitochondria and chloroplasts. Evidence for this chemiosmotic mechanism for photophosphorylation was actually discovered earlier (figure 8.16) and formed the background for experiments using the mitochondrial ATP synthase.

Figure 8.16 The Jagendorf acid bath experiment.

SCIENTIFIC THINKING

Hypothesis: *Photophosphorylation is coupled to electron transport by a proton gradient.*

Prediction: *If a proton gradient can be formed artificially, then isolated chloroplasts will phosphorylate ADP in the dark.*

Test: *Isolated chloroplasts are incubated in acid medium, then transferred in the dark to a basic medium to create an artificial proton gradient.*

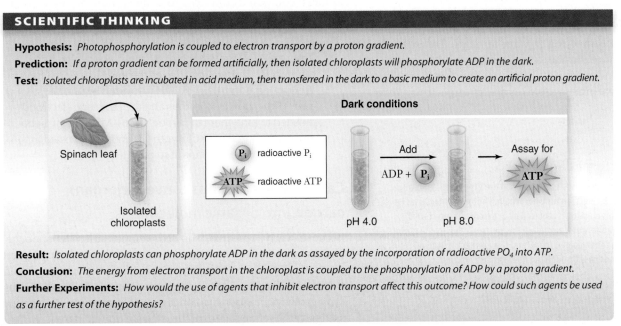

Result: *Isolated chloroplasts can phosphorylate ADP in the dark as assayed by the incorporation of radioactive PO_4 into ATP.*

Conclusion: *The energy from electron transport in the chloroplast is coupled to the phosphorylation of ADP by a proton gradient.*

Further Experiments: *How would the use of agents that inhibit electron transport affect this outcome? How could such agents be used as a further test of the hypothesis?*

The production of additional ATP

The passage of an electron pair from water to NADPH in noncyclic photophosphorylation generates one molecule of NADPH and slightly more than one molecule of ATP. But as you will learn later in this chapter, building organic molecules takes more energy than that—it takes 1.5 ATP molecules per NADPH molecule to fix carbon.

To produce the extra ATP, many plant species are capable of short-circuiting photosystem I, switching photosynthesis into a *cyclic photophosphorylation* mode, so that the light-excited electron leaving photosystem I is used to make ATP instead of NADPH. The energetic electrons are simply passed back to the b_6-f complex, rather than passing on to $NADP^+$. The b_6-f complex pumps protons into the thylakoid space, adding to the proton gradient that drives the chemiosmotic synthesis of ATP. The relative proportions of cyclic and noncyclic photophosphorylation in these plants determine the relative amounts of ATP and NADPH available for building organic molecules.

Thylakoid structure reveals components' locations

The four complexes responsible for the light-dependent reactions—namely photosystems I and II, cytochrome b_6-f, and ATP synthase—are not randomly arranged in the thylakoid. Researchers are beginning to image these complexes with the atomic force microscope, which can resolve nanometer scale structures, and a picture is emerging in which photosystem II is found primarily in the grana, whereas photosystem I and ATP synthase are found primarily in the stroma lamella. Photosystem I and ATP synthase may also be found in the edges of the grana that are not stacked. The cytochrome b_6-f complex is found in the borders between grana and stroma lamella. One possible model for the arrangement of the complexes is shown in figure 8.17.

The thylakoid itself is no longer thought of only as stacked disks. Some models of the thylakoid, based on electron microscopy and other imaging, depict the grana as folds of the interconnecting stroma lamella. This kind of arrangement is more similar to the folds seen in bacterial photosynthesis, and it would therefore allow for more flexibility in how the various complexes are arranged relative to one another.

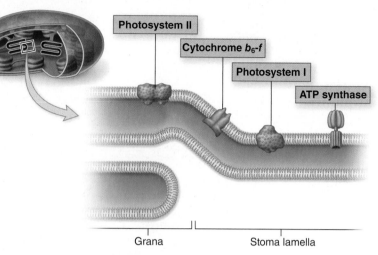

Figure 8.17 Model for the arrangement of complexes within the thylakoid. The arrangement of the two kinds of photosystems and the other complexes involved in photosynthesis is not random. Photosystem II is concentrated within grana, especially in stacked areas. Photosystem I and ATP synthase are concentrated in stroma lamella and the edges of grana. The cytochrome b_6-f complex is in the margins between grana and stroma lamella. This is one possible model for this arrangement.

8.6 Carbon Fixation: The Calvin Cycle

> **Learning Outcomes**
> 1. Describe carbon fixation.
> 2. Demonstrate how six CO_2 molecules can be used to make one glucose.

Carbohydrates contain many C—H bonds and are highly reduced compared with CO_2. To build carbohydrates, cells use energy and a source of electrons produced by the light-dependent reactions of the thylakoids:

1. **Energy.** ATP (provided by cyclic and noncyclic photophosphorylation) drives the endergonic reactions.
2. **Reduction potential.** NADPH (provided by photosystem I) provides a source of protons and the energetic electrons needed to bind them to carbon atoms. Much of the light energy captured in photosynthesis ends up invested in the energy-rich C—H bonds of sugars.

Calvin cycle reactions convert inorganic carbon into organic molecules

Because early research showed temperature dependence, photosynthesis was predicted to involve enzyme-catalyzed reactions. These reactions form a cycle of enzyme-catalyzed steps much like the Krebs cycle of respiration. Unlike the Krebs cycle, however, carbon fixation is geared toward producing new compounds, so the nature of the cycles is quite different.

The cycle of reactions that allow carbon fixation is called the **Calvin cycle,** after its discoverer, Melvin Calvin (1911–1997). Because the first intermediate of the cycle, phosphoglycerate, contains three carbon atoms, this process is also called **C₃ photosynthesis.**

The key step in this process—the event that makes the reduction of CO_2 possible—is the attachment of CO_2 to a highly specialized organic molecule. Photosynthetic cells produce this molecule by reassembling the bonds of two intermediates in glycolysis—fructose 6-phosphate and glyceraldehyde 3-phosphate (G3P)—to form the energy-rich 5-carbon sugar **ribulose 1,5-bisphosphate (RuBP).**

CO_2 reacts with RuBP to form a transient 6-carbon intermediate that immediately splits into two molecules of the three-carbon *3-phosphoglycerate (PGA).* This overall reaction is called the *carbon fixation reaction* because inorganic carbon (CO_2) has been incorporated into an organic form: the acid PGA. The enzyme that carries out this reaction, **ribulose bisphosphate carboxylase/oxygenase** (usually abbreviated **rubisco**) is a large, 16-subunit enzyme found in the chloroplast stroma.

Carbon is transferred through cycle intermediates, eventually producing glucose

We will consider how the Calvin cycle can produce one molecule of glucose, although this glucose is not produced directly by the cycle (figure 8.18). In a series of reactions, six molecules of CO_2 are bound to six RuBP by rubisco to produce 12 molecules

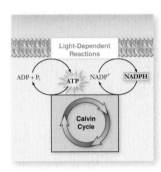

Figure 8.18 The Calvin cycle. The Calvin cycle accomplishes carbon fixation: converting inorganic carbon in the form of CO_2 into organic carbon in the form of carbohydrates. The cycle can be broken down into three phases: (1) carbon fixation, (2) reduction, and (3) regeneration of RuBP. For every six CO_2 molecules fixed by the cycle, a molecule of glucose can be synthesized from the products of the reduction reactions, G3P. The cycle uses the ATP and NADPH produced by the light reactions.

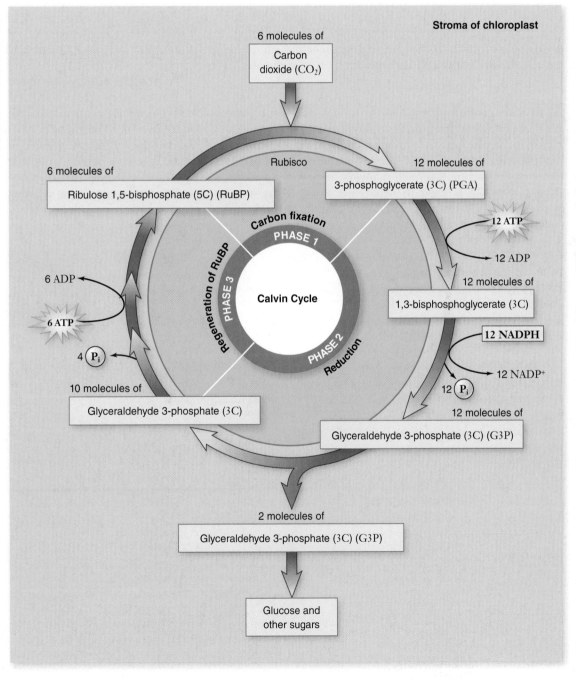

of PGA (containing $12 \times 3 = 36$ carbon atoms in all, 6 from CO_2 and 30 from RuBP). The 36 carbon atoms then undergo a cycle of reactions that regenerates the six molecules of RuBP used in the initial step (containing $6 \times 5 = 30$ carbon atoms). This leaves two molecules of *glyceraldehyde 3-phosphate (G3P)* (each with three carbon atoms) as the net gain. (You may recall G3P as also being the product of the first half of glycolysis, described in chapter 7.) These two molecules of G3P can then be used to make one molecule of glucose.

The net equation of the Calvin cycle is:

$$6CO_2 + 18\ ATP + 12\ NADPH + water \longrightarrow$$
$$2\ glyceraldehyde\ 3\text{-}phosphate + 16\ P_i + 18\ ADP + 12\ NADP^+$$

With six full turns of the cycle, six molecules of carbon dioxide enter, two molecules of G3P are produced, and six molecules of RuBP are regenerated. Thus six turns of the cycle produce two G3P that can be used to make a single glucose molecule. The six turns of the cycle also incorporated six CO_2 molecules, providing enough carbon to synthesize glucose, although the six carbon atoms do not all end up in this molecule of glucose.

Phases of the cycle

The Calvin cycle can be thought of as divided into three phases: (1) carbon fixation, (2) reduction, and (3) regeneration of RuBP. The carbon fixation reaction generates two molecules of the 3-carbon acid PGA; PGA is then reduced to G3P by reactions that are essentially a reverse of part of glycolysis; finally, the PGA is used to regenerate RuBP. Three turns around the cycle incorporate enough carbon to produce a new molecule of G3P, and six turns incorporate enough carbon to synthesize one glucose molecule.

We now know that light is required *indirectly* for different segments of the CO_2 reduction reactions. Five of the Calvin cycle enzymes—including rubisco—are light-activated; that is, they become functional or operate more efficiently in the presence of light. Light also promotes transport of required 3-carbon intermediates across chloroplast membranes. And finally, light promotes the influx of Mg^{2+} into the chloroplast stroma, which further activates the enzyme rubisco.

Output of the Calvin cycle

Glyceraldehyde 3-phosphate is a 3-carbon sugar, a key intermediate in glycolysis. Much of it is transported out of the chloroplast to the cytoplasm of the cell, where the reversal of several reactions in glycolysis allows it to be converted to fructose 6-phosphate and glucose 1-phosphate. These products can then be used to form sucrose, a major transport sugar in plants. (Sucrose, table sugar, is a disaccharide made of fructose and glucose.)

In times of intensive photosynthesis, G3P levels rise in the stroma of the chloroplast. As a consequence, some G3P in the chloroplast is converted to glucose 1-phosphate. This takes place in a set of reactions analogous to those occurring in the cytoplasm, by reversing several reactions similar to those of glycolysis. The glucose 1-phosphate is then combined into an insoluble polymer, forming long chains of starch stored as bulky starch grains in the cytoplasm. These starch grains represent stored glucose for later use.

Figure 8.19 Chloroplasts and mitochondria: completing an energy cycle. Water and O_2 cycle between chloroplasts and mitochondria within a plant cell, as do glucose and CO_2. Cells with chloroplasts take in CO_2 and H_2O and produce glucose and O_2. Cells without chloroplasts, such as animal cells, take in glucose and O_2 and produce CO_2 and H_2O. This leads to global cycling of carbon through photosynthesis and respiration (see figure 57.1).

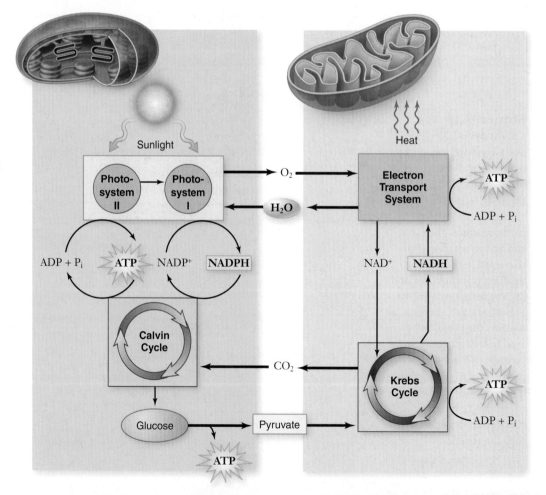

The energy cycle

The energy-capturing metabolisms of the chloroplasts studied in this chapter and the mitochondria studied in chapter 7 are intimately related (figure 8.19). Photosynthesis uses the products of respiration as starting substrates, and respiration uses the products of photosynthesis as starting substrates. The production of glucose from G3P even uses part of the ancient glycolytic pathway, run in reverse. Also, the principal proteins involved in electron transport and ATP production in plants are evolutionarily related to those in mitochondria.

Photosynthesis is but one aspect of plant biology, although it is an important one. In chapters 36 through 41, we examine plants in more detail. We have discussed photosynthesis as a part of cell biology because photosynthesis arose long before plants did, and because most organisms depend directly or indirectly on photosynthesis for the energy that powers their lives.

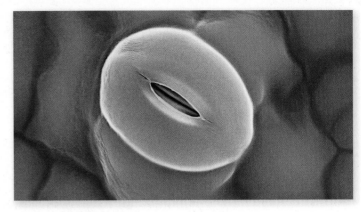

Figure 8.20 Stoma. A closed stoma in the leaf of a tobacco plant. Each stoma is formed from two guard cells whose shape changes with turgor pressure to open and close. Under dry conditions plants close their stomata to conserve water.

> #### Learning Outcomes Review 8.6
>
> Carbon fixation takes place in the stroma of the chloroplast, where inorganic CO_2 is incorporated into an organic molecule. The key intermediate is the 5-carbon sugar RuBP that combines with CO_2 in a reaction catalyzed by the enzyme rubisco. The cycle can be broken down into three stages: carbon fixation, reduction, and regeneration of RuBP. ATP and NADPH from the light reactions provide energy and electrons for the reduction reactions, which produce G3P. Glucose is synthesized when two molecules of G3P are combined.
>
> ■ *How does the Calvin cycle compare with glycolysis?*

8.7 Photorespiration

> #### Learning Outcomes
>
> 1. *Distinguish between how rubisco acts to make RuBP and how it oxidizes RuBP.*
> 2. *Compare the function of carbon fixation in the C_3, C_4, and CAM pathways.*

Evolution does not necessarily result in optimum solutions. Rather, it favors workable solutions that can be derived from features that already exist. Photosynthesis is no exception. Rubisco, the enzyme that catalyzes the key carbon-fixing reaction of photosynthesis, provides a decidedly suboptimal solution. This enzyme has a second enzymatic activity that interferes with carbon fixation, namely that of *oxidizing* RuBP. In this process, called **photorespiration,** O_2 is incorporated into RuBP, which undergoes additional reactions that actually release CO_2. Hence, photorespiration releases CO_2, essentially undoing carbon fixation.

Photorespiration reduces the yield of photosynthesis

The carboxylation and oxidation of RuBP are catalyzed at the same active site on rubisco, and CO_2 and O_2 compete with each other at this site. Under normal conditions at 25°C, the rate of the carboxylation reaction is four times that of the oxidation reaction, meaning that 20% of photosynthetically fixed carbon is lost to photorespiration.

This loss rises substantially as temperature increases, because under hot, arid conditions, specialized openings in the leaf called *stomata* (singular, *stoma*) (figure 8.20) close to conserve water. This closing also cuts off the supply of CO_2 entering the leaf and does not allow O_2 to exit (figure 8.21). As a result, the low-CO_2 and high-O_2 conditions within the leaf favor photorespiration.

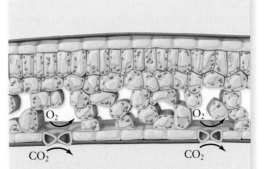

Under hot, arid conditions, leaves lose water by evaporation through openings in the leaves called stomata.

The stomata close to conserve water but as a result, O_2 builds up inside the leaves, and CO_2 cannot enter the leaves.

Figure 8.21 Conditions favoring photorespiration. In hot, arid environments, stomata close to conserve water, which also prevents CO_2 from entering and O_2 from exiting the leaf. The high-O_2/low-CO_2 conditions favor photorespiration.

Figure 8.22 Comparison of C₃ and C₄ pathways of carbon fixation. *a.* The C_3 pathway uses the Calvin cycle to fix carbon. All reactions occur in mesophyll cells using CO_2 that diffuses in through stomata. *b.* The C_4 pathway incorporates CO_2 into a 4-carbon molecule of malate in mesophyll cells. This is transported to the bundle sheath cells where it is converted back into CO_2 and pyruvate, creating a high level of CO_2. This allows efficient carbon fixation by the Calvin cycle.

Plants that fix carbon using only C_3 photosynthesis (the Calvin cycle) are called **C₃ plants** (figure 8.22*a*). Other plants add CO_2 to phosphoenolpyruvate (PEP) to form a 4-carbon molecule. This reaction is catalyzed by the enzyme PEP *carboxylase.* This enzyme has two advantages over rubisco: it has a much greater affinity for CO_2 than rubisco, and it does not have oxidase activity.

The 4-carbon compound produced by PEP carboxylase undergoes further modification, only to be eventually decarboxylated. The CO_2 released by this decarboxylation is then used by rubisco in the Calvin cycle. This allows CO_2 to be pumped directly to the site of rubisco, which increases the local concentration of CO_2 relative to O_2, minimizing photorespiration. The 4-carbon compound produced by PEP carboxylase allows CO_2 to be stored in an organic form, to then be released in a different cell, or at a different time to keep the level of CO_2 high relative to O_2.

The reduction in the yield of carbohydrate as a result of photorespiration is not trivial. C_3 plants lose between 25% and 50% of their photosynthetically fixed carbon in this way. The rate depends largely on temperature. In tropical climates, especially those in which the temperature is often above 28°C, the problem is severe, and it has a major effect on tropical agriculture.

The two main groups of plants that initially capture CO_2 using PEP carboxylase differ in how they maintain high levels of CO_2 relative to O_2. In **C₄ plants** (figure 8.22*b*), the capture of CO_2 occurs in one cell and the decarboxylation occurs in an adjacent cell. This represents a spatial solution to the problem of photorespiration. The second group, **CAM plants,** perform both reactions in the same cell, but capture CO_2 using PEP carboxylase at night, then decarboxylate during the day. CAM stands for **crassulacean acid metabolism,** after the plant family Crassulaceae (the stonecrops, or hens-and-chicks), in which it was first discovered. This mechanism represents a temporal solution to the photorespiration problem.

C₄ plants have evolved to minimize photorespiration

The C_4 plants include corn, sugarcane, sorghum, and a number of other grasses. These plants initially fix carbon using PEP carboxylase in mesophyll cells. This reaction produces the organic acid oxaloacetate, which is converted to malate and transported to bundle-sheath cells that surround the leaf veins. Within the bundle-sheath cells, malate is decarboxylated to produce pyruvate and CO_2 (figure 8.23). Because the

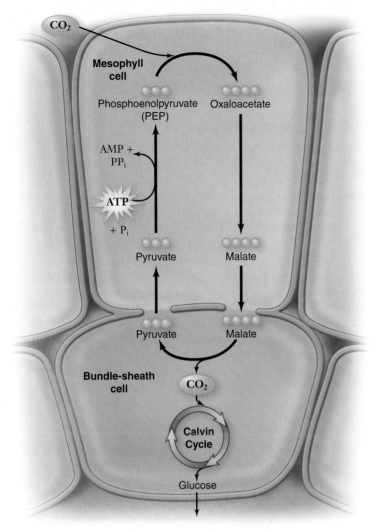

Figure 8.23 Carbon fixation in C$_4$ plants. This process is called the C$_4$ pathway because the first molecule formed, oxaloacetate, contains four carbons. The oxaloacetate is converted to malate, which moves into bundle-sheath cells where it is decarboxylated back to CO$_2$ and pyruvate. This produces a high level of CO$_2$ in the bundle-sheath cells that can be fixed by the usual C$_3$ Calvin cycle with little photorespiration. The pyruvate diffuses back into the mesophyll cells, where it is converted back to PEP to be used in another C$_4$ fixation reaction.

bundle-sheath cells are impermeable to CO$_2$, the local level of CO$_2$ is high and carbon fixation by rubisco and the Calvin cycle is efficient. The pyruvate produced by decarboxylation is transported back to the mesophyll cells, where it is converted back to PEP, thereby completing the cycle.

The C$_4$ pathway, although it overcomes the problems of photorespiration, does have a cost. The conversion of pyruvate back to PEP requires breaking two high-energy bonds in ATP. Thus each CO$_2$ transported into the bundle-sheath cells cost the equivalent of two ATP. To produce a single glucose, this requires 12 additional ATP compared with the Calvin cycle alone. Despite this additional cost, C$_4$ photosynthesis is advantageous in hot dry climates where photorespiration would remove more than half of the carbon fixed by the usual C$_3$ pathway alone.

Figure 8.24 Carbon fixation in CAM plants. CAM plants also use both C$_4$ and C$_3$ pathways to fix carbon and minimize photorespiration. In CAM plants, the two pathways occur in the same cell but are separated in time: The C$_4$ pathway is utilized to fix carbon at night, then CO$_2$ is released from these accumulated stores during the day to drive the C$_3$ pathway. This achieves the same effect of minimizing photorespiration while also minimizing loss of water by opening stomata at night when temperatures are lower.

The Crassulacean acid pathway splits photosynthesis into night and day

A second strategy to decrease photorespiration in hot regions has been adopted by the CAM plants. These include many succulent (water-storing) plants, such as cacti, pineapples, and some members of about two dozen other plant groups.

In these plants, the stomata open during the night and close during the day (figure 8.24). This pattern of stomatal opening and closing is the reverse of that in most plants. CAM plants initially fix CO$_2$ using PEP carboxylase to produce oxaloacetate. The oxaloacetate is often converted into other organic acids, depending on the particular CAM plant. These organic compounds accumulate during the night and are stored in the vacuole. Then during the day, when the stomata are closed, the organic acids are decarboxylated to yield high levels of CO$_2$. These high levels of CO$_2$ drive the Calvin cycle and minimize photorespiration.

Like C$_4$ plants, CAM plants use both C$_3$ and C$_4$ pathways. They differ in that they use both of these pathways in the same cell: the C$_4$ pathway at night and the C$_3$ pathway during the day. In C$_4$ plants the two pathways occur in different cells.

Learning Outcomes Review 8.7

Rubisco can also oxidize RuBP under conditions of high O$_2$ and low CO$_2$. In plants that use only C$_3$ metabolism (Calvin cycle), up to 20% of fixed carbon is lost to this photorespiration. Plants adapted to hot, dry environments are capable of storing CO$_2$ as a 4-carbon molecule and avoiding some of this loss; they are called C$_4$ plants. In CAM plants, CO$_2$ is fixed at night into a C$_4$ organic compound; in the daytime, this compound is used as a source of CO$_2$ C$_3$ metabolism when stomata are closed to prevent water loss.

■ **How do C$_4$ plants and CAM plants differ?**

Chapter Review

8.1 Overview of Photosynthesis

Photosynthesis is the conversion of light energy into chemical energy (figure 8.2).

Photosynthesis combines CO_2 and H_2O, producing glucose and O_2.
Photosynthesis has three stages: absorbing light energy, using this energy to synthesize ATP and NADPH, and using the ATP and NADPH to convert CO_2 to organic molecules. The first two stages consist of light-dependent reactions, and the third stage of light-independent reactions.

In plants, photosynthesis takes place in chloroplasts.
Chloroplasts contain internal thylakoid membranes and a fluid matrix called stroma. The photosystems involved in energy capture are found in the thylakoid membranes, and enzymes for assembling organic molecules are in the stroma.

8.2 The Discovery of Photosynthetic Processes

Plants do not increase mass from soil and water alone.
Early investigations revealed that plants produce O_2 from carbon dioxide and water in the presence of light.

Photosynthesis includes both light-dependent and light-independent reactions.
The light-dependent reactions require light; the light-independent reactions occur in both daylight and darkness. The rate of photosynthesis depends on the amount of light, the CO_2 concentration, and temperature.

O_2 comes from water, not from CO_2.
The use of isotopes revealed the individual origins and fates of different molecules in photosynthetic reactions.

ATP and NADPH from light-dependent reactions reduce CO_2 to make sugars.
Carbon fixation requires ATP and NADPH, which are products of the light-dependent reactions. As long as these are available, CO_2 is reduced by enzymes in the stroma to form simple sugars.

8.3 Pigments

Light is a form of energy.
Light exists both as a wave and as a particle (photon). Light can remove electrons from some metals by the photoelectric effect, and in photosynthesis, chloroplasts act as photoelectric devices.

Each pigment has a characteristic absorption spectrum (figure 8.5).
Chlorophyll a is the only pigment that can convert light energy into chemical energy. Chlorophyll b is an accessory pigment that increases the harvest of photons for photosynthesis.
Carotenoids and other accessory pigments further increase a plant's ability to harvest photons.

8.4 Photosystem Organization (figure 8.10)

Production of one O_2 molecule requires many chlorophyll molecules.
Measurement of O_2 output led to the idea of photosystems—clusters of pigment molecules that channel energy to a reaction center.

A generalized photosystem contains an antenna complex and a reaction center.
A photosystem is a network of chlorophyll a, accessory pigments, and proteins embedded in the thylakoid membrane. Pigment molecules of the antenna complex harvest photons and feed light energy to the reaction center. The reaction center is composed of

two chlorophyll a molecules in a protein matrix that pass an excited electron to an electron acceptor.

8.5 The Light-Dependent Reactions

The light reactions can be broken down into four processes: primary photoevent, charge separation, electron transport, and chemiosmosis.

Some bacteria use a single photosystem (figure 8.12).
An excited electron moves along a transport chain and eventually returns to the photosystem. This cyclic process is used to generate a proton gradient. In some bacteria, this can also produce NADPH.

Chloroplasts have two connected photosystems (figure 8.14).
Photosystem I transfers electrons to $NADP^+$, reducing it to NADPH. Photosystem II replaces electrons lost by photosystem I. Electrons lost from photosystem II are replaced by electrons from oxidation of water, which also produces O_2.

The two photosystems work together in noncyclic photophosphorylation (figure 8.14).
Photosystem II and photosystem I are linked by an electron transport chain; the b_6-f complex in this chain pumps protons into the thylakoid space.

ATP is generated by chemiosmosis.
ATP synthase is a channel enzyme; as protons flow through the channel down their gradient, ADP is phosphorylated producing ATP, similar to the mechanism in mitochondria. Plants can make additional ATP by cyclic photophosphorylation.

Thylakoid structure reveals components' locations.
Imaging studies suggest that photosystem II is primarily found in the grana, while photosystem I and ATP synthase are found in the stroma lamella.

8.6 Carbon Fixation: The Calvin Cycle (figure 8.18)

Calvin cycle reactions convert inorganic carbon into organic molecules.
The Calvin cycle, also known as C_3 photosynthesis, uses CO_2, ATP, and NADPH to build simple sugars.

Carbon is transferred through cycle intermediates, eventually producing glucose.
The Calvin cycle occurs in three stages: carbon fixation via the enzyme rubisco's action on RuBP and CO_2; reduction of the resulting 3-carbon PGA to G3P, generating ATP and NADPH; and regeneration of RuBP. Six turns of the cycle fix enough carbon to produce two excess G3Ps used to make one molecule of glucose.

8.7 Photorespiration

Photorespiration reduces the yield of photosynthesis.
Rubisco can catalyze the oxidation of RuBP, reversing carbon fixation. Dry, hot conditions tend to increase this reaction.

C_4 plants have evolved to minimize photorespiration.
C_4 plants fix carbon by adding CO_2 to a 3-carbon molecule, forming oxaloacetate. Carbon is fixed in one cell by the C_4 pathway, then CO_2 is released in another cell for the Calvin cycle (figure 8.23).

The Crassulacean acid pathway splits photosynthesis into night and day.
CAM plants use the C_4 pathway during the day when stomata are closed, and the Calvin cycle at night in the same cell (figure 8.24).

UNDERSTAND

1. The *light-dependent* reactions of photosynthesis are responsible for the production of
   a. glucose.
   b. CO_2.
   c. ATP and NADPH.
   d. H_2O.

2. Which region of a chloroplast is associated with the capture of light energy?
   a. Thylakoid membrane
   b. Outer membrane
   c. Stroma
   d. Both a and c are correct.

3. The colors of light that are most effective for photosynthesis are
   a. red, blue, and violet.
   b. green, yellow, and orange.
   c. infrared and ultraviolet.
   d. All colors of light are equally effective.

4. During noncyclic photosynthesis, photosystem I functions to _____, and photosystem II functions to _____.
   a. synthesize ATP; produce O_2
   b. reduce $NADP^+$; oxidize H_2O
   c. reduce CO_2; oxidize NADPH
   d. restore an electron to its reaction center; gain an electron from water

5. How is a reaction center pigment in a photosystem different from a pigment in the antenna complex?
   a. The reaction center pigment is a chlorophyll molecule.
   b. The antenna complex pigment can only reflect light.
   c. The reaction center pigment loses an electron when it absorbs light energy.
   d. The antenna complex pigments are not attached to proteins.

6. The ATP and NADPH from the light reactions are used
   a. in glycolysis in roots.
   b. directly in most biochemical reactions in the cell.
   c. during the reactions of the Calvin cycle to produce glucose.
   d. to synthesize chlorophyll.

7. The carbon fixation reaction converts
   a. inorganic carbon into an organic acid.
   b. CO_2 into glucose.
   c. inactive rubisco into active rubisco.
   d. an organic acid into CO_2.

8. C_4 plants initially fix carbon by
   a. the same pathway as C_3 plants, but they modify this product.
   b. incorporating CO_2 into oxaloacetate, which is converted to malate.
   c. incorporating CO_2 into citrate via the Krebs cycle.
   d. incorporating CO_2 into glucose via reverse glycolysis.

APPLY

1. The overall flow of electrons in the light reactions is from
   a. antenna pigments to the reaction center.
   b. H_2O to CO_2.
   c. photosystem I to photosystem II.
   d. H_2O to NADPH.

2. If you could measure pH within a chloroplast, where would it be lowest?
   a. In the stroma
   b. In the lumen of the thylakoid

c. In the cytoplasm immediately outside the chloroplast
d. In the antenna complex

3. The excited electron from photosystem I
   a. can be returned to the reaction center to generate ATP by cyclic photophosphorylation.
   b. is replaced by oxidizing H_2O.
   c. is replaced by an electron from photosystem II.
   d. Both a and c are correct.

4. If the Calvin cycle runs through six turns
   a. all of the fixed carbon will end up in the same glucose molecule.
   b. 12 carbons will be fixed by the process.
   c. enough carbon will be fixed to make one glucose, but they will not all be in the same molecule.
   d. one glucose will be converted into six CO_2.

5. Which of the following are similarities between the structure and function of mitochondria and chloroplasts?
   a. They both create internal proton gradients by electron transport.
   b. They both generate CO_2 by oxidation reactions.
   c. They both have a double membrane system.
   d. Both a and c are correct.

6. Given that the C_4 pathway gets around the problems of photorespiration, why don't all plants use it?
   a. It is a more recent process, and many plants have not had time to evolve this pathway.
   b. It requires extra enzymes that many plants lack.
   c. It requires special transport tissues that many plants lack.
   d. It also has an energetic cost.

7. If the thylakoid membrane became leaky to ions, what would you predict to be the result on the light reactions?
   a. It would stop ATP production.
   b. It would stop NADPH production.
   c. It would stop the oxidation of H_2O.
   d. All of the choices are correct.

8. The overall process of photosynthesis
   a. results in the reduction of CO_2 and the oxidation of H_2O.
   b. results in the reduction of H_2O and the oxidation of CO_2.
   c. consumes O_2 and produces CO_2.
   d. produces O_2 from CO_2.

SYNTHESIZE

1. Compare and contrast the fixation of carbon in C_3, C_4, and CAM plants.

2. Diagram the relationship between the reactants and products of photosynthesis and respiration.

3. Do plant cells need mitochondria? Explain your answer.

ONLINE RESOURCE

www.ravenbiology.com

Understand, Apply, and Synthesize—enhance your study with animations that bring concepts to life and practice tests to assess your understanding. Your instructor may also recommend the interactive eBook, individualized learning tools, and more.

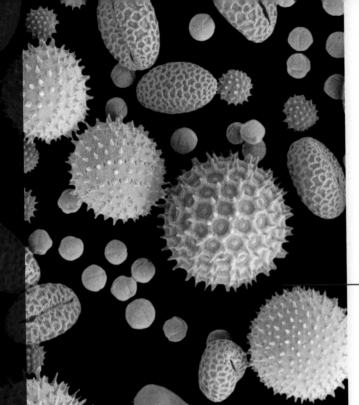

Chapter 9

Cell Communication

Chapter Contents

Introduction

Springtime is a time of rebirth and renewal. Trees that have appeared dead produce new leaves and buds, and flowers sprout from the ground. For sufferers of seasonal allergy, this is not quite such a pleasant time. The pollen in the micrograph and other allergens produced stimulate the immune system to produce the molecule histamine and other molecules that form cellular signals. These signals cause inflammation, mucus secretion, vasodilation, and other responses that together cause the runny nose, itching, watery eyes, and other symptoms that make up the allergic reaction. We treat allergy symptoms by using drugs called antihistamines that interfere with this cellular signaling. The popular drug loratadine (better known as Claritin), for example, acts by blocking the receptor for histamine, thus preventing its action.

We will begin this chapter with a general overview of signaling, and the kinds of receptors cells use to respond to signals. Then we will look in more detail at how these different types of receptors can elicit a response from cells, and finally, how cells make connections with one another.

9.1   Overview of Cell Communication

Learning Outcomes

1. *Discriminate between methods of signaling based on distance from source to reception.*
2. *Describe how phosphorylation can affect protein function.*

Communication between cells is common in nature. Cell signaling occurs in all multicellular organisms, providing an indispensable mechanism for cells to influence one another. Effective signaling requires a signaling molecule, called a **ligand,** and a molecule to which the signal binds, called a **receptor protein.** The interaction of these two components initiates the process of *signal transduction,* which converts the information in the signal into a cellular response (figure 9.1).

The cells of multicellular organisms use a variety of molecules as signals, including but not limited to, peptides, large proteins, individual amino acids, nucleotides, and steroids and other lipids. Even dissolved gases such as NO (nitric oxide) are used as signals.

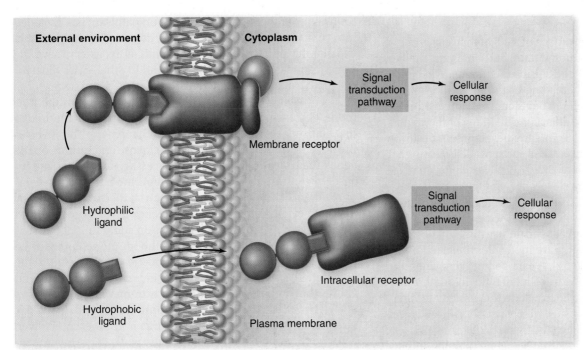

Figure 9.1 Overview of cell signaling. Cell signaling involves a signal molecule called a ligand, a receptor, and a signal transduction pathway that produces a cellular response. The location of the receptor can either be intracellular, for hydrophobic ligands that can cross the membrane, or in the plasma membrane, for hydrophilic ligands that cannot cross the membrane.

Any cell of a multicellular organism is exposed to a constant stream of signals. At any time, hundreds of different chemical signals may be present in the environment surrounding the cell. Each cell responds only to certain signals, however, and ignores the rest, like a person following the conversation of one or two individuals in a noisy, crowded room.

How does a cell "choose" which signals to respond to? The number and kind of receptor molecules determine this. When a ligand approaches a receptor protein that has a complementary shape, the two can bind, forming a complex. This binding induces a change in the receptor protein's shape, ultimately producing a response in the cell via a signal transduction pathway. In this way, a given cell responds to the signaling molecules that fit the particular set of receptor proteins it possesses and ignores those for which it lacks receptors.

Signaling is defined by the distance from source to receptor

Cells can communicate through any of four basic mechanisms, depending primarily on the distance between the signaling and responding cells (figure 9.2). These mechanisms are (1) direct contact, (2) paracrine signaling, (3) endocrine signaling, and (4) synaptic signaling.

In addition to using these four basic mechanisms, some cells actually send signals to themselves, secreting signals that bind to specific receptors on their own plasma membranes. This process, called *autocrine signaling,* is thought to play an important role in reinforcing developmental changes, and it is an important component of signaling in the immune system (chapter 51).

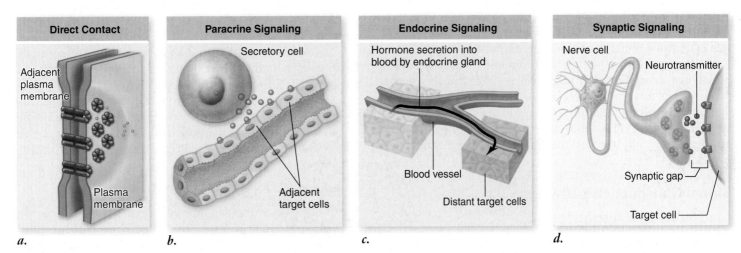

Figure 9.2 Four kinds of cell signaling. Cells communicate in several ways. *a.* Two cells in direct contact with each other may send signals across gap junctions. *b.* In paracrine signaling, secretions from one cell have an effect only on cells in the immediate area. *c.* In endocrine signaling, hormones are released into the organism's circulatory system, which carries them to the target cells. *d.* Chemical synapse signaling involves transmission of signal molecules, called neurotransmitters, from a neuron over a small synaptic gap to the target cell.

Direct contact

As you saw in chapter 5, the surface of a eukaryotic cell is richly populated with proteins, carbohydrates, and lipids attached to and extending outward from the plasma membrane. When cells are very close to one another, some of the molecules on the plasma membrane of one cell can be recognized by receptors on the plasma membrane of an adjacent cell. Many of the important interactions between cells in early development occur by means of direct contact between cell surfaces. Cells also signal through gap junctions (figure 9.2*a*). We'll examine contact-dependent interactions more closely later in this chapter.

Paracrine signaling

Signal molecules released by cells can diffuse through the extracellular fluid to other cells. If those molecules are taken up by neighboring cells, destroyed by extracellular enzymes, or quickly removed from the extracellular fluid in some other way, their influence is restricted to cells in the immediate vicinity of the releasing cell. Signals with such short-lived, local effects are called **paracrine** signals (figure 9.2*b*).

Like direct contact, paracrine signaling plays an important role in early development, coordinating the activities of clusters of neighboring cells. The immune response in vertebrates also involves paracrine signaling between immune cells (chapter 51).

Endocrine signaling

A released signal molecule that remains in the extracellular fluid may enter the organism's circulatory system and travel widely throughout the body. These longer-lived signal molecules, which may affect cells very distant from the releasing cell, are called **hormones,** and this type of intercellular communication is known as **endocrine signaling** (figure 9.2*c*). Chapter 45 discusses endocrine signaling in detail. Both animals and plants use this signaling mechanism extensively.

Synaptic signaling

In animals, the cells of the nervous system provide rapid communication with distant cells. Their signal molecules, **neurotransmitters,** do not travel to the distant cells through the circulatory system as hormones do. Rather, the long, fiberlike extensions of nerve cells release neurotransmitters from their tips very close to the target cells (figure 9.2*d*). The association of a neuron and its target cell is called a **chemical synapse,** and this type of intercellular communication is called **synaptic signaling.** Whereas paracrine signals move through the fluid between cells, neuro-transmitters cross the synaptic gap and persist only briefly. We will examine synaptic signaling more fully in chapter 44.

Signal transduction pathways lead to cellular responses

The types of signaling outlined earlier are descriptive and say nothing about how cells respond to signals. The events that occur within the cell on receipt of a signal are called **signal transduction.** These events form discrete pathways that lead to a cellular response to the signal received by receptors.

Knowledge of these signal transduction pathways has exploded in recent years and indicates a high degree of complexity that explains how in some cases different cell types can have the same response to different signals, and in other cases different cell types can have a different response to the same signal.

For example, a variety of cell types respond to the hormone glucagon by mobilizing glucose as part of the body's mechanism to control blood glucose (chapter 45). This involves breaking down stored glycogen into glucose and turning on the genes that encode the enzymes necessary to synthesize glucose. In contrast, the hormone epinephrine has diverse effects on different cell types. We have all been startled or frightened by a sudden event. Your heart beats faster, you feel more alert, and you can even feel the hairs on your skin stand up. All of this is due in part to your body releasing the hormone epinephrine (also called adrenaline) into the bloodstream. This leads to the heightened state of alertness and increased heart rate and energy that prepare us to respond to extreme situations.

These differing effects of epinephrine depend on the different cell types with receptors for this hormone. In the liver, cells are stimulated to mobilize glucose while in the heart muscle cells contract more forcefully to increase blood flow. In addition, blood vessels respond by expanding in some areas and contracting in others to redirect blood flow to the liver, heart, and skeletal muscles. These different reactions depend on the fact that each cell type has a receptor for epinephrine, but different sets of proteins that respond to this signal.

Phosphorylation is key in control of protein function

The function of a signal transduction pathway is to change the behavior or nature of a cell. This action may require changing the composition of proteins that make up a cell or altering the activity of cellular proteins. Many proteins are inactive or nonfunctional as they are initially synthesized and require modification after synthesis for activation. In other cases, a protein may be deactivated by modification. A major source of control for protein function is the addition or removal of phosphate groups, called **phosphorylation** or **dephosphorylation,** respectively.

As you learned in preceding chapters, the end result of the metabolic pathways of cellular respiration and photosynthesis was the phosphorylation of ADP to ATP. The ATP synthesized by these processes can donate phosphate groups to proteins. The phosphorylation of proteins alters their function by either turning their activity on or off. This is one way that the information from extracellular signals can result in changes in cellular activities.

Protein kinases

The class of enzyme that adds phosphate groups from ATP to proteins is called a *protein kinase*. These phosphate groups can be added to the three amino acids that have an OH as part of their R group, namely serine, threonine, and tyrosine. We categorize protein kinases as either serine–threonine or tyrosine kinases based on the amino acids they modify (figure 9.3). Most cytoplasmic protein kinases fall into the serine–threonine kinase class.

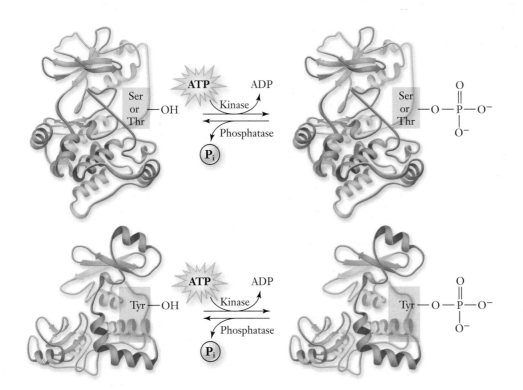

Figure 9.3 Phosphorylation of proteins. Many proteins are controlled by their phosphorylation state: that is, they are activated by phosphorylation and deactivated by dephosphorylation or the reverse. The enzymes that add phosphate groups are called kinases. These form two classes depending on the amino acid the phosphate is added to, either serine–threonine kinases or tyrosine kinases. The action of kinases is reversed by protein phosphatase enzymes.

Phosphatases

Part of the reason for the versatility of phosphorylation as a form of protein modification is that it is reversible. Another class of enzymes called **phosphatases** removes phosphate groups, reversing the action of kinases (see figure 9.3). Thus, a protein activated by a kinase will be deactivated by a phosphatase, and a protein deactivated by a kinase will be activated by a phosphatase.

Learning Outcomes Review 9.1

Cell communication involves chemical signals, or ligands, that bind to cellular receptors. Binding of ligand to receptor initiates signal transduction pathways that lead to a cellular response. Different cells may have the same response to one signal and the same signal can also elicit different responses in different cells. The phosphorylation–dephosphorylation of proteins is a common mechanism of controlling protein function found in signaling pathways.

■ *How are receptor ligand interactions similar to enzyme substrate interactions?*

9.2 Receptor Types

Learning Outcome

1. *Contrast the different types of receptors.*

The first step in understanding cell signaling is to consider the receptors themselves. Cells must have a specific receptor to be able to respond to a particular signaling molecule. The interaction of a receptor and its ligand is an example of molecular recognition, a process in which one molecule fits specifically based on its complementary shape with another molecule. This interaction causes subtle changes in the structure of the receptor, thereby activating it. This is the beginning of any signal transduction pathway.

Receptors are defined by location

The nature of these receptor molecules depends on their location and on the kind of ligands they bind. Intracellular receptors bind hydro-phobic ligands, which can easily cross the membrane, inside the cell. In contrast, cell surface or membrane receptors bind hydrophilic ligands, which cannot easily cross the membrane, outside the cell (see figure 9.1). Membrane receptors consist of transmembrane proteins that are in contact with both the cytoplasm and the extracellular environment. Table 9.1 summarizes the types of receptors and communication mechanisms discussed in this chapter.

Membrane receptors include three subclasses

When a receptor is a transmembrane protein, the ligand binds to the receptor outside of the cell and never actually crosses the plasma membrane. In this case, the receptor itself, and not the signaling molecule is responsible for information crossing the membrane. Membrane receptors can be categorized based on their structure and function.

Channel-linked receptors

Chemically gated ion channels are receptor proteins that allow the passage of ions (figure 9.4*a*). The receptor proteins that bind many neurotransmitters have the same basic structure. Each is a membrane protein with multiple transmembrane domains, meaning that the chain of amino acids threads back and forth across the plasma membrane several times. In the center of the protein is a pore that connects the extracellular fluid with the cytoplasm. The pore is big enough for ions to pass through, so the protein functions as an **ion channel.**

TABLE 9.1	Receptors Involved in Cell Signaling		
Receptor Type	**Structure**	**Function**	**Example**
Intracellular Receptors	No extracellular signal-binding site	Receives signals from lipid-soluble or noncharged, nonpolar small molecules	Receptors for NO, steroid hormone, vitamin D, and thyroid hormone
Cell Surface Receptors			
Chemically gated ion channels	Multipass transmembrane protein forming a central pore	Molecular "gates" triggered chemically to open or close	Neurons
Enzymatic receptors	Single-pass transmembrane protein	Binds signal extracellularly; catalyzes response intracellularly	Phosphorylation of protein kinases
G protein-coupled receptors	Seven-pass transmembrane protein with cytoplasmic binding site for G protein	Binding of signal to receptor causes GTP to bind a G protein; G protein, with attached GTP, detaches to deliver the signal inside the cell	Peptide hormones, rod cells in the eyes

The channel is said to be chemically gated because it opens only when a chemical (the neurotransmitter) binds to it. The type of ion that flows across the membrane when a chemically gated ion channel opens depends on the shape and charge structure of the channel. Sodium, potassium, calcium, and chloride ions all have specific ion channels.

The acetylcholine receptor found in muscle cell membranes functions as an Na^+ channel. When the receptor binds to its ligand, the neurotransmitter acetylcholine, the channel opens allowing Na^+ to flow into the muscle cell. This is a critical step linking the signal from a motor neuron to muscle cell contraction (chapter 46).

Enzymatic receptors

Many cell surface receptors either act as enzymes or are directly linked to enzymes (figure 9.4b). When a signal molecule binds to the receptor, it activates the enzyme. In almost all cases,

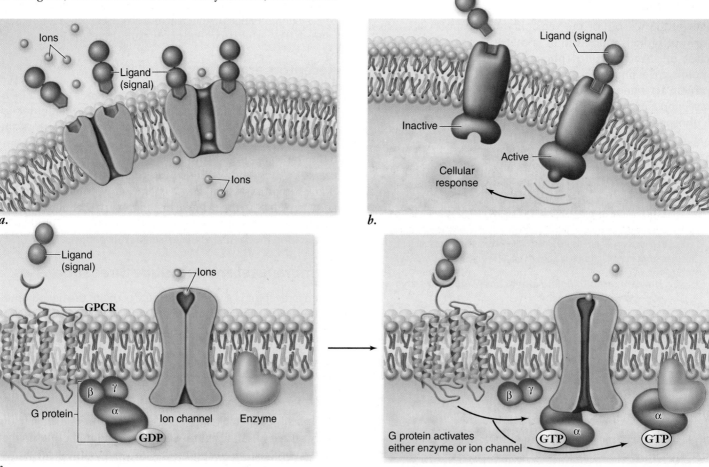

Figure 9.4 Cell surface receptors. *a.* Chemically gated ion channels form a pore in the plasma membrane that can be opened or closed by chemical signals. They are usually selective, allowing the passage of only one type of ion. *b.* Enzymatic receptors bind to ligands on the extracellular surface. A catalytic region on their cytoplasmic portion transmits the signal across the membrane by acting as an enzyme in the cytoplasm. *c.* G protein-coupled receptors (GPCR) bind to ligands outside the cell and to G proteins inside the cell. The G protein then activates an enzyme or ion channel, transmitting signals from the cell's surface to its interior.

these enzymes are **protein kinases,** enzymes that add phosphate groups to proteins. We discuss these receptors in detail in a later section of this chapter.

G Protein-coupled receptors

A third class of cell surface receptors acts indirectly on enzymes or ion channels in the plasma membrane with the aid of an assisting protein, called a **G protein.** The G protein, which is so named because it binds the nucleotide *guanosine triphosphate* (GTP), can be thought of as being inserted between the receptors and the enzyme (effector). That is, the ligand binds to the receptor, activating it, which activates the G protein, which in turn activates the effector protein (figure 9.4*c*). These receptors are also discussed in detail later on.

Membrane receptors can generate second messengers

Some enzymatic receptors and most G protein-coupled receptors utilize other substances to relay the message within the cytoplasm. These other substances, small molecules or ions called **second messengers,** alter the behavior of cellular proteins by binding to them and changing their shape. (The original signal molecule is considered the "first messenger.") Two common second messengers are **cyclic adenosine monophosphate (cyclic AMP,** or **cAMP)** and calcium ions. The role of these second messengers will be explored in more detail in a later section.

Learning Outcome Review 9.2

Receptors may be internal (intracellular receptors) or external (membrane receptors). Membrane receptors include channel-linked receptors, enzymatic receptors, and G protein-coupled receptors. Signal transduction through membrane receptors often involves the production of a second signaling molecule, or second messenger, inside the cell.

■ *Would a hydrophobic molecule be expected to have an internal or membrane receptor?*

Learning Outcomes

1. *Describe the chemical nature of ligands for intracellular receptors.*
2. *Diagram the pathway of signal transduction through intracellular receptors.*

Many cell signals are lipid-soluble or very small molecules that can readily pass through the plasma membrane of the target cell and into the cell, where they interact with an *intracellular receptor*. Some of these ligands bind to protein receptors located in the cytoplasm, others pass across the nuclear membrane as well and bind to receptors within the nucleus.

Steroid hormone receptors affect gene expression

Of all of the receptor types discussed in this chapter, the action of the steroid hormone receptors is the simplest and most direct.

Steroid hormones form a large class of compounds, including cortisol, estrogen, progesterone, and testosterone, that share a common nonpolar structure. Estrogen, progesterone, and testosterone are involved in sexual development and behavior (chapter 52). Other steroid hormones, such as cortisol, also have varied effects depending on the target tissue, ranging from the mobilization of glucose to the inhibition of white blood cells to control inflammation. Their anti-inflammatory action is the basis of their use in medicine.

The nonpolar structure allows these hormones to cross the membrane and bind to intracellular receptors. The location of steroid hormone receptors prior to hormone binding is cytoplasmic, but their primary site of action is in the nucleus. Binding of the hormone to the receptor causes the complex to

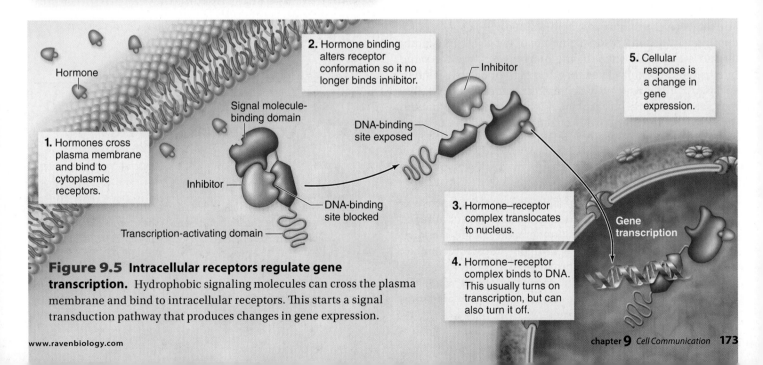

Figure 9.5 Intracellular receptors regulate gene transcription. Hydrophobic signaling molecules can cross the plasma membrane and bind to intracellular receptors. This starts a signal transduction pathway that produces changes in gene expression.

shift from the cytoplasm to the nucleus (figure 9.5). As the ligand–receptor complex makes it all the way to the nucleus of the cell, these receptors are often called **nuclear receptors.**

Steroid receptor action

The primary function of steroid hormone receptors, as well as receptors for a number of other small, lipid-soluble signal molecules such as vitamin D and thyroid hormone, is to act as regulators of gene expression (see chapter 16).

All of these receptors have similar structures; the genes that code for them appear to be the evolutionary descendants of a single ancestral gene. Because of their structural similarities, they are all part of the *nuclear receptor superfamily.*

Each of these receptors has three functional domains—

1. a hormone-binding domain,
2. a DNA-binding domain, and
3. a domain that can interact with coactivators to affect the level of gene transcription.

In its inactive state, the receptor typically cannot bind to DNA because an inhibitor protein occupies the DNA-binding site. When the signal molecule binds to the hormone-binding site, the conformation of the receptor changes, releasing the inhibitor and exposing the DNA-binding site, allowing the receptor to attach to specific nucleotide sequences on the DNA (see figure 9.5). This binding activates (or, in a few instances, suppresses) particular genes, usually located adjacent to the hormone-binding sequences. In the case of cortisol, which is a glucocorticoid hormone that can increase levels of glucose in cells, a number of different genes involved in the synthesis of glucose have binding sites for the hormone receptor complex.

The lipid-soluble ligands that intracellular receptors recognize tend to persist in the blood far longer than water-soluble signals. Most water-soluble hormones break down within minutes, and neurotransmitters break down within seconds or even milliseconds. In contrast, a steroid hormone such as cortisol or estrogen persists for hours.

Specificity and the role of coactivators

The target cell's response to a lipid-soluble cell signal can vary enormously, depending on the nature of the cell. This characteristic is true even when different target cells have the same intracellular receptor. Given that the receptor proteins bind to specific DNA sequences, which are the same in all cells, this may seem puzzling. It is explained in part by the fact that the receptors act in concert with **coactivators,** and the number and nature of these molecules can differ from cell to cell. Thus, a cell's response depends on not only the receptors but also the coactivators present.

The hormone estrogen has different effects in uterine tissue than in mammary tissue. This differential response is mediated by coactivators and not by the presence or absence of a receptor in the two tissues. In mammary tissue, a critical coactivator is lacking and the hormone–receptor complex instead interacts with another protein that acts to reduce gene expression. In uterine tissue, the coactivator is present, and the expression of genes that encode proteins involved in preparing the uterus for pregnancy are turned on.

Other intracellular receptors act as enzymes

A very interesting example of a receptor acting as an enzyme is found in the receptor for nitric oxide (NO). This small gas molecule diffuses readily out of the cells where it is produced and passes directly into neighboring cells, where it binds to the enzyme guanylyl cyclase. Binding of NO activates this enzyme, enabling it to catalyze the synthesis of *cyclic guanosine monophosphate (cGMP),* an intracellular messenger molecule that produces cell-specific responses such as the relaxation of smooth muscle cells.

When the brain sends a nerve signal to relax the smooth muscle cells lining the walls of vertebrate blood vessels, acetylcholine released by the nerve cell binds to receptors on epithelial cells. This causes an increase in intracellular Ca^{2+} in the epithelial cell that stimulates nitric oxide synthase to produce NO. The NO diffuses into the smooth muscle, where it increases the level of cGMP, leading to relaxation. This relaxation allows the vessel to expand and thereby increases blood flow. This explains the use of nitroglycerin to treat the pain of angina caused by constricted blood vessels to the heart. The nitroglycerin is converted by cells to NO, which then acts to relax the blood vessels.

The drug sildenafil (better known as Viagra) also functions via this signal transduction pathway by binding to and inhibiting the enzyme cGMP phosphodiesterase, which breaks down cGMP. This keeps levels of cGMP high, thereby stimulating production of NO. The reason for Viagra's selective effect is that it binds to a form of cGMP phosphodiesterase found in cells in the penis. This allows relaxation of smooth muscle in erectile tissue, thereby increasing blood flow.

Learning Outcomes Review 9.3

Hydrophobic signaling molecules can cross the membrane and bind to intracellular receptors. The steroid hormone receptors act by directly influencing gene expression. On binding hormone, the hormone–receptor complex moves into the nucleus to turn on (or sometimes turn off) gene expression. This may also require a coactivator that functions with the hormone–receptor complex. Thus, the cell's response to a hormone depends on the presence of a receptor and coactivators as well.

■ *Would these types of intracellular receptors be fast acting, or have effects of longer duration?*

9.4 Signal Transduction Through Receptor Kinases

Learning Outcomes

1. *Compare the function of RTKs to steroid hormone receptors.*
2. *Describe how information crosses the membrane in RTKs.*
3. *Explain the role of kinase cascades in signal transduction.*

Earlier you read that protein kinases phosphorylate proteins to alter protein function and that the most common kinases act on the amino acids serine, threonine, and tyrosine. The receptor tyrosine kinases (RTKs) influence the cell cycle, cell migration, cell metabolism, and cell proliferation—virtually all aspects of the cell are affected by signaling through these receptors. Alterations to the function of these receptors and their signaling pathways can lead to cancers in humans and other animals.

Some of the earliest examples of cancer-causing genes, or oncogenes, involve RTK function (discussed in chapter 10). The avian erythroblastosis virus carries an altered form of the epidermal growth factor receptor that lacks most of its extracellular domain. When this virus infects a cell the altered receptors produced are stuck in the "on" state. The continuous signaling from this receptor leads to cells that have lost the normal controls over growth.

Receptor tyrosine kinases recognize hydrophilic ligands and form a large class of membrane receptors in animal cells. Plants possess receptors with a similar overall structure and function, but they are serine–threonine kinases. These plant receptors have been named **plant receptor kinases.**

Because these receptors are performing similar functions in plant and animal cells but differ in their substrates, the duplication and divergence of each kind of receptor kinase probably occurred after the plant–animal divergence. The proliferation of these types of signaling molecules is thought to coincide with the independent evolution of multicellularity in each group.

In this section, we will concentrate on the RTK family of receptors that has been extensively studied in a variety of animal cells.

RTKs are activated by autophosphorylation

Receptor tyrosine kinases have a relatively simple structure consisting of a single transmembrane domain that anchors them in the membrane, an extracellular ligand-binding domain, and an intracellular kinase domain. This kinase domain contains the catalytic site of the receptor, which acts as a protein kinase that adds phosphate groups to tyrosines. On ligand binding to a specific receptor, two of these receptor–ligand complexes associate together (often referred to as dimerization) and phosphorylate each other, a process called *autophosphorylation* (figure 9.6).

The autophosphorylation event transmits across the membrane the signal that began with the binding of the ligand to the receptor. The next step, propagation of the signal in the cytoplasm, can take a variety of different forms. These forms include activation of the tyrosine kinase domain to

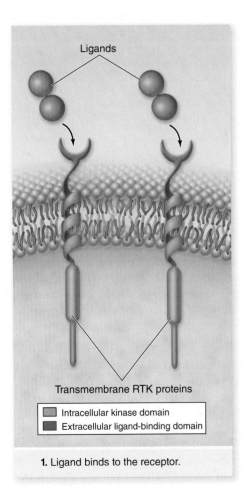

1. Ligand binds to the receptor.

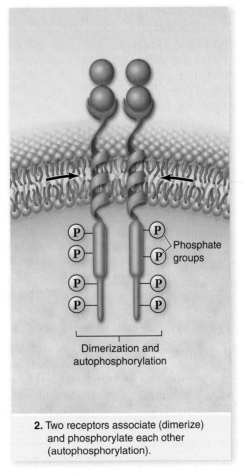

2. Two receptors associate (dimerize) and phosphorylate each other (autophosphorylation).

3. Response proteins bind to phosphotyrosine on receptor. Receptor can phosphorylate other response proteins.

Figure 9.6 Activation of a receptor tyrosine kinase (RTK). These membrane receptors bind hormones or growth factors that are hydrophilic and cannot cross the membrane. The receptor is a transmembrane protein with an extracellular ligand binding domain and an intracellular kinase domain. Signal transduction pathways begin with response proteins binding to phosphotyrosine on receptor, and by receptor phosphorylation of response proteins.

phosphorylate other intracellular targets or interaction of other proteins with the phosphorylated receptor.

The cellular response after activation depends on the possible response proteins in the cell. Two different cells can have the same receptor yet a different response, depending on what response proteins are present in the cytoplasm. For example, fibroblast growth factor stimulates cell division in fibroblasts but stimulates nerve cells to differentiate rather than to divide.

Phosphotyrosine domains mediate protein–protein interactions

One way that the signal from the receptor can be propagated in the cytoplasm is via proteins that bind specifically to phosphorylated tyrosines in the receptor. When the receptor is activated, regions of the protein outside of the catalytic site are phosphorylated. This creates "docking" sites for proteins that bind specifically to phosphotyrosine. The proteins that bind to these phosphorylated tyrosines can initiate intracellular events to convert the signal from the ligand into a response (see figure 9.6).

The insulin receptor

The use of docking proteins is illustrated by the insulin receptor. The hormone insulin is part of the body's control system to maintain a constant level of blood glucose. The role of insulin is to lower blood glucose, acting by binding to an RTK. Another protein called the *insulin response protein* binds to the phosphorylated receptor and is itself phosphorylated. The insulin response protein passes the signal on by binding to additional proteins that lead to the activation of the enzyme glycogen synthase, which converts glucose to glycogen (figure 9.7), thereby lowering blood glucose. Other proteins activated by the insulin receptor act to inhibit the synthesis of enzymes involved in making glucose, and to increase the number of glucose transporter proteins in the plasma membrane.

Adapter proteins

Another class of proteins, **adapter proteins,** can also bind to phosphotyrosines. These proteins themselves do not participate in signal transduction but act as a link between the receptor and proteins that initiate downstream signaling events. For example, the Ras protein discussed later is activated by adapter proteins binding to a receptor.

Protein kinase cascades can amplify a signal

One important class of cytoplasmic kinases are **mitogen-activated protein (MAP) kinases.** A *mitogen* is a chemical that stimulates cell division by activating the normal pathways that control division. The MAP kinases are activated by a signaling module called a *phosphorylation cascade* or a **kinase cascade.** This module is a series of protein kinases that phosphorylate each other in succession. The final step in the cascade is the activation by phosphorylation of MAP kinase itself (figure 9.8).

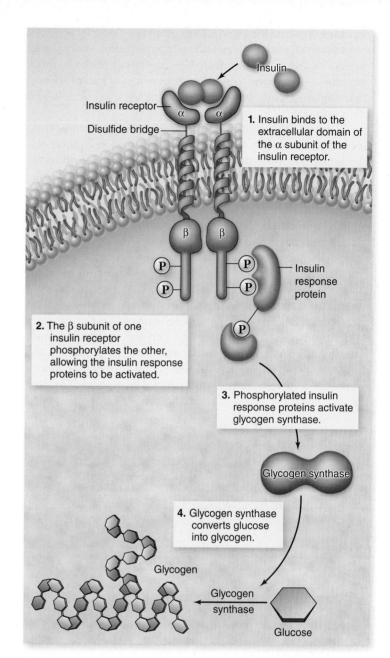

Figure 9.7 The insulin receptor. The insulin receptor is a receptor tyrosine kinase that initiates a variety of cellular responses related to glucose metabolism. One signal transduction pathway that this receptor mediates leads to the activation of the enzyme glycogen synthase. This enzyme converts glucose to glycogen.

One function of a kinase cascade is to amplify the original signal. Because each step in the cascade is an enzyme, it can act on a number of substrate molecules. With each enzyme in the cascade acting on many substrates this produces a large amount of the final product (see figure 9.8). This allows a small number of initial signaling molecules to produce a large response.

The cellular response to this cascade in any particular cell depends on the targets of the MAP kinase, but usually involves phosphorylating transcription factors that then activate gene expression (chapter 16). An example of this kind of signaling through growth factor receptors is provided in chapter 10 and

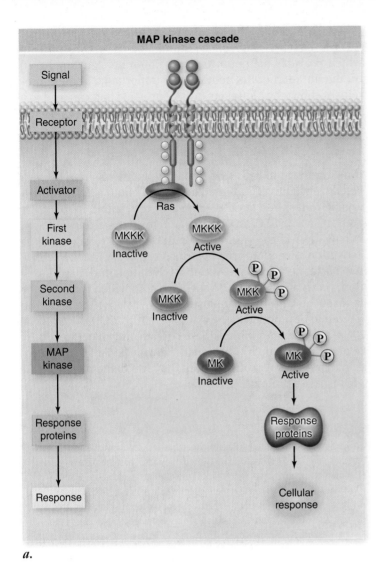

a.

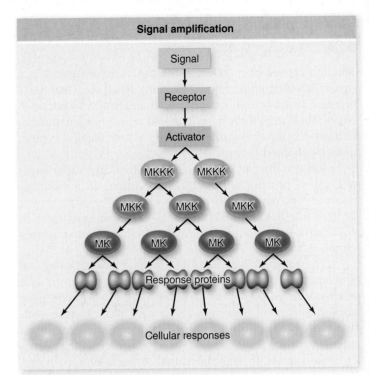

b.

Figure 9.8 MAP kinase cascade leads to signal amplification. *a.* Phosphorylation cascade is shown as a flowchart on the left. The corresponding cellular events are shown on the right, beginning with the receptor in the plasma membrane. Each kinase is named starting with the last, the MAP kinase (MK), which is phosphorylated by a MAP kinase kinase (MKK), which is in turn phosphorylated by a MAP kinase kinase kinase (MKKK). The cascade is linked to the receptor protein by an activator protein. *b.* At each step the enzymatic action of the kinase on multiple substrates leads to amplification of the signal.

illustrates how signal transduction initiated by a growth factor can control the process of cell division through a kinase cascade.

Scaffold proteins organize kinase cascades

The proteins in a kinase cascade need to act sequentially to be effective. One way the efficiency of this process can be increased is to organize them in the cytoplasm. Proteins called *scaffold proteins* are thought to organize the components of a kinase cascade into a single protein complex, the ultimate in a signaling module. The scaffold protein binds to each individual kinase such that they are spatially organized for optimal function (figure 9.9).

The advantages of this kind of organization are many. A physically arranged sequence is clearly more efficient than one that depends on diffusion to produce the appropriate order of events. This organization also allows the segregation of signaling modules in different cytoplasmic locations.

The disadvantage of this kind of organization is that it reduces the amplification effect of the kinase cascade. Enzymes held in one place are not free to find new substrate molecules, but must rely on substrates being nearby.

The best studied example of a scaffold protein comes from mating behavior in budding yeast. Yeast cells respond to mating pheromones with changes in cell morphology and gene expression, mediated by a protein kinase cascade. A protein called Ste5 was originally identified as a protein required for mating behavior, but no enzymatic activity could be detected for this protein. It has now been shown that this protein interacts with all of the members of the kinase cascade and acts as a scaffold protein that organizes the cascade and insulates it from other signaling pathways.

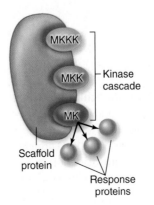

Figure 9.9 Kinase cascade can be organized by scaffold proteins. The scaffold protein binds to each kinase in the cascade, organizing them so each substrate is next to its enzyme. This organization also sequesters the kinases from other signaling pathways in the cytoplasm.

Ras is a small G protein that acts as a molecular switch

The link between the RTK and the MAP kinase cascade is a small GTP-binding protein (G protein) called **Ras.** Like all G proteins, Ras is actively bound to GTP, and inactively bound to GDP. The Ras protein is mutated in many human tumors, indicative of its central role in linking growth factor receptors to their cellular response.

Ras was the first protein identified in a large superfamily of small G proteins with over 150 members in the human genome. The superfamily consists of five subgroups, one of which is the Ras family. These small G proteins are found in eukaryotes from yeast to vertebrates, indicating their ancient origin.

The roles of these small G proteins vary, affecting cell proliferation, the cytoskeleton, membrane transport, and nuclear transport. They are an excellent example of how gene duplication and diversification allow evolution to create modular units with diverse functions. The common feature of all members of the family is to act as a molecular switch linking external signals to internal signal transduction pathways (figure 9.10).

The Ras switch is flipped by exchanging GDP for GTP, and by Ras hydrolyzing GTP to GDP. The link to outside signals comes from other proteins that affect the switch: guanine nucleotide exchange factors (GEFs) stimulate the exchange of GDP for GTP activating Ras. When a growth factor receptor is activated, it binds to an adapter protein that acts as a GEF. The activated Ras protein then activates the first kinase in the MAP kinase cascade (see figure 9.8 and chapter 10).

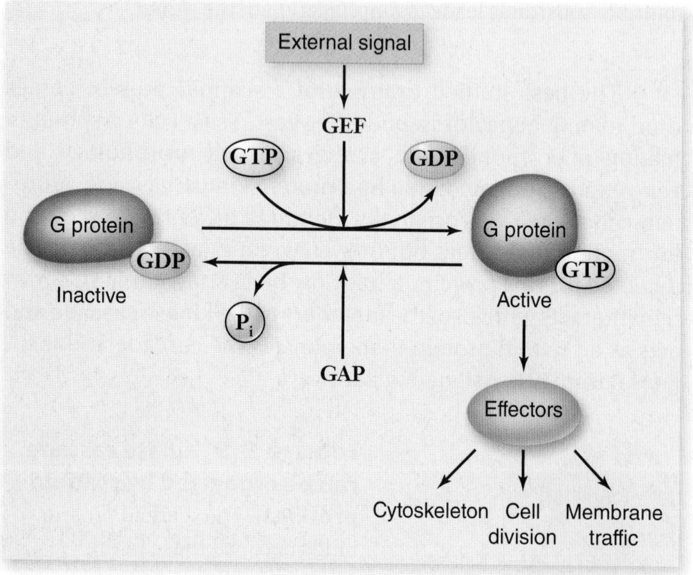

The action of Ras can be terminated by its intrinsic GTPase activity. This can be stimulated by a GAP protein, which provides the opportunity to fine-tune signaling based on the duration of Ras activity. The importance of these proteins is shown by mutations in GAP proteins that can lead to a predisposition for specific cancers such as neurofibromatosis.

RTKs are inactivated by internalization

It is important to cells that signaling pathways are only activated transiently. Continued activation could render the cell unable to respond to other signals or to respond inappropriately to a signal that is no longer relevant. Consequently, inactivation is as important for the control of signaling as activation. Receptor tyrosine kinases can be inactivated by two basic mechanisms—dephosphorylation and internalization. Internalization is by endocytosis, in which the receptor is taken up into the cytoplasm in a vesicle where it can be degraded or recycled.

The enzymes in the kinase cascade are all controlled by dephosphorylation by phosphatase enzymes. This leads to termination of the response at both the level of the receptor and the response proteins.

Learning Outcomes Review 9.4

Receptor tyrosine kinases (RTKs) are membrane receptors that can phosphorylate tyrosine. When activated, they autophosphorylate, creating binding domains for other proteins. These proteins transmit the signal inside the cell. One form of signaling pathway involves the MAP kinase cascade, a series of kinases that each activate the next in the series. This ends with a MAP kinase that activates transcription factors to alter gene expression.

■ *Ras protein is mutated in many human cancers. What are possible reasons for this?*

9.5 Signal Transduction Through G Protein-Coupled Receptors

Learning Outcomes

1. Contrast signaling through GPCRs and RTKs.
2. Relate the function of second messengers to signal transduction pathways.

The single largest category of receptor type in animal cells is **G protein-coupled receptors (GPCRs),** so named because the receptors act by coupling with a G protein. These receptors bind diverse ligands, including ions, organic odorants, peptides, proteins, and lipids. Light-sensing receptors are also part of this family, so we could even count photons as "ligands."

Figure 9.10 **Small G proteins act as molecular switches.** Small G proteins, such as Ras, link external signals to internal signal transduction pathways. External signals activate guanine nucleotide exchange proteins (GEF), which activate the G protein. The G protein can be inactivated by its weak intrinsic GTPase activity, which can be stimulated by activating proteins (GAP).

This superfamily of proteins also has a characteristic structure with seven transmembrane domains that anchor the receptors in the membrane. This arrangement of seven transmembrane domains is highly conserved and is used to search for new members in sequenced genomes. The analysis of many animal genomes indicates that GPCRs are the largest gene family in most animals. They have been found in virtually all types of eukaryotic organisms, indicating an ancient origin with duplication and divergence leading to a wide array of signaling pathways.

The latest count of genes encoding GPCRs in the human genome is 799, with about half of these encoding odorant receptors involved in the sense of taste and smell. In the mouse, over 1000 different odorant receptors are involved in the sense of smell. The family of GPCRs has been subdivided into five groups based on structure and function: Rhodopsin, Secretin, Adhesion, Glutamate, and Frizzled/Taste 2. The names refer to the first discovered member of each group; for example, Rhodopsin is the GPCR involved in light sensing in mammals. In this section, we will concentrate on the basic mechanism of activation and some of the possible signal transduction pathways.

G proteins link receptors with effector proteins

The function of the G protein in signaling by GPCRs is to provide a link between a receptor that receives signals and effector proteins that produce cellular responses. The G protein functions as a switch that is turned on by the receptor. In its "on" state, the G protein activates effector proteins to cause a cellular response.

All G proteins are active when bound to GTP and inactive when bound to GDP. The main difference between the G proteins in GPCRs and the small G proteins described earlier is that these G proteins are composed of three subunits, called α, β, and γ. As a result, they are often called *heterotrimeric G proteins*. When a ligand binds to a GPCR and activates its associated G protein, the G protein exchanges GDP for GTP and dissociates into two parts consisting of the G_{α} subunit bound to GTP, and the G_{β} and G_{γ} subunits together ($G_{\beta\gamma}$). The signal can then be propagated by either the G_{α} or the $G_{\beta\gamma}$ components, thereby acting to turn on effector proteins. The hydrolysis of bound GTP to GDP by G_{α} causes reassociation of the heterotrimer and restores the "off" state of the system (figure 9.11).

The effector proteins are usually enzymes. An effector protein might be a protein kinase that phosphorylates proteins to directly propagate the signal, or it may produce a second messenger to initiate a signal transduction pathway.

Effector proteins produce multiple second messengers

Often, the effector proteins activated by G proteins produce a second messenger. Two of the most common effectors are *adenylyl cyclase* and *phospholipase C*, which produce cAMP and IP$_3$ plus DAG, respectively.

Cyclic AMP

All animal cells studied thus far use cAMP as a second messenger (chapter 45). When a signaling molecule binds to a GPCR that uses the enzyme **adenylyl cyclase** as an effector, a large

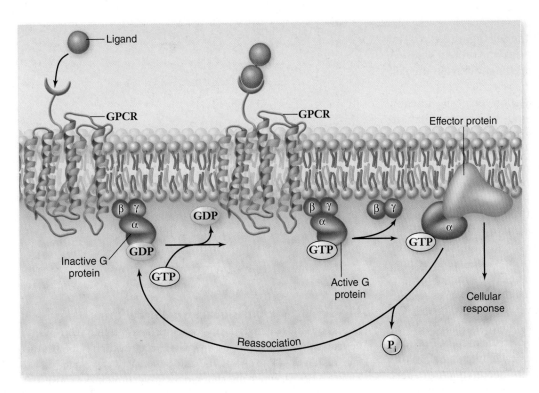

Figure 9.11 The action of G protein-coupled receptors. G protein-coupled receptors act through a heterotrimeric G protein that links the receptor to an effector protein. When ligand binds to the receptor, it activates an associated G protein, exchanging GDP for GTP. The active G protein complex dissociates into G_{α} and $G_{\beta\gamma}$. The G_{α} subunit (bound to GTP) is shown activating an effector protein. The effector protein may act directly on cellular proteins or produce a second messenger to cause a cellular response. G_{α} can hydrolyze GTP inactivating the system, then reassociate with $G_{\beta\gamma}$.

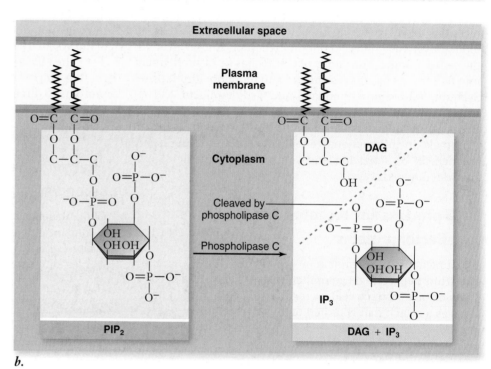

Figure 9.12 Production of second messengers. Second messengers are signaling molecules produced within the cell. *a.* The nucleotide ATP is converted by the enzyme adenylyl cyclase into cyclic AMP, or cAMP, and pyrophosphate (PP$_i$). *b.* The inositol phospholipid PIP$_2$ is composed of two lipids and a phosphate attached to glycerol. The phosphate is also attached to the sugar inositol. This molecule can be cleaved by the enzyme phospholipase C to produce two different second messengers: DAG, made up of the glycerol with the two lipids, and IP$_3$, inositol triphosphate.

amount of cAMP is produced within the cell (figure 9.12*a*). The cAMP then binds to and activates the enzyme protein kinase A (PKA), which adds phosphates to specific proteins in the cell (figure 9.13).

The effect of this phosphorylation on cell function depends on the identity of the cell and the proteins that are phosphorylated. In muscle cells, for example, PKA activates an enzyme necessary to break down glycogen and inhibits another enzyme necessary to synthesize glycogen. This leads to an increase in glucose available to the muscle. By contrast, in the kidney the action of PKA leads to the production of water channels that can increase the permeability of tubule cells to water.

Disruption of cAMP signaling can have a variety of effects. The symptoms of the disease cholera are due to altered cAMP levels in cells in the gut. The bacterium *Vibrio cholerae* produces a toxin that binds to a GPCR in the epithelium of the gut, causing it to be locked into an "on" state. This causes a large increase in intracellular cAMP that, in these cells, causes Cl$^-$ ions to be transported out of the cell. Water follows the Cl$^-$, leading to diarrhea and dehydration characteristic of the disease.

The molecule cAMP is also an extracellular signal. In the slime mold *Dictyostelium discoideum,* secreted cAMP acts as a signal for aggregation under conditions of starvation.

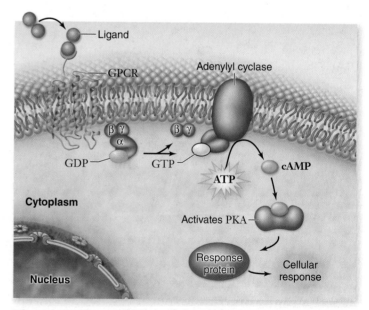

Figure 9.13 cAMP signaling pathway. Extracellular signal binds to a GPCR, activating a G protein. The G protein then activates the effector protein adenylyl cyclase, which catalyzes the conversion of ATP to cAMP. The cAMP then activates protein kinase A (PKA), which phosphorylates target proteins to cause a cellular response.

Question: *What is the receptor for cAMP?*

Hypothesis: *A previously identified G protein-coupled receptor is the cAMP receptor.*

Prediction: *If the function of the cAMP receptor is removed, then cells will not respond to starvation by aggregating.*

Test: *Use G protein-coupled receptor gene to direct synthesis of antisense RNA complementary to the normal mRNA. This will eliminate gene expression by the cellular copy of the G protein-coupled receptor.*

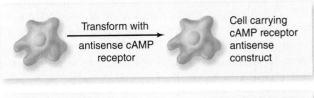

Transform with antisense cAMP receptor → Cell carrying cAMP receptor antisense construct

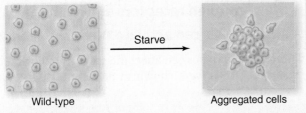

Wild-type → Starve → Aggregated cells

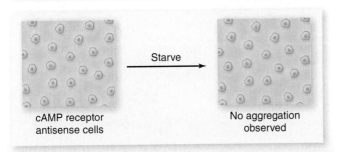

cAMP receptor antisense cells → Starve → No aggregation observed

Result: *Cells transformed with the antisense construct do not aggregate normally.*

Conclusion: *Previously identified G protein-coupled receptor is the cAMP receptor, which controls the aggregation response.*

Further Experiments: *How can this kind of experiment be used to unravel other aspects of this signaling system?*

Figure 9.14 The receptor for cAMP in *D. discoideum* is a GPCR.

Experiments have shown that the receptor for this signal is also a GPCR (figure 9.14).

Inositol phosphates

A common second messenger is produced from the molecules called inositol phospholipids. These are inserted into the plasma membrane by their lipid ends and have the *inositol phosphate* portion protruding into the cytoplasm. The most common inositol phospholipid is phosphatidylinositol-4,5-bisphosphate (PIP_2). This molecule is a substrate of the effector protein phospholipase C, which cleaves PIP_2 to yield **diacylglycerol (DAG)** and **inositol-1,4,5-trisphosphate (IP_3)** (see figure 9.12*b*).

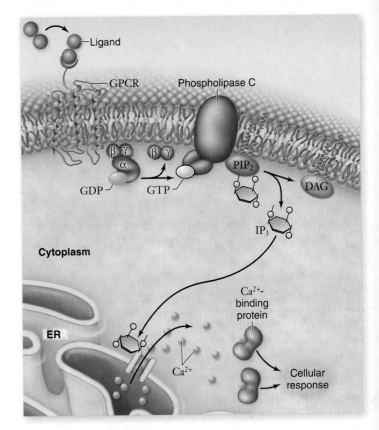

Figure 9.15 Inositol phospholipid and Ca²⁺ signaling.
Extracellular signal binds to a GPCR activating a G protein. The G protein activates the effector protein phospholipase C, which converts PIP_2 to DAG and IP_3. IP_3 is then bound to a channel-linked receptor on the endoplasmic reticulum (ER) membrane, causing the ER to release stored Ca²⁺ into the cytoplasm. The Ca²⁺ then binds to Ca²⁺-binding proteins such as calmodulin and PKC to cause a cellular response.

Both of these compounds then act as second messengers with a variety of cellular effects. DAG, like cAMP, can activate a protein kinase, in this case protein kinase C (PKC).

Calcium

Calcium ions (Ca²⁺) serve widely as second messengers. Ca²⁺ levels inside the cytoplasm are normally very low (less than 10^{-7} M), whereas outside the cell and in the endoplasmic reticulum, Ca²⁺ levels are quite high (about 10^{-3} M). The endoplasmic reticulum has receptor proteins that act as ion channels to release Ca²⁺. One of the most common of these receptors can bind the second messenger IP_3 to release Ca²⁺, linking signaling through inositol phosphates with signaling by Ca²⁺ (figure 9.15).

The result of the outflow of Ca²⁺ from the endoplasmic reticulum depends on the cell type. For example, in skeletal muscle cells Ca²⁺ stimulates muscle contraction but in endocrine cells it stimulates the secretion of hormones.

Ca²⁺ initiates some cellular responses by binding to *calmodulin,* a 148-amino-acid cytoplasmic protein that contains four binding sites for Ca²⁺ (figure 9.16). When four Ca²⁺ ions are bound to calmodulin, the calmodulin/Ca²⁺ complex is able to bind to other proteins to activate them. These proteins include

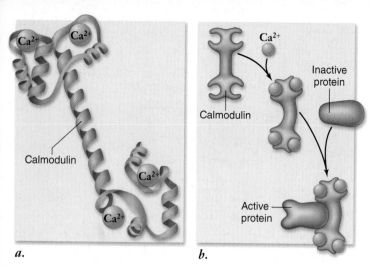

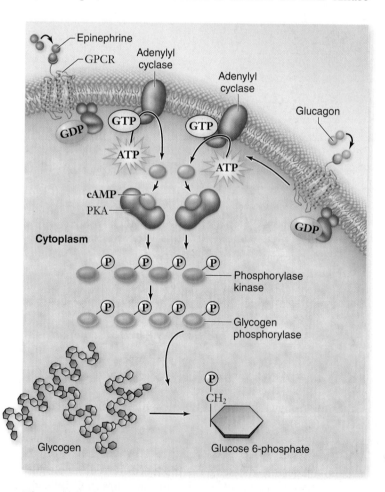

Figure 9.16 Calmodulin. *a.* Calmodulin is a protein containing 148 amino acid residues that mediates Ca²⁺ function. *b.* When four Ca²⁺ are bound to the calmodulin molecule, it undergoes a conformational change that allows it to bind to other cytoplasmic proteins and effect cellular responses.

protein kinases, ion channels, receptor proteins, and cyclic nucleotide phosphodiesterases. These many uses of Ca²⁺ make it one of the most versatile second messengers in cells.

Different receptors can produce the same second messengers

As mentioned previously, the two hormones glucagon and epinephrine can both stimulate liver cells to mobilize glucose. The reason that these different signals have the same effect is that they both act by the same signal transduction pathway to stimulate the breakdown and inhibit the synthesis of glycogen.

The binding of either hormone to its receptor activates a G protein that simulates adenylyl cyclase. The production of cAMP leads to the activation of PKA, which in turn activates another protein kinase called phosphorylase kinase. Activated phosphorylase kinase then activates glycogen phosphorylase, which cleaves off units of glucose 6-phosphate from the glycogen polymer (figure 9.17). The action of multiple kinases again leads to amplification such that a few signaling molecules result in a large number of glucose molecules being released.

At the same time, PKA also phosphorylates the enzyme glycogen synthase, but in this case it inhibits the enzyme, thus preventing the synthesis of glycogen. In addition, PKA phosphorylates other proteins that activate the expression of genes encoding the enzymes needed to synthesize glucose. This convergence of signal transduction pathways from different receptors leads to the same result—glucose is mobilized.

Receptor subtypes can lead to different effects in different cells

We also saw earlier how a single signaling molecule, epinephrine, can have different effects in different cells. One way this happens is through the existence of multiple forms of the same

receptor. The receptor for epinephrine actually has nine different subtypes, or isoforms. These are encoded by different genes and are actually different receptor molecules. The sequences of these proteins are very similar, especially in the ligand-binding domain, which allows them to bind epinephrine. They differ mainly in their cytoplasmic domains, which interact with G proteins. This leads to different isoforms activating different G proteins, thereby leading to different signal transduction pathways.

Thus, in the heart, muscle cells have one isoform of the receptor that, when bound to epinephrine, activates a G protein that activates adenylyl cyclase, leading to increased cAMP. This increases the rate and force of contraction. In the intestine, smooth muscle cells have a different isoform of the receptor that, when bound to epinephrine, activates a different G protein that inhibits adenylyl cyclase, which decreases cAMP. This has the result of relaxing the muscle.

G protein-coupled receptors and receptor tyrosine kinases can activate the same pathways

Different receptor types can affect the same signaling module. For example, RTKs were shown to activate the MAP kinase

Figure 9.17 Different receptors can activate the same signaling pathway. The hormones glucagon and epinephrine both act through GPCRs. Each of these receptors acts via a G protein that activates adenylyl cyclase, producing cAMP. The activation of PKA begins a kinase cascade that leads to the breakdown of glycogen.

cascade, but GPCRs can also activate this same cascade. Similarly, the activation of phospholipase C was mentioned previously in the context of GPCR signaling, but it can also be activated by RTKs.

This cross-reactivity may appear to introduce complications into cell function, but in fact it provides the cell with an incredible amount of flexibility. Cells have a large, but limited number of intracellular signaling modules, which can be turned on and off by different kinds of membrane receptors. This leads to signaling networks that interconnect possible cellular effectors with multiple incoming signals.

The Internet represents an example of a network in which many different kinds of computers are connected globally. This network can be broken down into subnetworks that are connected to the overall network. Because of the nature of the connections, when you send an e-mail message across the Internet, it can reach its destination through many different pathways. Likewise, the cell has interconnected networks of signaling pathways in which many different signals, receptors, and response proteins are interconnected. Specific pathways

like the MAP kinase cascade, or signaling through second messengers like cAMP and Ca^{2+}, represent subnetworks within the global signaling network. A specific signal can activate different pathways in different cells, or different signals can activate the same pathway. We do not yet understand the cell at this level, but the field of systems biology is moving toward such global understanding of cell function.

Learning Outcomes Review 9.5

Signaling through GPCRs uses a three-part system—a receptor, a G protein, and an effector protein. G proteins are active when bound to GTP and inactive when bound to GDP. A ligand binding to the receptor activates the G protein, which then activates the effector protein. Effector proteins include adenylyl cyclase, which produces the second messenger cAMP. Another effector protein, phospholipase C, cleaves the inositol phosphates and results in the release of Ca^{2+} from the ER.

■ *There are far more GPCRs than any other receptor type. What is a possible explanation for this?*

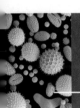

Chapter Review

9.1 Overview of Cell Communication (figure 9.1)

Cell communication requires signal molecules, called ligands, binding to specific receptor proteins producing a cellular response.

Signaling is defined by the distance from source to receptor (figure 9.2).

Direct contact—molecules on the plasma membrane of one cell contact the receptor molecules on an adjacent cell.

Paracrine signaling—short-lived signal molecules are released into the extracellular fluid and influence neighboring cells.

Endocrine signaling—long-lived hormones enter the circulatory system and are carried to target cells some distance away.

Synaptic signaling—short-lived neurotransmitters are released by neurons into the gap, called a synapse, between nerves and target cells.

Signal transduction pathways lead to cellular responses.

Intracellular events initiated by a signaling event are called signal transduction.

Phosphorylation is key in control of protein function.

Proteins can be controlled by phosphate added by kinase and removed by phosphatase enzymes.

9.2 Receptor Types (figure 9.4)

Receptors are defined by location.

Receptors are broadly defined as intracellular or cell-surface receptors (membrane receptors).

Membrane receptors are transmembrane proteins that transfer information across the membrane, but not the signal molecule.

Membrane receptors include three subclasses.

Channel-linked receptors are chemically gated ion channels that allow specific ions to pass through a central pore.

Enzymatic receptors are enzymes activated by binding a ligand; these enzymes are usually protein kinases.

G protein-coupled receptors interact with G proteins that control the function of effector proteins: enzymes or ion channels.

Membrane receptors can generate second messengers.

Some enzymatic and most G protein-coupled receptors produce second messengers, to relay messages in the cytoplasm.

9.3 Intracellular Receptors (figure 9.5)

Many cell signals are lipid-soluble and readily pass through the plasma membrane and bind to receptors in the cytoplasm or nucleus.

Steroid hormone receptors affect gene expression.

Steroid hormones bind cytoplasmic receptors, then are transported to the nucleus. Thus, they are called nuclear receptors. These can directly affect gene expression, usually activating transcription of the genes they control.

Nuclear receptors have three functional domains: hormone-binding, DNA-binding, and transcription-activating domains.

Ligand binding changes receptor shape, releasing an inhibitor occupying the DNA-binding site.

A cell's response to a lipid-soluble signal depends on the hormone–receptor complex and the other protein coactivators present.

Other intracellular receptors act as enzymes.

9.4 Signal Transduction Through Receptor Kinases

Receptor kinases in plants and animals recognize hydrophilic ligands and influence the cell cycle, cell migration, cell metabolism, and cell proliferation.

Because they are involved in growth control, alterations of receptor kinases and their signaling pathways can lead to cancer.

RTKs are activated by autophosphorylation.

The activated receptor can also phosphorylate other intracellular proteins.

Phosphotyrosine domains mediate protein–protein interactions.

Adapter proteins can bind to phosphotyrosine and act as links between the receptors and downstream signaling events.

Protein kinase cascades can amplify a signal.

Scaffold proteins organize kinase cascades.

Scaffold proteins and protein kinases form a single complex where the enzymes act sequentially and are optimally functional.

Internalized receptors are degraded or recycled.

Ras is a small G protein that acts as a molecular switch.

Small G proteins act as molecular switches linking external signals to signal transduction pathways.

RTKs are inactivated by internalization.

9.5 Signal Transduction Through G Protein-Coupled Receptors (figure 9.11)

G protein-coupled receptors function through activation of G proteins.

G proteins link receptors with effector proteins.

G proteins are active bound to GTP and inactive bound to GDP. Receptors promote exchange of GDP for GTP.

The activated G protein dissociates into two parts, G_α and $G_{\beta\gamma}$, each of which can act on effector proteins.

G_α also hydrolyzes GTP to GDP to inactivate the G protein.

Effector proteins produce multiple second messengers.

Two common effector proteins are adenylyl cyclase and phospholipase C, which produce second messengers known as cAMP, and DAG and IP_3, respectively.

Ca^{2+} is also a second messenger. Ca^{2+} release is triggered by IP_3 binding to channel-linked receptors in the ER.

Ca^{2+} can bind to a cytoplasmic protein calmodulin, which in turn activates other proteins, producing a variety of responses.

Different receptors can produce the same second messengers.

Different GPCR receptors can converge to activate the same effector enzyme and thus produce the same second messenger.

Receptor subtypes can lead to different effects in different cells.

Epinephrine causes increased contraction in heart muscle but relaxation in smooth muscle.

G protein-coupled receptors and receptor tyrosine kinases can activate the same pathways.

Both RTKs and GPCRs can activate MAP kinase cascades.

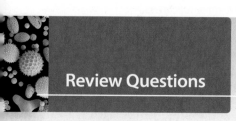

Review Questions

UNDERSTAND

1. Paracrine signaling is characterized by ligands that are
   a. produced by the cell itself.
   b. secreted by neighboring cells.
   c. present on the plasma membrane of neighboring cells.
   d. secreted by distant cells.

2. Signal transduction pathways
   a. are necessary for signals to cross the membrane.
   b. include the intracellular events stimulated by an extracellular signal.
   c. include the extracellular events stimulated by an intracellular signal.
   d. are only found in cases where the signal can cross the membrane.

3. The function of a _____ is to add phosphates to proteins, whereas a _____ functions to remove the phosphates.
   a. tyrosine; serine
   b. protein phosphatase; protein dephosphatase
   c. protein kinase; protein phosphatase
   d. receptor; ligand

4. Which of the following receptor types is not a membrane receptor?
   a. Channel-linked receptor
   b. Enzymatic receptor
   c. G protein-coupled receptor
   d. Steroid hormone receptors

5. How does the function of an intracellular receptor differ from that of a membrane receptor?
   a. The intracellular receptor binds a ligand.
   b. The intracellular receptor binds DNA.
   c. The intracellular receptor activates a kinase.
   d. The intracellular receptor functions as a second messenger.

6. Signaling through receptor tyrosine kinases often
   a. leads to the production of the second messenger cAMP.
   b. leads to the production of the second messenger IP_3.
   c. stimulates gene expression directly.
   d. leads to the activation of a cascade of kinase enzymes.

7. What is the function of Ras during tyrosine kinase cell signaling?
   a. It activates the opening of channel-linked receptors.
   b. It is an enzyme that synthesizes second messengers.
   c. It links the receptor protein to the MAP kinase pathway.
   d. It phosphorylates other enzymes as part of a pathway.

8. Which of the following best describes the immediate effect of ligand binding to a G protein-coupled receptor?
   a. The G protein trimer releases a GDP and binds a GTP.
   b. The G protein trimer dissociates from the receptor.
   c. The G protein trimer interacts with an effector protein.
   d. The α subunit of the G protein becomes phosphorylated.

APPLY

1. The action of steroid hormones is often longer-lived than that of peptide hormones. This is because they
   a. enter the cell and act like enzymes for a longer period of time.
   b. they turn on gene expression to produce proteins that persist in the cell.
   c. result in the production of second messengers that act directly on cellular processes.
   d. stimulate G proteins that act directly on cellular processes.

2. The ion Ca^{2+} can act as a second messenger because it is
   a. produced by the enzyme calcium synthase.
   b. normally at a high level in the cytoplasm.
   c. normally at a low level in the cytoplasm.
   d. stored in the cytoplasm.

3. Different receptors can have the same effect on a cell. One reason for this is that
   a. most receptors produce the same second messenger.
   b. different isoforms of receptors bind different ligands, but stimulate the same signaling pathway.
   c. signal transduction pathways intersect: the same pathway can be stimulated by different receptors.
   d. all receptors converge on the same signal transduction pathways.

4. In comparing small G proteins like Ras and GPCR proteins, we can say that
   a. both proteins have intrinsic GTPase activity that stops signaling.
   b. both proteins are active bound to GTP.
   c. Ras is active bound to GDP and GPCRs are active bound to GTP.
   d. both a and b are true.

5. The same signal can have different effects in different cells because there
   a. are different receptor subtypes that initiate different signal transduction pathways.
   b. may be different coactivators in different cells.
   c. may be different target proteins in different cells' signal transduction pathways.
   d. All of the choices are correct.

6. The receptors for steroid hormones and peptide hormones are fundamentally different because
   a. of the great difference in size of the molecule.
   b. peptides are one of the four major polymers and steroids are simple ringed structures.
   c. peptides are hydrophilic and steroids are hydrophobic.
   d. peptides are hydrophobic and steroids are hydrophilic.

SYNTHESIZE

1. Describe the common features found in all examples of cellular signaling discussed in this chapter. Provide examples to illustrate your answer.

2. The sheet of cells that form the gut epithelium folds into peaks called villi and valleys called crypts. The cells within the crypt region secrete a protein, Netrin-1, that becomes concentrated within the crypts. Netrin-1 is the ligand for a receptor protein that is found on the surface of all gut epithelial cells. Netrin-1 binding triggers a signal pathway that promotes cell growth. Gut epithelial cells undergo apoptosis (cell death) in the absence of Netrin-1 ligand binding.
   a. How would you characterize the type of signaling (autocrine, paracrine, endocrine) found in this system?
   b. Predict where the greatest amount of cell growth and cell death would occur in the epithelium.
   c. The loss of the Netrin-1 receptor is associated with some types of colon cancer. Suggest an explanation for the link between this signaling pathway and tumor formation.

ONLINE RESOURCE

www.ravenbiology.com

Understand, Apply, and Synthesize—enhance your study with animations that bring concepts to life and practice tests to assess your understanding. Your instructor may also recommend the interactive eBook, individualized learning tools, and more.

Chapter **10**

How Cells Divide

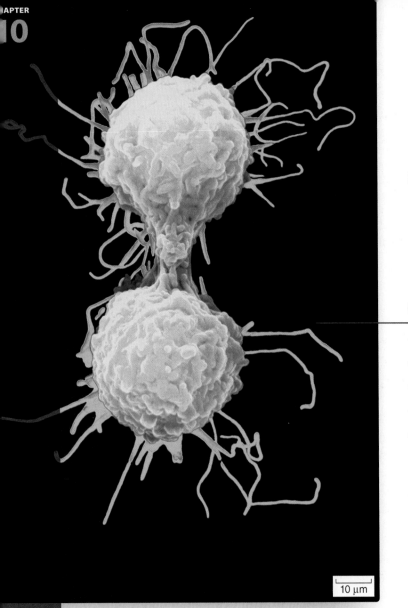

10 μm

Chapter Contents

Introduction

All species of organisms—bacteria, alligators, the weeds in a lawn—grow and reproduce. From the smallest creature to the largest, all species produce offspring like themselves and pass on the hereditary information that makes them what they are. In this chapter, we examine how cells, like the white blood cell shown in the figure, divide and reproduce. Cell division is necessary for the growth of organisms, for wound healing, and to replace cells that are lost regularly, such as those in your skin and in the lining of your gut. The mechanism of cell reproduction and its biological consequences have changed significantly during the evolution of life on Earth. The process is complex in eukaryotes, involving both the replication of chromosomes and their separation into daughter cells. Much of what we are learning about the causes of cancer relates to how cells control this process, and in particular their tendency to divide, a mechanism that in broad outline remains the same in all eukaryotes.

Bacterial Cell Division

Learning Outcome

1. **Describe the process of binary fission.**

Bacteria divide as a way of reproducing themselves. Although bacteria exchange DNA, they do not have a sexual cycle like eukaryotes. Thus all growth in a bacterial population is due to division to produce new cells. The reproduction of bacteria is clonal—that is, each cell produced by cell division is an identical copy of the original cell.

Binary fission is a simple form of cell division

Cell division in both bacterial and eukaryotic cells produces two new cells with the same genetic information as the original. Despite the differences in these cell types, the essentials of the process are the same: duplication and segregation of genetic information into daughter cells, and division of cellular contents. We begin by looking at the simpler process, **binary fission,** which occurs in bacteria.

Most bacteria have a genome made up of a single, circular DNA molecule. In spite of its apparent simplicity, the DNA molecule of the bacterium *Escherichia coli* is actually on the order of 500 times longer than the cell itself! Thus, this "simple" structure is actually packaged very tightly to fit into the cell. Although not found in a nucleus, the DNA is located in a region called the *nucleoid* that is distinct from the cytoplasm around it.

The compaction and organization of the nucleoid involves a class of proteins called structural maintenance of chromosome, or SMC, proteins. These are ancient proteins that have diversified over evolutionary time to fulfill a variety of roles related to DNA organization in different lineages. In eukaryotes the cohesin and condensin proteins discussed later in the chapter are SMC proteins.

During binary fission, the chromosome is replicated, and the two products are partitioned to each end of the cell prior to the actual division of the cell. One key feature of bacterial cell division is that replication and partitioning of the chromosome occur as a concerted process. In contrast, DNA replication in eukaryotic cells occurs early in division, and chromosome separation occurs much later.

Proteins control chromosome separation and septum formation

Binary fission begins with the replication of the bacterial DNA at a specific site—the origin of replication (see chapter 14)—and proceeds both directions around the circular DNA to a specific site of termination (figure 10.1). The cell grows by elongation, and division occurs roughly at midcell. For many years, it was thought that newly replicated *E. coli* DNA molecules were passively segregated by attachment to and growth of the membrane as the cell elongated. Experiments that follow the movement of the origin of replication show that it is at

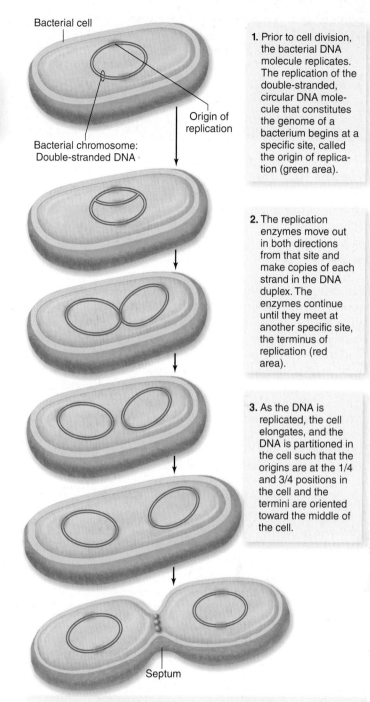

Bacterial cell

Bacterial chromosome:
Double-stranded DNA

Origin of
replication

1. Prior to cell division, the bacterial DNA molecule replicates. The replication of the double-stranded, circular DNA molecule that constitutes the genome of a bacterium begins at a specific site, called the origin of replication (green area).

2. The replication enzymes move out in both directions from that site and make copies of each strand in the DNA duplex. The enzymes continue until they meet at another specific site, the terminus of replication (red area).

3. As the DNA is replicated, the cell elongates, and the DNA is partitioned in the cell such that the origins are at the 1/4 and 3/4 positions in the cell and the termini are oriented toward the middle of the cell.

Septum

4. Septation then begins, in which new membrane and cell wall material begin to grow and form a septum at approximately the midpoint of the cell. A protein molecule called FtsZ (orange dots) facilitates this process.

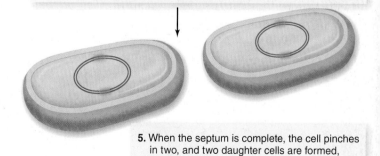

5. When the septum is complete, the cell pinches in two, and two daughter cells are formed, each containing a bacterial DNA molecule.

Figure 10.1 Binary fission.

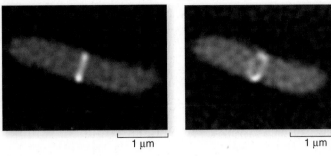

Figure 10.2 The FtsZ protein. In these dividing *E. coli* bacteria, the FtsZ protein is labeled with fluorescent dye to show its location during binary fission. The protein assembles into a ring at approximately the midpoint of the cell, where it facilitates septation and cell division. Bacteria carrying mutations in the *FtsZ* gene are unable to divide.

midcell prior to replication, then the newly replicated origins move toward opposite ends of the cell. This movement is faster than the rate of elongation, showing that growth alone is not enough. The origins appear to be captured at the one quarter and three quarter positions relative to the length of the cell, which will be midcell of the resulting daughter cells.

Although the actual mechanism of chromosome segregation is unclear, the order of events is not. During replication, first the origin, then the rest of the newly replicated chromosomes are moved to opposite ends of the cell as two new nucleoids are assembled. The final event of replication is decatenation (untangling) of the final replication products.

After replication and segregation, the midcell region is cleared of daughter nucleoids, and division occurs. The force behind chromosome segregation has been attributed to DNA replication itself, transcription, and the polymerization of actin-like molecules. At this point, no single model appears to explain the process, and it may involve more than one.

The cell's other components are partitioned by the growth of new membrane and production of the **septum** (see figure 10.1). This process, termed **septation,** usually occurs at the midpoint of the cell. It begins with the formation of a ring composed of many copies of the protein FtsZ (figure 10.2). Next, accumulation of a number of other proteins occurs, including ones embedded in the membrane. This structure contracts inward radially until the cell pinches off into two new cells. The midcell location of the FtsZ ring is caused by an oscillation between the two poles of an inhibitor of FtsZ formation.

The FtsZ protein is found in most prokaryotes, including archaea. It can form filaments and rings, and recent three-dimensional crystals show a high degree of similarity to eukaryotic tubulin. However, its role in bacterial division is quite different from the role of tubulin in mitosis in eukaryotes.

The evolution of eukaryotic cells included much more complex genomes composed of multiple linear chromosomes housed in a membrane-bounded nucleus. These complex genomes may be possible due to the evolution of mechanisms that delay chromosome separation after replication. Although it is unclear how this ability to keep chromosomes together evolved, it does seem more closely related to binary fission than we once thought (figure 10.3).

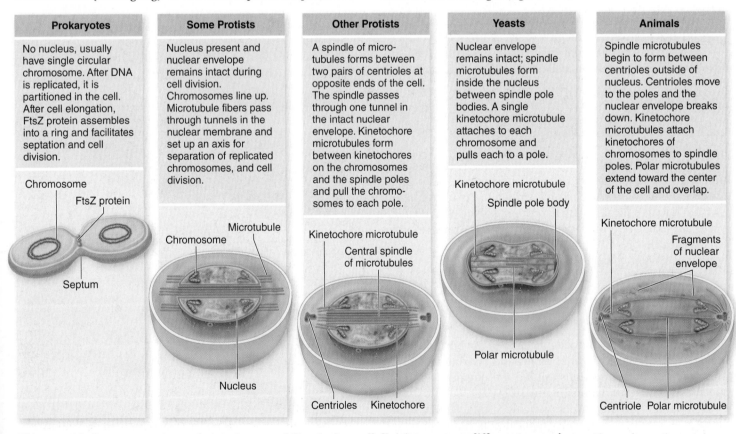

Figure 10.3 A comparison of protein assemblies during cell division among different organisms. The prokaryotic protein FtsZ has a structure that is similar to that of the eukaryotic protein tubulin. Tubulin is the protein component of microtubules, which are fibers that eukaryotic cells use to construct the spindle apparatus that is used to separate chromosomes.

10.2 Eukaryotic Chromosomes

Learning Outcomes

1. *Describe the structure of eukaryotic chromosomes.*
2. *Distinguish between homologues and sister chromatids.*
3. *Contrast replicated and nonreplicated chromosomes.*

TABLE 10.1	Chromosome Number in Selected Eukaryotes
Group	**Total Number of Chromosomes**
F U N G I	
Neurospora (haploid)	7
Saccharomyces (a yeast)	16
I N S E C T S	
Mosquito	6
Drosophila	8
Honeybee	diploid females 32, haploid males 16
Silkworm	56
P L A N T S	
Haplopappus gracilis	2
Garden pea	14
Corn	20
Bread wheat	42
Sugarcane	80
Horsetail	216
Adder's tongue fern	1262
V E R T E B R A T E S	
Opossum	22
Frog	26
Mouse	40
Human	46
Chimpanzee	48
Horse	64
Chicken	78
Dog	78

Chromosomes were first observed by the German embryologist Walther Flemming (1843–1905) in 1879, while he was examining the rapidly dividing cells of salamander larvae. When Flemming looked at the cells through what would now be a rather primitive light microscope, he saw minute threads within their nuclei that appeared to be dividing lengthwise. Flemming called their division **mitosis,** based on the Greek word *mitos,* meaning "thread."

Chromosome number varies among species

Since their initial discovery, chromosomes have been found in the cells of all eukaryotes examined. Their number may vary enormously from one species to another. A few kinds of organisms have only a single pair of chromosomes, whereas some ferns have more than 500 pairs (table 10.1). Most eukaryotes have between 10 and 50 chromosomes in their body cells.

Human cells each have 46 chromosomes, consisting of 23 nearly identical pairs (figure 10.4). Each of these 46 chromosomes contains hundreds or thousands of genes that play important roles in determining how a person's body develops and functions. Human embryos missing even one chromosome, a condition called *monosomy,* do not survive in most cases. Having an extra copy of any one chromosome, a condition called *trisomy,* is usually fatal except where the smallest chromosomes are involved. (You'll learn more about human chromosome abnormalities in chapter 13.)

Eukaryotic chromosomes exhibit complex structure

Researchers have learned a great deal about chromosome structure and composition in the more than 125 years since

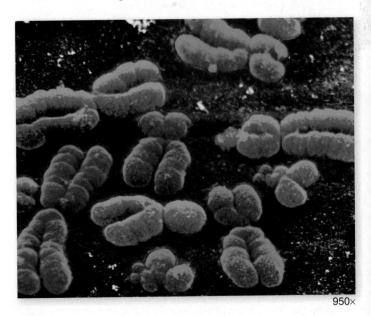

950×

Figure 10.4 Human chromosomes. This scanning electron micrograph shows human chromosomes as they appear immediately before nuclear division. Each DNA molecule has already replicated, forming identical copies held together at a visible constriction called the centromere. False color has been added to the chromosomes.

their discovery. But despite intense research, the exact structure of eukaryotic chromosomes during the cell cycle remains unclear. The structures described in this chapter represent the currently accepted model.

Composition of chromatin

Chromosomes are composed of **chromatin,** a complex of DNA and protein; most chromosomes are about 40% DNA and 60% protein. A significant amount of RNA is also associated with chromosomes because chromosomes are the sites of RNA synthesis.

Each chromosome contains a single DNA molecule that runs uninterrupted through the chromosome's entire length. A typical human chromosome contains about 140 million (1.4×10^8) nucleotides in its DNA. If we think of each nucleotide as a "word," then the amount of information an average chromosome contains would fill about 280 printed books of 1000 pages each, with 500 "words" per page.

If we could lay out the strand of DNA from a single chromosome in a straight line, it would be about 5 cm (2 in.) long. Fitting such a strand into a cell nucleus is like cramming a string the length of a football field into a baseball—and that's only 1 of 46 chromosomes! In the cell, however, the DNA is compacted, allowing it to fit into a much smaller space than would otherwise be possible.

The organization of chromatin in the nondividing nucleus is not well understood, but geneticists have recognized for years that some domains of chromatin, called **heterochromatin,** are not expressed, and other domains of chromatin, called **euchromatin,** are expressed. This genetically measurable state is also related to the physical state of chromatin, although researchers are just beginning to see the details.

Chromosome structure

If we gently disrupt a eukaryotic nucleus and examine the DNA with an electron microscope, we find that it resembles a string of beads (figure 10.5). Every 200 nucleotides (nt), the DNA duplex (double strand) is coiled around a core of eight **histone proteins.** Unlike most proteins, which have an overall negative charge, histones are positively charged because of an abundance of the basic amino acids arginine and lysine. Thus, they are strongly attracted to the negatively charged phosphate groups of the DNA, and the histone cores act as "magnetic forms" that promote and guide the coiling of the DNA. The complex of DNA and histone proteins is termed a **nucleosome.**

The DNA wrapped in nucleosomes is further coiled into an even more compact structure called the *solenoid*. The precise path of this higher order folding of chromatin is still a subject of debate, but it leads to a fiber with a diameter of 30 nm

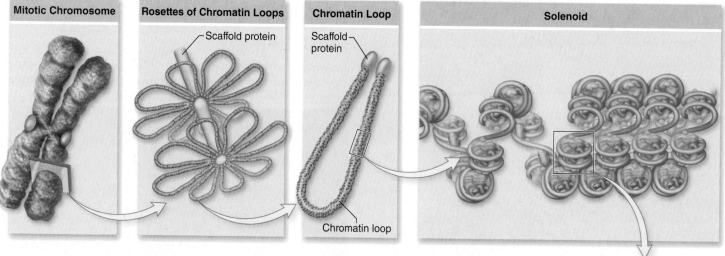

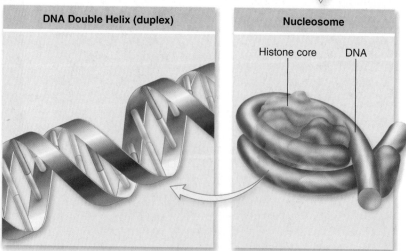

Figure 10.5 **Levels of eukaryotic chromosomal organization.** Each chromosome consists of a long double-stranded DNA molecule. These strands require further packaging to fit into the cell nucleus. The DNA duplex is tightly bound to and wound around proteins called histones. The DNA-wrapped histones are called nucleosomes. The nucleosomes are further coiled into the solenoid. This solenoid is then organized into looped domains. The precise organization of mitotic chromosomes is unknown, but the solenoid is further condensed around a preexisting scaffolding of proteins. The arrangement shown is one of many possibilities.

and thus is called the 30-nm fiber. This 30-nm fiber is the usual state of interphase (nondividing) chromatin.

During mitosis, a scaffold of proteins is assembled that allows the organization of even more compact chromosomes, which can be more readily separated by the mitotic machinery described later. The exact nature of the compaction is unknown, but one longstanding model involves looping of chromatin fibers from the scaffold like the fibers on a wire brush. This process is aided by a complex of proteins called condensin, which are evolutionarily related to the bacterial SMC that compact the nucleoid.

Chromosome karyotypes

Chromosomes vary in size, staining properties, the location of the centromere (a constriction found on all chromosomes, described shortly), the relative length of the two arms on either side of the centromere, and the positions of constricted regions along the arms. The particular array of chromosomes an individual organism possesses is called its **karyotype.** The karyotype in figure 10.6 shows the set of chromosomes from a normal human cell.

When defining the number of different chromosomes in a species, geneticists count the **haploid (n)** number of chromosomes. This refers to one complete set of chromosomes necessary to define an organism. For humans and many other species, the total number of chromosomes in a cell is called the

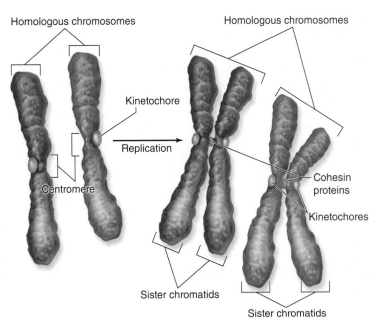

Figure 10.7 The difference between homologous chromosomes and sister chromatids. Homologous chromosomes are the maternal and paternal copies of the same chromosome—say, chromosome number 16. Sister chromatids are the two replicas of a single chromosome held together at their centromeres by cohesin proteins after DNA replication. The kinetochore (described later in the chapter) is composed of proteins found at the centromere that attach to microtubules during mitosis.

diploid **(2n)** number, which is twice the haploid number. For humans, the haploid number is 23 and the diploid number is 46. Diploid chromosomes reflect the equal genetic contribution that each parent makes to offspring. We refer to the maternal and paternal chromosomes as being **homologous,** and each one of the pair is termed a **homologue.**

Chromosome replication

Chromosomes as seen in a karyotype are only present for a brief period during cell division. Prior to replicating, each chromosome is composed of a single DNA molecule that is arranged into the 30-nm fiber described earlier. After replication, each chromosome is composed of two identical DNA molecules held together by a complex of proteins called **cohesins.** As the chromosomes become more condensed and arranged about the protein scaffold, they become visible as two strands that are held together at the centromere. At this point, we still call this one chromosome, but it is composed of two **sister chromatids** (figure 10.7).

The fact that the products of replication are held together is critical to the division process. One problem that a cell must solve is how to ensure that each new cell receives a complete set of chromosomes. If we were designing a system, we might use some kind of label to identify each chromosome, much like most of us use when we duplicate files on a computer. Instead of labeling chromosomes, the cell glues replication products together at the centromere. The process of mitosis then separates all of these copies at the same time, ensuring that each daughter cell gets one copy of each chromosome.

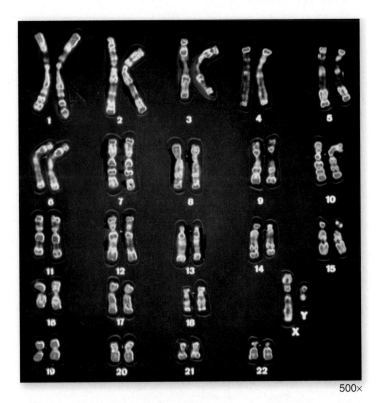

500×

Figure 10.6 A human karyotype. The individual chromosomes that make up the 23 pairs differ widely in size and in centromere position. In this preparation of a male karyotype, the chromosomes have been specifically stained to indicate differences in their composition and to distinguish them clearly from one another. Notice that members of a chromosome pair are very similar but not identical.

10.3 Overview of the Eukaryotic Cell Cycle

Learning Outcome

1. Describe the eukaryotic cell cycle.

Compared with prokaryotes, the increased size and more complex organization of eukaryotic genomes required radical changes in the partitioning of replicated genomes into daughter cells. The **cell cycle** requires the duplication of the genome, its accurate segregation, and the division of cellular contents.

The cell cycle is divided into five phases

The cell cycle is divided into phases based on the key events of genome duplication and segregation. The cell cycle is usually diagrammed as in figure 10.8.

■ **G₁ (gap phase 1)** is the primary growth phase of the cell. The term *gap phase* refers to its filling the gap between cytokinesis and DNA synthesis. For most cells, this is the longest phase.

■ **S (synthesis)** is the phase in which the cell synthesizes a replica of the genome.

■ **G₂ (gap phase 2)** is the second growth phase, and preparation for separation of the newly replicated genome. This phase fills the gap between DNA synthesis and the beginning of mitosis. During this phase microtubules begin to reorganize to form a spindle.

   G_1, S, and G_2 together constitute **interphase,** the portion of the cell cycle between cell divisions.

■ **Mitosis** is the phase of the cell cycle in which the spindle apparatus assembles, binds to the chromosomes, and moves the sister chromatids apart. Mitosis is the essential step in the separation of the two daughter genomes. It is traditionally subdivided into five stages: prophase, prometaphase, metaphase, anaphase, and telophase.

■ **Cytokinesis** is the phase of the cell cycle when the cytoplasm divides, creating two daughter cells. In animal

cells, the microtubule spindle helps position a contracting ring of actin that constricts like a drawstring to pinch the cell in two. In cells with a cell wall, such as plant cells, a plate forms between the dividing cells.

Mitosis and cytokinesis together are usually referred to collectively as M phase, to distinguish the dividing phase from interphase.

The duration of the cell cycle varies depending on cell type

The time it takes to complete a cell cycle varies greatly. Cells in animal embryos can complete their cell cycle in under 20 min; the shortest known animal nuclear division cycles occur in fruit fly embryos (8 min). These cells simply divide their nuclei as quickly as they can replicate their DNA, without cell growth. Half of their cycle is taken up by S, half by M, and essentially none by G_1 or G_2.

Because mature cells require time to grow, most of their cycles are much longer than those of embryonic tissue. Typically, a dividing mammalian cell completes its cell cycle in about 24 hr, but some cells, such as certain cells in the human liver, have cell cycles lasting more than a year. During the cycle, growth occurs throughout the G_1 and G_2 phases, as well as during the S phase. The M phase takes only about an hour, a small fraction of the entire cycle.

Most of the variation in the length of the cell cycle between organisms or cell types occurs in the G_1 phase. Cells often pause in G_1 before DNA replication and enter a resting state called the **G₀ phase;** cells may remain in this phase for

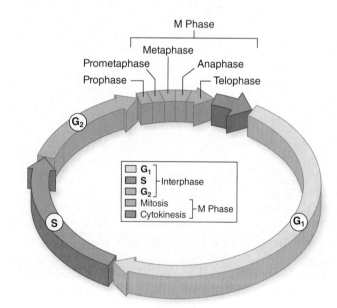

Figure 10.8 The cell cycle. The cell cycle is depicted as a circle. The first gap phase, G_1, involves growth and preparation for DNA synthesis. During S phase, a copy of the genome is synthesized. The second gap phase, G_2, prepares the cell for mitosis. During mitosis, replicated chromosomes are partitioned. Cytokinesis divides the cell into two cells with identical genomes.

days to years before resuming cell division. At any given time, most of the cells in an animal's body are in G_0 phase. Some, such as muscle and nerve cells, remain there permanently; others, such as liver cells, can resume G_1 phase in response to factors released during injury.

Learning Outcome Review 10.3

Cell division in eukaryotes is a complex process that involves five phases: a first gap phase (G_1); a DNA synthesis phase (S); a second gap phase (G_2); mitosis (M), during which chromatids are separated; and cytokinesis in which a cell becomes two separate cells.

■ *When during the cycle is a cell irreversibly committed to dividing?*

10.4 Interphase: Preparation for Mitosis

Learning Outcomes

1. *Describe the events that take place during interphase.*
2. *Illustrate the connection between sister chromatids after S phase.*

The events that occur during interphase—the G_1, S, and G_2 phases—are very important for the successful completion of mitosis. During G_1, cells undergo the major portion of their growth. During the S phase, each chromosome replicates to produce two sister chromatids, which remain attached to each other at the centromere. In the G_2 phase, the chromosomes coil even more tightly.

The **centromere** is a point of constriction on the chromosome containing repeated DNA sequences that bind specific proteins. These proteins make up a disklike structure called the **kinetochore.** This disk functions as an attachment site for microtubules necessary to separate the chromosomes during cell division (figure 10.9). As seen in figure 10.6, each chromosome's centromere is located at a characteristic site along the length of the chromosome.

After the S phase, the sister chromatids appear to share a common centromere, but at the molecular level the DNA of the centromere has actually already replicated, so there are two complete DNA molecules. This means that two chromatids are held together by cohesin proteins at the centromere, and each chromatid has its own set of kinetochore proteins (figure 10.10). In multicellular animals, most of the cohesins that hold sister chromatids together after replication appear to be replaced by condensin as the chromosomes are condensed. This leaves the chromosomes still attached tightly at the centromere, but loosely attached elsewhere.

The cell grows throughout interphase. The G_1 and G_2 segments of interphase are periods of active growth, during which proteins are synthesized and cell organelles are

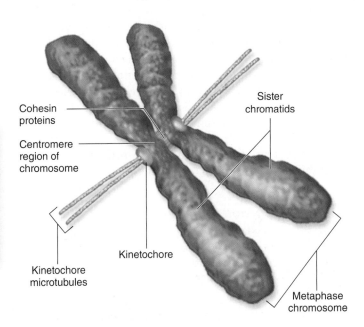

Figure 10.9 Kinetochores. Separation of sister chromatids during mitosis depends on microtubules attaching to proteins found in the kinetochore. These kinetochore proteins are assembled on the centromere of chromosomes. The centromeres of the two sister chromatids are held together by cohesin proteins.

produced. The cell's DNA replicates only during the S phase of the cell cycle.

After the chromosomes have replicated in S phase, they remain fully extended and uncoiled, although cohesin proteins are associated with them at this stage. In G_2 phase,

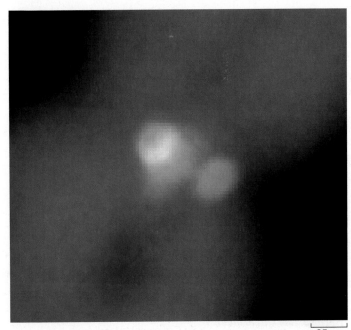

Figure 10.10 Proteins found at the centromere. In this image DNA, a cohesin protein, and a kinetochore protein have all been labeled with a different-colored fluorescent dye. Cohesin *(red)*, which holds centromeres together, lies between the sister chromatids *(blue)*. Each sister chromatid has its own separate kinetochore *(green)*.

they begin the process of condensation, coiling ever more tightly. Special *motor proteins* are involved in the rapid final condensation of the chromosomes that occurs early in mitosis. Also during G_2 phase, the cells begin to assemble the machinery they will later use to move the chromosomes to opposite poles of the cell. In animal cells, a pair of microtubule-organizing centers called *centrioles* replicate, producing one for each pole. All eukaryotic cells undertake an extensive synthesis of **tubulin,** the protein that forms microtubules.

Learning Outcomes Review 10.4

Interphase includes the G_1, S, and G_2 phases of the cell cycle. During interphase, the cell grows; replicates chromosomes, organelles, and centrioles; and synthesizes components needed for mitosis, including tubulin. Cohesin proteins hold chromatids together at the centromere of each chromosome.

■ *How would a mutation that deleted cohesin proteins affect cell division?*

10.5 M Phase: Chromosome Segregation and the Division of Cytoplasmic Contents

Learning Outcomes

1. *Describe the phases of mitosis.*
2. *Explain the importance of metaphase.*
3. *Compare cytokinesis in plants and animals.*

The process of mitosis is one of the most dramatic and beautiful biological processes that we can easily observe. In our attempts to understand this process, we have divided it into discrete phases but it should always be remembered that this is a dynamic, continuous process, not a set of discrete steps. This process is shown both schematically and in micrographs in figure 10.11.

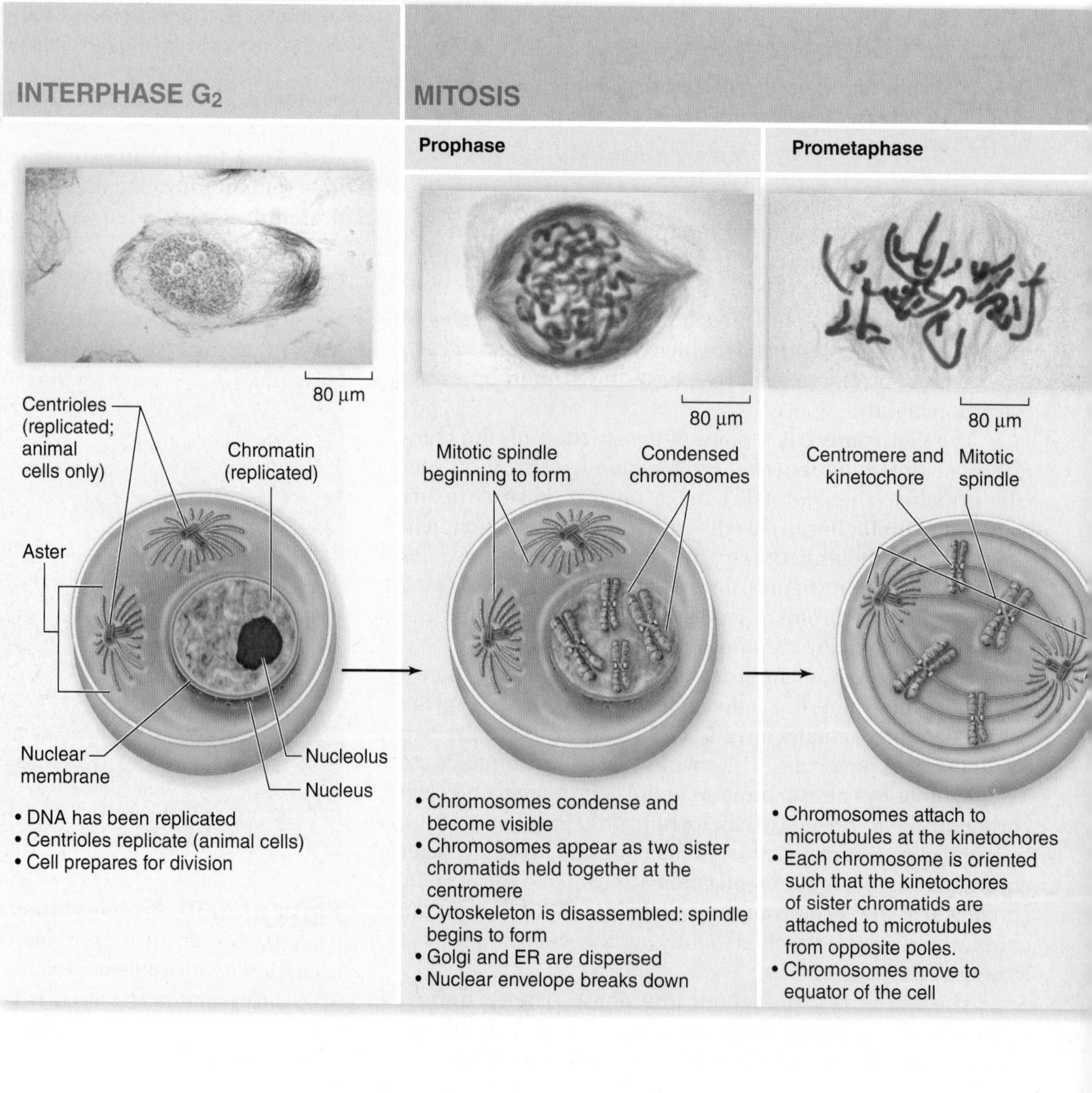

Figure 10.11 **Mitosis and cytokinesis.**
Mitosis is conventionally divided into five stages—prophase, prometaphase, metaphase, anaphase, and telophase—which together act to separate duplicated chromosomes. This is followed by cytokinesis, which divides the cell into two separate cells. Photos depict mitosis and cytokinesis in a plant, the African blood lily (*Haemanthus katharinae*), with chromosomes stained blue and microtubules stained red. Drawings depict mitosis and cytokinesis in animal cells.

INTERPHASE G_2

80 μm

Centrioles (replicated; animal cells only)
Chromatin (replicated)
Aster
Nuclear membrane
Nucleolus
Nucleus

- DNA has been replicated
- Centrioles replicate (animal cells)
- Cell prepares for division

MITOSIS

Prophase

80 μm

Mitotic spindle beginning to form
Condensed chromosomes

- Chromosomes condense and become visible
- Chromosomes appear as two sister chromatids held together at the centromere
- Cytoskeleton is disassembled: spindle begins to form
- Golgi and ER are dispersed
- Nuclear envelope breaks down

Prometaphase

80 μm

Centromere and kinetochore
Mitotic spindle

- Chromosomes attach to microtubules at the kinetochores
- Each chromosome is oriented such that the kinetochores of sister chromatids are attached to microtubules from opposite poles.
- Chromosomes move to equator of the cell

During prophase, the mitotic apparatus forms

When the chromosome condensation initiated in G_2 phase reaches the point at which individual condensed chromosomes first become visible with the light microscope, the first stage of mitosis, **prophase,** has begun. The condensation process continues throughout prophase; consequently, chromosomes that start prophase as minute threads appear quite bulky before its conclusion. Ribosomal RNA synthesis ceases when the portion of the chromosome bearing the rRNA genes is condensed.

The spindle and centrioles

The assembly of the **spindle** apparatus that will later separate the sister chromatids occurs during prophase. The normal microtubule structure in the cell disassembled in the G_2 phase is replaced by the spindle. In animal cells, the two centriole pairs formed during G_2 phase begin to move apart early in prophase, forming between them an axis of microtubules referred to as spindle fibers. By the time the centrioles reach the opposite poles of the cell, they have established a bridge of microtubules, called the spindle apparatus, between them. In plant cells, a similar bridge of microtubular fibers forms between opposite poles of the cell, although centrioles are absent in plant cells.

In animal cell mitosis, the centrioles extend a radial array of microtubules toward the nearby plasma membrane when they reach the poles of the cell. This arrangement of microtubules is called an **aster.** Although the aster's function is not fully understood, it probably braces the centrioles against the membrane and stiffens the point of microtubular attachment during the retraction of the spindle. Plant cells, which have rigid cell walls, do not form asters.

Breakdown of the nuclear envelope

During the formation of the spindle apparatus, the nuclear envelope breaks down, and the endoplasmic reticulum reabsorbs its components. At this point, the microtubular spindle fibers extend completely across the cell, from one pole to the other. Their orientation determines the plane in which the cell will subsequently divide, through the center of the cell at right angles to the spindle apparatus.

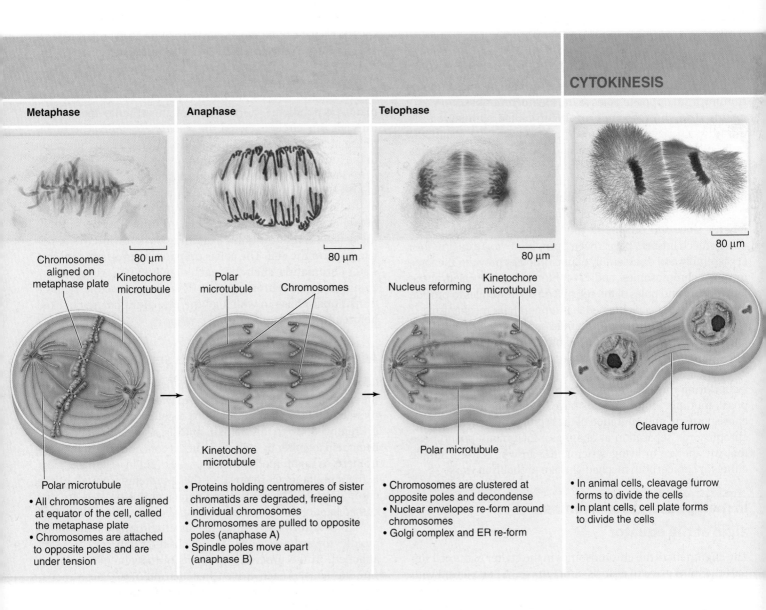

Metaphase

Chromosomes aligned on metaphase plate | Kinetochore microtubule | 80 μm

Polar microtubule

- All chromosomes are aligned at equator of the cell, called the metaphase plate
- Chromosomes are attached to opposite poles and are under tension

Anaphase

Polar microtubule | Chromosomes | 80 μm

Kinetochore microtubule

- Proteins holding centromeres of sister chromatids are degraded, freeing individual chromosomes
- Chromosomes are pulled to opposite poles (anaphase A)
- Spindle poles move apart (anaphase B)

Telophase

Nucleus reforming | Kinetochore microtubule | 80 μm

Polar microtubule

- Chromosomes are clustered at opposite poles and decondense
- Nuclear envelopes re-form around chromosomes
- Golgi complex and ER re-form

CYTOKINESIS

80 μm

Cleavage furrow

- In animal cells, cleavage furrow forms to divide the cells
- In plant cells, cell plate forms to divide the cells

During prometaphase, chromosomes attach to the spindle

The transition from prophase to **prometaphase** occurs following the disassembly of the nuclear envelope. During prometaphase the condensed chromosomes become attached to the spindle by their kinetochores. Each chromosome possesses two kinetochores, one attached to the centromere region of each sister chromatid (see figure 10.9).

Microtubule attachment

As prometaphase continues, a second group of microtubules grow from the poles of the cell toward the centromeres. These microtubules are captured by the kinetochores on each pair of sister chromatids. This results in the kinetochores of each sister chromatid being connected to opposite poles of the spindle.

This bipolar attachment is critical to the process of mitosis; any mistakes in microtubule positioning can be disastrous. For example, the attachment of the kinetochores of both sister chromatids to the same pole leads to a failure of sister chromatid separation, and they will be pulled to the same pole ending up in the same daughter cell, with the other daughter cell missing that chromosome.

Movement of chromosomes to the cell center

Each chromosome is attached to the spindle by microtubules running from opposite poles to the kinetochores of sister chromatids. The chromosomes are being pulled simultaneously toward each pole, leading to a jerky motion that eventually pulls all of the chromosomes to the equator of the cell. At this point, the chromosomes are arranged at the equator, with sister chromatids under tension and oriented toward opposite poles by their kinetochore microtubules.

The force that moves chromosomes has been of great interest since the process of mitosis was first observed. Two basic mechanisms have been proposed to explain this: (1) assembly and disassembly of microtubules provides the force to move chromosomes, and (2) motor proteins located at the kinetochore and poles of the cell pull on microtubules to provide force. Data have been obtained that support both mechanisms.

In support of the microtubule-shortening proposal, isolated chromosomes can be pulled by microtubule disassembly. The spindle is a very dynamic structure, with microtubules being added to at the kinetochore and shortened at the poles, even during metaphase. In support of the motor protein proposal, multiple motor proteins have been identified as kinetochore proteins, and inhibition of the motor protein dynein slows chromosome separation at anaphase. Like many phenomena that we analyze in living systems, the answer is not a simple either–or choice; both mechanisms are probably at work.

In metaphase, chromosomes align at the equator

The alignment of the chromosomes in the center of the cell signals the third stage of mitosis, **metaphase.** When viewed with a light microscope, the chromosomes appear to array themselves in a circle along the inner circumference of the cell, just

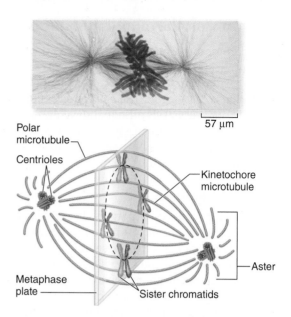

Figure 10.12 **Metaphase.** In metaphase, the chromosomes are arrayed at the midpoint of the cell. The imaginary plane through the equator of the cell is called the metaphase plate. As the spindle itself is a three-dimensional structure, the chromosomes are arrayed in a rough circle on the metaphase plate.

as the equator girdles the Earth (figure 10.12). An imaginary plane perpendicular to the axis of the spindle that passes through this circle is called the *metaphase plate.* The metaphase plate is not an actual structure, but rather an indication of the future axis of cell division.

Positioned by the microtubules attached to the kinetochores of their centromeres, all of the chromosomes line up on the metaphase plate. At this point their centromeres are neatly arrayed in a circle, equidistant from the two poles of the cell, with microtubules extending back toward the opposite poles of the cell. The cell is prepared to properly separate sister chromatids, such that each daughter cell will receive a complete set of chromosomes. Thus metaphase is really a transitional phase in which all the preparations are checked before the action continues.

At anaphase, the chromatids separate

Of all the stages of mitosis, shown in figure 10.11, **anaphase** is the shortest and the most amazing to watch. It begins when the proteins holding sister chromatids together at the centromere are removed. Up to this point in mitosis, sister chromatids have been held together by cohesin proteins concentrated at the centromere, as mentioned earlier. The key event in anaphase, then, is the simultaneous removal of these proteins from all of the chromosomes. The control and details of this process are discussed later on in the context of control of the entire cell cycle.

Freed from each other, the sister chromatids are pulled rapidly toward the poles to which their kinetochores are attached. In the process, two forms of movement take place simultaneously, each driven by microtubules. These movements are often called anaphase A and anaphase B to distinguish them.

First, during anaphase A, the *kinetochores are pulled toward the poles* as the microtubules that connect them to the poles shorten. This shortening process is not a contraction; the microtubules do not get any thicker. Instead, tubulin subunits are removed from the kinetochore ends of the microtubules. As more subunits are removed, the chromatid-bearing microtubules are progressively disassembled, and the chromatids are pulled ever closer to the poles of the cell.

Second, during anaphase B, the *poles move apart* as microtubular spindle fibers physically anchored to opposite poles slide past each other, away from the center of the cell (figure 10.13). Because another group of microtubules attach the chromosomes to the poles, the chromosomes move apart, too. If a flexible membrane surrounds the cell, it becomes visibly elongated.

When the sister chromatids separate in anaphase, the accurate partitioning of the replicated genome—the essential element of mitosis—is complete.

During telophase, the nucleus re-forms

In **telophase,** the spindle apparatus disassembles as the microtubules are broken down into tubulin monomers that can be used to construct the cytoskeletons of the daughter cells. A nuclear envelope forms around each set of sister chromatids, which can now be called chromosomes because they are no longer attached at the centromere. The chromosomes soon begin to uncoil into the more extended form that permits gene expression. One of the early group of genes expressed after mitosis is complete are the rRNA genes, resulting in the reappearance of the nucleolus.

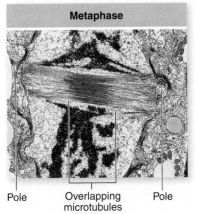

Figure 10.13 Microtubules slide past each other as the chromosomes separate. In these electron micrographs of dividing diatoms, the overlap of the microtubules lessens markedly during spindle elongation as the cell passes from metaphase to anaphase. During anaphase B the poles move farther apart as the chromosomes move toward the poles.

Metaphase

Pole   Overlapping   Pole
        microtubules

Late Anaphase

Pole   Overlapping   Pole   2 µm
        microtubules

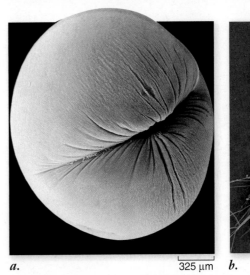

a.   325 µm   *b.*   25 µm

Figure 10.14 Cytokinesis in animal cells. *a.* A cleavage furrow forms around a dividing frog egg. *b.* The completion of cytokinesis in an animal cell. The two daughter cells are still joined by a thin band of cytoplasm occupied largely by microtubules.

Telophase can be viewed as a reversal of the process of prophase, bringing the cell back to the state of interphase. Mitosis is complete at the end of telophase. The eukaryotic cell has partitioned its replicated genome into two new nuclei positioned at opposite ends of the cell. Other cytoplasmic organelles, including mitochondria and chloroplasts (if present), were reassorted to areas that will separate and become the daughter cells.

Cell division is still not complete at the end of mitosis, however, because the division of the cell body proper has not yet begun. The phase of the cell cycle when the cell actually divides is called **cytokinesis.** It generally involves the cleavage of the cell into roughly equal halves.

In animal cells, a belt of actin pinches off the daughter cells

In animal cells and the cells of all other eukaryotes that lack cell walls, cytokinesis is achieved by means of a constricting belt of actin filaments. As these filaments slide past one another, the diameter of the belt decreases, pinching the cell and creating a **cleavage furrow** around the cell's circumference (figure 10.14*a*).

As constriction proceeds, the furrow deepens until it eventually slices all the way into the center of the cell. At this point, the cell is divided in two (figure 10.14*b*).

In plant cells, a cell plate divides the daughter cells

Plant cell walls are far too rigid to be squeezed in two by actin filaments. Instead, these cells assemble membrane components in their interior, at right angles to the spindle apparatus. This expanding membrane partition, called a **cell plate,** continues to grow outward until it reaches the interior surface of the plasma membrane and fuses with it, effectively dividing

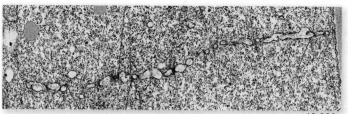

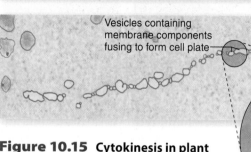

19,000×

Vesicles containing
membrane components
fusing to form cell plate

Cell wall

Figure 10.15 Cytokinesis in plant cells. In this photomicrograph and companion drawing, a cell plate is forming between daughter nuclei. The cell plate forms from the fusion of Golgi-derived vesicles. Once the plate is complete, there will be two cells.

the cell in two (figure 10.15). Cellulose is then laid down on the new membranes, creating two new cell walls. The space between the daughter cells becomes impregnated with pectins and is called a *middle lamella*.

In fungi and some protists, daughter nuclei are separated during cytokinesis

In most fungi and some groups of protists, the nuclear membrane does not dissolve, and as a result, all the events of mitosis occur entirely *within* the nucleus. Only after mitosis is complete in these organisms does the nucleus divide into two daughter nuclei; then, during cytokinesis, one nucleus goes to each daughter cell. This separate nuclear division phase of the cell cycle does not occur in plants, animals, or most protists.

After cytokinesis in any eukaryotic cell, the two daughter cells contain all the components of a complete cell. Whereas mitosis ensures that both daughter cells contain a full complement of chromosomes, no similar mechanism ensures that organelles such as mitochondria and chloroplasts are distributed equally between the daughter cells. But as long as at least one of each organelle is present in each cell, the organelles can replicate to reach the number appropriate for that cell.

Learning Outcomes Review 10.5

Mitosis is divided into phases: prophase, prometaphase, metaphase, anaphase, and telophase. The early phases involve restructuring the cell to create the microtubule spindle that pulls chromosomes to the equator of the cell in metaphase. Chromatids for each chromosome remain attached at the centromere by cohesin proteins. Chromatids are then pulled to opposite poles during anaphase when cohesin proteins are destroyed. The nucleus is re-formed in telophase, and cytokinesis then divides the cell cytoplasm and organelles. In animal cells, actin pinches the cell in two; in plant cells, a cell plate forms in the middle of the dividing cell.

■ *What would happen to a chromosome that loses cohesin protein between sister chromatids before metaphase?*

Learning Outcomes

1. **Distinguish the role of checkpoints in the control of the cell cycle.**
2. **Characterize the role of the anaphase-promoting complex/cyclosome in mitosis.**
3. **Describe cancer in terms of cell cycle control.**

Our knowledge of how the cell cycle is controlled, although still incomplete, has grown enormously in the past 30 years. Our current view integrates two basic concepts. First, the cell cycle has two irreversible points: the replication of genetic material and the separation of the sister chromatids. Second, the cell cycle can be put on hold at specific points called *checkpoints*. At any of these checkpoints, the process is checked for accuracy and can be halted if there are errors. This leads to extremely high fidelity overall for the entire process. The checkpoint organization also allows the cell cycle to respond to both the internal state of the cell, including nutritional state and integrity of genetic material, and to signals from the environment, which are integrated at major checkpoints.

Research uncovered cell cycle control factors

The history of investigation into control of the cell cycle is instructive in two ways. First, it allows us to place modern observations into context; second, we can see how biologists using very different approaches often end up at the same place. The following brief history introduces three observations and then shows how they can be integrated into a single mechanism.

Discovery of MPF

Research on the activation of frog oocytes led to the discovery of a substance that was first called *maturation-promoting factor (MPF)*. Frog oocytes, which go on to become egg cells, become arrested near the end of their development at the G_2 stage before meiosis I, which is the division leading to the production of gametes (chapter 11). They remain in this arrested state and await hormonal signaling to complete this division process.

Cytoplasm taken from a variety of actively dividing cells could prematurely induce cell division when injected into oocytes (figure 10.16). These experiments indicated the presence of a positive regulator of cell cycle progression in the cytoplasm of dividing cells: MPF. These experiments also fit well with cell fusion experiments done with mitotic and interphase cells that also indicated a cytoplasmic positive regulator that could induce mitosis (see figure 10.16).

Further studies highlighted two key aspects of MPF. First, MPF activity varied during the cell cycle: low in early G_2, rising throughout this phase, and then peaking in mitosis (figure 10.17). Second, the enzymatic activity of MPF involved

Hypothesis: *There are positive regulators of cell division.*

Prediction: *Frog oocytes are arrested in G₂ of meiosis I. They can be induced to mature (undergo meiosis) by progesterone treatment. If maturing oocytes contain a positive regulator of cell division, injection of cytoplasm should induce an immature oocyte to undergo meiosis.*

Test: *Oocytes are induced with progesterone, then cytoplasm from these maturing cells is injected into immature oocytes.*

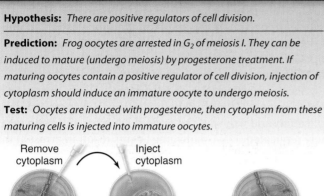

Remove cytoplasm   Inject cytoplasm

Progesterone-treated oocyte   Arrested oocyte   Oocyte in meiosis I

Result: *Injected oocytes progress from G₂ into meiosis I.*

Conclusion: *The progesterone treatment causes production of a positive regulator of maturation: Maturation Promoting Factor (MPF).*

Prediction: *If mitosis is driven by positive regulators, then cytoplasm from a mitotic cell should cause a G₁ cell to enter mitosis.*

Test: *M phase cells are fused with G₁ phase cells, then the nucleus from the G₁ phase cell is monitored microscopically.*

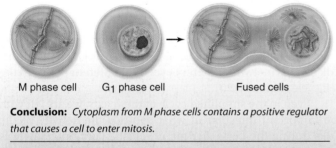

M phase cell   G₁ phase cell   Fused cells

Conclusion: *Cytoplasm from M phase cells contains a positive regulator that causes a cell to enter mitosis.*

Further Experiments: *How can both of these experiments be rationalized? What would be the next step in characterizing these factors?*

Figure 10.16 Discovery of positive regulator of cell division.

the phosphorylation of proteins. This second point is not surprising given the importance of phosphorylation as a reversible switch on the activity of proteins (see chapter 9). The first observation indicated that MPF itself was not always active, but rather was being regulated with the cell cycle, and the second showed the possible enzymatic activity of MPF.

Discovery of cyclins

Other researchers examined proteins produced during the early divisions in sea urchin embryos. They identified proteins that were produced in synchrony with the cell cycle, and named them **cyclins** (see figure 10.17). These observations were extended in another marine invertebrate, the surf clam. Two forms of cyclin were found that cycled at slightly different times, reaching peaks at the G₁/S and G₂/M boundaries.

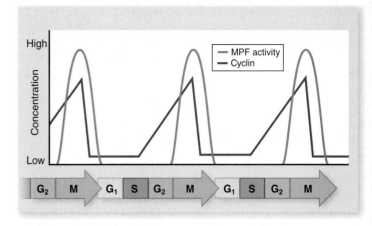

Figure 10.17 Correlation of MPF activity, amount of cyclin protein, and stages of the cell cycle. Cyclin concentration and MPF activity are shown plotted vs. stage of the cell cycle. MPF activity changes in a repeating pattern through the cell cycle. This also correlates with the level of mitotic cyclin in the cell, which shows a similar pattern. The reason for this correlation is that cyclin is actually one component of MPF, the other being a cyclin-dependent kinase (Cdk). Together these act as a positive regulator of cell division.

Despite much effort, no identified enzymatic activity was associated with these proteins. Their hallmark was the timing of their production and not any intrinsic activity.

Genetic analysis of the cell cycle

Geneticists using two different yeasts, budding yeast and fission yeast, as model systems set out to determine the genes necessary for control of the cell cycle. By isolating mutants that were halted during division, they identified genes that were necessary for cell cycle progression. These studies indicated that in yeast, there were two critical control points: the commitment to DNA synthesis, called START, as it meant committing to divide, and the commitment to mitosis. One particular gene, named *cdc2,* from fission yeast, was shown to be critical for passing both of these boundaries.

MPF is cyclin plus cdc2

All of these findings came together in an elegant fashion with the following observations. First, the protein encoded by the *cdc2* gene was shown to be a protein kinase. Second, the purification and identification of MPF showed that it was composed of both a cyclin component and a kinase component. Last, the kinase itself was the cdc2 protein!

The cdc2 protein was the first identified **cyclin-dependent kinase (Cdk),** that is, a protein kinase enzyme that is only active when complexed with cyclin. This finding led to the renaming of MPF as *mitosis*-promoting factor, as its role was clearly more general than simply promoting the maturation of frog oocytes.

These Cdk enzymes are the key positive drivers of the cell division cycle. They are often called the engine that drives cell division. The control of the cell cycle in higher eukaryotes is much more complex than the simple single-engine cycle of yeast, but the yeast model remains a useful framework for understanding more complex regulation. The discovery of Cdks and their role in the cell cycle is an excellent example of the progressive nature of science.

The cell cycle can be halted at three checkpoints

Although we have divided the cell cycle into phases and subdivided mitosis into stages, the cell recognizes three points at which the cycle can be delayed or halted. The cell uses these three checkpoints to both assess its internal state and integrate external signals (figure 10.18): G_1/S, G_2/M, and late metaphase (the spindle checkpoint). Passage through these checkpoints is controlled by the Cdk enzymes described earlier and also in the following section.

G_1/S checkpoint

The **G_1/S checkpoint** is the primary point at which the cell "decides" whether or not to divide. This checkpoint is therefore the primary point at which external signals can influence events of the cycle. It is the phase during which growth factors (discussed later on) affect the cycle and also the phase that links cell division to cell growth and nutrition.

In yeast systems, where the majority of the genetic analysis of the cell cycle has been performed, this checkpoint is called START. In animals, it is called the restriction point (R point). In all systems, once a cell has made this irreversible commitment to replicate its genome, it has committed to divide. Damage to DNA can halt the cycle at this point, as can starvation conditions or lack of growth factors.

G_2/M checkpoint

The **G_2/M checkpoint** has received a large amount of attention because of its complexity and its importance as the stimulus for the events of mitosis. Historically, Cdks active at this checkpoint were first identified as MPFs, a term that has now evolved into **M phase-promoting factor (MPF).**

Passage through this checkpoint represents the commitment to mitosis. This checkpoint assesses the success of DNA replication and can stall the cycle if DNA has not been accurately replicated. DNA-damaging agents result in arrest at this checkpoint as well as at the G_1/S checkpoint.

Spindle checkpoint

The **spindle checkpoint** ensures that all of the chromosomes are attached to the spindle in preparation for anaphase. The second irreversible step in the cycle is the separation of chromosomes during anaphase, and therefore it is critical that they are properly arrayed at the metaphase plate.

Cyclin-dependent kinases drive the cell cycle

The primary molecular mechanism of cell cycle control is phosphorylation, which you may recall is the addition of a phosphate group to the amino acids serine, threonine, and tyrosine in proteins (chapter 9). The enzymes that accomplish this phosphorylation are the Cdks (figure 10.19).

The action of Cdks

The first important cell cycle kinase was identified in fission yeast and named Cdc2 (now also called Cdk1). In yeast, this Cdk can partner with different cyclins at different points in the cell cycle (figure 10.20).

Even in the simplified cycle of the yeasts, we are left with the important question of what controls the activity of the Cdks during the cycle. For many years, a common view was that cyclins drove the cell cycle—that is, the periodic synthesis and destruction of cyclins acted as a clock. More recently, it has become clear that the Cdc2 kinase is also itself controlled

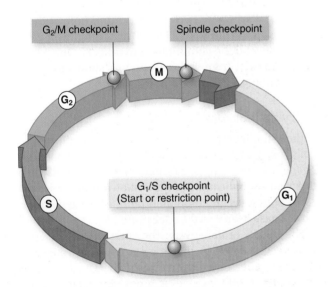

Figure 10.18 Control of the cell cycle. Cells use a centralized control system to check whether proper conditions have been achieved before passing three key checkpoints in the cell cycle.

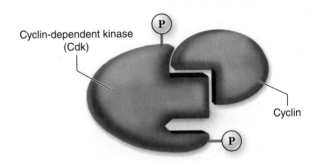

Figure 10.19 Cdk enzyme forms a complex with cyclin. Cdk is a protein kinase that activates numerous cell proteins by phosphorylating them. Cyclin is a regulatory protein required to activate Cdk. This complex is also called mitosis-promoting factor (MPF). The activity of Cdk is also controlled by the pattern of phosphorylation: phosphorylation at one site (represented by the red site) inactivates the Cdk, and phosphorylation at another site (represented by the green site) activates the Cdk.

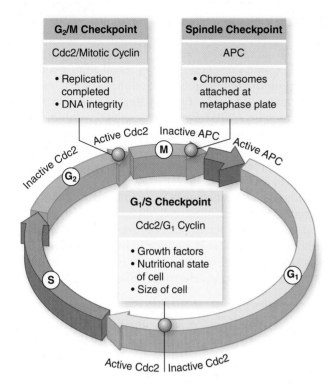

Figure 10.20 Checkpoints of the yeast cell cycle.
The simplest cell cycle that has been studied in detail is the fission yeast. This is controlled by three main checkpoints and a single Cdk enzyme, called Cdc2. The Cdc2 enzyme partners with different cyclins to control the G_1/S and G_2/M checkpoints. The spindle checkpoint is controlled by the anaphase-promoting complex (APC).

by phosphorylation: Phosphorylation at one site activates Cdc2, and phosphorylation at another site inactivates it (see figure 10.19). Full activation of the Cdc2 kinase requires complexing with a cyclin and the appropriate pattern of phosphorylation.

As the G_1/S checkpoint is approached, the triggering signal in yeast appears to be the accumulation of G_1 cyclins. These form a complex with Cdc2 to create the active G_1/S Cdk, which phosphorylates a number of targets that bring about the increased enzyme activity for DNA replication.

The action of MPF

MPF and its role at the G_2/M checkpoint has been extensively analyzed in a number of different experimental systems. The control of MPF is sensitive to agents that disrupt or delay replication and to agents that damage DNA. It was once thought that MPF was controlled solely by the level of the M phase-specific cyclins, but it has now become clear that this is not the case.

Although M phase cyclin is necessary for MPF function, activity is controlled by inhibitory phosphorylation of the kinase component, Cdc2. The critical signal in this process is the removal of the inhibitory phosphates by a protein, phosphatase. This action forms a molecular switch based on positive feedback because the active MPF further activates its own activating phosphatase.

The checkpoint assesses the balance of the kinase that adds inhibitory phosphates with the phosphatase that removes them. Damage to DNA acts through a complex pathway that includes damage sensing and a response to tip the balance toward the inhibitory phosphorylation of MPF. Later on, we describe how some cancers overcome this inhibition.

The anaphase-promoting complex

The molecular details of the sensing system at the spindle checkpoint are not clear. The presence of all chromosomes at the metaphase plate and the tension on the microtubules between opposite poles are both important. The signal is transmitted through the **anaphase-promoting complex,** also called the *cyclosome (APC/C).*

The function of the APC/C is to trigger anaphase itself. As described earlier, the sister chromatids at metaphase are still held together by the protein complex cohesin. The APC does not act directly on cohesin, but rather acts by marking a protein called *securin* for destruction. The securin protein acts as an inhibitor of another protease called *separase* that is specific for one component of the cohesin complex. Once inhibition is lifted, separase destroys cohesin.

This process has been analyzed in detail in budding yeast, where it has been shown that the separase enzyme specifically degrades a component of cohesin called Scc1. This leads to the release of the sister chromatids and results in their sudden movement toward opposite poles during anaphase.

In vertebrates, most cohesin is removed from the sister chromatids during chromosome condensation, possibly with cohesin being replaced by condensin. At metaphase, the majority of the cohesin that remains on vertebrate chromatids is concentrated at the centromere (see figure 10.10). The destruction of this cohesin explains the anaphase movement of chromosomes and the apparent "division" of the centromeres.

The APC/C has two main roles in mitosis: it activates the protease that removes the cohesins holding sister chromatids together, and it is necessary for the destruction of mitotic cyclins to drive the cell out of mitosis. The APC/C complex marks proteins for destruction by the proteosome, the organelle responsible for the controlled degradation of proteins (chapter 16). The signal to degrade a protein is the addition of a molecule called *ubiquitin,* and the APC/C acts as a ubiquitin ligase. As we learn more about the APC/C and its functions, it is clear that the control of its activity is a key regulator of the cell cycle.

In multicellular eukaryotes, many Cdks and external signals act on the cell cycle

The major difference between more complex animals and single-celled eukaryotes such as fungi and protists is twofold: First, multiple Cdks control the cycle as opposed to the single Cdk in yeasts; and second, animal cells respond to a greater variety of external signals than do yeasts, which primarily respond to signals necessary for mating.

In higher eukaryotes there are more Cdk enzymes and more cyclins that can partner with these multiple Cdks, but their basic role is the same as in the yeast cycle. A more complex cell cycle is shown in figure 10.21. These more complex controls allow the integration of more input into control of the cycle. With the evolution of more complex forms of organization (tissues, organs, and organ systems), more complex forms of cell cycle control evolved as well.

A multicellular body's organization cannot be maintained without severely limiting cell proliferation—so that only certain cells divide, and only at appropriate times. The way cells inhibit individual growth of other cells is apparent in mammalian cells growing in tissue culture: A single layer of cells expands over a culture plate until the growing border of cells comes into contact with neighboring cells, and then the cells stop dividing. If a sector of cells is cleared away, neighboring cells rapidly refill that sector and then stop dividing again on cell contact.

How are cells able to sense the density of the cell culture around them? When cells come in contact with one another, receptor proteins in the plasma membrane activate a signal transduction pathway that acts to inhibit Cdk action. This prevents entry into the cell cycle.

Growth factors and the cell cycle

Growth factors act by triggering intracellular signaling systems. Fibroblasts, for example, possess numerous receptors on their plasma membranes for one of the first growth factors to be identified, **platelet-derived growth factor (PDGF).** The PDGF receptor is a receptor tyrosine kinase (RTK) that initiates a MAP kinase cascade to stimulate cell division (discussed in chapter 9).

PDGF was discovered when investigators found that fibroblasts would grow and divide in tissue culture only if the growth medium contained blood serum. Serum is the liquid that remains in blood after clotting; blood plasma, the liquid from which cells have been removed without clotting, would not work. The researchers hypothesized that platelets in the blood clots were releasing into the serum one or more factors required for fibroblast growth. Eventually, they isolated such a factor and named it PDGF.

Growth factors such as PDGF can override cellular controls that otherwise inhibit cell division. When a tissue is injured, a blood clot forms, and the release of PDGF triggers neighboring cells to divide, helping to heal the wound. Only a tiny amount of PDGF (approximately 10^{-10} M) is required to stimulate cell division in cells with PDGF receptors.

Characteristics of growth factors

Over 50 different proteins that function as growth factors have been isolated, and more undoubtedly exist. A specific cell surface receptor recognizes each growth factor, its binding site fitting that growth factor precisely. These growth factor receptors often initiate MAP kinase cascades in which the final kinase enters the nucleus and activates transcription factors by phosphorylation. These transcription factors stimulate the production of G_1 cyclins and the proteins that are necessary for cell cycle progression (figure 10.22).

The cellular selectivity of a particular growth factor depends on which target cells bear its unique receptor. Some growth factors, such as PDGF and epidermal growth factor (EGF), affect a broad range of cell types, but others affect only specific types. For example, nerve growth factor (NGF) promotes the growth of certain classes of neurons, and erythropoietin triggers cell division in red blood cell precursors. Most animal cells need a combination of several different growth factors to overcome the various controls that inhibit cell division.

The G₀ phase

If cells are deprived of appropriate growth factors, they stop at the G_1 checkpoint of the cell cycle. With their growth and division arrested, they remain in this dormant G_0 phase.

The ability to enter G_0 accounts for the incredible diversity seen in the length of the cell cycle in different tissues. Epithelial cells lining the human gut divide more than twice a day, constantly renewing this lining. By contrast, liver cells divide only once every year or two, spending most of their time in the G_0 phase. Mature neurons and muscle cells usually never leave G_0.

Cancer is a failure of cell cycle control

The unrestrained, uncontrolled growth of cells in humans leads to the disease called **cancer.** Cancer is essentially a disease of cell division—a failure of cell division control.

The p53 gene

One of the critical players in this control system has been identified. Officially dubbed *p53,* this gene plays a key role in the G_1 checkpoint of cell division.

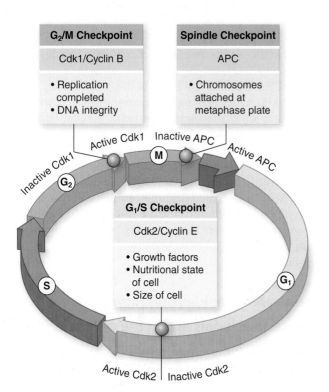

Figure 10.21 Checkpoints of the mammalian cell cycle. The more complex mammalian cell cycle is shown. This cycle is still controlled through three main checkpoints. These integrate internal and external signals to control progress through the cycle. These inputs control the state of two different Cdk–cyclin complexes and the anaphase-promoting complex (APC).

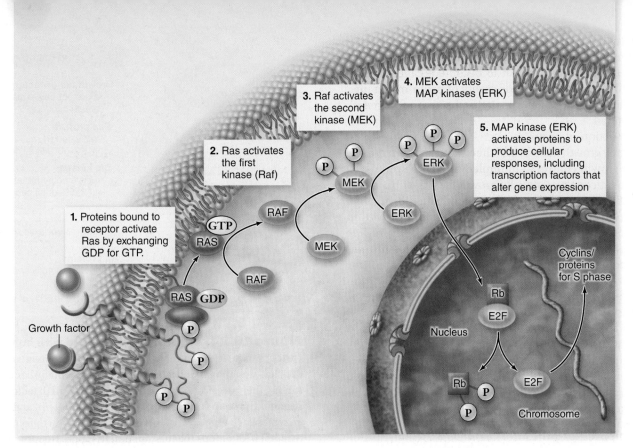

Figure 10.22 The cell proliferation-signaling pathway. Binding of a growth factor sets in motion a MAP kinase intracellular signaling pathway (described in chapter 9), which activates nuclear regulatory proteins that trigger cell division. In this example, when the nuclear retinoblastoma protein (Rb) is phosphorylated, another nuclear protein (the transcription factor E2F) is released and is then able to stimulate the production of cyclin and other proteins necessary for S phase.

The gene's product, the p53 protein, monitors the integrity of DNA, checking that it is undamaged. If the p53 protein detects damaged DNA, it halts cell division and stimulates the activity of special enzymes to repair the damage. Once the DNA has been repaired, p53 allows cell division to continue. In cases where the DNA damage is irreparable, p53 then directs the cell to kill itself.

By halting division in damaged cells, the *p53* gene prevents the development of many mutated cells, and it is therefore considered a **tumor-suppressor gene** although its activities are not limited to cancer prevention. Scientists have found that *p53* is entirely absent or damaged beyond use in the majority of cancerous cells they have examined. It is precisely because *p53* is nonfunctional that cancer cells are able to repeatedly undergo cell division without being halted at the G_1 checkpoint (figure 10.23).

Proto-oncogenes

The disease we call cancer is actually many different diseases, depending on the tissue affected. The common theme in all

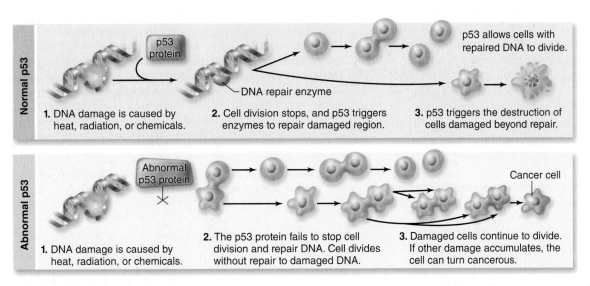

**Figure 10.23
Cell division, cancer, and p53 protein.**
Normal p53 protein monitors DNA, destroying cells that have irreparable damage to their DNA. Abnormal p53 protein fails to stop cell division and repair DNA. As damaged cells proliferate, cancer develops.

cases is the loss of control over the cell cycle. Research has identified numerous so-called **oncogenes,** genes that can, when introduced into a cell, cause it to become a cancer cell. This identification then led to the discovery of **proto-oncogenes,** which are normal cellular genes that become oncogenes when mutated.

The action of proto-oncogenes is often related to signalling by growth factors, and their mutation can lead to loss of growth control in multiple ways. Some proto-oncogenes encode receptors for growth factors, and others encode proteins involved in signal transduction that act after growth factor receptors. If a receptor for a growth factor becomes mutated such that it is permanently "on," the cell is no longer dependent on the presence of the growth factor for cell division. This is analogous to a light switch that is stuck on: The light will always be on. PDGF and EGF receptors both fall into the category of proto-oncogenes. Only one copy of a proto-oncogene needs to undergo this mutation for uncontrolled division to take place; thus, this change acts like a dominant mutation.

The number of proto-oncogenes identified has grown to more than 50 over the years. This line of research connects our understanding of cancer with our understanding of the molecular mechanisms governing cell cycle control.

Tumor-suppressor genes

After the discovery of proto-oncogenes, a second category of genes related to cancer was identified: the tumor-suppressor genes. We mentioned earlier that the *p53* gene acts as a tumor-suppressor gene, and a number of other such genes exist.

Both copies of a tumor-suppressor gene must lose function for the cancerous phenotype to develop, in contrast to the mutations in proto-oncogenes. Put another way, the proto-oncogenes act in a dominant fashion, and tumor suppressors act in a recessive fashion.

The first tumor-suppressor identified was the **retinoblastoma susceptibility gene (Rb),** which predisposes individuals for a rare form of cancer that affects the retina of the eye. Despite the fact that a cell heterozygous for a mutant *Rb* allele is normal, it is inherited as a dominant in families. The reason is that inheriting a single mutant copy of *Rb* means the individual has only one "good" copy left, and during the hundreds of thousands of divisions that occur to produce the retina, any error that damages the remaining good copy leads to a cancerous cell. A single cancerous cell in the retina then leads to the formation of a retinoblastoma tumor.

The role of the Rb protein in the cell cycle is to integrate signals from growth factors. The Rb protein is called a "pocket protein" because it has binding pockets for other proteins. Its role is therefore to bind important regulatory proteins and prevent them from stimulating the production of the necessary cell cycle proteins, such as cyclins or Cdks (see figure 10.21) discussed previously.

The binding of Rb to other proteins is controlled by phosphorylation: When it is dephosphorylated, it can bind a variety

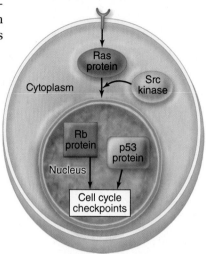

Mammalian cell

Proto-oncogenes
Growth factor receptor: more per cell in many breast cancers.
Ras protein: activated by mutations in 20–30% of all cancers.
Src kinase: activated by mutations in 2–5% of all cancers.

Tumor-suppressor Genes
Rb protein: mutated in 40% of all cancers.
p53 protein: mutated in 50% of all cancers.

Figure 10.24 Key proteins associated with human cancers. Mutations in genes encoding key components of the cell division-signaling pathway are responsible for many cancers. Among them are proto-oncogenes encoding growth factor receptors, protein relay switches such as Ras protein, and kinase enzymes such as Src, which act after Ras and growth factor receptors. Mutations that disrupt tumor-suppressor proteins, such as Rb and p53, also foster cancer development.

of regulatory proteins, but loses this capacity when phosphorylated. The action of growth factors results in the phosphorylation of Rb protein by a Cdk. This then brings us full circle, because the phosphorylation of Rb releases previously bound regulatory proteins, resulting in the production of S phase cyclins that are necessary for the cell to pass the G_1/S boundary and begin chromosome replication.

Figure 10.24 summarizes the types of genes that can cause cancer when mutated.

Learning Outcomes Review 10.6

Cyclin proteins are produced in synchrony with the cell cycle. These proteins complex with cyclin-dependent kinases to drive the cell cycle. Three checkpoints exist in the cell cycle: the G_1/S checkpoint, the G_2/M checkpoint, and the spindle checkpoint. The cell cycle can be halted at these checkpoints if the process is not accurate. The anaphase-promoting complex/cyclosome (APC/C) triggers anaphase by lifting inhibition on a protease that removes cohesin holding chromatids together. The loss of cell cycle control leads to cancer, which can occur by a combination of two basic mechanisms: proto-oncogenes that gain function to become oncogenes, and tumor-suppressor genes that lose function and allow cell proliferation.

■ *How can you distinguish between a tumor suppressor gene and a proto-oncogene?*

10.1 Bacterial Cell Division

Binary fission is a simple form of cell division.

Prokaryotic cell division is clonal, resulting in two identical cells. Bacterial DNA replication and partitioning of the chromosome are concerted processes.

Proteins control chromosome separation and septum formation.

DNA replication begins at a specific point, the origin, and proceeds bidirectionally to a specific termination site. Newly replicated chromosomes are segregated to opposite poles at the same time as they are replicated. New cells are separated by septation, which involves insertion of new cell membrane and other cellular materials at the midpoint of the cell. A ring of FtsZ and proteins embedded in the cell membrane expands radially inward, pinching the cell into two new cells.

10.2 Eukaryotic Chromosomes

Chromosome number varies among species.

The gain or loss of chromosomes is usually lethal.

Eukaryotic chromosomes exhibit complex structure.

Chromosomes are composed of chromatin, a complex of DNA, and protein. Heterochromatin is not expressed and euchromatin is expressed. The DNA of a single chromosome is a very long, double-stranded fiber. The DNA is wrapped around a core of eight histones to form a nucleosome, which can be further coiled into a 30-nm fiber in interphase cells. During mitosis, chromosomes are further condensed by arranging coiled 30-nm fibers radially around a protein scaffold.

Newly replicated chromosomes remain attached at a constricted area called a centromere, consisting of repeated DNA sequences. After replication, a chromosome consists of two sister chromatids held together at the centromere by a complex of proteins called cohesins (figure 10.7).

10.3 Overview of the Eukaryotic Cell Cycle (figure 10.8)

The cell cycle is divided into five phases.

The phases of the cell cycle are gap 1 (G_1), synthesis (S), gap 2 (G_2), mitosis, and cytokinesis (C). G_1, S, and G_2 are collectively called interphase, and mitosis and cytokinesis together are called M phase.

The duration of the cell cycle varies depending on cell type.

The length of a cell cycle varies with age, cell type, and species. Cells can exit G_1 and enter a nondividing phase called G_0; the G_0 phase can be temporary or permanent.

10.4 Interphase: Preparation for Mitosis

G_1, S, and G_2 are the three subphases of interphase. G_1 is the primary growth phase; during S phase, DNA synthesis occurs. G_2 phase occurs after S phase and before mitosis.

The centromere binds proteins assembled into a disklike structure called a kinetochore where microtubules attach during mitosis. The centromeric DNA is replicated, but the two DNA strands are held together by cohesin proteins.

10.5 M Phase: Chromosome Segregation and the Division of Cytoplasmic Contents (figure 10.11)

During prophase, the mitotic apparatus forms.

In prophase, chromosomes condense, the spindle is formed, and the nuclear envelope disintegrates. In animals cells, centriole pairs separate and migrate to opposite ends of the cell, establishing the axis of nuclear division.

During prometaphase, chromosomes attach to the spindle.

In metaphase, chromosomes align at the equator.

Chromatids of each chromosome are connected to opposite poles by kinetochore microtubules. They are held at the equator of the cell by the tension of being pulled toward opposite poles.

At anaphase, the chromatids separate.

At this point, cohesin proteins holding sister chromatids together at the centromeres are destroyed, and the chromatids are pulled to opposite poles. This movement is called anaphase A, and the movement of poles farther apart is called anaphase B.

During telophase, the nucleus re-forms.

Telophase reverses the events of prophase and prepares the cell for cytokinesis.

In animal cells, a belt of actin pinches off the daughter cells.

A contractile ring of actin under the membrane contracts during cytokinesis.

In plant cells, a cell plate divides the daughter cells.

Fusion of vesicles produces a new membrane in the middle of the cell to produce the cell plate.

In fungi and some protists, daughter nuclei are separated during cytokinesis.

10.6 Control of the Cell Cycle (figure 10.18)

Research uncovered cell cycle control factors.

Experiments showed that there are positive regulators of mitosis, and that there are proteins produced in synchrony with the cell cycle (cyclins). The positive regulators are cyclin-dependent kinases (Cdks). Cdks are complexes of a kinase and a regulatory molecule called cyclin. They phosphorylate proteins to drive the cell cycle.

The cell cycle can be halted at three checkpoints.

Checkpoints are points at which the cell can assess the accuracy of the process and stop if needed. The G_1/S checkpoint is a commitment to divide; the G_2/M checkpoint ensures DNA integrity; and the spindle checkpoint ensures that all chromosomes are attached to spindle fibers, with bipolar orientation.

Cyclin-dependent kinases drive the cell cycle.

The cycle progresses by the action of Cdks. Yeast have only one CDK enzyme; vertebrates have more than four enzymes. During the G_1 phase, G_1 cyclin combines with Cdc2 kinase to form the Cdk that triggers entry into S phase.

The anaphase-promoting complex/cyclosome (APC/C) activates a protease that removes cohesins holding the centromeres of sister chromatids together; the result is to trigger anaphase, separating the chromatids and drawing them to opposite poles. The APC/C also triggers destruction of mitotic cyclins to exit mitosis.

In multicellular eukaryotes, many Cdks and external signals act on the cell cycle.

Growth factors, like platelet-derived growth factor (PDGF), stimulate cell division. This acts through a MAP kinase cascade that results in the production of cyclins and activation of Cdks to stimulate cell division in fibroblasts after tissue injury.

Cancer is a failure of cell cycle control.

Mutations in proto-oncogenes have dominant, gain-of-function effects leading to cancer. Mutations in tumor-suppressor genes are recessive; loss of function of both copies leads to cancer.

UNDERSTAND

1. Binary fission in prokaryotes does not require the
   a. replication of DNA.
   b. elongation of the cell.
   c. separation of daughter cells by septum formation.
   d. assembly of the nuclear envelope.

2. Chromatin is composed of
   a. RNA and protein.   c. sister chromatids.
   b. DNA and protein.   d. chromosomes.

3. What is a nucleosome?
   a. A region in the cell's nucleus that contains euchromatin
   b. A region of DNA wound around histone proteins
   c. A region of a chromosome made up of multiple loops of chromatin
   d. A 30-nm fiber found in chromatin

4. What is the role of cohesin proteins in cell division?
   a. They organize the DNA of the chromosomes into highly condensed structures.
   b. They hold the DNA of the sister chromatids together.
   c. They help the cell divide into two daughter cells.
   d. They connect microtubules and chromosomes.

5. The kinetochore is a structure that functions to
   a. connect the centromere to microtubules.
   b. connect centrioles to microtubules.
   c. aid in chromosome condensation.
   d. aid in chromosomes cohesion.

6. Separation of the sister chromatids occurs during
   a. prophase.   c. anaphase.
   b. prometaphase.   d. telophase.

7. Why is cytokinesis an important part of cell division?
   a. It is responsible for the proper separation of genetic information.
   b. It is responsible for the proper separation of the cytoplasmic contents.
   c. It triggers the movement of a cell through the cell cycle.
   d. It allows cells to halt at checkpoints.

8. What steps in the cell cycle represent irreversible commitments?
   a. The S/G_2 checkpoint   c. Anaphase
   b. The G_1/S checkpoint   d. Both b and c are correct.

APPLY

1. Cyclin-dependent kinases (Cdks) are regulated by
   a. the periodic destruction of cyclins.
   b. bipolar attachment of chromosomes to the spindle.
   c. DNA synthesis.
   d. Both a and b are correct.

2. The bacterial SMC proteins, eukaryotic cohesin proteins, and condensin proteins share a similar structure. Functionally they all
   a. interact with microtubules.
   b. can act as kinase enzymes.
   c. interact with DNA to compact or hold strands together.
   d. connect chromosomes to cytoskeletal elements.

3. Genetically, proto-oncogenes act in a dominant fashion. This is because
   a. there is only one copy of each proto-oncogene in the genome.
   b. they act in a gain-of-function fashion to turn on the cell cycle.
   c. they act in a loss-of-function fashion to turn off the cell cycle.
   d. they require that both genomic copies are altered to affect function.

4. The metaphase to anaphase transition involves
   a. new force being generated to pull the chromatids apart.
   b. an increase in force on sister chromatids to pull them apart.
   c. completing DNA replication of centromeres allowing chromosomes to be pulled apart.
   d. loss of cohesion between sister chromatids.

5. The main difference between bacterial cell division and eukaryotic cell division is that
   a. since bacteria only have one chromosome, they can count the number of copies in the cell.
   b. eukaryotes mark their chromosomes to identify them and bacteria do not.
   c. bacterial DNA replication and chromosome segregation are concerted processes but in eukaryotes they are separated in time.
   d. None of the above is correct.

6. In animal cells, cytokinesis is accomplished by a contractile ring containing actin. The related process in bacteria is
   a. chromosome segregation, which also appears to use an actin-like protein.
   b. septation via a ring of FtsZ protein, which is an actin-like protein.
   c. cytokinesis, which requires formation of a cell plate via vesicular fusion.
   d. septation via a ring of FtsZ protein, which is a tubulin-like protein.

SYNTHESIZE

1. Regulation of the cell cycle is very complex and involves multiple proteins. In yeast, a complex of cdc2 and a mitotic cyclin is responsible for moving the cell past the G_2/M checkpoint. The activity of the cyclin-dependent kinase cdc2 is inhibited when it is phosphorylated by the kinase, Wee-1. What would you predict would be the phenotype of a Wee-1 mutant yeast? What other genes could be altered in a Wee-1 deficient mutant strain that would make the cells act normally?

2. Review your knowledge of signaling pathways (chapter 9). Create an outline illustrating how a growth factor (ligand) can lead to the production of a cyclin protein that would trigger S phase.

3. Compare and contrast how mutations in cellular proto-oncogenes and in tumor suppressor genes can lead to cancer cells.

ONLINE RESOURCE

www.ravenbiology.com

Understand, Apply, and Synthesize—enhance your study with animations that bring concepts to life and practice tests to assess your understanding. Your instructor may also recommend the interactive eBook, individualized learning tools, and more.

Chapter

11

Sexual Reproduction and Meiosis

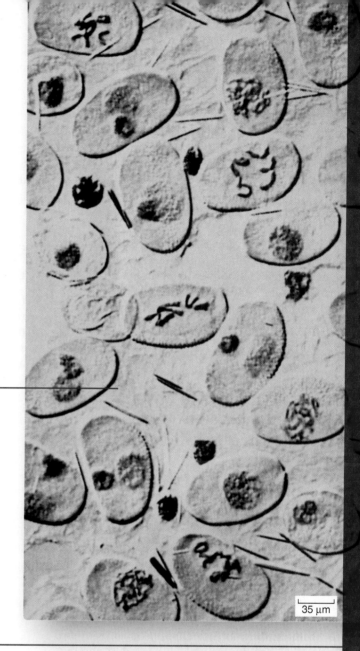

35 μm

Chapter Contents

Introduction

Most animals and plants reproduce sexually. Gametes of opposite sex unite to form a cell that, dividing repeatedly by mitosis, eventually gives rise to an adult body with some 100 trillion cells. The gametes that form the initial cell are the products of a special form of cell division called meiosis, visible in the photo above, and the subject of this chapter. Meiosis is far more intricate than mitosis, and the details behind it are not as well understood. The basic process, however, is clear. Also clear are the profound consequences of sexual reproduction: It plays a key role in generating the tremendous genetic diversity that is the raw material of evolution.

11.1 Sexual Reproduction Requires Meiosis

Learning Outcomes

1. *Characterize the function of meiosis in sexual reproduction.*
2. *Distinguish between germ-line and somatic cells.*

The essence of sexual reproduction is the genetic contribution of two cells. This mode of reproduction imposes difficulties for sexually reproducing organisms that biologists recognized early on. We are only recently making progress on the underlying mechanism for the elaborate behavior of chromosomes during meiosis. To begin, we briefly consider the history of meiosis and its relationship to sexual reproduction.

Meiosis reduces the number of chromosomes

Only a few years after Walther Flemming's discovery of chromosomes in 1879, Belgian cytologist Edouard van Beneden was surprised to find different numbers of chromosomes in different types of cells in the roundworm *Ascaris*. Specifically, he observed that the **gametes** (eggs and sperm) each contained two chromosomes, but all of the nonreproductive cells, or **somatic cells,** of embryos and mature individuals each contained four.

From his observations, van Beneden proposed in 1883 that an egg and a sperm, each containing half the complement of chromosomes found in other cells, fuse to produce a single cell called a **zygote.** The zygote, like all of the cells ultimately derived from it, contains two copies of each chromosome. The fusion of gametes to form a new cell is called **fertilization,** or **syngamy.**

It was clear even to early investigators that gamete formation must involve some mechanism that reduces the number of chromosomes to half the number found in other cells. If it did not, the chromosome number would double with each fertilization, and after only a few generations, the number of chromosomes in each cell would become impossibly large. For example, in just 10 generations, the 46 chromosomes present in human cells would increase to over 47,000 (46×2^{10}).

The number of chromosomes does not explode in this way because of a special reduction division, **meiosis.** Meiosis occurs during gamete formation, producing cells with half the normal number of chromosomes. The subsequent fusion of two of these cells ensures a consistent chromosome number from one generation to the next.

Sexual life cycles have both haploid and diploid stages

Meiosis and fertilization together constitute a cycle of reproduction. Two sets of chromosomes are present in the somatic cells of adult individuals, making them *diploid* cells, but only one set is present in the gametes, which are thus *haploid.* Reproduction that involves this alternation of meiosis and fertilization is called **sexual reproduction.** Its outstanding characteristic is that offspring inherit chromosomes from *two* parents (figure 11.1). You, for example, inherited 23 chromosomes from your mother (maternal homologue), and 23 from your father (paternal homologue).

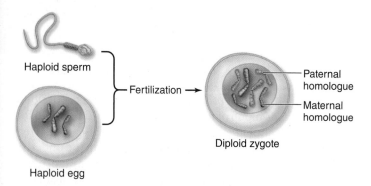

Figure 11.1 Diploid cells carry chromosomes from two parents. A diploid cell contains two versions of each chromosome, a maternal homologue contributed by the haploid egg of the mother, and a paternal homologue contributed by the haploid sperm of the father.

The life cycles of all sexually reproducing organisms follow a pattern of alternation between diploid and haploid chromosome numbers, but there is some variation in the life cycles. Many types of algae, for example, spend the majority of their life cycle in a haploid state. The zygote undergoing meiosis produces haploid cells that then undergo mitosis. Some plants and some algae alternate between a multicellular haploid phase and a multicellular diploid phase (specific examples can be found in chapters 30 and 31). In most animals, the diploid state dominates; the zygote first undergoes mitosis to produce diploid cells. Then later in the life cycle, some of these diploid cells undergo meiosis to produce haploid gametes (figure 11.2).

Germ-line cells are set aside early in animal development

In animals, the single diploid zygote undergoes mitosis to give rise to all of the cells in the adult body. The cells that will eventually undergo meiosis to produce gametes are set aside from somatic cells early in the course of development. These cells are referred to as **germ-line cells.**

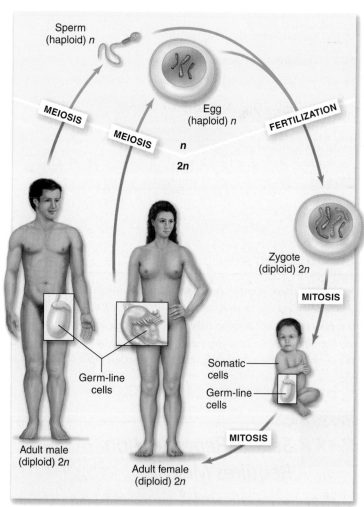

Figure 11.2 The sexual life cycle in animals. In animals, the zygote undergoes mitotic divisions and gives rise to all the cells of the adult body. Germ-line cells are set aside early in development and undergo meiosis to form the haploid gametes (eggs or sperm). The rest of the body cells are called somatic cells.

Both the somatic cells and the gamete-producing germ-line cells are diploid, but whereas somatic cells undergo mitosis to form genetically identical, diploid daughter cells, gamete-producing germ-line cells undergo meiosis to produce haploid gametes (see figure 11.2).

Learning Outcomes Review 11.1

Sexual reproduction involves the genetic contribution of two cells, each from a different individual. Meiosis produces haploid cells with half the number of chromosomes. Fertilization then unites these haploid cells to restore the diploid state of the next generation. Only germ-line cells are capable of meiosis. All other cells in the body, termed somatic cells, can undergo only mitotic division.

■ *Germ-line cells undergo meiosis, but how can the body maintain a constant supply of these cells?*

11.2 Features of Meiosis

Learning Outcomes

1. *Describe how homologous chromosomes pair during meiosis.*
2. *Explain why meiosis I is called the reductive division.*

The mechanism of meiotic cell division varies in important details in different organisms. These variations are particularly evident in the chromosomal separation mechanisms: Those found in protists and fungi are very different from those in plants and animals, which we describe here.

Meiosis in a diploid organism consists of two rounds of division, called **meiosis I** and **meiosis II,** with each round containing prophase, metaphase, anaphase, and telophase stages. Before describing the details of this process, we first examine the features of meiosis that distinguish it from mitosis.

Homologous chromosomes pair during meiosis

During early prophase I of meiosis, homologous chromosomes find each other and become closely associated, a process called pairing, or **synapsis** (figure 11.3*a*). Despite a long history of investigation, molecular details remain unclear.

Biologists have used electron microscopy, data from genetic crosses, and biochemical analysis to shed light on synapsis. Thus far the results of their investigations have not been integrated into a complete picture.

The synaptonemal complex

It is clear that homologous chromosomes find their proper partners and become intimately associated during prophase I. This process includes the formation in many species of an elaborate structure called the **synaptonemal complex,** consisting of the homologues paired closely along a lattice of proteins between them. The structure of the synaptonemal complex appears similar in all systems that have been examined, although its exact function is unclear. A representative example is shown in figure 11.3*b*. The result is that all four chromatids of the two homologues are closely associated during this phase of meiosis. This structure is also called a *tetrad* or *bivalent.*

The exchange of genetic material between homologues

While homologues are paired during prophase I, another process unique to meiosis occurs: genetic **recombination,** or **crossing over.** This process literally allows the homologues to exchange chromosomal material. The cytological observation of this phenomenon is called crossing over, and its detection genetically is called recombination—because alleles of genes

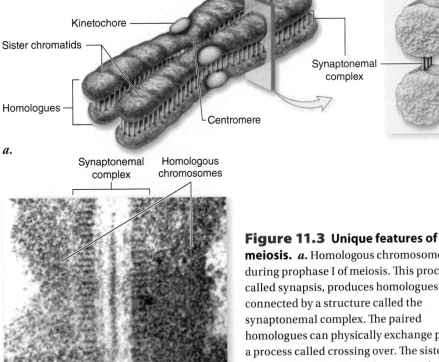

a.

b.   138 nm

Figure 11.3 Unique features of meiosis. *a.* Homologous chromosomes pair during prophase I of meiosis. This process, called synapsis, produces homologues connected by a structure called the synaptonemal complex. The paired homologues can physically exchange parts, a process called crossing over. The sister chromatids of each homologue are also held together by cohesin proteins, which is not shown for clarity. *b.* The synaptonemal complex of the ascomycete *Neotiella rutilans,* a cup fungus.

that were formerly on separate homologues can now be found on the same homologue. (Genetic recombination is covered in detail in chapter 13.)

The sites of crossing over are called **chiasmata** (singular, *chiasma*), and these sites of contact are maintained until anaphase I. The physical connection of homologues due to crossing over and the continued connection of the sister chromatids lock homologues together.

Homologue association and separation

The association between the homologues persists throughout meiosis I and dictates the behavior of the chromosomes. During metaphase I, the paired homologues move to the metaphase plate and become oriented with homologues of each pair attached to opposite poles of the spindle. By contrast, in mitosis homologues behave independently of one another.

Then, during anaphase I, homologues are pulled to opposite poles for each pair of chromosomes. This again is in contrast to mitosis, in which sister chromatids, not homologues, are pulled to opposite poles.

You can now see why the first division is termed the "reduction division"—it results in daughter cells that contain one homologue from each chromosome pair. The second meiotic division does not further reduce the number of chromosomes; it will merely separate the sister chromatids for each homologue.

Meiosis features two divisions with one round of DNA replication

The most obvious distinction between meiosis and mitosis is the simple observation that meiosis involves two successive divisions with no replication of genetic material between them. One way to view this is that DNA replication must be suppressed between the two meiotic divisions. Because of the behavior of chromosomes during meiosis I, the resulting cells contain one replicated copy of each chromosome. A division that acts like mitosis, without DNA replication, converts these cells into ones with a single copy of each chromosome. This is the last key to understanding meiosis: The second meiotic division is like mitosis with no chromosome duplication.

Learning Outcomes Review 11.2

Meiosis is characterized by the pairing of homologous chromosomes during prophase I. In many species, an elaborate structure called the synaptonemal complex forms between homologues. During this pairing, homologues may exchange chromosomal material at sites called chiasmata. In meiosis I, the homologues separate from each other, reducing the chromosome number to the haploid state (thus the reductive division). It is followed by a second division without replication, during which sister chromatids become separated. The result of meiosis I and II is four haploid cells.

■ *If sister chromatids separated at the first division, would meiosis still work?*

Learning Outcomes

1. Describe the behavior of chromosomes through both meiotic divisions.
2. Explain the importance of monopolar attachment of homologous pairs at metaphase I.
3. Differentiate between the events of anaphase I and anaphase II of meiosis.

To understand meiosis, it is necessary to carefully follow the behavior of chromosomes during each division. The first meiotic division depends on each homologous pair behaving as a unit and not as individual chromosomes, as they do in mitosis. This is accomplished by a complex set of processes that together join homologues until anaphase I, when they are separated.

Prophase I sets the stage for the reductive division

Meiotic cells have an interphase period that is similar to mitosis with G_1, S, and G_2 phases. After interphase, germ-line cells enter meiosis I. In prophase I, the DNA coils tighter, and individual chromosomes first become visible under the light microscope as a matrix of fine threads. Because the DNA has already replicated before the onset of meiosis, each of these threads actually consists of two sister chromatids joined at their centromeres. In prophase I, homologous chromosomes become closely associated in synapsis, exchange segments by crossing over, and then separate.

Synapsis

During interphase in germ-line cells, the ends of the chromatids seem to be attached to the nuclear envelope at specific sites. The sites the homologues attach to are adjacent, so that during prophase I the members of each homologous pair of chromosomes are brought close together. Homologous pairs then align side by side, apparently guided by heterochromatin sequences, in the process of synapsis.

This association joins homologues along their entire length. The sister chromatids of each homologue are also joined by the cohesin complex in a process called *sister chromatid cohesion*. Sister chromatid cohesion also occurs in mitosis, but in meiosis the cohesin complex contains a meiosis-specific cohesin. This brings all four chromatids for each set of paired homologues into close association.

Crossing over

Along with the synaptonemal complex that forms during prophase I (see figure 11.3), another kind of structure appears at the same time that recombination occurs. These are called *recombination nodules,* and they are thought to contain the enzymatic machinery necessary to break and rejoin chromatids of homologous chromosomes.

Crossing over involves a complex series of events in which DNA segments are exchanged between nonsister chromatids. Reciprocal crossovers between nonsister chromatids are controlled such that each chromosome arm usually has one or a few crossovers per meiosis, no matter what the size of the chromosome. Human chromosomes typically have two or three.

When crossing over is complete, the synaptonemal complex breaks down, and the homologous chromosomes become less tightly associated but remain attached by chiasmata. At this point, there are four chromatids for each type of chromosome (two homologous chromosomes, each of which consists of two sister chromatids).

The four chromatids are held together in two ways: (1) The two sister chromatids of each homologue, the products of DNA replication, are held together by cohesin proteins (sister chromatid cohesion); and (2) exchange of material by crossing over between homologues locks all four chromatids together.

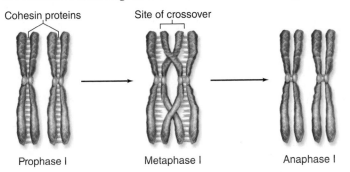

While the elaborate behavior of chromosome pairing is taking place, other events must occur during prophase I. The nuclear envelope must be dispersed, along with the interphase structure of microtubules. The microtubules re-form into a spindle, just as in mitosis.

During metaphase I, paired homologues align

Because of the events of prophase I, each of the paired homologues are locked together as a bivalent. As these bivalents capture spindle fibers, they move to the center of the cell, where

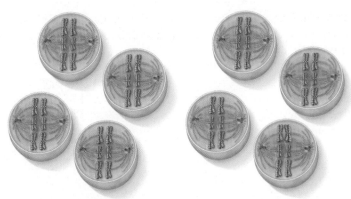

Figure 11.5 Random orientation of chromosomes on the metaphase plate. The number of possible chromosome orientations equals 2 raised to the power of the number of chromosome pairs. In this hypothetical cell with three chromosome pairs, eight (2^3) possible orientations exist. Each orientation produces gametes with different combinations of parental chromosomes.

they are aligned as paired homologues and not individual chromosomes.

The kinetochores of sister chromatids act as a unit to capture polar microtubules. This results in microtubules from opposite poles becoming attached to the kinetochores of *homologues,* and not to those of sister chromatids (figure 11.4).

The ability of sister centromeres to behave as a unit during meiosis I is not understood. It has been suggested, based on electron microscope data, that the centromere–kinetochore complex of sister chromatids is compacted during meiosis I, allowing them to function as a single unit.

The monopolar attachment of kinetochores of sister chromatids would be disastrous in mitosis, but it is critical to meiosis I. It produces tension on the paired homologues, pulling them to the equator of the cell. In this way, each joined pair of homologues lines up on the metaphase plate (see figure 11.4).

The orientation of each pair on the spindle axis is random; either the maternal or the paternal homologue may be oriented toward a given pole (figure 11.5; see also figure 11.6).

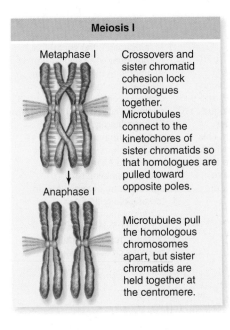

Meiosis I	
Metaphase I	Crossovers and sister chromatid cohesion lock homologues together. Microtubules connect to the kinetochores of sister chromatids so that homologues are pulled toward opposite poles.
Anaphase I	Microtubules pull the homologous chromosomes apart, but sister chromatids are held together at the centromere.

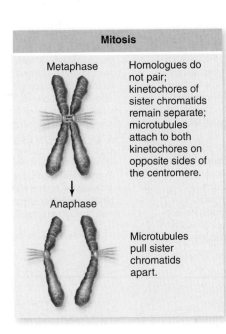

Mitosis	
Metaphase	Homologues do not pair; kinetochores of sister chromatids remain separate; microtubules attach to both kinetochores on opposite sides of the centromere.
Anaphase	Microtubules pull sister chromatids apart.

Figure 11.4 Alignment of chromosomes differs between meiosis I and mitosis. In metaphase I of meiosis I, the chiasmata and connections between sister chromatids hold homologous chromosomes together; paired kinetochores for sister chromatids of each homologue become attached to microtubules from one pole. By the end of meiosis I, connections between sister chromatid arms, but not centromeres, are broken as microtubules shorten, pulling the homologous chromosomes apart. In mitosis, microtubules from opposite poles attach to the kinetochore of each sister centromere; when the connections between sister centromeres are broken microtubules shorten, pulling the sister chromatids to opposite poles.

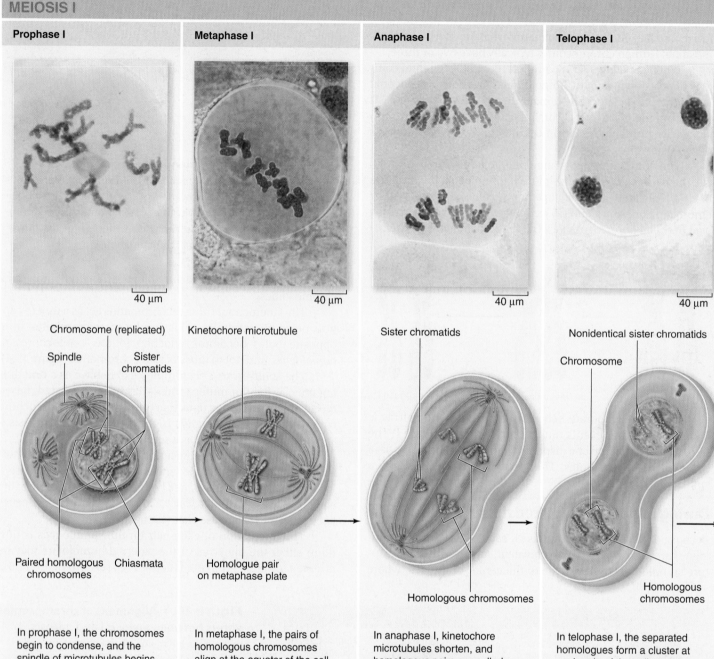

Prophase I

In prophase I, the chromosomes begin to condense, and the spindle of microtubules begins to form. The DNA has been replicated, and each chromosome consists of two sister chromatids attached at the centromere. The cell illustrated here has four chromosomes, or two pairs of homologues. Homologous chromosomes pair along their entire length during synapsis. Crossing over occurs, forming chiasmata, which hold homologous chromosomes together.

Metaphase I

In metaphase I, the pairs of homologous chromosomes align at the equator of the cell. Chiasmata keep homologous pairs together and microtubules from opposite poles attach to sister kinetochores of each homologue, producing tension. A kinetochore microtubule from one pole of the cell attaches to one homologue of a chromosome, while a kinetochore microtubule from the other cell pole attaches to the other homologue of a pair.

Anaphase I

In anaphase I, kinetochore microtubules shorten, and homologous pairs are pulled apart. One duplicated homologue goes to one pole of the cell, and the other duplicated homologue goes to the other pole. Sister chromatids do not separate. This is in contrast to mitosis, in which duplicated homologues line up individually on the metaphase plate, and sister chromatids are pulled apart in anaphase.

Telophase I

In telophase I, the separated homologues form a cluster at each pole of the cell, and the nuclear envelope re-forms around each daughter cell nucleus. Cytokinesis may occur. The resulting two cells have half the number of chromosomes of the original cell: In this example, each nucleus contains two chromosomes (versus four in the original cell). Each chromosome consists of two sister chromatids, but sister chromatids are not identical because crossing over has occurred.

Figure 11.6 The stages of meiosis. Meiosis in plant cells (photos) and animal cells (drawings) is shown.

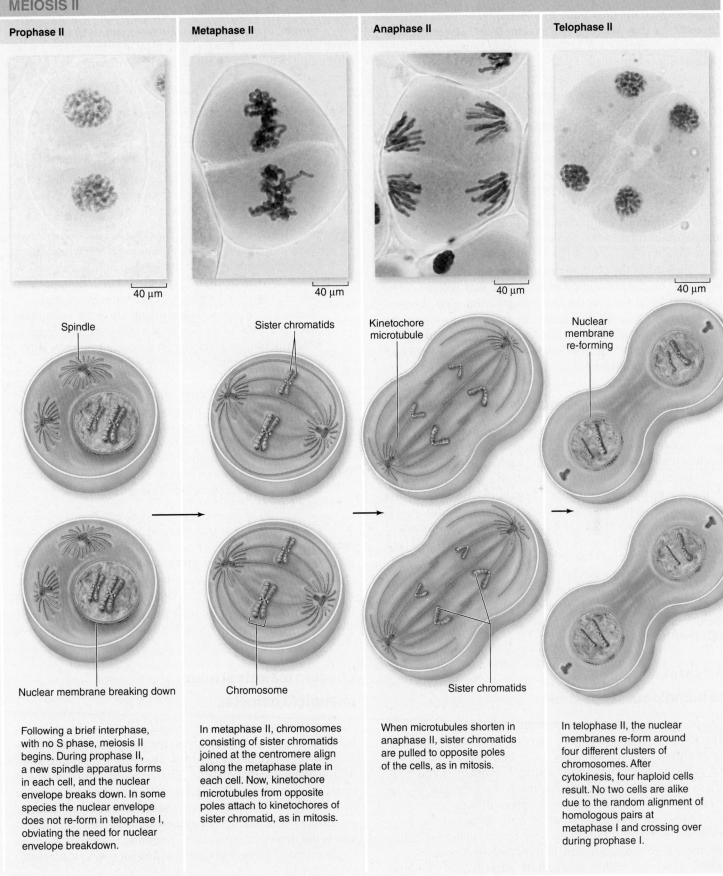

Prophase II

Spindle

Nuclear membrane breaking down

Following a brief interphase, with no S phase, meiosis II begins. During prophase II, a new spindle apparatus forms in each cell, and the nuclear envelope breaks down. In some species the nuclear envelope does not re-form in telophase I, obviating the need for nuclear envelope breakdown.

Metaphase II

Sister chromatids

Chromosome

In metaphase II, chromosomes consisting of sister chromatids joined at the centromere align along the metaphase plate in each cell. Now, kinetochore microtubules from opposite poles attach to kinetochores of sister chromatid, as in mitosis.

Anaphase II

Kinetochore microtubule

Sister chromatids

When microtubules shorten in anaphase II, sister chromatids are pulled to opposite poles of the cells, as in mitosis.

Telophase II

Nuclear membrane re-forming

In telophase II, the nuclear membranes re-form around four different clusters of chromosomes. After cytokinesis, four haploid cells result. No two cells are alike due to the random alignment of homologous pairs at metaphase I and crossing over during prophase I.

40 μm   40 μm   40 μm   40 μm

Anaphase I results from the differential loss of sister chromatid cohesion along the arms

In anaphase I, the microtubules of the spindle fibers begin to shorten. As they shorten, the connections between homologues at chiasmata are broken, allowing homologues to be pulled to opposite poles.

Anaphase I comes about by the release of sister chromatid cohesion along the chromosome arms, but not at the centromeres. This release is the result of the destruction of meiosis-specific cohesin in a process analogous to anaphase in mitosis. The difference is that the destruction is inhibited at the centromeres by a mechanism that is discussed later in the chapter.

As a result of this release, the homologues are pulled apart, but not the sister chromatids. Each homologue moves to one pole, taking both sister chromatids with it. When the spindle fibers have fully contracted, each pole has a complete haploid set of chromosomes consisting of one member of each homologous pair.

Because of the random orientation of homologous chromosomes on the metaphase plate, a pole may receive either the maternal or the paternal homologue from each chromosome pair. As a result, the genes on different chromosomes assort independently; that is, meiosis I results in the **independent assortment** of maternal and paternal chromosomes into the gametes (see chapter 12).

Telophase I completes meiosis I

By the beginning of telophase I, the chromosomes have segregated into two clusters, one at each pole of the cell. Now the nuclear membrane re-forms around each daughter nucleus.

Because each chromosome within a daughter nucleus had replicated before meiosis I began, each now contains two sister chromatids attached by a common centromere. Note that *the sister chromatids are no longer identical* because of the crossing over that occurred in prophase I (see figure 11.6); as you will see, this change has important implications for genetic variability.

Cytokinesis, the division of the cytoplasm and its contents, may or may not occur after telophase I. The second meiotic division, meiosis II, occurs after an interval of variable length.

Achiasmate segregation of homologues is possible

The preceding description of meiosis I relies on the observation that homologues are held together by chiasmata and by sister chromatid cohesion. This connection produces the critical behavior of chromosomes during metaphase I and anaphase I, when paired homologues move together to the metaphase plate and then move to opposite poles.

Although this connection of homologues is the rule, there are exceptions. In fruit fly *(Drosophila)* males for example, there is no recombination, and yet meiosis proceeds accurately, a process called **achiasmate segregation** ("without

chiasmata"). This seems to involve an alternative mechanism for joining homologues and then allowing their segregation during anaphase I. Telomeres and other heterochromatic sequences have been implicated, but the details are not known.

Despite these exceptions, the vast majority of species that have been examined use the formation of chiasmata and sister chromatid cohesion to hold homologues together for segregation during anaphase I.

Meiosis II is like a mitotic division without DNA replication

Typically, interphase between meiosis I and meiosis II is brief and does not include an S phase: Meiosis II resembles a normal mitotic division. Prophase II, metaphase II, anaphase II, and telophase II follow in quick succession (see figure 11.6).

Prophase II. At the two poles of the cell, the clusters of chromosomes enter a brief prophase II, each nuclear envelope breaking down as a new spindle forms.

Metaphase II. In metaphase II, spindle fibers from opposite poles bind to kinetochores of each sister chromatid, allowing each chromosome to migrate to the metaphase plate as a result of tension on the chromosomes from polar microtubules pulling on sister centromeres. This process is the same as metaphase during a mitotic division.

Anaphase II. The spindle fibers contract, and the cohesin complex joining the centromeres of sister chromatids is finally destroyed, allowing sister chromatids to be pulled to opposite poles. This process is essentially the same as anaphase during a mitotic division.

Telophase II. Finally, the nuclear envelope re-forms around the four sets of daughter chromosomes. Cytokinesis then follows.

The final result of this division is four cells, each containing a complete haploid set of chromosomes. The cells that contain these haploid nuclei may develop directly into gametes, as they do in animals. Alternatively, they may themselves divide mitotically, as they do in plants, fungi, and many protists, eventually producing greater numbers of gametes or, as in some plants and insects, adult individuals with varying numbers of chromosome sets.

Errors in meiosis produce aneuploid gametes

It is critical that the process of meiosis be accurate because any failure produces gametes without the correct number of chromosomes. Failure of chromosomes to move to opposite poles during either meiotic division is called *nondisjunction,* and it produces one gamete that lacks a chromosome and one that has two copies. Gametes with an improper number of chromosomes are called **aneuploid gametes.** In humans, this condition is the most common cause of spontaneous abortion. The implications of aneuploid gametes are explored in more detail in chapter 13.

11.4 Summing Up: Meiosis Versus Mitosis

The key to meiosis is understanding the differences between meiosis and mitosis. The basic machinery in both processes is the same, but the behavior of chromosomes is distinctly different during the first meiotic division (figure 11.7).

Meiosis is characterized by four distinct features:

1. Homologous pairing and crossing over joins maternal and paternal homologues during meiosis I.
2. Sister chromatids remain connected at the centromere and segregate together during anaphase I.
3. Kinetochores of sister chromatids are attached to the same pole in meiosis I and to opposite poles in mitosis.
4. DNA replication is suppressed between the two meiotic divisions.

Although the underlying molecular mechanisms are unclear, we will consider what we know of each of these features in the following sections.

Homologous pairing is specific to meiosis

The pairing of homologues during prophase I of meiosis is the first deviation from mitosis and sets the stage for all of the subsequent differences (see figure 11.7). How homologues find each other and become aligned is one of the great mysteries of meiosis. Some cytological evidence implicates telomeres and other specific sites as being necessary for pairing, but this finding does little to clarify the essential process.

The process of sister chromatid cohesion is similar to mitosis, but involves cohesin proteins that contain meiosis-specific subunits. In yeast, the protein Rec8 replaces the mitotic Scc1 protein as part of the cohesin complex. You saw in chapter 10 that Scc1 is destroyed during anaphase of mitosis to allow sister chromatids to be pulled to opposite poles. The replacement of this critical cohesin component with a meiosis-specific version seems to be a common feature in systems analyzed to date.

Synaptonemal complex proteins have been identified in diverse species, but these proteins show little sequence conservation, but do have similarities in structure where this has been analyzed. This may explain the similarity of structures observed cytologically. The transverse elements, while showing no sequence conservation, do share the feature of coiled-coil domains that promote protein–protein interactions.

The molecular details of the recombination process that produces crossing over are complex, but many of the proteins involved have been identified. The process is initiated with the introduction of a double-strand break in one homologue. This explains the similarity in the machinery necessary for meiotic recombination and the machinery involved in the repair of double-strand breaks in DNA. Recombination probably first evolved as a repair mechanism and was later co-opted for use in disjoining chromosomes. The importance of recombination for proper disjunction is clear from the observation in many organisms that loss of function for recombination proteins also results in higher levels of meiotic nondisjunction.

Sister chromatid cohesion is maintained through meiosis I but released in meiosis II

Meiosis I is characterized by the segregation of homologues, not sister chromatids, during anaphase. For this separation to occur, the centromeres of sister chromatids must cosegregate, or move to the same pole, during anaphase I. This means that meiosis-specific cohesin proteins must first be removed from the chromosome arms, then later from sister centromeres.

Homologues are joined by chiasmata, and sister chromatid cohesion around the site of exchange then holds homologues together. The destruction of Rec8 protein on the chromosome arms appears to be what allows homologues to be pulled apart at anaphase I.

This leaves the key distinction between meiosis and mitosis being the maintenance of sister chromatid cohesion at the centromere during all of meiosis I, but the loss of cohesion from the chromosome arms during anaphase I (see figure 11.7). Recently, some light was shed on this problem with the identification of conserved proteins, called Shugoshin (a Japanese term meaning "guardian spirit") required for cohesin protection from separase-mediated cleavage during meiosis I (figure 11.8). Mice have two Shugoshins: Sgo-1 and Sgo-2. Depletion of Sgo-2 results in early sister chromatid separation. This leaves the problem of why Sgo-2 acts only at anaphase I and not anaphase II. It has been suggested that the tension produced by anaphase II causes Sgo-2 to migrate from the centromere to the kinetochore.

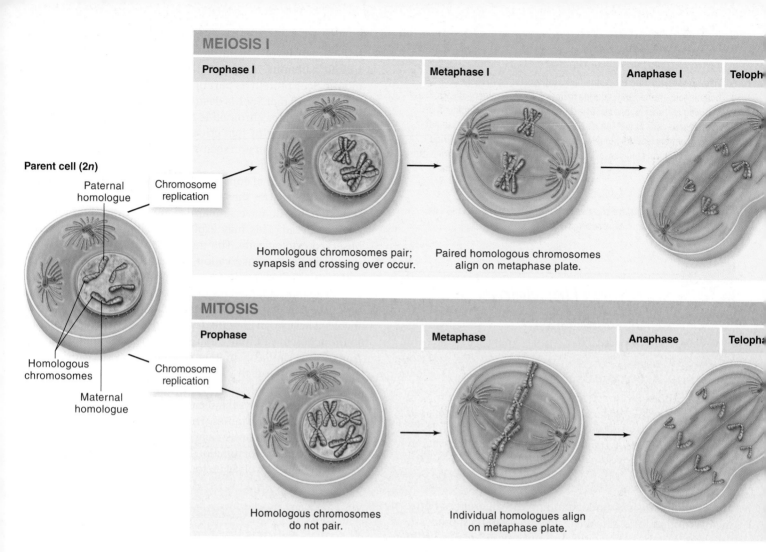

MEIOSIS I

Prophase I | Metaphase I | Anaphase I | Teloph

Parent cell (2n)

Paternal homologue

Chromosome replication

Homologous chromosomes

Maternal homologue

Homologous chromosomes pair; synapsis and crossing over occur.

Paired homologous chromosomes align on metaphase plate.

MITOSIS

Prophase | Metaphase | Anaphase | Telopha

Chromosome replication

Homologous chromosomes do not pair.

Individual homologues align on metaphase plate.

Sister kinetochores are attached to the same pole during meiosis I

The cosegregation of sister centromeres requires that the kinetochores of sister chromatids are attached to the same pole during meiosis I. This attachment is in contrast to both mitosis (see figure 11.7) and meiosis II, in which sister kinetochores must become attached to opposite poles.

The underlying basis of this monopolar attachment of sister kinetochores is unclear, but it seems to be based on structural differences between centromere–kinetochore complexes in meiosis I and in mitosis. Mitotic kinetochores visualized with the electron microscope appear to be recessed, making bipolar attachment more likely. Meiosis I kinetochores protrude more, making monopolar attachment easier.

It is clear that both the maintenance of sister chromatid cohesion at the centromere and monopolar attachment are required for the segregation of homologues that distinguishes meiosis I from mitosis.

Replication is suppressed between meiotic divisions

After a mitotic division, a new round of DNA replication must occur before the next division. For meiosis to succeed in halving the number of chromosomes, this replication must be suppressed between the two divisions. The detailed mechanism of suppression of replication between meiotic division is unknown. One clue is the observation that the level of one of the cyclins, cyclin B, is reduced between meiotic divisions, but is not lost completely, as it is between mitotic divisions.

During mitosis, the destruction of mitotic cyclin is necessary for a cell to enter another division cycle. The result of this maintenance of cyclin B between meiotic divisions in germ-line cells is the failure to form initiation complexes necessary for DNA replication to proceed. This failure to form initiation complexes appears to be critical to suppressing DNA replication.

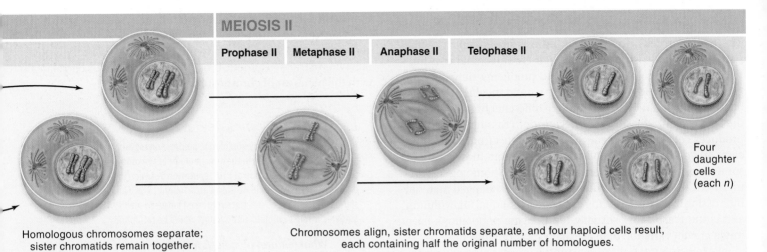

MEIOSIS II

Prophase II   Metaphase II   Anaphase II   Telophase II

Four daughter cells (each *n*)

Homologous chromosomes separate; sister chromatids remain together.

Chromosomes align, sister chromatids separate, and four haploid cells result, each containing half the original number of homologues.

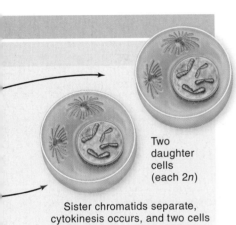

Two daughter cells (each 2*n*)

Sister chromatids separate, cytokinesis occurs, and two cells result, each containing the original number of homologues.

Figure 11.7 A comparison of meiosis and mitosis. Meiosis involves two nuclear divisions with no DNA replication between them. It thus produces four daughter cells, each with half the original number of chromosomes. Crossing over occurs in prophase I of meiosis. Mitosis involves a single nuclear division after DNA replication. It thus produces two daughter cells, each containing the original number of chromosomes.

? Inquiry question If the chromosomes of a mitotic cell behaved the same as chromosomes in meiosis I, would the resulting cells have the proper chromosomal constitution?

SCIENTIFIC THINKING

Question: *Why are cohesin proteins at the centromeres of sister chromatids not destroyed at anaphase I of meiosis?*

Hypothesis: *Meiosis-specific cohesin component Rec8 is protected by another protein at centromeres.*

Prediction: *If Rec8 and the centromere protecting protein are both expressed in mitotic cells, chromosome separation will be prevented. This is lethal to a dividing cell.*

Test: *Fission yeast strain is designed to produce Rec8 instead of normal mitotic cohesin. These cells are transformed with a cDNA library that expresses all cellular proteins. Transformed cells are duplicated onto media containing dye for dead cells (allows expression of Rec8 and cDNA), and media that will result in loss of plasmid cDNA (expresses only Rec8). Cells containing cDNA for protecting protein will be dead in presence of Rec8.*

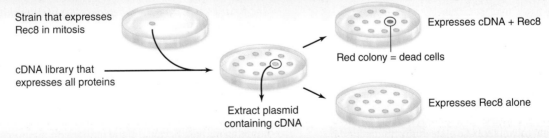

Strain that expresses Rec8 in mitosis

cDNA library that expresses all proteins

Extract plasmid containing cDNA

Expresses cDNA + Rec8

Red colony = dead cells

Expresses Rec8 alone

Result: *Transformed cells that die on the plates where Rec8 is coexpressed with cDNA identify the protecting protein. When the cDNA is extracted and analyzed, the encoded protein localizes to the centromeres of meiotic cells.*

Conclusion: *This screen identifies a protein with Rec8 protecting activity.*

Further Experiments: *If the gene encoding the protecting protein is deleted from cells, what would be the expected phenotype? In mitotic cells? In meiotic cells?*

Figure 11.8 Identification of meiosis-specific cohesin protector.

Meiosis produces cells that are not identical

The daughter cells produced by mitosis are identical to the parental cell, at least in terms of their chromosomal constitution. This exact copying is critical to producing new cells for growth, for development, and for wound healing. Meiosis, because of the random orientation of different chromosomes at the first meiotic division and because of crossing over, rarely produces cells that are identical. The gametes from meiosis all carry an entire haploid set of chromosomes, but these chromosomes are a mixture of maternal and paternal homologues; furthermore, the homologues themselves have exchanged material by crossing over. The resulting variation is essential for evolution and is the reason that sexually reproducing populations have much greater variation than asexually reproducing ones.

Meiosis is not only critical for the process of sexual reproduction, but is also the foundation for understanding the basis of heredity. The different cells produced by meiosis form the basis for understanding the behavior of observable traits in genetic crosses. In the next two chapters we will follow the behavior of traits in genetic crosses and see how this correlates with the behavior of chromosomes in meiosis.

Learning Outcomes Review 11.4

Meiosis is characterized by homologue pairing and crossing over; by loss of sister chromatid cohesion in the arms, but not at the centromere at the first division; by the suppression of DNA replication between the two meiotic divisions; and by sister kinetochores attachment to the same pole of the spindle. If replication were not suppressed between meiosis I and meiosis II, gametes would be diploid, and zygotes would be tetraploid.

■ **What features of meiosis lead to genetic variation in the products?**

Chapter Review

11.1 Sexual Reproduction Requires Meiosis
(figure 11.2)

Meiosis reduces the number of chromosomes.

Eggs and sperm are haploid ($1n$) cells, which contain one set of all chromosomes, and products of meiotic division.

Sexual life cycles have both haploid and diploid stages.

During fertilization, or syngamy, the fusion of two haploid gametes results in a diploid ($2n$) zygote, which contains two sets of chromosomes. Meiosis and fertilization constitute a reproductive cycle in sexual organisms as they alternate between diploid and haploid chromosome numbers. Somatic cells divide by mitosis and form the body of an organism.

Germ-line cells are set aside early in animal development.

Cells that eventually will form haploid gametes by meiosis are called germ-line cells. These are set aside early in development in animals.

11.2 Features of Meiosis

Homologous chromosomes pair during meiosis.

The pairing of homologous chromosomes, called synapsis, occurs during early prophase I. Paired homologues are often joined by the synaptonemal complex (figure 11.3). During synapsis, crossing over occurs between homologous chromosomes, exchanging chromosomal material. Because the homologues are paired, they move as a unit to the metaphase plate during metaphase I. During anaphase I, homologues of each pair are pulled to opposite poles, producing two cells that each have one complete set of chromosomes.

Meiosis features two divisions with one round of DNA replication.

Meiosis II is like mitosis but without replication of DNA. Sister chromatids are pulled to opposite poles to yield four haploid cells.

11.3 The Process of Meiosis (figures 11.6 & 11.7)

Prophase I sets the stage for the reductive division.

Meiotic cells have an interphase period similar to mitosis with G_1, S, and G_2 phases. This is followed by prophase I in which homologous chromosomes align along their entire length. The sister chromatids are held together by cohesin proteins. Homologues exchange chromosomal material by crossing over, which assists in holding the homologues together during meiosis I. The nuclear envelope disperses and the spindle apparatus forms.

During metaphase I, paired homologues align.

Spindle fibers attach to the kinetochores of the homologues; the kinetochores of sister chromatids behave as a single unit. Homologues of each pair become attached by kinetochore microtubules to opposite poles, and homologous pairs move to the metaphase plate as a unit. The orientation of each homologous pair on the equator is random; either the maternal or paternal homologue may be oriented toward a given pole.

Anaphase I results from the differential loss of sister chromatid cohesion along the arms.

During anaphase I the homologues of each pair are pulled to opposite poles as kinetochore microtubules shorten. Loss of sister chromatid cohesion on the arms but not at the centromeres allows homologues to separate, but sister chromatids to stay together. This is due to the loss of cohesin proteins on the arms but not at the centromere. At the end of anaphase I each pole has a complete set of haploid chromosomes, consisting of one member of each homologous pair. Because of the random orientation of homologous pairs at metaphase I, meiosis I results in the independent assortment of maternal and paternal chromosomes in gametes.

Telophase I completes meiosis I.

During telophase I the nuclear envelope re-forms around each daughter nucleus. This phase does not occur in all species. Cytokinesis may or may not occur after telophase I.

Achiasmate segregation of homologues is possible.

Although homologues are usually held together by chiasmata, some systems are able to segregate chromosomes without this.

Meiosis II is like a mitotic division without DNA replication.

A brief interphase with no DNA replication occurs after meiosis I. During meiosis II, cohesin proteins at the centromeres that hold sister chromatids together are destroyed, allowing each to migrate to opposite poles of the cell. The result of meiosis I and II is four cells, each containing haploid sets of chromosomes that are not identical. Once completed, the haploid cells may produce gametes or divide mitotically to produce even more gametes or haploid adults.

Errors in meiosis produce aneuploid gametes.

Errors occur during meiosis because of nondisjunction, the failure of chromosomes to move to opposite poles. It may result in aneuploid gametes: one gamete with no chromosome, and another gamete with two copies of a chromosome.

11.4 Summing Up: Meiosis Versus Mitosis

Four distinct features of meiosis I are not found in mitosis: Maternal and paternal homologues pair, and exchange genetic information by crossing over; the kinetochores of sister chromatids function as a unit during meiosis I, allowing sister chromatids to cosegregate during anaphase I; kinetochores of sister chromatids are connected to a single pole in meiosis I and to opposite poles in mitosis; and DNA replication is suppressed between meiosis I and meiosis II.

Homologous pairing is specific to meiosis.

How homologues find each other during meiosis is not known. The proteins of the synaptonemal complex do not seem to be conserved in different species, but there are meiosis-specific cohesin proteins. These are involved in the differential destruction of cohesins on the arms versus the centromere during meiosis I. The recombination process that occurs between paired homologues is better known. This process uses proteins involved in DNA repair and starts with a double-stranded break in DNA.

Sister chromatid cohesion is maintained through meiosis I but released in meiosis II.

Shugoshin protein protects centromeric cohesin in anaphase I, so that sister chromatids remain connected. Cohesins on the arms are not protected and are thus degraded during anaphase I, allowing homologues to move to opposite poles.

Sister kinetochores are attached to the same pole during meiosis I.

Kinetochores of sister chromatids must be attached to the same spindle fibers (monopolar attachment) to segregate together.

Replication is suppressed between meiotic divisions.

Suppression of replication may be related to the maintenance of some cyclin proteins that are degraded at the end of mitosis.

Meiosis produces cells that are not identical.

Because of the independent assortment of homologues and the process of crossing over, gametes show great variation.

Review Questions

UNDERSTAND

1. In comparing somatic cells and gametes, somatic cells are
   a. diploid with half the number of chromosomes.
   b. haploid with half the number of chromosomes.
   c. diploid with twice the number of chromosomes.
   d. haploid with twice the number of chromosomes.

2. What are *homologous* chromosomes?
   a. The two halves of a replicated chromosome
   b. Two identical chromosomes from one parent
   c. Two genetically identical chromosomes, one from each parent
   d. Two genetically similar chromosomes, one from each parent

3. Chiasmata form
   a. between homologous chromosomes.
   b. sister chromatids.
   c. between replicated copies of the same chromosomes.
   d. sex chromosomes but not autosomes.

4. Crossing over involves each of the following with the exception of
   a. the transfer of DNA between two nonsister chromatids.
   b. the transfer of DNA between two sister chromatids.
   c. the formation of a synaptonemal complex.
   d. the alignment of homologous chromosomes.

5. During anaphase I
   a. sister chromatids separate and move to the poles.
   b. homologous chromosomes move to opposite poles.
   c. homologous chromosomes align at the middle of the cell.
   d. all the chromosomes align independently at the middle of the cell.

6. At metaphase I the kinetochores of sister chromatids are
   a. attached to microtubules from the same pole.
   b. attached to microtubules from opposite poles.
   c. held together with cohesin proteins.
   d. not attached to any microtubules.

7. What occurs during anaphase of meiosis II?
   a. The homologous chromosomes align.
   b. Sister chromatids are pulled to opposite poles.
   c. Homologous chromosomes are pulled to opposite poles.
   d. The haploid chromosomes line up.

APPLY

1. Which of the following does *not* contribute to genetic diversity?
   a. Independent assortment
   b. Recombination
   c. Metaphase of meiosis II
   d. Metaphase of meiosis I

2. How does DNA replication differ between mitosis and meiosis?

   a. DNA replication takes less time in meiosis because the cells are haploid.
   b. During meiosis, there is only one round of replication for two divisions.
   c. During mitosis, there is only one round of replication every other division.
   d. DNA replication is exactly the same in mitosis and meiosis.

3. Which of the following is NOT a distinct feature of meiosis?

   a. Pairing and exchange of genetic material between homologous chromosomes
   b. Attachment of sister kinetochores to spindle microtubules
   c. Movement of sister chromatids to the same pole
   d. Suppression of DNA replication

4. Which phase of meiosis I is most similar to the comparable phase in mitosis?

   a. Prophase I   c. Anaphase I
   b. Metaphase I   d. Telophase I

5. Structurally, meiotic cohesins have different components than mitotic cohesins. This leads to the following functional difference:

   a. During metaphase I, the sister kinetochores become attached to the same pole.
   b. Centromeres remain attached during anaphase I of meiosis.
   c. Centromeres remain attached through both divisions.
   d. Centromeric cohesins are destroyed at anaphase I, and cohesins along the arms are destroyed at anaphase II.

6. Mutations that affect DNA repair often also affect the accuracy of meiosis. This is because

   a. the proteins involved in the repair of double-strand breaks are also involved in crossing over.
   b. the proteins involved in DNA repair are also involved in sister chromatid cohesion.
   c. DNA repair only occurs on condensed chromosomes such as those found in meiosis.
   d. cohesin proteins are also necessary for DNA repair.

SYNTHESIZE

1. Diagram the process of meiosis for an imaginary cell with six chromosomes in a diploid cell.

   a. How many homologous pairs are present in this cell? Create a drawing that distinguishes between homologous pairs.
   b. Label each homologue to indicate whether it is maternal (M) or paternal (P).
   c. Draw a new cell showing how these chromosomes would arrange themselves during metaphase of meiosis I. Do all the maternal homologues have to line up on the same side of the cell?
   d. How would this picture differ if you were diagramming anaphase of meiosis II?

2. Mules are the offspring of the mating of a horse and a donkey. Mules are unable to reproduce. A horse has a total of 64 chromosomes, whereas donkeys have 62 chromosomes. Use your knowledge of meiosis to predict the diploid chromosome number of a mule. Propose a possible explanation for the inability of mules to reproduce.

3. Compare the processes of *independent assortment* and *crossing over*. Which process has the greatest influence on genetic diversity?

4. Aneuploid gametes are cells that contain the wrong number of chromosomes. Aneuploidy occurs as a result of *nondisjunction*, or lack of separation of the chromosomes during either phase of meiosis.

   a. At what point in meiotic cell division would nondisjunction occur?
   b. Imagine a cell had a diploid chromosome number of four. Create a diagram to illustrate the effects of nondisjunction of one pair of homologous chromosomes in meiosis I versus meiosis II.

ONLINE RESOURCE

www.ravenbiology.com

Understand, Apply, and Synthesize—enhance your study with animations that bring concepts to life and practice tests to assess your understanding. Your instructor may also recommend the interactive eBook, individualized learning tools, and more.

Chapter

12

Patterns of Inheritance

Chapter Contents

Introduction

Every living creature is a product of the long evolutionary history of life on Earth. All organisms share this history, but as far as we know, only humans wonder about the processes that led to their origin and investigate the possibilities. We are far from understanding everything about our origins, but we have learned a great deal. Like a partially completed jigsaw puzzle, the boundaries of this elaborate question have fallen into place, and much of the internal structure is becoming apparent. In this chapter, we discuss one piece of the puzzle—the enigma of heredity. Why do individuals, like the children in this picture, differ so much in appearance despite the fact that we are all members of the same species? And, why do members of a single family tend to resemble one another more than they resemble members of other families?

12.1 The Mystery of Heredity

Learning Outcomes

1. *Describe explanations for inheritance prior to Mendel.*
2. *Explain the advantages of Mendel's experimental system.*

As far back as written records go, patterns of resemblance among the members of particular families have been noted and commented on (figure 12.1), but there was no coherent model to explain these patterns. Before the 20th century, two concepts provided the basis for most thinking about heredity. The first was that heredity occurs within species. The second was that traits are transmitted directly from parents to offspring. Taken together, these ideas led to a view of inheritance as resulting from a blending of traits within fixed, unchanging species.

Figure 12.1 Heredity and family resemblance. Family resemblances are often strong—a visual manifestation of the mechanism of heredity.

Inheritance itself was viewed as traits being borne through fluid, usually identified as blood, that led to their blending in offspring. This older idea persists today in the use of the term "bloodlines" when referring to the breeding of domestic animals such as horses.

Taken together, however, these two classical assumptions led to a paradox. If no variation enters a species from outside, and if the variation within each species blends in every generation, then all members of a species should soon have the same appearance. It is clear that this does not happen—individuals within most species differ from one another, and they differ in characteristics that are transmitted from generation to generation.

Early plant biologists produced hybrids and saw puzzling results

The first investigator to achieve and document successful experimental **hybridizations** was Josef Kölreuter, who in 1760 cross-fertilized (or crossed, for short) different strains of tobacco and obtained fertile offspring. The hybrids differed in appearance from both parent strains. When individuals within the hybrid generation were crossed, their offspring were highly variable. Some of these offspring resembled plants of the hybrid generation (their parents), but a few resembled the original strains (their grandparents). The variation observed in second-generation offspring contradicts the theory of direct transmission. This can be seen as the beginning of modern genetics.

Over the next hundred years, other investigators elaborated on Kölreuter's work. T. A. Knight, an English landholder, in 1823 crossed two varieties of the garden pea, *Pisum sativum* (figure 12.2). One of these varieties had green seeds, and the other had yellow seeds. Both varieties were **true-breeding,** meaning that the offspring produced from self-fertilization remained uniform from one generation to the next. All of the progeny (offspring)

of the cross between the two varieties had yellow seeds. Among the offspring of these hybrids, however, some plants produced yellow seeds and others, less common, produced green seeds.

Other investigators made observations similar to Knight's, namely that alternative forms of observed traits were being distributed among the offspring. A modern geneticist would say the alternative forms of each trait were **segregating** among the progeny of a mating, meaning that some offspring exhibited one form of a trait (yellow seeds), and other offspring from the same mating exhibited a different form (green seeds). This segregation of alternative forms of a trait provided the clue that led Gregor Mendel to his understanding of the nature of heredity.

Within these deceptively simple results were the makings of a scientific revolution. Nevertheless, another century passed before the process of segregation was fully appreciated.

Mendel used mathematics to analyze his crosses

Born in 1822 to peasant parents in Austria, Gregor Mendel (figure 12.3) was educated in a monastery and went on to study science and mathematics at the University of Vienna, where he failed his examinations for a teaching certificate. He returned to the monastery and spent the rest of his life there, eventually becoming abbot. In the garden of the monastery, Mendel initiated his own series of experiments on plant hybridization. The results of these experiments would ultimately change our views of heredity irrevocably.

Practical considerations for use of the garden pea

For his experiments, Mendel chose the garden pea, the same plant Knight and others had studied. The choice was a good one for several reasons. First, many earlier investigators had produced hybrid peas by crossing different varieties, so Mendel knew that he could expect to observe segregation of traits among the offspring.

Figure 12.2 The garden pea, *Pisum sativum.* Easy to cultivate and able to produce many distinctive varieties, the garden pea was a popular experimental subject in investigations of heredity as long as a century before Gregor Mendel's experiments.

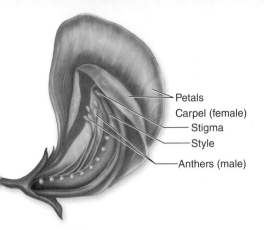

Petals
Carpel (female)
Stigma
Style
Anthers (male)

1. The anthers are cut away on the purple flower.

2. Pollen is obtained from the white flower.

3. Pollen is transferred to the purple flower.

4. All progeny result in purple flowers.

Figure 12.3 **How Mendel conducted his experiments.** In a pea plant flower, petals enclose both the male anther (containing pollen grains, which give rise to haploid sperm) and the female carpel (containing ovules, which give rise to haploid eggs). This ensures self-fertilization will take place unless the flower is disturbed. Mendel collected pollen from the anthers of a white flower, then placed that pollen onto the stigma of a purple flower with anthers removed. This cross-fertilization yields all hybrid seeds that give rise to purple flowers. Using pollen from a white flower to fertilize a purple flower gives the same result.

? **Inquiry question** What confounding problems could have been seen if Mendel had chosen another plant with exposed male and female structures?

Second, a large number of pure varieties of peas were available. Mendel initially examined 34 varieties. Then, for further study, he selected lines that differed with respect to seven easily distinguishable traits, such as round versus wrinkled seeds and yellow versus green seeds, the latter a trait that Knight had studied.

Third, pea plants are small and easy to grow, and they have a relatively short generation time. A researcher can therefore conduct experiments involving numerous plants, grow several generations in a single year, and obtain results relatively quickly.

A fourth advantage of studying peas is that both the male and female sexual organs are enclosed within each pea flower (see figure 12.3), and gametes produced by the male and female parts of the same flower can fuse to form viable offspring, a process termed **self-fertilization.** This self-fertilization takes place automatically within an individual flower if it is not disturbed. It is also possible to prevent self-fertilization by removing a flower's male parts before fertilization occurs, then introduce pollen from a different strain, thus performing *cross-pollination* that results in *cross-fertilization* (see figure 12.3).

Mendel's experimental design

Mendel was careful to focus on only a few specific differences between the plants he was using and to ignore the countless other differences he must have seen. He also had the insight to realize that the differences he selected must be comparable. For example, he recognized that trying to study the inheritance of round seeds versus tall height would be useless.

Mendel usually conducted his experiments in three stages:

1. Mendel allowed plants of a given variety to self-cross for multiple generations to assure himself that the traits he

was studying were indeed true-breeding, that is, transmitted unchanged from generation to generation.
2. Mendel then performed crosses between true-breeding varieties exhibiting alternative forms of traits. He also performed **reciprocal crosses:** using pollen from a white-flowered plant to fertilize a purple-flowered plant, then using pollen from a purple-flowered plant to fertilize a white-flowered plant.
3. Finally, Mendel permitted the hybrid offspring produced by these crosses to self-fertilize for several generations, allowing him to observe the inheritance of alternative forms of a trait. Most important, he counted the numbers of offspring exhibiting each trait in each succeeding generation.

This quantification of results is what distinguished Mendel's research from that of earlier investigators, who only noted differences in a qualitative way. Mendel's mathematical analysis of experimental results led to the inheritance model that we still use today.

Learning Outcomes Review 12.1

Prior to Mendel, concepts of inheritance did not form a consistent model. The dominant view was of blending inheritance, in which traits of parents were carried by fluid and "blended" in offspring. Plant hybridizers before Mendel, however, had already cast doubt on this model by observing characteristics in hybrids that seemed to change in second-generation offspring. Mendel's experiments with plants involved quantifying types of offspring and mathematically analyzing his observations.

■ *Which was more important to Mendel's success: his approach, or his choice of experimental material?*

12.2 Monohybrid Crosses: The Principle of Segregation

A *monohybrid cross* is a cross that follows only two variations on a single trait, such as white- and purple-colored flowers. This deceptively simple kind of cross can lead to important conclusions about the nature of inheritance.

The seven characteristics, or characters, Mendel studied in his experiments possessed two variants that differed from one another in ways that were easy to recognize and score (figure 12.4). We examine in detail Mendel's crosses with flower color. His experiments with other characters were similar, and they produced similar results.

The F_1 generation exhibits only one of two traits, without blending

When Mendel crossed white-flowered and purple-flowered plants, the hybrid offspring he obtained did not have flowers of intermediate color, as the hypothesis of blending inheritance would predict. Instead, in every case the flower color of the offspring resembled that of one of their parents. These offspring are customarily referred to as the **first filial generation,** or F_1. In a cross of white-flowered and purple-flowered plants, the F_1 offspring all had purple flowers, as other scientists had reported before Mendel.

Mendel referred to the form of each trait expressed in the F_1 plants as **dominant,** and to the alternative form that was not expressed in the F_1 plants as **recessive.** For each of the seven pairs of contrasting traits that Mendel examined, one of the pair proved to be dominant and the other recessive.

The F_2 generation exhibits both traits in a 3:1 ratio

After allowing individual F_1 plants to mature and self-fertilize, Mendel collected and planted the seeds from each plant to see what the offspring in the **second filial generation,** or F_2, would look like. He found that although most F_2 plants had purple flowers, some exhibited white flowers, the recessive trait. Although hidden in the F_1 generation, the recessive trait had reappeared among some F_2 individuals.

Believing the proportions of the F_2 types would provide some clue about the mechanism of heredity, Mendel counted the numbers of each type among the F_2 progeny. In the cross between the purple-flowered F_1 plants, he obtained a total of 929 F_2 individuals. Of these, 705 (75.9%) had purple flowers, and 224 (24.1%) had white flowers (see figure 12.4). Approximately ¼ of the F_2 individuals, therefore, exhibited the recessive form of the character.

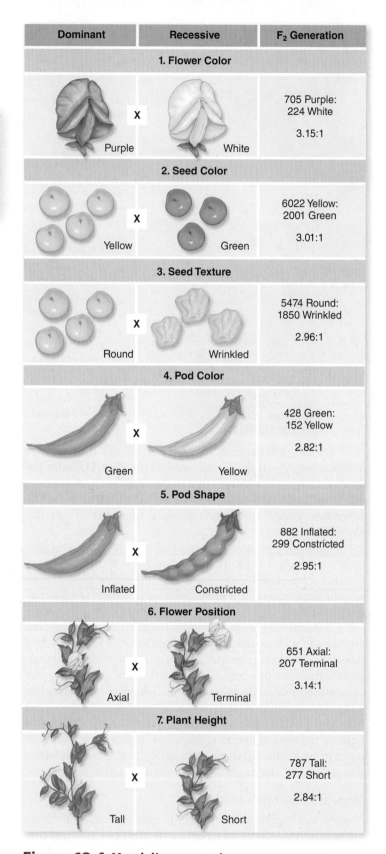

Dominant	Recessive	F_2 Generation
1. Flower Color		
Purple	White	705 Purple: 224 White 3.15:1
2. Seed Color		
Yellow	Green	6022 Yellow: 2001 Green 3.01:1
3. Seed Texture		
Round	Wrinkled	5474 Round: 1850 Wrinkled 2.96:1
4. Pod Color		
Green	Yellow	428 Green: 152 Yellow 2.82:1
5. Pod Shape		
Inflated	Constricted	882 Inflated: 299 Constricted 2.95:1
6. Flower Position		
Axial	Terminal	651 Axial: 207 Terminal 3.14:1
7. Plant Height		
Tall	Short	787 Tall: 277 Short 2.84:1

Figure 12.4 Mendel's seven traits. Mendel studied how differences among varieties of peas were inherited when the varieties were crossed. Similar experiments had been done before, but Mendel was the first to quantify the results and appreciate their significance. Results are shown for seven different monohybrid crosses. The F_1 generation is not shown in the table.

Mendel obtained the same numerical result with the other six characters he examined: Of the F_2 individuals, ¾ exhibited the dominant trait, and ¼ displayed the recessive trait (see figure 12.4). In other words, the dominant-to-recessive ratio among the F_2 plants was always close to 3:1.

The 3:1 ratio is actually 1:2:1

Mendel went on to examine how the F_2 plants passed traits to subsequent generations. He found that plants exhibiting the recessive trait were always true-breeding. For example, the white-flowered F_2 individuals reliably produced white-flowered offspring when they were allowed to self-fertilize. By contrast, only ⅓ of the dominant, purple-flowered F_2 individuals (¼ of all F_2 offspring) proved true-breeding, but ⅔ were not. This last class of plants produced dominant and recessive individuals in the third filial generation (F_3) in a 3:1 ratio.

This result suggested that, for the entire sample, the 3:1 ratio that Mendel observed in the F_2 generation was really a disguised 1:2:1 ratio: ¼ true-breeding dominant individuals, ½ not-true-breeding dominant individuals, and ¼ true-breeding recessive individuals (figure 12.5).

 Data analysis In the previous set of crosses, if the purple F_1 were backcrossed to the white parent, what would be the phenotypic ratio? The genotypic ratio?

Mendel's Principle of Segregation explains monohybrid observations

From his experiments, Mendel was able to understand four things about the nature of heredity:

- The plants he crossed did not produce progeny of intermediate appearance, as a hypothesis of blending inheritance would have predicted. Instead, different plants inherited each trait intact, as a discrete characteristic.
- For each pair of alternative forms of a trait, one alternative was not expressed in the F_1 hybrids, although it reappeared in some F_2 individuals. *The trait that "disappeared" must therefore be latent (present but not expressed) in the F_1 individuals.*
- The pairs of alternative traits examined were segregated among the progeny of a particular cross, some individuals exhibiting one trait and some the other.
- These alternative traits were expressed in the F_2 generation in the ratio of ¾ dominant to ¼ recessive. This characteristic 3:1 segregation is referred to as the **Mendelian ratio** for a monohybrid cross.

Mendel's five-element model

To explain these results, Mendel proposed a simple model that has become one of the most famous in the history of science, containing simple assumptions and making clear predictions. The model has five elements:

1. Parents do not transmit physiological traits directly to their offspring. Rather, they transmit discrete information for the traits, what Mendel called "factors." We now call these factors *genes*.

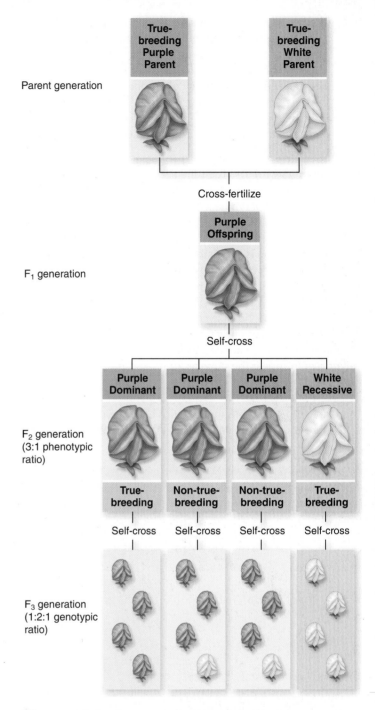

Figure 12.5 The F_2 generation is a disguised 1:2:1 ratio. By allowing the F_2 generation to self-fertilize, Mendel found from the offspring (F_3) that the ratio of F_2 plants was 1 true-breeding dominant: 2 not-true-breeding dominant: and 1 true-breeding recessive.

2. Each individual receives one copy of each gene from each parent. We now know that genes are carried on chromosomes, and each adult individual is diploid, with one set of chromosomes from each parent.
3. Not all copies of a gene are identical. The alternative forms of a gene are called **alleles.** When two haploid gametes containing the same allele fuse during fertilization, the resulting offspring is said to be **homozygous.** When the two haploid gametes contain different alleles, the resulting offspring is said to be **heterozygous.**

4. The two alleles remain discrete—they neither blend with nor alter each other. Therefore, when the individual matures and produces its own gametes, the alleles segregate randomly into these gametes.

5. The presence of a particular allele does not ensure that the trait it encodes will be expressed. In heterozygous individuals, only one allele is expressed (the dominant one), and the other allele is present but unexpressed (the recessive one).

Geneticists now refer to the total set of alleles that an individual contains as the individual's **genotype.** The physical appearance or other observable characteristics of that individual, which result from an allele's expression, is termed the individual's **phenotype.** In other words, the genotype is the blueprint, and the phenotype is the visible outcome in an individual.

This also allows us to present Mendel's ratios in more modern terms. The 3:1 ratio of dominant to recessive is the monohybrid phenotypic ratio. The 1:2:1 ratio of homozygous dominant to heterozygous to homozygous recessive is the monohybrid genotypic ratio. The genotypic ratio "collapses" into the phenotypic ratio due to the action of the dominant allele making the heterozygote appear the same as homozygous dominant.

The principle of segregation

Mendel's model accounts for the ratios he observed in a neat and satisfying way. His main conclusion—that alternative alleles for a character segregate from each other during gamete formation and remain distinct—has since been verified in many other organisms. It is commonly referred to as Mendel's first law of heredity, or the **Principle of Segregation.** It can be simply stated as: *The two alleles for a gene segregate during gamete formation and are rejoined at random, one from each parent, during fertilization.*

The physical basis for allele segregation is the behavior of chromosomes during meiosis. As you saw in chapter 11, homologues for each chromosome disjoin during anaphase I of meiosis. The second meiotic division then produces gametes that contain only one homologue for each chromosome.

It is a tribute to Mendel's intellect that his analysis arrived at the correct scheme, even though he had no knowledge of the cellular mechanisms of inheritance; neither chromosomes nor meiosis had yet been described.

The Punnett square allows symbolic analysis

To test his model, Mendel first expressed it in terms of a simple set of symbols. He then used the symbols to interpret his results.

Consider again Mendel's cross of purple-flowered with white-flowered plants. By convention, we assign the symbol P (uppercase) to the dominant allele, associated with the production of purple flowers, and the symbol p (lowercase) to the recessive allele, associated with the production of white flowers.

In this system, the genotype of an individual that is true-breeding for the recessive white-flowered trait would be designated

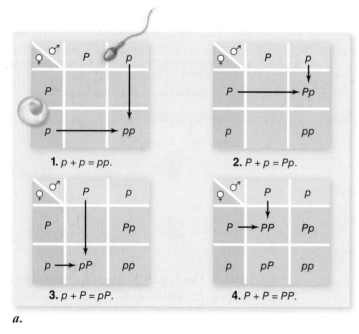

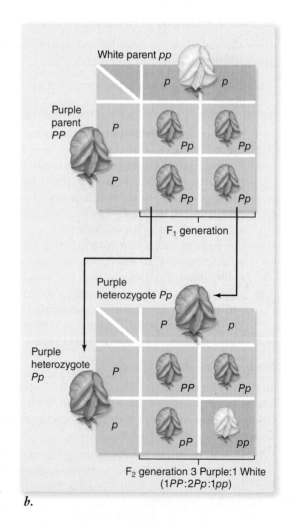

Figure 12.6 Using a Punnett square to analyze Mendel's cross.
a. To make a Punnett square, place the different female gametes along the side of a square and the different male gametes along the top. Each potential zygote is represented as the intersection of a vertical line and a horizontal line. *b.* In Mendel's cross of purple by white flowers, each parent makes only one type of gamete. The F_1 are all purple, Pp, heterozygotes. These F_1 offspring make two types of gametes that can be combined to produce three kinds of F_2 offspring: PP homozygous dominant (purple); Pp heterozygous (also purple); and pp homozygous recessive (white). The phenotypic ratio is 3 purple:1 white. The genotypic ratio is 1 PP:2 Pp:1 pp.

TABLE 12.1 Some Dominant and Recessive Traits in Humans

Recessive Traits	Phenotypes	Dominant Traits	Phenotypes
Albinism	Lack of melanin pigmentation	Middigital hair	Presence of hair on middle segment of fingers
Alkaptonuria	Inability to metabolize homogentisic acid	Brachydactyly	Short fingers
Red-green color blindness	Inability to distinguish red or green wavelengths of light	Huntington disease	Degeneration of nervous system, starting in middle age
Cystic fibrosis	Abnormal gland secretion, leading to liver degeneration and lung failure	Phenylthiocarbamide (PTC) sensitivity	Ability to taste PTC as bitter
Duchenne muscular dystrophy	Wasting away of muscles during childhood	Camptodactyly	Inability to straighten the little finger
Hemophilia	Inability of blood to clot properly, some clots form but the process is delayed	Hypercholesterolemia (the most common human Mendelian disorder)	Elevated levels of blood cholesterol and risk of heart attack
Sickle cell anemia	Defective hemoglobin that causes red blood cells to curve and stick together	Polydactyly	Extra fingers and toes

pp. Similarly, the genotype of a true-breeding purple-flowered individual would be designated *PP.* In contrast, a heterozygote would be designated *Pp* (dominant allele first). Using these conventions and denoting a cross between two strains with ×, we can symbolize Mendel's original purple × white cross as *PP* × *pp.*

Because a white-flowered parent (*pp*) can produce only *p* gametes, and a true-breeding purple-flowered parent (*PP, homozygous dominant*) can produce only *P* gametes, the union of these gametes can produce only heterozygous *Pp* offspring in the F_1 generation. Because the *P* allele is dominant, all of these F_1 individuals are expected to have purple flowers.

When F_1 individuals are allowed to self-fertilize, the *P* and *p* alleles segregate during gamete formation to produce both *P* gametes and *p* gametes. Their subsequent union at fertilization to form F_2 individuals is random.

The F_2 possibilities may be visualized in a simple diagram called a **Punnett square,** named after its originator, the English geneticist R. C. Punnett (figure 12.6*a*). Mendel's model, analyzed in terms of a Punnett square, clearly predicts that the F_2 generation should consist of ¾ purple-flowered plants and ¼ white-flowered plants, a phenotypic ratio of 3:1 (figure 12.6*b*).

Some human traits exhibit dominant/recessive inheritance

A number of human traits have been shown to display both dominant and recessive inheritance (table 12.1 provides a sample of these). Researchers cannot perform controlled crosses in humans the way Mendel did with pea plants; instead geneticists study crosses that have already been performed—in other words, family histories. The organized methodology we use is a **pedigree,** a consistent graphical representation of matings and offspring over multiple generations for a particular trait. The information in the pedigree may allow geneticists to deduce a model for the mode of inheritance of the trait. In analyzing these pedigrees, it is important to realize that disease-causing alleles are usually quite rare in the general population.

A dominant pedigree: Juvenile glaucoma

One of the most extensive pedigrees yet produced traced the inheritance of a form of blindness caused by a dominant allele. The disease allele causes a form of hereditary juvenile glaucoma. The disease causes degeneration of nerve fibers in the optic nerve, leading to blindness.

This pedigree followed inheritance over three centuries, following the origin back to a couple in a small town in northwestern France who died in 1495. A small portion of this pedigree is shown in figure 12.7. The dominant nature of the trait is

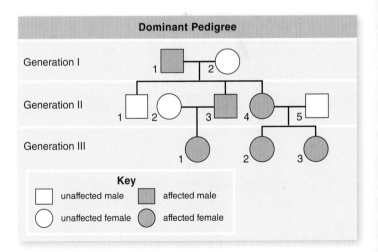

Figure 12.7 Dominant pedigree for hereditary juvenile glaucoma. Males are shown as squares and females are shown as circles. Affected individuals are shown shaded. The dominant nature of this trait can be seen in the trait appearing in every generation, a feature of dominant traits.

 Data analysis If one of the affected females in the third generation married an unaffected male, could she produce unaffected offspring? If so, what are the chances of having unaffected offspring?

obvious from the fact that every generation shows the trait. This is extremely unlikely for a recessive trait as it would require large numbers of unrelated individuals to be carrying the disease allele.

A recessive pedigree: Albinism

An example of inheritance of a recessive human trait is albinism, a condition in which the pigment melanin is not produced. Long thought to be due to a single gene, multiple genes are now known that lead to albinism; the common feature is the loss of pigment from hair, skin, and eyes. The loss of pigment makes albinistic individuals sensitive to the sun. The tanning effect we are all familiar with from exposure to the sun is due to increased numbers of pigment-producing cells, and increased production of pigment. This is lacking in albinistic individuals due to the lack of any pigment to begin with.

The pedigree in figure 12.8 is for a form of albinism due to a nonfunctional allele of the enzyme tyrosinase, which is required for the formation of melanin pigment. The genetic characteristics of this form of albinism are: females and males are affected equally, most affected individuals have unaffected parents, a single affected parent usually does not have affected offspring, and affected offspring are more frequent when parents are related. Each of these features can be seen in figure 12.8, and all of this fits a recessive mode of inheritance.

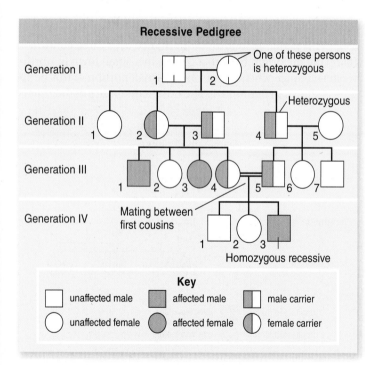

Figure 12.8 Recessive pedigree for albinism. One of the two individuals in the first generation must be heterozygous and individuals II-2 and II-4 must be heterozygous. Notice that for each affected individual, neither parent is affected, but both must be heterozygous (carriers). The double line indicates a consanguineous mating (between relatives) that, in this case, produced affected offspring.

? Inquiry question From the standpoint of genetic disease, why is it never advisable for close relatives to mate and have children?

12.3 Dihybrid Crosses: The Principle of Independent Assortment

The Principle of Segregation explains the behavior of alternative forms of a single trait in a monohybrid cross. The next step is to extend this to follow the behavior of two different traits in a single cross: a **dihybrid cross.**

With an understanding of the behavior of single traits, Mendel went on to ask if different traits behaved independently in hybrids. He first established a series of true-breeding lines of peas that differed in two of the seven characters he had studied. He then crossed contrasting pairs of the true-breeding lines to create heterozygotes. These heterozygotes are now doubly heterozygous, or dihybrid. Finally, he self-crossed the dihybrid F_1 plants to produce an F_2 generation, and counted all progeny types.

Traits in a dihybrid cross behave independently

Consider a cross involving different seed shape alleles (round, *R,* and wrinkled, *r*) and different seed color alleles (yellow, *Y,* and green, *y*). Crossing round yellow (*RR YY*) with wrinkled green (*rr yy*), produces heterozygous F_1 individuals having the same phenotype (namely round and yellow) and the same genotype (*Rr Yy*). Allowing these dihybrid F_1 individuals to self-fertilize produces an F_2 generation.

The F_2 generation exhibits four types of progeny in a 9:3:3:1 ratio

In analyzing these results, we first consider the number of possible phenotypes. We expect to see the two parental phenotypes: round yellow and wrinkled green. If the traits behave independently, then we can also expect one trait from each parent to produce plants with round green seeds and others with wrinkled yellow seeds.

Next consider what types of gametes the F_1 individuals can produce. Again, we expect the two types of gametes found in the parents: *RY* and *ry*. If the traits behave independently, then we can also expect the gametes *Ry* and *rY*. Using modern language, two genes each with two alleles can be combined four ways to produce these gametes: *RY, ry, Ry,* and *rY.*

A dihybrid Punnett square

We can then construct a Punnett square with these gametes to generate all possible progeny. This is a 4 × 4 square with 16 possible outcomes. Filling in the Punnett square produces all possible offspring (figure 12.9). From this we can see that there are 9 round yellow, 3 wrinkled yellow, 3 round green, and 1 wrinkled green. This predicts a phenotypic ratio of 9:3:3:1 for traits that behave independently.

Mendel's Principle of Independent Assortment explains dihybrid results

What did Mendel actually observe? From a total of 556 seeds from self-fertilized dihybrid plants, he observed the following results:

- 315 round yellow (signified *R__ Y__*, where the underscore indicates the presence of either allele),
- 108 round green *(R__ yy),*
- 101 wrinkled yellow *(rr Y__),* and
- 32 wrinkled green *(rr yy).*

These results are very close to a 9:3:3:1 ratio. (The expected 9:3:3:1 ratio from this many offspring would be 313:104:104:35.)

The alleles of two genes appeared to behave independently of each other. Mendel referred to this phenomenon as the traits assorting independently. Note that this *independent assortment* of different genes in no way alters the segregation of individual pairs of alleles for each gene. Round versus wrinkled seeds occur in a ratio of approximately 3:1 (423:133); so do yellow versus green seeds (416:140). Mendel obtained similar results for other pairs of traits.

We call this Mendel's second law of heredity, or the **Principle of Independent Assortment.** This can also be stated simply: *In a dihybrid cross, the alleles of each gene assort independently.* A more precise statement would be: *the segregation of different allele pairs is independent.* This statement more closely ties independent assortment to the behavior of chromosomes during meiosis (see chapter 11). The independent alignment of different homologous chromosome pairs during metaphase I leads to the independent segregation of the different allele pairs.

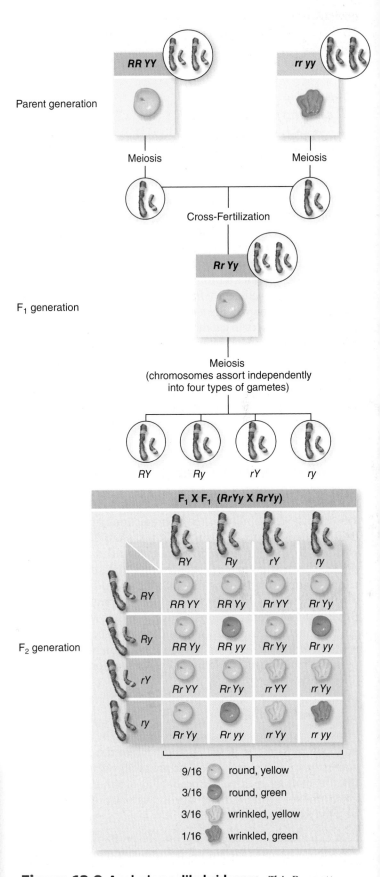

Figure 12.9 Analyzing a dihybrid cross. This Punnett square shows the results of Mendel's dihybrid cross between plants with round yellow seeds and plants with wrinkled green seeds. The ratio of the four possible combinations of phenotypes is predicted to be 9:3:3:1, the ratio that Mendel found.

Learning Outcomes Review 12.3

Mendel's analysis of dihybrid crosses revealed that the segregation of allele pairs for different traits is independent; this finding is known as Mendel's Principle of Independent Assortment. When individuals that differ in two traits are crossed, and their progeny are intercrossed, the result is four different types that occur in a ratio of 9:3:3:1, Mendel's dihybrid ratio. This occurs because of the independent behavior of different homologous pairs of chromosomes during meiosis I.

- *Which is more important in terms of explaining Mendel's laws, meiosis I or meiosis II?*

Probability: Predicting the Results of Crosses

Learning Outcomes

1. Explain the rule of addition and the rule of multiplication.
2. Apply the rules of probability to genetic crosses.

Probability allows us to predict the likelihood of the outcome of random events. Because the behavior of different chromosomes during meiosis is independent, we can use probability to predict the outcome of crosses. The probability of an event that is certain to happen is equal to 1. In contrast, an event that can never happen has a probability of 0. Therefore, probabilities for all other events have fractional values, between 0 and 1. For instance, when you flip a coin, two outcomes are possible; there is only one way to get the event "heads" so the probability of heads is one divided by two, or ½. In the case of genetics, consider a pea plant heterozygous for the flower color alleles P and p. This individual can produce two types of gametes in equal numbers, again due to the behavior of chromosomes during meiosis. There is one way to get a P gamete, so the probability of any particular gamete carrying a P allele is 1 divided by 2 or ½, just like the coin toss.

Two probability rules help predict monohybrid cross results

We can use probability to make predictions about the outcome of genetic crosses using only two simple rules. Before we describe these rules and their uses, we need another definition. We say that two events are *mutually exclusive* if both cannot happen at the same time. The heads and tails of a coin flip are examples of mutually exclusive events. Notice that this is different from two consecutive coin flips where you can get two heads or two tails. In this case, each coin flip represents an *independent event*. It is the distinction between independent and mutually exclusive events that forms the basis for our two rules.

The rule of addition

Consider a six-sided die instead of a coin: for any roll of the die, only one outcome is possible, and each of the possible outcomes are mutually exclusive. The probability of any particular number coming up is ⅙. The probability of either of two different numbers is the sum of the individual probabilities, or restated as the **rule of addition:**

For two mutually exclusive events, the probability of either event occurring is the sum of the individual probabilities.

Probability of rolling either a 2 or a 6
is = ⅙ + ⅙ = ²⁄₆ = ⅓

To apply this to our cross of heterozygous purple F_1, four mutually exclusive outcomes are possible: PP, Pp, pP, and pp. The

probability of being heterozygous is the same as the probability of being either Pp or pP, or ¼ plus ¼, or ½.

Probability of F_2 heterozygote = ¼Pp + ¼pP = ½

In the previous example, of 379 total offspring, we would expect about 190 to be heterozygotes. (The actual number is 189.5.)

The rule of multiplication

The second rule, and by far the most useful for genetics, deals with the outcome of independent events. This is called the **product rule,** or **rule of multiplication,** and it states that the probability of two independent events both occurring is the *product* of their individual probabilities.

We can apply this to a monohybrid cross in which offspring are formed by gametes from each of two parents. For any particular outcome then, this is due to two independent events: the formation of two different gametes. Consider the purple F_1 parents from earlier. They are all Pp (heterozygotes), so the probability that a particular F_2 individual will be pp (homozygous recessive) is the probability of receiving a p gamete from the male (½) times the probability of receiving a p gamete from the female (½), or ¼:

Probability of pp homozygote = ½p (male parent) × ½p
(female parent) = ¼pp

This is actually the basis for the Punnett square that we used before. Each cell in the square was the product of the probabilities of the gametes that contribute to the cell. We then use the addition rule to sum the probabilities of the mutually exclusive events that make up each cell.

We can use the result of a probability calculation to predict the number of homozygous recessive offspring in a cross between heterozygotes. For example, out of 379 total offspring, we would expect about 95 to exhibit the homozygous recessive phenotype. (The actual calculated number is 94.75.)

Dihybrid cross probabilities are based on monohybrid cross probabilities

Probability analysis can be extended to the dihybrid case. For our purple F_1 by F_1 cross, there are four possible outcomes, three of which show the dominant phenotype. Thus the probability of any offspring showing the dominant phenotype is ¾, and the probability of any offspring showing the recessive phenotype is ¼. Now we can use this and the product rule to predict the outcome of a dihybrid cross. We will use our example of seed shape and color from earlier, but now examine it using probability.

If the alleles affecting seed shape and seed color segregate independently, then the probability that a particular pair of alleles for seed shape would occur together with a particular pair of alleles for seed color is the product of the individual probabilities for each pair. For example, the probability that an individual with wrinkled green seeds ($rr\ yy$) would appear in the F_2 generation would be equal to the probability of obtaining wrinkled seeds (¼) times the probability of obtaining green seeds (¼), or ¹⁄₁₆.

Probability of $rr\ yy$ = ¼ rr × ¼ yy = ¹⁄₁₆ $rr\ yy$

Because of independent assortment, we can think of the dihybrid cross of consisting of two independent monohybrid crosses; since these are independent events, the product rule applies. So, we can calculate the probabilities for each dihybrid phenotype:

Probability of round yellow ($R\_\_ Y\_\_$) =
$\frac{3}{4} R\_\_ \times \frac{3}{4} Y\_\_ = \frac{9}{16}$

Probability of round green ($R\_\_ yy$) =
$\frac{3}{4} R\_\_ \times \frac{1}{4} yy = \frac{3}{16}$

Probability of wrinkled yellow ($rr Y\_\_$) =
$\frac{1}{4} rr \times \frac{3}{4} Y\_\_ = \frac{3}{16}$

Probability of wrinkled green ($rr yy$) =
$\frac{1}{4} rr \times \frac{1}{4} yy = \frac{1}{16}$

The hypothesis that color and shape genes are independently sorted thus predicts that the F$_2$ generation will display a 9:3:3:1 phenotypic ratio. These ratios can be applied to an observed total offspring to predict the expected number in each phenotypic group. The underlying logic and the results are the same as obtained using the Punnett square.

 Data analysis Purple-flowered, round, yellow peas are crossed to white-flowered, wrinkled, green peas to yield a purple-flowered, round, yellow F$_1$. If this F$_1$ is self-crossed, what proportion of progeny should be purple-flowered, round, yellow?

Learning Outcomes Review 12.4

The rule of addition states that the probability of either of two events occurring is the sum of their individual probabilities. The rule of multiplication states that the probability of two independent events both occurring is the product of their individual probabilities. These rules can be applied to genetic crosses to determine the probability of particular genotypes and phenotypes. Results can then be compared against these predictions.

- **If genes A and B assort independently, in a cross of Aa Bb by aa Bb, what is the probability of having the dominant phenotype for both genes?**

12.5 The Testcross: Revealing Unknown Genotypes

Learning Outcome

1. Interpret data from test crosses to infer unknown genotypes.

To test his model further, Mendel devised a simple and powerful procedure called the **testcross.** In a testcross, an individual with unknown genotype is crossed with the homozygous recessive genotype—that is, the recessive parental variety. The contribution of the homozygous recessive parent can be ignored, because this parent can contribute only recessive alleles.

Consider a purple-flowered pea plant. It is impossible to tell whether such a plant is homozygous or heterozygous simply by looking at it. To learn its genotype, you can perform a testcross to a white-flowered plant. In this cross, the two possible test plant genotypes will give different results (figure 12.10):

Alternative 1: Unknown individual is homozygous dominant (PP) $PP \times pp$: All offspring have purple flowers (Pp).

Alternative 2: Unknown individual is heterozygous (Pp) $Pp \times pp$: ½ of offspring have white flowers (pp), and ½ have purple flowers (Pp).

Put simply, the appearance of the recessive phenotype in the offspring of a testcross indicates that the test individual's genotype is heterozygous.

For each pair of alleles Mendel investigated, he observed phenotypic F$_2$ ratios of 3:1 (see figure 12.4) and testcross ratios of 1:1, just as his model had predicted. Testcrosses can also be used to determine the genotype of an individual when two genes are involved. Mendel often performed testcrosses to verify the genotypes of dominant-appearing F$_2$ individuals.

An F$_2$ individual exhibiting both dominant traits ($A\_\_ B\_\_$) might have any of the following genotypes: $AABB$,

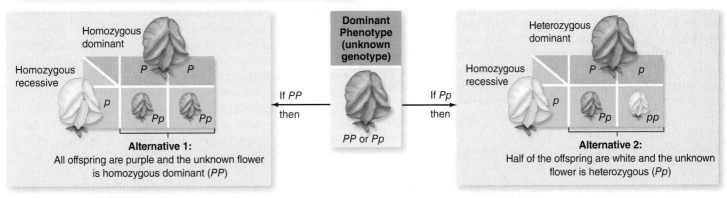

Figure 12.10 Using a testcross to determine unknown genotypes. Individuals with a dominant phenotype, such as purple flowers, can be either homozygous for the dominant allele, or heterozygous. Crossing an unknown purple plant to homozygous recessive (*white*) allows determination of its genotype. The Punnett "square" for each alternative shows only one row for the homozygous recessive white strain because they produce only *p*-bearing gametes.

AaBB, AABb, or AaBb. By crossing dominant-appearing F_2 individuals with homozygous recessive individuals (that is, $A\_\_ B\_\_ \times aabb$), Mendel was able to determine whether either or both of the traits bred true among the progeny, and so to determine the genotype of the F_2 parent.

 Data analysis Diagram all four possible testcrosses to determine genotypes for individuals that appear dominant for two traits.

Testcrossing is a powerful tool that simplifies genetic analysis. We will use this method of analysis in the next chapter, when we explore genetic mapping.

Learning Outcome Review 12.5

Individuals showing the dominant phenotype can be either homozygous dominant or heterozygous. Unknown genotypes can be revealed using a testcross, which is a cross to a homozygous recessive individual. Heterozygotes produce both dominant and recessive phenotypes in equal numbers as a result of the testcross.

■ *In a dihybrid testcross of a doubly heterozygous individual, what would be the expected phenotypic ratio?*

12.6 Extensions to Mendel

Learning Outcomes

1. *Describe how assumptions in Mendel's model result in oversimplification.*
2. *Discuss a genetic explanation for continuous variation.*
3. *Explain the genetic basis for observed alterations to Mendel's ratios.*

Although Mendel's results did not receive much notice during his lifetime, three different investigators independently rediscovered his pioneering paper in 1900, 16 years after his death. They came across it while searching the literature in preparation for publishing their own findings, which closely resembled those Mendel had presented more than 30 years earlier.

In the decades following the rediscovery of Mendel's ideas, many investigators set out to test them. However, scientists attempting to confirm Mendel's theory often had trouble obtaining the same simple ratios he had reported.

The reason that Mendel's simple ratios were not obtained had to do with the traits that others examined. A number of assumptions are built into Mendel's model that are oversimplifications. These assumptions include that each trait is specified by a single gene with two alternative alleles; that there are no environmental effects; and that gene products act independently. The idea of dominance also hides a wealth of biochemical complexity. In the following sections, you'll see how Mendel's simple ideas can be extended to provide a more complete view of genetics (table 12.2).

In polygenic inheritance, more than one gene can affect a single trait

Often, the relationship between genotype and phenotype is more complicated than a single allele producing a single trait. Most phenotypes also do not reflect simple two-state cases like purple or white flowers.

Consider Mendel's crosses between tall and short pea plants. In reality, the "tall" plants actually have normal height, and the "short" plants are dwarfed by an allele at a single gene. But in most species, including humans, height varies over a continuous range, rather than having discrete values. This continuous distribution of a phenotype has a simple genetic explanation: more than one gene is at work. The mode of inheritance operating in this case is often called **polygenic inheritance.**

In reality, few phenotypes result from the action of only one gene. Instead, most characters reflect multiple additive contributions to the phenotype by several genes. When multiple genes act jointly to influence a character, such as height or weight, the character often shows a range of small differences. When these genes segregate independently, a gradation in the degree of difference can be observed when a group consisting of many individuals is examined (figure 12.11). We call this gradation **continuous variation,** and we call such traits **quantitative traits.** The greater the number of genes influencing a character, the more continuous the expected distribution of the versions of that character.

This continuous variation in traits is similar to blending different colors of paint: Combining one part red with seven parts white, for example, produces a much lighter shade of pink than does combining five parts red with three parts white. Different ratios of red to white result in a continuum of shades, ranging from pure red to pure white.

Often, variations can be grouped into categories, such as different height ranges. Plotting the numbers in each height category produces a curve called a *histogram,* such as that shown in figure 12.11. The bell-shaped histogram approximates an idealized *normal distribution,* in which the central tendency is characterized by the mean, and the spread of the curve indicates the amount of variation.

Even simple-appearing traits can have this kind of polygenic basis. For example, human eye colors are often described in simple terms with brown dominant to blue, but this is actually incorrect. Extensive analysis indicates multiple genes are involved in determining eye color. This leads to more complex inheritance patterns than initially reported. For example, blue-eyed parents can have brown-eyed offspring, although it is rare. It is interesting to note that most phenotypic variation in eye color can be explained by the interaction of two to four genes. In the developing field of forensic genetics, attempts are being made to predict such phenotypes as eye, hair, and skin color by analysis of unknown samples.

In pleiotropy, a single gene can affect more than one trait

Not only can more than one gene affect a single trait, but a single gene can affect more than one trait. Considering the

TABLE 12.2 When Mendel's Laws/Results May Not Be Observed

Genetic Occurrence	Definition	Examples
Polygenic inheritance	More than one gene can affect a single trait.	• Four genes are involved in determining eye color. • Human height
Pleiotropy	A single gene can affect more than one trait.	• A pleiotropic allele dominant for yellow fur in mice is recessive for a lethal developmental defect. • Cystic fibrosis • Sickle cell anemia
Multiple alleles for one gene	Genes may have more than two alleles.	ABO blood types in humans
Dominance is not always complete	• In incomplete dominance the heterozygote is intermediate. • In codominance no single allele is dominant, and the heterozygote shows some aspect of both homozygotes.	• Japanese four o'clocks • Human blood groups
Environmental factors	Genes may be affected by the environment.	Siamese cats
Gene interaction	Products of genes can interact to alter genetic ratios.	• The production of a purple pigment in corn • Coat color in mammals

complexity of biochemical pathways and the interdependent nature of organ systems in multicellular organisms, this should be no surprise.

An allele that has more than one effect on phenotype is said to be **pleiotropic.** The pioneering French geneticist Lucien Cuenot studied yellow fur in mice, a dominant trait, and

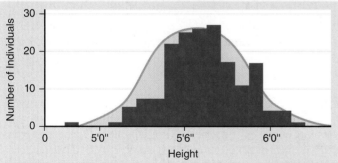

Figure 12.11 Height is a continuously varying trait.
The photo and accompanying graph show variation in height among students of the 1914 class at the Connecticut Agricultural College. Because many genes contribute to height and tend to segregate independently of one another, the cumulative contribution of different combinations of alleles to height forms a *continuous* distribution of possible heights, in which the extremes are much rarer than the intermediate values. Variation can also arise due to environmental factors such as nutrition.

found he was unable to obtain a pure-breeding yellow strain by crossing individual yellow mice with each other. Individuals homozygous for the yellow allele died, because the yellow allele was pleiotropic: One effect was yellow coat color, but another was a lethal developmental defect.

 Data analysis When Cuenot crossed yellow mice, what ratio of yellow to wild-type mice did he observe?

A pleiotropic allele may be dominant with respect to one phenotypic consequence (yellow fur) and recessive with respect to another (lethal developmental defect). Pleiotropic effects are difficult to predict, because a gene that affects one trait often performs other, unknown functions.

Pleiotropic effects are characteristic of many inherited disorders in humans, including cystic fibrosis and sickle cell anemia (discussed in chapter 13). In these disorders, multiple symptoms (phenotypes) can be traced back to a single gene defect. Cystic fibrosis patients exhibit clogged blood vessels, overly sticky mucus, salty sweat, liver and pancreas failure, and several other symptoms. It is often difficult to deduce the nature of the primary defect from the range of a gene's pleiotropic effects. As it turns out, all these symptoms of cystic fibrosis are pleiotropic effects of a single defect, a mutation in a gene that encodes a chloride ion transmembrane channel.

Genes may have more than two alleles

Mendel always looked at genes with two alternative alleles. Although any diploid individual can carry only two alleles for a gene, there may be more than two alleles in a population. The example of ABO blood types in humans, described later on, involves an allelic series with three alleles.

If you think of a gene as a sequence of nucleotides in a DNA molecule, then the number of possible alleles is huge because even a single nucleotide change could produce a new allele. In reality, the number of alleles possible for any gene is constrained, but usually more than two alleles exist for any gene in an outbreeding population. The dominance relationships of these alleles cannot be predicted, but can be determined by observing the phenotypes for the various heterozygous combinations.

Dominance is not always complete

Mendel's idea of dominant and recessive traits can seem hard to explain in terms of modern biochemistry. For example, if a recessive trait is caused by the loss of function of an enzyme encoded by the recessive allele, then why should a heterozygote, with only half the activity of this enzyme, have the same appearance as a homozygous dominant individual?

The answer is that enzymes usually act in pathways and not alone. These pathways, as you have seen in earlier chapters, can be highly complex in terms of inputs and outputs, and they can sometimes tolerate large reductions in activity of single enzymes in the pathway without reductions in the level of the end-product. When this is the case, complete dominance will be observed; however, not all genes act in this way.

Incomplete dominance

In **incomplete dominance,** the heterozygote is intermediate in appearance between the two homozygotes. For example, in a cross between red- and white-flowering Japanese four o'clocks, described in figure 12.12, all the F_1 offspring have pink flowers—indicating that neither red nor white flower color was dominant. Looking only at the F_1, we might conclude that this is a case of blending inheritance. But when two of the F_1 pink flowers are crossed, they produce red-, pink-, and white-flowered plants in a 1:2:1 ratio. In this case the phenotypic ratio is the same as the genotypic ratio because all three genotypes can be distinguished.

Codominance

Most genes in a population possess several different alleles, and often no single allele is dominant; instead, each allele has its own effect, and the heterozygote shows some aspect of the phenotype of both homozygotes. The alleles are said to be **codominant.**

Codominance can be distinguished from incomplete dominance by the appearance of the heterozygote. In incomplete dominance, the heterozygote is intermediate between the two homozygotes, whereas in codominance, some aspect of both alleles is seen in the heterozygote. One of the clearest human examples is found in the human blood groups.

The different phenotypes of human blood groups are based on the response of the immune system to proteins on the surface of red blood cells. In homozygotes a single type of protein is found on the surface of cells, and in heterozygotes, two kinds of protein are found, leading to codominance.

The human ABO blood group system

The gene that determines ABO blood types encodes an enzyme that adds sugar molecules to proteins on the surface of red blood cells. These sugars act as recognition markers for the immune system (see chapter 51). The gene that encodes the enzyme, designated I, has three common alleles: I^A, whose product adds galactosamine; I^B, whose product adds galactose; and i, which codes for a protein that does not add a sugar.

Hypothesis: *The pink F_1 observed in a cross of red and white Japanese four o'clock flowers is due to failure of dominance and is not an example of blending inheritance.*

Prediction: *If pink F_1 are self-crossed, they will yield progeny the same as the Mendelian monohybrid genotypic ratio. This would be 1 red: 2 pink: 1 white.*

Test: *Perform the cross and count progeny.*

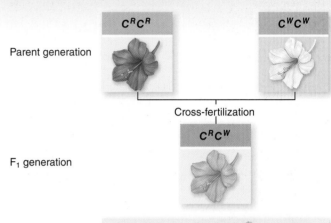

Result: *When this cross is performed, the expected outcome is observed.*

Conclusion: *Flower color in Japanese four o'clock plants exhibits incomplete dominance.*

Further Experiments: *How many offspring would you need to count to be confident in the observed ratio?*

Figure 12.12 Incomplete dominance. In a cross between a red-flowered (genotype C^RC^R) Japanese four o'clock and a white-flowered one (C^WC^W), neither allele is dominant. The heterozygous progeny have pink flowers and the genotype C^RC^W. If two of these heterozygotes are crossed, the phenotypes of their progeny occur in a ratio of 1:2:1 (red:pink:white).

The three alleles of the I gene can be combined to produce six different genotypes. An individual heterozygous for the I^A and I^B alleles produces both forms of the enzyme and exhibits both galactose and galactosamine on red blood cells. Because both alleles are expressed simultaneously in heterozygotes, the I^A and I^B alleles are codominant. Both I^A and I^B are dominant over the i allele, because both I^A and I^B alleles lead to sugar addition,

Alleles	Blood Type	Sugars Exhibited	Donates and Receives
I^AI^A, I^Ai (I^A dominant to i)	A	Galactosamine	Receives A and O Donates to A and AB
I^BI^B, I^Bi (I^B dominant to i)	B	Galactose	Receives B and O Donates to B and AB
I^AI^B (codominant)	AB	Both galactose and galactosamine	Universal receiver Donates to AB
ii (i is recessive)	O	None	Receives O Universal donor

Figure 12.13 ABO blood groups illustrate both codominance and multiple alleles. There are three alleles of the I gene: I^A, I^B, and i. I^A and I^B are both dominant to i (see types A and B), but codominant to each other (see type AB). The genotypes that give rise to each blood type are shown with the associated phenotypes in terms of sugars added to surface proteins and the body's reaction after a blood transfusion.

whereas the i allele does not. The different combinations of the three alleles produce four different phenotypes (figure 12.13):

1. Type A individuals add only galactosamine. They are either I^AI^A homozygotes or I^Ai heterozygotes (two genotypes).
2. Type B individuals add only galactose. They are either I^BI^B homozygotes or I^Bi heterozygotes (two genotypes).
3. Type AB individuals add both sugars and are I^AI^B heterozygotes (one genotype).
4. Type O individuals add neither sugar and are ii homozygotes (one genotype).

These four different cell-surface phenotypes are called the **ABO blood groups.**

A person's immune system can distinguish among these four phenotypes. If a type A individual receives a transfusion of type B blood, the recipient's immune system recognizes the "foreign" antigen (galactose) and attacks the donated blood cells, causing them to clump, or agglutinate. The same thing would happen if the donated blood is type AB. However, if the donated blood is type O, no immune attack occurs, because there are no galactose antigens.

In general, any individual's immune system can tolerate a transfusion of type O blood, and so type O is termed the "universal donor." Because neither galactose nor galactosamine is foreign to type AB individuals (whose red blood cells have both sugars), those individuals may receive any type of blood, and type AB is termed the "universal recipient." Nevertheless, matching blood is preferable for any transfusion.

Phenotypes may be affected by the environment

Another assumption, implicit in Mendel's work, is that the environment does not affect the relationship between genotype and phenotype. For example, the soil in the abbey yard where Mendel performed his experiments was probably not uniform, and yet its possible effect on the expression of traits was ignored. But in reality, although the expression of genotype produces phenotype, the environment can affect this relationship.

Environmental effects are not limited to the external environment. For example, the alleles of some genes encode heat-sensitive products that are affected by differences in internal body temperature. The ch allele in Himalayan rabbits and Siamese cats encodes a heat-sensitive version of the enzyme tyrosinase, which as you may recall is involved in albinism (figure 12.14). The Ch version of the enzyme is inactivated at temperatures above about 33°C. At the surface of the torso and head of these animals, the temperature is above 33°C and tyrosinase is inactive, producing a whitish coat. At the extremities, such as the tips of the ears and tail, the temperature is usually below 33°C and the enzyme is active, allowing production of melanin that turns the coat in these areas a dark color.

? Inquiry question Many studies of identical twins separated at birth have revealed phenotypic differences in their development (height, weight, etc.). If these are identical twins, can you propose an explanation for these differences?

In epistasis, interactions of genes alter genetic ratios

The last simplistic assumption in Mendel's model is that the products of genes do not interact. But the products of genes may not act independently of one another, and the interconnected behavior of gene products can change the ratio expected by independent assortment, even if the genes are on different chromosomes that do exhibit independent assortment.

Given the interconnected nature of metabolism, it should not come as a surprise that many gene products are not independent. Genes that act in the same metabolic pathway, for example, should show some form of dependence at the level of function. In such cases, the ratio Mendel would predict is not readily observed, but it is still there in an altered form.

Temperature below 33°C, tyrosinase active, dark pigment

Temperature above 33°C, tyrosinase inactive, no pigment

Figure 12.14 Siamese cat. The pattern of coat color is due to an allele that encodes a temperature-sensitive form of the enzyme tyrosinase.

In the tests of Mendel's ideas that followed the rediscovery of his work, scientists had trouble obtaining Mendel's simple ratios, particularly with dihybrid crosses. Sometimes, it was not possible to identify successfully each of the four phenotypic classes expected, because two or more of the classes looked alike.

An example of this comes from the analysis of particular varieties of corn, *Zea mays*. Some commercial varieties exhibit a purple pigment called anthocyanin in their seed coats,

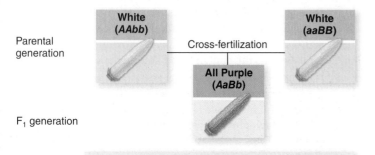

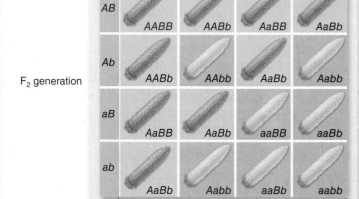

9/16 Purple: 7/16 White

a.

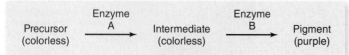

b.

Figure 12.15 How epistasis affects grain color.
a. Crossing some white varieties of corn yields an all purple F₁. Self-crossing the F₁ yields 9 purple:7 white. This can be explained by the presence of two genes, each encoding an enzyme necessary for the production of purple pigment. Unless both enzymes are active (genotype is $A\_B\_$), no pigment is expressed. *b.* The biochemical pathway for pigment production with enzymes encoded by A and B genes.

 Data analysis Mouse coat color is affected by a number of genes, including one that causes total loss of pigment (albinism) and another that leads to black/brown fur. A black mouse is crossed to another black mouse, yielding progeny with a ratio of 9 black:3 brown:4 albino. How can you explain these data if these two genes segregate independently?

whereas others do not. In 1918, geneticist R. A. Emerson crossed two true-breeding corn varieties, each lacking anthocyanin pigment. Surprisingly, all of the F₁ plants produced purple seeds.

When two of these pigment-producing F₁ plants were crossed to produce an F₂ generation, 56% were pigment producers and 44% were not. This is clearly not what Mendel's ideas would lead us to expect. Emerson correctly deduced that two genes were involved in producing pigment, and that the second cross had thus been a dihybrid cross. According to Mendel's theory, gametes in a dihybrid cross could combine in 16 equally possible ways—so the puzzle was to figure out how these 16 combinations could occur in the two phenotypic groups of progeny. Emerson multiplied the fraction that were pigment producers (0.56) by 16 to obtain 9, and multiplied the fraction that lacked pigment (0.44) by 16 to obtain 7. Emerson therefore had a *modified ratio* of 9:7 instead of the usual 9:3:3:1 ratio (figure 12.15).

This modified ratio is easily rationalized by considering the function of the products encoded by these genes. When gene products act sequentially, as in a biochemical pathway, an allele expressed as a defective enzyme early in the pathway blocks the flow of material through the rest of the pathway. In this case, it is impossible to judge whether the later steps of the pathway are functioning properly. This type of gene interaction, in which one gene can interfere with the expression of another, is the basis of the phenomenon called **epistasis.**

The pigment anthocyanin is the product of a two-step biochemical pathway:

$$\begin{array}{ccccc} & \text{enzyme 1} & & \text{enzyme 2} & \\ \textbf{starting molecule} & \longrightarrow & \textbf{intermediate} & \longrightarrow & \textbf{anthocyanin} \\ \text{(colorless)} & & \text{(colorless)} & & \text{(purple)} \end{array}$$

To produce pigment, a plant must possess at least one functional copy of each enzyme's gene. The dominant alleles encode functional enzymes, and the recessive alleles encode nonfunctional enzymes. Of the 16 genotypes predicted by random assortment, 9 contain at least one dominant allele of both genes; they therefore produce purple progeny. The remaining 7 genotypes lack dominant alleles at *either or both* loci (3 + 3 + 1 = 7) and so produce colorless progeny, giving the phenotypic ratio of 9:7 that Emerson observed (see figure 12.15).

You can see that although this ratio is not the expected dihybrid ratio, it is a modification of the expected ratio.

Learning Outcomes Review 12.6

Mendel's model assumes that each trait is specified by one gene with only two alleles, no environmental effects alter a trait, and gene products act independently. All of these prove to be oversimplifications. Traits produced by the action of multiple genes (polygenic inheritance) have continuous variation. One gene can affect more than one trait (pleiotropy). Genes may have more than two alleles, and these may not show simple dominance. In incomplete dominance, the heterozygote is intermediate between the two homozygotes, and in codominance the heterozygote shows aspects of both homozygotes, both of which alter the monohybrid ratio. The action of genes is not always independent, which can result in modified dihybrid ratios.

■ *In the cross in figure 12.15, what proportion of F₂ will be white because they are homozygous recessive for one of the two genes?*

12.1 The Mystery of Heredity

Early plant biologists produced hybrids and saw puzzling results.
Plant breeders noticed that some forms of a trait can disappear in one generation only to reappear later, that is, they segregate rather than blend.

Mendel used mathematics to analyze his crosses.
Mendel's experiments involved reciprocal crosses between true-breeding pea varieties followed by one or more generations of self-fertilization. His mathematical analysis of experimental results led to the present model of inheritance.

12.2 Monohybrid Crosses: The Principle of Segregation (figure 12.5)

The F_1 generation exhibits only one of two traits, without blending.
Mendel called the trait visible in the F_1 the dominant trait; the other he termed recessive.

The F_2 generation exhibits both traits in a 3:1 ratio.
When F_1 plants are self-fertilized, the F_2 shows a consistent ratio of 3 dominant:1 recessive. We call this 3:1 ratio the Mendelian monohybrid ratio.

The 3:1 ratio is actually 1:2:1.
Mendel then examined the F_2 and found the recessive F_2 plants always bred true, but only one out of three dominant F_2 bred true. This means the 3:1 ratio is actually 1 true-breeding dominant:2 non-true-breeding dominant:1 recessive.

Mendel's Principle of Segregation explains monohybrid observations.
Traits are determined by discrete factors we now call genes. These exist in alternative forms we call alleles. Individuals carrying two identical alleles for a gene are said to be homozygous, and individuals carrying different alleles are said to be heterozygous. The genotype is the entire set of alleles of all genes possessed by an individual. The phenotype is the individual's appearance due to these alleles.

The Principle of Segregation states that during gamete formation, the two alleles of a gene separate (segregate). Parental alleles then randomly come together to form the diploid zygote. The physical basis of segregation is the separation of homologues during anaphase of meiosis I.

The Punnett square allows symbolic analysis.
Punnett squares are formed by placing the gametes from one parent along the top of the square with the gametes from the other parent along the side. Zygotes formed from gamete combinations form the blocks of the square (figure 12.6).

Some human traits exhibit dominant/recessive inheritance.
Certain human traits have been found to have a Mendelian basis (table 12.1). Inheritance patterns in human families can be analyzed and inferred using a pedigree diagram of earlier generations.

12.3 Dihybrid Crosses: The Principle of Independent Assortment (figure 12.9)

Traits in a dihybrid cross behave independently.
If parents differing in two traits are crossed, the F_1 will be all dominant. Each F_1 parent can produce four different gametes that can be combined to produce 16 possible outcomes in the F_2. This yields a phenotypic ratio of 9:3:3:1 of the four possible phenotypes.

Mendel's Principle of Independent Assortment explains dihybrid results.
The Principle of Independent Assortment states that different traits segregate independently of one another. The physical basis of independent assortment is the independent behavior of different pairs of homologous chromosomes during meiosis I.

12.4 Probability: Predicting the Results of Crosses

Two probability rules help predict monohybrid cross results.
The rule of addition states that the probability of two independent events occurring is the sum of their individual probabilities. The rule of multiplication, or product rule, states that the probability of two independent events *both* occurring is the product of their individual probabilities.

Dihybrid cross probabilities are based on monohybrid cross probabilities.
A dihybrid cross is essentially two independent monohybrid crosses. The product rule applies and can be used to predict the cross's outcome.

12.5 The Testcross: Revealing Unknown Genotypes (figure 12.10)

In a testcross, an unknown genotype is crossed with a homozygous recessive genotype. The F_1 offspring will all be the same if the unknown genotype is homozygous dominant. The F_1 offspring will exhibit a 1:1 dominant:recessive ratio if the unknown genotype is heterozygous.

12.6 Extensions to Mendel

In polygenic inheritance, more than one gene can affect a single trait.
Many traits, such as human height, are due to multiple additive contributions by many genes, resulting in continuous variation.

In pleiotropy, a single gene can affect more than one trait.
A pleiotropic effect occurs when an allele affects more than one trait. These effects are difficult to predict.

Genes may have more than two alleles.
There may be more than two alleles of a gene in a population. Given the possible number of DNA sequences, this is not surprising.

Dominance is not always complete.
In incomplete dominance the heterozygote exhibits an intermediate phenotype; the monohybrid genotypic and phenotypic ratios are the same (figure 12.12). Codominant alleles each contribute to the phenotype of a heterozygote.

Phenotypes may be affected by the environment.
Genotype determines phenotype, but the environment will have an effect on this relationship. Environment means both external and internal factors. For example, in Siamese cats, a temperature-sensitive enzyme produces more pigment in the colder peripheral areas of the body.

In epistasis, interactions of genes alter genetic ratios.
Genes encoding enzymes that act in a single biochemical pathway are not independent. In corn, anthocyanin pigment production requires the action of two enzymes. Doubly heterozygous individuals for these enzymes yield a 9:7 ratio when self-crossed (figure 12.15).

UNDERSTAND

1. What property distinguished Mendel's investigation from previous studies?

   a. Mendel used true-breeding pea plants.
   b. Mendel quantified his results.
   c. Mendel examined many different traits.
   d. Mendel examined the segregation of traits.

2. The F_1 generation of the monohybrid cross purple (PP) × white (pp) flower pea plants should

   a. all have white flowers.
   b. all have a light purple or blended appearance.
   c. all have purple flowers.
   d. have ¾ purple flowers, and ¼ white flowers.

3. The F_1 plants from the previous question are allowed to self-fertilize. The phenotypic ratio for the F_2 should be

   a. all purple.
   b. 1 purple:1 white.
   c. 3 purple:1 white.
   d. 3 white:1 purple.

4. Which of the following is NOT a part of Mendel's five-element model?

   a. Traits have alternative forms (what we now call alleles).
   b. Parents transmit discrete traits to their offspring.
   c. If an allele is present it will be expressed.
   d. Traits do not blend.

5. An organism's _____ is/are determined by its _____.

   a. genotype; phenotype
   b. phenotype; genotype
   c. alleles; phenotype
   d. genes; alleles

6. Phenotypes like height in humans, which show a continuous distribution, are usually the result of

   a. an alteration of dominance for multiple alleles of a single gene.
   b. the presence of multiple alleles for a single gene.
   c. the action of one gene on multiple phenotypes.
   d. the action of multiple genes on a single phenotype.

APPLY

1. Japanese four o'clocks that are red and tall are crossed to white short ones, producing an F_1 that is pink and tall. If these genes assort independently, and the F_1 is self-crossed, what would you predict for the ratio of F_2 phenotypes?

   a. 3 red tall:1 white short
   b. 1 red tall:2 pink short:1 white short
   c. 3 pink tall:6 red tall:3 white tall:1 pink short:2 red short:1 white short
   d. 3 red tall:6 pink tall:3 white tall:1 red short:2 pink short:1 white short

2. If the two genes in the previous question showed complete linkage, what would you predict for an F_2 phenotypic ratio?

   a. 1 red tall:2 pink short:1 white short
   b. 1 red tall:2 red short:1 white short
   c. 1 pink tall:2 red tall:1 white short
   d. 1 red tall:2 pink tall:1 white short

3. What is the probability of obtaining an individual with the genotype bb from a cross between two individuals with the genotype Bb?

   a. ½
   b. ¼
   c. ⅛
   d. 0

4. In a cross of $Aa\ Bb\ cc\ X\ Aa\ Bb\ Cc,$ what is the probability of obtaining an individual with the genotype $AA\ Bb\ Cc$?

   a. $1/16$
   b. $3/16$
   c. $1/64$
   d. $3/64$

5. When you cross true-breeding tall and short tobacco plants you get an F_1 that is intermediate in height. When this F_1 is self-crossed, it yields an F_2 with a continuous distribution of heights. What is the best explanation for these data?

   a. Height is determined by a single gene with incomplete dominance.
   b. Height is determined by a single gene with many alleles.
   c. Height is determined by the additive effects of many genes.
   d. Height is determined by epistatic genes.

6. Mendel's model assumes that each trait is determined by a single factor with alternate forms. We now know that this is too simplistic and that

   a. a single gene may affect more than one trait.
   b. a single trait may be affected by more than one gene.
   c. a single gene always affects only one trait, but traits may be affected by more than one gene.
   d. a single gene can affect more than one trait, and traits may be affected by more than one gene.

SYNTHESIZE

1. Create a Punnett square for the following crosses and use this to predict phenotypic ratio for dominant and recessive traits. Dominant alleles are indicated by uppercase letters and recessive are indicated by lowercase letters. For parts b and c, predict ratios using probability and the product rule.

   a. A monohybrid cross between individuals with the genotype Aa and Aa
   b. A dihybrid cross between two individuals with the genotype $AaBb$
   c. A dihybrid cross between individuals with the genotype $AaBb$ and $aabb$

2. Explain how the events of meiosis can explain both segregation and independent assortment.

3. In mice, there is a yellow strain that when crossed yields 2 yellow:1 black. How could you explain this observation? How could you test this with crosses?

4. In mammals, a variety of genes affect coat color. One of these is a gene with mutant alleles that results in the complete loss of pigment, or albinism. Another controls the type of dark pigment with alleles that lead to black or brown colors. The albinistic trait is recessive, and black is dominant to brown. Two black mice are crossed and yield 9 black:4 albino:3 brown. How would you explain these results?

ONLINE RESOURCE

www.ravenbiology.com

Understand, Apply, and Synthesize—enhance your study with animations that bring concepts to life and practice tests to assess your understanding. Your instructor may also recommend the interactive eBook, individualized learning tools, and more.

Chapter 13

Chromosomes, Mapping, and the Meiosis–Inheritance Connection

Chapter Contents

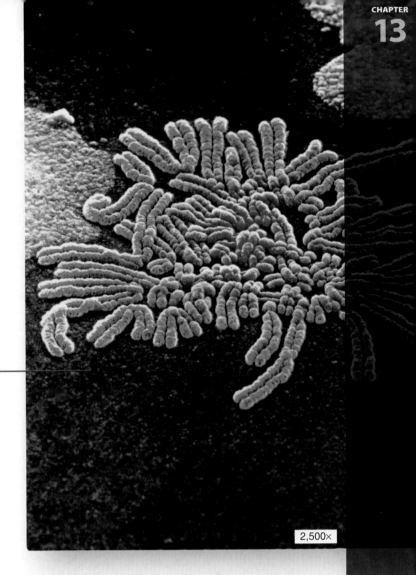

2,500×

Introduction

Mendel's experiments opened the door to understanding inheritance, but many questions remained. In the early part of the 20th century, we did not know the nature of the factors whose behavior Mendel had described. The next step, which involved many researchers in the early part of the century, was uniting information about the behavior of chromosomes, seen in the picture, and the inheritance of traits. The basis for Mendel's principles of segregation and independent assortment lie in events that occur during meiosis.

The behavior of chromosomes during meiosis not only explains Mendel's principles, but leads to new and different approaches to the study of heredity. The ability to construct genetic maps is one of the most powerful tools of classical genetic analysis. The tools of genetic mapping developed in flies and other organisms in combination with information from the Human Genome Project now allow us to determine the location of genes and isolate those that are involved in genetic diseases.

Sex Linkage and the Chromosomal Theory of Inheritance

Learning Outcomes

1. Describe sex-linked inheritance in fruit flies.
2. Explain the evidence for genes being on chromosomes.

A central role for chromosomes in heredity was first suggested in 1900 by the German geneticist Carl Correns, in one of the papers announcing the rediscovery of Mendel's work. Soon after, observations that similar chromosomes paired with one another during meiosis led directly to the **chromosomal theory of inheritance,** first formulated by the American Walter Sutton in 1902.

Morgan correlated the inheritance of a trait with sex chromosomes

In 1910, Thomas Hunt Morgan, studying the fruit fly *Drosophila melanogaster,* discovered a mutant male fly with white eyes instead of red (figure 13.1).

Morgan immediately set out to determine whether this new trait would be inherited in a Mendelian fashion. He first crossed the mutant male to a normal red-eyed female to see whether the red-eyed or white-eyed trait was dominant. All of the F_1 progeny had red eyes, so Morgan concluded that red eye color was dominant over white.

The F_1 cross

Following the experimental procedure that Mendel had established long ago, Morgan then crossed the red-eyed flies from the F_1 generation with each other. Of the 4252 F_2 progeny Morgan examined, 782 (18%) had white eyes. Although the ratio of red eyes to white eyes in the F_2 progeny was greater than 3:1, the results of the cross nevertheless provided clear evidence that eye color segregates. However, something about the outcome was strange and totally unpredicted by Mendel's theory—*all of the white-eyed F_2 flies were males!* (figure 13.2)

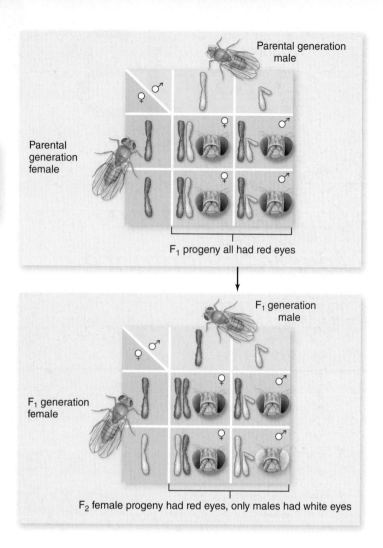

F_1 progeny all had red eyes

F_2 female progeny had red eyes, only males had white eyes

Testcross

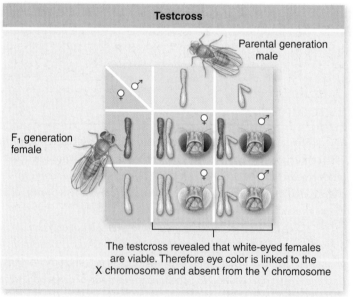

The testcross revealed that white-eyed females are viable. Therefore eye color is linked to the X chromosome and absent from the Y chromosome

Figure 13.2 The chromosomal basis of sex linkage. White-eyed male flies are crossed to red-eyed females. The F_1 flies all have red eyes, as expected for a recessive white-eye allele. In the F_2, all of the white-eyed flies are male because the Y chromosome lacks the white-eye (*white*) gene. Inheritance of the sex chromosomes correlates with eye color, showing the *white* gene is on the X chromosome.

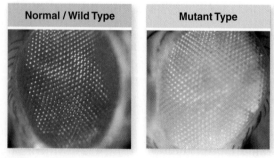

Figure 13.1 Red-eyed (wild-type) and white-eyed (mutant) *Drosophila.* Mutations are heritable alterations in genetic material. By studying the inheritance pattern of white and red alleles (located on the X chromosome), Morgan first demonstrated that genes are on chromosomes.

The testcross

Morgan sought an explanation for this result. One possibility was simply that white-eyed female flies don't exist; such individuals might not be viable for some unknown reason. To test this idea, Morgan testcrossed the female F_1 progeny with the original white-eyed male. He obtained white-eyed and red-eyed flies of both sexes in a 1:1:1:1 ratio, just as Mendel's theory had predicted (figure 13.2). Therefore, white-eyed female flies are viable. Given that white-eyed females can exist, Morgan turned to the nature of the chromosomes in males and females for an explanation.

The gene for eye color lies on the X chromosome

In *Drosophila*, the sex of an individual is determined by the number of copies it has of a particular chromosome, the **X chromosome.** Observations of *Drosophila* chromosomes revealed that female flies have two X chromosomes, but male flies have only one. In males, the single X chromosome pairs in meiosis with a dissimilar partner called the **Y chromosome.** These two chromosomes are termed **sex chromosomes** because of their association with sex.

During meiosis, a female produces only X-bearing gametes, but a male produces both X-bearing and Y-bearing gametes. When fertilization involves an X sperm, the result is an XX zygote, which develops into a female; when fertilization involves a Y sperm, the result is an XY zygote, which develops into a male.

The solution to Morgan's puzzle is that the gene causing the white-eye trait in *Drosophila* resides only on the X chromosome—it is absent from the Y chromosome. (We now know that the Y chromosome in flies carries almost no functional genes.) A trait determined by a gene on the X chromosome is said to be **sex-linked,** or X-linked, because it is associated with the sex of the individual. Knowing the white-eye trait is recessive to the red-eye trait, we can now see that Morgan's result was a natural consequence of the Mendelian segregation of chromosomes (see figure 13.2).

Morgan's experiment was one of the most important in the history of genetics because it presented the first clear evidence that the genes determining Mendelian traits do indeed reside on the chromosomes, as Sutton had proposed. Mendelian traits segregate in genetic crosses because homologues separate during gamete formation.

Learning Outcomes Review 13.1

Morgan showed that the trait for white eyes in *Drosophila* segregated with the sex of offspring. X and Y chromosomes also segregate with sex. This correlates the behavior of a trait with the behavior of chromosomes. This finding supported the chromosomal theory of inheritance, which states that traits are carried on chromosomes.

■ *What are the expectations for a cross of white-eyed females to red-eyed males?*

13.2 Sex Chromosomes and Sex Determination

Learning Outcomes

1. Describe the relationship between sex chromosomes and sex determination.
2. Explain the genetic consequences of dosage compensation in mammals.

The structure and number of sex chromosomes vary in different species (table 13.1). In the fruit fly, *Drosophila*, females are XX and males XY, which is also the case for humans and other mammals. However, in birds, the male has two Z chromosomes, and the female has a Z and a W chromosome. Some insects, such as grasshoppers, have no Y chromosome—females are XX and males are characterized as XO (O indicates the absence of a chromosome).

In humans, the Y chromosome generally determines maleness

In chapter 10, you learned that humans have 46 chromosomes (23 pairs). Twenty-two of these pairs are perfectly matched in both males and females and are called **autosomes.** The remaining pair are the sex chromosomes: XX in females, and XY in males.

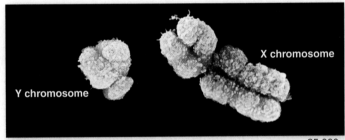

Y chromosome

X chromosome

35,000×

TABLE 13.1	Sex Determination in Some Organisms	Female	Male
Humans, *Drosophila*		XX	XY
Birds		ZW	ZZ
Grasshoppers		XX	XO
Honeybees		Diploid	Haploid

The Y chromosome in males is highly condensed. Because few genes on the Y chromosome are expressed, recessive alleles on a male's single X chromosome have no *active* counterpart on the Y chromosome.

The "default" setting in human embryonic development leads to female development. Some of the active genes on the Y chromosome, notably the *SRY* gene, are responsible for the masculinization of genitalia and secondary sex organs, producing features associated with "maleness" in humans. Consequently, any individual with *at least one Y chromosome* is normally a male.

The exceptions to this rule actually provide support for this mechanism of sex determination. For example, movement of part of the Y chromosome to the X chromosome can cause otherwise XX individuals to develop as male. There is also a genetic disorder that causes a failure to respond to the androgen hormones (androgen insensitivity syndrome) that causes XY individuals to develop as female. Lastly, mutations in *SRY* itself can cause XY individuals to develop as females.

This form of sex determination seen in humans is shared among mammals, but is not universal in vertebrates. Among fishes and some species of reptiles, environmental factors can cause changes in the expression of this sex-determining gene, and thus in the sex of the adult individual.

Some human genetic disorders display sex linkage

From ancient times, people have noted conditions that seem to affect males to a greater degree than females. Red-green color blindness is one well-known condition that is more common in males because the gene affected is carried on the X chromosome.

Another example is hemophilia, a disease that affects a single protein in a cascade of proteins involved in the formation of blood clots. Thus, in an untreated hemophiliac, even minor cuts will not stop bleeding. This form of hemophilia is caused by an X-linked recessive allele; women who are heterozygous for the allele are asymptomatic carriers, and men who receive an X chromosome with the recessive allele exhibit the disease.

The allele for hemophilia was introduced into a number of different European royal families by Queen Victoria of England. Because these families kept careful genealogical records, we have an extensive pedigree for this condition. In the five generations after Victoria, ten of her male descendants have had hemophilia as shown in the pedigree in figure 13.3.

The Russian house of Romanov inherited this condition through Alexandra Feodorovna, a granddaughter of Queen

Figure 13.3 The royal hemophilia pedigree. Queen Victoria, shown at the bottom center of the photo, was a carrier for hemophilia. Two of Victoria's four daughters, Alice and Beatrice, inherited the hemophilia allele from Victoria. Two of Alice's daughters are standing behind Victoria (wearing feathered boas): Princess Irene of Prussia *(right)* and Alexandra *(left)*, who would soon become czarina of Russia. Both Irene and Alexandra were also carriers of hemophilia. From the pedigree, it is clear that Alice introduced hemophilia into the Russian and Prussian royal houses, and Victoria's daughter Beatrice introduced it into the Spanish royal house. Victoria's son Leopold, himself a victim, also transmitted the disorder in a third line of descent. Half-shaded symbols represent carriers with one normal allele and one defective allele; fully shaded symbols represent affected individuals.

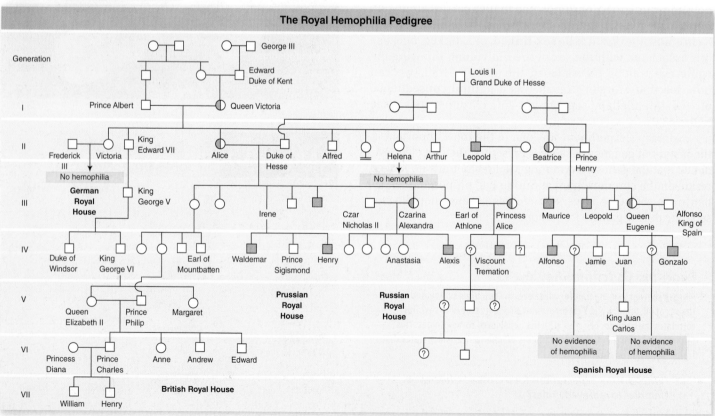

Victoria. She married Czar Nicholas II, and their only son, Alexis, was afflicted with the disease. The entire family was executed during the Russian revolution. (Recently, a woman who had long claimed to be Anastasia, a surviving daughter, was shown not to be a Romanov using modern genetic techniques to test her remains.)

Ironically, this condition has not affected the current British royal family, because Victoria's son Edward, who became King Edward VII, did not receive the hemophilia allele. All of the subsequent rulers of England are his descendants.

Dosage compensation prevents doubling of sex-linked gene products

Although males have only one copy of the X chromosome and females have two, female cells do not produce twice as much of the proteins encoded by genes on the X chromosome. Instead, one of the X chromosomes in females is inactivated early in embryonic development, shortly after the embryo's sex is determined. This inactivation is an example of **dosage compensation,** which ensures an equal level of expression from the sex chromosomes despite a differing number of sex chromosomes in males and females. (In *Drosophila,* by contrast, dosage compensation is achieved by increasing the level of expression on the male X chromosome.)

Which X chromosome is inactivated in females varies randomly from cell to cell. If a woman is heterozygous for a sex-linked trait, some of her cells will express one allele and some the other. The inactivated X chromosome is highly condensed, making it visible as an intensely staining **Barr body**, seen below, attached to the nuclear membrane.

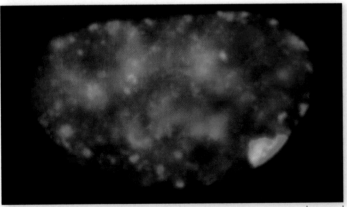

4 μm

X-chromosome inactivation can lead to genetic mosaics

X-chromosome inactivation to produce dosage compensation is not unique to humans but is true of all mammals. Females that are heterozygous for X-chromosome alleles are **genetic mosaics:** Their individual cells may express different alleles, depending on which chromosome is inactivated.

One example is the calico cat, a female that has a patchy distribution of dark fur, orange fur, and white fur (figure 13.4). The dark fur and orange fur are due to heterozygosity for a gene on the

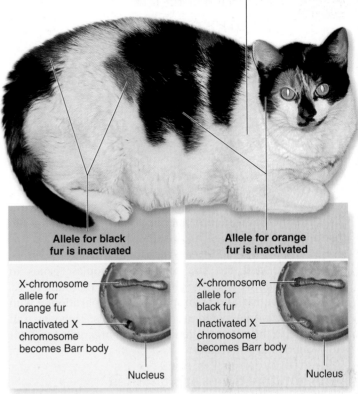

Second gene causes patchy distribution of pigment: white fur = no pigment, orange or black fur = pigment

Allele for black fur is inactivated

X-chromosome allele for orange fur

Inactivated X chromosome becomes Barr body

Nucleus

Allele for orange fur is inactivated

X-chromosome allele for black fur

Inactivated X chromosome becomes Barr body

Nucleus

Figure 13.4 A calico cat. The cat is heterozygous for alleles of a coat color gene that produce either black fur or orange fur. This gene is on the X chromosome, so the different-colored fur is due to inactivation of one X chromosome. The patchy distribution and white color is due to a second gene that is epistatic to the coat color gene and thus masks its effects.

X chromosome that determines pigment color. One allele results in dark fur, and another allele results in orange fur. Which of these colors is observed in any particular patch is due to inactivation of one X chromosome: If the chromosome containing the orange allele is inactivated, then the fur will be dark, and vice versa.

The patchy distribution of color, and the presence of white fur, is due to a second gene that is epistatic to the fur color gene (see chapter 12). That is, the presence of this second gene produces a patchy distribution of pigment, with some areas totally lacking pigment. In the areas that lack pigment, the effect of either fur color allele is masked. Thus, in this one animal we can see an excellent example of both epistasis and X inactivation.

Learning Outcomes Review 13.2

Sex determination begins with the presence or absence of certain chromosomes termed the sex chromosomes. Additional factors may influence sex determination in different species. In humans, males are XY, and therefore they exhibit recessive traits for alleles on the X chromosome. In mammalian females, one X chromosome in each cell becomes inactivated to balance the levels of gene expression. This random inactivation can lead to genetic mosaics.

■ *Would you expect an XXX individual to be viable? If so, would that individual be male or female?*

Exceptions to the Chromosomal Theory of Inheritance

Learning Outcome

1. *Describe the inheritance pattern for genes contained in a chloroplast or mitochondrion DNA.*

Although the chromosomal theory explains most inheritance, there are exceptions. Primarily, these are due to the presence of DNA in organelle genomes, specifically in mitochondria and chloroplasts. Non-Mendelian inheritance via organelles was studied in depth by Ruth Sager, who in the face of universal skepticism constructed the first map of chloroplast genes in *Chlamydomonas,* a unicellular green alga, in the 1960s and 1970s.

Mitochondria and chloroplasts are not partitioned with the nuclear genome by the process of meiosis. Thus any trait that is due to the action of genes in these organelles will not show Mendelian inheritance.

Mitochondrial genes are inherited from the female parent

Organelles are usually inherited from only one parent, generally the mother. When a zygote is formed, it receives an equal contribution of the nuclear genome from each parent, but it gets all of its mitochondria from the egg cell, which contains a great deal more cytoplasm (and thus organelles). As the zygote divides, these original mitochondria divide as well and are partitioned randomly.

As a result, the mitochondria in every cell of an adult organism can be traced back to the original maternal mitochondria present in the egg. This mode of uniparental (one-parent) inheritance from the mother is called **maternal inheritance.**

In humans, the disease Leber's hereditary optic neuropathy (LHON) shows maternal inheritance. The genetic basis of this disease is a mutant allele for a subunit of NADH dehydrogenase. The mutant allele reduces the efficiency of electron flow in the electron transport chain in mitochondria (see chapter 7), in turn reducing overall ATP production. Some nerve cells in the optic system are particularly sensitive to reduction in ATP production, resulting in neural degeneration.

A mother with this disease will pass it on to all of her progeny, whereas a father with the disease will not pass it on to any of his progeny. Note that this condition differs from sex-linked inheritance because males and females are equally affected.

Chloroplast genes may also be passed on uniparentally

The inheritance pattern of chloroplasts is also usually maternal, although both paternal and biparental inheritance of chloroplasts may be observed in some species. Carl Correns first hypothesized in 1909 that chloroplasts were responsible for

inheritance of variegation (mixed green and white leaves) in the plant commonly known as the four o'clock *(Mirabilis jalapa)*. The offspring exhibited the phenotype of the female parent, regardless of the male's phenotype.

In Sager's work on *Chlamydomonas,* resistance to the antibiotic streptomycin was shown to be transmitted via the chloroplast DNA from only the mt$^+$ mating type. The mt$^-$ mating type does not contribute chloroplast DNA to the zygote formed by fusion of mt$^+$ and mt$^-$ gametes.

Learning Outcome Review 13.3

The genomes of mitochondria and chloroplasts divide independently of the nucleus. These organelles are carried in the cytoplasm of the egg cell, so any traits determined by these genomes are maternally inherited and thus do not follow Mendelian rules. In some species, however, chloroplasts may be passed on paternally or biparentally.

■ *How can you explain the lack of mt$^-$ chloroplast DNA in Chlamydomonas zygotes from mt$^-$ by mt$^+$ crosses?*

Genetic Mapping

Learning Outcomes

1. *Describe how genes on the same chromosome will segregate.*
2. *Explain the relationship between frequency of recombinant progeny and map distance.*
3. *Calculate map distances from the frequency of recombinants in testcrosses.*

We have seen that Mendelian traits are determined by genes located on chromosomes and that the independent assortment of Mendelian traits reflects the independent assortment of chromosomes in meiosis. This is fine as far as it goes, but it is still incomplete. Of Mendel's seven traits in figure 12.4, six are on different chromosomes and two are on the same chromosome, yet all show independent assortment with one another. The two on the same chromosome should not behave the same as those that are on different chromosomes. In fact, organisms generally have many more genes that assort independently than the number of chromosomes. This means that independent assortment cannot be due only to the random alignment of different chromosomes during meiosis.

Inquiry question Mendel did not examine plant height and pod shape in his dihybrid crosses. The genes for these traits are very close together on the same chromosome. How would this have changed Mendel's results?

The solution to this problem is found in an observation that was introduced in chapter 11: the crossing over of homologues during meiosis. In prophase I of meiosis, homologues appear to physically exchange material by crossing over (figure 13.5). In chapter 11, you saw how this was part of the mechanism that allows homologues, and not sister chromatids, to disjoin at anaphase I.

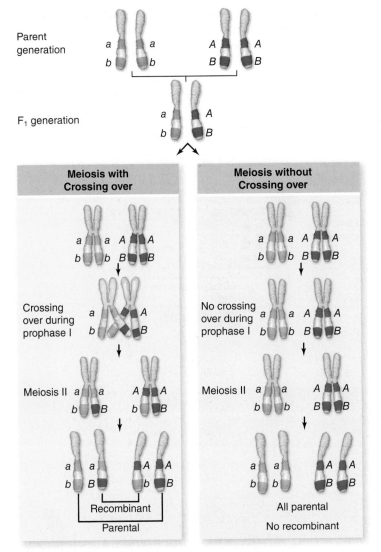

Figure 13.5 Crossing over exchanges alleles on homologues. When a crossover occurs between two loci, it leads to the production of recombinant chromosomes. If no crossover occurs, then the chromosomes will carry the parental combination of alleles.

Genetic recombination exchanges alleles on homologues

Consider a dihybrid cross performed using the Mendelian framework. Two true-breeding parents that each differ with respect to two traits are crossed, producing doubly heterozygous F_1 progeny. If the genes for the two traits are on a single chromosome, then during meiosis we would expect alleles for both loci to segregate together and produce only gametes that resemble the two parental types. But if a crossover occurs between the two loci, then each homologue would carry one allele from each parent and produce gametes that combine these parental traits (see figure 13.5). We call gametes with this new combination of alleles *recombinant* gametes as they are formed by recombining the parental alleles.

The first investigator to provide evidence for this was Morgan, who studied three genes on the X chromosome of *Drosophila*. He found an excess of parental types, which he explained as due to the genes all being on the X chromosome and therefore coinherited (inherited together). He went

further, suggesting that the recombinant genotypes were due to crossing over between homologues during meiosis.

Experiments performed independently by Barbara McClintock and Harriet Creighton in maize and by Curt Stern in *Drosophila* provided evidence for this physical exchange of genetic material. The experiment done by Creighton and McClintock is detailed in figure 13.6. In this experiment, they used a chromosome with two alterations visible under a microscope: a knob on one end of the chromosome and an extension of the other end making it longer. In addition to these visible markers, this chromosome also carried a gene that determines kernel color (colored or colorless) and a gene that determines kernel texture (waxy or starchy).

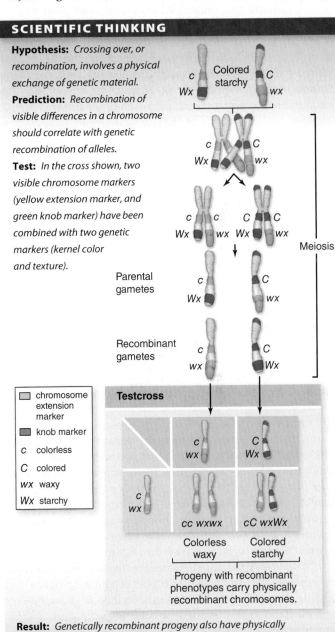

SCIENTIFIC THINKING

Hypothesis: Crossing over, or recombination, involves a physical exchange of genetic material.

Prediction: Recombination of visible differences in a chromosome should correlate with genetic recombination of alleles.

Test: In the cross shown, two visible chromosome markers (yellow extension marker, and green knob marker) have been combined with two genetic markers (kernel color and texture).

Result: Genetically recombinant progeny also have physically recombinant chromosomes.

Conclusion: A physical exchange of genetic material accompanied genetic recombination.

Further Experiments: This experiment was performed using maize. What other genetic model system would you use to test this?

Figure 13.6 The Creighton and McClintock experiment.

chapter **13** *Chromosomes, Mapping, and the Meiosis–Inheritance Connection* **245**

The long chromosome, which also had the knob, carried the dominant colored allele for kernel color *(C)* and the recessive waxy allele for kernel texture *(wx)*. Heterozygotes were constructed with this chromosome paired with a visibly normal chromosome carrying the recessive colorless allele for kernel color *(c)* and the dominant starchy allele for kernel texture *(Wx)* (see figure 13.6). These plants appeared colored and starchy because they were heterozygous for both loci, and they were also heterozygous for the two visibly distinct chromosomes.

These plants, heterozygous for both chromosomal and genetic markers, were testcrossed to colorless waxy plants with normal appearing chromosomes. The progeny were analyzed for both physical recombination (using a microscope to observe chromosome appearance) and genetic recombination (by examining the phenotype of progeny). The results were striking: All of the progeny that were genetically recombinant (appear colored starchy or colorless waxy) also now had only one of the chromosomal markers. That is, genetic recombination was accompanied by physical exchange of chromosomal material.

Recombination is the basis for genetic maps

The ability to map the location of genes on chromosomes using data from genetic crosses is one of the most powerful tools of genetics. The insight that allowed this technique, like many great insights, is so simple as to seem obvious in retrospect.

Morgan had already suggested that the frequency with which a particular group of recombinant progeny appeared was a reflection of the relative location of genes on the chromosome. An undergraduate in Morgan's laboratory, Alfred Sturtevant put this observation on a quantitative basis. Sturtevant reasoned that the frequency of recombination observed in crosses could be used as a measure of genetic distance. That is, as physical distance on a chromosome increases, so does the probability of recombination (crossover) occurring between the gene loci. Using this logic, the frequency of recombinant gametes produced is a measure of their distance apart on a chromosome.

Linkage data

To be able to measure recombination frequency easily, investigators use a testcross instead of intercrossing the F_1 progeny as Mendel did. In a testcross, as described earlier, the phenotypes of the progeny reflect the gametes produced by the doubly heterozygous F_1 individual. In the case of recombination, progeny that appear parental have not undergone crossover, and progeny that appear recombinant have experienced a crossover between the two loci in question (see figure 13.5).

When genes are close together, the number of recombinant progeny is much lower than the number of parental progeny, and the genes are defined on this basis as being **linked.** The number of recombinant progeny divided by total progeny gives a value defined as the **recombination frequency.** This value is converted to a percentage, and each 1% of recombination is termed a **map unit.** This unit has been named the centimorgan (cM) for T. H. Morgan, although it is also called simply a map unit (m.u.) as well.

Constructing maps

Constructing genetic maps then becomes a simple process of performing testcrosses with doubly heterozygous individuals

and counting progeny to determine percent recombination. This is best shown with an example using a two-point cross.

Drosophila homozygous for two mutations, vestigial wings *(vg)* and black body *(b)*, are crossed to flies homozygous for the wild type, or normal alleles, of these genes *(vg⁺ b⁺)*. The doubly heterozygous F_1 progeny are then testcrossed to homozygous

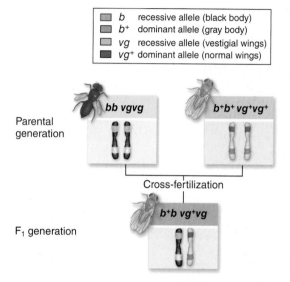

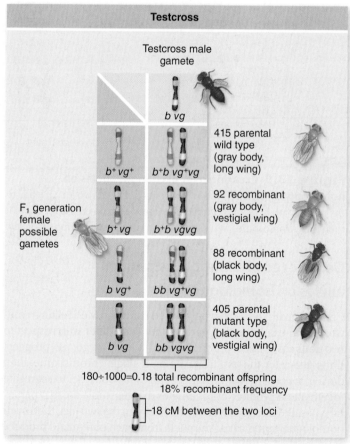

Figure 13.7 Two-point cross to map genes. Flies homozygous for long wings *(vg⁺)* and gray bodies *(b⁺)* are crossed to flies homozygous for vestigial wings *(vg)* and black bodies *(b)*. Both vestigial wing and black body are recessive to the normal (wildtype) long wing and gray body. The F_1 progeny are then testcrossed to homozygous vestigial black to produce the progeny for mapping. Data are analyzed in the text.

recessive individuals *(vg b/vg b)*, and progeny are counted (figure 13.7). The data are shown here:

vestigial wings, black body *(vg b)*	405	(parental)
long wings, gray body *(vg⁺ b⁺)*	415	(parental)
vestigial wings, gray body *(vg b⁺)*	92	(recombinant)
long wings, black body *(vg⁺ b)*	88	(recombinant)
Total Progeny	1000	

The numbers of recombinant progeny are added together, and this sum is divided by total progeny to produce the recombination frequency. The recombination frequency is 92 + 88 divided by 1000, or 0.18. Converting this number to a percentage yields 18 cM as the map distance between these two loci.

Multiple crossovers can yield independent assortment results

As the distance separating loci increases, the probability of recombination occurring between them during meiosis also increases. What happens when more than one recombination event occurs?

If homologues undergo two crossovers between loci, then the parental combination is restored. This leads to an underestimate of the true genetic distance because not all events can be noted. As a result, the relationship between true distance on a chromosome and the recombination frequency is not linear. It begins as a straight line, but the slope decreases; the curve levels off at a recombination frequency of 0.5 (figure 13.8).

At long distances, multiple events between loci become frequent. In this case, odd numbers of crossovers (1, 3, 5) produce recombinant gametes, and no crossover or even numbers of crossovers (0, 2, 4) produce parental gametes. At large enough distances, these frequencies are about equal, leading to the number of recombinant gametes being equal to the number of parental gametes, and the loci exhibit independent assortment! This is how Mendel could use two loci on the same chromosome and have them assort independently.

 Data analysis What would Mendel have observed in a dihybrid cross if the two loci were 10 cM apart on the same chromosome? Is this likely to have led him to the idea of independent assortment?

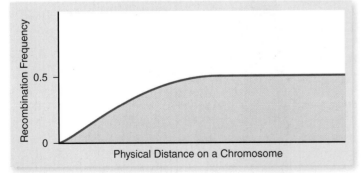

Figure 13.8 Relationship between true distance and recombination frequency. As distance on a chromosome increases, the recombinants are not all detected due to double crossovers. This leads to a curve that levels off at 0.5.

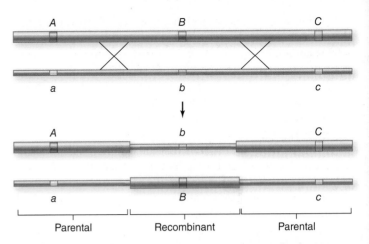

Figure 13.9 Use of a three-point cross to order genes. In a two-point cross, the outside loci appear parental for double crossovers. With the addition of a third locus, the two crossovers can still be detected because the middle locus will be recombinant. This double crossover class should be the least frequent, so whatever locus has recombinant alleles in this class must be in the middle.

Three-point crosses can be used to put genes in order

Because multiple crossovers reduce the number of observed recombinant progeny, longer map distances are not accurate. As a result, when geneticists try to construct maps from a series of two-point crosses, determining the order of genes is problematic. Using three loci instead of two, or a three-point cross, can help solve the problem.

In a three-point cross, the gene in the middle allows us to see recombination events on either side. For example, a double crossover for the two outside loci is actually a single crossover between the middle locus and each outside locus (figure 13.9).

The probability of two crossovers is equal to the product of the probability of each individual crossover, each of which is relatively low. Therefore, in any three-point cross, the class of offspring with two crossovers is the least frequent class. Analyzing these individuals to see which locus is recombinant identifies the locus that lies in the middle of the three loci in the cross (see figure 13.9).

In practice, geneticists use three-point crosses to determine the order of genes, then use data from the closest two-point crosses to determine distances. Longer distances are generated by simple addition of shorter distances. This avoids using inaccurate measures from two-point crosses between distant loci.

Genetic maps can be constructed for the human genome

Human genes can be mapped, but the data must be derived from historical pedigrees, such as those of the royal families of Europe mentioned earlier. The principle is the same—genetic distance is still proportional to recombination frequency—but the analysis requires the use of complex statistics and summing data from many families.

The difficulty of mapping in humans

Looking at nonhuman animals with extensive genetic maps, the majority of genetic markers have been found at loci where alleles cause morphological changes, such as variant eye color, body color, or wing morphology in flies. In humans, such alleles generally, but not always, correspond to what we consider disease states. As recently as the early 1980s, the number of markers for the human genome numbered in the hundreds. Because the human genome is so large, however, this low number of markers would never provide dense enough coverage to use for mapping.

Another consideration is that the disease-causing alleles are those that we wish to map, but they occur at low frequencies in the population. Any one family would be highly unlikely to carry multiple disease alleles, the segregation of which would allow for mapping.

Anonymous markers

This situation changed with the development of **anonymous markers,** genetic markers that can be detected using molecular techniques, but that do not cause a detectable phenotype. The nature of these markers has evolved with technology, leading to a standardized set of markers scattered throughout the genome. These markers, which have a relatively high density, can be detected using techniques that are easy to automate. As a result of analysis, geneticists now have several thousand markers to work with, instead of hundreds, and have produced a human genetic map that would have been unthinkable 25 years ago (figure 13.10). (In the following chapters of this unit, you'll learn about some of the molecular techniques that have been developed for use with genomes.)

Single-nucleotide polymorphisms (SNPs)

The information developed from sequencing the human genome can then be used to identify and map single bases that differ between individuals. Any differences between individuals in populations are termed *polymorphisms;* polymorphisms affecting a single base of a gene locus are called **single-nucleotide polymorphisms (SNPs).** Over 3.1 million such differences have been identified and are being placed on both the genetic map and the human genome sequence. This confluence of techniques will enable the ultimate resolution of genetic analysis.

The recent progress in gene mapping applies to more than just the relatively small number of genes that show simple Mendelian inheritance. The development of a high-resolution genetic map, and the characterization of millions of SNPs, opens up the possibility of being able to characterize complex quantitative traits in humans as well.

On a more practical level, the types of molecular markers described earlier are used in forensic analysis. Although not quite as rapid as some television programs would have you believe, this does allow rapid DNA testing of crime scene samples to help eliminate or confirm crime suspects and for paternity testing.

Learning Outcomes Review 13.4

Crossing over during meiosis exchanges alleles on homologues. This recombination of alleles can be used to map the location of genes. Genes that are close together are said to be linked, and exhibit an excess of parental versus recombinant types in a testcross. The frequency of recombination in testcrosses is used as a measure of genetic distance. Loci separated by large distances have multiple crossovers between them, which can lead to independent assortment.

■ *If two genes assort independently, can you tell if they are on a single chromosome and far apart or on two different chromosomes?*

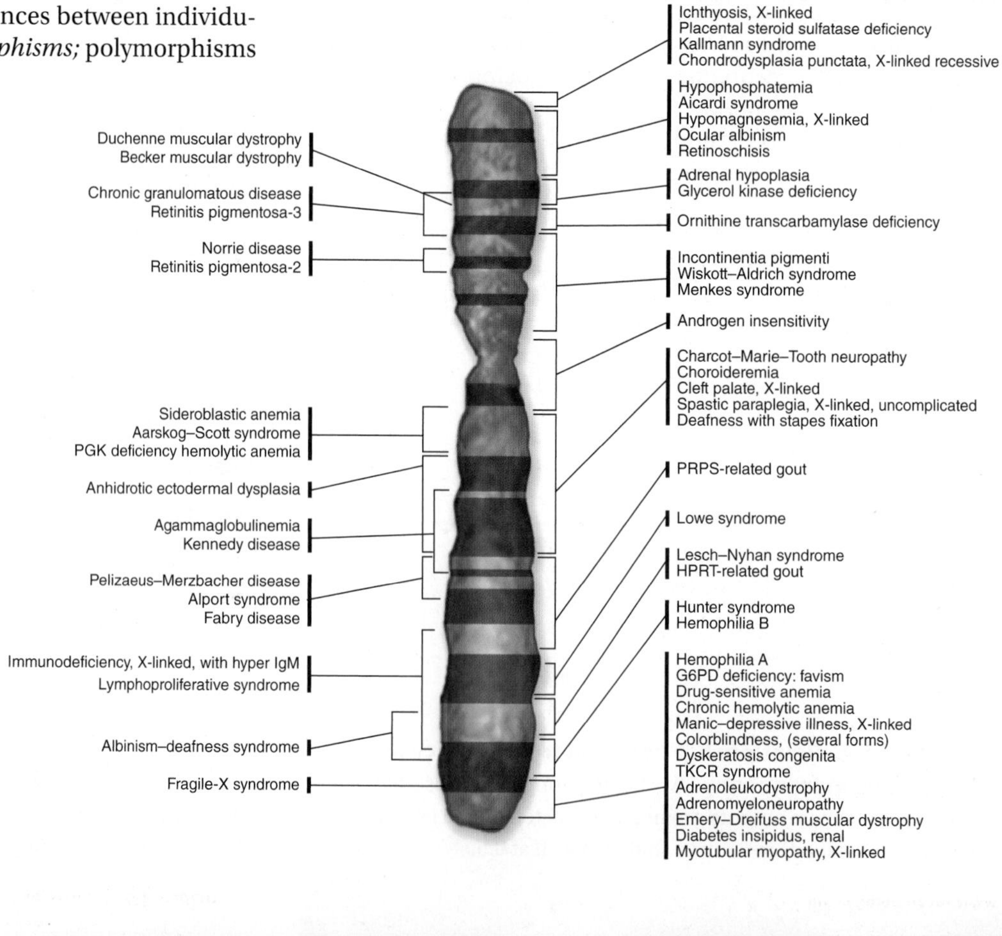

Figure 13.10 The human X-chromosome gene map. Only a partial map for the human X chromosome is presented here; a more detailed map would require a much larger figure. The black bands represent staining patterns that can be seen under the microscope, and the constriction represents the centromere. Analysis of the sequence of the X chromosome indicates 1098 genes on the X chromosome. Many of these may have mutant alleles that can affect disease states. By analyzing inheritance patterns of affected and unaffected individuals, the 59 diseases shown have been traced to specific segments of the X chromosome, indicated by brackets.

Ichthyosis, X-linked
Placental steroid sulfatase deficiency
Kallmann syndrome
Chondrodysplasia punctata, X-linked recessive

Hypophosphatemia
Aicardi syndrome
Hypomagnesemia, X-linked
Ocular albinism
Retinoschisis

Adrenal hypoplasia
Glycerol kinase deficiency

Ornithine transcarbamylase deficiency

Incontinentia pigmenti
Wiskott–Aldrich syndrome
Menkes syndrome

Androgen insensitivity

Charcot–Marie–Tooth neuropathy
Choroideremia
Cleft palate, X-linked
Spastic paraplegia, X-linked, uncomplicated
Deafness with stapes fixation

PRPS-related gout

Lowe syndrome

Lesch–Nyhan syndrome
HPRT-related gout

Hunter syndrome
Hemophilia B

Hemophilia A
G6PD deficiency: favism
Drug-sensitive anemia
Chronic hemolytic anemia
Manic–depressive illness, X-linked
Colorblindness, (several forms)
Dyskeratosis congenita
TKCR syndrome
Adrenoleukodystrophy
Adrenomyeloneuropathy
Emery–Dreifuss muscular dystrophy
Diabetes insipidus, renal
Myotubular myopathy, X-linked

Duchenne muscular dystrophy
Becker muscular dystrophy

Chronic granulomatous disease
Retinitis pigmentosa-3

Norrie disease
Retinitis pigmentosa-2

Sideroblastic anemia
Aarskog–Scott syndrome
PGK deficiency hemolytic anemia

Anhidrotic ectodermal dysplasia

Agammaglobulinemia
Kennedy disease

Pelizaeus–Merzbacher disease
Alport syndrome
Fabry disease

Immunodeficiency, X-linked, with hyper IgM
Lymphoproliferative syndrome

Albinism–deafness syndrome

Fragile-X syndrome

13.5 Selected Human Genetic Disorders

Learning Outcomes

1. Explain how mutations can cause disease.
2. Describe the consequences of nondisjunction in humans.
3. Recognize how genomic imprinting can lead to non-Mendelian inheritance.

Diseases that run in families have been known for many years. These can be nonlife-threatening like albinism, or may result in premature death like Huntington's, which were used as examples of recessive and dominant traits in humans previously. A small sample of diseases due to alterations of alleles of a single gene is provided in table 13.2. We will discuss the nature of these genetic changes later in chapter 15. In this section we discuss some of the genetic disorders that have been found in human populations.

Sickle cell anemia is due to altered hemoglobin

The first human disease shown to be the result of a mutation in a protein was sickle cell anemia. It is caused by a defect in the oxygen carrier molecule, hemoglobin, that leads to impaired oxygen delivery to tissues. The defective hemoglobin molecules stick to one another, leading to stiff, rodlike structures that alter the shape of the red blood cells that carry them. These

Figure 13.11 Sickle cell anemia. In individuals homozygous for the sickle cell trait, many of the red blood cells have sickled or irregular shapes, such as the cell on the far left.

red blood cells take on a characteristic shape that led to the name "sickle cell" (figure 13.11).

Individuals homozygous for the sickle cell allele exhibit intermittent illness and reduced life span. Individuals heterozygous for the sickle cell allele are indistinguishable from normal individuals in a normal oxygen environment, although their red cells do exhibit reduced ability to carry oxygen.

The sickle cell allele is particularly prevalent in people of African descent. In some regions of Africa, up to 45% of the population is heterozygous for the trait, and 6% are

TABLE 13.2	Some Important Genetic Disorders			
Disorder	**Symptom**	**Defect**	**Dominant/Recessive**	**Frequency Among Human Births**
Cystic fibrosis	Mucus clogs lungs, liver, and pancreas	Failure of chloride ion transport mechanism	Recessive	1/2500 (Caucasians)
Sickle cell anemia	Blood circulation is poor	Abnormal hemoglobin molecules	Recessive	1/600 (African Americans)
Tay–Sachs disease	Central nervous system deteriorates in infancy	Defective enzyme (hexosaminidase A)	Recessive	1/3500 (Ashkenazi Jews)
Phenylketonuria	Brain fails to develop in infancy, treatable with dietary restriction	Defective enzyme (phenylalanine hydroxylase)	Recessive	1/12,000
Hemophilia	Blood fails to clot	Defective blood-clotting factor VIII	X-linked recessive	1/10,000 (Caucasian males)
Huntington disease	Brain tissue gradually deteriorates in middle age	Production of an inhibitor of brain cell metabolism	Dominant	1/24,000
Muscular dystrophy (Duchenne)	Muscles waste away	Degradation of myelin coating of nerves stimulating muscles	X-linked recessive	1/3700 (males)
Hypercholesterolemia	Excessive cholesterol levels in blood lead to heart disease	Abnormal form of cholesterol cell surface receptor	Dominant	1/500

homozygous. This proportion of heterozygotes is higher than would be expected on the basis of chance alone. It turns out that heterozygosity confers a greater resistance to the blood-borne parasite that causes malaria. In regions of central Africa where malaria is endemic, the sickle cell allele also occurs at a high frequency.

The sickle cell allele is not the end of the story for the β-globin gene; a large number of other alterations of this gene have been observed that lead to anemias. In fact, for hemoglobin, which is composed of two α-globins and two β-globins, over 700 structural variants have been cataloged. It is estimated that 7% of the human population worldwide are carriers for different inherited hemoglobin disorders.

The Human Gene Mutation Database has cataloged the nature of many disease alleles, including the sickle cell allele. The majority of alleles seem to be simple changes. Almost 57% of the close to 85,000 alleles in the Human Gene Mutation Database are single-base substitutions. Another 24% are due to small insertions or deletions of less than 20 bases. This careful survey of disease-causing alterations has also revealed more large-scale changes. This is now termed *copy number variation (CNV)* and appears more important than previously thought.

Nondisjunction of chromosomes changes chromosome number

The failure of homologues or sister chromatids to separate properly during meiosis is called **nondisjunction.** This failure leads to the gain or loss of a chromosome, a condition called **aneuploidy.** The frequency of aneuploidy in humans is surprisingly high, being estimated to occur in 5% of conceptions.

Nondisjunction of autosomes

Humans who have lost even one copy of an autosome are called **monosomics,** and generally do not survive embryonic development. In all but a few cases, humans who have gained an extra autosome (called **trisomics**) also do not survive. Data from clinically recognized spontaneous abortions indicate levels of aneuploidy as high as 35%.

Five of the smallest human autosomes—those numbered 13, 15, 18, 21, and 22—can be present as three copies and still allow the individual to survive, at least for a time. The presence of an extra chromosome 13, 15, or 18 causes severe developmental defects, and infants with such a genetic makeup die within a few months. In contrast, individuals who have an extra copy of chromosome 21 or, more rarely, chromosome 22, usually survive to adulthood. In these people, the maturation of the skeletal system is delayed, so they generally are short and have poor muscle tone. Their mental development is also affected, and children with trisomy 21 show some degree of intellectual disability.

The developmental defect produced by trisomy 21 (figure 13.12) was first described in 1866 by J. Langdon Down; for this reason, it is called Down syndrome. About 1 in every 750 children exhibits Down syndrome, and the frequency is comparable in all racial groups. Similar conditions also occur in chimpanzees and other related primates.

In humans, the defect occurs when a particular small portion of chromosome 21 is present in three copies instead of two. In 97% of the cases examined, all of chromosome 21 is

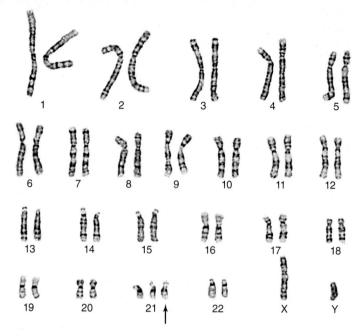

Figure 13.12 Down syndrome. As shown in this male karyotype, Down syndrome is associated with trisomy of chromosome 21 (arrow shows third copy of chromosome 21).

present in three copies. In the other 3%, a small portion of chromosome 21 containing the critical segment has been added to another chromosome by a process called *translocation* (see chapter 15); it exists along with the normal two copies of chromosome 21. This latter condition is known as *translocation Down syndrome.*

In mothers younger than 20 years of age, the risk of giving birth to a child with Down syndrome is about 1 in 1700; in mothers 20 to 30 years old, the risk is only about 1 in 1400. However, in mothers 30 to 35 years old, the risk rises to 1 in 750, and by age 45, the risk is as high as 1 in 16 (figure 13.13).

Primary nondisjunctions are far more common in women than in men because all of the eggs a woman will ever produce have developed to the point of prophase in meiosis I by the time she is born. By the time a woman has children, her eggs are as old as she is. Therefore, there is a much greater chance for cell-division problems of various kinds, including those that cause primary nondisjunction, to accumulate over time in female gametes. In contrast, men produce new sperm daily. For this reason, the age of the mother is more critical than that of the father for couples contemplating childbearing.

Nondisjunction of sex chromosomes

Individuals who gain or lose a sex chromosome do not generally experience the severe developmental abnormalities caused by similar changes in autosomes. Although such individuals have somewhat abnormal features, they often reach maturity and in some cases may be fertile.

X chromosome nondisjunction. When X chromosomes fail to separate during meiosis, some of the gametes produced possess both X chromosomes, and so are XX gametes; the other gametes have no sex chromosome and are designated "O" (figure 13.14).

If an XX gamete combines with an X gamete, the resulting XXX zygote develops into a female with one functional

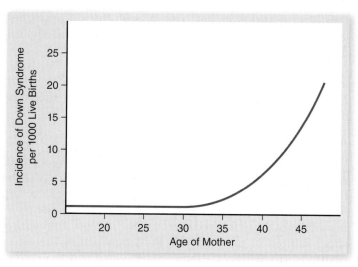

Figure 13.13 Correlation between maternal age and the incidence of Down syndrome. As women age, the chances they will bear a child with Down syndrome increase. After a woman reaches 35, the frequency of Down syndrome rises rapidly.

 Data analysis Over a five-year period between ages 20 and 25, the incidence of Down syndrome increases 0.1 per thousand; over a five-year period between ages 35 and 40, the incidence increases to 8.0 per thousand, 80 times as great. The period of time is the same in both instances. What has changed?

X chromosome and two Barr bodies. She may be taller in stature but is otherwise normal in appearance.

If an XX gamete instead combines with a Y gamete, the effects are more serious. The resulting XXY zygote develops into a male who has many female body characteristics and, in some cases but not all, diminished mental capacity. This condition, called *Klinefelter syndrome,* occurs in about 1 out of every 500 male births.

If an O gamete fuses with a Y gamete, the resulting OY zygote is nonviable and fails to develop further; humans cannot survive when they lack the genes on the X chromosome. But if an O gamete fuses with an X gamete, the XO zygote develops into a sterile female of short stature, with a webbed neck and sex organs that never fully mature during puberty. The mental abilities of an XO individual are in the low-normal range. This condition, called *Turner syndrome,* occurs roughly once in every 5000 female births.

Y chromosome nondisjunction. The Y chromosome can also fail to separate in meiosis, leading to the formation of YY gametes. When these gametes combine with X gametes, the XYY zygotes develop into fertile males of normal appearance. The frequency of the XYY genotype *(Jacob syndrome)* is about 1 per 1000 newborn males.

Genomic imprinting depends on the parental origin of alleles

By the late 20th century, geneticists were confident that they understood the basic mechanisms governing inheritance. It

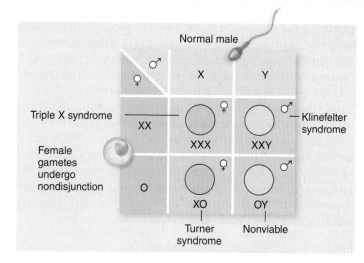

Figure 13.14 How nondisjunction can produce abnormalities in the number of sex chromosomes. When nondisjunction occurs in the production of female gametes, the gamete with two X chromosomes (XX) produces Klinefelter males (XXY) and triple-X females (XXX). The gamete with no X chromosome (O) produces Turner females (XO) and nonviable OY males lacking any X chromosome.

 Inquiry question Can you think of two nondisjunction scenarios that would produce an XXY male?

came as quite a surprise to find that for some genes inheritance depends on the parent of origin. Even stranger, the only two groups that show this pattern are flowering plants and mammals. In **genomic imprinting,** the phenotype caused by a specific allele is exhibited when the allele comes from one parent, but not from the other.

The basis for genomic imprinting is the expression of a gene depending on passage through maternal or paternal germ lines. Some genes are inactivated in the paternal germ line and therefore are not expressed in the zygote. Other genes are inactivated in the maternal germ line, with the same result. This condition makes the zygote effectively haploid for an imprinted gene. The expression of variant alleles of imprinted genes depends on the parent of origin. Furthermore, imprinted genes seem to be concentrated in particular regions of the genome. These regions include genes that are both maternally and paternally imprinted.

Prader–Willi and Angelman syndromes

An example of genomic imprinting in humans involves the two diseases Prader–Willi syndrome (PWS) and Angelman syndrome (AS). The effects of PWS include respiratory distress, obesity, short stature, mild intellectual disability, and obsessive–compulsive behavior. The effects of AS include developmental delay, severe intellectual disability, hyperactivity, aggressive behavior, and inappropriate laughter.

Genetic studies have implicated genes on chromosome 15 for both disorders, but the pattern of inheritance is complementary. The most common cause of both syndromes is a deletion of material on chromosome 15 and, in fact, the same deletion can cause either syndrome. The determining factor is the parental origin of the normal and deleted chromosomes. If the chromosome with the deletion is paternally inherited it causes PWS; if the chromosome with the deletion is maternally inherited it causes AS.

The region of chromosome 15 that is lost is subject to imprinting, with some genes being inactivated in the maternal germ line, and others in the paternal germ line. In PWS, genes are inactivated in the maternal germ line, such that deletion or other functional loss of paternally derived alleles produces the syndrome. The opposite is true for AS syndrome: Genes are inactivated in the paternal germ line, such that loss of maternally derived alleles leads to the syndrome.

Imprinting Is an Example of Epigenetics

Genomic imprinting is actually an example of a more general phenomenon: **epigenetic inheritance.** An epigenetic trait is defined as a stably heritable phenotype resulting from changes in a chromosome without alteration in the DNA sequence. This seems contradictory, but it illustrates the point that the sequence of bases in genes is not the end of the story. Another example from this chapter is X-chromosome inactivation, a phenomenon in which an entire chromosome is silenced. This is inherited through mitotic divisions.

As we will see in chapter 16, the control of gene expression involves the interaction of regulatory proteins with DNA and also with the proteins that are involved in chromosome structure. In some well studied cases, the pattern of imprinting that occurs in the male and female germ line is due to male- and female-specific patterns of DNA methylation and alterations to the proteins that are involved in chromosome structure.

Some genetic defects can be detected early in pregnancy

Although most genetic disorders cannot yet be cured, we are learning a great deal about them, and progress toward successful therapy is being made in many cases. In the absence of a cure, however, the only recourse is to try to avoid producing children with these conditions. The process of identifying parents at risk for having children with genetic defects and of assessing the genetic state of early embryos is called **genetic counseling.**

Pedigree analysis

One way of assessing risks is through pedigree analysis, often employed as an aid in genetic counseling. By analyzing a person's pedigree, it is sometimes possible to estimate the likelihood that the person is a carrier for certain disorders. For example, if a counseling client's family history reveals that a relative has been afflicted with a recessive genetic disorder, such as cystic fibrosis, it is possible that the client is a heterozygous carrier of the recessive allele for that disorder.

When a couple is expecting a child, and pedigree analysis indicates that both of them have a significant chance of being heterozygous carriers of a deleterious recessive allele, the pregnancy is said to be high-risk. In such cases, a significant probability exists that their child will exhibit the clinical disorder.

Another class of high-risk pregnancy is that in which the mothers are older than 35. As discussed earlier, the frequency of Down syndrome increases dramatically in the pregnancies of older women (see figure 13.13).

Amniocentesis

When a pregnancy is diagnosed as high-risk, many women elect to undergo **amniocentesis,** a procedure that permits the prenatal diagnosis of many genetic disorders. In the fourth month of pregnancy, a sterile hypodermic needle is inserted into the expanded uterus of the mother, removing a small sample of the amniotic fluid that bathes the fetus (figure 13.15). Within the fluid are free-floating cells derived from the fetus; once removed, these cells can be grown in cultures in the laboratory.

During amniocentesis, the position of the needle and that of the fetus are usually observed by means of *ultrasound.* The sound waves used in ultrasound are not harmful to mother or fetus, and they permit the person withdrawing the amniotic fluid to do so without damaging the fetus. In addition, ultrasound can be used to examine the fetus for signs of major abnormalities. However, about 1 out of 200 amniocentesis procedures may result in fetal death and miscarriage.

Chorionic villi sampling

In recent years, physicians have increasingly turned to a new, less invasive procedure for genetic screening called **chorionic villi sampling (CVS).** Using this method, the physician removes cells from the chorion, a membranous part of the placenta that nourishes the fetus (figure 13.15). This procedure can be used earlier in pregnancy (by the eighth week) and yields results much more rapidly than does amniocentesis. Risks from chorionic villi sampling are comparable to those for amniocentesis.

To test for certain genetic disorders, genetic counselors look for three characteristics in the cultures of cells obtained from amniocentesis or chorionic villi sampling. First, analysis of the karyotype can reveal aneuploidy (extra or missing chromosomes) and gross chromosomal alterations. Second, in many cases it is possible to test directly for the proper functioning of enzymes involved in genetic disorders. The lack of normal enzymatic activity signals the presence of the disorder. As examples, the lack of the enzyme responsible for breaking down phenylalanine indicates phenylketonuria (PKU); the absence of the enzyme responsible for the breakdown of gangliosides indicates Tay–Sachs disease; and so forth. Additionally, with information from the Human Genome Project, more disease alleles for genetic disorders are known. If there are a small number of alleles for a specific disease in the population, these can be identified as well.

With the changes in human genetics brought about by the Human Genome Project (see chapter 18), it is possible to design tests for many more diseases. Difficulties still exist in

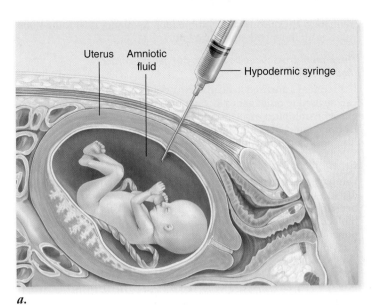

a.

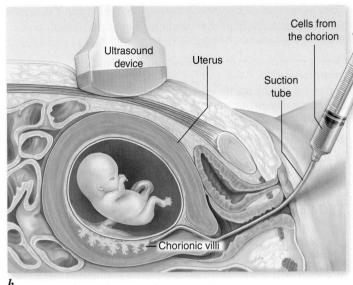

b.

Figure 13.15 Two ways to obtain fetal cells. *a.* In amniocentesis, a needle is inserted into the amniotic cavity, and a sample of amniotic fluid containing some free cells derived from the fetus is withdrawn into a syringe. *b.* In chorionic villi sampling, cells are removed by suction with a tube inserted through the cervix. This can be done as early as the eighth to tenth week. In each case, the cells can be grown in culture, then examined for karyotypes, and used in biochemical and genetic tests.

discerning the number and frequency of disease-causing alleles, but these problems are not insurmountable. At present, tests for at least 13 genes with alleles that lead to clinical syndromes are available. This number is bound to rise and to be expanded to include alleles that do not directly lead to disease states but that predispose a person for a particular disease.

? Inquiry question Based on what you read in this chapter, what reasons could a mother have to undergo CVS, considering its small but potential risks?

Learning Outcomes Review 13.5

Mutations in DNA that result in altered proteins can cause hereditary diseases. Pedigree studies and genetic testing may clarify the risk of disease. At the chromosome level, nondisjunction during meiosis can result in gametes with too few or too many chromosomes, most of which produce inviable offspring. Imprinting refers to inactivation of alleles depending on which parent the alleles come from; offspring in whom imprinting occurs appear haploid for the affected gene even though they are diploid.

■ *During spermatogenesis, is there any difference in outcome between first- and second-division nondisjunction?*

Chapter Review

13.1 Sex Linkage and the Chromosomal Theory of Inheritance

Morgan correlated the inheritance of a trait with sex chromosomes (figure 13.2).
Morgan crossed red-eyed and white-eyed flies and found differences in inheritance based on the sex of offspring. All white-eyed offspring were males, but testcrosses showed that white-eyed females were possible, supporting the idea that the white-eye gene was on the X chromosome.

The gene for eye color lies on the X chromosome.
The inheritance of eye color in *Drosophila* segregates with the X chromosome, a phenomenon termed sex-linked inheritance.

13.2 Sex Chromosomes and Sex Determination

Sex determination in animals is usually associated with a chromosomal difference. In some animals, females have two similar sex chromosomes and males have sex chromosomes that differ. In other species, females have sex chromosomes that differ (table 13.1).

In humans, the Y chromosome generally determines maleness.
The Y chromosome is highly condensed and does not have active counterparts to most genes on the X chromosome. The *SRY* gene on the Y chromosome is responsible for the masculinization of genitalia and secondary sex organs. An XY individual can develop into a sterile female due to mutations in the *SRY* gene or the failure of the embryo to respond to androgens.

Some human genetic disorders display sex linkage (figure 13.3).

Human genetic disorders show sex linkage when the relevant gene is on the X chromosome; hemophilia is an example.

Dosage compensation prevents doubling of sex-linked gene products.

In fruit flies, males double the gene expression from their single X chromosome. In mammals, one of the X chromosomes in a female is randomly inactivated during development.

X-chromosome inactivation can lead to genetic mosaics.

In a mammalian female that is heterozygous for X-chromosome alleles, X inactivation produces a mosaic pattern, as shown in the coat color of calico cats (figure 13.4).

13.3 Exceptions to the Chromosomal Theory of Inheritance

Mitochondrial genes are inherited from the female parent.

Mitochondria have their own genomes and divide independently; they are passed to offspring in the cytoplasm of the egg cell.

Chloroplast genes may also be passed on uniparentally.

Chloroplasts also reside in the cytoplasm, have their own genomes, and divide independently. They are usually inherited maternally.

13.4 Genetic Mapping

Mendel's independent assortment is too simplistic. Genes on the same chromosome may or may not segregate independently.

Genetic recombination exchanges alleles on homologues.

Homologous chromosomes may exchange alleles by crossing over (figure 13.5). This occurs by breakage and rejoining of chromosomes as shown by crosses in which chromosomes carry both visible and genetic markers (figure 13.6).

Recombination is the basis for genetic maps.

Genes close together on a single chromosome are said to be linked. The farther apart two linked genes are, the greater the frequency of recombination. This allows genetic maps to be constructed based on recombination frequency. A map unit is expressed as the percentage of recombinant progeny.

Multiple crossovers can yield independent assortment results.

The probability of multiple crossovers increases with distance between two genes and results in an underestimate of recombination

frequency. The maximum recombination frequency is 50%, the same value as for independent assortment.

Three-point crosses can be used to put genes in order (figure 13.9).

If three genes are used instead of two, data from multiple crossovers can be used to order genes. Longer map distances fail to reflect the effect of multiple crossovers and thus underestimate true distance. By evaluating intervening genes with less separation, more accurate distances can be obtained.

Genetic maps can be constructed for the human genome.

Human genetic mapping was difficult because it required multiple disease-causing alleles segregating in a family. The process has been made easier by the use of anonymous markers, identifiable molecular markers that do not cause a phenotype. Single-nucleotide polymorphisms (SNPs) can be used to detect differences between individuals for identification.

13.5 Selected Human Genetic Disorders

Sickle cell anemia is due to altered hemoglobin.

The phenotypes in sickle cell anemia can all be traced to alterations in the structure of hemoglobin that affect the shape of red blood cells. Over 700 variants of hemoglobin structure have been characterized, some of which also cause disorders.

Nondisjunction of chromosomes changes chromosome number.

Nondisjunction is the failure of homologues or sister chromatids to separate during meiosis. The result is aneuploidy: monosomy or trisomy of a chromosome in the zygote. Most aneuploidies are lethal, but some, such as trisomy 21 in humans (Down syndrome), can result in viable offspring. X-chromosome nondisjunction occurs when X chromosomes fail to separate during meiosis. The resulting gamete carries either XX or O (zero sex chromosomes) (figure 13.14). Y-chromosome nondisjunction results in YY gametes.

Genomic imprinting depends on the parental origin of alleles.

In genomic imprinting, the expression of a gene depends on whether it passes through the maternal or paternal germ line. Imprinted genes appear to be inactivated by methylation. Imprinting produces a haploid phenotype.

Some genetic defects can be detected early in pregnancy.

Genetic defects in humans can be determined by pedigree analysis, amniocentesis, or chorionic villi sampling.

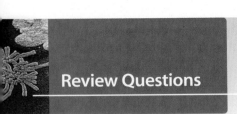

Review Questions

UNDERSTAND

1. Why is the white-eye phenotype always observed in males carrying the white-eye allele?
   a. Because the trait is dominant
   b. Because the trait is recessive
   c. Because the allele is located on the X chromosome and males only have one X
   d. Because the allele is located on the Y chromosome and only males have Y chromosomes

2. In an organism's genome, *autosomes* are
   a. the chromosomes that differ between the sexes.
   b. chromosomes that are involved in sex determination.
   c. only inherited from the mother (maternal inheritance).
   d. all of the chromosomes other than sex chromosomes.

3. What cellular process is responsible for genetic recombination?
   a. The independent alignment of homologous pairs during meiosis I
   b. Separation of the homologues in meiosis I
   c. Separation of the chromatids during meiosis II
   d. Crossing over between homologues
4. The map distance between two genes is determined by the
   a. recombination frequency.
   b. frequency of parental types.
   c. ratio of genes to length of a chromosome.
   d. ratio of parental to recombinant progeny.
5. How many map units separate two alleles if the recombination frequency is 0.07?
   a. 700 cM   b. 70 cM   c. 7 cM   d. 0.7 cM
6. How does maternal inheritance of mitochondrial genes differ from sex linkage?
   a. Mitochondrial genes do not contribute to the phenotype of an individual.
   b. Because mitochondria are inherited from the mother, only females are affected.
   c. Since mitochondria are inherited from the mother, females and males are equally affected.
   d. Mitochondrial genes must be dominant. Sex-linked traits are typically recessive.
7. Which of the following genotypes due to nondisjunction of sex chromosomes is lethal?
   a. XXX   b. XXY   c. OY   d. XO

APPLY

1. A recessive sex-linked gene in humans leads to a loss of sweat glands. A woman heterozygous for this will
   a. have no sweat glands.
   b. have normal sweat glands.
   c. have patches of skin with and without sweat glands.
   d. have an excess of sweat glands.
2. As real genetic distance increases, the distance calculated by recombination frequency becomes an
   a. overestimate due to multiple crossovers that cannot be scored.
   b. underestimate due to multiple crossovers that cannot be scored.
   c. underestimate due to multiple crossovers adding to recombination frequency.
   d. overestimate due to multiple crossovers adding to recombination frequency.
3. Down syndrome is the result of trisomy for chromosome 21. Why is this trisomy viable and trisomy for most other chromosomes is not?
   a. Chromosome 21 is a large chromosome and excess genetic material is less harmful.
   b. Chromosome 21 behaves differently in meiosis I than the other chromosomes.
   c. Chromosome 21 is a small chromosome with few genes so this does less to disrupt the genome.
   d. Chromosome 21 is less prone to nondisjunction than other chromosomes.

4. Genes that are on the same chromosome can show independent assortment
   a. when they are far enough apart for two crossovers to occur.
   b. when they are far enough apart that odd numbers of crossovers is about equal to even.
   c. only if recombination is low for that chromosome.
   d. only if the genes show genomic imprinting.
5. The A and B gene are 10 cM apart on a chromosome. If an A B/a b heterozygote is testcrossed to a b/a b, how many of each progeny class would you expect out of 100 total progeny?
   a. 25 A B, 25 a b, 25 A b, 25 a B
   b. 10 A B, 10 a b
   b. 45 A B, 45 a b
   d. 45 A B, 45 a b, 5 A b, 5 a B
6. During the process of spermatogenesis, a nondisjunction event that occurs during the second division would be
   a. worse than the first division because all four meiotic products would be aneuploid.
   b. better than the first division because only two of the four meiotic products would be aneuploid.
   c. the same outcome as the first division with all four products aneuploid.
   d. the same outcome as the first division as only two products would be aneuploid.

SYNTHESIZE

1. Color blindness is caused by a sex-linked, recessive gene. If a woman, whose father was color blind, marries a man with normal color vision, what percentage of their children will be color blind? What percentage of male children? Of female children?
2. Assume that the genes for seed color and seed shape are located on the same chromosome. A plant heterozygous for both genes is testcrossed wrinkled green with the following results:

green, wrinkled	645
green, round	36
yellow, wrinkled	29
yellow, round	590

   What were the genotypes of the parents, and how far apart are these genes?
3. Is it possible to have a calico cat that is male? Why or why not?

ONLINE RESOURCE

www.ravenbiology.com

Understand, Apply, and Synthesize—enhance your study with animations that bring concepts to life and practice tests to assess your understanding. Your instructor may also recommend the interactive eBook, individualized learning tools, and more.

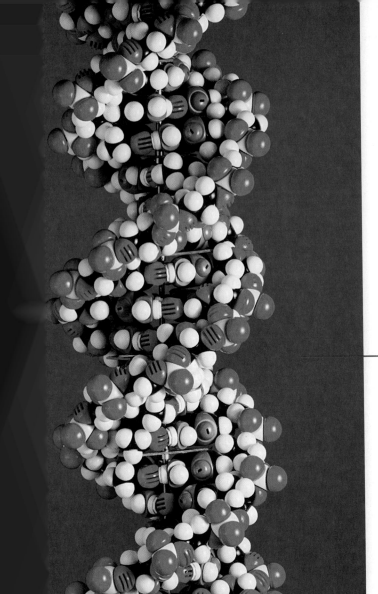

14

DNA: The Genetic Material

Chapter Contents

Introduction

The rediscovery of Mendel at the turn of the 20th century led to a period of rapid discovery of genetic mechanisms detailed in the previous two chapters. One question not directly answered for more than 50 years was perhaps the most simple: What are genes actually made of? Genes were known to be on chromosomes, but they are complex structures composed of DNA, RNA, and protein. This chapter describes the chain of experiments that led to our current understanding of DNA, modeled in the picture above, and of the molecular mechanisms of heredity. These experiments are among the most elegant in science. The elucidation of the structure of DNA was the beginning of a molecular era, whose pace is only accelerating today.

The Nature of the Genetic Material

ing Outcomes

scribe the experiments of Griffith and Avery.
aluate the evidence for DNA as genetic material.

In the previous two chapters, you learned about the nature of inheritance and how genes, which contain the information to specify traits, are located on chromosomes. This finding led to the question of what part of the chromosome actually contains the genetic information. Specifically, biologists wondered about the chemical identity of the genetic information. They knew that chromosomes are composed primarily of both protein and DNA. Which of these organic molecules actually makes up the genes?

Starting in the late 1920s and continuing for about 30 years, a series of investigations addressed this question.

DNA consists of four chemically similar nucleotides. In contrast, protein contains 20 different amino acids that are much more chemically diverse than nucleotides. These characteristics seemed initially to indicate greater informational capacity in protein than in DNA.

However, experiments began to reveal evidence in favor of DNA. We describe three of those major findings in this section.

Griffith finds that bacterial cells can be transformed

The first clue came in 1928 with the work of the British microbiologist Frederick Griffith. Griffith was trying to make a vaccine that would protect against influenza, which was thought at the time to be caused by the bacteria *Streptococcus pneumoniae*. There are two forms of this bacteria: The normal virulent form that causes pneumonia, and a mutant, nonvirulent form that does not. The normal virulent form of this bacterium is referred to as the S form because it forms smooth colonies on a culture dish. The mutant, nonvirulent form, which lacks an enzyme needed to manufacture the polysaccharide coat, is called the R form because it forms rough colonies.

Griffith performed a series of simple experiments in which mice were infected with these bacteria, then monitored for disease symptoms (figure 14.1). Mice infected with the virulent S form died from pneumonia, whereas infection with the nonvirulent R form had no effect. This result shows that the polysaccharide coat is necessary for virulence. If the virulent S form is first heat-killed, infection does not harm the mice, showing that the coat itself is not sufficient to cause disease. Lastly, infecting mice with a mixture of heat-killed S form with live R form caused pneumonia and death in the mice. This was unexpected as neither treatment alone caused disease. Furthermore, high levels of live S form bacteria were found in the lungs of the dead mice.

Somehow, the information specifying the polysaccharide coat had passed from the dead, virulent S bacteria to the live, coatless R bacteria in the mixture, permanently altering the coatless R bacteria into the virulent S variety. Griffith called this transfer of virulence from one cell to another **transformation.** Our modern interpretation is that genetic material was actually transferred between the cells.

Avery, MacLeod, and McCarty identify the transforming principle

The agent responsible for transforming *Streptococcus* went undiscovered until 1944. In a classic series of experiments, Oswald Avery and his coworkers Colin MacLeod and Maclyn McCarty identified the substance responsible for transformation in Griffith's experiment.

They first prepared the mixture of dead S *Streptococcus* and live R *Streptococcus* that Griffith had used. Then they removed as much of the protein as they could from their preparation, eventually achieving 99.98% purity. They found that despite the removal of nearly all protein, the transforming activity was not reduced.

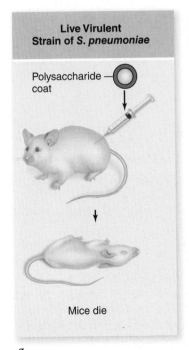

Live Virulent Strain of *S. pneumoniae*

Polysaccharide coat

Mice die

a.

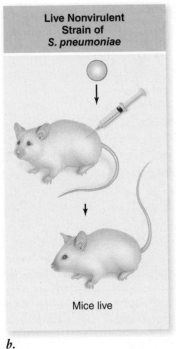

Live Nonvirulent Strain of *S. pneumoniae*

Mice live

b.

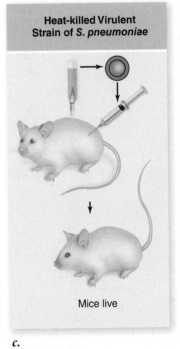

Heat-killed Virulent Strain of *S. pneumoniae*

Mice live

c.

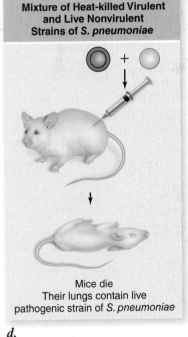

Mixture of Heat-killed Virulent and Live Nonvirulent Strains of *S. pneumoniae*

Mice die
Their lungs contain live pathogenic strain of *S. pneumoniae*

d.

Figure 14.1 Griffith's experiment. Griffith was trying to make a vaccine against pneumonia and instead discovered transformation. *a.* Injecting live virulent bacteria into mice produces pneumonia. Injection of nonvirulent bacteria (*b*) or heat-killed virulent bacteria (*c*) had no effect. *d.* However, a mixture of heat-killed virulent and live nonvirulent bacteria produced pneumonia in the mice. This indicates the genetic information for virulence was transferred from dead, virulent cells to live, nonvirulent cells, transforming them from nonvirulent to virulent.

Moreover, the properties of this substance resembled those of DNA in several ways:

1. The elemental composition agreed closely with that of DNA.
2. When spun at high speeds in an ultracentrifuge, it migrated to the same level (density) as DNA.
3. Extracting lipids and proteins did not reduce transforming activity.
4. Protein-digesting enzymes did not affect transforming activity, nor did RNA-digesting enzymes.
5. DNA-digesting enzymes destroyed all transforming activity.

These experiments supported the identity of DNA as the substance transferred between cells by transformation and indicated that the genetic material, at least in this bacterial species, is DNA.

Hershey and Chase demonstrate that phage genetic material is DNA

Avery's results were not widely accepted at first because many biologists continued to believe that proteins were the repository of hereditary information. But additional evidence supporting Avery's conclusion was provided in 1952 by Alfred Hershey and Martha Chase, who experimented with viruses that infect bacteria. These viruses are called **bacteriophages,** or more simply, **phages.**

Viruses, described in more detail in chapter 27, are much simpler than cells; they generally consist of genetic material (DNA or RNA) surrounded by a protein coat. The phage used in these experiments is called a *lytic* phage because infection causes the cell to burst, or lyse. When such a phage infects a bacterial cell, it first binds to the cell's outer surface and then injects its genetic information into the cell. There, the viral genetic information is expressed by the bacterial cell's machinery, leading to production of thousands of new viruses. The buildup of viruses eventually causes the cell to lyse, releasing progeny phage.

The phage used by Hershey and Chase contains only DNA and protein, and therefore it provides the simplest possible system to differentiate the roles of DNA and protein. Hershey and Chase set out to identify the molecule that the phage injects into the bacterial cells. To do this, they needed a method to label both DNA and protein in unique ways that would allow them to be distinguished. Nucleotides contain

SCIENTIFIC THINKING

Hypothesis: *DNA is the genetic material in bacteriophage.*

Prediction: *The phage life cycle requires reprogramming the cell to make phage proteins. The information for this must be introduced into the cell during infection.*

Test: *DNA can be specifically labeled using radioactive phosphate (^{32}P), and protein can be specifically labeled using radioactive sulfur (^{35}S). Phage are grown on either ^{35}S or ^{32}P, then used to infect cells in two experiments. The phage heads remain attached to the outside of the cell and can be removed by brief agitation in a blender. The cell suspension can be collected by centrifugation, leaving the phage heads in the supernatant.*

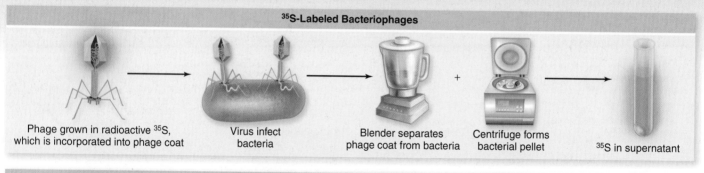

^{35}S-Labeled Bacteriophages

Phage grown in radioactive ^{35}S, which is incorporated into phage coat → Virus infect bacteria → Blender separates phage coat from bacteria + Centrifuge forms bacterial pellet → ^{35}S in supernatant

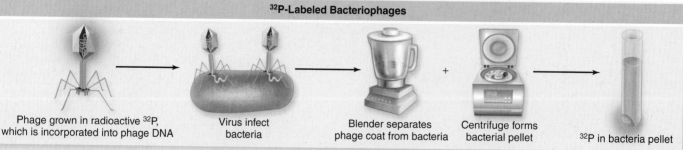

^{32}P-Labeled Bacteriophages

Phage grown in radioactive ^{32}P, which is incorporated into phage DNA → Virus infect bacteria → Blender separates phage coat from bacteria + Centrifuge forms bacterial pellet → ^{32}P in bacteria pellet

Result: *When the experiment is done, only ^{32}P makes it into the cell in any significant quantity.*

Conclusion: *Thus, DNA must be the molecule that is used to reprogram the cell.*

Further Experiments: *How does this experiment complement or extend the work of Avery on the identity of the transforming principle?*

Figure 14.2 Hershey–Chase experiment showed DNA is genetic material for phage.

phosphorus, but proteins do not, and some amino acids contain sulfur, but DNA does not. Thus, the radioactive ^{32}P isotope can be used to label DNA specifically, and the isotope ^{35}S can be used to label proteins specifically. The two isotopes are easily distinguished based on the particles they emit when they decay.

Two experiments were performed (figure 14.2). In one, viruses were grown on a medium containing ^{32}P, which was incorporated into DNA; in the other, viruses were grown on medium containing ^{35}S, which was incorporated into coat proteins. Each group of labeled viruses was then allowed to infect separate bacterial cultures.

After infection, the bacterial cell suspension was agitated in a blender to remove the infecting viral particles from the surfaces of the bacteria. This step ensured that only the part of the virus that had been injected into the bacterial cells—that is, the genetic material—would be detected.

Each bacterial suspension was then centrifuged to produce a pellet of cells for analysis. In the ^{32}P experiment, a large amount of radioactive phosphorus was found in the cell pellet, but in the ^{35}S experiment, very little radioactive sulfur was found in the pellet (see figure 14.2). Hershey and Chase deduced that DNA, and not protein, constituted the genetic information that viruses inject into bacteria.

Learning Outcomes Review 14.1

Experiments with pneumonia-causing bacteria showed that virulence could be passed from one cell to another, a phenomenon termed transformation. When the factor responsible for transformation was purified, it was shown to be DNA. Labeling experiments with phage also indicated that the genetic material was DNA and not protein.

■ *Why was protein an attractive candidate for the genetic material?*

Learning Outcomes

1. *Explain how the Watson–Crick structure rationalized the data available to them.*
2. *Evaluate the significance of complementarity for DNA structure and function.*

A Swiss chemist, Friedrich Miescher, discovered DNA in 1869, only four years after Mendel's work was published—although it is unlikely that Miescher knew of Mendel's experiments.

Miescher extracted a white substance from the nuclei of human cells and fish sperm. The proportion of nitrogen and phosphorus in the substance was different from that found in any other known constituent of cells, which convinced Miescher that he had discovered a new biological substance. He called this substance "nuclein" because it seemed to be specifically associated with the nucleus. Because Miescher's nuclein was slightly acidic, it came to be called *nucleic acid.*

DNA's components were known, but its three-dimensional structure was a mystery

Although the three-dimensional structure of the DNA molecule was not elucidated until Watson and Crick, it was known that it contained three main components (figure 14.3):

1. a five-carbon sugar
2. a phosphate (PO_4) group

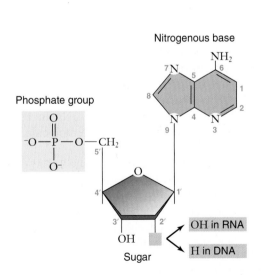

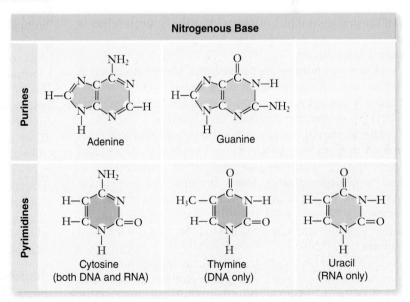

Figure 14.3 Nucleotide subunits of DNA and RNA. The nucleotide subunits of DNA and RNA are composed of three components: a five-carbon sugar (deoxyribose in DNA and ribose in RNA); a phosphate group; and a nitrogenous base (either a purine or a pyrimidine).

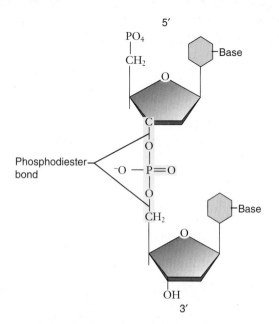

Figure 14.4   A phosphodiester bond.

3. a nitrogen-containing (nitrogenous) base. The base may be a **purine** (adenine, A, or guanine, G), a two-ringed structure; or a **pyrimidine** (thymine, T, or cytosine, C), a single-ringed structure. RNA contains the pyrimidine uracil (U) in place of thymine.

The convention in organic chemistry is to number the carbon atoms of a molecule and then to use these numbers to refer to any functional group attached to a carbon atom (see chapter 3). In the ribose sugars found in nucleic acids, four of the carbon atoms together with an oxygen atom form a five-membered ring. As illustrated in figure 14.3, the carbon atoms are numbered 1′ to 5′, proceeding clockwise from the oxygen atom; the prime symbol (′) indicates that the number refers to a carbon in a sugar rather than to the atoms in the bases attached to the sugars.

Under this numbering scheme, the phosphate group is attached to the 5′ carbon atom of the sugar, and the base is attached to the 1′ carbon atom. In addition, a free hydroxyl (—OH) group is attached to the 3′ carbon atom.

The 5′ phosphate and 3′ hydroxyl groups allow DNA and RNA to form long chains of nucleotides by the process of dehydration synthesis (see chapter 3). The linkage is called a **phosphodiester bond** because the phosphate group is now linked to the two sugars by means of a pair of ester bonds (figure 14.4). Many thousands of nucleotides can join together via these linkages to form long nucleic acid polymers.

Linear strands of DNA or RNA, no matter how long, almost always have a free 5′ phosphate group at one end and a free 3′ hydroxyl group at the other. Therefore, every DNA and RNA molecule has an intrinsic polarity, and we can refer unambiguously to each end of the molecule. By convention, the sequence of bases is usually written in the 5′-to-3′ direction.

Chargaff, Franklin, and Wilkins obtained some structural evidence

To understand the model that Watson and Crick proposed, we need to review the evidence that they had available to construct their model.

Chargaff's rules

A careful study carried out by Erwin Chargaff showed that the nucleotide composition of DNA molecules varied in complex ways, depending on the source of the DNA. This strongly suggested that DNA was not a simple repeating polymer and that it might have the information-encoding properties genetic material requires. Despite DNA's complexity, however, Chargaff observed an important underlying regularity in the ratios of the bases found in native DNA: *The amount of adenine present in DNA always equals the amount of thymine, and the amount of guanine always equals the amount of cytosine.* Two important findings from this work are often called *Chargaff's rules:*

1. The proportion of A always equals that of T, and the proportion of G always equals that of C, or: A = T, and G = C.
2. The ratio of G–C to A–T varies with different species.

As mounting evidence indicated that DNA stored the hereditary information, investigators began to puzzle over how such a seemingly simple molecule could carry out such a complex coding function.

X-ray diffraction patterns of DNA

The technique of X-ray diffraction provided more direct information about the possible structure of DNA. In X-ray diffraction, crystals of a molecule are bombarded with a beam of X-rays. The rays are bent, or diffracted, by the molecules they encounter, and the diffraction pattern is recorded on photographic film. The patterns resemble the ripples created by tossing a rock into a smooth lake. When analyzed mathematically, the diffraction pattern can yield information about the three-dimensional structure of a molecule.

The problem with using this technique with DNA was that in the 1950s, it was impossible to obtain true crystals of natural DNA. However, British researcher Maurice Wilkins learned how to prepare uniformly oriented DNA fibers, and with graduate student Ray Gosling succeeded in obtaining the first crude diffraction information on natural DNA in 1950. Their early X-ray photos suggested that the DNA molecule has the shape of a helix.

The British chemist Rosalind Franklin (figure 14.5a) continued this work, perfecting the technique to obtain ever clearer "pictures" of the oriented DNA fibers. The clearest of these images (figure 14.5b) confirmed that DNA was a helix, and allowed calculation of the dimensions of the molecule, indicating a diameter of about 2 nm and a complete helical turn every 3.4 nm.

Tautomeric forms of bases

One piece of evidence important to Watson and Crick was the form of the bases themselves. Because of the alternating double and single bonds in the bases, they actually exist in equilibrium between two different forms when in solution. The different forms have to do with keto (C=O) versus enol

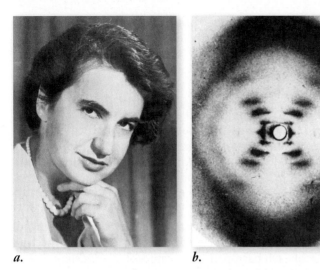

Figure 14.5 Rosalind Franklin's X-ray diffraction patterns. *a.* Rosalind Franklin. *b.* This X-ray diffraction photograph of DNA fibers, made in 1953 by Rosalind Franklin, was interpreted to show the helical structure of DNA.

(C—OH) groups and amino (—NH₂) versus imino (=NH) groups that are attached to the bases. These structural forms are called *tautomers.*

The importance of this distinction is that the two forms exhibit very different hydrogen-bonding possibilities. The predominant forms of the bases contain the keto and amino groups (see figure 14.3), but a prominent biochemistry text of the time actually contained the opposite, and incorrect, information. Legend has it that Watson learned the correct forms while having lunch with a biochemist friend.

The Watson–Crick model fits the available evidence

Learning informally of Franklin's results before they were published in 1953, American chemist James Watson and English molecular biologist Francis Crick, two young investigators at Cambridge University, quickly worked out a likely structure for the DNA molecule (figure 14.6), which we now know was substantially correct. Watson and Crick did not perform a single experiment themselves related to DNA structure; rather, they built detailed molecular models based on the information available.

The key to the model was their understanding that each DNA molecule is actually made up of *two* chains of nucleotides that are intertwined—the double helix.

The phosphodiester backbone

The two strands of the double helix are made up of long polymers of nucleotides, and as described earlier, each strand is made up of repeating sugar and phosphate units joined by phosphodiester bonds (figure 14.7). We call this the *phosphodiester backbone* of the molecule. The two strands of the

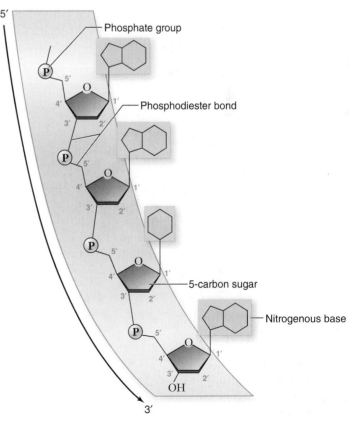

Figure 14.6 The DNA double helix. James Watson *(left)* and Francis Crick *(right)* deduced the structure of DNA in 1953 from Chargaff's rules, knowing the proper tautomeric forms of the bases and using Franklin's diffraction studies.

Figure 14.7 Structure of a single strand of DNA. The phosphodiester backbone is composed of alternating sugar and phosphate groups. The bases are attached to each sugar.

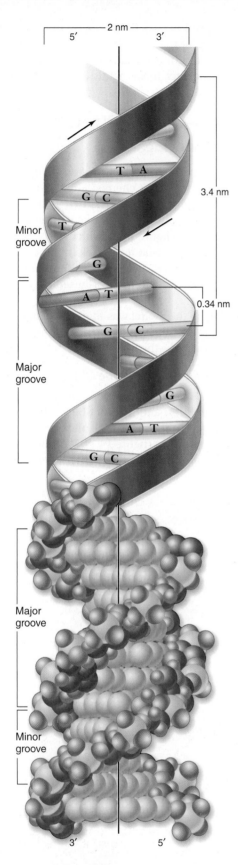

Figure 14.8 The double helix. Shown with the phosphodiester backbone as a ribbon on top and a space-filling model on the bottom. The bases protrude into the interior of the helix where they hold it together by base-pairing. The backbone forms two grooves, the larger major groove and the smaller minor groove.

backbone are then wrapped about a common axis forming a double helix (figure 14.8). The helix is often compared to a spiral staircase, in which the two strands of the double helix are the handrails on the staircase.

Complementarity of bases

Watson and Crick proposed that the two strands were held together by formation of hydrogen bonds between bases on opposite strands. These bonds would result in specific **base-pairs:** Adenine (A) can form two hydrogen bonds with thymine (T) to form an A–T base-pair, and guanine (G) can form three hydrogen bonds with cytosine (C) to form a G–C base-pair (figure 14.9).

Note that this configuration also pairs a two-ringed purine with a single-ringed pyrimidine in each case, so that the diameter of each base-pair is the same. This consistent diameter is indicated by the X-ray diffraction data.

We refer to this pattern of base-pairing as *complementary,* which means that although the strands are not identical, they each can be used to specify the other by base-pairing. If the sequence of one strand is ATGC, then the complementary strand sequence must be TACG. This characteristic becomes critical for DNA replication and expression, as you will see later in this chapter.

The Watson–Crick model also explained Chargaff's results: In a double helix, adenine forms two hydrogen bonds with thymine, but it will not form hydrogen bonds properly with cytosine. Similarly, guanine forms three hydrogen bonds with cytosine, but it will not form hydrogen bonds properly with thymine. Because of this base-pairing, adenine and thymine always occur in the same proportions in any DNA molecule, as do guanine and cytosine.

Figure 14.9 Base-pairing holds strands together. The hydrogen bonds that form between A and T and between G and C are shown with dashed lines. These produce AT and GC base-pairs that hold the two strands together. This always pairs a purine with a pyrimidine, keeping the diameter of the double helix constant.

 Data analysis Explain how the Watson–Crick model accounts for the data discussed in the text.

Antiparallel configuration

As stated earlier, a single phosphodiester strand has an inherent polarity, meaning that one end terminates in a 3′ OH and the other end terminates in a 5′ PO₄. Strands are thus referred to as having either a 5′-to-3′ or a 3′-to-5′ polarity. Two strands could be put together in two ways: with the polarity the same in each (parallel) or with the polarity opposite (antiparallel). Native double-stranded DNA always has the antiparallel configuration, with one strand running 5′ to 3′ and the other running 3′ to 5′ (see figure 14.8). In addition to its complementarity, this antiparallel nature also has important implications for DNA replication.

The Watson–Crick DNA molecule

In the Watson and Crick model, each DNA molecule is composed of two complementary phosphodiester strands that each form a helix with a common axis. These strands are antiparallel, with the bases extending into the interior of the helix. The bases from opposite strands form base-pairs with each other to join the two complementary strands (see figures 14.8 and 14.9).

Although the hydrogen bonds between each individual base-pair are low-energy bonds, the sum of bonds between the many base-pairs of the polymer has enough energy that the entire molecule is stable. To return to our spiral staircase analogy—the backbone is the handrails, the base-pairs are the steps.

Although the Watson–Crick model provided a rational structural for DNA, researchers had to answer further questions about how DNA could be replicated, a crucial step in cell division, and also about how cells could repair damaged or otherwise altered DNA. We explore these questions in the rest of this chapter. (In the following chapter, we continue with the genetic code and the connection between the code and protein synthesis.)

Learning Outcomes Review 14.2

Chargaff showed that in DNA, the amount of adenine was equal to the amount of thymine, and the amount of guanosine was equal to that of cytosine. X-ray diffraction studies by Franklin and Wilkins indicated that DNA formed a helix. Watson and Crick built a model consisting of two antiparallel strands wrapped in a helix about a common axis. The two strands are held together by hydrogen bonds between the bases: adenine pairs with thymine and guanine pairs with cytosine. The two strands are thus complementary to each other.

■ *Why was information about the proper tautomeric form of the bases critical?*

14.3 Basic Characteristics of DNA Replication

Learning Outcomes

1. Illustrate the products of semiconservative replication.
2. Describe the requirements for DNA replication.

The accurate replication of DNA prior to cell division is a basic and crucial function. Research has revealed that this complex process requires the participation of a large number of cellular proteins. Before geneticists could look for these details, however, they needed to perform some groundwork on the general mechanisms.

Meselson and Stahl demonstrate the semiconservative mechanism

The Watson–Crick model immediately suggested that the basis for copying the genetic information is complementarity. One chain of the DNA molecule may have any conceivable base sequence, but this sequence completely determines the sequence of its partner in the duplex.

In replication, the sequence of parental strands must be duplicated in daughter strands. That is, one parental helix with two strands must yield two daughter helices with four strands. The two daughter molecules are then separated during the course of cell division.

Three models of DNA replication are possible (figure 14.10):

1. In a *conservative model,* both strands of the parental duplex would remain intact (conserved), and new DNA copies would consist of all-new molecules. Both daughter strands would contain all-new molecules.

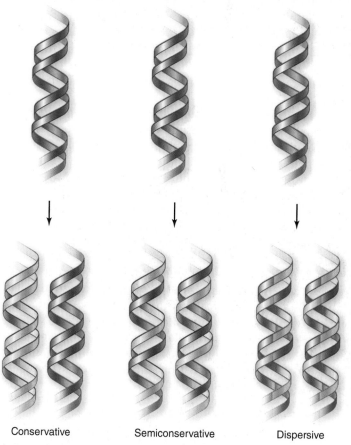

Conservative   Semiconservative   Dispersive

Figure 14.10 Three possible models for DNA replication. The conservative model produces one entirely new molecule and conserves the old. The semiconservative model produces two hybrid molecules of old and new strands. The dispersive model produces hybrid molecules with each strand a mixture of old and new.

2. In a **semiconservative model,** one strand of the parental duplex remains intact in daughter strands (semiconserved); a new complementary strand is built for each parental strand consisting of new molecules. Daughter strands would consist of one parental strand and one newly synthesized strand.

3. In a *dispersive model,* copies of DNA would consist of mixtures of parental and newly synthesized strands; that is, the new DNA would be dispersed throughout each strand of both daughter molecules after replication.

Notice that these three models suggest general mechanisms of replication, without specifying any molecular details of the process.

The Meselson–Stahl experiment

The three models for DNA replication were evaluated in 1958 by Matthew Meselson and Franklin Stahl. To distinguish between these models, they labeled DNA and then followed the labeled DNA through two rounds of replication (figure 14.11).

The label Meselson and Stahl used was a heavy isotope of nitrogen (^{15}N), not a radioactive label. Molecules containing ^{15}N have a greater density than those containing the common ^{14}N isotope. Ultracentrifugation can be used to separate molecules that have different densities.

Bacteria were grown in a medium containing ^{15}N, which became incorporated into the bases of the bacterial DNA. After several generations, the DNA of these bacteria was denser than that of bacteria grown in a medium containing the normally available ^{14}N. Meselson and Stahl then transferred the bacteria from the ^{15}N medium to ^{14}N medium and collected the DNA at various time intervals.

The DNA for each interval was dissolved in a solution containing a heavy salt, cesium chloride. This solution was spun at very high speeds in an ultracentrifuge. The enormous centrifugal forces caused cesium ions to migrate toward the bottom of the centrifuge tube, creating a gradient of cesium concentration, and thus of density. Each DNA strand floated or sank in the gradient until it reached the point at which its density exactly matched the density of the cesium at that location. Because ^{15}N strands are denser than ^{14}N strands, they migrated farther down the tube.

The DNA collected immediately after the transfer of bacteria to new ^{14}N medium was all of one density equal to that of ^{15}N DNA alone. However, after the bacteria completed a first round of DNA replication, the density of their DNA had decreased to a value intermediate between ^{14}N DNA alone and ^{15}N DNA. After the second round of replication, two density classes of DNA were observed: one intermediate and one equal to that of ^{14}N DNA (see figure 14.11).

Interpretation of the Meselson–Stahl findings

Meselson and Stahl compared their experimental data with the results that would be predicted on the basis of the three models.

1. The conservative model was not consistent with the data because after one round of replication, two densities should have been observed: DNA strands would either be all-heavy (parental) or all-light (daughter). This model is rejected.

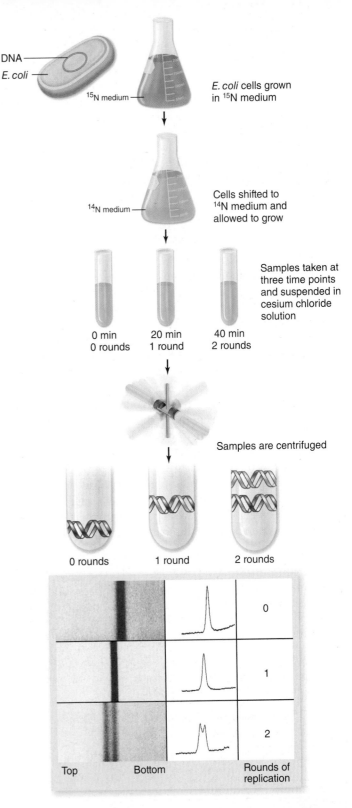

Figure 14.11 The Meselson–Stahl experiment. Bacteria grown in heavy ^{15}N medium are shifted to light ^{14}N medium and grown for two rounds of replication. Samples are taken at time points corresponding to zero, one, and two rounds of replication and centrifuged in cesium chloride to form a gradient. The actual data are shown at the bottom with the interpretation of semiconservative replication shown schematically.

 Data analysis What would you predict for the products of a third round of replication?

2. The semiconservative model is consistent with all observations: After one round of replication, a single density would be predicted because all DNA molecules would have a light strand and a heavy strand. After two rounds of replication, half of the molecules would have two light strands, and half would have a light strand and a heavy strand—and so two densities would be observed. Therefore, the results support the semiconservative model.

3. The dispersive model was consistent with the data from the first round of replication, because in this model, every DNA helix would consist of strands that are mixtures of ½ light (new) and ½ heavy (old) molecules. But after two rounds of replication, the dispersive model would still yield only a single density; DNA strands would be composed of ¾ light and ¼ heavy molecules. Instead, two densities were observed. Therefore, this model is also rejected.

The basic mechanism of DNA replication is semiconservative. At the simplest level, then, DNA is replicated by opening up a DNA helix and making copies of both strands to produce two daughter helices, each consisting of one old strand and one new strand.

DNA replication requires a template, nucleotides, and a polymerase enzyme

Replication requires three things: something to copy, something to do the copying, and the building blocks to make the copy. The parental DNA molecules serve as a template, enzymes perform the actions of copying the template, and the building blocks are nucleoside triphosphates.

The process of replication can be thought of as having a beginning where the process starts; a middle where the majority of building blocks are added; and an end where the process is finished. We use the terms *initiation, elongation,* and *termination* to describe a biochemical process. Although this may seem overly simplistic, in fact, discrete functions are usually required for initiation and termination that are not necessary for elongation.

A number of enzymes work together to accomplish the task of assembling a new strand, but the enzyme that actually matches the existing DNA bases with complementary nucleotides and then links the nucleotides together to make the new strand is **DNA polymerase** (figure 14.12). All DNA polymerases that have been examined have several common features. They all add new bases to the 3′ end of existing

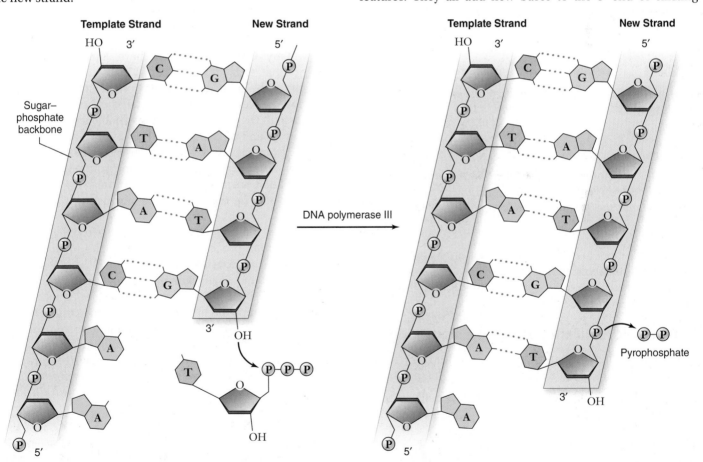

Figure 14.12 Action of DNA polymerase. DNA polymerases add nucleotides to the 3′ end of a growing chain. The nucleotide added depends on the base that is in the template strand. Each new base must be complementary to the base in the template strand. With the addition of each new nucleoside triphosphate, two of its phosphates are cleaved off as pyrophosphate.

? Inquiry question Why do you think it is important that the sugar–phosphate backbone of DNA is held together by covalent bonds, and the cross-bridges between the two strands are held together by hydrogen bonds?

strands. That is, they synthesize in a 5′-to-3′ direction by extending a strand base-paired to the template. All DNA polymerases also require a *primer* to begin synthesis; they cannot begin without a strand of RNA or DNA base-paired to the template. RNA polymerases do not have this requirement, so they usually synthesize the primers.

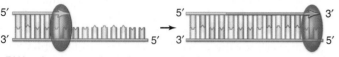

RNA polymerase makes primer   DNA polymerase extends primer

Learning Outcomes Review 14.3

Meselson and Stahl showed that the basic mechanism of replication is semiconservative: Each new DNA helix is composed of one old strand and one new strand. The process of replication requires a template to copy, nucleoside triphosphate building blocks, and the enzyme DNA polymerase. DNA polymerases synthesize DNA in a 5′-to-3′ direction from a primer, usually RNA.

■ *In the Meselson–Stahl experiment, what would the results be if the DNA was denatured prior to separation by ultracentrifugation?*

14.4 Prokaryotic Replication

Learning Outcomes

1. *Describe the functions of* E. coli *DNA polymerases.*
2. *Explain why replication is discontinuous on one strand.*
3. *Diagram the functions found at the replication fork.*

To build up a more detailed picture of replication, we first concentrate on prokaryotic replication using *E. coli* as a model. We can then look at eukaryotic replication primarily in how it differs from the prokaryotic system.

Prokaryotic replication starts at a single origin

Replication in *E. coli* initiates at a specific site, the origin (called *oriC*), and ends at a specific site, the terminus. The sequence of *oriC* consists of repeated nucleotides that bind an initiator protein and an AT-rich sequence that can be opened easily during initiation of replication. (A–T base-pairs have only two hydrogen bonds, compared with the three hydrogen bonds in G–C base-pairs.)

After initiation, replication proceeds bidirectionally from this unique origin to the unique terminus (figure 14.13). We call the DNA controlled by an origin a **replicon.** In this case, the chromosome plus the origin forms a single replicon.

 ### E. coli has at least three different DNA polymerases

As mentioned earlier, DNA polymerase refers to a group of enzymes responsible for the building of a new DNA strand from the template. The first DNA polymerase isolated in *E. coli* was given the name **DNA polymerase I (Pol I).** At first, investigators assumed this polymerase was responsible for the bulk synthesis of DNA during replication. A mutant was isolated, however, that had no Pol I activity, but could still replicate its chromosome. Two additional polymerases were isolated from this strain of *E. coli* and were named **DNA polymerase II (Pol II)** and **DNA polymerase III (Pol III).** As with all other known polymerases, all three of these enzymes synthesize polynucleotide strands only in the 5′-to-3′ direction and require a primer.

Many DNA polymerases have additional enzymatic activity that aids their function. This activity is a nuclease activity, or the ability to break phosphodiester bonds between nucleotides. Nucleases are classified as either **endonucleases** (which cut DNA internally) or **exonucleases** (which chew away at an end of DNA). DNA Pol I, Pol II, and Pol III have 3′-to-5′ exonuclease activity, which serves as a proofreading function because it allows the enzyme to remove a mispaired base. In addition, the DNA Pol I enzyme also has a 5′-to-3′ exonuclease activity, the importance of which will become clear shortly.

The three different polymerases have different roles in the replication process. DNA Pol III is the main replication enzyme; it is responsible for the bulk of DNA synthesis. DNA Pol I acts on the lagging strand to remove primers and replace them with DNA. The Pol II enzyme does not appear to play a role in replication but is involved in DNA repair processes.

For many years, these three polymerases were thought to be the only DNA polymerases in *E. coli,* but recently several new ones have been identified. There are now five known polymerases, although not all are active in DNA replication.

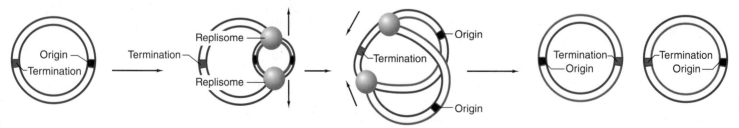

Figure 14.13 Replication is bidirectional from a unique origin. Replication initiates from a unique origin. Two separate replisomes are loaded onto the origin and initiate synthesis in the opposite directions on the chromosome. These two replisomes continue in opposite directions until they come to a unique termination site.

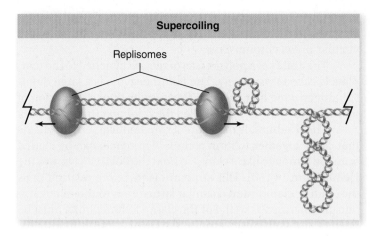

Supercoiling

Replisomes

No Supercoiling

Replisomes

DNA gyrase

Figure 14.14 Unwinding the helix causes torsional strain. If the ends of a linear DNA molecule are constrained, as they are in the cell, unwinding the helix produces torsional strain. This can cause the double helix to further coil in space (supercoiling). The enzyme DNA gyrase can relieve supercoiling.

Unwinding DNA requires energy and causes torsional strain

Although some DNA polymerases can unwind DNA as they synthesize new DNA, another class of enzymes has the single function of unwinding DNA strands to make this process more efficient. Enzymes that use energy from ATP to unwind the DNA template are called **helicases.**

The single strands of DNA produced by helicase action are unstable because the process exposes the hydrophobic bases to water. Cells solve this problem by using a protein, called single-strand-binding protein (SSB), to coat exposed single strands.

The unwinding of the two strands introduces torsional strain in the DNA molecule. Imagine two rubber bands twisted together. If you now unwind the rubber bands, what happens? The rubber bands, already twisted about each other, will further coil in space. When this happens with a DNA molecule it is called **supercoiling** (figure 14.14). The branch of mathematics that studies how forms twist and coil in space is called *topology*, and therefore we describe this coiling of the double helix as the *topological state* of DNA. This state describes how the double helix itself coils in space. You have already seen an example of this coiling with DNA wrapped about histone proteins in the nucleosomes of eukaryotic chromosomes (see chapter 10).

Enzymes that can alter the topological state of DNA are called **topoisomerases.** Topoisomerase enzymes act to relieve the torsional strain caused by unwinding and to prevent this supercoiling from happening. **DNA gyrase** is the topoisomerase involved in DNA replication (see figure 14.14).

Replication is semidiscontinuous

Earlier, DNA was described as being antiparallel—meaning that one strand runs in the 3′-to-5′ direction, and its complementary strand runs in the 5′-to-3′ direction. The antiparallel nature of DNA combined with the nature of the polymerase enzymes puts constraints on the replication process. Because polymerases can synthesize DNA in only one direction, and the two DNA strands run in opposite directions, polymerases on the two strands must be synthesizing DNA in opposite directions (figure 14.15).

The requirement of DNA polymerases for a primer means that on one strand primers need to be added as the helix is

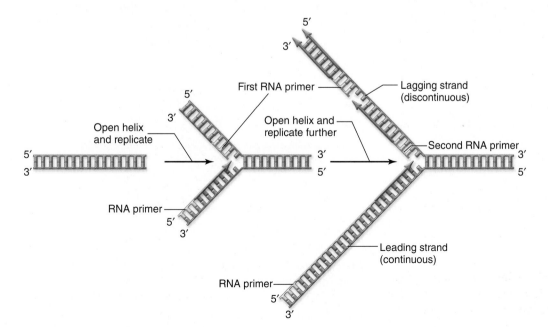

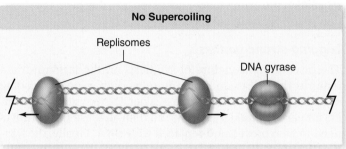

Figure 14.15 Replication is semidiscontinuous. The 5′-to-3′ synthesis of the polymerase and the antiparallel nature of DNA mean that only one strand, the leading strand, can be synthesized continuously. The other strand, the lagging strand, must be made in pieces, each with its own primer.

opened up (see figure 14.15). This means that one strand can be synthesized in a continuous fashion from an initial primer, but the other strand must be synthesized in a discontinuous fashion with multiple priming events and short sections of DNA being assembled. The strand that is continuous is called the **leading strand,** and the strand that is discontinuous is the **lagging strand.** DNA fragments synthesized on the lagging strand are named **Okazaki fragments** in honor of the man who first experimentally demonstrated discontinuous synthesis. They introduce a need for even more enzymatic activity on the lagging strand, as is described next.

Synthesis occurs at the replication fork

The partial opening of a DNA helix to form two single strands has a forked appearance, and is thus called the **replication fork.** All of the enzymatic activities that we have discussed plus a few more are found at the replication fork (table 14.1). Synthesis on the leading strand and on the lagging strand proceed in different ways, however.

Priming

The primers required by DNA polymerases during replication are synthesized by the enzyme *DNA primase.* This enzyme is an RNA polymerase that synthesizes short stretches of RNA 10–20 bp (base-pairs) long that function as primers for DNA polymerase. Later on, the RNA primer is removed and replaced with DNA.

Leading-strand synthesis

Synthesis on the leading strand is relatively simple. A single priming event is required, and then the strand can be extended indefinitely by the action of DNA Pol III. If the enzyme remains attached to the template, it can synthesize around the entire circular *E. coli* chromosome.

The ability of a polymerase to remain attached to the template is called *processivity.* The Pol III enzyme is a large multi-subunit enzyme that has high processivity due to the action of one subunit of the enzyme, called the β *subunit* (figure 14.16a).

The β subunit is made up of two identical protein chains that come together to form a circle. This circle can be loaded onto the template like a clamp to hold the Pol III enzyme to the DNA (figure 14.16b). This structure is therefore referred to as the "sliding clamp," and a similar structure is found in eukaryotic polymerases as well. For the clamp to function, it must be opened and then closed around the DNA. A multisubunit protein called the clamp loader accomplishes this task. This function is also found in eukaryotes.

Lagging-strand synthesis

The discontinuous nature of synthesis on the lagging strand requires the cell to do much more work than on the leading strand (see figure 14.15). Primase is needed to synthesize primers for each Okazaki fragment, and then all these RNA primers need to be removed and replaced with DNA. Finally, the fragments need to be stitched together.

DNA Pol III accomplishes the synthesis of Okazaki fragments. The removal and replacement of primer segments, however, is accomplished by DNA Pol I. Using its 5′-to-3′ exonuclease activity, it can remove primers in front and then replace them by using its usual 5′-to-3′ polymerase activity. The synthesis is

TABLE 14.1	DNA Replication Enzymes of *E. coli*		
Protein	**Role**	**Size (kDa)**	**Molecules per Cell**
Helicase	Unwinds the double helix	300	20
Primase	Synthesizes RNA primers	60	50
Single-strand binding protein	Stabilizes single-stranded regions	74	300
DNA gyrase	Relieves torque	400	250
DNA polymerase III	Synthesizes DNA	≈900	20
DNA polymerase I	Erases primer and fills gaps	103	300
DNA ligase	Joins the ends of DNA segments; DNA repair	74	300

a.

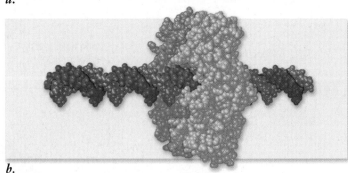

b.

Figure 14.16 The DNA polymerase sliding clamp. *a.* The β subunit forms a ring that can encircle DNA. *b.* The β subunit is shown attached to the DNA. This forms the "sliding clamp" that keeps the polymerase attached to the template.

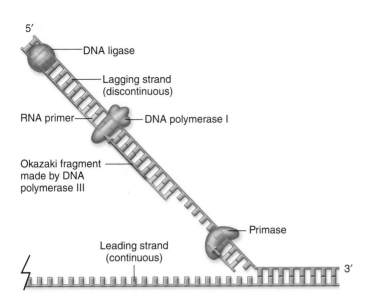

Figure 14.17 Lagging-strand synthesis. The action of primase synthesizes the primers needed by DNA polymerase III (not shown). These primers are removed by DNA polymerase I using its 5′-to-3′ exonuclease activity, then extending the previous Okazaki fragment to replace the RNA. The nick between Okazaki fragments after primer removal is sealed by DNA ligase.

primed by the previous Okazaki fragment, which is composed of DNA and has a free 3′ OH that can be extended.

This leaves only the last phosphodiester bond to be formed where synthesis by Pol I ends. This is done by **DNA ligase,** which seals this "nick," eventually joining the Okazaki fragments into complete strands. All of this activity on the lagging strand is summarized in figure 14.17.

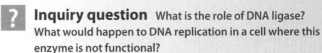

Inquiry question What is the role of DNA ligase? What would happen to DNA replication in a cell where this enzyme is not functional?

Termination

Termination occurs at a specific site located roughly opposite *oriC* on the circular chromosome. The last stages of replication produce two daughter molecules that are intertwined like two rings in a chain. These intertwined molecules are unlinked by the same enzyme that relieves torsional strain at the replication fork—DNA gyrase.

The replisome contains all the necessary enzymes for replication

The enzymes involved in DNA replication form a macromolecular assembly called the **replisome.** This assembly can be thought of as the "replication organelle," just as the ribosome is the organelle that synthesizes protein. The replisome has two main subcomponents: the *primosome,* and a complex of two DNA Pol III enzymes, one for each strand. The primosome is composed of primase and helicase, along with a number of accessory proteins. The need for constant priming on the lagging strand explains the need for the primosome complex as part of the replisome.

The two Pol III complexes include two synthetic core subunits, each with its own β subunit. The entire replisome complex is held together by a number of proteins that includes the clamp loader. The clamp loader is required to periodically load a β subunit on the lagging strand and to transfer the Pol III to this new β subunit (figure 14.18).

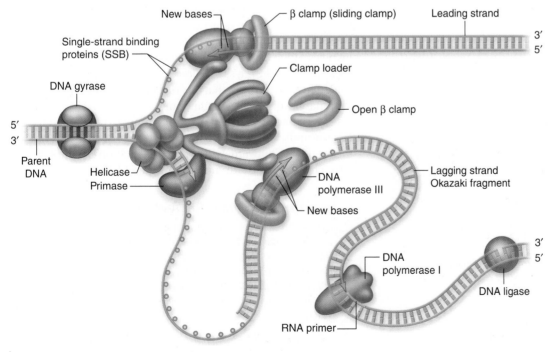

Figure 14.18 The replication fork. A model for the structure of the replication fork with two polymerase III enzymes held together by a large complex of accessory proteins. These include the "clamp loader," which loads the β subunit sliding clamp periodically on the lagging strand. The polymerase III on the lagging strand periodically releases its template and reassociates along with the β clamp. The loop in the lagging-strand template allows both polymerases to move in the same direction despite DNA being antiparallel. Primase, which makes primers for the lagging-strand fragments, and helicase are also associated with the central complex. Polymerase I removes primers and ligase joins the fragments together.

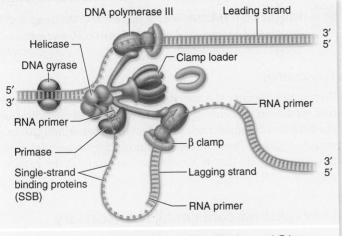

1. A DNA polymerase III enzyme is active on each strand. Primase synthesizes new primers for the lagging strand.

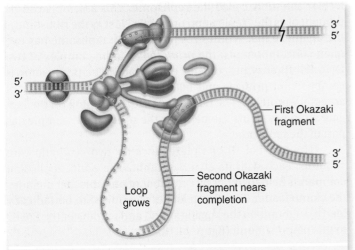

2. The "loop" in the lagging-strand template allows replication to occur 5′-to-3′ on both strands, with the complex moving to the left.

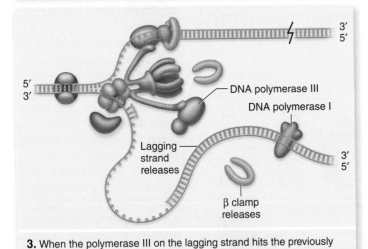

3. When the polymerase III on the lagging strand hits the previously synthesized fragment, it releases the β clamp and the template strand. DNA polymerase I attaches to remove the primer.

Figure 14.19 DNA synthesis by the replisome. The semidiscontinuous synthesis of DNA is illustrated in stages using the model from figure 14.18.

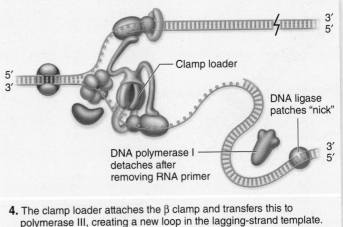

4. The clamp loader attaches the β clamp and transfers this to polymerase III, creating a new loop in the lagging-strand template. DNA ligase joins the fragments after DNA polymerase I removes the primers.

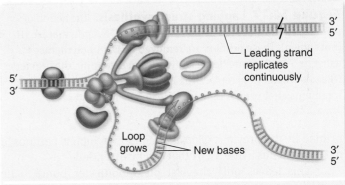

5. After the β clamp is loaded, the DNA polymerase III on the lagging strand adds bases to the next Okazaki fragment.

Even given the difficulties with lagging-strand synthesis, the two Pol III enzymes in the replisome are active on both leading and lagging strands simultaneously. How can the two strands be synthesized in the same direction when the strands are antiparallel? The model first proposed, still with us in some form, involves a loop formed in the lagging strand, so that the polymerases can move in the same direction (see figure 14.18). Current evidence also indicates that this replication complex is probably stationary, with the DNA strand moving through it like thread in a sewing machine, rather than the complex moving along the DNA strands. This stationary complex also pushes the newly synthesized DNA outward, which may aid in chromosome segregation. This process is summarized in figure 14.19.

Learning Outcomes Review 14.4

E. coli has three DNA polymerases: DNA Pol I, II, and III. Synthesis on one strand is discontinuous because DNA is antiparallel, and polymerases only synthesize in the 5′-to-3′ direction. Replication occurs at the replication fork, where the two strands are separated. Assembled here is a massive complex, the replisome, containing DNA polymerase III, primase, helicase, and other proteins. The lagging strand requires DNA polymerase I to remove the primers and replace them with DNA, and ligase to join Okazaki fragments.

■ *How are the nuclease functions of the different polymerases used during replication?*

Eukaryotic Replication

Learning Outcomes

1. *Compare eukaryotic replication with prokaryotic.*
2. *Explain the function of telomeres.*
3. *Evaluate the role of telomerase in cell division.*

Eukaryotic replication is complicated by two main factors: the larger amount of DNA organized into multiple chromosomes, and the linear structure of the chromosomes. This process requires new enzymatic activities only for dealing with the ends of chromosomes; otherwise the basic enzymology is the same.

Eukaryotic replication requires multiple origins

The sheer amount of DNA and how it is packaged constitute a problem for eukaryotes (figure 14.20). Eukaryotes usually have multiple chromosomes that are each larger than the *E. coli*

110,000×

Figure 14.20 DNA of a single human chromosome. This chromosome has been relieved of most of its packaging proteins, leaving the DNA in its native form. The residual protein scaffolding appears as the dark material in the lower part of the micrograph.

chromosome. If only a single unique origin existed for each chromosome, the length of time necessary for replication would be prohibitive. This problem is solved by the use of multiple origins of replication for each chromosome, resulting in multiple *replicons*.

The origins are not as sequence-specific as *oriC*, and their recognition seems to depend on chromatin structure as well as on sequence. The number of origins used can also be adjusted during the course of development, so that early on, when cell divisions need to be rapid, more origins are activated. Each origin must be used only once per cell cycle.

The enzymology of eukaryotic replication is more complex

The replication machinery of eukaryotes is similar to that found in bacteria, but it is larger and more complex. The initiation phase of replication requires more factors to assemble both helicase and primase complexes onto the template, then load the polymerase with its sliding clamp unit.

The eukaryotic primase is interesting in that it is a complex of both an RNA polymerase and a DNA polymerase. It first makes short RNA primers, then extends these with DNA to produce the final primer. The reason for this added complexity is unclear.

The main replication polymerase itself is also a complex of two different enzymes that work together. One is called *DNA polymerase epsilon* (pol ε) and the other *DNA polymerase delta* (pol δ). The sliding clamp subunit that allows the enzyme complex to stay attached to the template is called PCNA (for proliferating cell nuclear antigen). This unusual name reflects the fact that PCNA was first identified as an antibody-inducing protein in proliferating (dividing) cells. The PCNA sliding clamp forms a trimer, but this structure is similar to the β subunit sliding clamp. The clamp loader is also similar to the bacterial structure. Despite the additional complexity, the action of the replisome is similar to that described earlier for *E. coli*, and the replication fork has essentially the same components.

Archaeal replication proteins are similar to eukaryotic proteins

Despite their lack of a membrane-bounded nucleus, Archaeal replication proteins are more similar to eukaryotes than to bacterial. The main replication polymerase is most similar to eukaryotic pol δ, and the sliding clamp is similar to the PCNA protein. The clamp loading complex is also more similar to eukaryotic than bacterial. The most interesting conclusion from all of these data are that all three domains of life have similar functions involved in replicating chromosomes. All three domains assemble similar protein complexes with clamp loader, sliding clamp, two polymerases, helicase, and primase at the replication fork.

Linear chromosomes have specialized ends

The specialized structures found on the ends of eukaryotic chromosomes are called **telomeres.** These structures protect

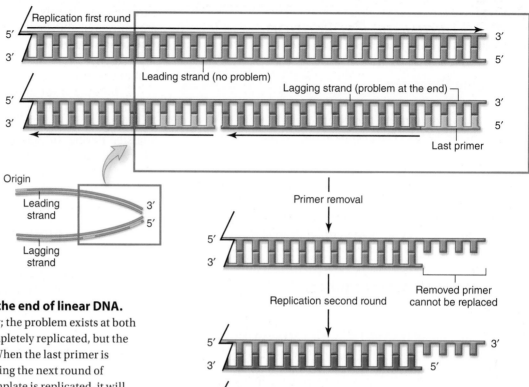

Figure 14.21 Replication of the end of linear DNA.
Only one end is shown for simplicity; the problem exists at both ends. The leading strand can be completely replicated, but the lagging strand cannot be finished. When the last primer is removed, it cannot be replaced. During the next round of replication, when this shortened template is replicated, it will produce a shorter chromosome.

the ends of chromosomes from nucleases and maintain the integrity of linear chromosomes. These telomeres are composed of specific DNA sequences, but they are not made by the replication complex.

Replicating ends

The very structure of a linear chromosome causes a cell problems in replicating the ends. The directionality of polymerases, combined with their requirement for a primer, create this problem.

Consider a simple linear molecule like the one in figure 14.21. Replication of one end of each template strand is simple, namely the 5′ end of the leading-strand template. When the polymerase reaches this end, synthesizing in the 5′-to-3′ direction, it eventually runs out of template and is finished.

But on the other strand's end, the 3′ end of the lagging strand, removal of the last primer on this end leaves a gap. This gap cannot be primed, meaning that the polymerase complex cannot finish this end properly. The result would be a gradual shortening of chromosomes with each round of cell division (see figure 14.21).

The action of telomerase

When the sequence of telomeres was determined, they were found to be composed of short repeated sequences of DNA. This repeating nature is easily explained by their synthesis. They are made by an enzyme called **telomerase,** which uses an internal RNA as a template and not the DNA itself (figure 14.22).

Figure 14.22 Action of telomerase. Telomerase contains an internal RNA that the enzyme uses as a template to extend the DNA of the chromosome end. Multiple rounds of synthesis by telomerase produce repeated sequences. This single strand is completed by normal synthesis using it as a template (not shown).

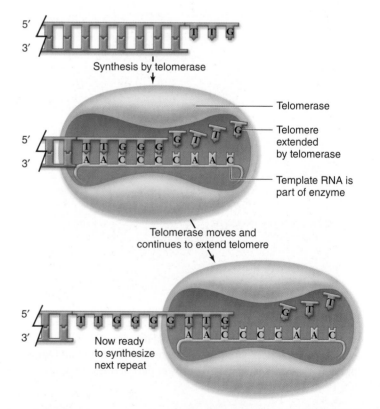

The use of the internal RNA template allows short stretches of DNA to be synthesized, composed of repeated nucleotide sequences complementary to the RNA of the enzyme. The other strand of these repeated units is synthesized by the usual action of the replication machinery copying the strand made by telomerase.

Telomerase, aging, and cancer

A gradual shortening of the ends of chromosomes occurs in the absence of telomerase activity. During embryonic and childhood development in humans, telomerase activity is high, but it is low in most somatic cells of the adult. The exceptions are cells that must divide as part of their function, such as lymphocytes. The activity of telomerase in somatic cells is kept low by preventing the expression of the gene encoding this enzyme.

Evidence for the shortening of chromosomes in the absence of telomerase was obtained by producing mice with no telomerase activity. These mice appear to be normal for up to six generations, but they show steadily decreasing telomere length that eventually leads to nonviable offspring.

This finding indicates a relationship between cell senescence (aging) and telomere length. Normal cells undergo only a specified number of divisions when grown in culture. This limit is at least partially based on telomere length.

Support for the relationship between senescence and telomere length comes from experiments in which telomerase was introduced into fibroblasts in culture. These cells have their lifespan increased relative to controls that have no added telomerase. Interestingly, these cells do not show the hallmarks of malignant cells, indicating that activation of telomerase alone does not make cells malignant.

A relationship has been found, however, between telomerase and cancer. Cancer cells do continue to divide indefinitely, and this would not be possible if their chromosomes were being continually shortened. Cancer cells generally show activation of telomerase, which allows them to maintain telomere length; but this is clearly only one aspect of conditions that allow them to escape normal growth controls.

? Inquiry question How does the structure of eukaryotic genomes affect replication? Does this introduce problems that are not faced by prokaryotes?

Learning Outcomes Review 14.5

Eukaryotic replication is complicated by a large amount of DNA organized into chromosomes, and by the linear nature of chromosomes. Eukaryotes replicate a large amount of DNA in a short time by using multiple origins of replication. Linear chromosomes end in telomeres, and the length of telomeres is correlated with the ability of cells to divide. The enzyme telomerase synthesizes the telomeres. Cancer cells show activation of telomerase, which extends the ability of the cells to divide.

■ *What might be the result of abnormal shortening of telomeres or a lack of telomerase activity?*

14.6 DNA Repair

Learning Outcomes

1. *Explain why DNA repair is critical for cells.*
2. *Describe the different forms of DNA repair.*

As you learned earlier, many DNA polymerases have 3'-to-5' exonuclease activity that allows "proofreading" of added bases. This action increases the accuracy of replication, but errors still occur. Without error correction mechanisms, cells would accumulate errors at an unacceptable rate, leading to high levels of deleterious or lethal mutations. A balance must exist between the introduction of new variation by mutation, and the effects of deleterious mutations on the individual.

Cells are constantly exposed to DNA-damaging agents

In addition to errors in DNA replication, cells are constantly exposed to agents that can damage DNA. These agents include radiation, such as UV light and X-rays, and chemicals in the environment. Agents that damage DNA can lead to mutations, and any agent that increases the number of mutations above background levels is called a **mutagen.**

The number of potentially mutagenic agents that organisms encounter is huge. Sunlight itself includes radiation in the UV range and is thus mutagenic. Ozone normally screens out much of the harmful UV radiation in sunlight, but some remains. The relationship between sunlight and mutations is shown clearly by the increase in skin cancer in regions of the southern hemisphere that are underneath a seasonal "ozone hole."

Organisms also may encounter mutagens in their diet in the form of either contaminants in food or natural plant products that can damage DNA. When a simple test was designed to detect mutagens, screening of possible sources indicated an amazing diversity of mutagens in the environment and in natural sources. As a result, consumer products are now screened to reduce the load of mutagens we are exposed to, but we cannot escape natural sources.

DNA repair restores damaged DNA

Cells cannot escape exposure to mutagens, but systems have evolved that enable cells to repair some damage. These DNA repair systems are vital to continued existence, whether a cell is a free-living, single-celled organism or part of a complex multicellular organism.

The importance of DNA repair is indicated by the multiplicity of repair systems that have been discovered and characterized. All cells that have been examined show multiple pathways for repairing damaged DNA and for reversing errors that occur during replication. These systems are not perfect, but they do reduce the mutational load on organisms to an acceptable level. In the rest of this section, we illustrate the action of DNA repair by concentrating on two examples drawn from these multiple repair pathways.

Repair can be either specific or nonspecific

DNA repair falls into two general categories: specific and nonspecific. Specific repair systems target a single kind of lesion in DNA and repair only that damage. Nonspecific forms of repair use a single mechanism to repair multiple kinds of lesions in DNA.

Photorepair: A specific repair mechanism

Photorepair is specific for one particular form of damage caused by UV light, namely the *thymine dimer*. Thymine dimers are formed by a photochemical reaction of UV light and adjacent thymine bases in DNA. The UV radiation causes the thymines to react, covalently linking them together: a thymine dimer (figure 14.23).

Repair of these thymine dimers can be accomplished by multiple pathways, including photorepair. In photorepair, an enzyme called a *photolyase* absorbs light in the visible range

and uses this energy to cleave the thymine dimer. This action restores the two thymines to their original state (see figure 14.23). It is interesting that sunlight in the UV range can cause this damage, and sunlight in the visible range can be used to repair the damage. Photorepair does not occur in cells deprived of visible light.

The photolyase enzyme has been found in many different species, ranging from bacteria, to single-celled eukaryotes, to humans. The ubiquitous nature of this enzyme illustrates the importance of this form of repair. For as long as cells have existed on Earth, they have been exposed to UV light and its potential to damage DNA.

Excision repair: A nonspecific repair mechanism

A common form of nonspecific repair is **excision repair**. In this pathway, a damaged region is removed, or excised, and is then replaced by DNA synthesis (figure 14.24). In *E. coli*, this action is accomplished by proteins encoded by the *uvr A, B,*

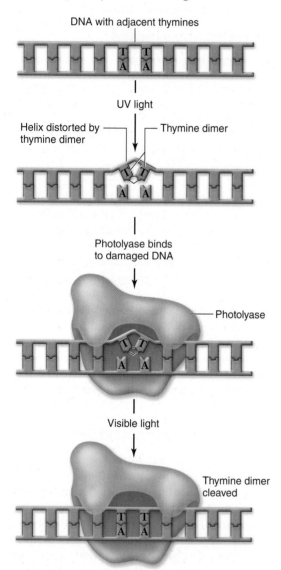

Figure 14.23 Repair of thymine dimer by photorepair. UV light can catalyze a photochemical reaction to form a covalent bond between two adjacent thymines, thereby creating a thymine dimer. A photolyase enzyme recognizes the damage and binds to the thymine dimer. The enzyme absorbs visible light and uses the energy to cleave the thymine dimer.

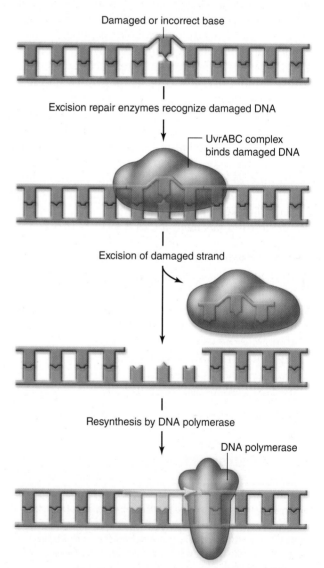

Figure 14.24 Repair of damaged DNA by excision repair. Damaged DNA is recognized by the uvr complex, which binds to the damaged region and removes it. Synthesis by DNA polymerase replaces the damaged region. DNA ligase finishes the process (not shown).

and *C* genes. Although these genes were identified based on mutations that increased sensitivity of the cell to UV light (hence the "uvr" in their names), their proteins can act on damage due to other mutagens.

Excision repair follows three steps: (1) recognition of damage, (2) removal of the damaged region, and (3) resynthesis using the information on the undamaged strand as a template (see figure 14.24). Recognition and excision are accomplished by the UvrABC complex. The UvrABC complex binds to damaged DNA and then cleaves a single strand on either side of the damage, removing it. In the synthesis stage, DNA pol I or pol II replaces the damaged DNA. This restores the original information in the damaged strand by using the information in the complementary strand.

Other repair pathways

Cells have other forms of nonspecific repair, and these fall into two categories: error-free and error-prone. It may seem strange to have an error-prone pathway, but it can be thought of as a last-ditch effort to save a cell that has been exposed to such massive damage that it has overwhelmed the error-free systems. In fact, this system in *E. coli* is part of what is called the "SOS response."

Cells can also repair damage that produces breaks in DNA. These systems use enzymes related to those that are involved in recombination during meiosis (see chapter 11). It is thought that recombination uses enzymes that originally evolved for DNA repair.

The number of different systems and the wide spectrum of damage that can be repaired illustrate the importance of maintaining the integrity of the genome. Accurate replication of the genome is useless if a cell cannot reverse errors that can occur during this process or repair damage due to environmental causes.

> **?** **Inquiry question** Cells are constantly exposed to DNA-damaging agents, ranging from UV light to by-products of oxidative metabolism. How does the cell deal with this, and what would happen if the cell had no way of dealing with this?

Learning Outcomes Review 14.6

The ability to repair DNA is critical because of replication errors and the constant presence of damaging agents that can cause mutation. Cells have multiple repair pathways; some of these systems are specific for a single type of damage, such as photorepair that reverses thymine dimers caused by UV light. Other systems are nonspecific, such as excision repair that removes and replaces damaged regions.

- **Could a cell survive with no form of DNA repair?**

Chapter Review

14.1 The Nature of the Genetic Material

Griffith finds that bacterial cells can be transformed.
Nonvirulent *S. pneumoniae* could take up an unknown substance from a virulent strain and become virulent.

Avery, MacLeod, and McCarty identify the transforming principle.
The transforming substance could be inactivated by DNA-digesting enzymes, but not by protein-digesting enzymes.

Hershey and Chase demonstrate that phage genetic material is DNA.
Radioactive labeling showed that the infectious agent of phage is its DNA, and not its protein.

14.2 DNA Structure

DNA's components were known, but its three-dimensional structure was a mystery.
The nucleotide building blocks for DNA contain deoxyribose and the bases adenine (A), guanine (G), cytosine (C), and thymine (T). Phosphodiester bonds are formed between the 5′ phosphate of one nucleotide and the 3′ hydroxyl of another nucleotide (figure 14.4).

Chargaff, Franklin, and Wilkins obtained some structural evidence.
Chargaff found equal amounts of adenine and thymine, and of cytosine and guanine, in DNA. The bases exist primarily in keto and enol forms that exhibit hydrogen bonding. X-ray diffraction studies by Franklin and Wilkins indicated that DNA had a helical structure.

The Watson–Crick model fits the available evidence (figures 14.8 & 14.9).
DNA consists of two antiparallel polynucleotide strands wrapped about a common helical axis. These strands are held together by hydrogen bonds forming specific base pairs (A/T and G/C). The two strands are complementary; one strand can specify the other.

14.3 Basic Characteristics of DNA Replication

Meselson and Stahl demonstrate the semiconservative mechanism (figure 14.11).
Semiconservative replication uses each strand of a DNA molecule to specify the synthesis of a new strand. Meselson and Stahl showed this by using a heavy isotope of nitrogen and separating the replication products. Replication produces two new molecules each composed of one new strand and one old strand.

DNA replication requires a template, nucleotides, and a polymerase enzyme.
All new DNA molecules are produced by DNA polymerase copying a template. All known polymerases synthesize new DNA in the 5′-to-3′ direction. These enzymes also require a primer. The building blocks used in replication are deoxynucleotide triphosphates with high-energy bonds; they do not require any additional energy.

14.4 Prokaryotic Replication

Prokaryotic replication starts at a single origin.

The *E. coli* origin has AT-rich sequences that are easily opened. The chromosome and its origin form a replicon.

E. coli *has at least three different DNA polymerases.*

Some DNA polymerases can also degrade DNA from one end, called exonuclease activity. Pol I, II, and III all have 3′-to-5′ exonuclease activity that can remove mispaired bases. Pol I can remove bases in the 5′-to-3′ direction, important to removing RNA primers.

Unwinding DNA requires energy and causes torsional strain.

DNA helicase uses energy from ATP to unwind DNA. The torsional strain introduced is removed by the enzyme DNA gyrase.

Replication is semidiscontinuous.

Replication is discontinuous on one strand (figure 14.15). The continuous strand is called the leading strand, and the discontinuous strand is called the lagging strand.

Synthesis occurs at the replication fork.

The partial opening of a DNA strand forms two single-stranded regions called the replication fork. At the fork, synthesis on the leading strand requires a single primer, and the polymerase stays attached to the template because of the β subunit that acts as a sliding clamp. On the lagging strand, DNA primase adds primers periodically, and DNA Pol III synthesizes the Okazaki fragments. DNA Pol I removes primer segments, and DNA ligase joins the fragments.

The replisome contains all the necessary enzymes for replication.

The replisome consists of two copies of Pol III, DNA primase, DNA helicase, and a number of accessory proteins. It moves in one direction by creating a loop in the lagging strand, allowing the antiparallel template strands to be copied in the same direction (figures 14.18 & 14.19).

14.5 Eukaryotic Replication

Eukaryotic replication requires multiple origins.

The sheer size and organization of eukaryotic chromosomes requires multiple origins of replication to be able to replicate DNA in the time available in S phase.

The enzymology of eukaryotic replication is more complex.

The eukaryotic primase synthesizes a short stretch of RNA and then switches to making DNA. This primer is extended by the main replication polymerase, which is a complex of two enzymes. The sliding clamp subunit was originally identified as protein produced by proliferating cells and is called PCNA.

Archaeal replication proteins are similar to eukaryotic proteins.

The replication proteins of archaea, including the sliding clamp, clamp loader, and DNA polymerases, are more similar to those of eukaryotes than to prokaryotes.

Linear chromosomes have specialized ends.

The ends of linear chromosomes are called telomeres. They are made by telomerase, not by the replication complex. Telomerase contains an internal RNA that acts as a template to extend the DNA of the chromosome end. Adult cells lack telomerase activity, and telomere shortening correlates with senescence.

14.6 DNA Repair

Cells are constantly exposed to DNA-damaging agents.

Errors from replication and damage induced by agents such as UV light and chemical mutagens can lead to mutations.

DNA repair restores damaged DNA.

Without repair mechanisms, cells would accumulate mutations until inviability occurred.

Repair can be either specific or nonspecific.

The enzyme photolyase uses energy from visible light to cleave thymine dimers caused by UV light. Excision repair is nonspecific. In prokaryotes, the uvr system can remove a damaged region of DNA.

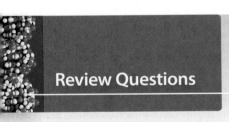

Review Questions

UNDERSTAND

1. What was the key finding from Griffith's experiments using live and heat-killed pathogenic bacteria?
   a. Bacteria with a smooth coat could kill mice.
   b. Bacteria with a rough coat are not lethal.
   c. DNA is the genetic material.
   d. Genetic material can be transferred from dead to live bacteria.

2. Which of the following is NOT a component of DNA?
   a. The pyrimidine uracil
   b. Five-carbon sugars
   c. The purine adenine
   d. Phosphate groups

3. Chargaff studied the composition of DNA from different sources and found that
   a. the number of phosphate groups always equals the number of five-carbon sugars.
   b. the proportions of A equal that of C and G equals T.
   c. the proportions of A equal that of T and G equals C.
   d. purines bind to pyrimidines.

4. The bonds that hold two complementary strands of DNA together are
   a. hydrogen bonds.
   b. peptide bonds.
   c. ionic bonds.
   d. phosphodiester bonds.

5. The basic mechanism of DNA replication is semiconservative with two new molecules,

   a. each with new strands.
   b. one with all new strands and one with all old strands.
   c. each with one new and one old strand.
   d. each with a mixture of old and new strands.

6. One common feature of all DNA polymerases is that they

   a. synthesize DNA in the 3′-to-5′ direction.
   b. synthesize DNA in the 5′-to-3′ direction.
   c. synthesize DNA in both directions by switching strands.
   d. do not require a primer.

7. Which of the following is *not* part of the Watson–Crick model of the structure of DNA?

   a. DNA is composed of two strands.
   b. The two DNA strands are oriented in parallel (5′-to-3′).
   c. Purines bind to pyrimidines.
   d. DNA forms a double helix.

APPLY

1. If one strand of a DNA is 5′ ATCGTTAAGCGAGTCA 3′, then the complementary strand would be:

   a. 5′ TAGCAATTCGCTCAGT 3′.
   b. 5′ ACTGAGCGAATTGCTA 3′.
   c. 5′ TGACTCGCTTAACGAT 3′.
   d. 5′ ATCGTTAAGCGAGTCA 3′.

2. Hershey and Chase used radioactive phosphorus and sulfur to

   a. label DNA and protein uniformly.
   b. differentially label DNA and protein.
   c. identify the transforming principle.
   d. Both b and c are correct.

3. The Meselson and Stahl experiment used a density label to be able to

   a. determine the directionality of DNA replication.
   b. differentially label DNA and protein.
   c. distinguish between newly replicated and old strands.
   d. distinguish between replicated DNA and RNA primers.

4. The difference in leading- versus lagging-strand synthesis is a consequence of

   a. only the physical structure of DNA.
   b. only the activity of DNA polymerase enzymes.
   c. both the physical structure of DNA and the action of polymerase enzyme.
   d. the larger size of the lagging strand.

5. If the activity of DNA ligase was removed from replication, this would have a greater affect on

   a. synthesis on the lagging strand versus the leading strand.
   b. synthesis on the leading strand versus the lagging strand.
   c. priming of DNA synthesis versus actual DNA synthesis.
   d. photorepair of DNA versus DNA replication.

6. Successful DNA synthesis requires all of the following *except*

   a. helicase.
   b. endonuclease.
   c. DNA primase.
   d. DNA ligase.

7. The synthesis of telomeres

   a. uses DNA polymerase, but without the sliding clamp.
   b. uses enzymes involved in DNA repair.
   c. requires telomerase, which does not use a template.
   d. requires telomerase, which uses an internal RNA as a template.

8. When mutations that affected DNA replication were isolated, two kinds were found. In cultures that were not synchronized (that is, not all dividing at the same time), one class put an immediate halt to replication, whereas the other put a much slower stop to the process. The first class affects functions at the replication fork like polymerase and primase. The second class affects functions necessary for

   a. elongation on the lagging but not the leading strand.
   b. elongation on the leading but not the lagging strand.
   c. initiation: cells complete replication but cannot start a new round.
   d. the sliding clamp: loss makes the polymerase slower.

SYNTHESIZE

1. The work by Griffith provided the first indication that DNA was the genetic material. Review the four experiments outlined in figure 14.1. Predict the likely outcome for the following variations on this classic research.

   a. Heat-killed pathogenic and heat-killed nonpathogenic
   b. Heat-killed pathogenic and live nonpathogenic in the presence of an enzyme that digests proteins (proteases)
   c. Heat-killed pathogenic and live nonpathogenic in the presence of an enzyme that digests DNA (endonuclease)

2. In the Meselson–Stahl experiment, a control experiment was done to show that the hybrid bands after one round of replication were in fact two complete strands, one heavy and one light. Using the same experimental setup as detailed in the text, how can this be addressed?

3. Enzyme function is critically important for the proper replication of DNA. Predict the consequence of a loss of function for each of the following enzymes.

   a. DNA gyrase
   b. DNA polymerase III
   c. DNA ligase
   d. DNA polymerase I

ONLINE RESOURCE

www.ravenbiology.com

Understand, Apply, and Synthesize—enhance your study with animations that bring concepts to life and practice tests to assess your understanding. Your instructor may also recommend the interactive eBook, individualized learning tools, and more.

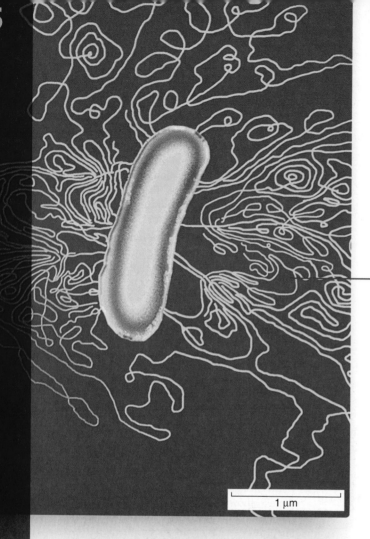

1 μm

Chapter 15

Genes and How They Work

Chapter Contents

Introduction

You've seen how genes specify traits and how those traits can be followed in genetic crosses. You've also seen that the information in genes resides in the DNA molecule; the picture above shows all the DNA within the entire E. coli *chromosome. Information in DNA is replicated by the cell and then partitioned equally during the process of cell division. The information in DNA is much like a blueprint for a building. The construction of the building uses the information in the blueprint, but requires building materials and carpenters and other skilled laborers using a variety of tools working together to actually construct the building. Similarly, the information in DNA requires nucleotide and amino acid building blocks, multiple forms of RNA, and many proteins acting in a coordinated fashion to make up the structure of a cell.*

We now turn to the nature of the genes themselves and how cells extract the information in DNA in the process of gene expression. Gene expression can be thought of as the conversion of genotype into the phenotype.

15.1 The Nature of Genes

Learning Outcomes

1. *Evaluate the evidence for the one-gene/one-polypeptide hypothesis.*
2. *Distinguish between transcription and translation.*
3. *List the roles played by RNA in gene expression.*

We know that DNA encodes proteins, but this knowledge alone tells us little about how the information in DNA can control cellular functions. Researchers had evidence that genetic mutations affected proteins, and in particular enzymes, long before the structure and code of DNA was known. In this section we review the evidence of the link between genes and enzymes.

Garrod concluded that inherited disorders can involve specific enzymes

In 1902, the British physician Archibald Garrod noted that certain diseases among his patients seemed to be more prevalent in particular families. By examining several generations of these families, he found that some of the diseases behaved as though they were the product of simple recessive alleles. Garrod concluded that these disorders were Mendelian traits, and that they had resulted from changes in the hereditary information in an ancestor of the affected families.

Garrod investigated several of these disorders in detail. In alkaptonuria, patients produced urine that contained homogentisic acid (alkapton). This substance oxidized rapidly when exposed to air, turning the urine black. In normal individuals, homogentisic acid is broken down into simpler substances. With considerable insight, Garrod concluded that patients suffering from alkaptonuria lack the enzyme necessary to catalyze this breakdown. He speculated that many other inherited diseases might also reflect enzyme deficiencies.

Beadle and Tatum showed that genes specify enzymes

From Garrod's finding, it took but a short leap of intuition to surmise that the information encoded within the DNA of chromosomes acts to specify particular enzymes. This point was not actually established, however, until 1941, when a series of experiments by George Beadle and Edward Tatum at Stanford University provided definitive evidence. Beadle and Tatum deliberately set out to create mutations in chromosomes and verified that they behaved in a Mendelian fashion in crosses. These alterations to single genes were analyzed for their effects on the organism (figure 15.1).

Neurospora crassa, *the bread mold*

One of the reasons Beadle and Tatum's experiments produced clear-cut results was their choice of experimental organism, the bread mold *Neurospora crassa*. This fungus can be grown readily in the laboratory on a defined medium consisting of only a carbon source (glucose), a vitamin (biotin), and inorganic salts. This type of medium is called "minimal" because it represents the minimal requirements to support growth. Any cells that can grow on minimal medium must be able to synthesize all necessary biological molecules.

Beadle and Tatum exposed *Neurospora* spores to X-rays, expecting that the DNA in some of the spores would experience damage in regions encoding the ability to make compounds needed for normal growth (see figure 15.1). Such a mutation would cause cells to be unable to grow on minimal medium. Such mutations are called **nutritional mutations** because cells carrying them grow only if the medium is supplemented with additional nutrients.

Nutritional mutants

To identify mutations causing metabolic deficiencies, Beadle and Tatum placed subcultures of individual fungal cells grown on a rich medium onto minimal medium. Any cells that had lost the ability to make compounds necessary for growth would not grow on minimal medium. Using this approach, Beadle and Tatum succeeded in isolating and identifying many nutritional mutants.

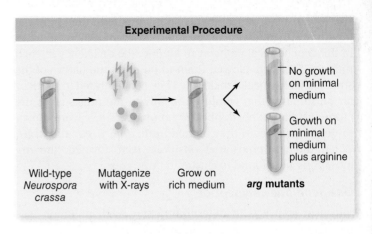

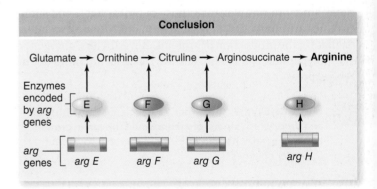

Figure 15.1   The Beadle and Tatum experiment.
Wild-type *Neurospora* were mutagenized with X-rays to produce mutants deficient in the synthesis of arginine (top panel). The specific defect in each mutant was identified by growing on medium supplemented with intermediates in the biosynthetic pathway for arginine (middle panel). A mutant will grow only on media supplemented with an intermediate produced after the defective enzyme in the pathway for each mutant. The enzymes in the pathway can then be correlated with genes on chromosomes (bottom panel).

Next, the researchers supplemented the minimal medium with different compounds known to be intermediates in this biochemical pathway to identify the deficiency in each mutant. This step allowed them to pinpoint the nature of the strain's biochemical deficiency. They concentrated in particular on mutants that would grow only in the presence of the amino acid arginine, dubbed *arg* mutants. These were shown to define four genes they named *argE, argF, argG,* and *argH.* When their chromosomal positions were located, the *arg* mutations were found to cluster in three areas.

One gene/one polypeptide

The next step was to determine where each mutation was blocked in the biochemical pathway for arginine biosynthesis. To do this, they supplemented the medium with each intermediate in the pathway to see which would support each mutant's growth. If the mutation affects an enzyme in the pathway that acts prior to the supplement, then growth should be supported—but not if the mutation affects a step after the intermediate used (see figure 15.1). Beadle and Tatum were able to isolate a mutant strain defective for each enzyme in the biosynthetic pathway. The mutation was always located at a specific chromosomal sites and each mutation had a unique location. Thus, each of the mutants they examined had a defect in a single enzyme, caused by a mutation at a single site on a chromosome.

Beadle and Tatum concluded that genes specify the structure of enzymes, and that each gene encodes the structure of one enzyme (see figure 15.1). They called this relationship the *one-gene/one-enzyme hypothesis.* Today, because many enzymes contain multiple polypeptide subunits, each encoded by a separate gene, the relationship is more commonly referred to as the **one-gene/one-polypeptide hypothesis.** This hypothesis clearly states the molecular relationship between genotype and phenotype.

As you learn more about genomes and gene expression, this clear relationship becomes overly simple. Eukaryotic genes are more complex than those of prokaryotes, and some enzymes are composed, at least in part, of RNA, itself an intermediate in the production of proteins. Nevertheless, one-gene/one-polypeptide is a useful starting point for thinking about gene expression.

 Data analysis If you made a double mutant with *argE* and *argG*, which kind(s) of media would this strain grow on? In general, what can a double mutant tell you about the order of genes?

The central dogma describes information flow in cells as DNA to RNA to protein

The conversion of genotype to phenotype requires information stored in DNA to be converted to protein. The nature of information flow in cells was first described by Francis Crick as the **central dogma of molecular biology.** Information passes in one direction from the gene (DNA) to an RNA copy of the gene, and the RNA copy directs the sequential assembly

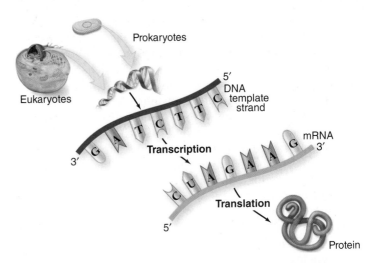

Figure 15.2 The central dogma of molecular biology. DNA is transcribed to make mRNA, which is translated to make a protein.

of a chain of amino acids into a protein (figure 15.2). Stated briefly,

$$DNA \longrightarrow RNA \longrightarrow protein$$

The central dogma provides an intellectual framework that describes information flow in biological systems. We call the DNA-to-RNA step **transcription** because it produces an exact copy of the DNA, much as a legal transcription contains the exact words of a court proceeding. The RNA-to-protein step is termed **translation** because it requires translating from the nucleic acid to the protein "languages."

Since the original formulation of the central dogma, a class of viruses called **retroviruses** was discovered that can convert their RNA genome into a DNA copy, using the viral enzyme **reverse transcriptase.** This conversion violates the direction of information flow of the central dogma, and the discovery forced an updating of the possible flow of information to include this "reverse" flow from RNA to DNA.

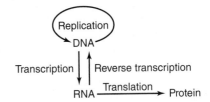

Transcription makes an RNA copy of DNA

The process of transcription produces an RNA copy of the information in DNA. That is, transcription is the DNA-directed synthesis of RNA by the enzyme RNA polymerase (figure 15.3). This process uses the principle of complementarity, described in chapter 14, to use DNA as a template to make RNA.

Because DNA is double-stranded and RNA is single-stranded, only one of the two DNA strands needs to be copied. We call the strand that is copied the **template strand.** The RNA transcript's sequence is complementary to the template strand.

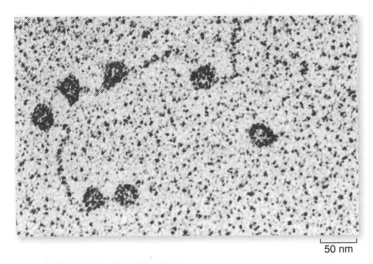

Figure 15.3 RNA polymerase. In this electron micrograph, the dark circles are RNA polymerase molecules synthesizing RNA from a DNA template.

The strand of DNA not used as a template is called the **coding strand.** It has the same sequence as the RNA transcript, except that U (uracil) in the RNA is T (thymine) in the DNA-coding strand. Another naming convention for the two strands of the DNA is to call the coding strand the sense strand, as it has the same "sense" as the RNA. The template strand would then be the antisense strand.

```
Coding (sense)      5′–TCAGCCGTCAGCT–3′  ⎤
Template (antisense) 3′–AGTCGGCAGTCGA–5′  ⎦ DNA
                        Transcription
                            ↓
          Coding 5′–UCAGCCGUCAGCU–3′  mRNA
```

The RNA transcript used to direct the synthesis of polypeptides is termed *messenger RNA (mRNA).* Its name reflects its use by the cell to carry the DNA message to the ribosome for processing.

> **?** **Inquiry question** RNA polymerase has no proofreading capacity. How does this affect the error rate in transcription compared with DNA replication? Why do you think it is more important for DNA polymerase than for RNA polymerase to proofread?

Translation uses information in RNA to synthesize proteins

The process of translation is by necessity much more complex than transcription. In this case, RNA cannot be used as a direct template for a protein because there is no complementarity—that is, a sequence of amino acids cannot be aligned to an RNA template based on any kind of "chemical fit." Molecular geneticists suggested that some kind of adapter molecule must exist that can interact with both RNA and amino acids, and *transfer RNA (tRNA)* was found to fill this role. This need for an intermediary adds a level of complexity to the process that is not seen in either DNA replication or transcription of RNA.

Translation takes place on the ribosome, the cellular protein-synthesis machinery, and it requires the participation of multiple kinds of RNA and many proteins. Here we provide an outline of the processes; all are described in detail in the sections that follow.

RNA has multiple roles in gene expression

All RNAs are synthesized from a DNA template by transcription. Gene expression requires the participation of multiple kinds of RNA, each with different roles in the overall process. Here is a brief summary of these roles, which are described in detail later.

Messenger RNA. Even before the details of gene expression were unraveled, geneticists recognized that there must be an intermediate form of the information in DNA that can be transported out of the eukaryotic nucleus to the cytoplasm for ribosomal processing. This hypothesis was called the "messenger hypothesis," and we retain this language in the name *messenger RNA* (mRNA).

Ribosomal RNA. The class of RNA found in ribosomes is called **ribosomal RNA (rRNA).** There are multiple forms of rRNA, and rRNA is found in both ribosomal subunits. This rRNA is critical to the function of the ribosome.

Transfer RNA. The intermediary adapter molecule between mRNA and amino acids, as mentioned earlier, is **transfer RNA (tRNA).** Transfer RNA molecules have amino acids covalently attached to one end and an anticodon that can base-pair with an mRNA codon at the other. The tRNAs act to interpret information in mRNA and to help position the amino acids on the ribosome.

Small nuclear RNA. Small nuclear RNAs (snRNAs) are part of the machinery that is involved in nuclear processing of eukaryotic "pre-mRNA." We discuss this splicing reaction later in the chapter.

SRP RNA. In eukaryotes, where some proteins are synthesized by ribosomes on the rough endoplasmic reticulum (RER), this process is mediated by the **signal recognition particle,** or **SRP,** described later in the chapter. The SRP contains both RNA and proteins.

Small RNAs. This class of RNA includes both **micro-RNA (miRNA)** and **small interfering RNA (siRNA).** These are involved in the control of gene expression discussed in chapter 16.

Learning Outcomes Review 15.1

Garrod showed that altered enzymes can cause metabolic disorders. Beadle and Tatum demonstrated that each gene encodes a unique enzyme. Genetic information flows from DNA (genes) to protein (enzymes) using messenger RNA as an intermediate. Transcription converts information in DNA into an RNA transcript, and translation converts this information into protein. RNA comes in several varieties having different functions; these include mRNA (the transcript), tRNA (the intermediary), and rRNA (in ribosomes), as well as snRNA, SNP RNA, and small RNAs (miRNA, siRNA).

- **Why do cells need an adapter molecule like tRNA between RNA and protein?**

Learning Outcomes

1. *Summarize the experiments that revealed the genetic code.*
2. *Describe the characteristics of the genetic code.*
3. *Identify the relationship between codons and amino acids.*

How does a sequence of nucleotides in a DNA molecule specify the sequence of amino acids in a polypeptide? The answer to this essential question came in 1961, through an experiment led by Francis Crick and Sydney Brenner. That experiment was so elegant and the result so critical to understanding the genetic code that we describe it here in detail.

The code is read in groups of three

Crick and Brenner reasoned that the genetic code most likely consisted of a series of blocks of information called **codons,** each corresponding to an amino acid in the encoded protein. They further hypothesized that the information within one codon was probably a sequence of three nucleotides. With four DNA nucleotides (G, C, T, and A), using two in each codon can produce only 4^2, or 16, different codons—not enough to code for 20 amino acids. However, three nucleotides results in 4^3, or 64, different combinations of three, more than enough.

Spaced or unspaced codons?

In theory, the sequence of codons in a gene could be punctuated with nucleotides between the codons that are not used, like the spaces that separate the words in this sentence. Alternatively, the codons could lie immediately adjacent to each other, forming a continuous sequence of nucleotides.

If the information in the genetic message is separated by spaces, then altering any single word would not affect the entire sentence. In contrast, if all of the words are run together but read in groups of three, then any alteration that is not in groups of three would alter the entire sentence. These two ways of using information in DNA imply different methods of translating the information into protein.

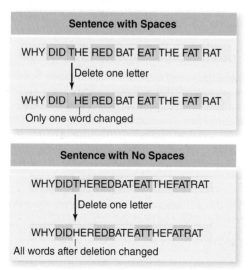

Determining that codons are unspaced

To choose between these alternative mechanisms, Crick and his colleagues used a chemical to create mutations that caused single-base insertions or deletions from a viral DNA molecule. They then showed that combining an insertion with a deletion restored function even though either one individually displayed loss of function. In this case, only the region between the insertion or deletion would be altered. By choosing a region of the gene that encoded a part of the protein not critical to function, this small change did not cause a change in phenotype.

When they combined a single deletion or two deletions near each other, the genetic message shifted, altering all of the amino acids after the deletion. When they made three deletions, however, the protein after the deletions was normal. They

SCIENTIFIC THINKING

Hypothesis: *The genetic code is read in groups of three bases.*

Prediction: *If the genetic code is read in groups of three, then deletion of one or two bases would shift the reading frame after the deletion. Deletion of three bases, however, would produce a protein with a single amino acid deleted but no change downstream.*

Test: *Single-base deletion mutants are collected, each of which exhibits a mutant phenotype. Three of these deletions in a single region are combined to assess the effect of deletion of three bases.*

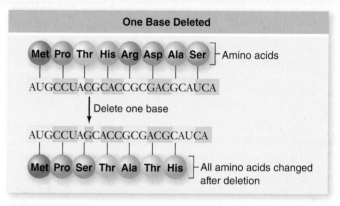

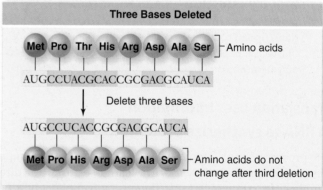

Result: *The combination of three deletions does not have the same drastic effect as the loss of one or two bases.*

Conclusion: *The genetic code is read in groups of three.*

Further Experiments: *If you also had mutants with single-base additions, what would be the effect of combining a deletion and an addition?*

Figure 15.4 **The genetic code is triplet.**

obtained the same results when they made additions to the DNA consisting of 1, 2, or 3 nt (nucleotides).

Thus, Crick and Brenner concluded that the genetic code is read in increments of three nucleotides (in other words, it is a triplet code), and that reading occurs continuously without punctuation between the 3-nt units (figure 15.4).

These experiments indicate the importance of the **reading frame** for the genetic message. Because there is no punctuation, the reading frame established by the first codon in the sequence determines how all subsequent codons are read. We now call the kinds of mutations that Crick and Brenner used **frameshift mutations** because they alter the reading frame of the genetic message.

Nirenberg and others deciphered the code

The determination of which of the 64 possible codons encoded each particular amino acids was one of the greatest triumphs of 20th-century biochemistry. Accomplishing this decryption depended on two related technologies: (1) cell-free biochemical systems that would support protein synthesis from a defined RNA and (2) the ability to produce synthetic, defined RNAs that could be used in the cell-free system.

During a five-year period from 1961 to 1966, work performed primarily in American biochemist Marshall Nirenberg's laboratory led to the elucidation of the genetic code. Nirenberg's group first showed that adding the synthetic RNA molecule polyU (an RNA molecule consisting of a string of uracil nucleotides) to their cell-free systems produced the polypeptide polyphenylalanine (a string of phenylalanine amino acids). Therefore, UUU encodes phenylalanine.

Next they used enzymes to produce RNA polymers with more than one nucleotide. These polymers allowed them to infer the composition of many of the possible codons, but not the order of bases in each codon.

The researchers then were able to use enzymes to synthesize defined 3-base sequences that could be tested for binding to the protein-synthesis machinery. This so-called *triplet-binding assay* allowed them to identify 54 of the 64 possible triplets.

The organic chemist H. Gobind Khorana provided the final piece of the puzzle by using organic synthesis to produce artificial RNA molecules of defined sequence, and then examining what polypeptides they directed in cell-free systems. The combination of all of these methods allowed the determination of all 64 possible 3-nt sequences, and the full genetic code was determined (table 15.1).

The code is degenerate but specific

Some obvious features of the code jump out of table 15.1. First, 61 of the 64 possible codons are used to specify amino acids. Three codons, UAA, UGA, and UAG, are reserved for another function: they signal "stop" and are known as **stop codons.** The only other form of "punctuation" in the code is that AUG is used to signal "start" and is therefore the **start codon.** In this case the codon has a dual function because it also encodes the amino acid methionine (Met).

| TABLE 15.1 | The Genetic Code |

First Letter	SECOND LETTER							Third Letter
	U		C		A		G	
U	UUU	Phe Phenylalanine	UCU	Ser Serine	UAU	Tyr Tyrosine	UGU	Cys Cysteine	U
	UUC		UCC		UAC		UGC		C
	UUA	Leu Leucine	UCA		UAA	"Stop"	UGA	"Stop"	A
	UUG		UCG		UAG	"Stop"	UGG	Trp Tryptophan	G
C	CUU	Leu Leucine	CCU	Pro Proline	CAU	His Histidine	CGU	Arg Arginine	U
	CUC		CCC		CAC		CGC		C
	CUA		CCA		CAA	Gln Glutamine	CGA		A
	CUG		CCG		CAG		CGG		G
A	AUU	Ile Isoleucine	ACU	Thr Threonine	AAU	Asn Asparagine	AGU	Ser Serine	U
	AUC		ACC		AAC		AGC		C
	AUA		ACA		AAA	Lys Lysine	AGA	Arg Arginine	A
	AUG	Met Methionine; "Start"	ACG		AAG		AGG		G
G	GUU	Val Valine	GCU	Ala Alanine	GAU	Asp Aspartate	GGU	Gly Glycine	U
	GUC		GCC		GAC		GGC		C
	GUA		GCA		GAA	Glu Glutamate	GGA		A
	GUG		GCG		GAG		GGG		G

A codon consists of three nucleotides read in the sequence shown. For example, ACU codes for threonine. The first letter, A, is in the First Letter column; the second letter, C, is in the Second Letter column; and the third letter, U, is in the Third Letter column. Each of the mRNA codons is recognized by a corresponding anticodon sequence on a tRNA molecule. Many amino acids are specified by more than one codon. For example, threonine is specified by four codons, which differ only in the third nucleotide (ACU, ACC, ACA, and ACG).

Figure 15.5 Transgenic pig. The piglet on the right is a conventional piglet. The piglet on the left was engineered to express a gene from jellyfish that encodes green fluorescent protein. The color of this piglet's nose is due to expression of this introduced gene. Such transgenic animals indicate the universal nature of the genetic code.

You can see that 61 codons are more than enough to encode 20 amino acids. That leaves lots of extra codons. One way to deal with this abundance would be to use only 20 of the 61 codons, but this is not what cells do. In reality, all 61 codons are used, making the code **degenerate,** which means that some amino acids are specified by more than one codon. The reverse, however, in which a single codon would specify more than one amino acid, is never found.

This degeneracy is not uniform. Some amino acids have only one codon, and some have up to six. In addition, the degenerate base usually occurs in position 3 of a codon, such that the first two positions are the same, and two or four of the possible nucleotides at position 3 encode the same amino acid. (The nature of protein synthesis on ribosomes explains how this codon usage works, and it is discussed later.)

The code is practically universal, but not quite

The genetic code is the same in almost all organisms. The universality of the genetic code is among the strongest evidence that all living things share a common evolutionary heritage. Because the code is universal, genes can be transferred from one organism to another and can be successfully expressed in their new host (figure 15.5). This universality of gene expression is central to many of the advances of genetic engineering discussed in chapter 17.

In 1979, investigators began to determine the complete nucleotide sequences of the mitochondrial genomes in humans, cattle, and mice. It came as something of a shock when these investigators learned that the genetic code used by these mammalian mitochondria was not quite the same as the "universal code" that has become so familiar to biologists.

In the mitochondrial genomes, what should have been a stop codon, UGA, was instead read as the amino acid tryptophan; AUA was read as methionine rather than as isoleucine; and AGA and AGG were read as stop codons rather than as arginine. Furthermore, minor differences from the universal code have also been found in the genomes of chloroplasts and in ciliates (certain types of protists).

Thus, it appears that the genetic code is not quite universal. Some time ago, presumably after they began their endosymbiotic existence, mitochondria and chloroplasts began to read the code differently, particularly the portion associated with "stop" signals.

> **? Inquiry question** The genetic code is almost universal. Why do you think it is nearly universal?

Learning Outcomes Review 15.2

The genetic code was shown to be nucleotide base triplets with two forms of punctuation and no spaces: three bases code for an amino acid, and the groups of three are read in order. Sixty-one codons specify amino acids, one of which also codes for "start," and three codons indicate "stop," for 64 total. Because some amino acids are specified by more than one codon, the code is termed degenerate. All codons encode only one amino acid, however.

■ *What would be the outcome if a codon specified more than one amino acid?*

15.3 Prokaryotic Transcription

Learning Outcomes

1. *Describe the transcription process in bacteria.*
2. *Differentiate among initiation, elongation, and termination of transcription.*
3. *Define the unique features of prokaryotic transcription.*

We begin an examination of gene expression by describing the process of transcription in prokaryotes. The later description of eukaryotic transcription will concentrate on their differences from prokaryotes.

Figure 15.6 Bacterial RNA polymerase and transcription initiation. *a.* RNA polymerase has two forms: core polymerase and holoenzyme. *b.* The σ subunit of the holoenzyme recognizes promoter elements at –35 and –10 and binds to the DNA. The helix is opened at the –10 region, and transcription begins at the start site at +1.

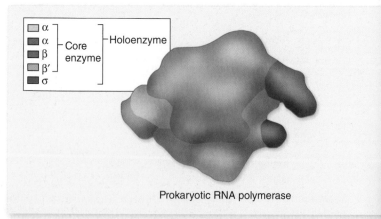

Prokaryotic RNA polymerase

a.

Prokaryotes have a single RNA polymerase

The single **RNA polymerase** of prokaryotes exists in two forms: the *core polymerase* and the *holoenzyme.* The core polymerase can synthesize RNA using a DNA template, but it cannot initiate synthesis accurately. The holoenzyme can accurately initiate synthesis.

The core polymerase is composed of four subunits: two identical α subunits, a β subunit, and a β′ subunit (figure 15.6a). The two α subunits help to hold the complex together and can bind to regulatory molecules. The active site of the enzyme is formed by the β and β′ subunits, which bind to the DNA template and the ribonucleotide triphosphate precursors.

The *holoenzyme,* which can properly initiate synthesis, is formed by the addition of a σ (sigma) subunit to the core polymerase (see figure 15.6a). Its ability to recognize specific signals in DNA allows RNA polymerase to locate the beginning of genes, which is critical to its function. Note that initiation of mRNA synthesis does not require a primer, in contrast to DNA replication.

Initiation occurs at promoters

Accurate initiation of transcription requires two sites in DNA: one called a **promoter** that forms a recognition and binding site for the RNA polymerase, and the actual **start site.** The polymerase also needs a signal to end transcription, which we call a **terminator.** We then refer to the region from promoter to terminator as a **transcription unit.**

The action of the polymerase moving along the DNA can be thought of as analogous to water flowing in a stream. We can speak of sites on the DNA as being "upstream" or "downstream" of the start site. We can also use this comparison to form a simple system for numbering bases in DNA to refer to positions in the transcription unit. The first base transcribed is called **+1,** and this numbering continues downstream until the last base is transcribed. Any bases upstream of the start site receive negative numbers, starting at **-1.**

The promoter is a short sequence found upstream of the start site and is therefore not transcribed by the polymerase. Two 6-base sequences are common to bacterial promoters: One

is located 35 nt upstream of the start site (–35), and the other is located 10 nt upstream of the start site (–10) (figure 15.6b). These two sites provide the promoter with asymmetry; they indicate not only the site of initiation, but also the direction of transcription.

The binding of RNA polymerase to the promoter is the first step in transcription. Promoter binding is controlled by the σ subunit of the RNA polymerase holoenzyme, which recognizes the –35 sequence in the promoter and positions the RNA polymerase at the correct start site, oriented to transcribe in the correct direction.

Once bound to the promoter, the RNA polymerase begins to unwind the DNA helix at the –10 site (see figure 15.6b). The polymerase covers a region of about 75 bp but only unwinds about 12–14 bp.

> **? Inquiry question** The prokaryotic promoter has two distinct elements that are not identical. How is this important to the initiation of transcription?

Elongation adds successive nucleotides

In prokaryotes, the transcription of the RNA chain usually starts with ATP or GTP. One of these forms the 5′ end of the chain, which grows in the 5′-to-3′ direction as ribonucleotides are added. As the RNA polymerase molecule leaves the promoter region, the σ factor is no longer required, although it may remain in association with the enzyme.

This process of leaving the promoter, called *clearance,* or *escape,* involves more than just synthesizing the first few nucleotides of the transcript and moving on, because the enzyme has made strong contacts to the DNA during initiation. It is necessary to break these contacts with the promoter region to be able to move progressively down the template. The enzyme goes through conformational changes during this clearance stage, and subsequently contacts less of the DNA than it does during the initial promoter binding.

The region containing the RNA polymerase, the DNA template, and the growing RNA transcript is called the **transcription bubble** because it contains a locally unwound

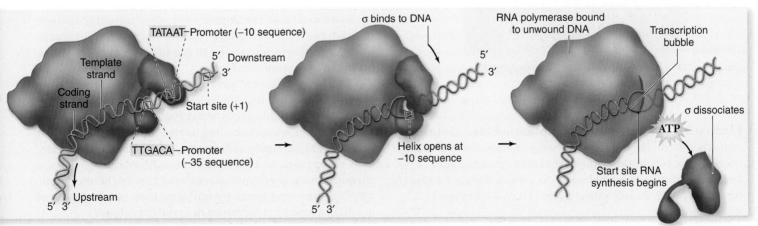

b.

"bubble" of DNA (figure 15.7). Within the bubble, the first 9 bases of the newly synthesized RNA strand temporarily form a helix with the template DNA strand. This stabilizes the positioning of the 3′ end of the RNA so it can interact with an incoming ribonucleotide triphosphate. The enzyme itself covers about 50 bp of DNA around this transcription bubble.

The transcription bubble created by RNA polymerase moves down the bacterial DNA at a constant rate, about 50 nt/sec, with the growing RNA strand protruding from the bubble. After the transcription bubble passes, the now-transcribed DNA is rewound as it leaves the bubble.

Termination occurs at specific sites

The end of a bacterial transcription unit is marked by terminator sequences that signal "stop" to the polymerase. Reaching these sequences causes the formation of phosphodiester bonds to cease, the RNA–DNA hybrid within the transcription bubble to dissociate, the RNA polymerase to release the DNA, and the DNA within the transcription bubble to rewind.

The simplest terminators consist of a series of G-C base-pairs followed by a series of A-T base-pairs. The RNA transcript of this stop region can form a double-stranded structure in the GC region called a *hairpin,* which is followed by four or more uracil (U) ribonucleotides (figure 15.8). Formation of the hairpin causes the RNA polymerase to pause,

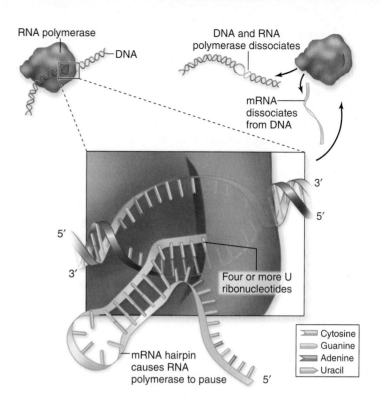

Figure 15.8 Bacterial transcription terminator. The self-complementary G–C region forms a double-stranded stem with a single-stranded loop called a hairpin. The stretch of U's forms a less stable RNA–DNA hybrid that falls off the enzyme.

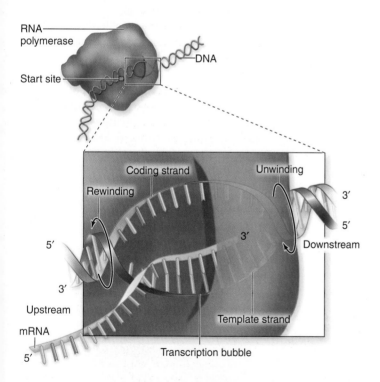

Figure 15.7 Model of a transcription bubble. The DNA duplex is unwound by the RNA polymerase complex, rewinding at the end of the bubble. One of the strands of DNA functions as a template, and nucleotide building blocks are added to the 3′ end of the growing RNA. There is a short region of RNA–DNA hybrid within the bubble.

placing it directly over the run of four uracils. The pairing of U with the DNA's A is the weakest of the four hybrid base-pairs, and it is not strong enough to hold the hybrid strands when the polymerase pauses. Instead, the RNA strand dissociates from the DNA within the transcription bubble, and transcription stops. A variety of protein factors also act at these terminators to aid in terminating transcription.

Prokaryotic transcription is coupled to translation

In prokaryotes, the mRNA produced by transcription begins to be translated before transcription is finished—that is, they are *coupled* (figure 15.9). As soon as a 5′ end of the mRNA becomes available, ribosomes are loaded onto this to begin translation. (This coupling cannot occur in eukaryotes because transcription occurs in the nucleus, and translation occurs in the cytoplasm.)

Another difference between prokaryotic and eukaryotic gene expression is that the mRNA produced in prokaryotes may contain multiple genes. Prokaryotic genes are often organized such that genes encoding related functions are clustered together. This grouping of functionally related genes is referred to as an **operon.** An operon is a single transcription unit that encodes multiple enzymes necessary for a biochemical pathway. By clustering genes by function, they can be regulated together, a topic that we return to in the next chapter.

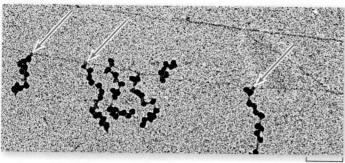

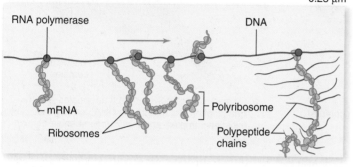

Figure 15.9 Transcription and translation are coupled in prokaryotes. In this micrograph of gene expression in *E. coli*, translation is occurring during transcription. The arrows point to RNA polymerase enzymes, and ribosomes are attached to the mRNAs extending from the polymerase. Polypeptides being synthesized by ribosomes, which are not visible in the micrograph, have been added to the last mRNA in the drawing.

15.4 Eukaryotic Transcription

Learning Outcomes

1. List the different eukaryotic RNA polymerases.
2. Differentiate promoters for the three polymerases.
3. Describe the processing of eukaryotic transcripts.

The basic mechanism of transcription by RNA polymerase is the same in eukaryotes as in prokaryotes; however, the details of the two processes differ enough that it is necessary to consider them separately. Here we concentrate only on how eukaryotic systems differ from prokaryotic systems, such as the bacterial system just discussed. All other features may be assumed to be the same.

Eukaryotes have three RNA polymerases

Unlike prokaryotes, which have a single RNA polymerase enzyme, eukaryotes have three different RNA polymerases, which are distinguished in both structure and function. The enzyme **RNA polymerase I** transcribes rRNA, **RNA polymerase II** transcribes mRNA and some small nuclear RNAs, and **RNA polymerase III** transcribes tRNA and some other small RNAs. Together, these three enzymes accomplish all transcription in the nucleus of eukaryotic cells.

Each polymerase has its own promoter

The existence of three different RNA polymerases requires different signals in the DNA to allow each polymerase to recognize where to begin transcription. Each polymerase recognizes a different promoter structure.

RNA polymerase I promoters

RNA polymerase I promoters at first puzzled biologists, because comparisons of rRNA genes between species showed no similarities outside the coding region. The current view is that these promoters are also specific for each species, and for this reason, cross-species comparisons do not yield similarities.

RNA polymerase II promoters

The RNA polymerase II promoters are the most complex of the three types, probably a reflection of the huge diversity of genes that are transcribed by this polymerase. When the first eukaryotic genes were isolated, many had a sequence called the **TATA box** upstream of the start site. This sequence was similar to the prokaryotic –10 sequence, and it was assumed that the TATA box was the primary promoter element. With the sequencing of entire genomes, many more genes have been analyzed, and this assumption has proved too simple. It has been replaced by the idea of a "core promoter" that can be composed of a number of different elements, including the TATA box. Additional control elements allow for tissue-specific and developmental time–specific expression (see chapter 16).

RNA polymerase III promoters

Promoters for RNA polymerase III also were a source of surprise for biologists in the early days of molecular biology who were examining the control of eukaryotic gene expression. A common technique for analyzing regulatory regions was to make successive deletions from the 5′ end of genes until enough was deleted to abolish specific transcription. The logic followed experiences with prokaryotes, in which the regulatory regions had been found at the 5′ end of genes. But in the case of tRNA genes, the 5′ deletions had no effect on

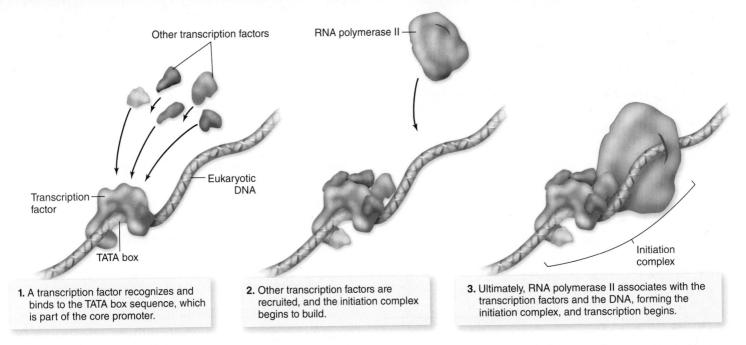

1. A transcription factor recognizes and binds to the TATA box sequence, which is part of the core promoter.

2. Other transcription factors are recruited, and the initiation complex begins to build.

3. Ultimately, RNA polymerase II associates with the transcription factors and the DNA, forming the initiation complex, and transcription begins.

Figure 15.10 Eukaryotic initiation complex. Unlike transcription in prokaryotic cells, in which the RNA polymerase recognizes and binds to the promoter, eukaryotic transcription requires the binding of transcription factors to the promoter before RNA polymerase II binds to the DNA. The association of transcription factors and RNA polymerase II at the promoter is called the initiation complex.

expression! The promoters were found to actually be internal to the gene itself. This has not proved to be the case for all polymerase III genes, but appears to be for most.

Initiation and termination differ from that in prokaryotes

The initiation at RNA polymerase II promoters is analogous to prokaryotic initiation but instead of a single factor allowing promoter recognition, eukaryotes use a host of **transcription factors.** These proteins are necessary to assemble RNA polymerase II on a promoter. The transcription factors interact with RNA polymerase II to form an initiation complex at the promoter (figure 15.10). We explore this complex in detail in chapter 16 when we describe the control of gene expression.

Curiously, it now appears that recruitment to the promoter is not the end of the story. Recent global analyses showed that 30% of human genes have Pol II paused 20–50 bp

downstream of the promoter. This promoter-proximal pausing can be relieved by elongation factors, and allows another level of control on transcription.

The termination of transcription for RNA polymerase II also differs from prokaryotes. Although termination sites exist, they are not well defined, and the end of the mRNA is not even formed by RNA polymerase II because the primary transcript is modified.

Eukaryotic transcripts are modified

A primary difference between prokaryotes and eukaryotes is the fate of the transcript itself. Prokaryotes translate the mRNA during transcription, but eukaryotes extensively modify the transcript in the nucleus before its translation in the cytoplasm. We call the RNA synthesized by RNA polymerase II the **primary transcript,** which is processed to produce the **mature mRNA.**

The 5′ cap

The first base in the transcript is usually an adenine (A) or a guanine (G), and this is modified by the addition of GTP to the 5′ PO_4 group, forming what is known as the **5′ cap** (figure 15.11). This cap is joined to the transcript by its 5′ end; the only such 5′-to-5′ bond found in nucleic acids. The G in the GTP is also modified by the addition of a methyl group, so it is often called a **methyl-G cap.** The cap is added while transcription is still in

Figure 15.11 Posttranscriptional modifications to 5′ and 3′ ends. Eukaryotic mRNA molecules are modified in the nucleus with the addition of a methylated GTP to the 5′ end of the transcript, called the 5′ cap, and a long chain of adenine residues to the 3′ end of the transcript, called the 3′ poly-A tail.

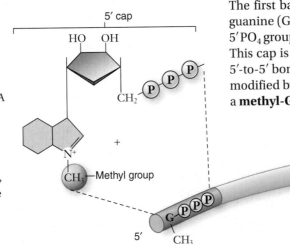

progress. This cap protects the 5′ end of the mRNA from degradation and participates in translation initiation.

The 3′ poly-A tail

A major difference between prokaryotes and eukaryotes is that in eukaryotes, the end of the transcript is not the end of the mRNA. The eukaryotic transcript is cleaved downstream of a specific site (AAUAAA) prior to the termination site. A series of adenine (A) residues, called the **3′ poly-A tail,** is added after this cleavage by the enzyme poly-A polymerase. Thus the end of the mRNA is not created by RNA polymerase II (see figure 15.11).

The enzyme poly-A polymerase is part of a complex that recognizes the poly-A site, cleaves the transcript, then adds 100–200 A's to the end. The poly-A tail appears to play a role in the stability of mRNAs by protecting them from degradation (see chapter 16).

Splicing of primary transcripts

Eukaryotic genes may contain noncoding sequences that have to be removed to produce the final mRNA. This process, called pre-mRNA splicing, is accomplished by an organelle called the **spliceosome.** This complex topic is discussed in the next section.

Learning Outcomes Review 15.4

Eukaryotes have three RNA polymerases called polymerase I, II, and III. Each synthesizes a different RNA and recognizes its own promoter. The RNA polymerase I promoter is species-specific. The polymerase II promoter is complex, but often includes a sequence called the TATA box. The polymerase III promoter is internal to the gene, rather than close to the 5′ end. Polymerase II is responsible for mRNA synthesis. The primary mRNA transcript is modified by addition of a 5′ cap and a 3′ poly-A tail consisting of 100–200 adenines. Noncoding regions are removed by splicing.

■ **Does the complexity of the eukaryotic genome require three polymerases?**

15.5 *Eukaryotic pre-mRNA Splicing*

Learning Outcomes

1. *Explain the relationship between genes and proteins in prokaryotes and eukaryotes.*
2. *Describe the splicing reaction for pre-mRNA.*
3. *Illustrate how splicing changes the nature of genes.*

The first genes isolated were prokaryotic genes found in *E. coli* and its viruses. A clear picture of the nature and some of the control of gene expression emerged from these systems before any eukaryotic genes were isolated. It was assumed that although details would differ, the outline of gene expression in eukaryotes would be similar. The world of biology was in for a shock with the isolation of the first genes from eukaryotic organisms.

Eukaryotic genes may contain interruptions

Many eukaryotic genes appeared to contain sequences that were not represented in the mRNA. It is hard to exaggerate how unexpected this finding was. A basic tenet of molecular biology based on *E. coli* was that a gene was *colinear* with its protein product, that is, the sequence of bases in the gene corresponds to the sequence of bases in the mRNA, which in turn corresponds to the sequence of amino acids in the protein.

In the case of eukaryotes, genes can be interrupted by sequences that are not represented in the mRNA and the protein. The term "split genes" was used at the time, but the nomenclature that has stuck describes the unexpected nature of these sequences. We call the noncoding DNA that interrupts the sequence of the gene "intervening sequences," or **introns,** and we call the coding sequences **exons** because they are expressed (figure 15.12).

The spliceosome is the splicing organelle

It is still true that the mature eukaryotic mRNA is colinear with its protein product, but a gene that contains introns is not. Imagine looking at an interstate highway from a satellite. Scattered randomly along the thread of concrete would be cars, some moving in clusters, others individually; most of the road

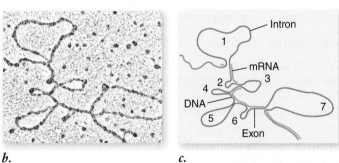

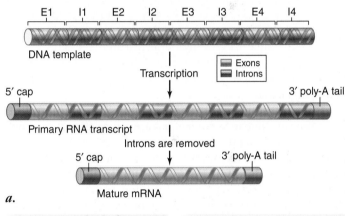

Figure 15.12 Eukaryotic genes contain introns and exons. *a.* Eukaryotic genes contain sequences that form the coding sequence called exons and intervening sequences called introns. *b.* An electron micrograph showing hybrids formed with the mRNA and the DNA of the ovalbumin gene, which has seven introns. Introns within the DNA sequence have no corresponding sequence in the mRNA and thus appear as seven loops. *c.* A schematic drawing of the micrograph.

 Data analysis Illustrate how the gene in figure 15.12 could encode multiple transcripts.

would be bare. That is what a eukaryotic gene is like—scattered exons embedded within much longer sequences of introns.

In humans, only 1 to 1.5% of the genome is devoted to the exons that encode proteins; 24% is devoted to the noncoding introns within which these exons are embedded.

The splicing reaction

The obvious question is—How do eukaryotic cells deal with the noncoding introns? The answer is that the primary transcript is cut and put back together to produce the mature mRNA. The latter process is referred to as **pre-mRNA splicing,** and it occurs in the nucleus prior to the export of the mRNA to the cytoplasm.

The intron–exon junctions are recognized by **small nuclear ribonucleoprotein particles,** called **snRNPs** (pronounced "snurps"). The snRNPs are complexes composed of snRNA and protein. These snRNPs then cluster together with other associated proteins to form a larger complex called the **spliceosome,** which is responsible for the splicing, or removal, of the introns.

For splicing to occur accurately, the spliceosome must be able to recognize intron–exon junctions. Introns all begin with the same 2-base sequence and end with another 2-base sequence that tags them for removal. In addition, within the intron there is a conserved A nucleotide, called the *branch point,* which is important for the splicing reaction (figure 15.13).

The splicing process begins with cleavage of the 5' end of the intron. This 5' end becomes attached to the 2' OH of the branch point A, forming a branched structure called a *lariat* due to its resemblance to a cowboy's lariat in a rope (see figure 15.13). The 3' end of the first exon is then used to displace the 3' end of the intron, joining the two exons together and releasing the intron as a lariat.

The processes of transcription and RNA processing do not occur in a linear sequence, but are rather all part of a concerted process that produces the mature mRNA. The capping reaction occurs during transcription, as does the splicing process. The RNA polymerase II enzyme itself helps to recruit the other factors necessary for modification of the primary transcript, and in this way the process of transcription and pre-mRNA processing are coupled.

Distribution of introns

No rules govern the number of introns per gene or the sizes of introns and exons. Some genes have no introns; others may have 50. The sizes of exons range from a few nucleotides to 7500 nt, and the sizes of introns are equally variable. The presence of introns partly explains why so little of a eukaryotic genome is actually composed of "coding sequences" (see chapter 18 for results from the Human Genome Project).

One explanation for the existence of introns suggests that exons represent functional domains of proteins, and that the intron–exon arrangements found in genes represent the shuffling of these functional units over long periods of evolutionary time. This hypothesis, called *exon shuffling,* was proposed soon after the discovery of introns and has been the subject of much debate over the years.

The recent flood of genomic data has shed light on this issue by allowing statistical analysis of the placement of introns and on intron–exon structure. This analysis has provided support for the exon shuffling hypothesis for many genes; however, it is also clearly

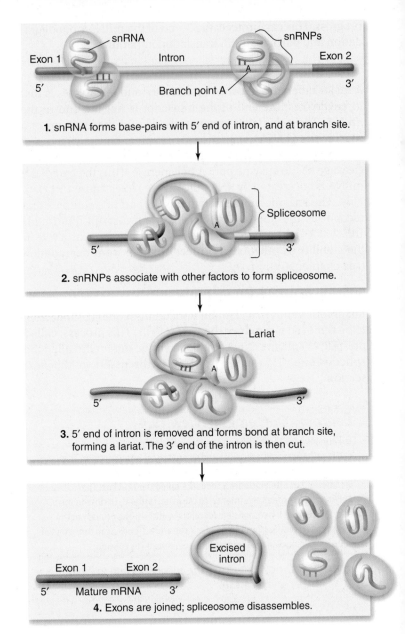

1. snRNA forms base-pairs with 5' end of intron, and at branch site.

2. snRNPs associate with other factors to form spliceosome.

3. 5' end of intron is removed and forms bond at branch site, forming a lariat. The 3' end of the intron is then cut.

4. Exons are joined; spliceosome disassembles.

Figure 15.13 Pre-mRNA splicing by the spliceosome. Particles called snRNPs contain snRNA that interacts with the 5' end of an intron and with a branch site internal to the intron. Several snRNPs come together with other proteins to form the spliceosome. As the intron forms a loop, the 5' end is cut and linked to a site near the 3' end of the intron. The intron forms a lariat that is excised, and the exons are spliced together. The spliceosome then disassembles and releases the spliced mRNA.

not universal, because all proteins do not show this kind of pattern. It is possible that introns do not have a single origin, and therefore cannot be explained by a single hypothesis.

Splicing can produce multiple transcripts from the same gene

One consequence of the splicing process is greater complexity in gene expression in eukaryotes. A single primary transcript can be spliced into different mRNAs by the inclusion of different sets of exons, a process called **alternative splicing.**

Evidence indicates that the normal pattern of splicing is important to an organism's function. Up to half of known human genetic disorders may be due to altered splicing. Mutations in the signals for splicing can introduce new splice sites or can abolish normal patterns of splicing. (In chapter 16 we consider how alternative splicing can be used to regulate gene expression.)

Although many specific cases of alternative splicing have been documented, the availability of the human genome and high throughput systems to analyze transcription have led to a flood of data comparing transcripts from different tissues to the genome. This has led to continuously increasing estimates of the frequency of alternative transcripts. If the latest estimates hold up, the conclusion is that alternative splicing is essentially universal. Two different groups arrived at estimates of more than 90% of human genes being alternatively spliced with more than 80% of these having minor isoforms that make up more than 15% of mRNAs for the gene.

It is important to note that these analyses are global surveys using next generation sequencing methods to analyze RNA populations from different tissues. The possible functions of the protein products of these splice variants have been investigated for only a small fraction of the potentially spliced genes. These analyses, however, do explain how the 25,000 genes of the human genome can encode the more than 100,000 different proteins reported to exist in human cells. The emerging field of proteomics addresses the number and functioning of proteins encoded by the human genome.

Learning Outcomes Review 15.5

In prokaryotes, genes appear to be colinear with their protein products. Eukaryotic genes, by contrast, contain exon regions, which are expressed, and intron sequences, which interrupt the exons. The introns are removed by the spliceosome in a process that leaves the exons joined together. Alternative splicing can generate different mRNAs, and thus different proteins, from the same gene. Recent estimates are that as many as half of human genes may be alternatively spliced.

■ *What advantages would alternative splicing confer on an organism?*

Learning Outcomes

1. *Explain why the tRNA charging reaction is critical to translation.*
2. *Identify the tRNA-binding sites in the ribosome.*

The ribosome is the key organelle in translation, but it also requires the participation of mRNA, tRNA, and a host of other factors. Critical to this process is the interaction of the ribosomes with tRNA and mRNA. To understand this, we first examine the structure of the tRNA adapter molecule and the ribosome itself.

Aminoacyl-tRNA synthetases attach amino acids to tRNA

Each amino acid must be attached to a tRNA with the correct anticodon for protein synthesis to proceed. This covalent attachment is accomplished by the action of activating enzymes called **aminoacyl-tRNA synthetases.** One of these enzymes is present for each of the 20 common amino acids.

tRNA structure

Transfer RNA is a bifunctional molecule that must be able to interact with mRNA and with amino acids. The structure of tRNAs is highly conserved in all living systems, and it can be formed into a cloverleaf type of structure based on intramolecular base-pairing that produces double-stranded regions. This primary structure is then folded in space to form an L-shaped molecule that has two functional ends: the **acceptor stem** and the **anticodon loop** (figure 15.14).

2D "Cloverleaf" Model	3D Ribbon-like Model	3D Space-filled Model	Icon

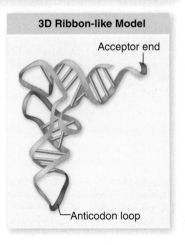
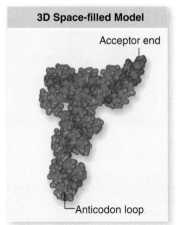
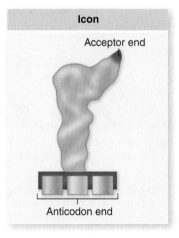

Figure 15.14   The structure of tRNA. Base-pairing within the molecule creates three stem and loop structures in a characteristic cloverleaf shape. The loop at the bottom of the cloverleaf contains the anticodon sequence, which can base-pair with codons in the mRNA. Amino acids are attached to the free, single-stranded —OH end of the acceptor stem. In its final three-dimensional structure, the loops of tRNA are folded into the final L-shaped structure.

The acceptor stem is the 3′ end of the molecule, which always ends in 5′ CCA 3′. The amino acid is attached to this end of the molecule. The anticodon loop is the bottom loop of the cloverleaf, and it can base-pair with codons in mRNA.

The charging reaction

The aminoacyl-tRNA synthetases must be able to recognize specific tRNA molecules as well as their corresponding amino acids. Although 61 codons code for amino acids, there are actually not 61 tRNAs in cells, although the number varies from species to species. Therefore, some aminoacyl-tRNA synthetases must be able to recognize more than one tRNA—but each recognizes only a single amino acid.

The reaction catalyzed by the enzymes is called the tRNA **charging reaction,** and the product is an amino acid joined to a tRNA, now called a *charged tRNA*. An ATP molecule provides energy for this endergonic reaction. The charged tRNA produced by the reaction is an activated intermediate that can undergo the peptide bond-forming reaction without an additional input of energy.

The charging reaction joins the acceptor stem to the carboxyl terminus of an amino acid (figure 15.15). Keeping this directionality in mind is critical to understanding the function of the ribosome, because each peptide bond will be formed between the amino group of one amino acid and the carboxyl group of another amino acid.

The correct attachment of amino acids to tRNAs is important because the ribosome does not verify this attachment. Ribosomes can only ensure that the codon–anticodon pairing is correct. In an elegant experiment, cysteine was converted chemically to alanine after the charging reaction, when the amino acid was already attached to tRNA. When this charged tRNA was used in an in vitro protein synthesis system, alanine was incor-porated in the place of cysteine, showing that the ribosome cannot "proofread" the amino acids attached to tRNA.

In a very real sense, therefore, the charging reaction is the actual translation step; amino acids are incorporated into a peptide based solely on the tRNA anticodon and its interaction with the mRNA.

The ribosome has multiple tRNA-binding sites

The synthesis of any biopolymer can be broken down into initiation, elongation, and termination—you have seen this division for DNA replication as well as for transcription. In the case of translation, or protein synthesis, all three of these steps take place on the ribosome, a large macromolecular assembly consisting of rRNA and proteins. Details of the process by which the two ribosome subunits are assembled during initiation are described shortly.

For the ribosome to function it must be able to bind to at least two charged tRNAs at once so that a peptide bond can be formed between their amino acids, as described in the previous overview. The bacterial ribosome contains three binding sites, summarized in figure 15.16:

- The **P site** (peptidyl) binds to the tRNA attached to the growing peptide chain.
- The **A site** (aminoacyl) binds to the tRNA carrying the next amino acid to be added.
- The **E site** (exit) binds the tRNA that carried the previous amino acid added (see figure 15.16).

Transfer RNAs move through these sites successively during the process of elongation. Relative to the mRNA, the sites are arranged 5′ to 3′ in the order E, P, and A. The incoming

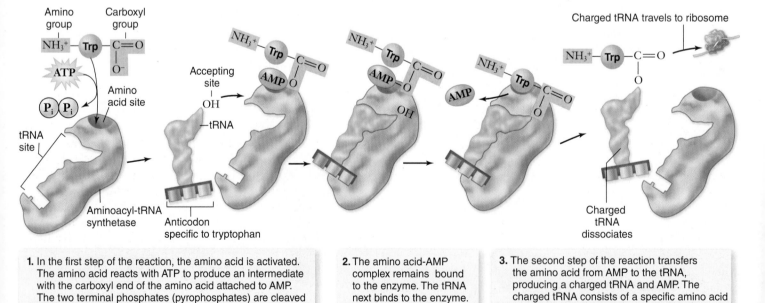

1. In the first step of the reaction, the amino acid is activated. The amino acid reacts with ATP to produce an intermediate with the carboxyl end of the amino acid attached to AMP. The two terminal phosphates (pyrophosphates) are cleaved from ATP in this reaction.

2. The amino acid-AMP complex remains bound to the enzyme. The tRNA next binds to the enzyme.

3. The second step of the reaction transfers the amino acid from AMP to the tRNA, producing a charged tRNA and AMP. The charged tRNA consists of a specific amino acid attached to the 3′ acceptor stem of its RNA.

Figure 15.15 tRNA charging reaction. There are 20 different aminoacyl-tRNA synthetase enzymes each specific for one amino acid, such as tryptophan (Trp). The enzyme must also recognize and bind to the tRNA molecules with anticodons specifying that amino acid, ACC for tryptophan. The reaction uses ATP and produces an activated intermediate that will not require further energy for peptide bond formation.

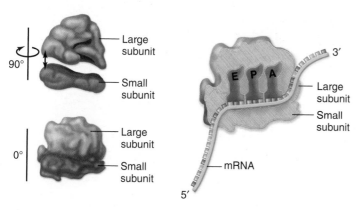

Figure 15.16 Ribosomes have two subunits. Ribosome subunits come together and apart as part of a ribosome cycle. The smaller subunit fits into a depression on the surface of the larger one. Ribosomes have three tRNA-binding sites: aminoacyl site (A), peptidyl site (P), and empty site (E).

charged tRNAs enter the ribosome at the A site, transit through the P site, and then leave via the E site.

The ribosome has both decoding and enzymatic functions

The two functions of the ribosome involve decoding the transcribed message and forming peptide bonds. The decoding function resides primarily in the small subunit of the ribosome. The formation of peptide bonds requires the enzyme **peptidyl transferase,** which resides in the large subunit.

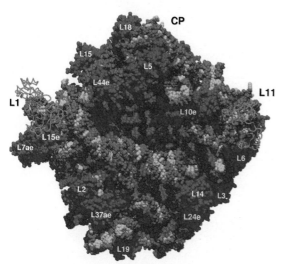

Figure 15.17 3-D structure of prokaryotic ribosome. The complete atomic structure of a prokaryotic large ribosomal subunit has been determined at 2.4-Å resolution. Bases of RNA are white, the polynucleotide backbone is red, and proteins are blue. The faces of each ribosomal subunit are lined with rRNA such that their interaction with tRNAs, amino acids, and mRNA all involve rRNA. Proteins are absent from the active site but abundant everywhere on the surface. The proteins stabilize the structure by interacting with adjacent RNA strands.

Our view of the ribosome has changed dramatically over time. Initially, molecular biologists assumed that the proteins in the ribosome carried out its function and that the rRNA was a structural scaffold necessary to hold the proteins in the correct position. Now this view has mostly been reversed; the ribosome is seen instead as rRNAs that are held in place by proteins. The faces of the two subunits that interact with each other are lined with rRNA, and the parts of both subunits that interact with mRNA, tRNA, and amino acids are also primarily rRNA (figure 15.17). It is now thought that the peptidyl transferase activity resides in an rRNA in the large subunit.

Learning Outcomes Review 15.6

Transfer RNA has two functional regions, one that bonds with an amino acid, and the other that can base-pair with mRNA. The tRNA charging reaction joins the carboxyl end of an amino acid to the 3′ acceptor stem of its tRNA; without charged tRNAs, translation cannot take place. This reaction is catalyzed by 20 different aminoacyl-tRNA synthetases, one for each amino acid. The ribosome has three different binding sites for tRNA, one for the tRNA adding to the growing peptide chain (P site), one for the next charged tRNA (A site), and one for the previous tRNA, which is now without an amino acid (E site). The ribosome can be thought of as having both a decoding function and an enzymatic function.

- *What would be the effect on translation of a mutant tRNA that has an anticodon complementary to a STOP codon?*

15.7 *The Process of Translation*

Learning Outcomes

1. *Describe the process of translation initiation.*
2. *Explain the elongation cycle.*
3. *Compare translation on the RER and in the cytoplasm.*

The process of translation is one of the most complex and energy-expensive tasks that cells perform. An overview of the process, as you saw earlier, is perhaps deceptively simple: The mRNA is threaded through the ribosome, while tRNAs carrying amino acids bind to the ribosome, where they interact with mRNA by base-pairing with the mRNA's codons. The ribosome and tRNAs position the amino acids such that peptide bonds can be formed between each new amino acid and the growing polypeptide.

Initiation requires accessory factors

As mentioned earlier, the start codon is AUG, which also encodes the amino acid methionine. The ribosome usually uses the first AUG it encounters in an mRNA strand to signal the start of translation.

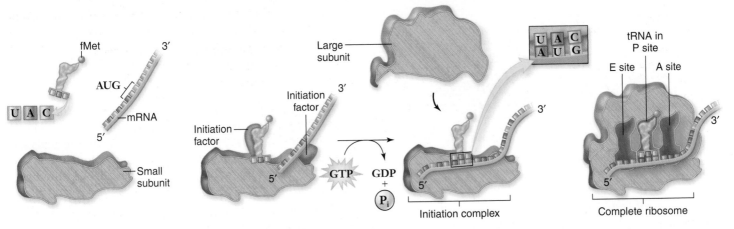

Figure 15.18 Initiation of translation. In prokaryotes, initiation factors play key roles in positioning the small ribosomal subunit, the initiator tRNA^fMet, and the mRNA. When the tRNA^fMet is positioned over the first AUG codon of the mRNA, the large ribosomal subunit binds, forming the E, P, and A sites where successive tRNA molecules bind to the ribosomes, and polypeptide synthesis begins. Ribosomal subunits are shown as a cutaway sectioned through the middle.

Prokaryotic initiation

In prokaryotes, the **initiation complex** includes a special **initiator tRNA** molecule charged with a chemically modified methionine, *N-formylmethionine*. The initiator tRNA is shown as tRNA^fMet. The initiation complex also includes the small ribosomal subunit and the mRNA strand (figure 15.18). The small subunit is positioned correctly on the mRNA due to a conserved sequence in the 5′ end of the mRNA called the **ribosome-binding sequence (RBS)** that is complementary to the 3′ end of a small subunit rRNA.

A number of initiation factors mediate this interaction of the ribosome, mRNA, and tRNA^fMet to form the initiation complex. These factors are involved in initiation only and are not part of the ribosome.

Once the complex of mRNA, initiator tRNA, and small ribosomal subunit is formed, the large subunit is added, and

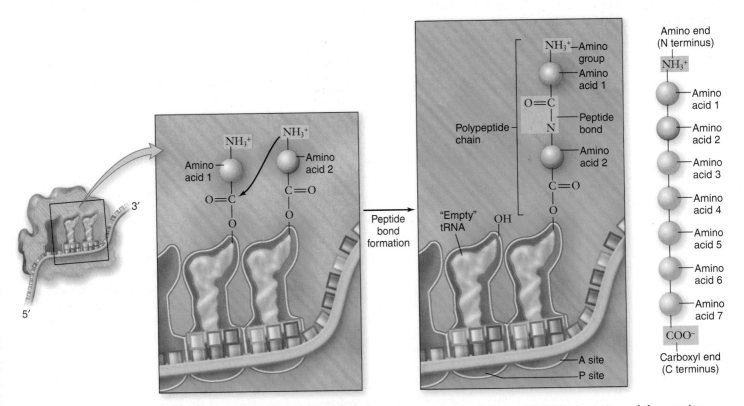

Figure 15.19 Peptide bond formation. Peptide bonds are formed between a "new" charged tRNA in the A site and the growing chain attached to the tRNA in the P site. The bond forms between the amino group of the new amino acid and the carboxyl group of the growing chain. This breaks the bond between the growing chain and its tRNA, transferring it to the A site as the new amino acid remains attached to its tRNA.

translation can begin. With the formation of the complete ribosome, the initiator tRNA is bound to the P site with the A site empty.

Eukaryotic initiation

Initiation in eukaryotes is similar, although it differs in two important ways. First, in eukaryotes, the initiating amino acid is methionine rather than *N*-formylmethionine. Second, the initiation complex is far more complicated than in prokaryotes, containing nine or more protein factors, many consisting of several subunits. Eukaryotic mRNAs also lack an RBS. The small subunit binds to the mRNA initially by binding to the 5′ cap of the mRNA.

Elongation adds successive amino acids

When the entire ribosome is assembled around the initiator tRNA and mRNA, the second charged tRNA can be brought to the ribosome and bind to the empty A site. This requires an **elongation factor** called **EF-Tu,** which binds to the charged tRNA and to GTP.

A peptide bond can then form between the amino acid of the initiator tRNA and the newly arrived charged tRNA in the A site. The geometry of this bond relative to the two charged tRNAs is critical to understanding the process. Remember that an amino acid is attached to a tRNA by its carboxyl terminus. The peptide bond is formed between the amino end of the incoming amino acid (in the A site) and the carboxyl end of the growing chain (in the P site) (figure 15.19).

The addition of successive amino acids is a series of events that occur in a cyclic fashion. Figure 15.20 shows the details of the elongation cycle.

1. **Matching tRNA anticodon with mRNA codon.** Each new charged tRNA comes to the ribosome bound to EF-Tu and GTP. The charged tRNA binds to the A site if its anticodon is complementary to the mRNA codon in the A site.

   After binding, GTP is hydrolyzed, and EF-Tu–GDP dissociates from the ribosome where it is recycled by another factor. This two-step binding and hydrolysis of GTP is thought to increase the accuracy of translation.

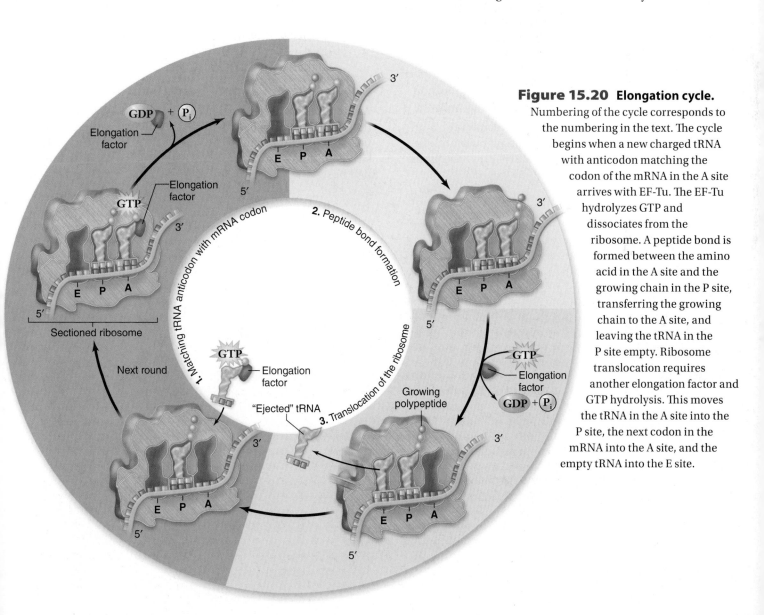

Figure 15.20 Elongation cycle. Numbering of the cycle corresponds to the numbering in the text. The cycle begins when a new charged tRNA with anticodon matching the codon of the mRNA in the A site arrives with EF-Tu. The EF-Tu hydrolyzes GTP and dissociates from the ribosome. A peptide bond is formed between the amino acid in the A site and the growing chain in the P site, transferring the growing chain to the A site, and leaving the tRNA in the P site empty. Ribosome translocation requires another elongation factor and GTP hydrolysis. This moves the tRNA in the A site into the P site, the next codon in the mRNA into the A site, and the empty tRNA into the E site.

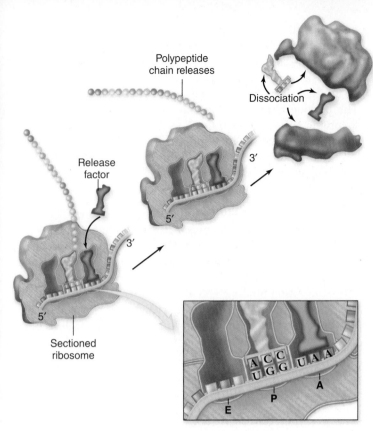

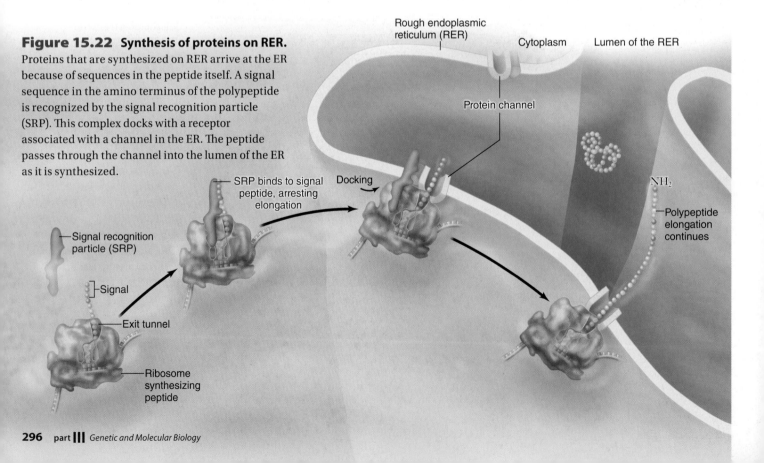

Figure 15.21 Termination of protein synthesis. There is no tRNA with an anticodon complementary to any of the three termination signal codons. When a ribosome encounters a termination codon, it stops translocating. A specific protein release factor facilitates the release of the polypeptide chain by breaking the covalent bond that links the polypeptide to the P site tRNA.

2. **Peptide bond formation.** Peptidyl transferase, located in the large subunit, catalyzes the formation of a peptide bond between the amino group of the amino acid in the A site and the carboxyl group of the growing chain. This also breaks the bond between the growing chain and the tRNA in the P site leaving it empty (no longer charged). The overall result of this is to transfer the growing chain to the tRNA in the A site.

3. **Translocation of the ribosome.** After the peptide bond has been formed, the ribosome moves relative to the mRNA and the tRNAs. The next codon in the mRNA shifts into the A site, and the tRNA with the growing chain moves to the P site. The uncharged tRNA formerly in the P site is now in the E site, and it will be ejected in the next cycle. This translocation step requires the accessory factor EF-G and the hydrolysis of another GTP.

This elongation cycle continues with each new amino acid added. The ribosome moves down the mRNA in a 5′-to-3′ direction, reading successive codons. The tRNAs move through the ribosome in the opposite direction, from the A site to the P site and finally the E site, before they are ejected as empty tRNAs, which can be charged with another amino acid and then used again.

Wobble pairing

As mentioned, there are fewer tRNAs than codons. This situation is easily rationalized because the pairing between the 3′ base of the codon and the 5′ base of the anticodon is less stringent than normal. In some tRNAs, the presence of modified bases with less accurate pairing in the 5′ position of the

Figure 15.22 Synthesis of proteins on RER. Proteins that are synthesized on RER arrive at the ER because of sequences in the peptide itself. A signal sequence in the amino terminus of the polypeptide is recognized by the signal recognition particle (SRP). This complex docks with a receptor associated with a channel in the ER. The peptide passes through the channel into the lumen of the ER as it is synthesized.

anticodon enhances this flexibility. This effect is referred to as **wobble pairing** because these tRNAs can "wobble" a bit on the mRNA, so that a single tRNA can "read" more than one codon in the mRNA.

 Inquiry question How is the wobble phenomenon related to the number of tRNAs and the degeneracy of the genetic code?

Termination requires accessory factors

Elongation continues in this fashion until a chain-terminating stop codon is reached (for example, UAA in figure 15.21). These stop codons do not bind to tRNA; instead, they are recognized by release factors, proteins that release the newly made polypeptide from the ribosome.

Proteins may be targeted to the ER

In eukaryotes, translation can occur either in the cytoplasm or on the RER. Proteins that are translated on the RER are targeted there based on their own initial amino acid sequence. The ribosomes found on the RER are actively translating and are not permanently bound to the ER.

A polypeptide that starts with a short series of amino acids called a **signal sequence** is specifically recognized and bound by a cytoplasmic complex of proteins called the **signal recognition particle (SRP).** The complex of signal sequence and SRP is in turn recognized by a receptor protein in the ER membrane. The binding of the ER receptor to the signal sequence/SRP complex holds the ribosome engaged in translation of the protein on the ER membrane, a process called *docking* (figure 15.22).

As the protein is assembled, it passes through a channel formed by the docking complex and into the interior ER compartment, the cisternal space. This is the basis for the docking metaphor—the ribosome is not actually bound to the ER itself, but with the newly synthesized protein entering the ER, the ribosome is like a boat tied to a dock with a rope.

The basic mechanism of protein translocation across membranes by the SRP and its receptor and channel complex has been conserved across all three cell types: eukaryotes, bacteria, and archaea. Given that only eukaryotic cells have an endomembrane system, this universality may seem curious; however, bacteria and archaea both export proteins through their plasma membrane, and the mechanism used is similar to the way in which eukaryotes move proteins into the cisternal space of the ER.

Once within the ER cisternal space, or lumen, the newly synthesized protein can be modified by the addition of sugars (glycosylation) and transported by vesicles to the Golgi apparatus (see chapter 4). This is the beginning of the protein-trafficking pathway that can lead to other intracellular targets, to incorporation into the plasma membrane, or to release outside of the cell itself.

15.8 *Summarizing Gene Expression*

Because of the complexity of the process of gene expression, it is worth stepping back to summarize some key points:

■ The process of gene expression converts information in the genotype into the phenotype.

■ A copy of the gene in the form of mRNA is produced by transcription, and the mRNA is used to direct the synthesis of a protein by translation.

■ Both transcription and translation can be broken down into initiation, an elongation cycle, and termination—processes that produce their respective polymers. (The same is true for DNA replication.)

■ Eukaryotic gene expression is much more complex than that of prokaryotes.

The structure of eukaryotic genes with interrupted coding sequences complicates both the process of gene expression and the nature of genetic information. It means that processing must occur between transcription and translation, and that one gene can produce multiple messages. Transcription in eukaryotes also takes place in the nucleus, whereas translation takes place in the cytoplasm. This necessitates that the mRNA be transported through nuclear pores to the cytoplasm prior to translation. The entire eukaryotic process is summarized in figure 15.23, and differences in gene expression between prokaryotes and in eukaryotes are summarized in table 15.2.

Figure 15.23 An overview of gene expression in eukaryotes.

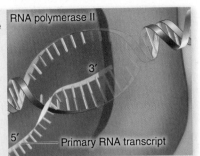

1. RNA polymerase II in the nucleus copies one strand of the DNA to produce the primary transcript.

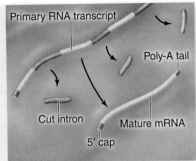

2. The primary transcript is processed by addition of a 5′ methyl-G cap, cleavage and polyadenylation of the 3′ end, and removal of introns. The mature mRNA is then exported through nuclear pores to the cytoplasm.

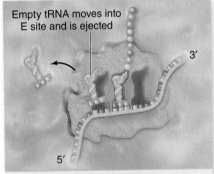

3. The 5′ cap of the mRNA associates with the small subunit of the ribosome. The initiator tRNA and large subunit are added to form an initiation complex.

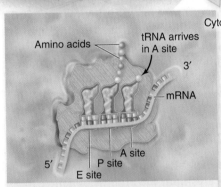

4. The ribosome cycle begins with the growing peptide attached to the tRNA in the P site. The next charged tRNA binds to the A site with its anticodon complementary to the codon in the mRNA in this site.

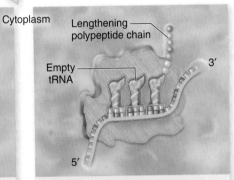

5. Peptide bonds form between the amino terminus of the next amino acid and the carboxyl terminus of the growing peptide. This transfers the growing peptide to the tRNA in the A site, leaving the tRNA in the P site empty.

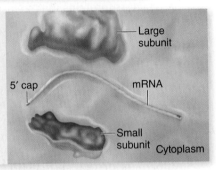

6. Ribosome translocation moves the ribosome relative to the mRNA and its bound tRNAs. This moves the growing chain into the P site, leaving the empty tRNA in the E site and the A site ready to bind the next charged tRNA.

TABLE 15.2	**Differences Between Prokaryotic and Eukaryotic Gene Expression**	
Characteristic	**Prokaryotes**	**Eukaryotes**
Introns	No introns, although some archaeal genes possess them.	Most genes contain introns.
Number of genes in mRNA	Several genes may be transcribed into a single mRNA molecule. Often these have related functions and form an operon, which helps coordinate regulation of biochemical pathways.	Only one gene per mRNA molecule; regulation of pathways accomplished in other ways.
Site of transcription and translation	No membrane-bounded nucleus, transcription and translation are coupled.	Transcription in nucleus; mRNA is transported to the cytoplasm for translation.
Initiation of translation	Begins at AUG codon preceded by special sequence that binds the ribosome.	Begins at AUG codon preceded by the 5′ cap (methylated GTP) that binds the ribosome.
Modification of mRNA after transcription	None; translation begins before transcription is completed. Transcription and translation are coupled.	A number of modifications while the mRNA is in the nucleus: Introns are removed and exons are spliced together; a 5′ cap is added; a poly-A tail is added.

Learning Outcomes

1. *Describe the effects of different point mutations.*
2. *Explain the nature of triplet repeat expansion.*
3. *List the different chromosomal mutations and their effects.*

Geneticists analyze the function of genes by looking at altered forms; that is, by finding or inducing mutations. The behavior of the protein produced from the altered gene provides information about how the normal protein functions. In terms of the organism, however, mutations are usually negative; most mutations have deleterious effects on the phenotype of the organism. In chapter 13, you saw how a number of genetic diseases, such as sickle cell anemia, are due to single-base changes. We now take this one step farther by considering how the DNA itself is altered. This ranges from the alteration of a single base, to the loss of genetic material (deletion), to the loss of an entire chromosome. Changing a single base can result in an amino acid substitution that can lead to a debilitating clinical phenotype. This is illustrated for the case of sickle cell anemia in figure 15.24. In the sickle cell allele, a single A is changed to a T, resulting in a glutamic acid being replaced with a valine. The substitution of nonpolar valine causes the β-chains to aggregate into polymers, which consequently alters the shape of the cells, leading to the disease state.

Point mutations affect a single site in the DNA

A mutation that alters a single base is termed a **point mutation.** The mutation can be either the substitution of one base for another, or the deletion or addition of a single base (or a small number of bases) (figure 15.25).

Base substitution

The substitution of one base pair for another in DNA is called a **base substitution mutation.** Because of the degenerate nature of the genetic code, base substitution may or may not alter the amino acid encoded. If the new codon from the base substitution still encodes the same amino acid, we say the mutation is *silent* (figure 15.25*b*). When base substitution changes an amino acid in a protein, it is also called a **missense mutation** as the "sense" of the codon produced after transcription of the mutant gene will be altered (figure 15.25*c*). These fall into two classes, *transitions* and *transversions.* A transition does not change the type of bases in the base pair, that is, a pyrimidine is substituted for a pyrimidine, or purine for purine. In contrast, a transversion does change the type of bases in a base pair, that is, pyrimidine to purine or the reverse. A variety of human genetic diseases, including sickle cell anemia, are caused by base substitutions.

Nonsense mutations

A special category of base substitution arises when a base is changed such that the transcribed codon is converted to a stop codon (see figure 15.25*d*). We call these **nonsense mutations** because the mutation does not make "sense" to the translation apparatus. The stop codon results in premature termination of translation and leads to a truncated protein. How short the resulting protein is depends on where a stop codon has been introduced in the gene.

Frameshift mutations

The addition or deletion of a single base has much more profound consequences than does the substitution of one base for another. These mutations are called *frameshift mutations* because they alter the reading frame in the mRNA downstream of the mutation. This class of mutations was used by Crick and Brenner, as described earlier in the chapter, to infer the nature of the genetic code.

Changing the reading frame early in a gene, and thus in its mRNA transcript, means that the majority of the protein will

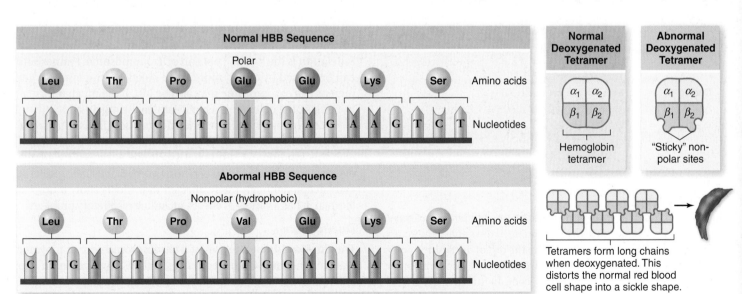

Figure 15.24 Sickle cell anemia is caused by an altered protein. Hemoglobin is composed of a tetramer of two α-globin and two β-globin chains. The sickle cell allele of the β-globin gene contains a single base change resulting in the substitution of Val for Glu. This creates a hydrophobic region on the surface of the protein that is "sticky" leading to their association into long chains that distort the shape of the red blood cells.

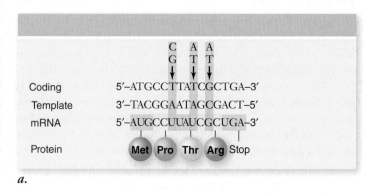

a.

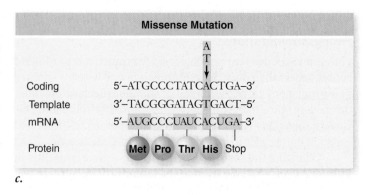

b.

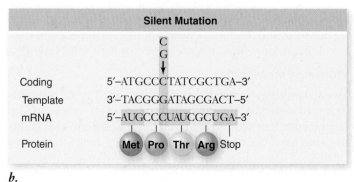

c.

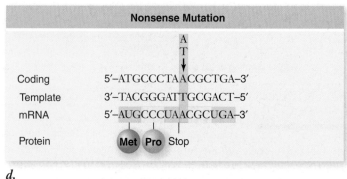

d.

Figure 15.25 Types of mutations. *a.* A hypothetical gene is shown with encoded mRNA and protein. Arrows above the gene indicate sites of mutations described in the rest of the figure. *b.* Silent mutation. A change in the third position of a codon is often silent due to degeneracy in the genetic code. In this case T/A to C/G mutation does not change the amino acid encoded (proline). *c.* Missense mutation. The G/C to A/T mutation changes the amino acid encoded from arginine to histidine. *d.* Nonsense mutation. The T/A to A/T mutation produces a UAA stop codon in the mRNA.

be altered. Frameshifts also can cause premature termination of translation because 3 in 64 codons are stop codons, which represents a high probability in the sequence that has been randomized by the frameshift.

Triplet repeat expansion mutations

Given the long history of molecular genetics, and the relatively short time that molecular analysis has been possible on humans, it is surprising that a new kind of mutation was discovered in humans. However, one of the first genes isolated that was associated with human disease, the gene for *Huntington disease,* provided a new kind of mutation. The gene for Huntington contains a triplet sequence of DNA that is repeated, and this repeat unit is expanded in the disease allele relative to the normal allele. Since this initial discovery, at least 20 other human genetic diseases appear to be due to this mechanism. The prevalence of this kind of mutation is unknown, but at present humans and mice are the only organisms in which they have been observed, implying that they may be limited to vertebrates, or even mammals. No such mutation has ever been found in *Drosophila,* for example.

The expansion of the triplet can occur in the coding region or in noncoding transcribed DNA. In the case of Huntington disease, the repeat unit is actually in the coding region of the gene where the triplet encodes glutamine, and expansion results in a polyglutamine region in the protein. A number of other neurodegenerative disorders also show this kind of mutation. In the case of fragile-X syndrome, an inherited form of intellectual disability, the repeat is in noncoding DNA.

Chromosomal mutations change the structure of chromosomes

Point mutations affect a single site in a chromosome, but more extensive changes can alter the structure of the chromosome itself, resulting in **chromosomal mutations.** Many human cancers are associated with chromosomal abnormalities, so these are of great clinical relevance. We briefly consider possible alterations to chromosomal structure, all of which are summarized in figure 15.26.

Deletions

A **deletion** is the loss of a portion of a chromosome. Frameshifts can be caused by one or more small deletions, but much larger regions of a chromosome may also be lost. If too much information is lost, the deletion is usually fatal to the organism.

One human syndrome that is due to a deletion is *cri-du-chat,* which is French for "cry of the cat" after the noise made by children with this syndrome. Cri-du-chat syndrome is caused by a large deletion from the short arm of chromosome 5. It usually results in early death, although many affected individuals show a normal lifespan. It has a variety of effects, including respiratory problems.

Duplications

The **duplication** of a region of a chromosome may or may not lead to phenotypic consequences. Effects depend upon the location of the "breakpoints" where the duplication occurred. If the duplicated region does not lie within a gene, there may be no effect. If the duplication occurs next to the original region, it is termed a *tandem duplication*. These tandem duplications are important in the evolution of families of related genes, such as the globin family that encode the protein hemoglobin.

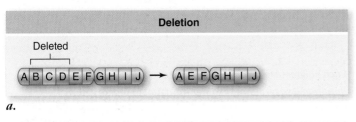

Deletion

Deleted

A B C D E F G H I J → A E F G H I J

a.

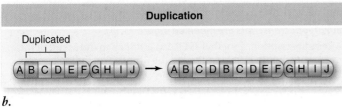

Duplication

Duplicated

A B C D E F G H I J → A B C D B C D E F G H I J

b.

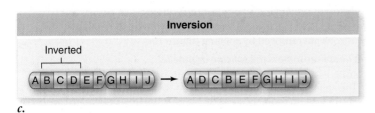

Inversion

Inverted

A B C D E F G H I J → A D C B E F G H I J

c.

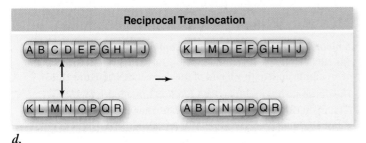

Reciprocal Translocation

A B C D E F G H I J   K L M D E F G H I J

↕   →

K L M N O P Q R   A B C N O P Q R

d.

Figure 15.26 Chromosomal mutations. Larger-scale changes in chromosomes are also possible. Material can be deleted *(a)*, duplicated *(b)*, and inverted *(c)*. Translocations occur when one chromosome is broken and becomes part of another chromosome. This often occurs where both chromosomes are broken and exchange material, an event called a reciprocal translocation *(d)*.

Inversions

An **inversion** results when a segment of a chromosome is broken in two places, reversed, and put back together. An inversion may not have an effect on phenotype if the sites where the inversion occurs do not break within a gene. In fact, although humans all have the "same" genome, the order of genes in all individuals in a population is not precisely the same due to inversions that occur in different lineages.

Translocations

If a piece of one chromosome is broken off and joined to another chromosome, we call this a **translocation.** Translocations are complex because they can cause problems during meiosis, particularly when two different chromosomes try to pair with each other during meiosis I.

Translocations can also move genes from one chromosomal region to another in a manner that changes the expression of genes in the region involved. Two forms of leukemia have been shown to be associated with translocations that move oncogenes into regions of a chromosome where they are expressed inappropriately in blood cells.

Mutations are the starting point of evolution

If no changes occurred in genomes over time, then there could be no evolution. Too much change, however, is harmful to the individual with a greatly altered genome. Thus a delicate balance must exist between the amount of new variation that arises in a species and the health of individuals in the species. This topic is explored in more detail later in the book when we consider evolution and population genetics (chapter 20).

The larger scale alteration of chromosomes has also been important in evolution, although its role is poorly understood. It is clear that gene families arise by the duplication of an ancestral gene, followed by the functional divergence of the duplicated copies. It is also clear that even among closely related species, the number and arrangements of genes on chromosomes can differ. Large-scale rearrangements may have occurred.

Our view of the nature of genes has changed with new information

In this and the preceding chapters, we have seen multiple views of genes. Mendel used crosses to follow traits determined by what we now call genes. The behavior of these genes can be predicted based on the behavior of chromosomes during meiosis. Morgan and others learned to map the location of genes on chromosomes. These findings led to the view of genes as abstract entities that could be followed through generations and mapped to chromosomal locations like "beads on a string," with the beads being genes and the string the chromosome.

The original molecular analysis of genes led to the simple one-gene/one-polypeptide paradigm. This oversimplification was changed when geneticists observed the alternative splicing of eukaryotic genes, which can lead to multiple protein products from the same genetic information. Furthermore, some genes do not encode proteins at all, but only RNA, which can either be a part of the gene expression machinery (rRNA, tRNA, and other forms) or can itself act as an enzyme. Other stretches of DNA are important for regulating genes but are not expressed. All of these findings make a simple definition of genes difficult.

We are left with the rich complexity of the nature of genes, which defies simple definition. To truly understand the nature of genes we must consider both their molecular nature as well as their phenotypic expression. This brings us full circle, back to the relationship between genotype and phenotype, with a much greater appreciation for the complexity of this relationship.

Learning Outcomes Review 15.9

Point mutations (single-base changes, additions, or deletions) include missense mutations that cause substitution of one amino acid for another, nonsense mutations that halt transcription, and frameshift mutations that throw off the correct reading of codons. Triplet repeat expansion is the abnormal duplication of a codon with each round of cell division. Mutations affecting chromosomes include deletions, duplications, inversions, and translocations.

■ **Would an inversion or duplication always be expected to have a phenotype?**

15.1 The Nature of Genes

Garrod concluded that inherited disorders can involve specific enzymes.
Garrod found that alkaptonuria is due to an altered enzyme.

Beadle and Tatum showed that genes specify enzymes.
Neurospora mutants unable to synthesize arginine were found to lack specific enzymes. Beadle and Tatum advanced the "one gene/one polypeptide" hypothesis (figure 15.1).

The central dogma describes information flow in cells as DNA to RNA to protein (figure 15.2).
We call the DNA strand copied to mRNA the template (antisense) strand; the other the coding (sense) strand.

Transcription makes an RNA copy of DNA.

Translation uses information in RNA to synthesize proteins.
An adapter molecule, tRNA, is required to connect the information in mRNA into the sequence of amino acids.

RNA has multiple roles in gene expression.

15.2 The Genetic Code

The code is read in groups of three.
Crick and Brenner showed that the code is nonoverlapping and is read in groups of three. This finding established the concept of reading frame.

Nirenberg and others deciphered the code.
A codon consists of 3 nucleotides, so there are 64 possible codons. Three codons signal "stop," and one codon signals "start" and also encodes methionine. Thus 61 codons encode the 20 amino acids.

The code is degenerate but specific.
Many amino acids have more than one codon, but each codon specifies only a single amino acid.

The code is practically universal, but not quite.
In some mitochondrial and protist genomes, a STOP codon is read as an amino acid; otherwise the code is universal.

15.3 Prokaryotic Transcription

Prokaryotes have a single RNA polymerase.
Prokaryotic RNA polymerase exists in two forms: core polymerase, which can synthesize mRNA; and holoenzyme, core plus σ factor, which can accurately initiate synthesis (figure 15.6).

Initiation occurs at promoters.
Initiation requires a start site and a promoter. The promoter is upstream of the start site, and binding of RNA polymerase holoenzyme to its –35 region positions the polymerase properly.

Elongation adds successive nucleotides.
Transcription proceeds in the 5′-to-3′ direction. The transcription bubble contains RNA polymerase, the locally unwound DNA template, and the growing mRNA transcript (figure 15.7).

Termination occurs at specific sites.
Terminators consist of complementary sequences that form a double-stranded hairpin loop where the polymerase pauses (figure 15.8).

Prokaryotic transcription is coupled to translation.
Translation begins while mRNAs are still being transcribed.

15.4 Eukaryotic Transcription

Eukaryotes have three RNA polymerases.
RNA polymerase I transcribes rRNA; polymerase II transcribes mRNA and some snRNAs; polymerase III transcribes tRNA.

Each polymerase has its own promoter.

Initiation and termination differ from that in prokaryotes.
Unlike prokaryotic promoters, RNA polymerase II promoters require a host of transcription factors. Although termination sites exist, the end of the mRNA is modified after transcription.

Eukaryotic transcripts are modified (figure 15.11).
After transcription, a methyl-GTP cap is added to the 5′ end of the transcript. A poly-A tail is added to the 3′ end. Noncoding internal regions are also removed by splicing.

15.5 Eukaryotic pre-mRNA Splicing

Eukaryotic genes may contain interruptions.
Coding DNA (an exon) is interrupted by noncoding introns. These introns are removed by splicing (figure 15.13).

The spliceosome is the splicing organelle.
snRNPs recognize intron–exon junctions and recruit spliceosomes. The spliceosome ultimately joins the 3′ end of the first exon to the 5′ end of the next exon.

Splicing can produce multiple transcripts from the same gene.

15.6 The Structure of tRNA and Ribosomes

Aminoacyl-tRNA synthetases attach amino acids to tRNA.
The tRNA charging reaction attaches the carboxyl terminus of an amino acid to the 3′ end of the correct tRNA (figure 15.15).

The ribosome has multiple tRNA-binding sites (figure 15.16).
A charged tRNA first binds to the A site, then moves to the P site where its amino acid is bonded to the peptide chain, and finally, without its amino acid, moves to the E site from which it is released.

The ribosome has both decoding and enzymatic functions.
Ribosomes hold tRNAs and mRNA in position for a ribosomal enzyme to form peptide bonds.

15.7 The Process of Translation

Initiation requires accessory factors.
In prokaryotes, initiation-complex formation is aided by the ribosome-binding sequence (RBS) of mRNA, complementary to a small subunit. Eukaryotes use the 5′ cap for the same function.

Elongation adds successive amino acids (figure 15.20).
As the ribosome moves along the mRNA, new amino acids from charged tRNAs are added to the growing peptide.

Termination requires accessory factors.
Stop codons are recognized by termination factors.

Proteins may be targeted to the ER.
In eukaryotes, proteins with a signal sequence in their amino terminus bind to the SRP, and this complex docks on the ER.

(15.8 Summary is omitted.)

15.9 Mutation: Altered Genes

Point mutations affect a single site in the DNA .
Base substitutions exchange one base for another, and frameshift mutations involve the addition or deletion of a base. Triplet repeat expansion mutations can cause genetic diseases.

Chromosomal mutations change the structure of chromosomes.
Chromosomal mutations include additions, deletions, inversions, or translocations.

Mutations are the starting point of evolution.

Our view of the nature of genes has changed with new information.

UNDERSTAND

1. The experiments with nutritional mutants in *Neurospora* by Beadle and Tatum provided evidence that
   a. bread mold can be grown in a lab on minimal media.
   b. X-rays can damage DNA.
   c. cells need enzymes.
   d. genes specify enzymes.

2. What is the *central dogma* of molecular biology?
   a. DNA is the genetic material.
   b. Information passes from DNA directly to protein.
   c. Information passes from DNA to RNA to protein.
   d. One gene encodes only one polypeptide.

3. In the genetic code, one codon
   a. consists of three bases.
   b. specifies a single amino acid.
   c. specifies more than one amino acid.
   d. Both a and b are correct.

4. Eukaryotic transcription differs from prokaryotic in that
   a. eukaryotes have only one RNA polymerase.
   b. eukaryotes have three RNA polymerases.
   c. prokaryotes have three RNA polymerases.
   d. Both a and c are correct.

5. An anticodon would be found on which of the following types of RNA?
   a. snRNA (small nuclear RNA)
   b. mRNA (messenger RNA)
   c. tRNA (transfer RNA)
   d. rRNA (ribosomal RNA)

6. RNA polymerase binds to a _____ to initiate _____.
   a. mRNA; translation
   b. promoter; transcription
   c. primer; transcription
   d. transcription factor; translation

7. During translation, the codon in mRNA is actually "read" by
   a. the A site in the ribosome.
   b. the P site in the ribosome.
   c. the anticodon in a tRNA.
   d. the anticodon in an amino acid.

APPLY

1. You have mutants that all affect the same biochemical pathway. If feeding an intermediate in the pathway supports growth, this tells you that the enzyme encoded by the affected gene
   a. acts after the intermediate used.
   b. acts before the intermediate used.
   c. must act to produce the intermediate.
   d. must not act to produce the intermediate.

2. The splicing process
   a. occurs in prokaryotes.
   b. joins introns together.
   c. can produce multiple mRNAs from the same transcript.
   d. only joins exons for each gene in one way.

3. The enzyme that forms peptide bonds is called peptidyl *transferase* because it transfers
   a. a new amino acid from a tRNA to the growing peptide.
   b. the growing peptide from a tRNA to the next amino acid.
   c. the peptide from one amino acid to another.
   d. the peptide from the ribosome to a charged tRNA.

4. In comparing gene expression in prokaryotes and eukaryotes
   a. eukaryotic genes can produce more than one protein.
   b. prokaryotic genes can produce more than one protein.
   c. both produce mRNAs that are colinear with the protein.
   d. Both a and c are correct.

5. The codon CCA could be mutated to produce
   a. a silent mutation.
   b. a codon for Lys.
   c. a Stop codon.
   d. Both a and b are correct.

6. An inversion will
   a. necessarily cause a mutant phenotype.
   b. only cause a mutant phenotype if the inversion breakpoints fall within a gene.
   c. halt transcription in the inverted region because the chromosome is now backward.
   d. interfere with translation of genes in the inverted region.

7. What is the relationship between mutations and evolution?
   a. Mutations make genes better.
   b. Mutations can create new alleles.
   c. Mutations happened early in evolution, but not now.
   d. There is no relationship between evolution and genetic mutations.

SYNTHESIZE

1. A template strand of DNA has the following sequence:

   3' – CGTTACCCGAGCCGTACGATTAGG – 5'

   Use the sequence information to determine
   a. the predicted sequence of the mRNA for this gene.
   b. the predicted amino acid sequence of the protein.

2. Frameshift mutations often result in truncated proteins. Explain this observation based on the genetic code.

3. Describe how each of the following mutations will affect the final protein product (protein begins with START codon). Name the type of mutation.
   Original template strand:
   3' – CGTTACCCGAGCCGTACGATTAGG – 5'
   a. 3' – CGTTACCCGAGCCGTAACGATTAGG – 5'
   b. 3' – CGTTACCCGATCCGTACGATTAGG – 5'
   c. 3' – CGTTACCCGAGCCGTTCGATTAGG – 5'

4. There are a number of features that are unique to bacteria, and others that are unique to eukaryotes. Could any of these features offer the possibility to control gene expression in a way that is unique to either eukaryotes or bacteria?

ONLINE RESOURCE

www.ravenbiology.com

Understand, Apply, and Synthesize—enhance your study with animations that bring concepts to life and practice tests to assess your understanding. Your instructor may also recommend the interactive eBook, individualized learning tools, and more.

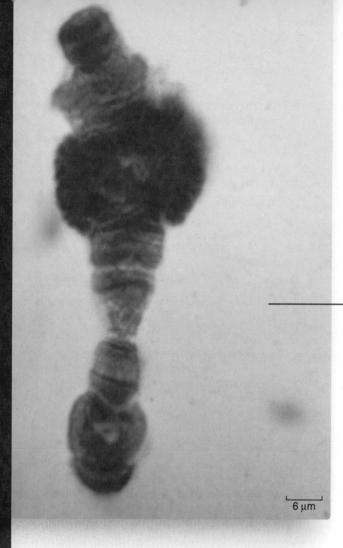

6 µm

Chapter

16

Control of Gene Expression

Chapter Contents

Introduction

In a symphony, various instruments play their own parts at different times; the musical score determines which instruments play when. Similarly, in an organism, different genes are expressed at different times, with a "genetic score," written in regulatory regions of the DNA, determining which genes are active when. The picture shows the expanded "puff" of this Drosophila *chromosome, which represents genes that are being actively expressed. Gene expression and how it is controlled is our topic in this chapter.*

16.1 Control of Gene Expression

Learning Outcomes

1. Identify when gene expression is usually controlled.
2. Describe the usual action of regulatory proteins.
3. List differences between control of gene expression in prokaryotes and eukaryotes.

Control of gene expression is essential to all organisms. In prokaryotes, cells adapt to environmental changes by changing gene expression. In multicellular eukaryotes, it is critical for directing development and maintaining homeostasis. In fact, different cell types in a multicellular organism have distinct functions based on the proteins they express. All cells in a multicellular organism share a set of "housekeeping" genes that sustain the cell, but they also express a unique set of proteins that distinguish each cell type.

Control can occur at all levels of gene expression

You learned in the previous chapter that gene expression is the conversion of genotype to phenotype—the flow of information from DNA to produce functional proteins that control cellular activities. This traditional view of gene expression includes controlling the process primarily at the level of transcription initiation. Although this view remains valid, evidence is accumulating that both the extent of the genome transcribed, and the control of this transcription in multicellular organisms is even more complex than previously expected.

In this chapter, we will develop the control of initiation of transcription in some detail because of its importance, and because it is still the best studied mechanism for the control of gene expression. With this framework in place, we will also consider how chromatin structure affects gene expression and how control can be exerted posttranscriptionally as well. The latter topic will lead us into the exciting new world of regulatory RNA molecules.

RNA polymerase is key to transcription, and it must have access to the DNA helix and must be capable of binding to the gene's promoter for transcription to begin. **Regulatory proteins** act by modulating the ability of RNA polymerase to bind to the promoter. This idea of controlling the access of RNA polymerase to a promoter is common to both prokaryotes and eukaryotes, but the details differ greatly, as you will see.

These regulatory proteins bind to specific nucleotide sequences on the DNA that are usually only 10–15 nt in length. (Even a large regulatory protein has a "footprint," or binding area, of only about 20 nt.) Hundreds of these regulatory sequences have been characterized, and each provides a binding site for a specific protein that is able to recognize the sequence. Binding of the protein either *blocks* transcription by getting in the way of RNA polymerase or *stimulates* transcription by facilitating the binding of RNA polymerase to the promoter.

Control strategies in prokaryotes are geared to adjust to environmental changes

Control of gene expression is accomplished very differently in prokaryotes than it is in eukaryotes. Prokaryotic cells have been shaped by evolution to grow and divide as rapidly as possible, enabling them to exploit transient resources. Proteins in prokaryotes turn over rapidly, allowing these organisms to respond quickly to changes in their external environment by changing patterns of gene expression.

In prokaryotes, the primary function of gene control is to adjust the cell's activities to its immediate environment. Changes in gene expression alter which enzymes are present in response to the quantity and type of nutrients and the amount of oxygen available. Almost all of these changes are fully reversible, allowing the cell to adjust its enzyme levels up or down in response to environment changes.

Control strategies in eukaryotes maintain homeostasis and drive development

The cells of multicellular organisms, in contrast, have been shaped by evolution to be protected from transient changes in their immediate environment. Most of them experience fairly constant conditions. Indeed, *homeostasis*—the maintenance of a constant internal environment—is a hallmark of multicellular organisms. Cells in such organisms respond to signals in their immediate environment (such as growth factors and hormones) by altering gene expression, and in doing so they participate in regulating the body as a whole.

Perhaps the most important role for controlled changes in gene expression is the development of the organism itself. This occurs by coordinated changes in gene expression that occur both over developmental time and in different tissues. Understanding this complex program has been a major goal of developmental genetics, and this work has uncovered circuits of gene expression that have been preserved over very long evolutionary time (see chapter 19). The same regulatory circuit may also be used within an organism to pattern different structures in different places at different developmental times. For example, the gene *sonic hedgehog* acts to pattern the neural tube, then later to pattern digits in developing limbs.

Unicellular eukaryotes also use different control mechanisms from those of prokaryotes. All eukaryotes have a membrane-bounded nucleus, use similar mechanisms to condense DNA into chromosomes, and have the same gene expression machinery, all of which differ from those of prokaryotes.

Learning Outcomes Review 16.1

Gene expression is usually controlled at the level of transcription initiation. Regulatory proteins bind to specific DNA sequences and affect the binding of RNA polymerase to promoters. Individual proteins may either prevent or stimulate transcription. In prokaryotes, regulation is focused on adjusting the cell's activities to the environment to ensure viability. In multicellular eukaryotes, regulation is geared to maintaining internal homeostasis, and even in unicellular forms, this control has mechanisms to deal with a bounded nucleus and multiple chromosomes.

■ *Would you expect the control of gene expression in a unicellular eukaryote like yeast to be more like that of humans or E. coli?*

16.2 Regulatory Proteins

Learning Outcomes

1. *Explain how proteins can interact with base pairs without unwinding the helix.*
2. *Describe the common features of DNA-binding motifs.*

The ability of certain proteins to bind to *specific* DNA regulatory sequences and either block transcription or facilitate the binding of RNA polymerase is the basis for transcriptional control. To understand how cells control gene expression, it is first necessary to gain a clear picture of this molecular recognition process.

Proteins can interact with DNA through the major groove

In the past, molecular biologists thought that the DNA helix had to unwind before proteins could distinguish one DNA sequence from another; only in this way, they reasoned, could regulatory proteins gain access to the hydrogen bonds between base-pairs. We now know it is unnecessary for the helix to unwind because proteins can bind to its outside surface, where the edges of the base-pairs are exposed.

Careful inspection of a DNA molecule reveals two helical grooves winding around the molecule, one deeper than the other. Within the deeper groove, called the **major groove,** the nucleotides' hydrogen bond donors and acceptors are accessible. The pattern created by these chemical groups is unique for each of the four possible base-pair arrangements, providing a ready way for a protein nestled in the groove to read the sequence of bases (figure 16.1).

DNA-binding domains interact with specific DNA sequences

Protein–DNA recognition is an area of active research; so far, the structures of over 30 regulatory proteins have been analyzed. Although each protein is unique in its fine details, the part of the protein that actually binds to the DNA is much less variable. Almost all of these proteins employ one of a small set of **DNA-binding motifs.** A motif, as described in chapter 3, is a form of three-dimensional substructure that is found in many proteins. These DNA-binding motifs share the property of interacting with specific sequences of bases, usually through the major groove of the DNA helix.

DNA-binding motifs are the key structure within the DNA-binding domain of these proteins. This domain is a functionally distinct part of the protein necessary to bind to DNA in a sequence-specific manner. Regulatory proteins also need to be able to interact with the transcription apparatus, which is accomplished by a different regulatory domain.

Note that two proteins that share the same DNA-binding domain do not necessarily bind to the same DNA sequence. The similarities in the DNA-binding motifs appear in their three-dimensional structure, and not in the specific contacts that they make with DNA.

Several common DNA-binding motifs are shared by many proteins

A limited number of common DNA-binding motifs are found in a wide variety of different proteins. Four of the best known are detailed in the following sections to give the sense of how DNA-binding proteins interact with DNA.

The helix-turn-helix motif

The most common DNA-binding motif is the **helix-turn-helix,** constructed from two α-helical segments of the protein linked by a short, nonhelical segment, the "turn" (figure 16.2a). As the first motif recognized, the helix-turn-helix motif has since been identified in hundreds of DNA-binding proteins.

A close look at the structure of a helix-turn-helix motif reveals how proteins containing such motifs interact with the major groove of DNA. The helical segments of the motif interact with one another, so that they are held at roughly right angles. When this motif is pressed against DNA, one of the

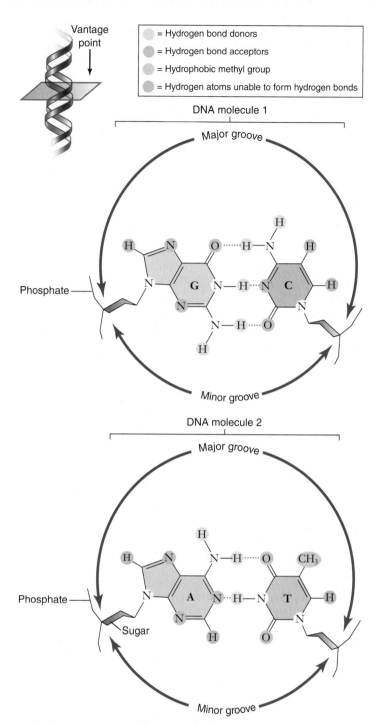

Figure 16.1 Reading the major groove of DNA. Looking down into the major groove of a DNA helix, we can see the edges of the bases protruding into the groove. Each of the four possible base-pair arrangements (two are shown here) extends a unique set of chemical groups into the groove, indicated in this diagram by differently colored circles. A regulatory protein can identify the base-pair arrangement by this characteristic signature.

helical segments (called the *recognition helix*) fits snugly in the major groove of the DNA molecule, and the other butts up against the outside of the DNA molecule, helping to ensure the proper positioning of the recognition helix.

Most DNA-regulatory sequences recognized by helix-turn-helix motifs occur in symmetrical pairs. Such sequences are bound by proteins containing two helix-turn-helix motifs separated by 3.4 nanometers (nm), the distance required for one turn of the DNA helix (see figure 16.2a). Having *two* protein–DNA-binding sites doubles the zone of contact between protein and DNA and greatly strengthens the affinity between them.

The homeodomain motif

A special class of helix-turn-helix motifs, the **homeodomain,** plays a critical role in development in a wide variety of eukaryotic organisms, including humans. These motifs were discovered when researchers began to characterize a set of homeotic mutations in *Drosophila* (mutations that cause one body part to be replaced by another). They found that the mutant genes encoded regulatory proteins. Normally these proteins would initiate key stages of development by binding to developmental switch-point genes. More than 50 of these regulatory proteins have been analyzed, and they all contain a nearly identical sequence of 60 amino acids, which was termed the *homeodomain*. The most conserved part of the homeodomain contains a recognition helix of a helix-turn-helix motif. The rest of the homeodomain forms the other two helices of this motif.

The zinc finger motif

A different kind of DNA-binding motif uses one or more zinc atoms to coordinate its binding to DNA. Called **zinc fingers**, these motifs exist in several forms. In one form, a zinc atom links an α-helical segment to a β-sheet segment so that the helical segment fits into the major groove of DNA.

This sort of motif often occurs in clusters, the β sheets spacing the helical segments so that each helix contacts the major groove. The effect is like a hand wrapped around the DNA with the fingers lying in the major groove. The more zinc fingers in the cluster, the more the protein associates with DNA.

The leucine zipper motif

In another DNA-binding motif, the name actually refers to a dimerization motif that allows different subunits of a protein to associate with the DNA. This so-called **leucine zipper** is created where a region on one subunit containing several hydrophobic amino acids (usually leucines) interacts with a similar region on the other subunit. This interaction holds the subunits together and creates a Y-shaped structure where the two arms of the Y are helical regions that each fit into the major groove of DNA but on opposite sides of the helix (figure 16.2b), holding the DNA like a pair of tongs.

Learning Outcomes Review 16.2

A DNA helix exhibits a major groove and a minor groove; regulatory proteins interact with DNA by accessing bases along the major groove. These proteins all contain DNA-binding motifs, and they often include one or two α-helical segments. These motifs form the active part of the DNA-binding domain, and another domain of the protein interacts with the transcription apparatus.

■ *What would be the effect of a mutation in a helix-turn-helix protein that altered the spacing of the two helices?*

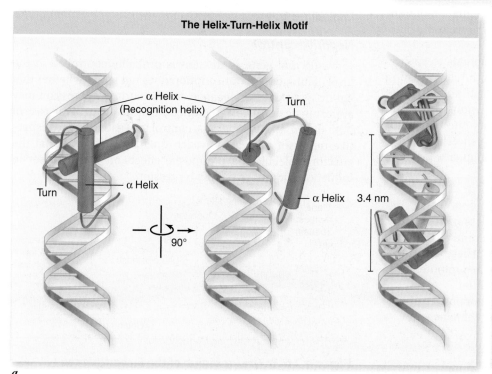

The Helix-Turn-Helix Motif

α Helix (Recognition helix)

Turn

α Helix

Turn

α Helix

3.4 nm

90°

a.

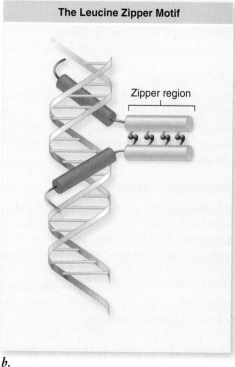

The Leucine Zipper Motif

Zipper region

b.

Figure 16.2 Major DNA-binding motifs. Two different DNA-binding motifs are pictured interacting with DNA. *a.* The helix-turn-helix motif binds to DNA using one α helix, the recognition helix, to interact with the major groove. The other helix positions the recognition helix. Proteins with this motif are usually dimers, with two identical subunits, each containing the DNA-binding motif. The two copies of the motif *(red)* are separated by 3.4 nm, precisely the spacing of one turn of the DNA helix. *b.* The leucine zipper acts to hold two subunits in a multisubunit protein together, thereby allowing α-helical regions to interact with DNA.

chapter **16** *Control of Gene Expression* **307**

16.3 *Prokaryotic Regulation*

The details of regulation can be revealed by examining mechanisms used by prokaryotes to control the initiation of transcription. Prokaryotes and eukaryotes share some common themes, but they have some profound differences as well. Later on we discuss eukaryotic systems and concentrate on how they differ from the simpler prokaryotic systems.

Control of transcription can be either positive or negative

Control at the level of transcription initiation can be either positive or negative. **Positive control** increases the frequency of initiation, and **negative control** decreases the frequency of initiation. Each of these forms of control are mediated by regulatory proteins, but the proteins have opposite effects.

Negative control by repressors

Negative control is mediated by proteins called **repressors.** Repressors are proteins that bind to regulatory sites on DNA called **operators** to prevent or decrease the initiation of transcription. They act as a kind of roadblock to prevent the polymerase from initiating effectively.

Repressors do not act alone; each responds to specific effector molecules. Effector binding can alter the conformation of the repressor to either enhance or abolish its binding to DNA. These repressor proteins are allosteric proteins with an active site that binds DNA and a regulatory site that binds effectors. Effector binding at the regulatory site changes the ability of the repressor to bind DNA (see chapter 6 for more details on allosteric proteins).

Positive control by activators

Positive control is mediated by another class of regulatory, allosteric proteins called *activators* that can bind to DNA and stimulate the initiation of transcription. These activators enhance the binding of RNA polymerase to the promoter to increase the frequency of transcription initiation.

Activators are the logical and physical opposites of repressors. Effector molecules can either enhance or decrease activator binding.

Prokaryotes adjust gene expression in response to environmental conditions

Changes in the environments that bacteria and archaea encounter often result in changes in gene expression. In general, genes encoding proteins involved in catabolic pathways (breaking down molecules) respond oppositely from genes encoding proteins involved in anabolic pathways (building up molecules). In the discussion that follows, we describe enzymes in the catabolic pathway that transports and utilizes the sugar lactose. Later we describe the anabolic pathway that synthesizes the amino acid tryptophan.

As mentioned in the preceding chapter, prokaryotic genes are often organized into operons, multiple genes that are part of a single transcription unit having a single promoter. Genes that are involved in the same metabolic pathway are often organized in this fashion. The proteins necessary for the utilization of lactose are encoded by the *lac* **operon,** and the proteins necessary for the synthesis of tryptophan are encoded by the *trp* **operon.**

? Inquiry question What advantage might a bacterium get by linking into a single operon several genes, all of the products of which contribute to a single biochemical pathway?

Induction and repression

If a bacterium encounters lactose, it begins to make the enzymes necessary to utilize lactose. When lactose is not present, however, there is no need to make these proteins. Thus, we say that the synthesis of the proteins is *induced* by the presence of lactose. **Induction** therefore occurs when enzymes for a certain pathway are produced in response to a substrate.

When tryptophan is available in the environment, a bacterium will not synthesize the enzymes necessary to make tryptophan. If tryptophan ceases to be available, then the bacterium begins to make these enzymes. **Repression** occurs when bacteria capable of making biosynthetic enzymes do not produce them. In the case of both induction and repression, the bacterium is adjusting to produce the enzymes that are optimal for its immediate environment.

Negative control

Knowing that gene expression is probably controlled at the level of initiation of transcription does not tell us whether that control is positive or negative. On the surface, repression may appear to be negative and induction positive; but in the case of both the *lac* and *trp* operons, control is negative by the respective repressor proteins for each operon. The key is that the effector molecules have opposite effects on the repressor in induction with those seen in repression.

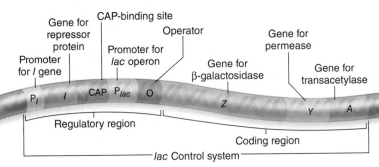

Figure 16.3 The *lac* region of the *Escherichia coli* chromosome. The *lac* operon consists of a promoter, an operator, and three genes (*lac Z, Y,* and *A*) that encode proteins required for the metabolism of lactose. In addition, there is a binding site for the catabolite activator protein (CAP), which affects RNA polymerase binding to the promoter. The *I* gene encodes the repressor protein, which can bind the operator and block transcription of the *lac* operon.

For either mechanism to work, the molecule in the environment, such as lactose or tryptophan, must produce the proper effect on the gene being regulated. In the case of *lac* induction, the presence of lactose must *prevent* a repressor protein from binding to its regulatory sequence. In the case of *trp* repression, by contrast, the presence of tryptophan must *cause* a repressor protein to bind to its regulatory sequence.

These responses are opposite because the needs of the cell are opposite in anabolic versus catabolic pathways. Each pathway is examined in detail in the following sections to show how protein–DNA interactions allow the cell to respond to environmental conditions.

The *lac* operon is negatively regulated by the *lac* repressor

The control of gene expression in the *lac* operon was elucidated by the pioneering work of Jacques Monod and François Jacob.

The *lac* operon consists of the genes that encode functions necessary to utilize lactose: β-galactosidase *(lacZ),* lactose permease *(lacY),* and lactose transacetylase *(lacA),* plus the regulatory regions necessary to control the expression of these genes (figure 16.3). In addition, the gene for the *lac* repressor *(lacI)* is linked to the rest of the *lac* operon and is thus considered part of the operon although it has its own promoter. The arrangement of the control regions upstream of the coding region is typical of most prokaryotic operons, although the linked repressor is not.

Action of the repressor

Initiation of transcription of the *lac* operon is controlled by the *lac* repressor. The repressor binds to the operator, which is adjacent to the promoter (figure 16.4a). This binding prevents RNA polymerase from binding to the promoter. This DNA binding is sensitive to the presence of lactose: The

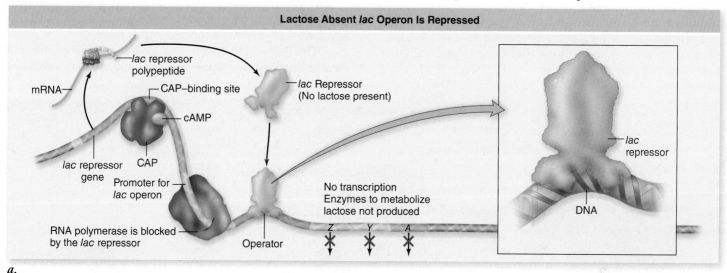

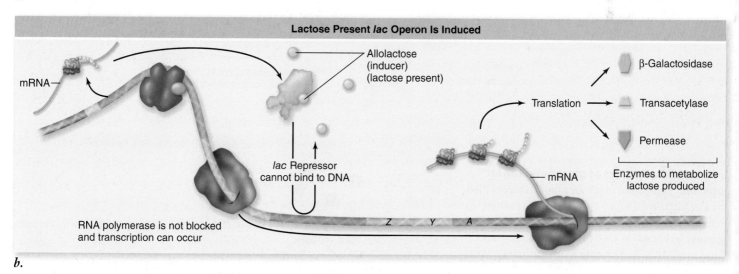

Figure 16.4 Induction of the *lac* operon. *a.* In the absence of lactose the *lac* repressor binds to DNA at the operator site, thus preventing transcription of the operon. When the repressor protein is bound to the operator site, the *lac* operon is shut down (repressed). *b.* The *lac* operon is transcribed (induced) when CAP is bound and when the repressor is not bound. Allolactose binding to the repressor alters the repressor's shape so it cannot bind to the operator site and block RNA polymerase activity.

Data analysis What would the phenotype be of a repressor mutation that prevents DNA binding? Inducer binding? How do these compare with a mutation in the operator that prevents repressor binding?

repressor binds DNA in the absence of lactose, but not in the presence of lactose.

Interaction of repressor and inducer

In the absence of lactose, the *lac* repressor binds to the operator, and the operon is repressed (see figure 16.4*a*). The effector that controls the DNA binding of the repressor is a metabolite of lactose, allolactose, which is produced when lactose is available. Allolactose binds to the repressor, altering its conformation so that it no longer can bind to the operator (figure 16.4*b*). The operon is now induced. Since allolactose allows induction of the operon, it is usually called the inducer.

As the level of lactose falls, allolactose concentrations decrease, making it no longer available to bind to the repressor and allowing the repressor to bind to DNA again. Thus this system of negative control by the *lac* repressor and its inducer, allolactose, allows the cell to respond to changing levels of lactose in the environment.

Even in the absence of lactose, the *lac* operon is expressed at a very low level. When lactose becomes available, it is transported into the cell and enough allolactose is produced that induction of the operon can occur.

The presence of glucose prevents induction of the *lac* operon

Glucose repression is a mechanism for the preferential use of glucose in the presence of other sugars such as lactose. If bacteria are grown in the presence of both glucose and lactose, the *lac* operon is not induced. As glucose is used up, the *lac* operon is induced, allowing lactose to be used as an energy source.

Despite the name *glucose repression,* this mechanism involves an activator protein that can stimulate transcription from multiple catabolic operons, including the *lac* operon. This activator, **catabolite activator protein (CAP),** is an allosteric protein with cAMP as an effector. This protein is also called **cAMP response protein (CRP)** because it binds cAMP, but we will use the name CAP to emphasize its role as a positive regulator. CAP alone does not bind to DNA, but binding of the effector cAMP to CAP changes its conformation such that it can bind to DNA (figure 16.5). The level of cAMP in cells is reduced in the presence of glucose so that no stimulation of transcription from CAP-responsive operons takes place.

The CAP–cAMP system was long thought to be the sole mechanism of glucose repression. But more recent research has

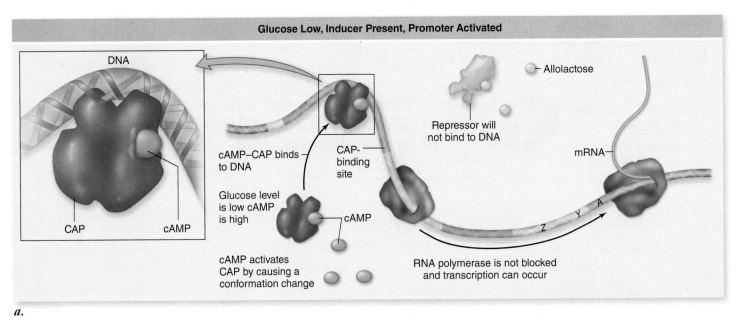

Glucose Low, Inducer Present, Promoter Activated

DNA

Allolactose

cAMP–CAP binds to DNA

CAP-binding site

Repressor will not bind to DNA

mRNA

Glucose level is low cAMP is high

cAMP

CAP   cAMP

cAMP activates CAP by causing a conformation change

RNA polymerase is not blocked and transcription can occur

Z   Y   A

a.

Figure 16.5 Effect of glucose on the *lac* operon. Expression of the *lac* operon is controlled by a negative regulator (repressor) and a positive regulator (CAP). The action of CAP is sensitive to glucose levels. *a.* For CAP to bind to DNA, it must bind to cAMP. When glucose levels are low, cAMP is abundant and binds to CAP. The CAP–cAMP complex causes the DNA to bend around it. This brings CAP into contact with RNA polymerase (not shown) making polymerase binding to the promoter more efficient. *b.* High glucose levels produce two effects: cAMP is scarce so CAP is unable to activate the promoter, and the transport of lactose is blocked (inducer exclusion).

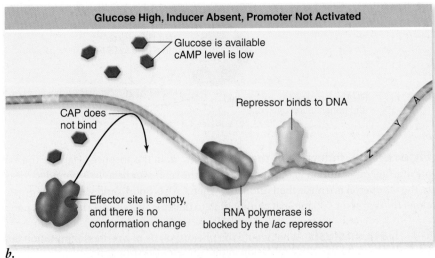

Glucose High, Inducer Absent, Promoter Not Activated

Glucose is available cAMP level is low

Repressor binds to DNA

CAP does not bind

A

Effector site is empty, and there is no conformation change

RNA polymerase is blocked by the *lac* repressor

Z   Y

b.

indicated that the presence of glucose inhibits the transport of lactose into the cell. This deprives the cell of the *lac* operon inducer, allolactose, allowing the repressor to bind to the operator. This mechanism, called **inducer exclusion,** is now thought to be the main form of glucose repression of the *lac* operon.

Given that inducer exclusion occurs, the role of CAP in the absence of glucose seems superfluous. But in fact, the positive control of CAP–cAMP is necessary because the promoter of the *lac* operon alone is not efficient in binding RNA polymerase. This inefficiency is overcome by the action of the positive control of the CAP–cAMP activator. Thus, the highest levels of expression occur in the absence of glucose and in the presence of lactose. In this case the presence of the activator, and absence of the repressor combine to produce the highest levels of expression (see figure 16.5).

The *trp* operon is controlled by the *trp* repressor

Like the *lac* operon, the *trp* operon consists of a series of genes that encode enzymes involved in the same biochemical pathway. In the case of the *trp* operon these enzymes are necessary for synthesizing tryptophan. The regulatory region that controls transcription of these genes is located upstream of the genes. The *trp* operon is controlled by a repressor encoded by a gene located outside the *trp* operon. The *trp* operon is continuously expressed in the absence of tryptophan and is not expressed in the presence of tryptophan.

The *trp* repressor is a helix-turn-helix protein that binds to the operator site located adjacent to the *trp* promoter (figure 16.6). In the absence of tryptophan, the *trp* repressor does not bind to its operator, allowing expression

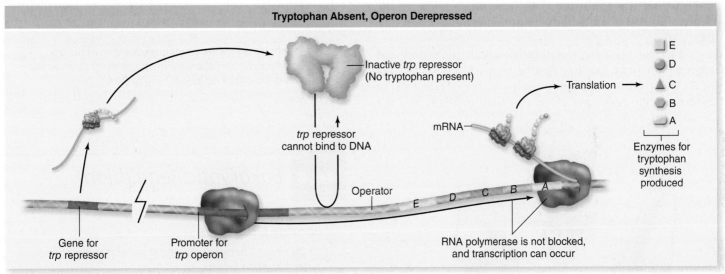

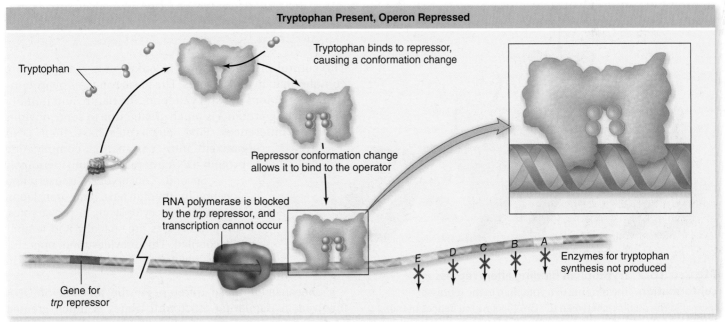

Figure 16.6 How the *trp* operon is controlled. The tryptophan operon encodes the enzymes necessary to synthesize tryptophan. *a.* The tryptophan repressor alone cannot bind to DNA. The promoter is free to function, and RNA polymerase transcribes the operon. *b.* When tryptophan is present, it binds to the repressor, altering its conformation so it now binds DNA. The tryptophan–repressor complex binds tightly to the operator, preventing RNA polymerase from initiating transcription.

of the operon, and production of the enzymes necessary to make tryptophan.

When levels of tryptophan rise, then tryptophan (the *corepressor*) binds to the repressor and alters its conformation, allowing it to bind to its operator. Binding of the repressor–corepressor complex to the operator prevents RNA polymerase from binding to the promoter. The actual change in repressor structure due to tryptophan binding is an alteration of the orientation of a pair of helix-turn-helix motifs that allows their recognition helices to fit into adjacent major grooves of the DNA (figure 16.7).

When tryptophan is present and bound to the repressor and this complex is bound to the operator, the operon is said to be *repressed*. As tryptophan levels fall, the repressor alone cannot bind to the operator, allowing expression of the operon. In this state, the operon is said to be **derepressed,** distinguishing this state from induction (see figure 16.6).

The key to understanding how both induction and repression can be due to negative regulation is knowledge of the behavior of repressor proteins and their effectors. In induction, the repressor alone can bind to DNA, and the inducer prevents DNA binding. In the case of repression, the repressor only binds DNA when bound to the corepressor. Induction and repression are excellent examples of how interactions of molecules can affect their structures, and how molecular structure is critical to function.

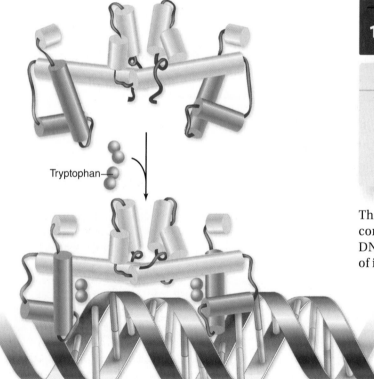

Figure 16.7 Tryptophan binding alters repressor conformation. The binding of tryptophan to the repressor increases the distance between the two recognition helices in the repressor, allowing the repressor to fit snugly into two adjacent portions of the major groove in DNA.

Tryptophan

⊢——— 3.4 nm ———⊣

Learning Outcomes Review 16.3

Induction occurs when expression of genes in a pathway is turned on in response to a substrate; repression occurs when expression is prevented in response to a substrate. The *lac* operon is negatively controlled by a repressor protein that binds to DNA, thus preventing transcription. When lactose is present, the operon is turned on; allolactose binds to the repressor, which then no longer binds to DNA. This operon is also positively regulated by an activator protein. The *trp* operon is negatively controlled by a repressor protein that must be bound to tryptophan in order to bind to DNA. In the absence of tryptophan, the repressor cannot bind DNA, and the operon is derepressed.

■ *What would be the effect on regulation of the* trp *operon of a mutation in the* trp *repressor that can still bind to* trp, *but no longer bind to DNA?*

16.4 Eukaryotic Regulation

Learning Outcomes

1. *Distinguish between the role of general and specific transcription factors.*
2. *Describe the formation of a Pol II initiation complex.*
3. *Explain how transcription factors can have an effect from a distance in the DNA.*

The control of transcription in eukaryotes is much more complex than in prokaryotes. The basic concepts of protein–DNA interactions are still valid, but the nature and number of interacting proteins is much greater due to some obvious differences. First, eukaryotes have their DNA organized into chromatin, complicating protein–DNA interactions considerably.

Second, eukaryotic transcription occurs in the nucleus, and translation occurs in the cytoplasm; in prokaryotes, these processes are spatially and temporally coupled. This provides more opportunities for regulation in eukaryotes than in prokaryotes.

Because of these differences, the amount of DNA involved in regulating eukaryotic genes is much greater. The need for a fine degree of flexible control is especially important for multicellular eukaryotes, with their complex developmental programs and multiple tissue types. General themes, however, emerge from this complexity.

Transcription factors can be either general or specific

In the preceding chapter we introduced the concept of transcription factors. Eukaryotic transcription requires a variety of these protein factors, which fall into two categories: *general transcription factors* and *specific transcription factors*. General factors are necessary for the assembly of a transcription apparatus and recruitment of RNA polymerase II to a promoter. Specific factors increase the level of transcription in certain cell types or in response to signals.

General transcription factors

Transcription of RNA polymerase II templates (the majority being genes that encode protein products) requires more than just RNA polymerase II to initiate transcription. A host of **general transcription factors** are also necessary to establish productive initiation. These factors are required for transcription to occur, but they do not increase the rate above this basal rate.

General transcription factors are named with letter designations that follow the abbreviation TFII, for "transcription factor RNA polymerase II." The most important of these factors, TFIID, contains the TATA-binding protein that recognizes the TATA box sequence found in many eukaryotic promoters.

Binding of TFIID is followed by binding of TFIIE, TFIIF, TFIIA, TFIIB, and TFIIH and a host of accessory factors called *transcription-associated factors,* TAFs. The *initiation complex* that results (figure 16.8) is clearly much more complex than the bacterial RNA polymerase holoenzyme binding to a promoter. And there is yet another level of complexity: The initiation complex, although capable of initiating synthesis at a basal level, does not achieve transcription at a high level without the participation of other, specific factors.

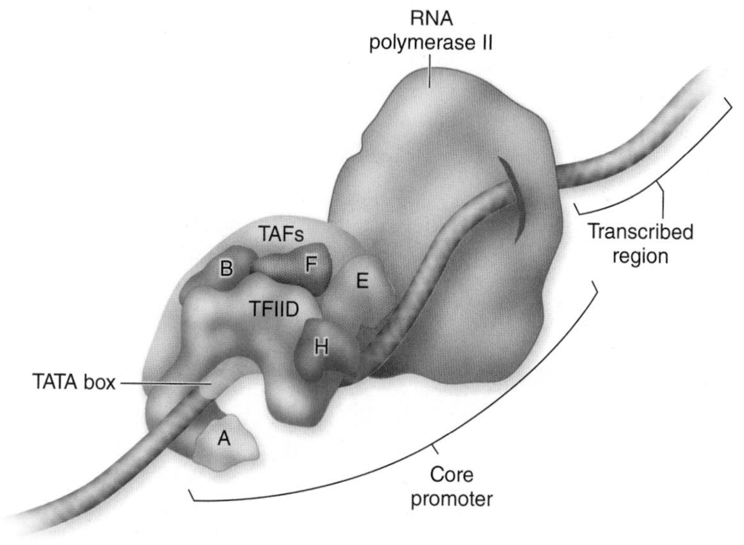

Specific transcription factors

Specific transcription factors act in a tissue- or time-dependent manner to stimulate higher levels of transcription than the basal level. The number and diversity of these factors are overwhelming. Some sense can be made of this proliferation of factors by concentrating on the DNA-binding motif, as opposed to the specific factors.

A key common theme that emerges from the study of these factors is that specific transcription factors, called *activators,* have a domain organization. Each factor consists of a DNA-binding domain and a separate activating domain that interacts with the transcription apparatus, and these domains are essentially independent in the protein. If the DNA-binding domains are "swapped" between different factors the binding specificity for the factors is switched without affecting their ability to activate transcription.

Promoters and enhancers are binding sites for transcription factors

Promoters, as mentioned in the preceding chapter, contain DNA-binding sites for general transcription factors. These factors then mediate the binding of RNA polymerase II to the promoter (and also the binding of RNA polymerases I and III to their specific promoters). In contrast, the holoenzyme portion of the RNA polymerase of prokaryotes can directly recognize a promoter and bind to it.

Enhancers were originally defined as DNA sequences necessary for high levels of transcription that can act independently of position or orientation. At first, this concept seemed counterintuitive, especially since molecular biologists had been conditioned by prokaryotic systems to expect control regions to be immediately upstream of the coding region. It turns out that enhancers are the binding site of the specific transcription factors. The ability of enhancers to act over large distances was at first puzzling, but investigators now think this action is accomplished by DNA bending to form a loop, positioning the enhancer closer to the promoter.

Although more important in eukaryotic systems, this looping was first demonstrated using prokaryotic

Figure 16.8 Formation of a eukaryotic initiation complex. The general transcription factor, TFIID, binds to the TATA box and is joined by the other general factors, TFIIE, TFIIF, TFIIA, TFIIB, and TFIIH. This complex is added to by a number of transcription-associated factors (TAFs) that together recruit the RNA Pol II molecule to the core promoter.

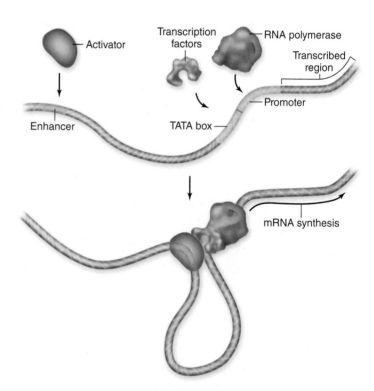

DNA-binding proteins (figure 16.9). The important point is that the linear distance separating two sites on the chromosome does not have to translate to great physical distance, because the flexibility of DNA allows bending and looping. An activator bound to an enhancer can thus be brought into contact with the transcription factors bound to a distant promoter (figure 16.10).

Coactivators and mediators link transcription factors to RNA polymerase II

Other factors specifically mediate the action of transcription factors. These *coactivators* and *mediators* are also necessary for activation of transcription by the transcription factor. They act by binding the transcription factor and then binding to another part of the transcription apparatus. Mediators are essential to the function of some transcription factors, but not all transcription factors require them. The number of coactivators is much smaller than the number of transcription factors because the same coactivator can be used with multiple transcription factors.

NtrC (activator)
Enhancer
Promoter
RNA polymerase

Bacterial RNA polymerase is loosely bound to the promoter. The activator (NtrC) binds at the enhancer.

ATP

ADP

5 nm

DNA loops around so that the activator comes into contact with the RNA polymerase.

RNA polymerase

Activator

mRNA synthesis

The activator triggers RNA polymerase activation, and transcription begins. DNA unloops.

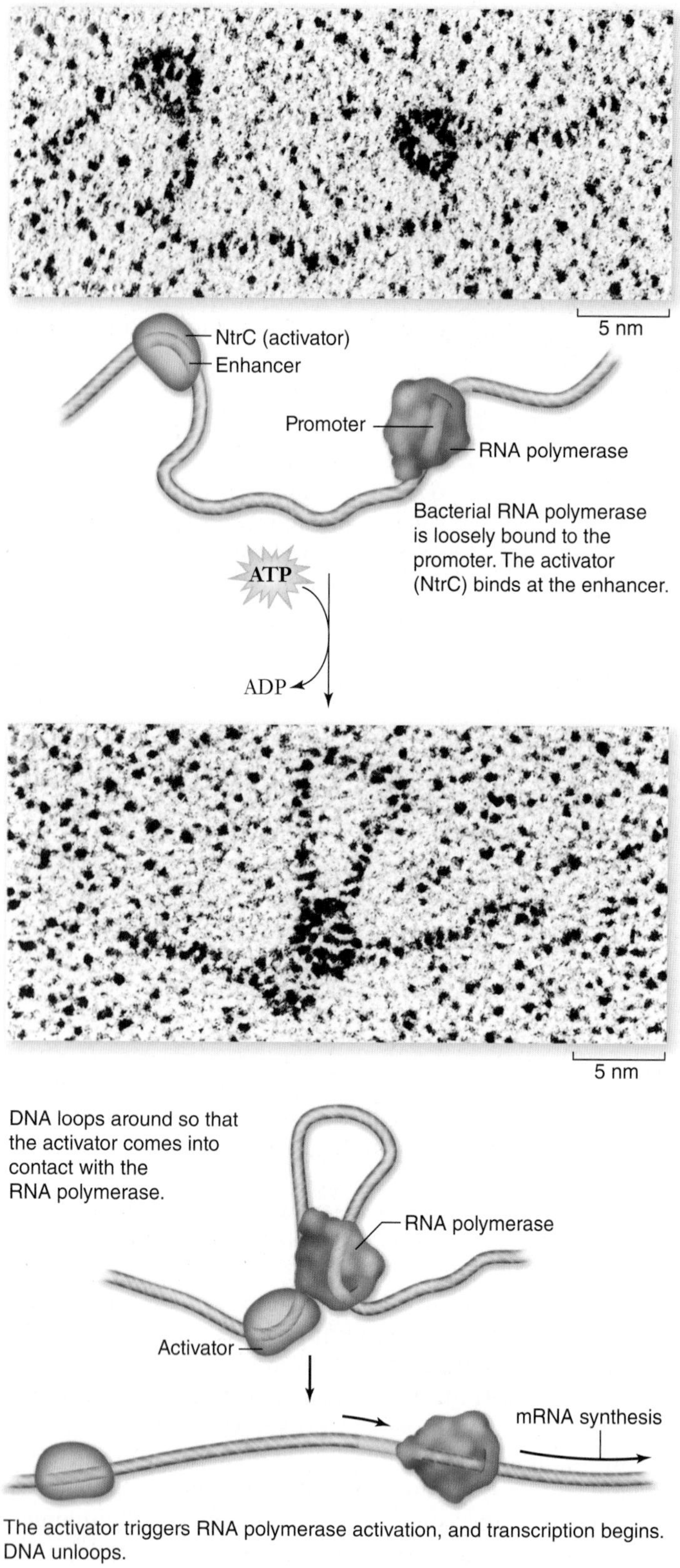

Figure 16.9 DNA looping caused by proteins. When the bacterial activator NtrC binds to an enhancer, it causes the DNA to loop over to a distant site where RNA polymerase is bound, thereby activating transcription. Although such enhancers are rare in prokaryotes, they are common in eukaryotes.

Activator
Transcription factors
RNA polymerase
Transcribed region
Enhancer
TATA box
Promoter

mRNA synthesis

Figure 16.10 How enhancers work. The enhancer site is located far away from the gene being regulated. Binding of an activator *(gray)* to the enhancer allows the activator to interact with the transcription factors *(blue)* associated with RNA polymerase, stimulating transcription.

The transcription complex brings things together

Although a few general principles apply to a broad range of situations, nearly every eukaryotic gene—or group of genes with coordinated regulation—represents a unique case. Virtually all genes that are transcribed by RNA polymerase II need the same suite of general factors to assemble an initiation complex, but the assembly of this complex and its ultimate level of transcription depend on specific transcription factors that in combination make up the **transcription complex** (figure 16.11).

The makeup of eukaryotic promoters, therefore, is either very simple, if we consider only what is needed for the initiation complex, or very complicated, if we consider all factors that may bind in a complex and affect transcription. This kind of combinatorial gene regulation leads to great flexibility because it can respond to the many signals a cell may receive affecting transcription, allowing integration of these signals.

? Inquiry question How do eukaryotes coordinate the activation of many genes whose transcription must occur at the same time?

Learning Outcomes Review 16.4

In eukaryotes, initiation requires general transcription factors that bind to the promoter and recruit RNA polymerase II to form an initiation complex. General factors produce the basal level of transcription. Specific transcription factors, which bind to enhancer sequences, can increase the level of transcription. Enhancers can act at a distance because DNA can loop, bringing an enhancer and a promoter closer together. Additional coactivators and mediators link certain specific transcription factors to RNA polymerase II.

■ *What would be the effect of a mutation that results in the loss of a general transcription factor versus the loss of a specific factor?*

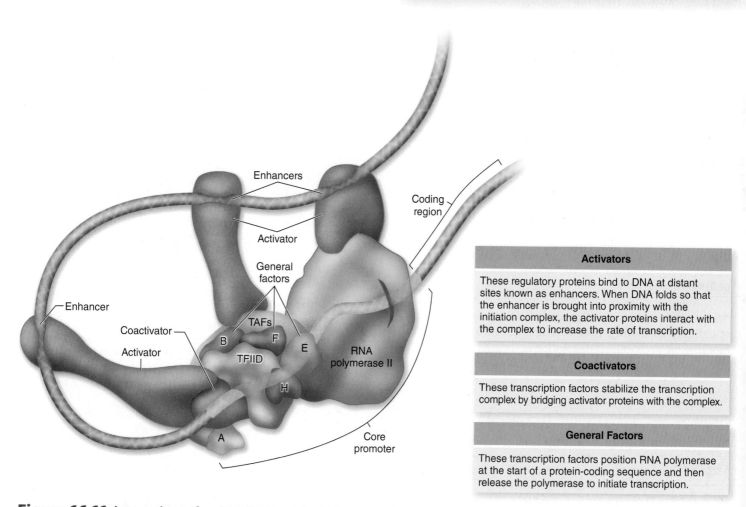

Activators

These regulatory proteins bind to DNA at distant sites known as enhancers. When DNA folds so that the enhancer is brought into proximity with the initiation complex, the activator proteins interact with the complex to increase the rate of transcription.

Coactivators

These transcription factors stabilize the transcription complex by bridging activator proteins with the complex.

General Factors

These transcription factors position RNA polymerase at the start of a protein-coding sequence and then release the polymerase to initiate transcription.

Figure 16.11 Interactions of various factors within the transcription complex. All specific transcription factors bind to enhancer sequences that may be distant from the promoter. These proteins can then interact with the initiation complex by DNA looping to bring the factors into proximity with the initiation complex. As detailed in the text, some transcription factors, called activators, can directly interact with the RNA polymerase II or the initiation complex, whereas others require additional coactivators.

Eukaryotic Chromatin Structure

Learning Outcomes

1. *Describe how chromatin structure can affect gene expression.*
2. *Explain the function of chromatin remodeling complexes.*

Eukaryotes have the additional gene expression hurdle of possessing DNA that is packaged into chromatin. The packaging of DNA first into nucleosomes and then into higher order chromatin structures is now thought to be directly related to the control of gene expression.

Chromatin structure at its lowest level is the organization of DNA and histone proteins into *nucleosomes* (see chapter 10). These nucleosomes may block binding of transcription factors and RNA polymerase II at the promoter.

The higher order organization of chromatin, which is not completely understood, appears to depend on the state of the histones in nucleosomes. Histones can be modified to result in a greater condensation of chromatin, making promoters even less accessible for protein–DNA interactions. A chromatin remodeling complex exists that can make DNA more accessible.

Both DNA and histone proteins can be modified

Chemical *methylation* of the DNA was once thought to play a major role in gene regulation in vertebrate cells. The addition of a methyl group to cytosine creates 5-methylcytosine, but this change has no effect on its base-pairing with guanine (figure 16.12). Similarly, the addition of a methyl group to uracil produces thymine, which clearly does not affect base-pairing with adenine.

Many inactive mammalian genes are methylated, and it was tempting to conclude that methylation caused the inactivation. But methylation is now viewed as having a less direct role, blocking the accidental transcription of "turned-off" genes. Vertebrate cells apparently possess a protein that binds to clusters of 5-methylcytosine, preventing transcriptional activators from gaining access to the DNA. DNA methylation in vertebrates thus ensures that once a gene is turned off, it stays off.

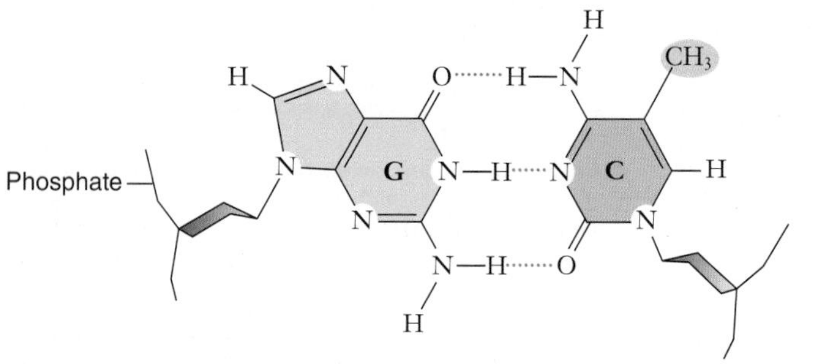

The histone proteins that form the core of the nucleosome (chapter 10) can also be modified. This modification is correlated with active versus inactive regions of chromatin, similar to the methylation of DNA just described. Histones can also be methylated, and this alteration is generally found in inactive regions of chromatin. Finally, histones can be modified by the addition of an acetyl group, and this addition is correlated with active regions of chromatin.

Some transcription activators alter chromatin structure

The control of eukaryotic transcription requires the presence of many different factors to activate transcription. Some activators seem to interact directly with the initiation complex or with coactivators that themselves interact with the initiation complex, as described earlier. Other cases are not so clear. The emerging consensus is that some coactivators have been shown to be histone acetylases. In these cases, it appears that transcription is increased by removing higher order chromatin structure that would prevent transcription (figure 16.13). Some corepressors have been shown to be histone deacetylases as well.

These observations have led to the suggestion that a "histone code" might exist, analogous to the genetic code.

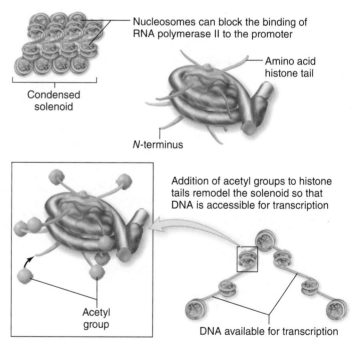

Figure 16.13 Histone modification affects chromatin structure. DNA in eukaryotes is organized first into nucleosomes and then into higher order chromatin structures. The histones that make up the nucleosome core have amino tails that protrude. These amino tails can be modified by the addition of acetyl groups. The acetylation alters the structure of chromatin, making it accessible to the transcription apparatus.

Figure 16.12 DNA methylation. Cytosine is methylated, creating 5-methylcytosine. Because the methyl group *(green)* is positioned to the side, it does not interfere with the hydrogen bonds of a G–C base-pair, but it can be recognized by proteins.

This histone code is postulated to underlie the control of chromatin structure and, thus, of access of the transcription machinery to DNA.

Chromatin-remodeling complexes also change chromatin structure

The outline of how alterations to chromatin structure can regulate gene expression are beginning to emerge. A key discovery is the existence of so-called **chromatin-remodeling complexes.** These large complexes of proteins include enzymes that modify histones and DNA and that also change chromatin structure itself.

One class of these remodeling factors, ATP-dependent chromatin remodeling factors, function as molecular motors that affect DNA and histones. These ATP-dependent remodeling factors use energy from ATP to alter the relationships between histones and DNA. They can catalyze four different changes in histone/DNA binding (figure 16.14): (1) nucleosome sliding along DNA, which changes the position of a nucleosome on the DNA; (2) create a remodeled state where

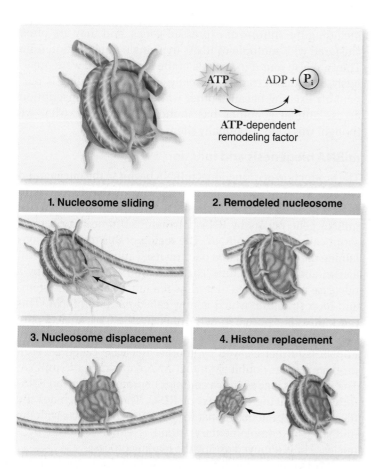

Figure 16.14 Function of ATP-dependent remodeling factors. ATP-dependent remodeling factors use the energy from ATP to alter chromatin structure. They can *(1)* slide nucleosomes along DNA to reveal binding sites for proteins; *(2)* create a remodeled state of chromatin where the DNA is more accessible; *(3)* completely remove nucleosomes from DNA; and *(4)* replace histones in nucleosomes with variant histones.

DNA is more accessible; (3) removal of nucleosomes from DNA; and (4) replacement of histones with variant histones. These functions all act to make DNA more accessible to regulatory proteins that in turn, affect gene expression.

Learning Outcomes Review 16.5

Eukaryotic DNA is packaged into chromatin, adding another structural challenge to transcription. Changes in chromatin structure correlate with modification of DNA and histones, and access to DNA by transcriptional regulators requires changes in chromatin structure. Some transcriptional activators modify histones by acetylation. Large chromatin-remodeling complexes include enzymes that alter the structure of chromatin, making DNA more accessible to regulatory proteins.

■ *Genes that are turned on in all cells are called "housekeeping" genes. Explain the idea behind this name.*

16.6 Eukaryotic Posttranscriptional Regulation

Learning Outcomes

1. *Explain how small RNAs can affect gene expression.*
2. *Differentiate between the different kinds of posttranscriptional regulation.*

The separation of transcription in the nucleus and translation in the cytoplasm in eukaryotes provides possible points of regulation that do not exist in prokaryotes. For many years we thought of this as "alternative" forms of regulation, but it now appears that they play a much more central role than previously suspected. In this section we will consider several of these mechanisms for controlling gene expression, beginning with the exciting new area of regulation by small RNAs.

Small RNAs act after transcription to control gene expression

Developmental genetics has provided important insights into the regulation of gene expression. A striking example is the discovery of small RNAs that affect gene expression. The mutant *lin-4* was known to alter developmental timing in the worm *C. elegans,* and genetic studies had shown that *lin-4* regulated another gene, *lin-14*. When Ambros, Lee, and Feinbaum isolated the *lin-4* gene in 1992, they found it did not encode a protein product. Instead, the *lin-4* gene encoded only two small RNA molecules, one of 22 nt and the other of 61 nt. Furthermore, the 22-nt RNA was derived from the longer 61-nt RNA. Further work showed that this small RNA was complementary to a region in *lin-14*. A model was developed in which the lin-4 RNA acted as a translational repressor of the lin-14 mRNA (figure 16.15). Although not called that at the time, this was the first identified **micro-RNA**, or **miRNA.**

A completely different line of inquiry involved the use of double-stranded RNAs to turn off gene expression. This has been shown to act via another class of small RNA called **small interfering RNAs**, or **siRNAs.** These may be experimentally introduced, derived from invading viruses, or even encoded in the genome. The use of siRNA to control gene expression revealed the existence of cellular mechanisms for the control of gene expression via small RNAs.

Since its discovery, gene silencing by small RNAs has been a source of great interest for both its experimental uses, and as an explanation for posttranslational control of gene expression. Recent research has uncovered a wealth of new types of small RNAs, but we will confine ourselves to the two classes of miRNA and siRNA, as these are well established and illustrate the RNA silencing machinery.

SCIENTIFIC THINKING

Hypothesis: *The region of the* lin-14 *gene complementary to the* lin-4 *miRNA controls* lin-14 *expression.*

Prediction: *If the* lin-4 *complementary region of the* lin-14 *gene is spliced into a reporter gene, then this reporter gene should show regulation similar to* lin-14.

Test: *Recombinant DNA is used to make two versions of a reporter gene (β-galactosidase). In transgenic worms (C. elegans), expression of the reporter gene produces a blue color.*

1. The β-galactosidase gene with the lin-14 *3′ untranslated region containing the* lin-4 *complementary region (shown below)*

2. The β-galactosidase gene with a control 3′ untranslated region with no lin-4 *complementary region (not shown)*

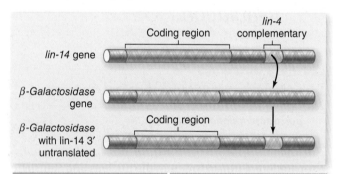

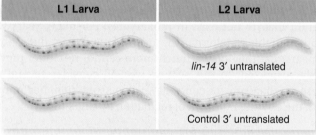

Result:

1. Transgenic worms with reporter gene plus lin-14 *3′ untranslated region show expression in L1 but not L2 stage larvae. This is the pattern expected for the* lin-14 *gene, which is controlled by* lin-4.

2. Transgenic worms with reporter gene with control 3′ untranslated region do not show expression pattern expected for control by lin-4.

Conclusion: *The 3′ untranslated region from* lin-14 *is sufficient to turn off gene expression in L2 larvae.*

Further Experiments: *What expression pattern would you predict for these constructs in a mutant that lacks* lin-4 *function?*

Figure 16.15 Control of *lin-14* gene expression. The *lin-14* gene is controlled by the *lin-4* gene. This is mediated by a region of the 3′ untranslated region of the *lin-14* mRNA that is complementary to *lin-4* miRNA.

miRNA genes

The discovery of the role of miRNAs in gene expression initially appeared to be confined to nematodes because the *lin-4* gene did not have any obvious homologues in other systems. Seven years later, a second gene, *let-7*, was discovered in the same pathway in *C. elegans*. The *let-7* gene also encoded a 22-nt RNA that could influence translation. In this case, homologues for *let-7* were immediately found in both *Drosophila* and humans.

As an increasing number of miRNAs were discovered in different organisms, miRNA gene discovery has turned to computer searching and high-throughput methods such as microarrays and new next-generation sequencing. A database devoted to miRNAs currently lists 695 known human miRNA sequences.

Genes for miRNA are found in a variety of locations, including the introns of expressed genes, and they are often clustered with multiple miRNAs in a single transcription unit. They are also found in regions of the genome that were previously considered transcriptionally silent. This finding is particularly exciting because other work looking at transcription across animal genomes has found that much of what we thought was transcriptionally silent is actually not.

miRNA biogenesis and function

The production of a functional miRNA begins in the nucleus and ends in the cytoplasm with an ~22-nt RNA that functions to repress gene expression (figure 16.16). The initial transcript of a miRNA gene occurs by RNA polymerase II producing a transcript called the pri-miRNA. The region of this transcript containing the miRNA can fold back on itself and base-pair to form a stem-and-loop structure. This is cleaved in the nucleus by a nuclease called Drosha that trims the miRNA to just the stem-and-loop structure, which is now called the pre-miRNA. This pre-miRNA is exported from the nucleus through a nuclear pore bound to the protein exportin 5. Once in the cytoplasm, the pre-miRNA is further cleaved by another nuclease called Dicer to produce a short double-stranded RNA containing the miRNA. The miRNA is loaded into a complex of proteins called an **RNA-induced silencing complex,** or **RISC.** The RISC includes the RNA-binding protein Argonaute (Ago), which interacts with the miRNA. The complementary strand is either removed by a nuclease or is removed during the loading process.

At this point, the RISC is targeted to repress the expression of other genes based on sequence complementarity to the miRNA. The complementary region is usually in the 3′ untranslated region of genes, and the result can be cleavage of the mRNA or inhibition of translation. It appears that in animals, the inhibition of translation is more common than the cleavage of the mRNA, although the precise mechanism of this inhibition is still unclear. In plants, the cleavage of the mRNA by the

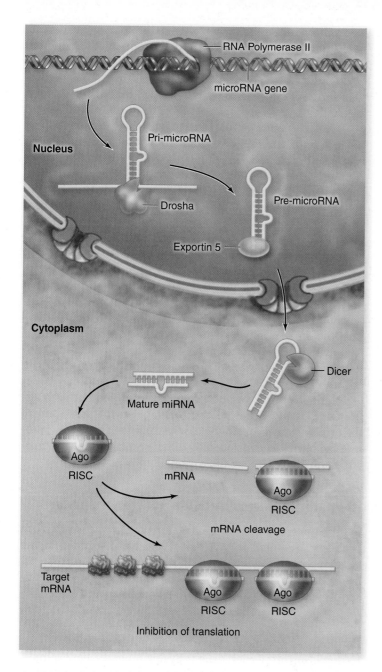

Figure 16.16 Biogenesis and function of miRNA. Genes for miRNAs are transcribed by RNA polymerase II to produce a pri-miRNA. This is processed by the Drosha nuclease to produce the pre-miRNA, which is exported from the nucleus bound to export factor Exportin 5. Once in the cytoplasm, the pre-miRNA is processed by Dicer nuclease to produce the mature miRNA. The miRNA is loaded into a RISC, which can act to either cleave target mRNAs, or to inhibit translation of target mRNAs.

RISC is common and seems to be related to the more precise complementarity found between plant miRNAs and their targets than that found in animal systems.

RNA interference

Small RNA-mediated gene silencing has been known for a number of years. Some confusion arose in the nomenclature in this area because work in different systems led to a profusion of names. However, RNA interference, cosuppression,

and posttranscriptional gene silencing all act through similar biochemical mechanisms. The term **RNA interference** is currently the most commonly used and involves the production of siRNAs.

The production of siRNAs is similar to that of miRNAs, except that they arise from a long piece of double-stranded RNA (figure 16.17). This can be either a very long region of self complementarity, or from two complementary RNAs. These long double-stranded RNAs are processed by Dicer to yield multiple siRNAs that are loaded into an Ago containing RISC. The siRNAs usually have near-perfect complementarity to their target mRNAs, and the result is cleavage of the mRNA by the siRNA containing RISC.

The source of the double-stranded RNA to produce siRNAs can be either from the cell or from outside the cell. From the cell itself, genes can produce RNAs with long regions of self-complementarity that fold back to produce a substrate for Dicer in the cytoplasm. They can also arise from repeated regions of the genome that contain transposable elements. Exogenous double-stranded RNAs can be introduced experimentally or by infection with a virus.

Small RNAs may have evolved to protect the genome

The observation that viral RNA can be degraded via the RNA-silencing pathway may point toward the evolutionary origins of small RNAs. A related observation is that RNA silencing can

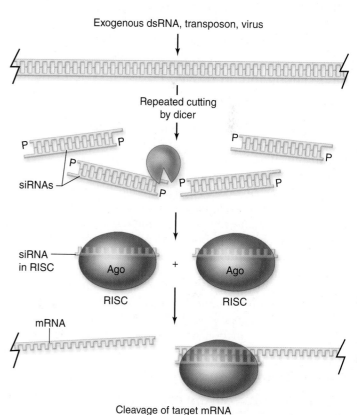

Figure 16.17 Biogenesis and function of siRNA. SiRNAs can arise from a variety of sources that all produce long double-stranded regions of RNA. The double-stranded RNA is processed by Dicer nuclease to produce a number of siRNAs that are each loaded onto their own RISC. The RISC then cleaves target mRNA.

control the action of transposons as well. In both mice and fruit flies, genetic evidence supports the involvement of the RNA interference machinery in the germ line where a specific class of small RNA appears to be involved in silencing transposons during spermatogenesis and oogenesis. Thus the origins of this mechanism may be an ancient pathway for protection of the genome from assault from both within and without. The conservation of key proteins suggests that the ancestor to all eukaryotes had some form of RNA-silencing pathway.

Distinguishing miRNAs and siRNAs

The biogenesis of both miRNA and siRNA involves cleavage by Dicer and incorporation into a RISC complex. The main thing that distinguishes these small RNAs is their targets: miRNAs tend to repress genes different from their origin, whereas endogenous siRNAs tend to repress the genes they were derived from. Additionally, siRNAs are used experimentally to turn off the expression of genes. This technique uses the cells' RNA-silencing machinery to turn off a gene by introducing a double-stranded RNA complementary to the gene.

The two classes of small RNA have other differences. When multiple species are examined, miRNAs tend to be evolutionarily conserved, but siRNAs do not. Although the biogenesis for both is similar in terms of the nucleases involved, the actual structure of the double-stranded RNAs is not the same. The transcript of miRNA genes form stem-loop structures containing the miRNA, but the double-stranded RNAs generating siRNAs may be bimolecular, or very long stem-loops. These longer double-stranded regions lead to multiple siRNAs, whereas only a single miRNA is generated from a pre-miRNA.

Small RNAs can mediate heterochromatin formation

RNA-silencing pathways have also been implicated in the formation of heterochromatin in fission yeast, plants, and *Drosophila*. In fission yeast, centromeric heterochromatin formation is driven by siRNAs produced by the action of the Dicer nuclease. This heterochromatin formation also involves modification of histone proteins and thus connects RNA interference with chromatin-remodeling complexes in this system. It is not yet clear how widespread this phenomenon is.

Plants are an interesting case in that they have a variety of small RNA species. The RNA interference pathway in plants is more complex than that in animals, with multiple forms of Dicer nuclease proteins and Argonaute RNA-binding proteins. One class of endogenous siRNA can lead to heterochromatin formation by DNA methylation and histone modification.

Alternative splicing can produce multiple proteins from one gene

The latest estimates of the frequency of alternative splicing mentioned in the preceding chapter emphasize its importance. However, the functional significance of these data is still not clear. Here we will consider some well characterized examples.

Alternative splicing can change the splicing events that occur during different stages of development or in different tissues. An example of developmental differences is found in *Drosophila,* in which sex determination is the result of a complex series of alternative splicing events that differ in males and females.

An excellent example of tissue-specific alternative splicing in action is found in two different human organs: the thyroid gland and the hypothalamus. The thyroid gland is responsible for producing hormones that control processes such as metabolic rate. The hypothalamus, located in the brain, collects information from the body (for example, salt balance) and releases hormones that in turn regulate the release of hormones from other glands, such as the pituitary gland. (You'll learn more about these glands in chapter 45.)

These two organs produce two distinct hormones: *calcitonin* and *CGRP* (calcitonin-gene-related peptide) as part of their function. Calcitonin controls calcium uptake and the balance of calcium in tissues such as bones and teeth. CGRP is involved in a number of neural and endocrine functions. Although these two hormones are used for very different physiological purposes, they are produced from the same transcript (figure 16.18).

The synthesis of one product versus another is determined by tissue-specific factors that regulate the processing of the primary transcript. In the case of calcitonin and CGRP, pre-mRNA splicing is controlled by different factors that are present in the thyroid and in the hypothalamus.

RNA editing alters mRNA after transcription

In some cases, the editing of mature mRNA transcripts can produce an altered mRNA that is not truly encoded in the genome—an unexpected possibility. RNA editing was first discovered as the insertion of uracil residues into some RNA transcripts in protozoa, and it was thought to be an anomaly.

RNA editing of a different sort has since been found in mammalian species, including humans. In this case, the editing involves chemical modification of a base to change its base-pairing properties, usually by deamination. For example, both deamination of cytosine to uracil and deamination of adenine to inosine have been observed (inosine pairs as G would during translation).

Apolipoprotein B

The human protein apolipoprotein B is involved in the transport of cholesterol and triglycerides. The gene that encodes this protein, *apoB,* is large and complex, consisting of 29 exons scattered across almost 50 kilobases (kb) of DNA.

The protein exists in two isoforms: a full-length APOB100 form and a truncated APOB48 form. The truncated form is due to an alteration of the mRNA that changes a codon for glutamine to one that is a stop codon. Furthermore, this editing occurs in a tissue-specific manner; the edited form appears only in the intestine, whereas the liver makes only the full-length form. The full-length APOB100 form is part of the low-density lipoprotein (LDL) particle that carries cholesterol. High levels of serum LDL are thought to be a

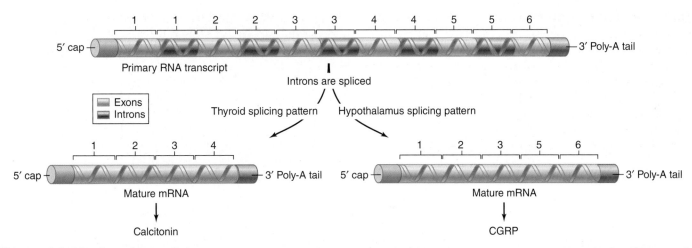

Figure 16.18 Alternative splicing. Many primary transcripts can be spliced in different ways to give rise to multiple mRNAs. In this example, in the thyroid the primary transcript is spliced to contain four exons encoding the protein calcitonin. In the hypothalamus the fourth exon, which contains the poly-A site used in the thyroid, is skipped and two additional exons are added to encode the protein calcitonin-gene-related peptide (CGRP).

major predictor of atherosclerosis in humans. It does not appear that editing has any effect on the levels of the intestine-specific transcript.

The 5-HT serotonin receptor

RNA editing has also been observed in some brain receptors for opiates in humans. One of these receptors, the serotonin (5-HT) receptor, is edited at multiple sites to produce a total of 12 different isoforms of the protein.

It is unclear how widespread these forms of RNA editing are, but they are further evidence that the information encoded within genes is not the end of the story for protein production.

mRNA must be transported out of the nucleus for translation

Processed mRNA transcripts exit the nucleus through the nuclear pores (described in chapter 4). The passage of a transcript across the nuclear membrane is an active process that requires the transcript to be recognized by receptors lining the interior of the pores. Specific portions of the transcript, such as the poly-A tail, appear to play a role in this recognition.

There is little hard evidence that gene expression is regulated at this point, although it could be. On average, about 10% of primary transcripts consists of exons that will make up mRNA sequences, but only about 5% of the total mRNA produced as primary transcript ever reaches the cytoplasm. This observation suggests that about half of the exons in primary transcripts never leave the nucleus, but it is unclear whether the disappearance of this mRNA is selective.

Initiation of translation can be controlled

The translation of a processed mRNA transcript by ribosomes in the cytoplasm involves a complex of proteins called *translation factors*. In at least some cases, gene expression is regulated by modification of one or more of these factors. In other instances, **translation repressor proteins** shut down transla-

tion by binding to the beginning of the transcript, so that it cannot attach to the ribosome.

In humans, the production of ferritin (an iron-storing protein) is normally shut off by a translation repressor protein called aconitase. Aconitase binds to a 30-nt sequence at the beginning of the ferritin mRNA, forming a stable loop to which ribosomes cannot bind. When iron enters the cell, the binding of iron to aconitase causes the aconitase to dissociate from the ferritin mRNA, freeing the mRNA to be translated and increasing ferritin production 100-fold.

The degradation of mRNA is controlled

Another aspect that affects gene expression is the stability of mRNA transcripts in the cell cytoplasm. Unlike prokaryotic mRNA transcripts, which typically have a half-life of about 3 min, eukaryotic mRNA transcripts are very stable. For example, β-globin gene transcripts have a half-life of over 10 hr, an eternity in the fast-moving metabolic life of a cell.

The transcripts encoding regulatory proteins and growth factors, however, are usually much less stable, with half-lives of less than 1 hr. What makes these particular transcripts so unstable? In many cases, they contain specific sequences near their 3′ ends that make them targets for enzymes that degrade mRNA. A sequence of A and U nucleotides near the 3′ poly-A tail of a transcript promotes removal of the tail, which destabilizes the mRNA.

Loss of the poly-A tail leads to rapid degradation by 3′ to 5′ RNA exonucleases. Another consequence of this loss is the stimulation of decapping enzymes that remove the 5′ cap leading to degradation by 5′ to 3′ RNA exonucleases.

Other mRNA transcripts contain sequences near their 3′ ends that are recognition sites for endonucleases, which cause these transcripts to be digested quickly. The short half-lives of the mRNA transcripts of many regulatory genes are critical to the function of those genes because they enable the levels of regulatory proteins in the cell to be altered rapidly.

A review of various methods of posttranscriptional control of gene expression is provided in figure 16.19.

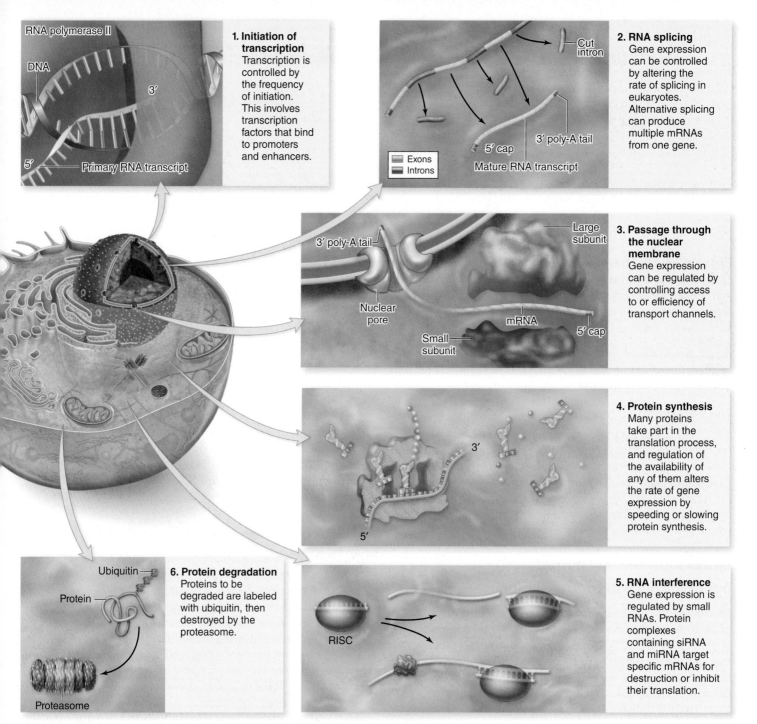

1. Initiation of transcription Transcription is controlled by the frequency of initiation. This involves transcription factors that bind to promoters and enhancers.

RNA polymerase II

DNA

3′

5′ ━ Primary RNA transcript

2. RNA splicing Gene expression can be controlled by altering the rate of splicing in eukaryotes. Alternative splicing can produce multiple mRNAs from one gene.

Cut intron

□ Exons
■ Introns

5′ cap

3′ poly-A tail

Mature RNA transcript

3. Passage through the nuclear membrane Gene expression can be regulated by controlling access to or efficiency of transport channels.

3′ poly-A tail

Nuclear pore

Large subunit

mRNA

5′ cap

Small subunit

4. Protein synthesis Many proteins take part in the translation process, and regulation of the availability of any of them alters the rate of gene expression by speeding or slowing protein synthesis.

3′

5′

6. Protein degradation Proteins to be degraded are labeled with ubiquitin, then destroyed by the proteasome.

Ubiquitin

Protein

Proteasome

5. RNA interference Gene expression is regulated by small RNAs. Protein complexes containing siRNA and miRNA target specific mRNAs for destruction or inhibit their translation.

RISC

Figure 16.19 Mechanisms for control of gene expression in eukaryotes.

Learning Outcomes Review 16.6

Small RNAs control gene expression by either selective degradation of mRNA, inhibition of translation, or alteration of chromatin structure. Multiple mRNAs can be formed from a single gene via alternative splicing, which can be tissue- and developmentally specific. The sequence of an mRNA transcript can also be altered by RNA editing.

■ **How could the phenomenon of RNA interference be used in drug design?**

16.7 Protein Degradation

Learning Outcomes

1. *Describe the role of ubiquitin in the degradation of proteins.*
2. *Explain the function of the proteasome.*

If all of the proteins produced by a cell during its lifetime remained in the cell, serious problems would arise. Protein labeling studies in the 1970s indicated that eukaryotic cells turn over proteins in a controlled manner. That is, proteins are continually being synthesized and degraded. Although this protein turnover is not as rapid as in prokaryotes, it indicates that a system regulating protein turnover is important.

Proteins can become altered chemically, rendering them nonfunctional; in addition, the need for any particular protein may be transient. Proteins also do not always fold correctly, or they may become improperly folded over time. These changes can lead to loss of function or other chemical behaviors, such as aggregating into insoluble complexes. In fact, a number of neurodegenerative diseases, such as Alzheimer dementia, Parkinson disease, and mad cow disease, are related to proteins that aggregate, forming characteristic plaques in brain cells. Thus, in addition to normal turnover of proteins, cells need a mechanism to get rid of old, unused, and incorrectly folded proteins.

Enzymes called **proteases** can degrade proteins by breaking peptide bonds, converting a protein into its constituent amino acids. Although there is an obvious need for these enzymes, they clearly cannot be floating around in the cytoplasm active at all times.

One way that eukaryotic cells handle such problems is to confine destructive enzymes to a specific cellular compartment. You may recall from chapter 4 that lysosomes are vesicles that contain digestive enzymes, including proteases. Lysosomes are used to remove proteins and old or nonfunctional organelles, but this system is not specific for particular proteins. Cells need another regulated pathway to remove proteins that are old or unused, but leave the rest of cellular proteins intact.

Addition of ubiquitin marks proteins for destruction

Eukaryotic cells solve this problem by marking proteins for destruction, then selectively degrading them. The mark that cells use is the attachment of a **ubiquitin** molecule. Ubiquitin, so named because it is found in essentially all eukaryotic cells (that is, it is ubiquitous), is a 76–amino-acid protein that can exist as an isolated molecule or in longer chains that are attached to other proteins.

The longer chains are added to proteins in a stepwise fashion by an enzyme called *ubiquitin ligase* (figure 16.20). This reaction requires ATP and other proteins, and it takes place in a multistep, regulated process. Proteins that have a ubiquitin chain attached are called *polyubiquitinated,* and this state is a signal to the cell to destroy this protein.

Two basic categories of proteins become ubiquitinated: those that need to be removed because they are improperly folded or nonfunctional, and those that are produced and degraded in a controlled fashion by the cell. An example of the latter are the cyclin proteins that help to drive the cell cycle (chapter 10). When these proteins have fulfilled their role in active division of the cell, they become polyubiquitinated and

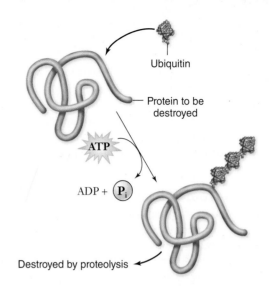

Figure 16.20 Ubiquitination of proteins. Proteins that are to be degraded are marked with ubiquitin. The enzyme ubiquitin ligase uses ATP to add ubiquitin to a protein. When a series of these have been added, the polyubiquitinated protein is destroyed.

are removed. In this way, a cell can control entry into cell division or maintain a nondividing state.

The proteasome degrades polyubiquitinated proteins

The cellular organelle that degrades proteins marked with ubiquitin is the **proteasome,** a large cylindrical complex that proteins enter at one end and exit the other as amino acids or peptide fragments (figure 16.21).

The proteasome complex contains a central region that has protease activity and regulatory components at each end. Although not membrane-bounded, this organelle can be thought of as a form of compartmentalization on a very small scale. By using a two-step process, first to mark proteins for

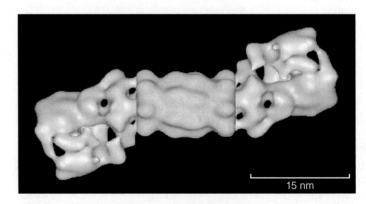

Figure 16.21 The *Drosophila* proteasome. The central complex contains the proteolytic activity, and the flanking regions act as regulators. Proteins enter one end of the cylinder and are cleaved to peptide fragments that exit the other end.

destruction, then to process them through a large complex, proteins to be degraded are isolated from the rest of the cytoplasm.

The process of ubiquitination followed by degradation by the proteasome is called the *ubiquitin–proteasome pathway*. It can be thought of as a cycle in that the ubiquitin added to proteins is not itself destroyed in the proteasome. As the proteins are degraded, the ubiquitin chain itself is simply cleaved back into ubiquitin units that can then be reused (figure 16.22).

Learning Outcomes Review 16.7

Control of protein degradation in eukaryotes involves addition of the protein ubiquitin, which marks the protein for destruction. The proteasome, a cylindrical complex with protease activity in its center, recognizes ubiquitinated proteins and breaks them down, much like a shredder destroys documents. Ubiquitin is recycled unchanged.

■ *If the ubiquitination process was not tightly controlled, what effect would this have on a cell?*

? **Inquiry question** What are two reasons a cell would polyubiquitinate a polypeptide?

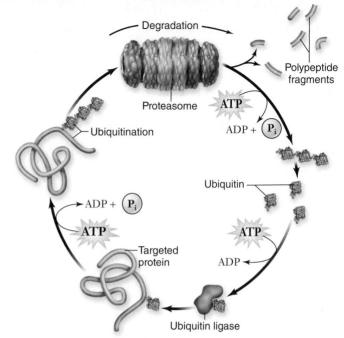

Figure 16.22 Degradation by the ubiquitin–proteasome pathway. Proteins are first ubiquitinated, then enter the proteasome to be degraded. In the proteasome, the polyubiquitin is removed and then is later "deubiquitinated" to produce single ubiquitin molecules that can be reused.

Chapter Review

16.1 Control of Gene Expression

Control can occur at all levels of gene expression.
Transcription is controlled by regulatory proteins that modulate the ability of RNA polymerase to bind to the promoter. These may either block transcription or stimulate it.

Control strategies in prokaryotes are geared to adjust to environmental changes.

Control strategies in eukaryotes maintain homeostasis and drive development.

16.2 Regulatory Proteins

Proteins can interact with DNA through the major groove.
A DNA double helix exhibits a major groove and a minor groove; bases in the major groove are accessible to regulatory proteins.

DNA-binding domains interact with specific DNA sequences.
A region of the regulatory protein that can bind to the DNA is termed a DNA-binding motif (figure 16.2).

Several common DNA-binding motifs are shared by many proteins.
Common motifs include the helix-turn-helix motif, the homeodomain motif, the zinc finger motif, and the leucine zipper.

16.3 Prokaryotic Regulation

Control of transcription can be either positive or negative.
Negative control is mediated by proteins called repressors that interfere with transcription. Positive control is mediated by a class of regulatory proteins called activators that stimulate transcription.

Prokaryotes adjust gene expression in response to environmental conditions.
The *lac* operon is induced in the presence of lactose; that is, the enzymes to utilize lactose are only produced when lactose is present. The *trp* operon is repressed; that is, the enzymes needed to produce tryptophan are turned off when tryptophan is present.

The lac operon is negatively regulated by the lac repressor.
The *lac* operon is induced when the effector (allolactose) binds to the repressor, altering its conformation such that it no longer binds DNA (figure 16.4).

The presence of glucose prevents induction of the lac operon.
Maximal expression of the *lac* operon requires positive control by catabolite activator protein (CAP) complexed with cAMP. When glucose is low, cAMP is high. Glucose repression involves both inducer exclusion, in which lactose is prevented from entering the cell, and the control of CAP function by the level of glucose.

The trp operon is controlled by the trp repressor.
The *trp* operon is repressed when tryptophan, acting as a corepressor, binds to the repressor, altering its conformation such

that it can bind to DNA and turn off the operon. This prevents expression in the presence of excess *trp*.

16.4 Eukaryotic Regulation

Transcription factors can be either general or specific.

General transcription factors are needed to assemble the transcription apparatus and recruit RNA polymerase II at the promoter. Specific factors act in a tissue- or time-dependent manner to stimulate higher rates of transcription.

Promoters and enhancers are binding sites for transcription factors.

General factors bind to the promoter to recruit RNA polymerase. Specific factors bind to enhancers, which may be distant from the promoter but can be brought closer by DNA looping.

Coactivators and mediators link transcription factors to RNA polymerase II (figure 16.11).

Some, but not all, transcription factors require a mediator. The number of coactivators is small because a single coactivator can be used with multiple transcription factors.

The transcription complex brings things together.

16.5 Eukaryotic Chromatin Structure

In eukaryotes, DNA is wrapped around proteins called histones, forming nucleosomes. These may block binding of transcription factors to promoters and enhancers.

Both DNA and histone proteins can be modified.

Methylation of DNA bases, primarily cytosine, correlates with genes that have been "turned off." Methylation is associated with inactive regions of chromatin.

Some transcription activators alter chromatin structure.

Acetylation of histones results in active regions of chromatin.

Chromatin-remodeling complexes also change chromatin structure.

Chromatin-remodeling complexes contain enzymes that move, reposition, and transfer nucleosomes.

16.6 Eukaryotic Posttranscriptional Regulation

Small RNAs act after transcription to control gene expression.

RNA interference is mediated by siRNAs formed by cleavage of double-stranded RNA by the Dicer nuclease. The siRNA is bound to a protein, Argonaute, in an RNA-induced silencing complex (RISC). The RISC can cleave mRNA or inhibit translation. Another class of small RNA, miRNA, is formed by the action of two nucleases, Drosha and Dicer, on RNA stem-and-loop structures. These also form a RISC that can either degrade mRNA or stop translation.

Small RNAs may have evolved to protect the genome.

Viral RNAs are degraded and transposons are silenced in the germ line by RNA interference. The origins of this machinery are ancient.

Small RNAs can mediate heterochromatin formation.

In fission yeast, *Drosophila,* and plants, RNA interference pathways lead to the formation of heterochromatin.

Alternative splicing can produce multiple proteins from one gene.

In response to tissue-specific factors, alternative splicing of pre-mRNA from one gene can result in multiple proteins.

RNA editing alters mRNA after transcription.

mRNA must be transported out of the nucleus for translation.

Initiation of translation can be controlled.

Translation factors may be modified to control initiation; translation repressor proteins can bind to the beginning of a transcript so that it cannot attach to the ribosome.

The degradation of mRNA is controlled.

An mRNA transcript is relatively stable, but it may carry targets for enzymes that degrade it more quickly as needed by the cell.

16.7 Protein Degradation

Addition of ubiquitin marks proteins for destruction.

In eukaryotes, proteins targeted for destruction have ubiquitin added to them as a marker.

The proteasome degrades polyubiquitinated proteins.

A cell organelle—the cylindrical proteasome—degrades ubiquitinated proteins that pass through it.

Review Questions

UNDERSTAND

1. In prokaryotes, control of gene expression usually occurs at the
   a. splicing of pre-mRNA into mature mRNA.
   b. initiation of translation.
   c. initiation of transcription.
   d. All of the choices are correct.

2. Regulatory proteins interact with DNA by
   a. unwinding the helix and changing the pattern of base-pairing.
   b. binding to the sugar–phosphate backbone of the double helix.
   c. unwinding the helix and disrupting base-pairing.
   d. binding to the major groove of the double helix and interacting with base-pairs.

3. In *E. coli*, induction in the *lac* operon and repression in the *trp* operon are both examples of
   a. negative control by a repressor.
   b. positive control by a repressor.
   c. negative control by an activator.
   d. positive control by a repressor.

4. The *lac* operon is controlled by two main proteins. These proteins
   a. both act in a negative fashion.
   b. both act in a positive fashion.
   c. act in the opposite fashion, one negative and one positive.
   d. act at the level of translation.

5. In eukaryotes, binding of RNA polymerase to a promoter requires the action of
   a. specific transcription factors.
   b. general transcription factors.
   c. repressor proteins.
   d. inducer proteins.

6. In eukaryotes, the regulation of gene expression occurs
   a. only at the level of transcription.
   b. only at the level of translation.
   c. at the level of transcription initiation, or posttranscriptionally.
   d. only posttranscriptionally.

7. In the *trp* operon, the repressor binds to DNA
   a. in the absence of *trp*.
   b. in the presence of *trp*.
   c. in either the presence or absence of *trp*.
   d. only when *trp* is needed in the cell.

APPLY

1. The *lac* repressor, the *trp* repressor and CAP are all
   a. negative regulators of transcription.
   b. positive regulators of transcription.
   c. allosteric proteins that bind to DNA and an effector.
   d. proteins that can bind DNA or other proteins.

2. Specific transcription factors in eukaryotes interact with enhancers, which may be a long distance from the promoter. These transcription factors then
   a. alter the structure of the DNA between enhancer and promoter.
   b. do not interact with the transcription apparatus.
   c. can interact with the transcription apparatus via DNA looping.
   d. can interact with the transcription apparatus by removing the intervening DNA.

3. Repression in the *trp* operon and induction in the *lac* operon are both mechanisms that
   a. would only be possible with positive regulation.
   b. allow the cell to control the level of enzymes to fit environmental conditions.
   c. would only be possible with negative regulation.
   d. cause the cell to make the enzymes from these two operons all the time.

4. Regulation by small RNAs and alternative splicing are similar in that both
   a. act after transcription.
   b. act via RNA/protein complexes.
   c. regulate the transcription machinery.
   d. Both a and b are correct.

5. Eukaryotic mRNAs differ from prokaryotic mRNAs in that they
   a. usually contain more than one gene.
   b. are colinear with the genes that encode them.
   c. are not colinear with the genes that encode them.
   d. Both a and c are correct.

6. In the cell cycle, cyclin proteins are produced in concert with the cycle. This likely involves
   a. control of initiation of transcription of cyclin genes, and ubiquitination of cyclin proteins.
   b. alternative splicing of cyclin genes to produce different cyclin proteins.
   c. RNA editing to produce the different cyclin proteins.
   d. transcription/translation coupling.

7. A mechanism of control in *E. coli* not discussed in this chapter involves pausing of ribosomes allowing a transcription terminator to form in the mRNA. In eukaryotic fission yeast, this mechanism should
   a. be common since they are unicellular.
   b. not be common since they are unicellular.
   c. not occur as transcription occurs in the nucleus and translation in the cytoplasm.
   d. not occur due to possibility of alternative splicing.

SYNTHESIZE

1. You have isolated a series of mutants affecting regulation of the *lac* operon. All of these are constitutive, that is, they express the *lac* operon all the time. You also have both mutant and wild-type alleles for each mutant in all combinations, and on F′ plasmids, which can be introduced into cells to make the cell diploid for the relevant genes. How would you use these tools to determine which mutants affect DNA binding sites on DNA, and which affect proteins that bind to DNA?

2. Examples of positive and negative control of transcription can be found in the regulation of expression of the bacterial operons *lac* and *trp*. Use these two operon systems to describe the difference between positive and negative regulation.

3. What forms of eukaryotic control of gene expression are unique to eukaryotes? Could prokaryotes use the mechanisms, or are they due to differences in these cell types?

4. The number and type of proteins found in a cell can be influenced by genetic mutation and regulation of gene expression. Discuss how these two processes differ.

ONLINE RESOURCE

www.ravenbiology.com

Understand, Apply, and Synthesize—enhance your study with animations that bring concepts to life and practice tests to assess your understanding. Your instructor may also recommend the interactive eBook, individualized learning tools, and more.

Chapter 17

Biotechnology

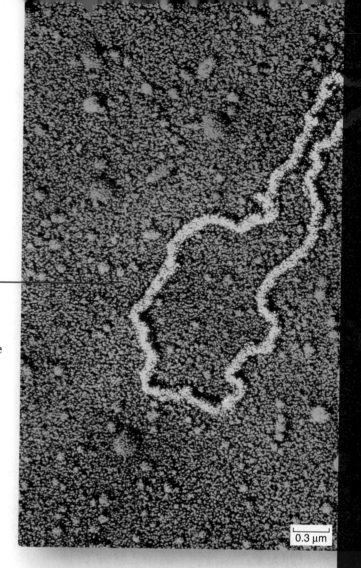

0.3 μm

Chapter Contents

Introduction

Biotechnology is the manipulation of living organisms resulting in a desired product or process. Over the past three decades, the development of new and powerful techniques for studying and manipulating DNA has revolutionized biology. The knowledge gained in the last 30 years is greater than that accrued during the history of biology. Biotechnology also affects more aspects of everyday life than any other area of biology. From the food on your table to the future of medicine, biotechnology touches your life.

Biotechnology includes the application of molecular biology principles you have studied to numerous aspects of life. The ability to isolate specific DNA sequences arose from the study and use of small DNA molecules found in bacteria, such as the plasmid pictured here. In this chapter, we explore these technologies and consider how they apply to specific problems of practical importance.

17.1 Recombinant DNA

Learning Outcomes

1. *Contrast the potential results of using breeding versus recombinant DNA.*
2. *Relate endogenous roles of enzymes to their recombinant DNA applications.*
3. *Explain why DNA fragments can be separated with gel electrophoresis and why it is useful.*

Over 15,000 years ago humans began domesticating dogs from wolves, and since that time selective breeding has led to the 155 existing breeds of dogs. Crop domestication followed, and the development of hybrid corn in the early 20th century substantially increased yield. Although creating new gene combinations through genetic crosses is not new, the ability to directly isolate and manipulate genetic material was one of the most profound changes to come about in the field of biology in the late 20th century. The construction of **recombinant DNA** molecules, that is, a single DNA molecule made from two different sources, began in the mid-1970s. The development of this technology, which has led to the entire field of biotechnology, is based on enzymes that can be used to manipulate DNA.

In the 1970s, the Indian-born American microbiologist Ananda Chakrabarty, at General Electric's Research and Development Center, was developing bacteria to consume oil spills. Four *Pseudomonas* strains had genes coding for single, distinct enzymes that digested the hydrocarbons in oil into methane. The genes were encoded in plasmids (small, circular DNA) in the bacteria. Together the four enzymes were more effective in dissipating an oil spill than any one alone. Chakrabarty combined the genes encoding the enzymes into a single plasmid, creating the first recombinant DNA. He sought a patent for the bacteria containing the recombinant DNA. In 1980, in the case of *Diamond versus Chakrabarty,* the Supreme Court ruled that Chakrabarty had the right to patent his oil-consuming bacteria because such bacteria did not occur in nature and existed only because of his ingenuity.

Restriction endonucleases cleave DNA at specific sites

Restriction endonucleases are the key to inserting a sequence of DNA from one organism into a piece of DNA, such as a plasmid, from another. The use of restriction enzymes revolutionized molecular biology because of their ability to cleave DNA at specific sites. As described in chapter 14, nucleases are enzymes that degrade DNA, and many were known prior to the isolation of the first restriction enzyme (*Hin*dII) in 1970. If a DNA sequence were a rope, then restriction enzymes would be a knife that always cut that rope into specific pieces.

Discovery and significance of restriction endonucleases

This site-specific cleavage activity, long sought by molecular biologists, was discovered from basic research into why bacterial viruses can infect some cells but not others. This phenomenon was termed host restriction. The bacteria produce enzymes that can cleave the invading viral DNA at specific sequences. The host cells protect their own DNA from cleavage by modifying bases at the cleavage sites; the restriction enzymes do not cleave the modified bacterial DNA. Since the initial discovery of these restriction endonucleases, hundreds more have been isolated that recognize and cleave different **restriction sites.**

The ability to cut DNA at specific places is significant in two ways: First, it allows physical maps to be constructed based on the positioning of cleavage sites for restriction enzymes. These restriction maps provide crucial data for identifying and working with DNA molecules (as discussed in detail in chapter 18).

Second, restriction endonuclease cleavage allows for the creation of recombinant molecules. The ability to construct recombinant molecules is critical to research because many steps in the process of cloning and manipulating DNA require the ability to combine molecules from different sources.

How restriction enzymes work

There are three types of restriction enzymes, but only type II cleaves at precise locations. Types I and III cleave with less precision and are not often used in cloning and manipulating DNA.

Type II enzymes enable creation of recombinant molecules; these enzymes recognize a specific DNA sequence,

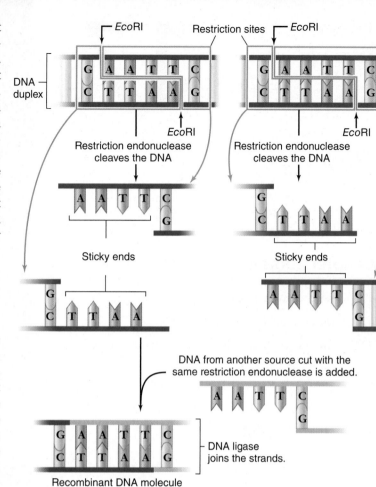

Figure 17.1 Many restriction endonucleases produce DNA fragments with sticky ends. The restriction endonuclease *Eco*RI always cleaves the sequence 5′-GAATTC-3′ between G and A. Because the same sequence occurs on both strands, both are cut. However, the two sequences run in opposite directions on the two strands. As a result, single-stranded tails called "sticky ends" are produced that are complementary to each other. These complementary ends can then be joined to a fragment from another DNA that is cut with the same enzyme. These two molecules can then be joined by DNA ligase to produce a recombinant molecule.

ranging from 4 bases to 12 bases, and cleave the DNA at a specific base within this sequence (figure 17.1). The recognition sites for most type II enzymes are palindromes. A linguistic **palindrome** is a word or phrase that reads the same forward and in reverse, such as the sentence: "Madam I'm Adam." The palindromic DNA sequence reads the same from 5′ to 3′ on one strand as it does on the complementary strand (see figure 17.1).

Given this kind of sequence, cutting the DNA at the same base on either strand can lead to staggered cuts that produce "sticky ends." These short, unpaired sequences are the same for any DNA that is cut by this enzyme. Thus, these sticky ends allow DNA molecules from different sources to be easily joined together (see figure 17.1). Although less common, some type II restriction enzymes, including *Pvu*II, can cut both strands in the same position, producing blunt, not sticky, ends. Blunt-cut ends can be joined with other blunt-cut ends.

Gel electrophoresis separates DNA fragments

Restriction endonucleases cut DNA into fragments of different sizes. Separating the fragments based on size makes it possible to select the DNA sequence of interest. The most common separation technique used is gel electrophoresis. This technique takes advantage of the negative charge on DNA molecules by using an electrical field to provide the force necessary to separate DNA molecules based on size.

The gel, which is made of either agarose or polyacrylamide and spread thinly on supporting material, provides a three-dimensional matrix that separates molecules based on size (figure 17.2). The gel is submerged in a buffer solution containing ions that can carry current and is subjected to an electrical field.

The strong negative charges from the phosphate groups in the DNA backbone cause it to migrate toward the positive pole (figure 17.2b). The gel acts as a sieve to separate DNA molecules based on size: The larger the molecule, the slower it will move through the gel matrix. Over a given period, smaller molecules migrate farther than larger ones. The DNA in gels can be visualized using a fluorescent dye that binds to DNA (figure 17.2c, d).

Electrophoresis is one of the most important methods in the toolbox of modern molecular biology, with uses ranging from DNA fingerprinting to DNA sequencing, both of which are described later on.

DNA ligase allows construction of recombinant plasmids

Once a specific restriction fragment is isolated, it can be spliced into a plasmid that has been cut with the same restriction enzyme. Another enzyme is needed, however, to join the two fragments together to create a stable DNA molecule. The

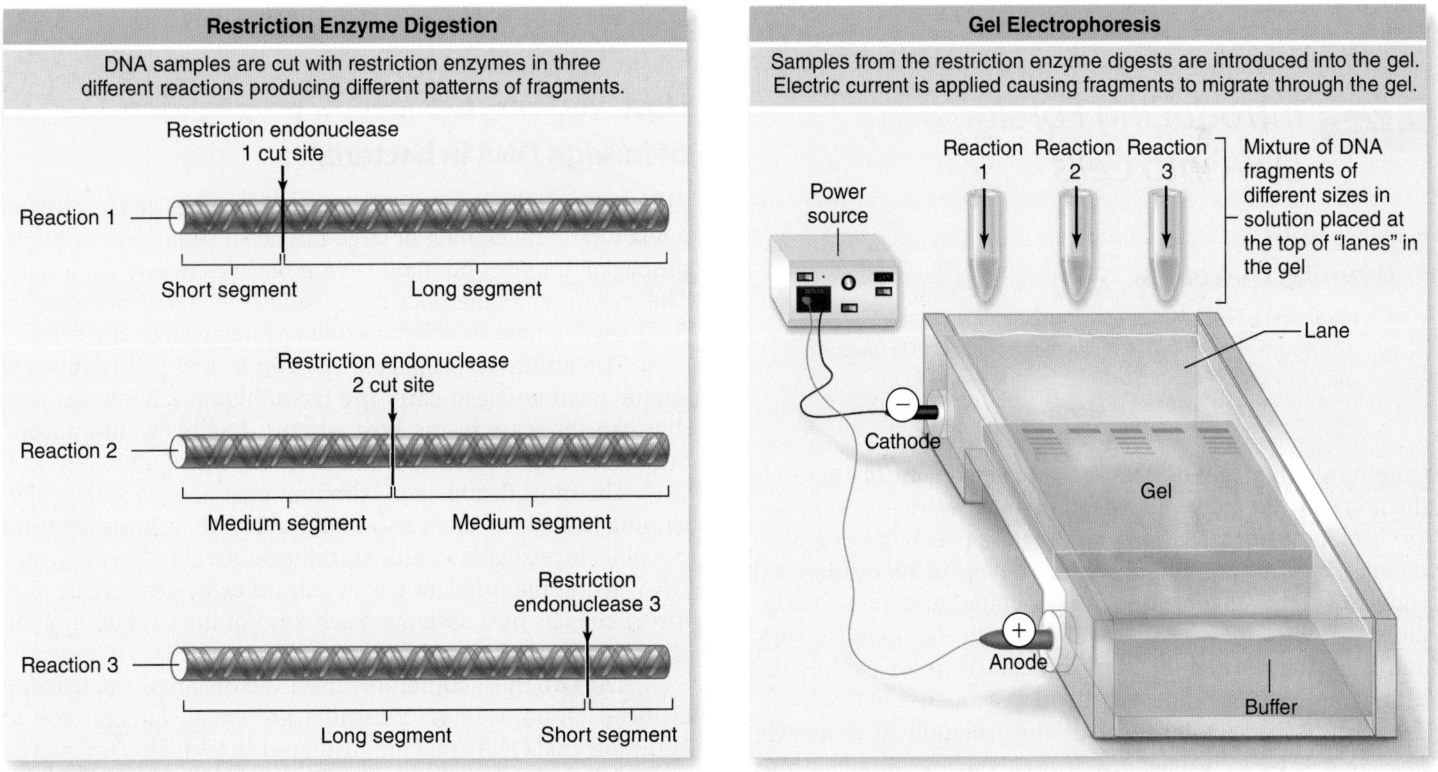

Restriction Enzyme Digestion

DNA samples are cut with restriction enzymes in three different reactions producing different patterns of fragments.

Restriction endonuclease 1 cut site

Reaction 1
Short segment | Long segment

Restriction endonuclease 2 cut site

Reaction 2
Medium segment | Medium segment

Restriction endonuclease 3

Reaction 3
Long segment | Short segment

a.

Gel Electrophoresis

Samples from the restriction enzyme digests are introduced into the gel. Electric current is applied causing fragments to migrate through the gel.

Power source

Reaction 1 · Reaction 2 · Reaction 3

Mixture of DNA fragments of different sizes in solution placed at the top of "lanes" in the gel

Cathode

Lane

Gel

Anode

Buffer

b.

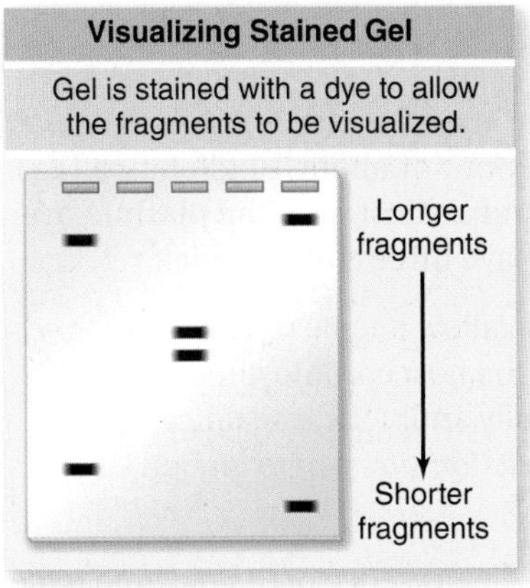

Visualizing Stained Gel

Gel is stained with a dye to allow the fragments to be visualized.

Longer fragments

Shorter fragments

c.

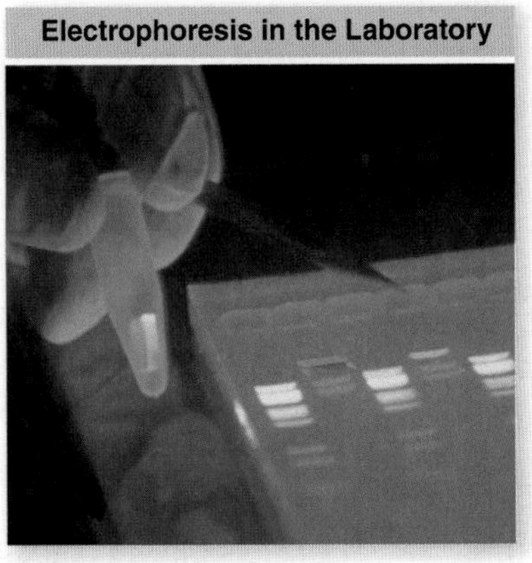

Electrophoresis in the Laboratory

d.

Figure 17.2 Gel electrophoresis. *a.* Three restriction enzymes are used to cut DNA into specific pieces depending on each enzyme's recognition sequence. *b.* The fragments are loaded into a gel (agarose or polyacrylamide), and an electrical current is applied. The DNA fragments migrate through the gel based on size, with larger ones moving more slowly. *c.* This results in a pattern of fragments separated based on size, with the smaller fragments migrating farther than larger ones. *d.* The fragments can be visualized by staining with the dye ethidium bromide. When the gel is exposed to UV light, the DNA with bound dye fluoresces, appearing as pink bands in the gel. In the photograph, one band of DNA has been excised from the gel for further analysis and can be seen glowing in the tube the technician holds.

enzyme DNA ligase accomplishes this by catalyzing the formation of a phosphodiester bond between adjacent phosphate and hydroxyl groups of DNA nucleotides. The action of ligase is to seal nicks in one or both strands (see figure 17.1). This is the same enzyme that joins Okazaki fragments on the lagging strand during DNA replication (see chapter 14).

Learning Outcomes Review 17.1

Restriction endonucleases are part of bacterial cells' strategies for fighting viral infection. Type II endonucleases cleave DNA at specific sites. DNA ligase can be used to link together fragments following action of restriction endonucleases. Gel electrophoresis employs electrical charge to separate DNA fragments according to size.

■ *Assess the effect of recombinant DNA on biotechnology.*

■ *Compare and contrast the endogenous roles of EcoRI and ligase in* E. coli *with their use in a molecular biology lab.*

17.2 Introducing Foreign DNA into Cells

Learning Outcomes

1. *Explain the role of a vector in molecular cloning.*
2. *Compare recombinant technology methods in bacteria and eukaryotes.*

Obtaining a fragment of DNA that encodes a gene of interest is the first step toward genetic engineering. Restriction enzymes are used to insert a DNA fragment into a plasmid, but a plasmid in isolation cannot replicate. To be useful, many identical copies of the fragment must be generated and stably maintained. The term **clone** refers to a genetically identical copy and is used in several different contexts. Here we explore the idea of molecular cloning, amplifying a sequence of DNA.

Molecular cloning involves the isolation of a specific sequence of DNA, usually one that encodes a particular protein product. This is sometimes called *gene cloning,* but the term *molecular cloning* is more accurate. In this section the focus is on the use of cells in molecular cloning.

Transformation allows introduction of foreign DNA into cells

In chapter 14 you learned that Frederick Griffith demonstrated that genetic material could be transferred between bacterial cells. This process, called *transformation,* is a natural process in the cells that Griffith was studying. The bacterium *E. coli,* used routinely in molecular biology laboratories, does not undergo natural transformation; but artificial transformation techniques have been developed to allow introduction of foreign DNA into *E. coli.* Through temperature shifts or application of an electrical charge, the *E. coli* membrane becomes transiently permeable to the foreign DNA. In this way, recombinant molecules can be propagated in a cell that will make many copies of the constructed molecules.

In general, the introduction of DNA from an outside source into a cell is referred to as transformation. This process is important in *E. coli* for molecular cloning and the propagation of cloned DNA. Researchers also want to be able to reintroduce DNA into the original cells from which it was isolated, including eukaryotic cells. A transformed cell can also be used to form all or part of a multicellular, eukaryotic organism, called a **transgenic organism.**

Here we focus on amplifying recombinant DNA sequences in transformed cells. Amplification and expression are not the same. For example, a eukaryotic gene can be amplified if it is inserted in a plasmid in *E. coli,* but if it has a eukaryotic promoter and/or eukaryotic introns, the bacterial cell will not be able to correctly transcribe and translate the gene. This distinction will be taken into consideration when we look at applications of molecular cloning later in the chapter.

Host–vector systems allow propagation of foreign DNA in bacteria

Although short sequences of DNA can be synthesized in vitro (in a test tube), the cloning of large unknown sequences requires propagation of recombinant DNA molecules in vivo (in a cell). The enzymes and methods described earlier allow biologists to produce, separate, and then introduce foreign DNA into cells.

The ability to propagate DNA in a host cell requires a **vector** (something to carry the recombinant DNA molecule) that can replicate in the host when it has been introduced. Such host–vector systems are crucial to molecular biology.

The most flexible and common host used for molecular cloning is the bacterium *E. coli,* but many other hosts are now possible. Investigators routinely reintroduce cloned eukaryotic DNA, using mammalian tissue culture cells, yeast cells, and insect cells as host systems. Each kind of host–vector system allows particular uses of the cloned DNA.

The two most commonly used vectors are plasmids and artificial chromosomes. **Plasmids** are small, circular extrachromosomal DNAs that are dispensable to the bacterial cell. Bacterial and eukaryotic artificial chromosomes are used to clone larger pieces of DNA.

Plasmid vectors

Plasmid vectors are typically used to clone relatively small pieces of DNA, up to a maximum of about 10 kilobases (kb). Larger inserts are not stable and are lost from the plasmid over time. A plasmid vector must have three components:

1. An *origin of replication* to allow it to be replicated in *E. coli* independently of the host chromosome,
2. A *selectable marker,* usually antibiotic resistance, and
3. *One or more unique restriction sites* where foreign DNA can be added.

The selectable marker allows the presence of the plasmid to be easily identified through genetic selection. For example, cells that contain a plasmid with an antibiotic resistance gene continue to live when plated on antibiotic-containing growth media, whereas cells that lack the plasmid will die (they are killed by the antibiotic).

A fragment of DNA is inserted by the techniques previously described into a region of the plasmid with restriction sites called the multiple-cloning site (MCS). This region contains a number of unique restriction sites such that when the plasmid is cut with the relevant restriction enzymes, a linear plasmid results. When DNA of interest is cut with the same restriction enzyme, it can then be ligated into this site. The plasmid is then introduced into cells by transformation (figure 17.3), and the fragment of DNA is amplified as the bacterial cells divide.

This region of the vector often has been engineered to contain another gene that becomes inactivated, a process called *insertional inactivation,* because it is now interrupted by the inserted DNA. One of the first cloning vectors, pBR322, used another antibiotic resistance gene for insertional activation; resistance to one antibiotic and sensitivity to the other indicated the presence of inserted DNA.

More recent vectors use the gene for β-galactosidase, an enzyme that cleaves galactoside sugars such as lactose. When the enzyme cleaves the artificial substrate X-gal, a blue color is produced. In these plasmids, insertion of foreign DNA interrupts the β-galactosidase gene, preventing a functional enzyme from being produced. When transformed cells are plated on a medium containing both antibiotic (to select for plasmid-containing cells) and X-gal, they remain white, whereas transformed cells with no inserted DNA are blue (see figure 17.3).

Artificial chromosomes

The size of DNA molecules that can be cloned in plasmid vectors has limited the large-scale analysis of genomes. To deal with this, geneticists decided to follow the strategy of cells and construct chromosomes, leading to the development of yeast artificial chromosomes (YACs) and bacterial artificial chromosomes (BACs). Progress has also been made on creating mammalian artificial chromosomes.

> **? Inquiry question** An investigator wishes to clone a 32-kb recombinant molecule. What do you think is the best vector to use?

Eukaryotic cell transformation is challenging

Transforming eukaryotic cells is more challenging than transforming bacteria. The primary experimental difficulty has been identifying a suitable vector for introducing recombinant DNA. Eukaryotic cells do not possess the many plasmids that bacteria have, so the choice of potential vectors is limited.

Two successful approaches for transforming animal cells are injecting DNA into the pronucleus of a fertilized egg or injecting embryonic stem cells into an embryo. Specific applications are explored in chapter 19. General approaches to transforming plant cells include electrically charging cells and employing "the gene gun," to bombard cells with tiny gold or tungsten particles coated with DNA. This technique has the advantage of being usable for any species, but it does not provide as precise engineering because the copy number of introduced genes is much harder to control. However, a bacterial pathogen has been quite effective in transforming plants.

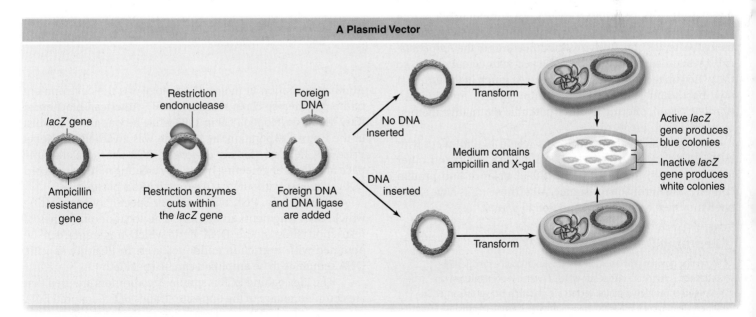

A Plasmid Vector

Figure 17.3 Molecular cloning with vectors. Plasmids are cut within the β-galactosidase gene *(lacZ),* and foreign DNA and DNA ligase are added. Foreign DNA inserted into *lacZ* interrupts the coding sequence, thus inactivating the gene. Plating cells on a medium containing the antibiotic ampicillin selects for plasmid-containing cells. The medium also contains X-gal, and when *lacZ* is intact *(top),* the expressed enzyme cleaves the X-gal, producing blue colonies. When *lacZ* is inactivated *(bottom),* X-gal is not cleaved, and colonies remain white.

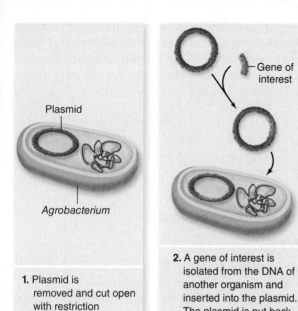
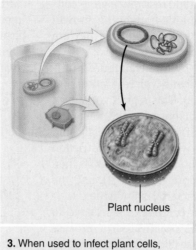
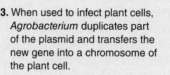

1. Plasmid is removed and cut open with restriction endonuclease.

2. A gene of interest is isolated from the DNA of another organism and inserted into the plasmid. The plasmid is put back into the *Agrobacterium.*

3. When used to infect plant cells, *Agrobacterium* duplicates part of the plasmid and transfers the new gene into a chromosome of the plant cell.

4. The plant cell divides, and each daughter cell receives the new gene. These cultured cells can be used to grow a new plant with the introduced gene.

Figure 17.4   The Ti plasmid. This *Agrobacterium tumefaciens* plasmid is used in plant genetic engineering.

Transforming plants with a bacterial pathogen

The most successful results thus far have been obtained with the **Ti (tumor-inducing) plasmid** of the plant bacterium *Agrobacterium tumefaciens,* which normally infects broadleaf plants such as tomato, tobacco, and soybean. This plant pathogen causes tumors to form on the plant, but the tumor-inducing genes in the tumor-inducing (Ti) plasmid in *Agrobacterium* can be removed. The **transfer DNA (T-DNA)** within the Ti plasmid integrates into the plant DNA, and researchers have succeeded in attaching other genes to this portion of the plasmid (figure 17.4). The characteristics of a number of plants that are susceptible to *Agrobacterium* infections have been altered using this technique. Recently, modifications of the *Agrobacterium* system have allowed it to be used with cereal plants, so the gene gun technology may not be used much in the future. A new bacterium has also been manipulated to function like *Agrobacterium,* offering another potential alternative method of engineering cereal crops.

Among the features scientists would like to affect with molecular cloning are resistance to disease, frost, and other forms of stress; increase in nutritional balance and protein content; and herbicide resistance. All of these traits have either been modified or are being modified in plants.

Learning Outcomes Review 17.2

Molecular cloning is the isolation and amplification of a specific DNA sequence. A vector is a carrier into which a sequence of interest may be introduced. The most common vectors are plasmids. The vector carries the DNA sequence into a cell, which then multiplies, copying its own DNA along with that of the vector.

■ *Review the essential steps needed to make multiple copies of a restriction digest DNA fragment that you have isolated using gel electrophoresis.*

17.3 Amplifying DNA Without a Vector—The Polymerase Chain Reaction

Learning Outcomes

1. *Explain how DNA can be amplified in the absence of a vector.*
2. *Compare and contrast DNA replication and the polymerase chain reaction.*

Another revolution in molecular biology was the development of the polymerase chain reaction (PCR). American biochemist Kary Mullis developed PCR in 1983 while he was a staff chemist at the Cetus Corporation; in 1993, he was awarded the Nobel Prize in Chemistry for his discovery. PCR can accelerate the pace of genetic engineering by quickly creating many clones of a DNA sequence without first inserting it into a plasmid.

Additionally, PCR offers greater specificity in selecting which DNA fragments to amplify. The location and types of restriction sites in the DNA limit which fragments can be obtained with restriction endonucleases. In PCR the specific DNA sequence to be amplified can be specified.

The idea behind PCR is simple: Two primers are used that are complementary to the opposite strands of a denatured DNA sequence. When DNA polymerase acts on these primers and the sequence of interest, the polymerase produces complementary strands, each containing the other primer. If this procedure is done cyclically, the result is a large quantity of a sequence corresponding to the DNA that lies between the two primers (figure 17.5). Simply put, PCR is DNA replication in vitro.

PCR mimics DNA replication

Two developments turned this simple concept into a powerful technique. First, each cycle requires denaturing the DNA after each round of synthesis, which is easily done by raising the temperature; however, this destroys most polymerase enzymes. The solution was to isolate a DNA polymerase from a thermophilic, or heat-loving bacterium. *Thermus aquaticus,* found in the hot springs in Yellowstone National Park, was an ideal candidate. The enzyme produced from the bacterium, called **Taq polymerase** for the first few letters of the bacterium's name, allows the reaction mixture to be repeatedly heated without destroying enzyme activity.

The second innovation was the development of machines with heating blocks that can be rapidly cycled over large temperature ranges with very accurate temperature control.

Thus each cycle of PCR involves three steps:

1. Denaturation (high temperature)
2. Annealing of primers (low temperature)
3. Synthesis (intermediate temperature)

Steps 1 to 3 are repeated, and the two copies become four. It is not necessary to add any more polymerase, because the heating step does not harm Taq polymerase. Each complete cycle, which takes only 1–2 min, doubles the number of DNA molecules. After 20 cycles, a single fragment produces more than a million (2^{20}) copies!

In this way, the process of PCR allows the **amplification** of a single DNA fragment from a small amount of a complex mixture of DNA. This result is similar to what is isolated using molecular cloning, but in the case of PCR, the DNA cannot be reintroduced directly into a cell. The PCR product can be analyzed using electrophoresis, cloned into a vector for other manipulations, or directly sequenced. The size of the fragment that can be synthesized in this way is limited, but it has been adapted for an amazing number of uses.

PCR has many applications

PCR, now fully automated, has revolutionized many aspects of science and medicine because it allows for the investigation of minute samples of DNA. In criminal investigations, DNA fingerprints can now be prepared from the cells in a tiny speck of dried blood or from the tissue at the base of a single human hair. In medicine, physicians can detect genetic defects in very early embryos by collecting a single cell and amplifying its DNA. Due to its sensitivity, speed, and ease of use, technicians now routinely use PCR methods for these applications.

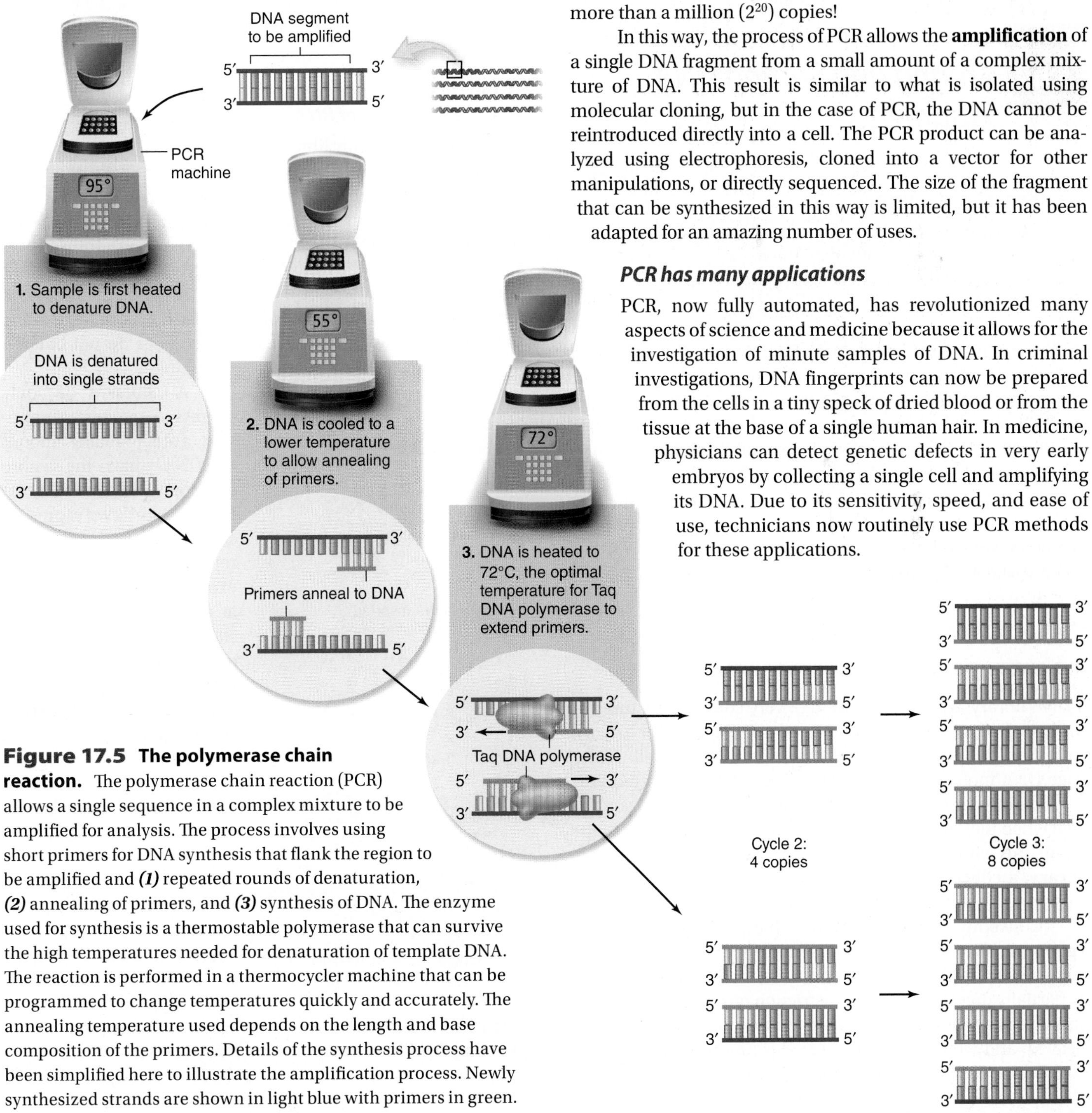

Figure 17.5 The polymerase chain reaction. The polymerase chain reaction (PCR) allows a single sequence in a complex mixture to be amplified for analysis. The process involves using short primers for DNA synthesis that flank the region to be amplified and *(1)* repeated rounds of denaturation, *(2)* annealing of primers, and *(3)* synthesis of DNA. The enzyme used for synthesis is a thermostable polymerase that can survive the high temperatures needed for denaturation of template DNA. The reaction is performed in a thermocycler machine that can be programmed to change temperatures quickly and accurately. The annealing temperature used depends on the length and base composition of the primers. Details of the synthesis process have been simplified here to illustrate the amplification process. Newly synthesized strands are shown in light blue with primers in green.

PCR has even been used to analyze mitochondrial DNA from the early human species *Homo neanderthalensis*. This application provided the first glimpse of data from extinct related species.

Learning Outcomes Review 17.3

The polymerase chain reaction (PCR) is a procedure that allows amplification of specific DNA sequences in vitro. PCR quickly produces a large amount of a specific DNA sequence from a small amount of starting material.

■ *In what ways are PCR and DNA replication similar? How do they differ?*

17.4 Storing and Sorting DNA Fragments

Learning Outcomes

1. *Describe how a DNA library is constructed and how you can find a specific clone in a library.*
2. *Explain the utility of making cDNA from RNA.*

So far we have considered single fragments of DNA that can be isolated and amplified using either restriction endonuclease digests that are inserted into plasmids and introduced into cells or PCR. Using these two methods, a large number of different DNA fragments can be isolated. Storing and sorting different DNA fragments requires a DNA library. It is also possible to isolate all the RNA in a specific tissue at a specific time and convert it to DNA fragments, which represent the expressed genes. These DNA libraries contain only DNA that is expressed as RNA in the cell.

DNA libraries may contain the entire genome of an organism

A DNA library is a representation of very complex mixtures in DNA, such as an entire genome, in a form that is easier to work with than the enormous chromosomes within a cell. If the huge DNA molecules in chromosomes can be converted into random fragments and inserted into a vector, such as plasmids, then when they are propagated in a host they will together represent the whole genome. This aggregate is termed a **DNA library,** a collection of DNAs in a vector that taken together represent the complex mixture of DNA (figure 17.6).

Conceptually the simplest possible kind of DNA library is a **genomic library**—a representation of the entire genome in a vector. Many copies of this genome are randomly fragmented by partially digesting it with a restriction enzyme that cuts frequently. By not cutting the DNA to completion, not all sites are cleaved, and which sites are cleaved is random. The random

fragments are then inserted into vectors and introduced into host cells. Genomic libraries are usually constructed in BACs.

A variety of different kinds of libraries can be made depending on the source DNA used. Any particular clone in the library contains only a single DNA, and all of them together make up the library. Keep in mind that unlike a library full of books, which is organized and catalogued, a DNA library is a random collection of overlapping DNA fragments. We explore how to find a sequence of interest in this random collection later in the chapter.

 Data analysis The human genome contains 3 billion base-pairs. If you construct a BAC library of the human genome with 500-bp fragments of DNA, what is the minimum number of clones in your library?

Using reverse transcriptase to make a DNA copy of RNA

In addition to genomic libraries, investigators often wish to isolate only the *expressed* part of genes. The structure of eukaryotic genes is such that the mRNA may be much smaller than the gene itself due to the presence of introns in the gene. After transcription by RNA polymerase II, the primary transcript is spliced to produce the mRNA (see chapter 15). Because of this, genomic libraries, which are crucial to understanding the structure of the gene, are not of much use if we want to express the gene in a bacterial species, whose genes do not contain introns and have no mechanism for splicing.

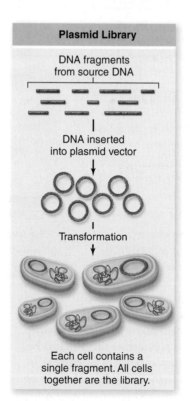

Figure 17.6
Creating DNA libraries.

A library of only expressed sequences represents a much smaller amount of DNA than the entire genome. The starting point for a DNA library of expressed sequences is isolated mRNA representing the genes expressed in a specific tissue at a specific developmental stage. Such a library of expressed sequences is made possible by the use of another enzyme: **reverse transcriptase.**

Reverse transcriptase was isolated from a class of viruses called retroviruses. The life cycle of a retrovirus requires making a DNA copy from its RNA genome. We can take advantage of the activity of the retrovirus enzyme to make DNA copies from isolated mRNA. DNA copies of mRNA are called **complementary DNA (cDNA)** (figure 17.7).

A cDNA library is made by first isolating mRNA from genes being expressed and then using the reverse transcriptase enzyme to make cDNA from the mRNA. The cDNA is then used to make a library, as mentioned earlier. These cDNA libraries are commonly made to represent the genes expressed in many different tissues or cells. Although all genomic libraries made from an individual will be identical, cDNA libraries from the same cells at different developmental stages or cells from different tissues will each be distinct. Questions about which genes influence physiological responses to the environment or development in an organism can be answered by comparing cDNA libraries.

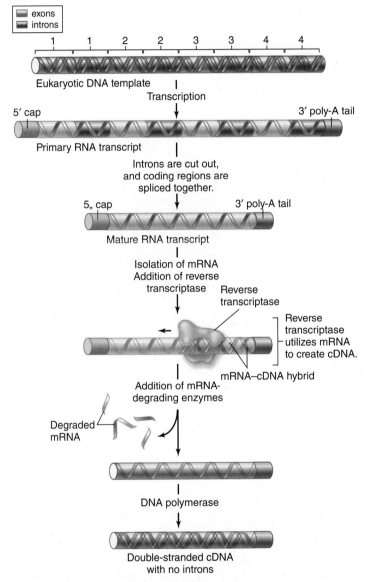

Figure 17.7 The formation of cDNA. A mature mRNA transcript is usually much smaller than the gene due to the loss of intron sequences by splicing. mRNA is isolated from the cytoplasm of a cell, which the enzyme reverse transcriptase uses as a template to make a DNA strand complementary to the mRNA. That newly made strand of DNA is the template for the enzyme DNA polymerase, which assembles a complementary DNA strand along it, producing cDNA—a double-stranded DNA version of the intron-free mRNA.

? Inquiry question Suppose you wanted a copy of a section of a eukaryotic genome that included the introns and exons. Would the creation of cDNA be a good way to go about this? Explain.

Learning Outcomes Review 17.4

DNA libraries are representations of complex mixtures of DNA, such as an entire genome or all the genes expressed in a tissue, stored in a host–vector system.

■ *How does a gene's sequence in a cDNA library compare with the genomic sequence of the gene?*

17.5 Analyzing and Creating DNA Differences

Learning Outcomes

1. *Explain the Southern blotting method of identifying genes.*
2. *Analyze and interpret the results of DNA fingerprinting.*
3. *Outline how DNA mutations can be created using recombinant DNA technology.*

Although all members of a species have the same genes, the alleles of these genes differ, contributing to variation among individuals. Advances in studying and manipulating DNA have led to new approaches to differentiating among alleles, which can be useful in identifying individuals. Closely related species have very similar genes that can also be distinguished with DNA analysis. In addition, DNA technology is used to create mutant alleles of a gene in an individual to better understand gene function. In this section we explore DNA analysis methods with a broad range of applications.

DNA differences can be detected using blotting methods

Once a gene has been cloned, it may be used as a probe to identify the same gene in a DNA library. Any single-stranded nucleic acid (DNA or RNA) can be tagged with a radioactive label or with another detectable label, such as a fluorescent dye. This can then be used as a probe to identify its complement in a complex mixture of DNA or RNA. This renaturing is termed *hybridization* because the combination of labeled probe and unlabeled DNA form a hybrid molecule through base-pairing.

A probe may also be used to identify the same or a similar gene in DNA isolated from a cell or tissue in the same or related

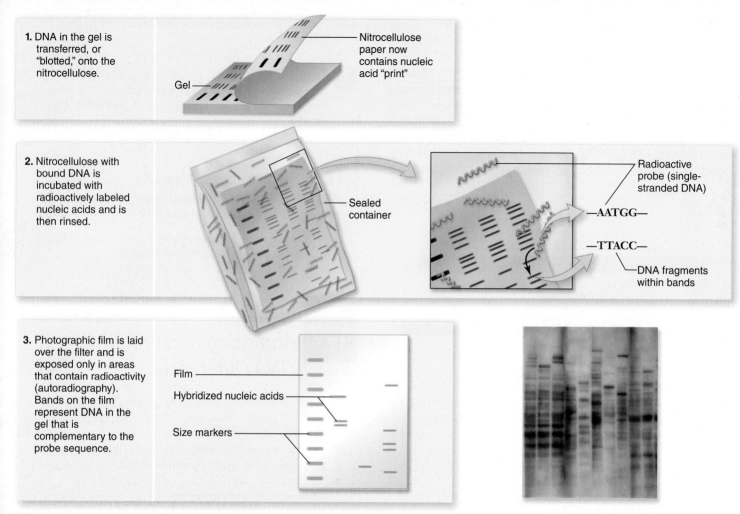

1. DNA in the gel is transferred, or "blotted," onto the nitrocellulose.

Gel

Nitrocellulose paper now contains nucleic acid "print"

2. Nitrocellulose with bound DNA is incubated with radioactively labeled nucleic acids and is then rinsed.

Sealed container

Radioactive probe (single-stranded DNA)

—AATGG—

—TTACC—

DNA fragments within bands

3. Photographic film is laid over the filter and is exposed only in areas that contain radioactivity (autoradiography). Bands on the film represent DNA in the gel that is complementary to the probe sequence.

Film

Hybridized nucleic acids

Size markers

Figure 17.8 **The Southern blot procedure.** Edwin M. Southern developed this procedure in 1975 to enable DNA fragments of interest to be visualized in a complex sample containing many other fragments of similar size. In steps 1–3, the DNA is separated on a gel, and then transferred ("blotted") onto a solid support medium such as nitrocellulose paper or a nylon membrane and denatured with alkaline chemicals into single strands. Sequences of interest can be detected by using a radioactively labeled probe. This probe (usually several hundred nucleotides in length) of single-stranded DNA (or an mRNA complementary to the gene of interest) is incubated with the filter containing the DNA fragments. All DNA fragments that contain nucleotide sequences complementary to the probe will form hybrids with the probe. Only a short segment of the probe and the complementary sequence are shown in step 3. The fragments differ in size, with the smallest moving the farthest in the gel. The fragments of interest are then detected using photographic film. A representative image is shown. The use of film for detection is being replaced by phosphor imagers, computer-controlled devices that have electronic sensors for light or radioactive emissions.

species (figure 17.8). In this procedure, called a **Southern blot,** DNA from the sample is cleaved into fragments with a restriction endonuclease, and the fragments are separated by gel electrophoresis. The double-stranded helix of each DNA fragment is then denatured into single strands by making the pH of the gel basic. Then the gel is "blotted" with a sheet of filter paper, transferring some of the DNA strands to the sheet.

Next, the filter is incubated with a labeled probe consisting of purified, single-stranded DNA corresponding to a specific gene (or mRNA transcribed from that gene). Any fragment that has a nucleotide sequence complementary to the probe's sequence hybridizes with the probe (see figure 17.8).

This kind of blotting technique has also been adapted for use with RNA and proteins. When mRNA is separated by electrophoresis, the technique is called a **Northern blot.** The methodology is the same except for the starting material (mRNA instead of DNA) and that no denaturation step is required. Proteins can also be separated by electrophoresis and blotted by a procedure called a **Western blot.** In this case both the electrophoresis and the detection step are different from Southern blotting. The detection, in this case, requires an antibody that can bind to one protein.

The names of these techniques all go back to the original investigator, the British biologist Edwin M. Southern; the Northern and Western blotting names were word play on Southern's name using the cardinal points of the compass.

DNA fingerprinting is used to identify particular genomes

In some cases, an investigator wants to do more than find a specific gene, but instead is looking for variation in the genes of different individuals. Identifying differences can be important in diagnosing a genetic disease, establishing biological relationship, identifying

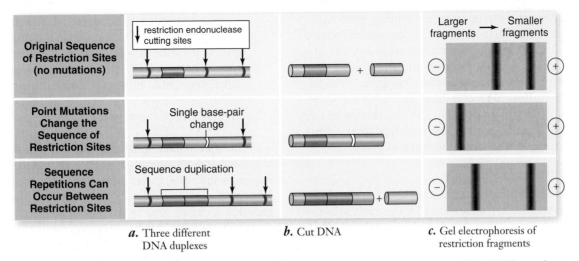

a. Three different
DNA duplexes

b. Cut DNA

c. Gel electrophoresis of
restriction fragments

Figure 17.9 **Restriction fragment length polymorphism (RFLP) analysis.** *a.* Three samples of DNA differ in their restriction sites due to a single base-pair substitution in one case and a sequence duplication in another case. *b.* When the samples are cut with a restriction endonuclease, different numbers and sizes of fragments are produced. *c.* Gel electrophoresis separates the fragments, and different banding patterns result.

the remains of missing persons or victims of a mass disaster, or convicting or exonerating an individual accused of a crime. Early on, **restriction fragment length polymorphisms,** or **RFLPs,** were most commonly used to distinguish individuals (figure 17.9).

Point mutations that change the sequence of DNA can eliminate sequences recognized by restriction enzymes or create new recognition sequences. For example, Huntington disease, cystic fibrosis, and sickle cell anemia are all caused by a single base-pair mutation and have associated RFLPs that have been used as molecular markers for diagnosis.

More commonly, short, repeated sequences vary among individuals. These variations are particularly useful in **DNA fingerprinting,** a process that compares DNA from several different regions of individual genomes for identification purposes. Short tandem repeats (STRs), typically 2–4 nt long, are not part of coding or regulatory regions of genes and mutate over generations so that the length of the repeats varies. We say that the population is **polymorphic** for these molecular markers. These markers can be used as DNA "fingerprints" in criminal investigations and other identification applications (figure 17.10).

STRs can be detected using RFLPs and Southern blotting, but currently PCR and automated DNA sequencing is the preferred method (see chapter 18 for DNA sequencing approaches). Since 1997, 13 STRs have been established as the standard of evidence for identification in court, and approved identification kits are available commercially. The 13 STRs form the basis of a federal profiling database called CODIS (Combined DNA Index System). New DNA fingerprints can be compared with those of known individuals in CODIS.

Since 1972, approximately 3000 people have been reported missing in California, and researchers in the California Department of Justice use STR fingerprints to try and match unidentified remains with samples from missing persons cases. This is done by comparing a database with the DNA fingerprints of relatives with a database with STR data obtained from all unidentified remains examined by California coroners. The goal is to provide closure for families and information for law enforcement officers.

DNA fingerprinting has also been used to exonerate wrongly convicted individuals who had been imprisoned for years before DNA analysis was widely available, as well as to identify individuals after catastrophes. After the September 11, 2001, attacks on the World Trade Centers in New York, DNA fingerprinting was the only means for identifying some of the victims. The DNA Shoah Project uses DNA fingerprinting to reunite families separated during the Holocaust. After a devastating earthquake in the Republic of Haiti in 2010, DNA fingerprinting was used to reunite 13 children with their families.

DNA differences can be created to determine gene function

In addition to identifying differences in DNA, recombinant technologies can be used to create differences. Creating

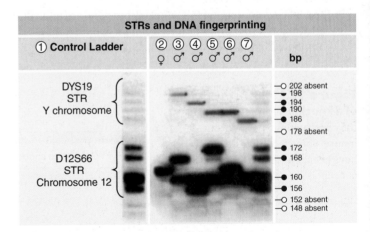

Figure 17.10 **Using STRs and DNA fingerprinting to identify individuals.** A Y-chromosome STR distinguishes between men and women *(top)* because it is absent in women *(column 2)*. The STR is different lengths in men, depending on the number of repeats (columns 3–7). A second STR found on chromosome 12 appears in both men and women *(bottom)*.

differences is a way to determine gene function. One of the most important technologies for research purposes is **in vitro mutagenesis**—the ability to create mutations at any site in a cloned gene to examine their effect on function. Rather than depending on mutations induced by chemical agents or radiation in intact organisms, which is time- and labor-intensive, the DNA itself is directly manipulated. The ultimate use of this approach is to be able to replace the wild-type gene with a mutant copy to test the function of the mutated gene.

"Knockout" mice

In mice, in vitro mutagenesis produces **knockout mice** in which a known gene is inactivated ("knocked out"). The effect of loss of this function is then assessed in the adult mouse, or if it is lethal, the stage of development at which function fails can be determined. The idea is simple, but the technology is quite complex. A streamlined description of the steps in this type of experiment are outlined as follows and illustrated in figure 17.11:

1. The cloned gene is disrupted by replacing it with a marker gene using recombinant DNA techniques. The marker gene codes for resistance to the antibiotic neomycin in bacteria, which allows mouse cells to survive when grown in a medium containing the related drug G418. The construction is done such that the marker gene is flanked by the DNA normally flanking the gene of interest in the chromosome.

2. The interrupted gene is introduced into **embryonic stem cells (ES cells).** These cells are derived from early embryos and can develop into different adult tissues. In these cells, the gene can recombine with the chromosomal copy of the gene based on the flanking DNA. This is the same kind of recombination used to map genes (see chapter 13). The knockout gene with the drug resistance gene does not have an origin of replication, and thus it will be lost if no recombination occurs. Cells are grown in medium containing G418 to select for recombination events. (Only those containing the marker gene can grow in the presence of G418.)

3. The ES cells containing the knocked-out gene are injected into an embryo early in its development, which is then implanted into a pseudopregnant female (one that has

been mated with a vasectomized male and as a result has a receptive uterus). The pups from this female have one copy of the gene of interest knocked out, and the phenotype is characterized. If the mutation is recessive and not lethal, transgenic animals can then be crossed to generate homozygous lines. These homozygous lines can be analyzed for phenotypes.

In conventional genetics, genes are identified based on mutants that show a particular phenotype. Molecular genetic techniques are then used to find the gene and isolate a molecular clone for analysis. The use of knockout mice is an example of **reverse genetics:** A cloned gene of unknown function is used to make a mutant that is deficient in that gene. A geneticist can then assess the effect on the entire organism of eliminating a single gene.

Sometimes this approach leads to surprises, such as happened when the gene for the p53 tumor suppressor was knocked out. Because this protein is found mutated in many human cancers and plays a key role in the regulation of the cell cycle (see chapter 10), it was thought to be essential—the knockout was expected to be lethal in the embryo. Instead, the mice were born normal; that is, development had proceeded normally. These mice do have a phenotype, however; they exhibit an increased incidence of tumors in a variety of tissues as they age.

RNA interference—RNAi

RNA interference (RNAi) provides another experimental approach to knockdown or knockout expression of a gene of interest. Unlike knockout mutations, which permanently alter the DNA, RNAi can target a specific RNA sequence so it is degraded and not translated into protein. Details of the mechanism of RNAi are presented in chapter 15. RNAi is used to determine the function of a gene in many organisms, including the nematode *Caenorhabditis elegans*. Silencing of the expression of a gene is initiated when double-stranded RNA (dsRNA) is inserted into cells. Three methods are successfully used to insert dsRNA into *C. elegans* worms; injecting dsRNA, soaking worms in dsRNA, and feeding worms *E. coli* that express the desired dsRNA.

The *C. elegans* genome has been fully sequenced. Coupling the feeding approach with library construction, it is now possible to test most of the genes in the genome. A library of

Figure 17.11 Construction of a knockout mouse. Steps in the construction of a knockout mouse. Some technical details have been omitted, but the basic concept is shown.

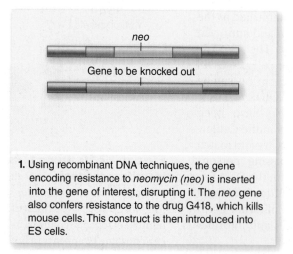

1. Using recombinant DNA techniques, the gene encoding resistance to *neomycin (neo)* is inserted into the gene of interest, disrupting it. The *neo* gene also confers resistance to the drug G418, which kills mouse cells. This construct is then introduced into ES cells.

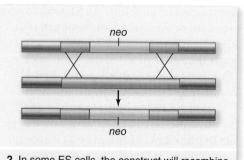

2. In some ES cells, the construct will recombine with the chromosomal copy of the gene to be knocked out. This replaces the chromosomal copy with the *neo* disrupted construct. This is the equivalent to a double crossover event in a genetic cross.

16,757 *E. coli* colonies contains 86% of the *C. elegans* genes that can be used to feed worms. Unlike knockout mutations, RNAi most often knocks down, but does not completely turn off a gene. The advantage to RNAi is that it works very quickly, and changes in phenotype provide information about the function of the gene that is knocked down.

Learning Outcomes Review 17.5

The Southern blotting technique allows identification of a target DNA sequence by separating single-stranded DNA fragments and hybridizing fragments of interest with a labeled probe. Genetic variation among individuals, including variation in STRs, can be used to differentiate individuals by separating RFLPs using gel electrophoresis. Conversely, variation can be created among individuals using recombinant DNA.

■ *Propose a strategy for distinguishing your DNA from your neighbor's, given restriction endonucleases, probes for the relevant RFLPs, and a well-equipped molecular biology lab.*

17.6 *Medical Applications*

Learning Outcomes

1. *Explain how recombinant DNA can be used in vaccine production.*
2. *Evaluate potential problems of gene therapy.*

The ability to clone individual genes for analysis ushered in an era of unprecedented advancement in research. The early days of genetic engineering led to a rash of start-up companies, many of which are no longer in business. At the same time, all of the major pharmaceutical companies either began research in this area or actively sought to acquire smaller companies with promising technology. The number of medical applications of this technology are far too numerous to mention here, but we highlight a few. Agricultural applications are discussed in the following section.

Eukaryotic genes can be expressed in bacterial cells

Bacterial cells can produce eukaryotic proteins if the differences in the control of transcription and translation discussed in chapter 16 are carefully considered and controlled. In 1982, the human insulin gene was first successfully expressed in *E. coli*. This was a technological breakthrough because individuals with diabetes who required insulin injections to regulate their blood glucose levels could now obtain human insulin more easily and cheaply via bacterial production than from the older method of extraction from pigs' pancreases. To successfully produce insulin in cultured *E. coli* cells, three challenges had to be met (figure 17.12):

1. A eukaryotic promoter is not recognized by the bacterial cellular machinery.
   The eukaryotic insulin promoter gene was inserted in a bacterial plasmid with a bacterial promoter at the 5′ end of the gene.
2. Eukaryotic genes have introns that bacteria cannot excise because they lack posttranscriptional modification.
   The regions of the insulin gene that coded for introns were removed before the gene was spliced into the bacterial plasmid.
3. The insulin peptide undergoes posttranslational modification that excises part of the peptide, creating two peptide sequences held together by a disulfide bond.
   Two DNA sequences that code for only the final, modified peptides were cloned into different plasmids and inserted into two different *E. coli*. The peptides are produced in two separate cultures, purified, and then combined to make human insulin.

Recombinant DNA may simplify vaccine production

Another area of potential significance involves the use of genetic engineering to produce vaccines against communicable diseases. Three types of vaccines are under investigation: *subunit vaccines, DNA vaccines,* and *plant-based vaccines.*

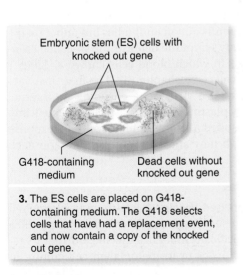

G418-containing medium   Dead cells without knocked out gene

Embryonic stem (ES) cells with knocked out gene

3. The ES cells are placed on G418-containing medium. The G418 selects cells that have had a replacement event, and now contain a copy of the knocked out gene.

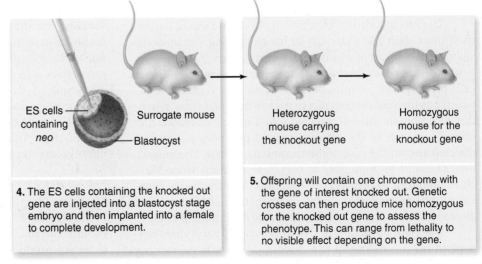

ES cells containing *neo*   Surrogate mouse   Blastocyst

Heterozygous mouse carrying the knockout gene

Homozygous mouse for the knockout gene

4. The ES cells containing the knocked out gene are injected into a blastocyst stage embryo and then implanted into a female to complete development.

5. Offspring will contain one chromosome with the gene of interest knocked out. Genetic crosses can then produce mice homozygous for the knocked out gene to assess the phenotype. This can range from lethality to no visible effect depending on the gene.

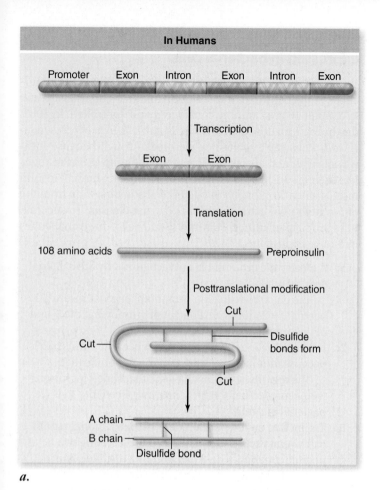

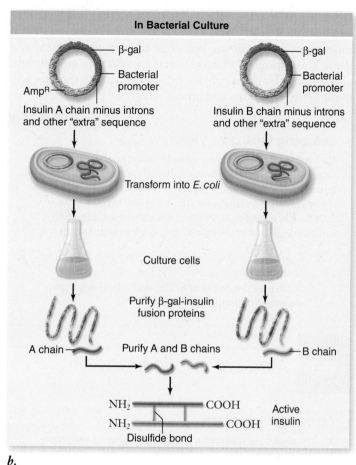

Figure 17.12 Genetically engineering *E. coli* to manufacture human insulin. Three modifications were required in bacterial culture (b): (1) eukaryotic promoters do not work in bacteria, (2) bacteria lack posttranscriptional modification and cannot remove introns, and (3) bacteria lack posttranscriptional modification so the single polypeptide could not be cleaved into two polypeptides.

Subunit vaccines

Subunit vaccines may be developed against pathogens, including the viruses that cause herpes and hepatitis and the parasitic protist that causes malaria. Genes encoding a part, or subunit, of a protein on the surface of the pathogen are cloned, inserted into a vector, and used to produce the vaccine. For example, genes encoding part of the polysaccharide coat of the herpes simplex virus or hepatitis B virus are spliced into a fragment of the vaccinia (cowpox) virus genome (figure 17.13).

The vaccinia virus, which British physician Edward Jenner used more than 200 years ago in his pioneering vaccinations against smallpox, is now used as a vector to carry the herpes or hepatitis viral coat gene into cultured mammalian cells. These cells produce many copies of the recombinant vaccinia virus, which has the outside coat of a herpes or hepatitis virus. When this recombinant virus is injected into a mouse or rabbit, the immune system of the infected animal produces antibodies directed against the coat of the recombinant virus. The animal then develops an immunity to herpes or hepatitis virus. Vaccines produced in this way are harmless because the vaccinia virus is benign, and only a small fragment of the DNA from the disease-causing virus is introduced via the recombinant virus.

The great attraction of this approach is that it does not depend on the nature of the disease. Malaria is caused by

Plasmodium falciparum, a mosquito-borne protist, and has been difficult to eradicate in developing countries. The subunit vaccine RTS,S/AS01E is the first successful vaccine for malaria and reduced the incidence of malaria in vaccinated individuals by almost a half. A wide variety of subunit vaccines are now being developed.

DNA vaccines

In 1995, the first clinical trials began to test a novel kind of **DNA vaccine,** one that depends not on antibodies but rather on the second arm of the body's immune defense, the so-called *cellular immune response,* in which blood cells known as killer T cells attack infected cells (see chapter 51). The first DNA vaccines spliced an influenza virus gene encoding an internal nucleoprotein into a plasmid, which was then injected into mice. The mice developed a strong cellular immune response to influenza. Although new and controversial, the approach offers great promise.

Plant-based vaccines

The Texas Plant-Expressed Vaccine Consortium has launched Project GreenVax, to use transgenic tobacco plants to produce subunit vaccines, specifically influenza vaccine. Currently vaccines are produced in eggs or in mammalian cell culture in

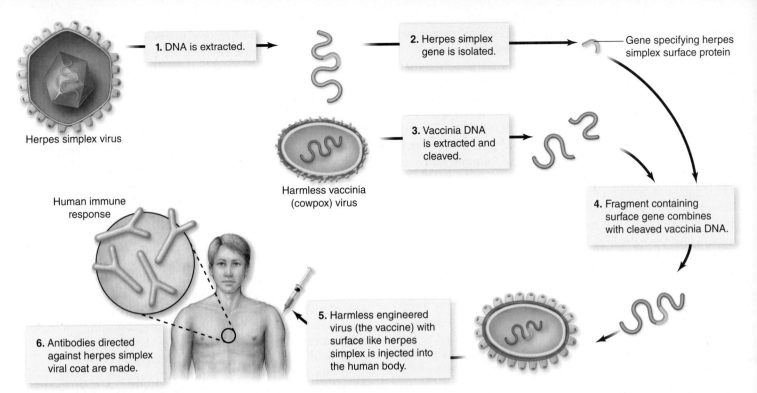

Figure 17.13 Strategy for constructing a subunit vaccine against herpes simplex. Recombinant DNA techniques can be used to construct vaccines for a single protein from a virus or bacterium. In this example, the protein is a surface protein from the herpes simplex virus.

1. DNA is extracted.

2. Herpes simplex gene is isolated.

Gene specifying herpes simplex surface protein

Herpes simplex virus

3. Vaccinia DNA is extracted and cleaved.

Harmless vaccinia (cowpox) virus

4. Fragment containing surface gene combines with cleaved vaccinia DNA.

Human immune response

5. Harmless engineered virus (the vaccine) with surface like herpes simplex is injected into the human body.

6. Antibodies directed against herpes simplex viral coat are made.

bioreactors (large fermentation tanks), which are costly and relatively slow processes. In contrast, large-scale, low-cost production is possible in plants that replace the bioreactors. Advantages include being able to quickly produce vaccines in response to new strains of influenza and to provide vaccines to parts of the world where availability is currently limited because of cost.

Project GreenVax facilities include processing areas to purify the vaccine produced by the plants. At some point, it may be possible to eliminate the purification processes and use edible plants so the vaccine could be delivered orally.

Gene therapy can treat genetic diseases directly

In 1990, researchers first attempted to combat genetic defects by the transfer of human genes. When a hereditary disorder is the result of a single defective gene, an obvious way to cure the disorder would be to add a working copy of the gene. This approach is being used in an attempt to combat cystic fibrosis, and it offers the potential of treating muscular dystrophy and a variety of other disorders (table 17.1).

Clinical trials for treating macular degeneration, a genetic eye disease that is a leading cause of blindness among adults in the United States, using an RNAi vector (see chapter 16) are promising. Individuals with a certain type of macular degeneration lose their sight because of the uncontrolled proliferation of blood vessels under the retina. For the patient, it is a lot like looking through a car windshield with broken wipers in the middle of a thunderstorm. RNAi gene therapy involves injection of double-stranded RNA coding for a gene necessary for blood vessel proliferation. The RNAi mechanism has the counterintuitive effect of suppressing production of the protein needed for blood vessel development, preventing progression of the disease. Other applications of RNAi to treat genetic disease have not developed as quickly. Despite the initial promise of RNAi, one of the key challenges is delivering the dsRNA to

TABLE 17.1	Diseases Being Treated in Clinical Trials of Gene Therapy
Disease	
Cancer (melanoma, renal cell, ovarian, neuroblastoma, brain, head and neck, lung, liver, breast, colon, prostate, mesothelioma, leukemia, lymphoma, multiple myeloma)	
SCID (severe combined immunodeficiency)	
Cystic fibrosis	
Gaucher disease	
Familial hypercholesterolemia	
Hemophilia	
Purine nucleoside phosphorylase deficiency	
α_1-Antitrypsin deficiency	
Fanconi anemia	
Hunter syndrome	
Chronic granulomatous disease	
Rheumatoid arthritis	
Peripheral vascular disease	
Acquired immunodeficiency syndrome (AIDS)	
Duchenne muscular dystrophy	
Macular degeneration (wet variety)	
Batten disease (neurological disorder)	

the targeted cells. The macular degeneration treatment works beautifully because the eye is readily accessible.

One disease that illustrates both the potential and the problems with gene therapy is **severe combined immunodeficiency disease (SCID).** This disease has multiple forms, including an X-linked form (X-SCID) and a form that lacks the enzyme adenosine deaminase (ADA-SCID).

Trials for both of these forms showed great initial promise, with patients exhibiting restoration of immune function. Unfortunately, problems arose in the case of the X-SCID trial when a patient developed a rare form of leukemia. Since that time, two other patients have developed the same leukemia, and it appears to be due to the gene therapy itself. The vector used to introduce the X-SCID gene integrated into the genome next to a proto-oncogene called *LMO2* in all three cases. Activation of this gene can cause childhood leukemia.

The insertion of a gene during gene therapy has always been a random event, and it has been a concern that the insertion could inactivate an essential gene, or turn on a gene inappropriately. That effect had not been observed prior to the X-SCID trial, despite a large number of genes introduced into blood cells in particular. For leukemia to occur in 15% of the patients treated implies that some influence of the genetic background associated with X-SCID potentiates this development. This possibility is supported by the observation that the ADA-SCID patients treated have not been affected thus far.

On the positive side, 15 children treated successfully are still alive, several of them after more than a decade after gene therapy, with functioning immune systems. On the negative side, three other children treated have developed leukemia. New approaches are being explored, and clinical trials for SCID have resumed.

Learning Outcomes Review 17.6

Recombinant DNA technology has allowed genes from eukaryotes, such as humans, to be isolated, inserted into vectors, and recombined into bacterial genomes, where the genes' products can be mass-produced. Gene therapy is the process of using genetic engineering to replace defective genes; however, in some cases unwanted effects result from random gene insertion.

■ *Create a flow chart to illustrate how a gene coding for an influenza coat protein can be used to create a plant-based influenza vaccine.*

17.7 Agricultural Applications

Learning Outcomes

1. *Compare recombinant technology techniques used in plants with those used in bacteria.*
2. *Describe the controversial issues in the use of GM plants.*

Perhaps no area of genetic engineering touches all of us so directly as the applications being used in agriculture today. Crops are being modified to resist disease, to be tolerant of herbicides, and for changes in nutritional and other content in a variety of ways.

Plant systems are also being used to produce pharmaceuticals by "biopharming," and domesticated animals are being genetically modified to produce biologically active compounds.

Pharmaceuticals can be produced by "biopharming"

The medicinal use of plants goes back as far as recorded history. In modern times, the pharmaceutical industry began by isolating biologically active compounds from plants. This approach began to change when in 1897, the Bayer company introduced acetylsalicylic acid, otherwise known as aspirin. This compound was a synthetic version of the compound salicylic acid, which was isolated from the bark of the white willow. The production of pharmaceuticals has since been dominated more by organic synthesis and less by the isolation of plant products.

One exception to this trend is cancer chemotherapeutic agents such as taxol, vinblastine, and vincristine, all of which were isolated from plant sources. In an interesting closing of the historical loop, the industry is now looking at using transgenic plants for the production of useful compounds.

The first human protein to be produced in plants was human serum albumin, which was produced in 1990 by both genetically engineered tobacco and potato plants. Since that time more than 20 proteins have been produced in transgenic plants. This first crop of transgenic pharmaceuticals is now undergoing regulatory examination.

Herbicide-resistant crops allow for no-till planting

Recently, broadleaf plants have been genetically engineered to be resistant to **glyphosate,** a powerful, biodegradable herbicide that kills most actively growing plants (figure 17.14). Glyphosate works by inhibiting an enzyme called 5-enolpyruvylshikimate-3-phosphate (EPSP) synthetase, which plants require to produce aromatic amino acids.

Humans do not make aromatic amino acids; we get them from our diet, so we are unaffected by glyphosate. To make glyphosate-resistant plants, scientists used a Ti plasmid to insert extra copies of the EPSP synthetase gene into plants. These engineered plants produce 20 times the normal level of EPSP synthetase, enabling them to synthesize proteins and grow despite glyphosate's suppression of the enzyme. In later experiments, a bacterial form of the EPSP synthetase gene that differs from the plant form by a single nucleotide was introduced into plants via Ti plasmids; the bacterial enzyme is not inhibited by glyphosate (see figure 17.14).

These advances are of great interest to farmers because a crop resistant to glyphosate does not have to be weeded through tilling—the field could simply be treated with the herbicide. Because glyphosate is a broad-spectrum herbicide, farmers no longer need to employ a variety of different herbicides, most of which kill only a few kinds of weeds. Furthermore, glyphosate breaks down readily in the environment, unlike many other herbicides commonly used in agriculture. A plasmid is actively being sought for the introduction of the EPSP synthetase gene into cereal plants that would also make them glyphosate-resistant.

At this point four important crop plants have been modified to be glyphosate-resistant: maize (corn), cotton, soybeans,

Hypothesis: *Petunias can acquire tolerance to the herbicide glyphosate by overexpressing EPSP synthase.*

Prediction: *Transgenic petunia plants with a chimeric EPSP synthase gene with strong promoter will be glyphosate tolerant.*

Test:

1. Use restriction enzymes and ligase to "paste" the cauliflower mosaic virus promoter (35S) to the EPSP synthase gene and insert the construct in Ti plasmids.

2. Transform Agrobacterium with the recombinant plasmid.

3. Infect petunia cells and regenerate plants. Regenerate uninfected plants as controls.

4. Challenge plants with glyphosate.

Result: *Glyphosate kills control plants, but not transgenic plants.*

Conclusion: *Additional EPSP synthase provides glyphosate tolerance.*

Further Experiments: *The transgenic plants are tolerant, but not resistant (note bleaching at shoot tip). How could you determine if additional copies of the gene would increase tolerance? Can you think of any downsides to expressing too much EPSP synthase in petunia?*

Figure 17.14 Genetically engineered herbicide resistance.

and canola. The use of glyphosate-resistant soy has been especially popular, accounting for 60% of the global area of genetically modified (GM) crops grown in nine countries worldwide. In the United States, 90% of soy currently grown is GM soy. Use of GM crops varies globally, with the Americas, led by the United States, the largest adopter. The area currently with the largest growth in the use of GM crops is Asia, and Europe has been the slowest to adopt their use.

Bt crops are resistant to some insect pests

Many commercially important plants are attacked by insects, and the usual defense against such attacks has been to apply insecticides. Over 40% of the chemical insecticides used today are targeted against boll weevils, bollworms, and other insects that eat cotton plants. Scientists have produced plants that are resistant to insect pests, removing the need to use many externally applied insecticides.

The approach is to insert into crop plants genes encoding proteins that are harmful to the insects that feed on the plants, but harmless to other organisms. The most commonly used protein is a toxin produced by the soil bacterium *Bacillus thuringiensis* (Bt toxin). When insects ingest Bt toxin, endogenous enzymes convert it into an insect-specific toxin, causing paralysis and death. Because these enzymes are not found in other animals, the protein is harmless to them.

The same four crops that have been modified for herbicide resistance have also been modified for insect resistance using the Bt toxin. The use of Bt maize is the second most common GM crop, representing 14% of global area of GM crops in

nine countries. The global distribution of these crops is also similar to the herbicide-resistant relatives.

Given the popularity of both of these types of crop modifications, it is not surprising that they have also been combined, so-called *stacked GM crops*, in both maize and cotton. Stacked crops now represent 9% of global area of GM crops.

Golden Rice shows the potential of GM crops

One of the successes of GM crops is the development of Golden Rice. The World Health Organization (WHO) estimates that vitamin A deficiency affects between 140 and 250 million preschool children worldwide, 250,000–500,000 of whom become blind. The deficiency is especially severe in developing countries where the major staple food is rice. Golden Rice has been genetically modified to produce β-carotene (provitamin A), which can be converted by enzymes in the body to vitamin A, thus alleviating the deficiency.

Golden Rice is named for its distinctive color imparted by the presence of β-carotene in the endosperm (the outer layer of rice that has been milled). Rice does not normally make β-carotene in endosperm tissue, but does produce a precursor, geranyl geranyl diphosphate, that can be converted by three enzymes, phytoene synthase, phytoene desaturase, and lycopene β-cyclase, to β-carotene. These three genes were engineered to be expressed in endosperm and introduced into rice to complete the biosynthetic pathway producing β-carotene in endosperm (figure 17.15).

This case of genetic engineering is interesting for two reasons. First, it introduces a new biochemical pathway in tissue of the transgenic plants. Second, it could not have been done by conventional breeding as no rice cultivar known produces these

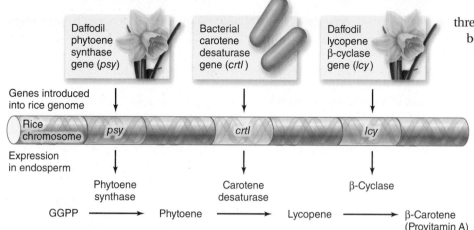

Figure 17.15 Construction of Golden Rice. Rice does not normally express the enzymes needed to synthesize β-carotene in endosperm. Three genes were added to the rice genome to allow expression of the pathway for β-carotene in endosperm. The source of the genes and the pathway for synthesis of β-carotene is shown. The result is Golden Rice, which contains enriched levels of β-carotene in endosperm.

enzymes in endosperm. The original constructs used two genes from daffodil and one from a bacterium (see figure 17.15). There are many reasons to expect failure in the introduction of a biochemical pathway without disrupting normal metabolism. That the original form of Golden Rice makes significant amounts of β-carotene in an otherwise healthy plant is impressive. A second-generation version that makes much higher levels of β-carotene has also been produced by using the gene for phytoene synthase from maize in place of the original daffodil gene.

Golden Rice was originally constructed in a public facility in Switzerland and made available for free with no commercial entanglements. Since its inception, Golden Rice has been improved on both by public groups and by industry scientists, and these improved versions are also being made available without commercial strings attached.

Marker assisted breeding accelerates breeding programs

High-yielding crops have a multitude of desirable traits. Breeders cross different plants to maximize desired gene combinations, but this is a very time-consuming process. **Marker assisted breeding** (MAB) combines classic plant breeding with molecular biology tools. Instead of screening for phenotypically obvious traits at maturity, breeders extract DNA from leaf tissue of young seedlings and screen for molecular markers (DNA sequences) that are associated with agriculturally important traits. Screening relies on the DNA fingerprinting techniques (described earlier in this chapter). Seedlings with the desired combination of molecular markers are raised to maturity and the remaining plants are discarded.

Molecular markers are often repetitive sequences, similar to the STRs used for fingerprinting. They are variants that tend to cosegregate with desirable traits, but the variation in the DNA is not necessarily in a gene known to code for that trait. For example, variation in the number of repeats in an STR near a corn gene coding for an enzyme that converts sugar to starch could be an indicator of the relative sweetness of the corn.

MAB is being used to breed for nematode resistance in soybeans. Fields of soybeans are being destroyed by this microscopic,

threadlike worm that bores into the roots of soybeans and use nutrients from the plant. Peking landraces of soybean from China are resistant to nematodes, but lack many of the traits in commercial lines that enhance yield and make it possible to mechanically harvest the soybeans. These plants are being bred with commercial lines, and molecular markers (MAB) are used to sort out promising offspring, saving vast amounts of time and growing space.

MAB is a tool that allows breeders to take advantage of the diversity in traditional breeding programs. The Food and Agricultural Organization of the United Nations proposes that MAB will play a significant role in breeding programs for crops as well as livestock, forestry, and fisheries globally.

GM crops raise a number of social issues

The adoption of GM crops has been resisted in some places for a variety of reasons. Some people have wondered about the safety of these crops for human consumption, the likelihood of introduced genes moving into wild relatives, and the possible loss of biodiversity associated with these crops.

Powerful forces have aligned on opposing sides in this debate. On the side in favor of the use of GM crops are the multinational companies that are utilizing this technology to produce seeds for the various GM crops and groups noting the benefits of GM crops like Golden Rice in feeding the developing world. On the other side are a variety of political organizations that are opposed to genetically modified foods. Scientists can be found on both sides of the controversy.

The controversy originally centered on the safety of introduced genes for human consumption. In the United States, this issue has been "settled" for the crops already mentioned, and a large amount of GM soy and maize is consumed in this country. Although some opponents still raise the issue of long-term use and allergic reactions, no negative effects have been documented so far. Existing crops will be monitored for adverse effects, and each new modification will require regulatory approval for human consumption.

Another concern is that genes of the GM crops will spread outside into non-GM crop, through gene flow. The amount of cross-pollination between plants of the same species varies. Soybeans tend to self-pollinate with limited outcrossing; but corn freely outcrosses, and so genes from GM plants more frequently move to non-GM corn plants. This is a concern for organic farmers with fields close to GM corn fields, as current regulations for organic certification exclude GM crops. The amount of outcrossing depends on the proximity of crops, wind speed, and direction, as well as temperature and humidity. For plants that depend on pollinators for reproduction, the range of species the pollinator visits and the distance it travels are also factors.

Gene flow can also occur between related species through hybridization. In the United States, at least 15 weedy species have hybridized with crop plants. For two of the major U.S. crops, corn and soybean, no closely related weedy species reproduce with them, so this is an unlikely mechanism for acquiring herbicide resistance. Sunflowers, however, were first domesticated in the United States, and the risk of a transgene moving into a weedy population is a concern. One study revealed that 10–33% of wild sunflowers had hybridized with domesticated varieties.

In the case of herbicide-resistant GM crop plants, the repeated application of a single herbicide over a number of years creates selective pressure on weedy species. Over time, weeds with resistance to the herbicide will increase in frequency, and the herbicide becomes ineffectual. Almost 200 weed species worldwide have acquired resistance to one or more herbicides. Management practices that reduce herbicide use and vary the herbicides used can slow the evolution of herbicide resistance.

Domesticated animals can also be genetically modified

Humans have been breeding and selecting domestic animals for thousands of years. With the advent of genetic engineering, this process can be accelerated, and genes can be introduced from other species.

The production of transgenic livestock is in an early stage, and it is hard to predict where it will go. At this point, one of the uses of biotechnology is not to construct transgenic animals, but to use DNA markers to identify animals and to map genes that are involved in such traits as palatability in food animals, texture of hair or fur, and other features of animal products. This information is then used in MAB. Molecular techniques combined with the ability to clone domestic animals (see chapter 19) could produce improved animals for economically desirable traits.

Transgenic animal technology has not been as successful as initially predicted. To date, no transgenic animal has been approved for human consumption. Early on, pigs were engineered to overproduce growth hormone in the hope that this would lead to increased and faster growth. These animals proved to have only slightly increased growth, and they had lower fat levels, which reduces flavor, as well as showing other deleterious effects.

One interesting idea for transgenics is the "Enviropig." This animal has been engineered with the gene for phytase under the control of a salivary gland-specific promoter. The enzyme phytase breaks down phosphorus in the feed and can reduce phosphate excretion by up to 65%. Phosphate is a major problem in pig waste, and reducing the amount of phosphate runoff into rivers and streams reduces the overgrowth of algae. Enviropigs can now be raised in Canada for research purposes, but it will likely be years before they make it to the consumer's table.

For over a decade, AquaBounty Technologies has been seeking approval from the Food and Drug Administration (FDA) to market its GM salmon that grows more rapidly than non-GM salmon because of a transgenic growth hormone gene (figure 17.16). The hormone gene was isolated from a related fish species, and there is no evidence that the protein could harm humans. The fish are all female triploids so they could not reproduce with wild relatives if they escaped into the wild, but they could compete with wild salmon for resources. The focus at the FDA was on whether or not to label the salmon as genetically modified in the grocery store, when in June 2011 the U.S. House of Representatives voted to ban the FDA from approving any GM salmon for human consumption. As with the Enviropig, GM salmon will not be on the menu any time soon.

a.

b.

Figure 17.16 Transgenic salmon grow more rapidly than wild salmon. *a.* The rate of growth in transgenic salmon compared with that for wild salmon. *b.* The size of the transgenic salmon is larger than a wild salmon of the same age.

Data analysis Based on the information in this figure, evaluate the claim that transgenic salmon are huge compared with wild salmon.

17.1 Recombinant DNA

Restriction endonucleases cleave DNA at specific sites.

DNA molecules fragmented by known type II restriction endonucleases can be recombined with other DNA cut with the same restriction endonucleases (figure 17.1).

Gel electrophoresis separates DNA fragments.

An electric field applied to a gel matrix causes DNA to migrate through the matrix, separating the DNA fragment by size. Smaller fragments migrate farther than large fragments (figure 17.2).

DNA ligase allows construction of recombinant molecules.

Just as in DNA replication, DNA ligase catalyzes formation of a phosphodiester bond between nucleotides, forming a recombinant molecule.

17.2 Introducing Foreign DNA into Cells

Transformation allows introduction of foreign DNA into cells.

Artificial transformation techniques introduce foreign DNA into bacterial and eukaryotic cells, which are then termed transgenic.

Host–vector systems allow propagation of foreign DNA in bacteria.

Plasmids and artificial chromosomes can be used as vectors. Foreign DNA is inserted using restriction enzymes and DNA ligase; once the vector is inside the host cell, it is replicated during the cell cycle.

Eukaryotic cell transformation is challenging.

Eukaryotic cells lack plasmids and cannot be transformed in the same way as bacteria. Other strategies have been developed and include injecting DNA into animal cells and using a bacterial pathogen to insert DNA into some plant cells (figure 17.4).

17.3 Amplifying DNA Without a Vector— The Polymerase Chain Reaction

PCR mimics DNA replication (figure 17.5).

The polymerase chain reaction (PCR) amplifies a single small DNA fragment using two short primers that flank the region to be amplified. Cyclic replication is accomplished via heating and cooling; a key factor is Taq polymerase, which is not denatured at high temperature.

PCR has many applications.

Because PCR can amplify even tiny amounts of DNA, it has many applications, ranging from DNA fingerprinting for forensics to genome sequencing of extinct species.

17.4 Storing and Sorting DNA Fragments

DNA libraries may contain the entire genome of an organism.

A DNA library is a complex mixture of DNAs collected into vectors that are randomly organized (figure 17.6).

A library can also be created for the expressed parts of the genome by isolating RNA and converting it to cDNA using the enzyme reverse transcriptase (figure 17.7).

17.5 Analyzing and Creating DNA Differences

DNA differences can be detected using blotting methods.

DNA can be reversibly denatured and renatured, resulting in single- and then double-stranded DNA. Renaturation of complementary strands from different sources is called hybridization. Known DNA can be labeled to identify complementary strands.

In Southern blotting, a complex mixture is separated by electrophoresis and transferred to filter paper (figure 17.8). Specific sequences of DNA can then be identified by hybridization. Similar techniques can identify mRNA (Northern blotting) and proteins (Western blotting).

DNA fingerprinting is used to identify particular genomes.

Regions of repetitive DNA sequences, including STRs, vary among individuals in terms of the number of repeats. This variation can be assessed using RFLPs to create distinct DNA fingerprints, which are used to identify individuals in criminal and missing person cases, as well as major disasters.

DNA differences can be created to determine gene function.

Reverse genetics approaches begin with a sequence of DNA and aim to find the function of that sequence. In knockout mice, a gene is inactivated by replacing the wild-type version with a mutant copy (figure 17.11).

RNAi can be used to knock down gene expression by inserting dsRNA into an organism. In this way, the function of the gene can be analyzed and clarified.

17.6 Medical Applications

Eukaryotic genes can be expressed in bacterial cells.

Bacterial production of human proteins, such as insulin, has allowed better results and has increased production to treat disease.

Recombinant DNA may simplify vaccine production.

Subunit vaccines produced in cultured cells have been shown to be effective in animals.

DNA vaccines, which alter the cellular immune response, are also promising. Both these approaches require further testing.

Gene therapy can treat genetic diseases directly.

Gene therapy involves inserting a normal gene to replace a defective one. Clinical trials for some therapies are underway, but the many challenges include safely inserting a foreign gene into the appropriate cells.

17.7 Agricultural Applications

Pharmaceuticals can be produced by "biopharming."

More than 20 proteins that are used as pharmaceuticals are being made by recombinant plants.

Herbicide-resistant crops allow for no-till planting.

Herbicide-resistant crops are widely used in the United States, reducing both the need for tilling and the associated fossil fuel consumption.

Bt crops are resistant to some insect pests.

Recombinant crops that produce Bt are resistant to insect damage.

Golden Rice shows the potential of GM crops.

Golden rice produces provitamin A, reducing blindness in developing countries where rice is a staple crop. Golden rice is an example of a not-for-profit effort to provide food security in the developing world.

Marker assisted breeding accelerates breeding programs.

By isolating DNA from the leaves of young seedlings in a breeding program and using DNA fingerprinting to compare individuals, only those with promising molecular markers are raised to maturity. This combination of conventional breeding with the use of molecular tools is called MAB and accelerates the rate of breeding programs substantially.

GM crops raise a number of social issues.

Concerns about GM plants include unintended allergic reactions to proteins inserted from a different organism, although no adverse affects have been documented yet. The spread of foreign genes into noncultivated plants in the environment through hybridization is being followed closely, and to date almost 200 weed species worldwide have acquired resistance to one or more herbicides.

Domesticated animals can also be genetically modified.

To date, results with transgenic animals have been mixed, and no recombinant meat or fish is currently available on grocery shelves.

UNDERSTAND

1. A recombinant DNA molecule is one that is

   a. produced through the process of crossing over that occurs in meiosis.
   b. constructed from DNA from different sources.
   c. constructed from novel combinations of DNA from the same source.
   d. produced through mitotic cell division.

2. What is the basis of separation of different DNA fragments by gel electrophoresis?

   a. The negative charge on DNA
   b. The size of the DNA fragments
   c. The sequence of the fragments
   d. The presence of a dye

3. The basic logic of organizing a genome into BAC libraries is to create

   a. a nested set of DNA fragments produced by restriction enzymes.
   b. a nested set of DNA fragments that each begin with different bases.
   c. primers to allow PCR amplification of the region between the primers.
   d. a nested set of DNA fragments that end with known bases.

4. A DNA library is

   a. an orderly array of all the genes within an organism.
   b. a collection of vectors.
   c. the collection of plasmids found within a single *E. coli.*
   d. a collection of DNA fragments representing the entire genome of an organism.

5. Molecular hybridization is used to

   a. generate cDNA from mRNA.
   b. introduce a vector into a bacterial cell.
   c. screen a DNA library.
   d. introduce mutations into genes.

6. In vitro mutagenesis is used to

   a. produce large quantities of mutant proteins.
   b. create mutations at specific sites within a gene.
   c. create random mutations within multiple genes.
   d. create organisms that carry foreign genes.

7. Insertion of a gene for a surface protein from a medically important virus such as herpes into a harmless virus is an example of

   a. a DNA vaccine.   c. gene therapy.
   b. reverse genetics.   d. a subunit vaccine.

8. What is a Ti plasmid?

   a. A vector that can transfer recombinant genes into plant genomes
   b. A vector that can be used to produce recombinant proteins in yeast
   c. A vector that is specific to cereal plants like rice and corn
   d. A vector that is specific to embryonic stem cells

APPLY

1. How is the gene for β-galactosidase used in the construction of a plasmid?

   a. The gene is a promoter that is sensitive to the presence of the sugar galactose.
   b. It is an origin of replication.
   c. It is a cloning site.
   d. It is a marker for insertion of DNA.

2. Which of the following statements is accurate for DNA replication in your cells, but not PCR?

   a. DNA primers are required.
   b. DNA polymerase is stable at high temperatures.
   c. Ligase is essential.
   d. dNTPs are necessary.

3. What potential problems must be considered in creating a transgenic bacterium with the human insulin gene to produce insulin?

   a. Introns in the human gene will not be processed after transcription.
   b. The bacterial cell will be unable to posttranslationally process the insulin peptide sequence.
   c. There is no way to get the bacterium to transcribe high levels of a human gene.
   d. Both a and b present problems.

SYNTHESIZE

1. Many human proteins, such as hemoglobin, are only functional as an assembly of multiple subunits. Assembly of these functional units occurs within the endoplasmic reticulum and Golgi apparatus of a eukaryotic cell. Discuss what limitations, if any, exist to the large-scale production of genetically engineered hemoglobin.

2. As a plant breeder your assignment is to integrate the resistance to root nematodes in a Chinese soybean into an otherwise robust soybean grown in Iowa. You have a set of STRs for both soybeans and information about which STRs have alleles that correspond with root nematode resistance. Using your knowledge of MAB and DNA fingerprinting, write a short proposal to your supervisor outlining a plan to breed for nematode resistance over the next three years.

ONLINE RESOURCE

www.ravenbiology.com

Understand, Apply, and Synthesize—enhance your study with animations that bring concepts to life and practice tests to assess your understanding. Your instructor may also recommend the interactive eBook, individualized learning tools, and more.

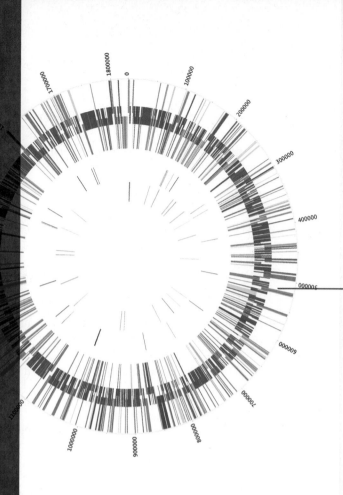

Chapter

Genomics

18

Chapter Contents

Introduction

The pace of discovery in biology in the last 30 years has been like the exponential growth of a population. Starting with the isolation of the first genes in the mid-1970s, researchers had accomplished the first complete genome sequence by the mid-1990s—that of the bacterial species Haemophilus influenzae, *shown in the picture (genes with similar functions are shown in the same color). By the turn of the 21st century, the molecular biology community had completed a draft sequence of the human genome. Put another way, scientific accomplishments moved from cloning a single gene, to determining the sequence of a million base-pairs in 20 years, then determining the sequence of 3 billion base-pairs in another 5 years, and now sequencing 20 billion base-pairs at one time. In the previous chapter you learned about the basic techniques of molecular biology. In this chapter you will see how those techniques have been applied to the analysis of whole genomes. This analysis integrates ideas from classical and molecular genetics with biotechnology, scaled and applied to whole genomes.*

18.1 Mapping Genomes

Learning Outcomes

1. *Distinguish between a genetic map and a physical map.*
2. *Explain how genetic and physical maps can be linked.*

We use maps to find our location, and depending on how accurately we wish to do this, we may use multiple maps with different resolutions. In genomics, we can locate a gene on a chromosome, in a subregion of a chromosome, and finally its precise location in the chromosome's DNA sequence. The DNA sequence level requires knowing the entire sequence of the genome, something that was once out of our reach technologically. Knowing the entire sequence is useless, however, without other kinds of maps; finding a single gene within the sequence of the human genome is like trying to find your house on a map of the world.

To overcome this difficulty, maps of genomes are constructed at different levels of resolution and using different kinds of information. We can distinguish between *genetic maps* and *physical maps*. **Genetic maps** are abstract maps that place the relative location of genes on chromosomes based on recombination frequency (see chapter 13). **Physical maps** use landmarks within DNA sequences, ranging from restriction sites (described in the preceding chapter) to the ultimate level of detail: the actual DNA sequence.

Different kinds of physical maps can be generated

To make sense of genome mapping, it is important to have physical landmarks on the genome that are at a lower level of resolution than the entire sequence. In fact, long before the Human Genome Project was even conceived, physical maps of DNA were needed as landmarks on cloned DNA. Two types of physical maps are (1) restriction maps, constructed using restriction enzymes and (2) chromosome-banding patterns, generated by cytological dye methods.

Restriction maps

Distances between "landmarks" on a physical map are measured in base-pairs (1000 base-pairs [bp] equal 1 kilobase [kb]). It is not necessary to know the DNA sequence of a segment of DNA in order to create a physical map, or to know whether the DNA encompasses information for a specific gene.

The first physical maps were created by cutting genomic DNA with different restriction enzymes, both singly and with combinations of enzymes (figure 18.1). The analysis of the patterns of fragments generated was used to generate a map.

In terms of larger pieces of DNA, this process is repeated and then used to put the pieces back together, based on size and overlap, into a contiguous segment of the genome, called a **contig.** Coincidently, the very first restriction enzymes to be isolated came from *Haemophilus,* which was also the first free-living genome to be completely sequenced.

Chromosome-banding patterns

Cytologists studying chromosomes with light microscopes found that by using different stains, they could produce reproducible patterns of bands on the chromosomes. In this way, they could identify all of the chromosomes and divide them into subregions based on banding pattern.

The use of different stains allows for the construction of a cytological map of the entire genome. These large-scale physical maps are like a map of an entire country, in that they encompass the whole genome, but at low resolution.

Cytological maps are used to characterize chromosomal abnormalities associated with human diseases, such as chronic myelogenous leukemia. In this disease, a reciprocal translocation occurs between chromosome 9 and

1. Multiple copies of a segment of DNA are cut with restriction enzymes.

2. The fragments produced by enzyme A only, by enzyme B only, and by enzymes A and B together are run side-by-side on a gel, which separates them according to size.

3. The fragments are arranged so that the smaller ones produced by the simultaneous cut can be grouped to generate the larger ones produced by the individual enzymes.

4. A physical map is constructed.

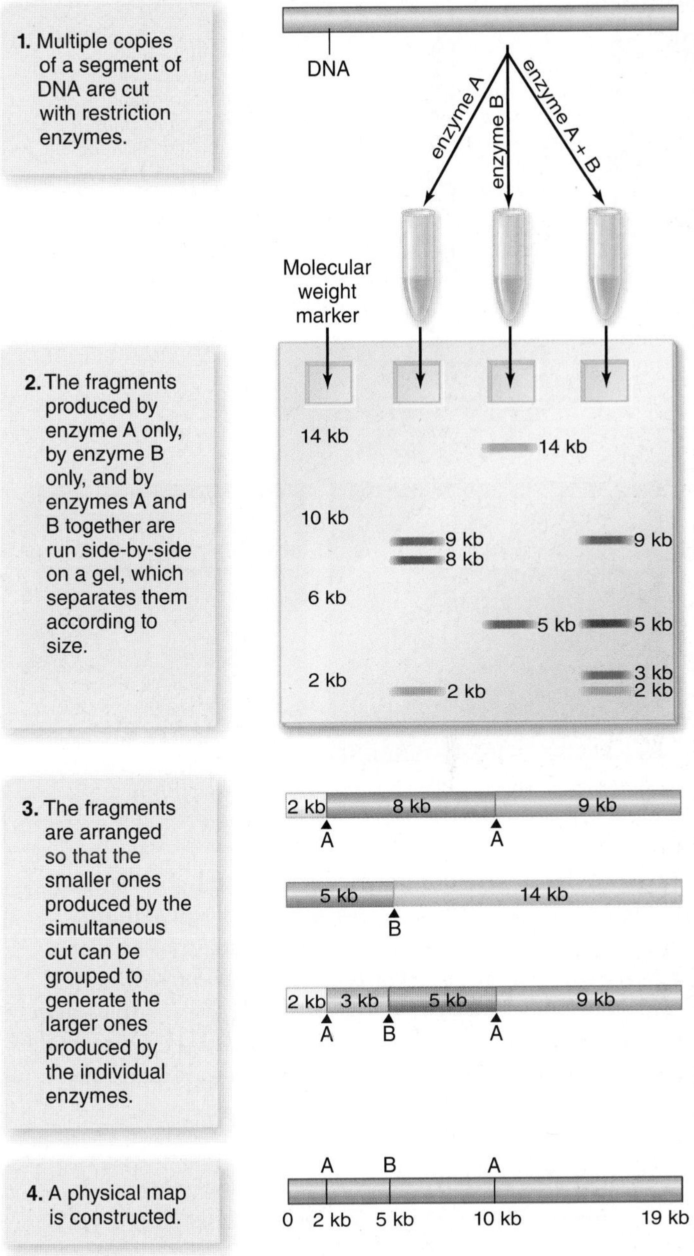

Figure 18.1 Restriction enzymes can be used to create a physical map. DNA is digested with two different restriction enzymes singly and in combination, then electrophoresed to separate the fragments. The location of sites can be deduced by comparing the sizes of fragments from the individual reactions with the combined reaction.

chromosome 22 (figure 18.2*a*), resulting in an altered form of tyrosine kinase that is always turned on, causing white blood cell proliferation.

The use of hybridization with cloned DNA has added to the utility of chromosome-banding analysis. In this case, because the hybridization involves whole chromosomes, it is called *in situ hybridization.* It is done using fluorescently labeled probes, and so its complete name is **fluorescence in situ hybridization (FISH)** (figure 18.2*b*).

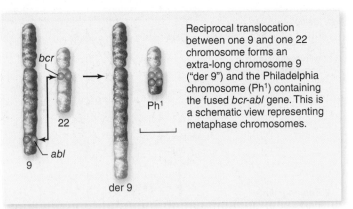

Reciprocal translocation between one 9 and one 22 chromosome forms an extra-long chromosome 9 ("der 9") and the Philadelphia chromosome (Ph¹) containing the fused *bcr-abl* gene. This is a schematic view representing metaphase chromosomes.

a.

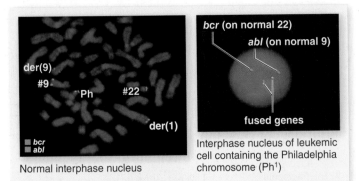

b.

Figure 18.2 Use of fluorescence in situ hybridization (FISH) to correlate cloned DNA with cytological maps.
a. Karyotype of human chromosomes showing the translocation between chromosomes 9 and 22. *b.* FISH using a *bcr* (green) and *abl* (red) probe. The yellow color indicates the fused genes (red plus green fluorescence combined). The *abl* gene and the fused *bcr-abl* gene both encode a tyrosine kinase, but the fused gene is always expressed.

? Inquiry question Why are there only three colored spots on the karyotype for two different genes?

Sequence-tagged sites provide a common language for physical maps

The construction of a physical map for a large genome requires the efforts of many laboratories in different locations. A variety of difficulties arose in comparing data from different labs, as well as integrating different types of landmarks used on physical and genetic maps.

In the early days of the Human Genome Project, this problem was addressed by the creation of a common molecular language that could be used to describe the different types of landmarks.

Defining common markers

Since all genetic information is ultimately based on DNA sequence, it was important for this common language to be sequence-based, but not to require generating a large amount of sequence for any landmark. The solution was the **sequence-tagged site,** or **STS.** This site is a small stretch of DNA that is unique in the genome, that is, it only occurs once.

The boundary of the STS is defined by PCR primers, so the presence of the STS can be identified by PCR using any DNA as a template (see chapter 17). These sites need to be only 200–500 bp long, an amount of sequence that can be determined easily. The STS can contain any other kind of landmark—for example, part of a cloned gene that has been genetically mapped, or a restriction site that is polymorphic. Any marker that has been mapped can be converted to an STS by sequencing only 200–500 bp of the entire marker.

The use of STSs

As maps are generated, new STSs are identified and added to a database that indicates the sequence of the STS, its location in the genome, and the PCR primers needed to identify it. Any researcher is then able to identify the presence or absence of any STS in the DNA that he or she is analyzing.

Fragments of DNA can be pieced together using STSs by identifying overlapping regions in fragments. Because of the high density of STSs in the human genome and the relative ease of identifying an STS in a DNA clone, investigators were able to develop physical maps on the huge scale of the 3.2-gigabase genome in the mid-1990s (figure 18.3). STSs provide a scaffold for assembling genome sequences.

Genetic maps provide a link to phenotypes

The first genetic (linkage) map was made in 1911 when Alfred Sturtevant mapped five genes in *Drosophila,* as described in chapter 13. Distances on a genetic map reflect the frequency of recombination between genes and are measured in centimorgans (cM) in honor of the geneticist Thomas Hunt Morgan. One centimorgan corresponds to 1% recombination frequency between two loci. Over 15,000 genes have been mapped on the *Drosophila* genome.

Linkage mapping can be done without knowing the DNA sequence of a gene. Computer programs make it possible to create a linkage map for a thousand genes at a time. But a few limitations to genetic maps still exist. One is that distances between genes determined by recombination frequencies do not directly correspond to physical distance on a chromosome. The sequence and conformation of DNA between genes varies, as does the frequency of recombination. Another limitation is that not all genes have obvious phenotypes that can be followed in segregating crosses.

The human genetic map is quite dense, with a marker roughly every 1 cM. This level of detail would have been unheard of 20 years ago, and it was made possible by development of molecular markers that do not cause a phenotype change.

The most common type of markers are short repeated sequences, called short tandem repeats, or STR loci, that differ in repeat length between individuals. These repeats are identified by using PCR to amplify the region containing the repeat, then analyzing the products using electrophoresis. Once a map is constructed using these markers, genes with alleles that cause a disease state can be mapped relative to the

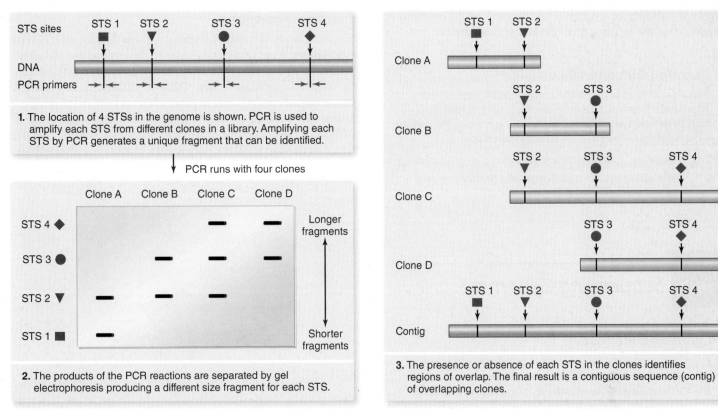

1. The location of 4 STSs in the genome is shown. PCR is used to amplify each STS from different clones in a library. Amplifying each STS by PCR generates a unique fragment that can be identified.

PCR runs with four clones

2. The products of the PCR reactions are separated by gel electrophoresis producing a different size fragment for each STS.

3. The presence or absence of each STS in the clones identifies regions of overlap. The final result is a contiguous sequence (contig) of overlapping clones.

Figure 18.3 Creating a physical map with sequence-tagged sites. The presence of landmarks called sequence-tagged sites, or STSs, in the human genome made it possible to begin creating a physical map large enough in scale to provide a foundation for sequencing the entire genome. *(1)* Primers *(green arrows)* that recognize unique STSs are added to cloned DNA, followed by DNA amplification via polymerase chain reaction (PCR). *(2)* PCR products are separated based on size on a DNA gel, and the STSs contained in each clone are identified. *(3)* Cloned DNA segments are aligned based on STSs to create a contig.

 Data analysis You could construct the physical map using a subset of the clones in panel 2. List the possible combinations that would allow you to construct the physical map with the fewest number of clones.

molecular landmarks. As described in chapter 17, databases of STR loci provide DNA fingerprints for identifying individuals in missing persons' cases, establishing relationship, identifying remains in mass tragedies, and for court proceedings.

Physical maps can be correlated with genetic maps

We need to be able to correlate genetic maps with physical maps, particularly genome sequences, to aid in finding physical sequences for genes that have been mapped genetically.

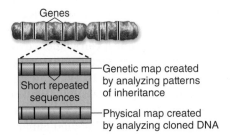

The problem in finding genes is that the resolution of genetic maps at present is not nearly as fine-grained as the genome sequence. Markers that are 1 cM apart may be as much as a million base-pairs apart.

Since the markers used to construct genetic maps are now primarily molecular markers, they can be easily located within a genome sequence. Similarly, any gene that has been cloned can be placed within the genome sequence and can also be mapped genetically. This provides an automatic correlation between the two maps. Genes that have been mapped genetically, but not isolated as molecular clones, present a problem because of the nature of genetic maps. Distances measured on genetic maps are not uniform due to variation in recombination frequency along the chromosome. So 1 cM of genetic distance translates to different numbers of base-pairs in different regions.

Different kinds of maps are stored in databases so they can be aligned and viewed. The National Center for Biotechnology Information (NCBI) is a branch of the National Library of Medicine, and it serves as the U.S. repository for these data and more. Similar databases exist in Europe and Japan, and all are kept current. An enormous storehouse of information is available for use by biological researchers worldwide.

Learning Outcomes Review 18.1

Maps of genomes can be either physical maps or genetic maps. Physical maps include cytogenetic maps of chromosome banding, or restriction maps. Genetic maps are correlated with physical maps by using DNA markers such as sequence-tagged sites (STSs) unique to each genome.

■ *What accounts for the difference between the proximity of banding sites on a karyotype and the number of base-pairs separating the two sites?*

18.2 Sequencing Genomes

Learning Outcomes

1. *Characterize the main hurdle to sequencing an entire genome and how it has been overcome.*
2. *Differentiate between clone-by-clone sequencing and shotgun sequencing.*

The ultimate physical map is the base-pair sequence of an entire genome. Large-scale DNA sequencing made genomics possible. Conceptually, all approaches to sequencing adapt DNA replication to an in vitro environment, using modified nucleotides to stop or pause replication and limiting the replication to just one strand of the DNA. The rapid advances in genomics have been enabled by newer and much faster automated sequencing technologies.

DNA sequencing provides information about genes and genomes

The development of sequencing technology has paralleled the advancement of molecular biology. The earliest approach was to generate a set of nested fragments that each begin with the same sequence and end in a specific base. When this set of fragments is separated by high-resolution gel electrophoresis, the result is a "ladder" of fragments in which each band consists of fragments that end in a specific base. By starting with the shortest fragment, one can then read the sequence by moving up the ladder.

The problem then became how to generate the sets of fragments that end in specific bases. In the early days of sequencing, both a chemical method and an enzymatic method were utilized. The chemical method involved organic reactions specific for the different bases that made breaks in the DNA chains at specific bases. The enzymatic method used DNA polymerase to synthesize chains, but it also included in the reaction modified nucleotides that could be incorporated but not extended: so-called *chain terminators*. The enzymatic method has proved more versatile, and it is easier to adapt to different uses.

Enzymatic sequencing

The enzymatic method of sequencing was developed by Fredrick Sanger, who also was the first to determine the complete sequence of a protein. This method uses dideoxynucleotides as chain terminators in DNA synthesis reactions. A **dideoxynucleotide** has H in place of OH at both the 2′ position and at the 3′ position. All DNA nucleotides lack —OH at the 2′ carbon of the sugar, but dideoxynucleotides have no 3′ —OH, which is needed for DNA polymerase to add new nucleotides. Thus, the chain is terminated.

The experimenter must perform four separate reactions, each with a single dideoxynucleotide, to generate a set of fragments that terminate in specific bases. Thus all of the fragments produced in the A reaction incorporate dideoxyadenosine and must end in A, and the same for the other three reactions with different terminators. When these fragments are separated by high-resolution gel electrophoresis, each reaction is run in a different track, or lane, to generate a pattern of nested fragments that can be read from the smallest fragment to fragments that are each longer by one base (figure 18.4a).

Remember that all DNA polymerase enzymes require a primer to begin synthesis (see chapter 14). With cloned DNA in a vector, the site of insertion is known, and short DNA molecules that are complementary to regions adjacent to the cloned DNA can be chemically synthesized for use as primers. This serves the dual purposes of providing a primer and ensuring that the first few bases sequenced are known because they are in the vector itself. This provides a landmark for determining where the sequence of interest begins. Using the sequence determined with the first set of reactions, new complementary primers can be designed near the end of this sequence and chemically synthesized to use in the next set of reactions to extend the region sequenced.

Automated sequencing

Large-scale genome sequencing requires the use of high-throughput automated methods and computer analysis. Genome sequencing is one case in which technology drove the science, rather than the other way around. In a few hours, an automated Sanger sequencer can sequence the same number of base-pairs that a technician could manually sequence in a year—up to 50,000 bp (figure 18.4b). With the current generation of technology, the rate of sequence generation is now five orders of magnitude greater than when the human genome was sequenced with automated Sanger sequencers. Without the automation of sequencing, it would have been

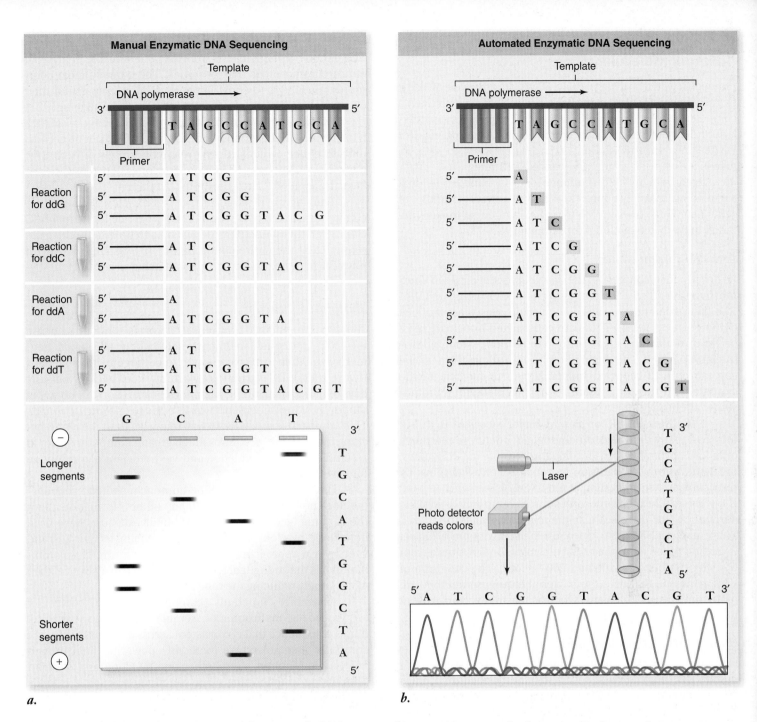

Figure 18.4 Manual and automated enzymatic DNA sequencing. The sequence to be determined is shown at the top as a template strand for DNA polymerase with a primer attached. *a.* In the manual method, four reactions were done, one for each nucleotide. For example, the A tube would contain dATP, dGTP, dCTP, dTTP, and ddATP. This leads to fragments that end in A due to the dideoxy terminator. The fragments generated in each reaction are shown along with the results of gel electrophoresis. *b.* In automated sequencing, each ddNTP is labeled with a different color fluorescent dye, which allows the reaction to be done in a single tube. The fragments generated by the reactions are shown. When these are electrophoresed in a capillary tube, a laser at the bottom of the tube excites the dyes, and each will emit a different color that is detected by a photodetector.

impossible to sequence large, eukaryotic genomes like that of humans.

New automated sequencing technology is even faster than automated Sanger sequencing. Modified, fluorescent nucleotides are still used in some sequencers, but they allow for a controlled pause rather than a complete stop to elongating the new strand of DNA. High-resolution cameras can capture the identity of each new base-pair as it is added so a sequence can be discerned from individual sequencing events, rather than analyzing a pool of terminated fragments. The new approach is termed sequencing by synthesis, but it still adapts the basics of DNA replication with the use of one, rather than two, primers to drive replication in a single direction.

Genome sequencing requires larger molecular clones

Although it would be ideal to isolate DNA from an organism, add it to a sequencer, and then come back in a week or two to pick up a computer-generated printout of the genome sequence, the process is not quite that simple. Sequencers provide accurate sequences for DNA segments up to 800 bp long. Even then, errors are possible. So, to reduce errors, each clone is sequenced 5–10 times.

Even with reliable sequence data in hand, individual sequencing runs produce a relatively small amount of sequence. Thus, the genome must be fragmented to generate individual molecular clones for sequencing

Artificial chromosomes

As described in chapter 17, the development of artificial chromosomes has allowed scientists to clone larger pieces of DNA. The first generation of these new vectors was yeast artificial chromosomes (YACs). These are constructed by using a yeast origin of replication and centromere sequence, then adding foreign DNA to it. The origin of replication allows the artificial chromosome to replicate independently of the rest of the genome, and the centromere sequences make the chromosome mitotically stable.

YACs were useful for cloning larger pieces of DNA but they had many drawbacks, including a tendency to rearrange or to lose portions of DNA by deletion. Despite the difficulties, the YACs were used early on to construct physical maps by restriction enzyme digestion of the YAC DNA.

The artificial chromosomes most commonly used now, particularly for large-scale sequencing, are made in *E. coli*. These bacterial artificial chromosomes (BACs) are a logical extension of the use of bacterial plasmids. BAC vectors accept DNA inserts between 100 and 200 kb long. The downside of BAC vectors is that, like the bacterial chromosome, they are maintained as a single copy, whereas plasmid vectors exist at high copy numbers.

Human artificial chromosomes

Human artificial chromosomes can introduce large segments of human DNA into cultured cells. These artificial chromosomes are usually constructed by fragmentation of chromosomes with centromere sequence. Although circular, some can still segregate correctly during mitosis up to 98% of the time. Construction of linear human artificial chromosomes is not yet possible.

Whole-genome sequencing is approached in two ways: clone-by-clone and shotgun

Sequencing an entire genome is an enormous task. Multiple copies of a genome are fragmented into chunks of overlapping sequences that must be assembled by matching the overlapping regions after sequencing. The shorter the sequences, the harder it is to piece together the puzzle. Two strategies are employed: assemble portions of a chromosome first and then figure out how the bigger pieces fit together (**clone-by-clone sequencing**) or try to assemble all the pieces at once, instead of in a stepwise fashion (**shotgun sequencing**).

Clone-by-clone sequencing

The cloning of large inserts in BACs facilitates the analysis of entire chromosomes and genomes. The strategy most commonly pursued is to construct a physical map first, and then use it to place the site of BAC clones for later sequencing.

Aligning large portions of a chromosome requires identifying regions that overlap between clones. This can be accomplished either by constructing restriction maps of each BAC clone or by identifying STSs found in clones. If two BAC clones have the same STS, then they must overlap.

The alignment of a number of BAC clones results in a contiguous stretch of DNA called a *contig*. The individual BAC clones can then be sequenced 500 bp at a time to produce the sequence of the entire contig (figure 18.5*a*). This strategy of physical mapping followed by sequencing is called clone-by-clone sequencing.

Shotgun sequencing

Shotgun sequencing, simply put, involves randomly cutting the DNA into small fragments, sequencing all cloned fragments, and then using a computer to put together the overlaps (figure 18.5*b*). This terminology actually goes back to the early days of molecular cloning when the construction of a library of randomly cloned fragments was referred to as *shotgun cloning*. This approach is much less labor-intensive than the clone-by-clone method, but it requires much greater computer power to assemble the final sequence and very efficient algorithms to find overlaps.

Unlike the clone-by-clone approach, shotgun sequencing does not tie the sequence to any other information about the genome (see figure 18.5*b*). Many investigators have used both clone-by-clone and shotgun-sequencing techniques, and such hybrid approaches are becoming the norm. This combination has the strength of tying the sequence to a physical map while greatly reducing the time involved.

Assembler programs compare multiple copies of sequenced regions in order to assemble a **consensus sequence,** that is, a sequence that is consistent across all copies. Although computer assemblers are incredibly powerful, final human analysis is required after both clone-by-clone and shotgun sequencing to determine when a genome sequence is sufficiently accurate to be useful to researchers.

The Human Genome Project used both sequencing methods

The vast scale of genomics ushered in a new way of doing biological research involving large teams. Although a single individual can isolate and manually sequence a molecular clone for a single gene, a huge genome like the human genome requires the collaborative efforts of hundreds of researchers.

The Human Genome Project originated in 1990 when a group of American scientists formed the International Human Genome Sequencing Consortium. The goal of this publicly funded effort was to use a clone-by-clone approach to sequence the human genome. Genetic and physical maps were used as scaffolding to sequence each chromosome.

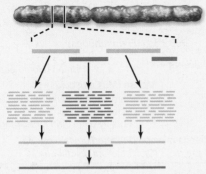

Clone-by-Clone Method

1. Large DNA clones are first isolated. These are arranged into contiguous sequences based on overlapping tagged sites.

2. Large clones are fragmented into smaller clones for sequencing.

3. The entire sequence is assembled from the overlapping larger clones.

a.

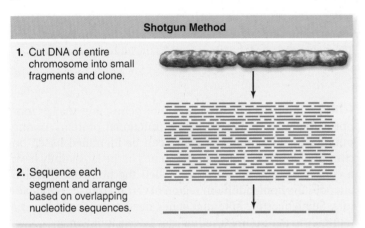

Shotgun Method

1. Cut DNA of entire chromosome into small fragments and clone.

2. Sequence each segment and arrange based on overlapping nucleotide sequences.

b.

Figure 18.5 Comparison of sequencing methods.
a. The clone-by-clone method uses large clones assembled into overlapping regions by STSs. Once assembled, these can be fragmented into smaller clones for sequencing. *b.* In the shotgun method the entire genome is fragmented into small clones and sequenced. Computer algorithms assemble the final DNA sequence based on overlapping nucleotide sequences.

In May 1998, American biologist Craig Venter, whose research group had sequenced *Haemophilus influenzae,* announced that his private company (Celera Genomics) would also endeavor to sequence the human genome. He proposed to shotgun-sequence the 3.2-gigabase genome in only two years. The Consortium rose to the challenge, and the race to sequence the human genome began. The upshot was a tie of sorts. On June 26, 2000, the groups jointly announced success, and each published its findings simultaneously in 2001. The Consortium's draft alone included 248 authors.

The draft sequence of the human genome was just the beginning. Gaps in the sequence are still being filled, and the map is constantly being refined. The most recent "finished" human sequence is down to only 260 gaps, a 400-fold reduction in gaps, and it now includes 99% of the euchromatic sequence, up from 95%. The reference sequence has an error rate of 1 per 100,000 bases. Newer sequencing technologies are being used to close the remaining gaps. A few individuals, including James Watson (who codiscovered the structure of

DNA) and both Venter and his colleague Francis Collins (who lead the U.S. team of the International Consortium), have now had their personal genomes sequenced. The cost for having one's genome sequenced is predicted to fall to $1000 in the next few years, making the process much more affordable and accessible. Many more people seeking personal sequencing raises many questions about genome privacy, including how private the information will remain.

Research on the whole genome can move ahead. Now that the ultimate physical map is in place and is being integrated with the genetic map, diseases that result from changes in more than one gene, such as diabetes, can be addressed. Comparisons with other genomes are already changing our understanding of genome evolution (see chapter 24).

Learning Outcomes Review 18.2

Because of the enormous size of genomes, sequencing requires the use of automated sequencers running many samples in parallel. Two approaches have been developed for whole-genome sequencing: one that uses clones already aligned by physical mapping (clone-by-clone sequencing), and one that involves sequencing random clones and using a computer to assemble the final sequence (shotgun sequencing). In either case, significant computing power is necessary to assemble a final sequence.

■ **Compare and contrast DNA replication and DNA sequencing.**

18.3 *Characterizing Genomes*

Learning Outcomes

1. **Describe the classes of DNA found in a genome.**
2. **Explain what an SNP is and why SNPs are helpful in characterizing genomes.**

Automated sequencing technology has produced huge amounts of sequence data, eventually sequencing entire genomes. This has allowed researchers studying complex problems to move beyond approaches restricted to the analysis of individual genes. However, sequencing projects in themselves are descriptive analyses that tell us nothing about the organization of genomes, let alone the function of gene products and how they may be interrelated. Additional research and evaluation has given us both answers and new puzzles.

The Human Genome Project found fewer genes than expected

For many years, geneticists had estimated the number of human genes to be around 100,000. This estimate, although based on some data, was really just a guess. Imagine researchers' surprise when the number turned out to be less than 25,000! This represents only about twice as many genes as

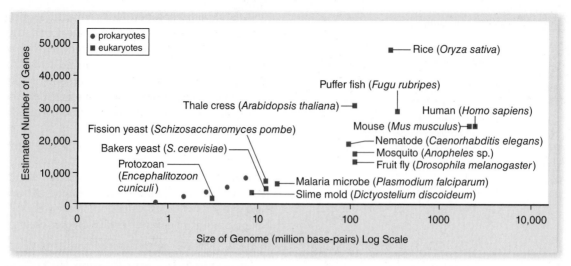

Figure 18.6 Size and complexity of genomes. In general, eukaryotic genomes are larger and have more genes than prokaryotic genomes, although the size of the organism is not the determining factor. The mouse genome is nearly as large as the human genome, and the rice genome contains more genes than both.

Drosophila and fewer genes than rice (figure 18.6). Clearly, the complexity of an organism is not a simple function of the number of genes in its genome.

The human transcriptome and proteome are far more complex than might be inferred from under 25,000 coding genes. As discussed in chapter 16, alternative splicing can produce multiple mRNAs and thus multiple proteins from a single gene. An analysis of the human genome revealed that about 95% of genes with multiple exons undergo alternative splicing. An estimated 100,000 alternative splicing events occur in the major tissues of humans. Understanding genome sequences is just the beginning of understanding how the blueprint in the genome is used to build an organism.

 Data analysis Estimate the number of splice variants that occur, on average, on each of the 25,000 genes in the human genome.

Finding genes in sequence data requires computer searches

Once a genome has been sequenced, the next step is to determine which regions of the genome contain which genes, and what those genes do. A lot of information can be mined from the sequence data. Using markers from physical maps and information from genetic maps, it is possible to find the sequence of the small percentage of genes that are identified by mutations with an observable (phenotypic) effect. Genes can also be found by comparing expressed sequences to genomic sequences. The analysis of expressed sequences is discussed later in this section.

Locating starts and stops

Information in the nucleotide sequence itself can also be used in the search for genes. A protein-coding gene begins with a start codon, such as ATG, and it contains no stop codons (TAA, TGA, or TAG) for a distance long enough to encode a protein. This coding region is referred to as an **open reading frame**

(ORF). Although ORFs are likely to be genes, they may or may not actually be translated into a functional protein. Among putative genes, families of genes can be identified based on common domains. For example, genes in the Hox family have a conserved, 180-bp sequence called the homeobox, which encodes the homeodomain region of certain transcription factors. Sequences for potential genes need to be tested experimentally to determine whether they have a function.

The addition of information to the basic sequence information, like identifying ORFs, is called sequence **annotation.** This process is what converts simple sequence data into something that we can recognize based on landmarks such as regions that are transcribed and regions that are known or thought to encode proteins.

 Inquiry question Given the sequence of a genome, how might you predict the number of genes in the genome? Why might your estimate be inaccurate?

Inferring function across species: the BLAST algorithm

It is also possible to search genome databases for sequences that are homologous to known genes in other species. A researcher who has isolated a molecular clone for a gene of unknown function can search the database for similar sequences to infer function. The tool that makes this possible is a search algorithm called BLAST (which stands for Basic Local Alignment Search Tool). Using a networked computer, one can submit a sequence to the BLAST server and get back a reply with all possible similar sequences contained in the sequence database.

Using these techniques, sequences that are not part of ORFs have been identified that have been conserved over millions of years of evolution. These sequences may be important for the regulation of the genes contained in the genome.

Using computer programs to search for genes, to compare genomes, and to assemble genomes are only a few of the new genomics approaches falling under the heading of **bioinformatics.**

Genomes contain both coding and noncoding DNA

When genome sequences are analyzed, regions that encode proteins and other regions that do not encode proteins are revealed. For many years investigators had known of the latter, but they did not know the extent and nature of the noncoding DNA. We first consider the types of coding DNA that have been found, then move on to look at types of noncoding DNA.

Protein-encoding DNA in eukaryotes

Four different classes of protein-encoding genes are found in eukaryotic genomes, differing largely in gene copy number.

Single-copy genes. Many genes exist as single copies on a particular chromosome. Most mutations in these genes result in recessive Mendelian inheritance.

Segmental duplications. Sometimes whole blocks of genes are copied from one chromosome to another, resulting in *segmental duplication.* Blocks of similar genes in the same order are found throughout the human genome. Chromosome 19 seems to have been the biggest borrower, sharing blocks of genes with 16 other chromosomes.

Multigene families. As more has been learned about eukaryotic genomes, many genes have been found to exist as parts of *multigene families,* groups of related but distinctly different genes that often occur together in clusters. About 10,000 multigene families with two or more genes are found in the human genome. Comparisons of mammalian gene families show that 164 of these gene families are evolving at accelerated rates. Biological functions of genes in these families include immune response and brain development. These multigene families may include silent copies called *pseudogenes,* which are inactivated by mutation.

Tandem clusters. Identical copies of genes can also be found in *tandem clusters.* These genes are transcribed simultaneously, increasing the amount of mRNA available for protein production. Tandem clusters also include genes that do not encode proteins, such as clusters of rRNA genes.

Noncoding DNA in eukaryotes

One of the most notable characteristics is the amount of non-coding DNA they possess. The Human Genome Project has revealed a particularly startling picture. Each of your cells has about 6 feet of DNA stuffed into it, but of that, less than 1 inch is devoted to genes! Nearly 99% of the DNA in your cells is non-protein-coding DNA.

True genes are scattered about the human genome in clumps among the much larger amount of noncoding DNA, like isolated oases in a desert. Seven major sorts of noncoding human DNA have been described. (Table 18.1 shows the composition of the human genome, including noncoding DNA.)

Noncoding DNA within genes. As discussed in chapter 15, a human gene is not simply a stretch of DNA, like the letters of a word. Instead, a human gene is made up of numerous fragments of protein-encoding information (exons) embedded within a much larger matrix of noncoding DNA (introns). Together, introns make up about 24% of the human genome and exons less than 1.5%.

Structural DNA. Some regions of the chromosomes remain highly condensed, tightly coiled, and untranscribed throughout the cell cycle. Called *constitutive heterochromatin,* these portions tend to be localized around the centromere or located near the ends of the chromosome, at the telomeres.

Simple sequence repeats. Scattered about chromosomes are **simple sequence repeats (SSRs).** An SSR is a 1- to 6-nt sequence such as CA or CGG, repeated like a broken record thousands and thousands of times. SSRs can arise from DNA replication errors. SSRs make up about 3% of the human genome.

Segmental duplications. Blocks of genomic sequences composed of from 10,000 to 300,000 bp have duplicated and moved either within a chromosome or to a nonhomologous chromosome.

Pseudogenes. These inactive genes may have lost function because of mutation.

Transposable elements. Fully 45% of the human genome consists of mobile bits of DNA called *transposable elements.*

TABLE 18.1	Classes of DNA Sequences Found in the Human Genome
Class	**Description**
Protein-encoding genes	Translated portions of the 25,000 genes scattered about the chromosomes
Introns	Noncoding DNA that constitutes the great majority of each human gene
Segmental duplications	Regions of the genome that have been duplicated
Pseudogenes (inactive genes)	Sequence that has characteristics of a gene but is not a functional gene
Structural DNA	Constitutive heterochromatin, localized near centromeres and telomeres
Simple sequence repeats	Stuttering repeats of a few nucleotides such as CGG, repeated thousands of times
Transposable elements	21%: Long interspersed elements (LINEs), which are active transposons 13%: Short interspersed elements (SINEs), which are active transposons 8%: Retrotransposons, which contain long terminal repeats (LTRs) at each end 3%: DNA transposon fossils
Noncoding RNA	RNAs that do not encode a protein but have regulatory functions, many of which are currently unknown

Some of these elements code for proteins, but many do not. Because of the significance of these elements, we describe them more fully in the following section.

microRNA genes. Hidden within the non-protein-coding DNA lies an extraordinary mechanism for controlling gene expression and development. Compact regulatory RNAs have a much larger role in directing development in complex organisms than we imagined even a few years ago. Specifically, DNA that was once considered "junk" has been shown to encode microRNAs, or miRNAs, which are processed after transcription to lengths of 21 to 23 nt, but never translated. About 10,000 unique miRNAs have been identified that are complementary to one or more mature mRNAs.

Long, noncoding RNA. In addition to the many small RNAs such as microRNAs that are not translated into protein but serve a regulatory role, tens of thousands of longer noncoding RNAs likely regulate gene expression. This recently discovered, hidden world of regulatory networks reveals a new level of complexity in the precise control of gene expression. Long, noncoding RNAs have important roles in physiology and development and are only beginning to be characterized.

Transposable elements: mobile DNA

Discovered by Barbara McClintock in 1950, **transposable elements,** also termed *transposons* and *mobile genetic elements,* are bits of DNA that are able to move from one location on a chromosome to another. Barbara McClintock received the 1983 Nobel Prize in physiology or medicine for discovery of these elements and their unexpected ability to change location.

Transposable elements move around in different ways. In some cases, the transposon is duplicated, and the duplicated DNA moves to a new place in the genome, so the number of copies of the transposon increases. Other types of transposons are excised without duplication and insert themselves elsewhere in the genome. The role of transposons in genome evolution is discussed in chapter 24.

Human chromosomes contain four sorts of transposable elements. Fully 21% of the genome consists of **long interspersed elements (LINEs).** These ancient and very successful elements are about 6000 bp long, and they contain all the equipment needed for transposition. LINEs encode a reverse transcriptase enzyme that can make a cDNA copy of the transcribed LINE RNA. The result is a double-stranded segment that can reinsert into the genome rather than undergo translation into a protein. Since these elements use an RNA intermediate, they are termed *retrotransposons.*

Short interspersed elements (SINEs) are similar to LINEs, but they cannot transpose without using the transposition machinery of LINEs. Nested within the genome's LINEs are over half a million copies of a SINE element called Alu (named for a restriction enzyme that cuts within the sequence). The Alu SINE is 300 bp and represents 10% of the human genome. Like a flea on a dog, Alu moves with the LINE it resides within. Just as a flea sometimes jumps to a different dog, so Alu sometimes uses the enzymes of its LINE to move to a new chromosome location. Alu can also jump right into genes, causing harmful mutations.

Two other sorts of transposable elements are also found in the human genome: 8% of the human genome is devoted to retrotransposons called **long terminal repeats (LTRs).** Although the transposition mechanism is a bit different from that of LINEs, LTRs also use reverse transcriptase to ensure that copies are double-stranded and can reintegrate into the genome.

Some 3% of the genome is devoted to dead transposons, elements that have lost the signals for replication and can no longer move.

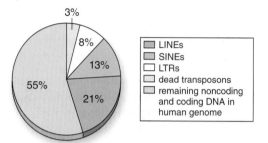

Inquiry question How do you think these repetitive elements would affect the determination of gene order?

Expressed sequence tags identify genes that are transcribed

Given the complexity of coding and noncoding DNA, it is important to be able to recognize regions of the genome that are actually expressed—that is, transcribed and then translated.

Because DNA is easier to work with than protein, one approach is to isolate mRNA, use this to make cDNA, then sequence one or both ends of as many cDNAs as possible. With automated sequencing, this task is not difficult, and these short sections of cDNA have been named **expressed sequence tags (ESTs).** An EST is another form of STS, and thus it can be included in physical maps. This technique does not tell us anything about the function of any particular EST, but it does provide one view, at the whole-genome level, of what genes are expressed, at least as mRNAs.

ESTs have been used to identify 87,000 cDNAs in different human tissues. About 80% of these cDNAs were previously unknown. The estimated 25,000 genes of the human genome can result in these 87,000 different cDNAs because of *alternative splicing* (figure 18.7).

SNPs are single-base differences between individuals

One fact becoming clear from analysis of the human genome is that a huge amount of genetic variation exists in our species. This information has practical use.

Single-nucleotide polymorphisms (SNPs) are sites where individuals differ by only a single nucleotide. To be classified as a polymorphism, an SNP must be present in at least 1% of the population. SNPs occur about every 100 to 300 bp in the 3 billion base-pair human genome. As of July 2011, 4.4 million non-redundant human SNPs had been identified and validated, representing about 30% of the variation available. These SNPs are being used to look for associations between genes. We

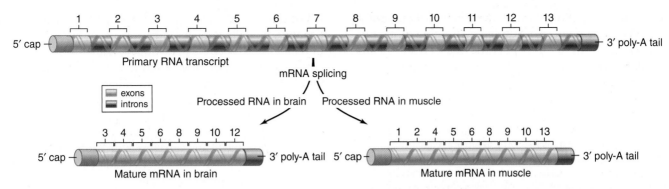

Figure 18.7 Alternative splicing can result in the production of different mRNAs from the same coding sequence. In some cells, exons can be excised along with neighboring introns, resulting in different proteins. Alternative splicing explains why 25,000 human genes can code for three to four times as many proteins.

expect that the genetic recombination occurring during meiosis randomizes all but the most tightly linked genes. We call the tendency for genes *not* to be randomized **linkage disequilibrium.** This kind of association can be used to map genes and when done at the level of the whole genome is called a **genome-wide association study**.

Analysis of SNPs shows that many cosegregate with specific genomic regions at almost 100% frequencies. This unexpected result has led to the idea of genomic **haplotypes,** or regions of chromosomes that are not being exchanged by recombination. The existence of haplotypes allows the genetic characterization of genomic regions by describing a small number of SNPs (figure 18.8). The SNPs have been mapped onto the human haplotypes, creating a haplotype map. A large number of SNPs have now been identified that are associated with disease phenotypes through

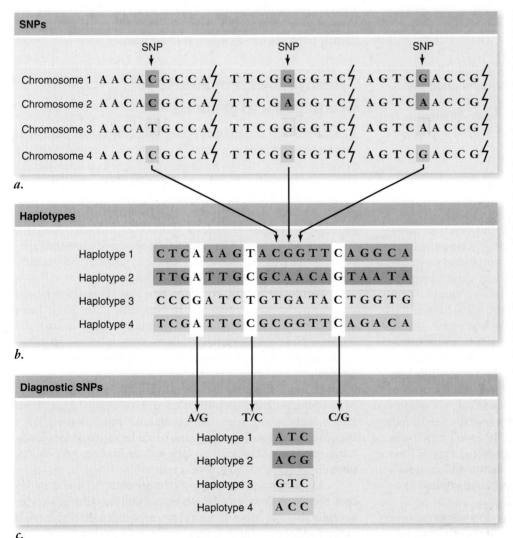

Figure 18.8 Construction of a haplotype map. Single-nucleotide polymorphisms (SNPs) are single-base differences between individuals. Sections of DNA sequences from four individuals are shown in (*a*), with three SNPs indicated by arrows. *b.* These three SNPs are shown aligned along with 17 other SNPs from this chromosomal region. This represents a haplotype map for this region of the chromosome. Haplotypes are regions of the genome that are not exchanged by recombination during meiosis. *c.* Haplotypes can be identified using a small number of diagnostic SNPs that differ between the different haplotypes. In this case, 3 SNPs out of the 20 in this region are all that are needed to uniquely identify each haplotype. This greatly facilitates locating disease-causing genes, as haplotypes represent large regions of the genome that behave as a single site during meiosis.

genome-wide association studies. Many diseases are multigenic, as well as having contributing environmental factors. One must be cautious about concluding too much from any given SNP variant.

Learning Outcomes Review 18.3

Coding sequences in a genome can be found as a single copy, as repeated clusters, as part of segmental duplications, or as part of a gene family. A significant amount of noncoding DNA is found in all eukaryotic organisms. Transposable elements are capable of movement in the genome and are found in all eukaryotic genomes. Single-nucleotide polymorphisms (SNPs) provide a way of identifying individual variation, and they have also revealed cases of nonrandom recombination (genomic haplotypes).

■ *What explanation could you suggest, based on principles of natural selection, for the many repeated transposable elements in the human genome?*

18.4 Comparing Genomes

Learning Outcome

1. *Describe the advances that have come from comparative genomics.*

Sequencing whole genomes has vastly expanded the range of traits available for evolutionary analysis. Comparing organisms at the level of whole genomes is giving us fresh insights into our shared genomes and the often subtle differences in DNA that correspond with notable morphological and behavioral differences.

Comparative genomics reveals conserved regions in genomes

With the large number of sequenced genomes, it is now possible to make comparisons at both the gene and genome level. The flood of information from different genomes has given rise to a new field: *comparative genomics.* One of the striking lessons learned from the sequence of the human genome is how very similar humans are to other organisms. More than half of the genes of *Drosophila* have human counterparts. Among mammals, the similarities are even greater. Humans have only 300 genes that have no counterpart in the mouse genome.

The use of comparative genomics to ask evolutionary questions is also a field of great promise. The comparison of the many prokaryotic genomes already indicates a greater degree of lateral gene transfer than was previously suspected. Sequenced animal genomes now include the chimpanzee, our closest living relative. The draft sequence of the chimp *(Pan troglodytes)* genome has just been completed, and comparisons between the chimp and human genome may allow us to unravel what makes us uniquely human.

The early returns from this sequencing effort confirm that our genomes differ by only 1.23% in terms of nucleotide substitutions. At first glance, the largest difference between our genomes actually appears to be in transposable elements. In humans, the SINEs have been threefold more active than in the chimp, but the chimp has acquired two elements that are not found in the human genome. The differences due to insertion and deletion of bases are fewer than substitutions but account for about 1.5% of the euchromatic sequence being unique in each genome.

The genome of an even closer, but extinct, relative, *Homo neanderthalensis* (Neandertal) is remarkably similar to our own. About half a million years ago the two shared a common ancestor in Africa. Then Neandertals headed north, eventually settling in Europe and Asia and dying out about 28,000 years ago. Humans migrated from Africa later and, for about 100,000 years, overlapped with Neanderthals in Europe. The most compelling evidence that humans and Neandertals interbred in Europe is the finding that Europeans and Asians, but not African's, share 1% to 4% of their genome with Neandertals (figure 18.9).

Enough DNA remained in 38,000- and 44,000-year-old Neandertal bones from Croatia that the genome could be sequenced and reconstructed. Of the nearly 10 million amino acids encoded in our genome, only 78 differences that could alter the shape and/or function of a protein were consistently found in humans and not Neanderthals. More than 200 other regions within the genome appear to have evolved since the human and Neanderthal branches split, but it is nothing that clearly points to our uniquely human traits.

Synteny allows comparison of unsequenced genomes

Similarities and differences between highly conserved genes can be investigated on a gene-by-gene basis between species. Genome science allows for a much larger scale approach to comparing genomes by taking advantage of synteny.

Synteny refers to the conserved arrangements of segments of DNA in related genomes. Physical mapping techniques can be used to look for synteny in genomes that have not been sequenced. Comparisons with the sequenced, syntenous segment in another species can provide information about the unsequenced genome.

To illustrate this, consider rice and its grain relatives corn, barley, and wheat. Only rice and corn have been sequenced. Even though these plants diverged more than 50 MYA, the chromosomes of rice, corn, wheat, and other grass crops show extensive synteny (figure 18.10). In a genomic sense, "rice is wheat."

By understanding the rice and corn genomes at the level of its DNA sequence, identification and isolation of genes from grains with larger genomes should be much easier. DNA sequence analysis of cereal grains could be valuable for identifying genes associated with disease resistance, crop yield, nutritional quality, and growth capacity.

As mentioned earlier, the rice genome has more genes than the human genome. However, rice still has a much smaller genome than its other grain relatives, which also represent a major food source for humans.

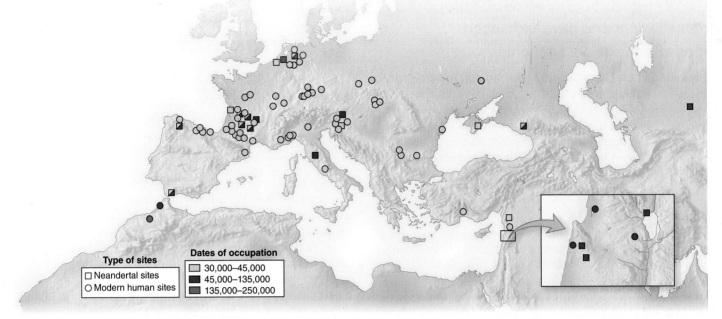

Figure 18.9 Europeans and Asians, but not Africans, share between 1% and 4% of their genomes with Neandertals. From 30,000 to 45,000 years ago humans and Neandertals coexisted in Europe, and possibly in the Middle East as early as 80,000 years ago. Interbreeding likely occurred after European and Asian ancestors left Africa.

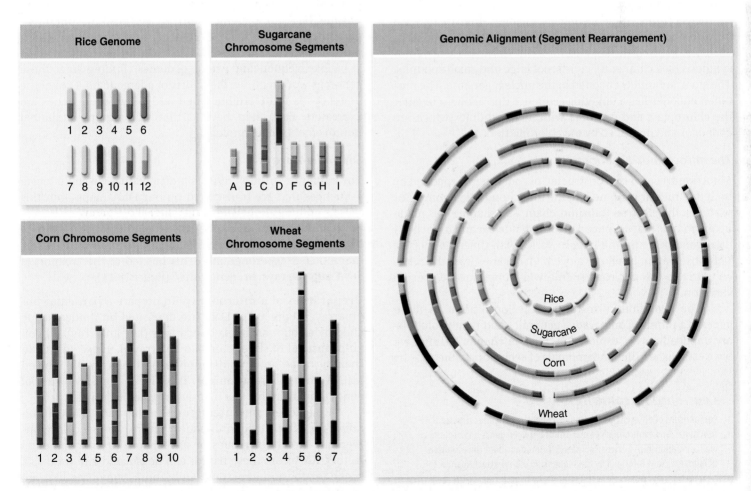

Figure 18.10 Grain genomes are rearrangements of similar chromosome segments. Shades of the same color represent pieces of DNA that are conserved among the different species but have been rearranged. By splitting the individual chromosomes of major grass species into segments and rearranging the segments, researchers have found that the genome components of rice, sugarcane, corn, and wheat are highly conserved. This implies that the order of the segments in the ancestral grass genome has been rearranged by recombination as the grasses have evolved.

Organelle genomes have exchanged genes with the nuclear genome

Mitochondria and chloroplasts are considered to be descendants of ancient bacterial cells living in eukaryotes as a result of endosymbiosis (see chapter 4). Their genomes have been sequenced in some species, and they are most like prokaryotic genomes. The chloroplast genome, having about 100 genes, is minute compared with the rice genome, with 32,000–55,000 genes.

The chloroplast genome

The chloroplast, a plant organelle that functions in photosynthesis, can independently replicate in the plant cell because it has its own genome. The DNA in the chloroplasts of all land plants have about the same number of genes, and they are present in about the same order. In contrast to the evolution of the DNA in the plant cell nucleus, chloroplast DNA has evolved at a more conservative pace and therefore shows a more easily interpretable evolutionary pattern when scientists study DNA sequence similarities. Chloroplast DNA is also not subject to modification caused by transposable elements or to mutations due to recombination.

Over time, some genetic exchange appears to have occurred between the nuclear and chloroplast genomes. For example, Rubisco, the key enzyme in the Calvin cycle of photosynthesis (see chapter 8), consists of large and small subunits. The small subunit is encoded in the nuclear genome. The protein it encodes has a targeting sequence that allows it to enter the chloroplast and combine with large subunits, which are coded for and produced by the chloroplast.

The mitochondrial genome

Mitochondria are also constructed of components encoded by both the nuclear genome and the mitochondrial genome. For example, the electron transport chain (see chapter 7) is made up of proteins that are encoded by both nuclear and mitochondrial genomes, and the pattern varies with different species. This observation implies a movement of genes from the mitochondria to the nuclear genome with some lineage-specific variation.

The evolutionary history of the localization of these genes is a puzzle. Comparative genomics and their evolutionary implications are explored in detail in chapter 24, after we have established the fundamentals of evolutionary theory.

Learning Outcome Review 18.4

Comparisons of different genomes allow geneticists to infer structural, functional, and evolutionary relationships between genes and proteins as well as relationships between species. Information about the evolution of humans is now informed by the sequencing of the extinct Neandertal genome.

■ *The human and Neandertal genomes are so similar that it is difficult to identify sequences that make us uniquely human. Are there other ways the two genomes could differ (consider the cereal synteny example)?*

From Genes to Proteins

Learning Outcomes

1. *Distinguish between genomics and proteomics.*
2. *Explain how gene expression can be analyzed.*

To fully understand how genes work, we need to characterize the proteins they produce. This information is essential to understanding cell biology, physiology, development, and evolution. In many ways, we continue to ask the same questions that Mendel asked, but at a much different level of organization.

Functional genomics reveals gene function at the genome level

Bioinformatics takes advantage of high-end computer technology to analyze the growing gene databases, look for relationships among genomes, and then hypothesize functions of genes based on sequence. Genomics is now shifting gears and moving back to hypothesis-driven science, to **functional genomics,** the study of the function of genes and their products.

Like sequencing whole genomes, finding how these genomes work requires the efforts of a large team. One of the first steps is to determine when and where these genes are expressed. Each step beyond that will require additional improvements in technology.

DNA microarrays

The earlier description of ESTs indicated that we could locate sequences that are transcribed on our DNA maps—but this tells us nothing about when and where these genes are turned on. To be able to analyze gene expression at the whole-genome level requires a representation of the genome that can be manipulated experimentally. This has led to the creation of **DNA microarrays,** or "gene chips" (figure 18.11).

Preparation of a microarray. To prepare a particular microarray, fragments of DNA are deposited on a microscope slide by a robot at indexed locations (i.e., an array). Silicon chips instead of slides can also be arrayed. These chips can then be used in hybridization experiments with labeled mRNA from different sources. This gives a high-level view of genes that are active and inactive in specific tissues.

Researchers are currently using a chip with 24,000 *Arabidopsis* genes on it to identify genes that are expressed developmentally in certain tissues or in response to environmental factors. RNA from these tissues can be isolated and used as a probe for these microarrays. Only those sequences that are expressed in the tissues will be present and will hybridize to the microarray.

Microarray analysis and cancer. One of the most exciting uses of microarrays has been the profiling of gene expression patterns in human cancers. Microarray analysis has revealed

Hypothesis: *Flowers and leaves will express some of the same genes.*

Prediction: *When mRNAs isolated from* Arabidopsis *flowers and from leaves are used as probes on an* Arabidopsis *genome microarray, the two different probe sets will hybridize to both common and unique sequences.*

Test:

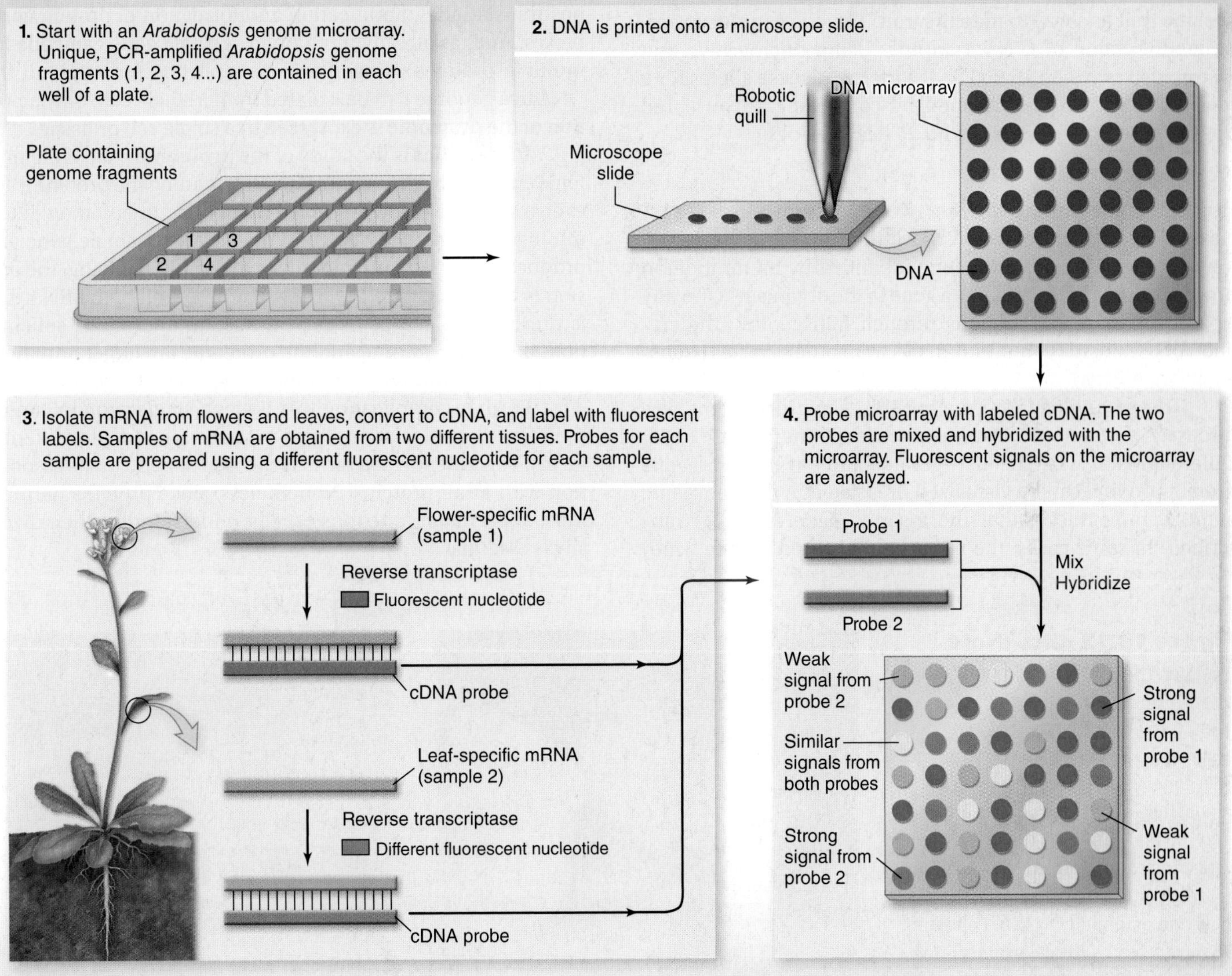

1. Start with an *Arabidopsis* genome microarray. Unique, PCR-amplified *Arabidopsis* genome fragments (1, 2, 3, 4...) are contained in each well of a plate.

Plate containing genome fragments

1 3
2 4

2. DNA is printed onto a microscope slide.

Robotic quill
DNA microarray
Microscope slide
DNA

3. Isolate mRNA from flowers and leaves, convert to cDNA, and label with fluorescent labels. Samples of mRNA are obtained from two different tissues. Probes for each sample are prepared using a different fluorescent nucleotide for each sample.

Flower-specific mRNA (sample 1)
Reverse transcriptase
Fluorescent nucleotide
cDNA probe
Leaf-specific mRNA (sample 2)
Reverse transcriptase
Different fluorescent nucleotide
cDNA probe

4. Probe microarray with labeled cDNA. The two probes are mixed and hybridized with the microarray. Fluorescent signals on the microarray are analyzed.

Probe 1
Probe 2
Mix
Hybridize

Weak signal from probe 2
Similar signals from both probes
Strong signal from probe 2
Strong signal from probe 1
Weak signal from probe 1

Result: *Yellow spots represent sequences that hybridized to cDNA from both flowers and leaves. Red spots represent genes expressed only in flowers. Green spots represent genes expressed only in leaves.*

Conclusion: *Some* Arabidopsis *genes are expressed in both flowers and leaves, but there are genes expressed in flowers but not leaves and leaves but not flowers.*

Further Experiments: *How could you use microarrays to determine whether the genes expressed in both flowers and leaves are housekeeping genes or are unique to flowers and leaves?*

Figure 18.11 Microarrays.

that different cancers have different gene expression patterns. These findings are already being used to diagnose and design specific treatments for particular cancers.

From a large body of data, several patterns emerge:

1. Specific cancer types can be reliably distinguished from other cancer types and from normal tissue based on microarray data.

2. Subtypes of particular cancers often have different gene expression patterns in microarray data.

3. Gene expression patterns from microarray data can be used to predict disease recurrence, tendency to metastasize, and treatment response.

This represents an important step forward in both the diagnosis and treatment of human cancers.

Microarray analysis and genome-wide association mapping

Genome-wide association (GWA), as mentioned earlier, is an approach that compares SNPs throughout the genome between members in a population with and without a specific trait. The goal is to find a SNP that correlates with a specific trait as a way to map the trait. The dog genome exemplifies the value of GWA mapping. Using microarrays that distinguish between 15,000 SNP variants, disease alleles for a recessive trait can be mapped by comparing 20 purebred dogs exhibiting the disease with 20 healthy dogs.

Transgenics

How can we determine whether two genes from different species having similar sequences have the same function? And, how can we be sure that a gene identified by an annotation program actually functions as a gene in the organism? One way to address these questions is through transgenics—the creation of organisms containing genes from other species (transgenic organisms).

The technology for creating transgenic organisms was discussed in chapter 17; it is illustrated for plants in figure 18.12. Different markers can be incorporated into the gene so that its protein product can be visualized or isolated in the transgenic plant, demonstrating that the inserted gene is being transcribed. In some cases, the transgene (inserted foreign gene) may affect a visible phenotype. Of course, transgenics are but one of many ways to address questions about gene function.

Proteomics moves from genes to proteins

Proteins are much more difficult to study than DNA because of posttranslational modification and formation of protein complexes. And, as already mentioned, a single gene can code for multiple proteins using alternative splicing. Although all the DNA in a genome can be isolated from a single cell, only a portion of the proteome is expressed in a single cell or tissue.

Proteomics is the study of the **proteome**—all of the proteins encoded by the genome. Understanding the proteome for even a single cell will be a much more difficult task than determining the sequence of a genome. Because a single gene can produce more than one protein by alternative splicing, the first step is to characterize the **transcriptome**—all of the RNA that is present in a cell or tissue. Because of alternative splicing, both the transcriptome and the proteome are larger and more complex than the simple number of genes in the genome.

Further complicating this issue, a single protein can be modified posttranslationally to produce functionally different forms. The function of a protein can also depend on its association with other proteins. Nonetheless, since proteins perform most of the major functions of cells, understanding their diversity is essential.

Figure 18.12 Growth of a transgenic plant. DNA containing a gene for herbicide resistance was transferred into wheat *(Triticum aestivum)*. The DNA also contains the *GUS* gene, which is used as a tag or label. The *GUS* gene produces an enzyme that catalyzes the conversion of a staining solution from clear to blue. *a.* Embryonic tissue just prior to insertion of foreign DNA. *b.* Following DNA transfer, callus cells containing the foreign DNA are indicated by color from the *GUS* gene *(dark blue spots)*. *c.* Shoot formation in the transgenic plants growing on a selective medium. Here, the gene for herbicide resistance in the transgenic plants allows growth on the selective medium containing the herbicide. *d.* Comparison of growth on the selection medium for transgenic plants bearing the herbicide resistance gene *(left)* and a nontransgenic plant *(right)*.

a. 2000 μm

b. 2500 μm

c.

d.

Predicting protein function

The use of new methods to quickly identify and characterize large numbers of proteins is the distinguishing feature between traditional protein biochemistry and proteomics. As with genomics, the challenge is one of scale.

Ideally, a researcher would like to be able to examine a nucleotide sequence and know what sort of functional protein the sequence specifies. Databases of protein structures in different organisms can be searched to predict the structure and function of genes known only by sequence, as identified in genome projects. Analysis of these data provides a clearer picture of how gene sequence relates to protein structure and function. Having a greater number of DNA sequences available allows for more extensive comparisons as well as identification of common structural patterns as groups of proteins continue to emerge.

Although there may be as many as a million different proteins, most are just variations on a handful of themes. The same shared structural motifs—barrels, helices, molecular zippers—are found in the proteins of plants, insects, and

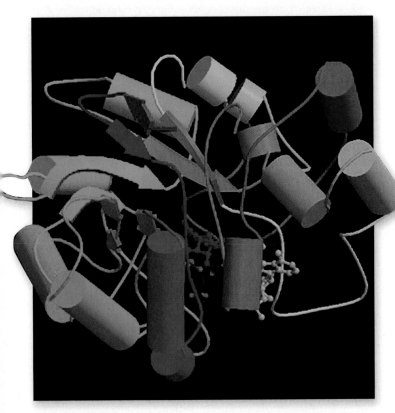

Figure 18.13 Computer-generated model of an enzyme. Searchable databases contain known protein structures, including human aldose reductase shown here. Secondary structural motifs are shown in different colors.

humans (figure 18.13; also see chapter 3 for more information on protein motifs). The maximum number of distinct motifs has been estimated to be fewer than 5000. About 1000 of these motifs have already been cataloged. Efforts are now under way to detail the shapes of all the common motifs.

Large-scale screens reveal protein–protein interactions

We often study proteins in isolation, compared with their normal cellular context. This approach is obviously artificial. One immediate goal of proteomics, therefore, is to map all the physical interactions between proteins in a cell. This is a daunting task that requires tools that can be automated, similarly to the way that genome sequencing was automated.

One approach is to use the yeast two-hybrid system, which integrates much of the technology discussed in this chapter. It takes advantage of one feature of eukaryotic gene regulation, namely that the structure of proteins that turn on eukaryotic gene expression—transcription factors—have a modular structure.

The *Gal4* gene of yeast encodes a transcriptional activator with modular structure consisting of a DNA-binding domain that binds sequences in *Gal4*-responsive promoters and an activation domain that interacts with the transcription apparatus to turn on transcription. The system uses two vectors: one containing a fragment of the *Gal4* gene that encodes the DNA-binding domain, and another containing a fragment of the *Gal4* gene that encodes the transcription activation domain. Neither of these alone can activate transcription.

When cDNAs are inserted into each of these two vectors in the proper reading frame, they are expressed as a single protein consisting of the protein of interest and part of the Gal4 activator protein (figure 18.14). These hybrid proteins are called *fusion proteins* since they are literally fused in the same polypeptide chain. The DNA-binding hybrid is called the *bait,* and the activating domain hybrid is called the *prey.*

These vectors are inserted into cells of different mating types that can be crossed. One of these vectors also contains a so-called *reporter gene* encoding a protein that can be assayed for enzymatic activity. The reporter gene is under control of a *Gal4*-responsive regulatory region, so that when active *Gal4* is present, the reporter gene is expressed and can be detected by an enzymatic assay.

The DNA-binding hybrid binds to DNA adjacent to the reporter gene. When the two proteins in bait and prey interact, the prey hybrid brings the activating domain into position to turn on gene expression from the reporter gene (see figure 18.13).

The beauty of this system is that it is both simple and flexible. It can be used with two known proteins or with a known protein in the bait vector and entire cDNA libraries in the prey vector. In the latter case, all of the possible interactions in a cell type can be mapped.

It is already clear that even more protein interactions occur in cells than anticipated. In the future these data will

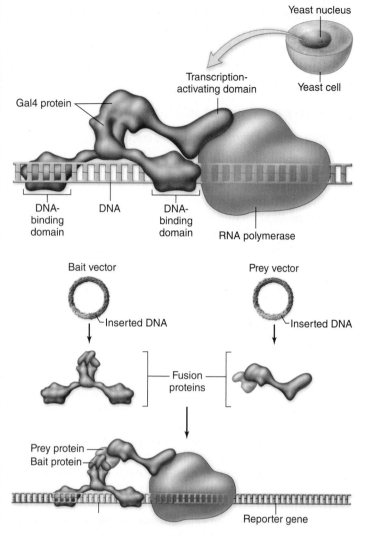

process, such as signal transduction. The technique can then be used to map all of the interacting proteins in a specific signaling pathway.

? Inquiry question What is the relationship among genome, transcriptome, and proteome?

Learning Outcomes Review 18.5

Functional genomics provides tools to begin to understand the functions of the genes in a genome. Microarrays enable evaluation of gene expression for many genes at once. Proteomics involves similar analysis of all the proteins coded by a genome, that is, an organism's proteome. Because of alternative splicing, this task is much more complex.

■ *Why is establishment of a species' transcriptome an important step in studying its proteome?*

18.6 Applications of Genomics

Learning Outcomes

1. List ways in which genomics could be applied to infectious disease research.
2. Explain how genomics could enhance crop production and nutritional yield.
3. Evaluate the issues of genome ownership and privacy.

Figure 18.14 The yeast two-hybrid system detects interacting proteins. The Gal4 protein is a transcriptional activator *(top)*. The *Gal4* gene has been split and engineered into two different vectors such that one will encode only the DNA-binding domain (bait vector) and the other the transcription-activating domain (prey vector). When other genes are spliced into these vectors, they produce fusion proteins containing part of Gal4 and the proteins to be tested. If the proteins being tested interact, this will restore *Gal4* function and activate expression of a reporter gene.

Space allows us to highlight only a few of the myriad applications of genomics to show the possibilities. The tools being developed truly represent a revolution in biology that will likely have a lasting influence on the way that we think about living systems.

Genomics can help to identify infectious diseases

The genomics revolution has yielded millions of new genes to be investigated. The potential of genomics to improve human health is enormous. Mutations in a single gene can explain some, but not most, hereditary diseases. With entire genomes to search, the probability of unraveling human, animal, and plant diseases is greatly improved.

Although proteomics will likely lead to new pharmaceuticals, the immediate effect of genomics is being seen in diagnostics. Both improved technology and gene discovery are enhancing the diagnosis of genetic abnormalities.

Diagnostics are also being used to identify individuals. For example, short tandem repeats (STRs), discovered through genomic research, were among the forensic diagnostic tools used to identify remains of victims of the September 11, 2001, terrorist attack on the World Trade Center in New York City.

form the basis for understanding the networks of protein interactions that make up the normal activities of a cell.

The yeast two-hybrid system can be automated once libraries of known cDNAs are available in each of the two vectors used. The use of two-hybrid screens has been applied to budding yeast to generate a map of all possible interacting proteins. This method is difficult to apply to more complex multicellular organisms, but in a technical tour-de-force, it has been applied to *Drosophila melanogaster* as well.

For vertebrates, the two-hybrid system is being applied more selectively, by concentrating on a biologically significant

The September 11 attacks were followed by an increased awareness and concern about biological weapons. Five people died and 17 more were infected with anthrax after envelopes containing anthrax spores were sent through the U.S. mail. A massive FBI investigation initially focused on the wrong individual, Steven J. Hatfill, a government scientist. Genome sequencing allowed exploration of possible sources of the deadly bacteria. A difference of only 10 bp between strains allowed the FBI to trace the source to a single vial of the bacteria used in a vaccine research program at U.S. Army Medical Research Institute for Infectious Diseases. By 2008, Hatfield was exonerated. Another researcher, Bruce E. Ivins, committed suicide just before being formally charged by the FBI with criminal activity in the 2001 anthrax attacks. Ivins had been working on vaccine development. In addition, substantial effort has been turned toward the use of genomic tools to distinguish between naturally occurring infections and intentional outbreaks of disease. The Centers for Disease Control and Prevention (CDC) have ranked bacteria and viruses that are likely targets for bioterrorism (table 18.2).

Genomics can help improve agricultural crops

Globally speaking, poor nutrition is the greatest impediment to human health. Much of the excitement about the rice genome project is based on its potential for improving the yield and nutritional quality of rice and other cereals worldwide. The development of Golden Rice (see chapter 17) is an

TABLE 18.2	High-Priority Pathogens for Genomic Research	
Pathogen	**Disease**	**Genome***
Variola major	Smallpox	Complete
Bacillus anthracis	Anthrax	Complete
Yersinia pestis	Plague	Complete
Clostridium botulinum	Botulism	Complete
Francisella tularensis	Tularemia	Complete
Filoviruses	Ebola and Marburg hemorrhagic fever	Both are complete
Arenaviruses	Lassa fever and Argentine hemorrhagic fever	Both are complete

* These viruses and bacteria have multiple strains. "Complete" indicates that at least one has been sequenced. For example, the Florida strain of anthrax was the first to be sequenced.

example of improved nutrition through genetic approaches, and access to the entire genome could potentially lead to more improvements. About one third of the world population obtains half its calories from rice (figure 18.15). In some regions, individuals consume up to 1.5 kg of rice daily. More than 500 million tons of rice is produced each year, but this may not be adequate to provide enough rice for the world in the future.

Due in large part to scientific advances in crop breeding and farming techniques, in the last 50 years world grain production has more than doubled, with an increase in cropland of only 1%. The world now farms a total area the size of South America, but without the scientific advances of the past 50 years, an area equal to the entire western hemisphere would need to be farmed to produce enough food for the world.

Unfortunately, water usage for crops has tripled in that time period, and quality farmland is being lost to soil erosion. Scientists are also concerned about the effects of global climate change on agriculture worldwide. Increasing the yield and quality of crops, especially on more marginal farmland, will depend on many factors—but genetic engineering, built on the findings of genomics projects, can contribute significantly to the solution.

Most crops grown in the United States produce less than half of their genetic potential because of environmental stresses (salt, water, and temperature), herbivores, and pathogens (figure 18.16). Identifying genes that can provide resistance to stress and pests is the focus of many current genomics research projects. Having access to entire genomic sequences will enhance the probability of identifying critical genes.

Figure 18.15 Rice field. Most of the rice grown globally is directly consumed by humans and is the dietary mainstay of 2 billion people.

Figure 18.16 Corn crop productivity well below its genetic potential due to drought stress. Corn production can be limited by water deficiencies due to the drought that occurs during the growing season in dry climates. Global climate change may increase drought stress in areas where corn is the major crop.

Synthetic biology extends the potential of genetic engineering

Synthetic biology is the next frontier beyond genetic engineering approaches described in chapter 17. It is now possible to synthetically construct an entire bacterial genome and insert it into a bacterium. Although this accomplishment has been touted as a synthetic cell or synthetic life, creating all the other cell components de novo is still on the horizon.

Synthetic biology can be used to creatively engineer a vast number of solutions. Biosensors are cells that respond to toxins or other molecules with a visible or otherwise measurable signal. Biofuel production, therapeutic treatment for disease, and creation of organisms to degrade environmental hazards are among the many promises of synthetic biology. Along with the huge benefits, the potential for misuse of the technology is leading to extensive ethical discussions.

Genomics raises ethical issues over ownership of genomic information

Genome science is also a source of ethical challenges and dilemmas. One example is the issue of gene patents. Actually, it is the use of a gene, not the gene itself, that is patentable. For a patent to be granted for a gene's use, the product and its function must be known.

The public genome consortia, supported by federal funding, have been driven by the belief that the sequence of genomes should be freely available to all and should not be patented. Private companies patent gene functions, but they often make sequence data available with certain restrictions. The physical sciences have negotiated the landscape of public and for-profit research for decades, but this is relatively new territory for biologists.

A March 2010 ruling in New York state's Southern District Court invalidated Myriad Genetics patents on the *BRCA1* and *BRCA2* genes. The molecular diagnostics company had a monopoly on these two genes, which are used in diagnosing breast cancer risk. From a patient perspective, the patents prevented individuals from seeking a second independent analysis of their *BRCA1* and *BRCA2* allele. Appeals are underway, and the controversy over gene patents continues.

Another ethical issue involves privacy. How sequence data are used is the focus of thoughtful and ongoing discussions. The Universal Declaration on the Human Genome and Human Rights states, "The human genome underlies the fundamental unity of all members of the human family, as well as the recognition of their inherent dignity and diversity. In a symbolic sense, it is the heritage of humanity."

Although we talk about "the" human genome, each of us has subtly different genomes that can be used to identify us. Genetic disorders such as cystic fibrosis and Huntington disease can already be identified by screening, but genomics will greatly increase the number of identifiable traits. The Genetic Information Nondiscrimination Act (GINA) was signed into law in 2008 to prevent discrimination based on genotype. Employers and health insurance companies may not request genetic tests or discriminate based on someone's genetic code. Life, disability, and long-term care insurance coverage are not covered by GINA, however. Members of the military are also excluded from GINA's privacy protection. The U.S. Armed Forces require DNA samples from members of the military for possible casualty identification. The genome privacy debate continues.

Behavioral genomics is an area that is also rich with possibilities and dilemmas. Very few behavioral traits can be accounted for by single genes. Two genes have been associated with fragile-X syndrome, and three with early-onset Alzheimer disease. Comparisons of multiple genomes will likely lead to the identification of multiple genes controlling a range of behaviors. Will this change the way we view acceptable behavior?

In Iceland, the parliament has voted to have a private company create a database from pooled medical, genetic, and genealogical information about all Icelanders, a particularly fascinating population from a genetic perspective. Because minimal migration or immigration has occurred there over the last 800 years, the information that can be mined from the Icelandic database is phenomenal. Ultimately, the value of that information has to be weighed, however, against any possible discrimination or stigmatization of individuals or groups.

? Inquiry question As of February 2008 a draft version of the corn genome had been sequenced. How could you use information from the corn and rice genome sequences to try to improve drought tolerance in corn?

Learning Outcomes Review 18.6

Genomics is one approach to better diagnosis, based on knowledge of infectious agents' genetic makeup; it also allows identification of individual disease strains. Genomics has enhanced DNA identification of remains. Agricultural crop yields and nutritional content could be improved if genes that confer disease resistance or increased synthesis can be identified.

■ *You are assigned to develop a biosensor for a toxin and are working with a bioluminescent gene. What part of the gene will you work with and why?*

Chapter Review

18.1 Mapping Genomes

Different kinds of physical maps can be generated.

Physical genetic maps include fully sequenced genomes, restriction maps, and maps of chromosome-banding patterns.

Sequence-tagged sites provide a common language for physical maps.

Any physical site can be used as a sequence-tagged site (STS), based on a small stretch of a unique DNA sequence that allows unambiguous identification of a fragment (figure 18.3).

Genetic maps provide a link to phenotypes.

Short tandem repeats (STRs) are the most common type of markers for distinguishing regions of the genome and assessing its phenotypic effects.

Physical maps can be correlated with genetic maps.

Physical and genetic maps can be correlated. Any gene that can be cloned can be placed within the genome sequence and mapped. However, absolute correspondence of distances cannot be accomplished.

18.2 Sequencing Genomes

DNA sequencing provides information about genes and genomes.

DNA sequencing technology is an adaptation of DNA replication in vitro that uses modified nucleotides and copies a single strand of the DNA. Modified nucleotides are labeled and stop or pause the extension of a new strand. A whole-genome sequence is the ultimate physical map.

Genome sequencing requires larger molecular clones.

Yeast artificial chromosomes (YACs) have allowed cloning of larger pieces of DNA, although their use has some drawbacks. Bacterial artificial chromosomes (BACs) are most commonly used now.

Whole-genome sequencing is approached in two ways: clone-by-clone and shotgun.

Clone-by-clone sequencing starts with known clones, often in BACs that can be aligned with each other.

Shotgun sequencing involves sequencing random clones, then using a computer to assemble the finished sequence.

The Human Genome Project used both sequencing methods.

By 2004, the "finished" sequence was announced, and it includes 99% of the euchromatic human DNA sequence.

18.3 Characterizing Genomes

The Human Genome Project found fewer genes than expected.

Although eukaryotic genomes are larger and have more genes than those of prokaryotes, the size of the organism is not always correlated with the size of the genome. The human genome contains only around 25,000 genes, fewer than found in rice (figure 18.7).

Finding genes in sequence data requires computer searches.

In a sequenced genome, protein-coding genes are identified by looking for open-reading frames (ORFs). An ORF begins with a start codon and contains no stop codon for a distance long enough to encode a protein. Genes are then grouped based on conserved regions.

Genomes contain both coding and noncoding DNA.

Protein-encoding DNA includes single-copy genes, segmental duplications, multigene families, and tandem clusters. Noncoding DNA in eukaryotes makes up about 99% of DNA. Approximately 45% of the human genome is composed of mobile transposable elements, including LINEs, SINEs, and LTRs.

Expressed sequence tags identify genes that are transcribed.

The number and location of expressed genes can be estimated by sequencing the ends of randomly selected cDNAs to produce expressed sequence tags (ESTs).

SNPs are single-base differences between individuals.

Single-nucleotide difference between individuals are called single-nucleotide polymorphisms (SNPs). To be classified as a polymorphism, an SNP must be present in at least 1% of the population. At least 50,000 SNPs are currently known in coding regions.

Genomic haplotypes are regions of chromosomes that are not exchanged by recombination. These regions can be used to map genes by association (figure 18.8).

18.4 Comparing Genomes

Comparative genomics reveals conserved regions in genomes.

More than half of the genes of *Drosophila* have human counterparts. The biggest difference between our genome and the chimpanzee genome is in transposable elements.

Synteny allows comparison of unsequenced genomes.

Synteny refers to the conserved arrangements of segments of DNA in related genomes (figure 18.9). Many separate species have been found to have large regions of synteny.

Organelle genomes have exchanged genes with the nuclear genome.

Both chloroplasts and mitochondria contain components that indicate exchange of genetic material with the nuclear genome.

18.5 From Genes to Proteins

Functional genomics reveals gene function at the genome level.

Functional genomics uses high-end computer technology to analyze gene function and gene products. DNA microarrays allow the expression of all of the genes in a cell to be monitored at once (figure 18.10).

Proteomics moves from genes to proteins.

Proteomics characterizes all of the proteins produced by a cell. The transcriptome is all the mRNAs present in a cell at a specific time. Protein microarrays can identify and characterize large numbers of proteins.

Large-scale screens reveal protein–protein interactions.

The yeast two-hybrid system is used to generate large-scale maps of interacting proteins; however, the scope of this task is daunting in humans, mice, and other vertebrates. Selective applications in specific areas, such as signal transduction, have been undertaken.

18.6 Applications of Genomics

Genomics can help to identify infectious diseases.

Genomics can help identify naturally occurring and intentional outbreaks of infectious diseases and tracing of disease strains.

Genomics can help improve agricultural crops.

Genomics can potentially increase the nutritional value of crops and alter their responses to environmental stresses, potentially helping to feed a growing population.

Synthetic biology extends the potential of genetic engineering.

The ability to synthesize entire genomes de novo makes it possible to engineer organisms to function as biosensors and chemical factories, clean up contaminated environments, and perform other yet to be imagined roles.

Genomics raises ethical issues over ownership of genomic information.

Questions regarding profit and ownership of genomic data provide ongoing challenges for the ethical use of scientific knowledge.

Review Questions

UNDERSTAND

1. A genetic map is based on the
   a. sequence of the DNA.
   b. relative position of genes on chromosomes.
   c. location of sites of restriction enzyme cleavage.
   d. banding pattern on a chromosome.

2. What is an STS?
   a. A unique sequence within the DNA that can be used for mapping
   b. A repeated sequence within the DNA that can be used for mapping
   c. An upstream element that allows for mapping of the 3′ region of a gene
   d. Both b and c are correct.

3. Which number represents the total number of genes in the human genome?
   a. 2500   c. 25,000
   b. 10,000   d. 100,000

4. An open reading frame (ORF) is distinguished by the presence of
   a. a stop codon.
   b. a start codon.
   c. a sequence of DNA long enough to encode a protein.
   d. All of the choices are correct.

5. What is a BLAST search?
   a. A mechanism for aligning consensus regions during whole-genome sequencing
   b. A search for similar gene sequences from other species
   c. A method of screening a DNA library
   d. A method for identifying ORFs

6. Which of the following is NOT an example of a protein-encoding gene?
   a. Single-copy gene   c. Pseudogene
   b. Tandem clusters   d. Multigene family

7. What is a proteome?
   a. The collection of all genes encoding proteins
   b. The collection of all proteins encoded by the genome
   c. The collection of all proteins present in a cell
   d. The amino acid sequence of a protein

8. Which of the following is NOT an example of noncoding DNA?
   a. Promoter   c. Pseudogene
   b. Intron   d. Exon

APPLY

1. An artificial chromosome is useful because it
   a. produces more consistent results than a natural chromosome.
   b. allows for the isolation of larger DNA sequences.
   c. provides a high copy number of a DNA sequence.
   d. is linear.

2. Comparisons between genomes is made easier because of
   a. synteny.
   b. haplotypes.
   c. transposons.
   d. expressed sequence tags.

3. Which of the following techniques relies on prior knowledge of overlapping sequences?
   a. Yeast two-hybrid system
   b. Shotgun method of genome sequencing
   c. FISH
   d. Clone-by-clone method of genome sequencing

4. The duplication of a gene due to uneven meiotic crossing over is thought to lead to the production of a
   a. segmental duplication.
   b. tandem duplication.
   c. simple sequence repeat.
   d. multigene family.

5. What information can be obtained from a DNA microarray?
   a. The sequence of a particular gene
   b. The presence of genes within a specific tissue
   c. The pattern of gene expression
   d. Differences between genomes

6. Which of the following is true regarding microarray technology and cancer?
   a. A DNA microarray can determine the type of cancer.
   b. A DNA microarray can measure the response of a cancer to therapy.
   c. A DNA microarray can be used to predict whether the cancer will metastasize.
   d. All of the choices are correct.

7. Which of the following techniques could be used to examine protein–protein interactions in a cell?
   a. Two-hybrid screens
   b. Protein structure databases
   c. Protein microarrays
   d. Both a and c are correct.

SYNTHESIZE

1. You are in the early stages of a genome-sequencing project. You have isolated a number of clones from a BAC library and mapped the inserts in these clones using STSs. Use the STSs shown to align the clones into a contiguous sequence of the genome (a contig).

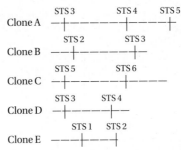

2. Genomic research can be used to determine if an outbreak of an infectious disease is natural or "intentional." Explain what a genomic researcher would be looking for in a suspected intentional outbreak of a disease like anthrax.

ONLINE RESOURCE

www.ravenbiology.com

Understand, Apply, and Synthesize—enhance your study with animations that bring concepts to life and practice tests to assess your understanding. Your instructor may also recommend the interactive eBook, individualized learning tools, and more.

Chapter

19

Cellular Mechanisms of Development

5.5 μm

Chapter Contents

Introduction

Recent work with different kinds of stem cells, like those pictured, have captured the hopes and imagination of the public. For thousands of years, humans have wondered how organisms arise, grow, change, and mature. We are now in an era when long-standing questions may be answered, and new possibilities for regenerative medicine seem on the horizon.

We have explored gene expression from the perspective of individual cells, examining the diverse mechanisms cells employ to control the transcription of particular genes. Now we broaden our perspective and look at the unique challenge posed by the development of a single cell, the fertilized egg, into a multicellular organism. In the course of this developmental journey, a pattern of gene expression takes place that causes particular lines of cells to proceed along different paths, spinning an incredibly complex web of cause and effect. Yet, for all its complexity, this developmental program works with impressive precision. In this chapter, we explore the mechanisms of development at the cellular and molecular level.

19.1 The Process of Development

Development can be defined as the process of systematic, gene-directed changes through which an organism forms the successive stages of its life cycle. Development is a continuum, and explorations of development can be focused on any point along this continuum. The study of development plays a central role in unifying the understanding of both the similarities and diversity of life on Earth.

We can divide the overall process of development into four subprocesses:

- **Cell Division.** A developing plant or animal begins as a fertilized egg, or zygote, that must undergo cell division to produce the new individual. In all cases early development involves extensive cell division, but in many cases it does not include much growth as the egg cell itself is quite large.

- **Differentiation.** As cells divide, orchestrated changes in gene expression result in differences between cells that ultimately result in cell specialization. In differentiated cells, certain genes are expressed at particular times, but other genes may not be expressed at all.

- **Pattern Formation.** Cells in a developing embryo must become oriented to the body plan of the organism the embryo will become. Pattern formation involves cells' abilities to detect positional information that guides their ultimate fate.
- **Morphogenesis.** As development proceeds, the form of the body—its organs and anatomical features—is generated. Morphogenesis may involve cell death as well as cell division and differentiation.

Despite the overt differences between groups of plants and animals, most multicellular organisms develop according to molecular mechanisms that are fundamentally very similar. This observation suggests that these mechanisms evolved very early in the history of multicellular life.

19.2 Cell Division

Learning Outcomes

1. Characterize the role of cell division in early development.
2. Describe the use of C. elegans to track cell lineages.
3. Distinguish differences in cell division between animals and plants.

When a frog tadpole hatches out of its protective coats, it is roughly the same overall mass as the fertilized egg from which it came. Instead of being made up of just one cell, however, the tadpole consists of about a million cells, which are organized into tissues and organs with different functions. Thus, the very first process that must occur during embryogenesis is cell division.

Immediately following fertilization, the diploid zygote undergoes a period of rapid mitotic divisions that ultimately result in an early embryo comprised of dozens to thousands of diploid cells. In animal embryos, the timing and number of these divisions are species-specific and are controlled by a set of molecules that we examined in chapter 10: the *cyclins* and *cyclin-dependent kinases (Cdks)*. These molecules exert control over checkpoints in the cycle of mitosis.

Development begins with cell division

In animal embryos, the period of rapid cell division following fertilization is called **cleavage.** During cleavage, the enormous mass of the zygote is subdivided into a larger and larger number of smaller and smaller cells, called **blastomeres** (figure 19.1). Hence, cleavage is not accompanied by any increase in the overall size of the embryo. The G_1 and G_2 phases of the cell cycle, during which a cell increases its mass and size, are extremely shortened or eliminated during cleavage (figure 19.2).

Because of the absence of the two gap/growth phases, the rapid rate of mitotic divisions during cleavage is never again approached in the lifetime of any animal. For example, zebrafish blastomeres divide once every several minutes during cleavage, to create an embryo with a thousand cells in just under 3 hr! In contrast, cycling adult human intestinal epithelial cells divide on average only once every 19 hr. A comparison of the different patterns of cleavage can be found in chapter 53.

When external sources of nutrients become available—for example, during larval feeding stages or after implantation of mammalian embryos—daughter cells can increase in size following cytokinesis, and an overall increase in the size of the organism occurs as more cells are produced.

Every cell division is known in the development of *C. elegans*

One of the most completely described models of development is the tiny nematode *Caenorhabditis elegans*. Only about 1 mm long, the adult worm consists of 959 somatic cells.

Because *C. elegans* is transparent, individual cells can be followed as they divide. By observing them, researchers have learned how each of the cells that make up the adult worm is derived from the fertilized egg. As shown on the lineage map in figure 19.3a, the egg divides into two cells, and these daughter cells continue to divide. Each horizontal line on the map represents one round of cell division. The length of each vertical line represents the time between cell divisions, and the end of each vertical line represents one fully differentiated cell. In figure 19.3b, the major organs of the worm are color-coded to match the colors of the corresponding groups of cells on the lineage map.

Some of these differentiated cells, such as some cells that generate the worm's external cuticle, are "born" after only 8 rounds of cell division; other cuticle cells require as many as 14 rounds. The cells that make up the worm's pharynx, or feeding organ, are born after 9 to 11 rounds of division, whereas cells in the gonads require up to 17 divisions.

Exactly 302 nerve cells are destined for the worm's nervous system. Exactly 131 cells are programmed to die, mostly within minutes of their "birth." The fate of each cell is the same in every *C. elegans* individual, except for the cells that will become eggs and sperm.

Figure 19.1 Cleavage divisions in a frog embryo. *a.* The first cleavage division divides the egg into two large blastomeres. *b.* After two more divisions, four small blastomeres sit on top of four large blastomeres, each of which continues to divide to produce *(c)* a compact mass of cells.

a. 0.8 mm

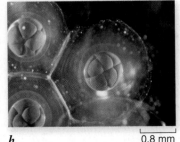
b. 0.8 mm

c. 0.8 mm

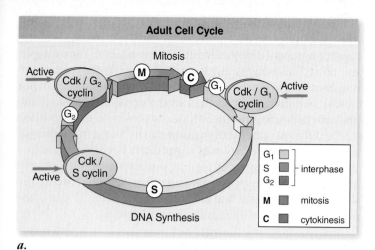

Adult Cell Cycle

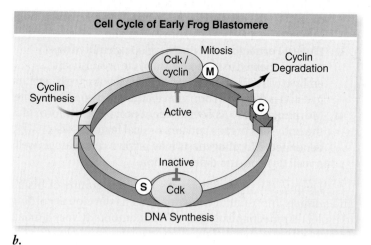

Cell Cycle of Early Frog Blastomere

a. *b.*

Figure 19.2 Cell cycle of adult cell and embryonic cell. In contrast to the cell cycle of adult somatic cells *(a)*, the dividing cells of early frog embryos lack G₁ and G₂ stages *(b)*, enabling the cleavage stage nuclei to rapidly cycle between DNA synthesis and mitosis. Large stores of cyclin mRNA are present in the unfertilized egg. Periodic degradation of cyclin proteins correlates with exiting from mitosis. Cyclin degradation and Cdk inactivation allow the cell to complete mitosis and initiate the next round of DNA synthesis.

Plant growth occurs in specific areas called meristems

A major difference between animals and plants is that most animals are mobile, at least in some phase of their life cycles, and therefore they can move away from unfavorable circumstances. Plants, in contrast, are anchored in position and must simply endure whatever environment they experience. Plants compensate for this restriction by allowing development to accommodate local circumstances.

Instead of creating a body in which every part is specified to have a fixed size and location, a plant assembles its body throughout its life span from a few types of modules, such as leaves, roots, branch nodes, and flowers. Each module has a rigidly controlled structure and organization, but how the modules are utilized is quite flexible—they can be adjusted to environmental conditions.

Figure 19.3 Studying embryonic cell division and development in the nematode.

Development in *C. elegans* has been mapped out such that the fate of each cell from the single egg cell has been determined. *a.* The lineage map shows the number of cell divisions from the egg, and the color coding links their placement in *(b)* the adult organism.

M. E. Challinor illustration. From Howard Hughes Medical Institute © as published in *From Egg to Adult*, 1992. Reprinted by permission.

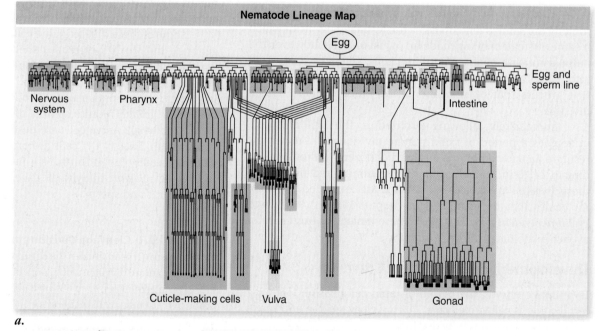

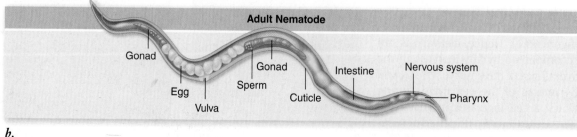

Plants develop by building their bodies outward, creating new parts from groups of stem cells that are contained in structures called **meristems.** As meristematic stem cells continually divide, they produce cells that can differentiate into the tissues of the plant.

This simple scheme indicates a need to control the process of cell division. We know that cell-cycle control genes are present in both yeast (fungi) and animal cells, implying that these are a eukaryotic innovation—and in fact, the plant cell cycle is regulated by the same mechanisms, namely through cyclins and cyclin-dependent kinases. In one experiment, overexpression of a Cdk inhibitor in transgenic *Arabidopsis thaliana* plants resulted in strong inhibition of cell division in leaf meristems, leading to significant changes in leaf size and shape.

Learning Outcomes Review 19.2

In animal embryos, a series of rapid cell divisions that skip the G_1 and G_2 phases convert the fertilized egg into many cells with no change in size. In the nematode *C. elegans,* every cell division leading to the adult form is known, and this pattern is invariant, allowing biologists to trace development in a cell-by-cell fashion. In plants, growth is restricted to specific areas called meristems, where undifferentiated stem cells are retained.

■ *How are early cell divisions in an embryo different from in an adult organism?*

19.3 Cell Differentiation

Learning Outcomes

1. *Describe the progressive nature of determination.*
2. *Illustrate with examples how cells become committed to developmental pathways.*
3. *Differentiate between the different types of stem cells.*

In chapter 16, we examined the mechanisms that control eukaryotic gene expression. These processes are critical for the development of multicellular organisms, in which life functions are carried out by different tissues and organs. In the course of development, cells become different from one another because of the differential expression of subsets of genes—not only at different times, but in different locations of the growing embryo. We now explore some of the mechanisms that lead to differential gene expression during development.

Cells become determined prior to differentiation

A human body contains more than 210 major types of differentiated cells. These differentiated cells are distinguishable from one another by the particular proteins that they synthesize, their morphologies, and their specific functions. A molecular decision to become a particular type of differentiated cell occurs prior to any overt changes in the cell. This molecular decision-making process is called **cell determination,** and it commits a cell to a particular developmental pathway.

Tracking determination

Determination is often not visible in the cell and can only be "seen" by experiment. The standard experiment to test whether a cell or group of cells is determined is to move the donor cell(s) to a different location in a host (recipient) embryo. If the cells of the transplant develop into the same type of cell as they would have if left undisturbed, then they are judged to be already determined (figure 19.4).

Determination has a time course; it depends on a series of intrinsic or extrinsic events, or both. For example, a cell in the prospective brain region of an amphibian embryo at the early gastrula stage (see chapter 53) has not yet been determined; if transplanted elsewhere in the embryo, it will develop according to the site of transplant. By the late gastrula stage,

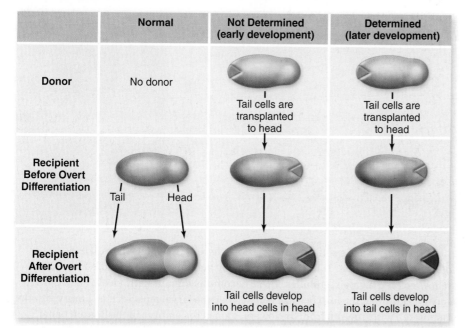

	Normal	Not Determined (early development)	Determined (later development)
Donor	No donor	Tail cells are transplanted to head	Tail cells are transplanted to head
Recipient Before Overt Differentiation	Tail — Head		
Recipient After Overt Differentiation		Tail cells develop into head cells in head	Tail cells develop into tail cells in head

Figure 19.4 The standard test for determination. The gray ovals represent embryos at early stages of development. The cells to the right normally develop into head structures, whereas the cells to the left usually form tail structures. If prospective tail cells from an early embryo are transplanted to the opposite end of a host embryo, they develop according to their new position into head structures. These cells are not determined. At later stages of development, the tail cells are determined since they now develop into tail structures after transplantation into the opposite end of a host embryo!

however, additional cell interactions have occurred, determination has taken place, and the cell will develop as neural tissue no matter where it is transplanted.

Determination often takes place in stages, with a cell first becoming partially committed, acquiring positional labels that reflect its location in the embryo. These labels can have a great influence on how the pattern of the body subsequently develops. In a chicken embryo, tissue at the base of the leg bud normally gives rise to the thigh. If this tissue is transplanted to the tip of the identical-looking wing bud, which would normally give rise to the wing tip, the transplanted tissue will develop into a toe rather than a thigh. The tissue has already been determined as leg, but it is not yet committed to being a particular part of the leg. Therefore, it can be influenced by the positional signaling at the tip of the wing bud to form a tip (but in this case, a tip of leg).

The molecular basis of determination

Cells initiate developmental changes by using transcription factors to change patterns of gene expression. When genes encoding these transcription factors are activated, one of their effects is to reinforce their own activation. This reinforcement makes the developmental switch deterministic, initiating a chain of events that leads down a particular developmental pathway.

Cells in which a set of regulatory genes have been activated may not actually undergo differentiation until some time later, when other factors interact with the regulatory protein and cause it to activate still other genes. Nevertheless, once the initial "switch" is thrown, the cell is fully committed to its future developmental path.

Cells become committed to follow a particular developmental pathway in one of two ways:

1. via the differential inheritance of cytoplasmic determinants, which are maternally produced and deposited into the egg during oogenesis; or
2. via cell–cell interactions.

The first situation can be likened to a person's social status being determined by who his or her parents are and what he or she has inherited. In the second situation, the person's social standing is determined by interactions with his or her neighbors. Clearly both can be powerful factors in the development and maturation of that individual.

Determination can be due to cytoplasmic determinants

Many invertebrate embryos provide good visual examples of cell determination through the differential inheritance of

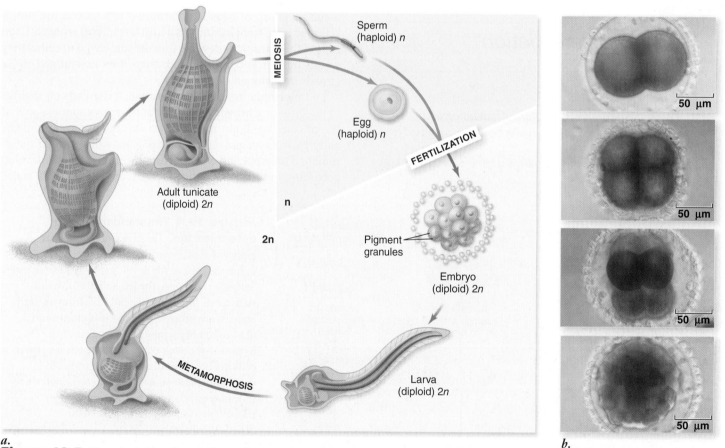

a.
Figure 19.5 Muscle determinants in tunicates. *a.* The life cycle of a solitary tunicate. Muscle cells that move the tail of the swimming tadpole are arranged on either side of the notochord and nerve cord. The tail is lost during metamorphosis into the sedentary adult. *b.* The egg of the tunicate *Styela* contains bright yellow-colored pigment granules. These become asymmetrically localized in the egg following fertilization, and cells that inherit the yellow-colored granules during cleavage will become the larval muscle cells. Embryos at the 2-cell, 4-cell, 8-cell, and 64-cell stages are shown. The tadpole tail will grow out from the lower region of the embryo in the bottom panel.

cytoplasmic determinants. Tunicates are marine invertebrates (see chapter 35), and most adults have simple, saclike bodies that are attached to the underlying substratum. Tunicates are placed in the phylum Chordata, however, due to the characteristics of their swimming, tadpolelike larval stage, which has a dorsal nerve cord and notochord (figure 19.5*a*). The muscles that move the tail develop on either side of the notochord.

In many tunicate species, yellow-colored pigment granules become asymmetrically localized in the egg following fertilization and subsequently segregate to the tail muscle cell progenitors during cleavage (figure 19.5*b*). When these pigment granules are shifted experimentally into other cells that normally do not develop into muscle, their fate is changed and they become muscle cells. Thus, the molecules that flip the switch for muscle development appear to be associated with the pigment granules.

The next step is to determine the identity of the molecules involved. Experiments indicate that the female parent provides the egg with mRNA encoded by the *macho-1* gene. The elimination of *macho-1* function leads to a loss of tail muscle in the tadpole, and the misexpression of *macho-1* mRNA leads to the formation of additional (ectopic) muscle cells from nonmuscle lineage cells. The *macho-1* gene product has been shown to be a transcription factor that can activate the expression of several muscle-specific genes.

Induction can lead to cell differentiation

In chapter 9, we examined a variety of ways by which cells communicate with one another. We can demonstrate the importance of cell–cell interactions in development by separating the cells of an early frog embryo and allowing them to develop independently.

Under these conditions, blastomeres from one pole of the embryo (the "animal pole") develop features of ectoderm, and blastomeres from the opposite pole of the embryo (the "vegetal pole") develop features of endoderm. None of the two separated groups of cells ever develop features characteristic of mesoderm, the third main cell type. If animal-pole cells and vegetal-pole cells are placed next to each other, however, some of the animal-pole cells develop as mesoderm. The interaction between the two cell types triggers a switch in the developmental path of these cells. This change in cell fate due to interaction with an adjacent cell is called **induction.** Signaling molecules act to alter gene expression in the target cells, in this case, some of the animal-pole cells.

Another example of inductive cell interactions is the formation of the notochord and mesenchyme, a specific tissue, in tunicate embryos. Muscle, notochord, and mesenchyme all arise from mesodermal cells that form at the vegetal margin of the 32-cell stage embryo. These prospective mesodermal cells receive signals from the underlying endodermal precursor cells that lead to the formation of notochord and mesenchyme (figure 19.6).

The chemical signal is a member of the *fibroblast growth factor (FGF)* family of signaling molecules. It induces the overlying marginal zone cells to differentiate into either notochord (anterior) or mesenchyme (posterior). The FGF receptor on the marginal zone cells is a receptor tyrosine kinase that

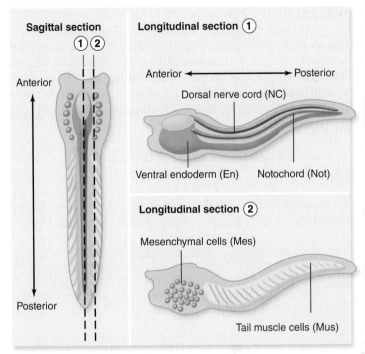

a.

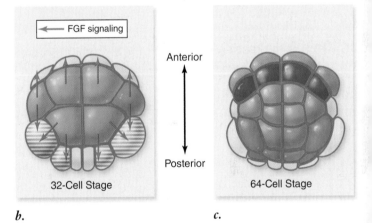

b.   *c.*

Figure 19.6 Inductive interactions contribute to cell fate specification in tunicate embryos. *a.* Internal structures of a tunicate larva. To the left is a sagittal section through the larva with dotted lines indicating two longitudinal sections. Section 1, through the midline of a tadpole, shows the dorsal nerve cord (NC), the underlying notochord (Not) and the ventral endoderm cells (En). Section 2, a more lateral section, shows the mesenchymal cells (Mes) and the tail muscle cells (Mus). *b.* View of the 32-cell stage looking up at the endoderm precursor cells. Fibroblast growth factor (FGF) secreted by these cells is indicated with light-green arrows. Only the surfaces of the marginal cells that directly border the endoderm precursor cells bind FGF signal molecules. Note that the posterior vegetal blastomeres also contain the *macho-1* determinants (red and white stripes). *c.* Cell fates have been fixed by the 64-cell stage. Colors are as in *(a)*. Cells on the anterior margin of the endoderm precursor cells become notochord and nerve cord, respectively, whereas cells that border the posterior margin of the endoderm cells become mesenchyme and muscle cells, respectively.

signals through a MAP kinase cascade to activate a transcription factor that turns on gene expression resulting in differentiation (figure 19.7).

This example is also a case of two cells responding differently to the same signal. The presence or absence of the *macho-1* muscle determinant discussed earlier controls this difference in cell fate. In the presence of *macho-1*, cells differentiate into mesenchyme; in its absence, cells differentiate into notochord. Thus, the combination of *macho-1* and FGF signaling leads to four different cell types (see figure 19.7)

Stem cells can divide and produce cells that differentiate

It is important, both during development, and even in the adult animal, to have cells set aside that can divide but are not determined for only a single cell fate. We call cells that are capable of continued division but that can also give rise to differentiated cells, **stem cells.** These cells can be characterized based on the degree to which they have become determined. At one extreme, we call a cell that can give rise to any tissue in an organism **totipotent.** In mammals, the only cells that can give rise to both the embryo and the extraembryonic membranes are the zygote and early blastomeres from the first few cell divisions. Cells that can give rise to all of the cells in the organism's body are called **pluripotent.** A stem cell that can give rise to a limited number of cell types, such as the cells that give rise to the different blood cell types, are called **multipotent.** Then at the other extreme, **unipotent** stem cells give rise to only a single cell type, such as the cells that give rise to sperm cells in males.

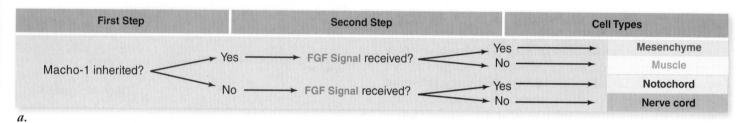

a.

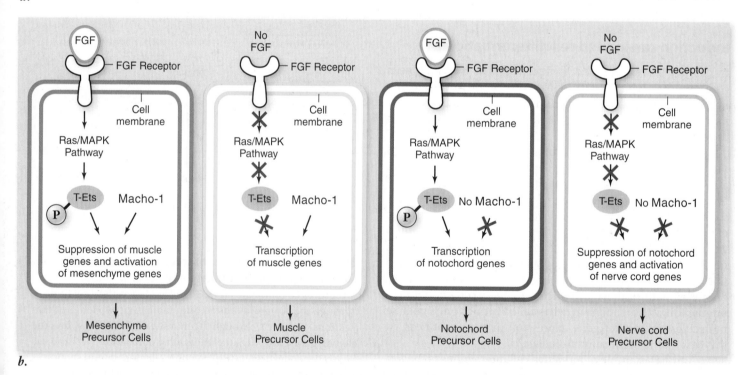

b.

Figure 19.7 **Model for cell fate specification by Macho-1 muscle determinant and FGF signaling.** *a.* Two-step model of cell fate specification in vegetal marginal cells of the tunicate embryo. The first step is inheritance (or not) of muscle *macho-1* mRNA. The second step is FGF signaling from the underlying endoderm precursor cells. *b.* Posterior vegetal margin cells inherit *macho-1* mRNA. Signaling by FGF activates a Ras/MAP kinase pathway that produces the transcription factor T-Ets. Macho-1 protein and T-Ets suppress muscle-specific genes and turn on mesenchyme specific genes (*green cells*). In cells with Macho-1 that do not receive the FGF signal, Macho-1 alone turns on muscle-specific cells (*yellow cells*). Anterior vegetal margin cells do not inherit *macho-1* mRNA. If these cells receive the FGF signal, T-Ets turns on notochord-specific genes (*purple cells*). In cells that lack Macho-1 and FGF, notochord-specific genes are suppressed and nerve cord-specific genes are activated (*gray cells*).

Data analysis What type of cells would develop if you injected embryos with a reagent that blocked the FGF receptor, thus preventing its signaling? What about with a reagent that turned on the FGF receptor, thereby causing it to be always on?

Embryonic stem cells are pluripotent cells derived from embryos

A form of pluripotent stem cells that has been derived in the laboratory are called embryonic stem cells (ES cells). These cells are made from mammalian embryos that have undergone the cleavage stage of development to produce a ball of cells called a blastocyst. The blastocyst consists of an outer ball of cells, the trophectoderm, which will become the placenta, and the inner cell mass that will go on to form the embryo (see chapter 53 for details). Embryonic stem cells can be isolated from the inner cell mass and grown in culture (figure 19.8). In mice, these cells have been studied extensively and have been shown to be able to develop into any type of cell in the tissues of the adult. However, these cells cannot give rise to the extraembryonic tissues that arise during development, so they are pluripotent, but not totipotent.

Once these cells were found in mice, it was only a matter of time before human ES cells were derived as well. In 1998, the first human ES cells (hES cells) were isolated and grown in culture. While there are differences between human and mouse ES cells, there are also substantial similarities. These embryonic stem cells hold great promise for regenerative medicine based on their potential to produce any cell type as described below. These cells have also been the source of much controversy and ethical discussion due to their embryonic origin.

Differentiation in culture

In addition to their possible therapeutic uses, ES cells offer a way to study the differentiation process in culture. The manipulation of these cells by additions to the culture media will allow us to tease out the factors involved in differentiation at the level of the actual cell undergoing the process. Early attempts at assessing differentiation in culture was plagued by the culture conditions. The medium in early experiments contained fetal calf serum (common in tissue culture), which is ill-defined, and varies lot-to-lot. More recently, more defined culture conditions have been found that allow greater reproducibility in controlling differentiation in culture.

Using more defined media, ES cells have been used to recapitulate in culture the early events in mouse development. Thus mouse ES cells can be used to first give rise to ectoderm, endoderm, and mesoderm, then these three cell types will give rise to the different cells each germ layer is determined to become. This work is in early stages but is tremendously exciting as it offers the promise of understanding the molecular cues that are involved in the stepwise determination of different cell types.

In humans, ES cells have been used to give rise to a variety of cell types in culture. For example, human ES cells have been shown to give rise to different kinds of blood cells in culture. Work is underway to produce hematopoietic stem cells in culture, which could be used to replace such cells in patients with diseases that affect blood cells. Human ES cells have also been used to produce cardiomyocytes in culture. These cells could be used to replace damaged heart tissue after heart attacks.

Learning Outcomes Review 19.3

Cell differentiation is preceded by determination, where the cell becomes committed to a developmental pathway, but has not yet differentiated. Differential inheritance of cytoplasmic factors can cause determination and differentiation, as can interactions between neighboring cells (induction). Inductive changes are mediated by signaling molecules that trigger transduction pathways. Stem cells are able to divide indefinitely, and they can give rise to differentiated cells. Embryonic stem cells are pluripotent cells that can give rise to all adult structures.

■ *How could you distinguish whether a cell becomes determined by induction or because of cytoplasmic factors?*

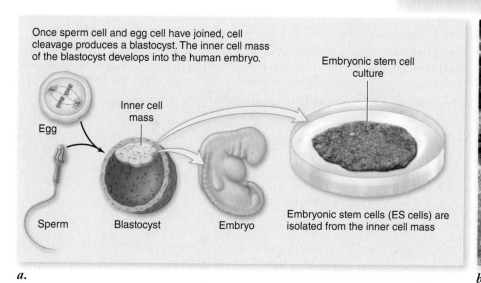

Once sperm cell and egg cell have joined, cell cleavage produces a blastocyst. The inner cell mass of the blastocyst develops into the human embryo.

Embryonic stem cell culture

Inner cell mass

Egg

Sperm

Blastocyst

Embryo

Embryonic stem cells (ES cells) are isolated from the inner cell mass

a.

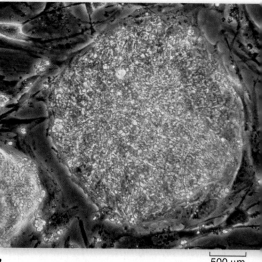

b.

500 μm

Figure 19.8 Isolation of embryonic stem cells. *a.* Early cell divisions lead to the blastocyst stage that consists of an outer layer and an inner cell mass, which will go on to form the embryo. Embryonic stem cells (ES cells) can be isolated from this stage by disrupting the embryo and plating the cells. Stem cells removed from a six-day blastocyst can be established in culture and maintained indefinitely in an undifferentiated state. *b.* Human embryonic stem cells. This mass in the photograph is a colony of undifferentiated human embryonic stem cells being studied in the developmental biologist James Thomson's research lab at the University of Wisconsin–Madison.

19.4 Nuclear Reprogramming

Learning Outcomes

1. *Contrast different methods of nuclear reprogramming.*
2. *Differentiate between reproductive and therapeutic cloning.*

The study of the process of determination and differentiation leads quite naturally to questions about whether this process can be reversed. This is of interest both in terms of the experimental possibilities to understand the basic process, and the prospect of creating patient-specific populations of specific cell types to replace cells lost to disease or trauma. This has led to a fascinating path with many twists and turns that has accelerated in the recent past. We will briefly consider the history of this topic, then look at the most recent results available.

Reversal of determination has allowed cloning

Experiments carried out in the 1950s showed that single cells from fully differentiated tissue of an adult plant could develop into entire, mature plants. The cells of an early cleavage stage mammalian embryo are also totipotent. When mammalian embryos naturally split in two, identical twins result. If individual blastomeres are separated from one another, any one of them can produce a completely normal individual. In fact, this type of procedure has been used to produce sets of four or eight identical offspring in the commercial breeding of particularly valuable lines of cattle.

Early research in amphibians

An early question in developmental biology was whether the production of differentiated cells during development involved irreversible changes to cells. Experiments carried out in the 1950s by Robert Briggs and Thomas King, and by John Gurdon in the 1960s and 1970s showed nuclei could be transplanted between cells. Using very fine pipettes (hollow glass tubes), these researchers sucked the nucleus out of a frog or toad egg and replaced the egg nucleus with a nucleus sucked out of a body cell taken from another individual.

The conclusions from these experiments are somewhat contradictory. On the one hand, cells do not appear to undergo any truly irreversible changes, such as loss of genes. On the other hand, the more differentiated the cell type, the less successful the nucleus in directing development when transplanted. This led to the concept of *nuclear reprogramming,* that is, a nucleus from a differentiated cell undergoes **epigenetic** changes that must be reversed to allow the nucleus to direct development. Epigenetic changes do not change a cell's DNA but are stable through cell divisions. The early work on amphibians showed that tadpoles' intestinal cell nuclei could be reprogrammed to produce viable adult frogs. These animals not only can be considered clones, but they show that tadpole nuclei can be completely reprogrammed. However, nuclei from adult differentiated cells could only be reprogrammed to produce tadpoles, but not viable, fertile adults. Thus this work showed that adult nuclei have remarkable developmental potential, but cannot be reprogrammed to be totipotent.

Early research in mammals

Given the work done in amphibians, much effort was put into nuclear transfer in mammals, primarily mice and cattle. Not only did this not result in reproducible production of cloned

Figure 19.9 Proof that determination in animals is reversible. Scientists combined a nucleus from an adult mammary cell with an enucleated egg cell to successfully clone a sheep, named Dolly, who grew to be a normal adult and bore healthy offspring. This experiment, the first successful cloning of an adult animal, shows that a differentiated adult cell can be used to drive all of development.

Data analysis The sheep used for the donor nucleus had a different pattern of pigmentation than the donor egg. Why is this important, and which animal should Dolly resemble?

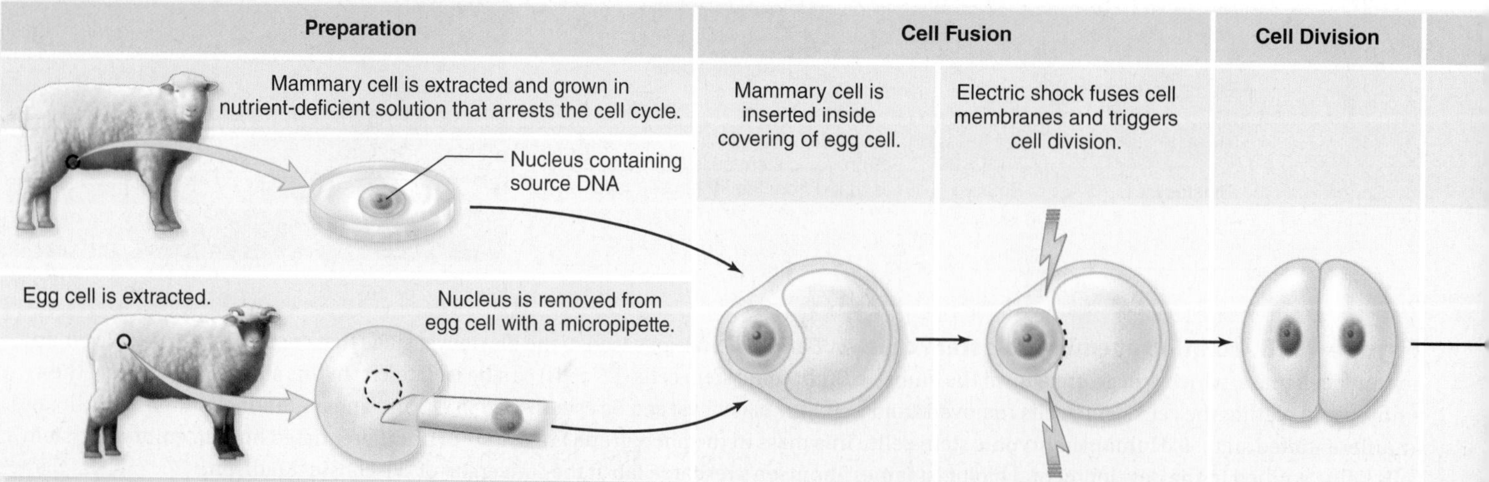

Preparation
Cell Fusion
Cell Division
Mammary cell is extracted and grown in nutrient-deficient solution that arrests the cell cycle.
Nucleus containing source DNA
Egg cell is extracted.
Nucleus is removed from egg cell with a micropipette.
Mammary cell is inserted inside covering of egg cell.
Electric shock fuses cell membranes and triggers cell division.

animals, but this work led to the discovery of imprinting through the production of embryos with only maternal or paternal input (see chapter 13 for more information on imprinting). These embryos never developed, and showed different kinds of defects depending on whether the maternal or paternal genome was the sole contributor.

Successful nuclear transplant in mammals

These results stood until a sheep was cloned using the nucleus from a cell of an early embryo in 1984. The key to this success was in picking a donor cell very early in development. This exciting result was soon replicated by others in a host of other organisms, including pigs and monkeys. Only early embryo cells seemed to work, however.

Geneticists at the Roslin Institute in Scotland reasoned that the egg and donated nucleus would need to be at the same stage of the cell cycle for successful development. To test this idea, they performed the following procedure (figure 19.9):

1. They removed differentiated mammary cells from the udder of a six-year-old sheep. The cells were grown in tissue culture, and then the concentration of serum nutrients was substantially reduced for five days, causing them to pause at the beginning of the cell cycle.
2. In parallel preparation, eggs obtained from a ewe were enucleated.
3. Mammary cells and egg cells were surgically combined in a process called **somatic cell nuclear transfer (SCNT)** in January of 1996. Mammary cells and eggs were fused to introduce the mammary nucleus into egg.
4. Twenty-nine of 277 fused couplets developed into embryos, which were then placed into the reproductive tracts of surrogate mothers.
5. A little over five months later, on July 5, 1996, one sheep gave birth to a lamb named Dolly, the first clone generated from a fully differentiated animal cell.

Dolly matured into an adult ewe, and she was able to reproduce the old-fashioned way, producing six lambs. Thus, Dolly established beyond all dispute that determination in animals is reversible—that with the right techniques, the nucleus of a fully differentiated cell *can* be reprogrammed to be totipotent.

Reproductive cloning has inherent problems

The term **reproductive cloning** refers to the process just described, in which scientists use SCNT to create an animal that is genetically identical to another animal. Since Dolly's birth in 1997, scientists have successfully cloned one or more cats, dogs, rabbits, rats, mice, cattle, goats, pigs, and mules. All of these procedures used some form of adult cell.

Low success rate and age-associated diseases

The efficiency in all reproductive cloning is quite low—only 3–5% of adult nuclei transferred to donor eggs result in live births. In addition, many clones that are born usually die soon thereafter of liver failure or infections. Many become oversized, a condition known as *large offspring syndrome (LOS)*. In 2003, three of four cloned piglets developed to adulthood, but all three suddenly died of heart failure at less than 6 months of age.

Dolly herself was euthanized at the relatively young age of six. Although she was put down because of virally induced lung cancer, she had been diagnosed with advanced-stage arthritis a year earlier. Thus, one difficulty in using genetic engineering and cloning to improve livestock is production of enough healthy animals.

Lack of imprinting

The reason for these problems lies in a phenomenon discussed in chapter 13: *genomic imprinting*. Imprinted genes are expressed differently depending on parental origin—that is, they are turned off in either egg or sperm, and this "setting" continues through development into the adult. Normal mammalian development depends on precise genomic imprinting.

The chemical reprogramming of the DNA, which occurs in adult reproductive tissue, takes months for sperm and years for eggs. During cloning, by contrast, the reprogramming of the donor DNA must occur within a few hours. The organization of the chromatin in a somatic cell is also quite different from that in a newly fertilized egg. Significant chromatin remodeling of the transferred donor nucleus must also occur if the cloned embryo is to survive. Cloning fails because there is likely not enough time in these few hours to get the remodeling and reprogramming jobs done properly.

Development	Implantation	Birth of Clone	Growth to Adulthood
Embryo begins to develop in vitro.	Embryo is implanted into surrogate mother.	After a five-month pregnancy, a lamb genetically identical to the sheep from which the mammary cell was extracted is born.	

Embryo

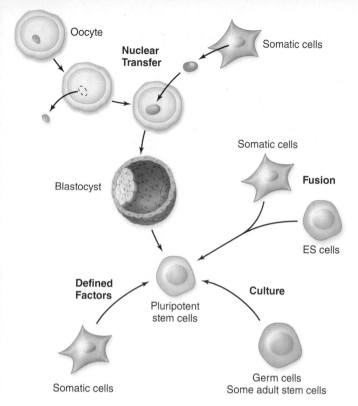

Figure 19.10 Methods to reprogram adult cell nuclei.
Cells taken from adult organisms can be reprogrammed to pluripotent cells in a number of different ways. Nuclei from somatic cells can be transplanted into oocytes as during cloning. Somatic cells can be fused to ES cells created by some other means. Germ cells, and some adult stem cells, after prolonged culture appear to be reprogrammed. Recent work has shown that somatic cells in culture can be reprogrammed by introduction of defined factors.

Nuclear reprogramming has been accomplished by use of defined factors

Stimulated by the discovery of ES cells and success in the reproductive cloning of mammals, work turned to finding ways to reprogram adult cells to pluripotency without the use of embryos (figure 19.10). One approach was to fuse an ES cell to a differentiated cell. These fusion experiments showed that the nucleus of the differentiated cell could be reprogrammed by exposure to ES cell cytoplasm. Of course, the resulting cells are tetraploid (four copies of the genome), which limits their experimental and practical utility. Another line of research showed that primordial germ cells explanted into culture can give rise to cells that act similar to ES cells after extended time in culture.

All of these different lines of inquiry showed that reprogramming of somatic nuclei was possible. Investigations into the characteristics of pluripotency identified a set of transcription factors that were active in ES cells. Then in 2006 it was shown that introducing genes that encode four of these transcription factors, Oct4, Sox2, c-Myc, and Klf4 could reprogram fibroblast cells in culture. Following introduction of the transcription factors genes, cells were selected that express a target gene regulated by Oct4 and Sox2, and these cells appeared to be pluripotent. These were named induced pluripotent stem cells, or iPS cells.

The protocol has been refined by selection for another target gene known to be critical to the pluripotent state: *Nanog*. These *Nanog*-expressing iPS cells appear to be similar to ES cells in terms of developmental potential, as well as gene expression pattern. There is some indication that their chromatin structure, and thus their epigenetic state, may not be the same as that of ES cells.

It is worth asking what this work has taught us about the pluripotent state and the differentiated state. It is becoming clear that reprogramming is a multistep process. When this is done in culture, only a subset of cells make each step, thus explaining why the entire process is inefficient. Starting from a fibroblast, cells first change shape, becoming more spherical, and divide more rapidly. They then reverse part of their developmental program, becoming more like epithelial cells, a so-called mesenchyme-to-epithelial transition.

Lastly, the stable expression of the core pluripotency regulatory factors Oct4, Sox2, and Nanog is established. The pluripotent state is maintained by a combination of transcription factors and chromatin structure (epigenetic changes).

This technology has now been used to construct ES cells from patients with the inherited neurological disorder spinal muscular atrophy. These ES cells differentiate in culture into motor neurons that show the phenotype of the disease. The ability to derive

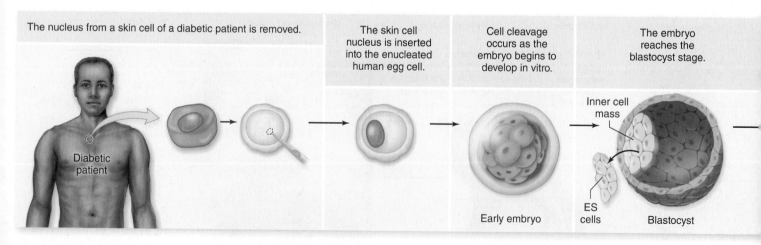

The nucleus from a skin cell of a diabetic patient is removed.

The skin cell nucleus is inserted into the enucleated human egg cell.

Cell cleavage occurs as the embryo begins to develop in vitro.

The embryo reaches the blastocyst stage.

Diabetic patient

Early embryo

Inner cell mass

ES cells

Blastocyst

disease-specific stem cells is an incredible advance for research on such diseases. This will allow us to study the cells affected by genetic diseases and to screen for possible therapeutics.

Pluripotent cell types themselves have potential for therapeutic applications. One way to solve the problem of graft rejection, such as in skin grafts in severe burn cases, is to produce patient-specific lines of ES cells. The first method to accomplish this was called **therapeutic cloning** and it uses the same SCNT procedure that created Dolly to assemble an embryo. The nucleus is removed from a skin cell and inserted into an egg whose nucleus has already been removed. The egg with its skin cell nucleus is allowed to form a blastocyst-stage embryo. This artificial embryo is then used to derive ES cells for transfer to injured tissue (figure 19.11).

Therapeutic cloning successfully addresses one key problem that must be solved before stem cells can be used to repair human tissues damaged by heart attack, nerve injury, diabetes, or Parkinson disease—the problem of immune acceptance. Since stem cells are cloned from a person's own tissues, they pass the immune system's "self" identity check, and the body readily accepts them. The first human trials using this technology were recently halted by the company Geron, reportedly for financial reasons. There is still great interest in this technology and the use of iPS cells would remove the ethical problems of embryo destruction, and the practical problem of the requirement for oocytes.

Learning Outcomes Review 19.4

Cloning has long been practiced in plants. In animals, cells from early-stage embryos are also totipotent, but attempts to use adult nuclei for cloning led to mixed results. The nucleus of a differentiated cell requires reprogramming to be totipotent. This appears to be necessary at least in part because of genomic imprinting. Nuclei may be reprogrammed by fusion with an embryonic stem cell, which produces a tetraploid cell, or through the introduction of four important transcription factors. That reprogramming is possible was shown by reproductive cloning via somatic cell nuclear transfer (SCNT). In therapeutic cloning, the goal is to produce replacement tissue using a patient's own cells.

■ *What changes must occur to produce a totipotent cell from a differentiated nucleus?*

19.5 Pattern Formation

Learning Outcomes

1. *Describe A/P axis formation in* Drosophila.
2. *Describe D/V axis formation in* Drosophila.
3. *Explain the importance of homeobox-containing genes in development.*

For cells in multicellular organisms to differentiate into appropriate cell types, they must gain information about their relative locations in the body. All multicellular organisms seem to use positional information to determine the basic pattern of body compartments and, thus, the overall architecture of the adult body. This positional information then leads to intrinsic changes in gene activity, so that cells ultimately adopt a fate appropriate for their location.

Pattern formation is an unfolding process. In the later stages, it may involve morphogenesis of organs (to be discussed later), but during the earliest events of development, the basic body plan is laid down, along with the establishment of the anterior–posterior (A/P, head-to-tail) axis and the dorsal–ventral (D/V, back-to-front) axis. Thus, pattern formation can be considered the process of taking a radially symmetrical cell and imposing two perpendicular axes to define the basic body plan, which in this way becomes bilaterally symmetrical. Developmental biologists use the term **polarity** to refer to the acquisition of axial differences in developing structures.

The fruit fly *Drosophila melanogaster* is the best understood animal in terms of the genetic control of early patterning. We will concentrate on the *Drosophila* system here, and later in chapter 53 we will examine axis formation in vertebrates in the context of their overall development.

A hierarchy of gene expression that begins with maternally expressed genes controls the development of *Drosophila*. To understand the details of these gene interactions, we first need to briefly review the stages of *Drosophila* development.

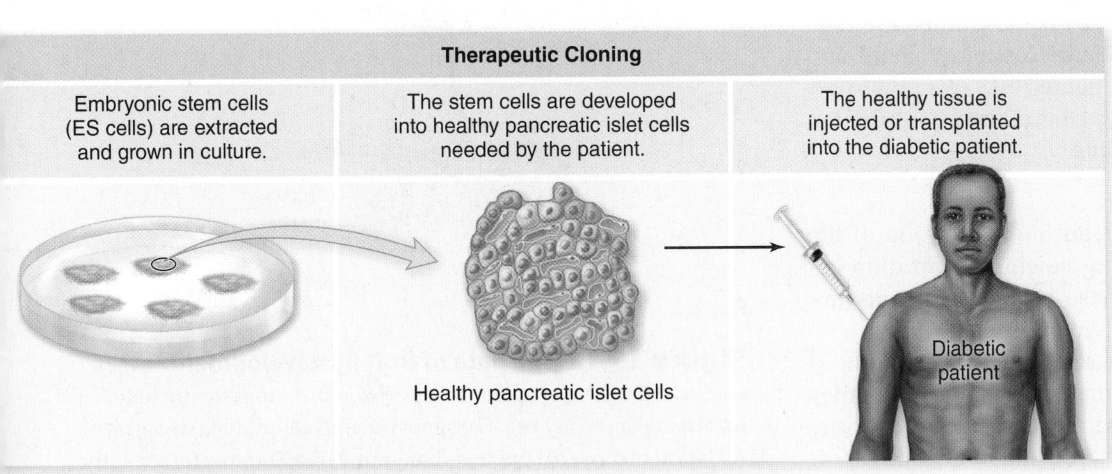

Therapeutic Cloning

Embryonic stem cells (ES cells) are extracted and grown in culture.

The stem cells are developed into healthy pancreatic islet cells needed by the patient.

The healthy tissue is injected or transplanted into the diabetic patient.

Healthy pancreatic islet cells

Diabetic patient

Figure 19.11 How human embryos might be used for therapeutic cloning. In therapeutic cloning, after initial stages to reproductive cloning, the embryo is broken apart and its embryonic stem cells are extracted. These are grown in culture and used to replace the diseased tissue of the individual who provided the DNA. This is useful only if the disease in question is not genetic, as the stem cells are genetically identical to the patient.

Drosophila embryogenesis produces a segmented larva

Drosophila and many other insects produce two different kinds of bodies during their development: the first, a tubular eating machine called a **larva,** and the second, an adult flying sex machine with legs and wings. The passage from one body form to the other, called **metamorphosis,** involves a radical shift in development (figure 19.12). In this chapter, we concentrate on the process of going from a fertilized egg to a larva, which is termed *embryogenesis.*

Prefertilization maternal contribution

The development of an insect like *Drosophila* begins before fertilization, with the construction of the egg. Specialized *nurse cells* that help the egg grow move some of their own maternally encoded mRNAs into the maturing oocyte (figure 19.12*a*).

Following fertilization, the maternal mRNAs are transcribed into proteins, which initiate a cascade of sequential gene activations. Embryonic nuclei do not begin to function (that is, to direct new transcription of genes) until approximately 10 nuclear divisions have occurred. Therefore, the action of maternal, rather than zygotic, genes determines the initial course of *Drosophila* development.

Postfertilization events

After fertilization, 12 rounds of nuclear division without cytokinesis produce about 4000 nuclei, all within a single cytoplasm. All of the nuclei within this **syncytial blastoderm** (figure 19.12*b*) can freely communicate with one another, but nuclei located in different sectors of the egg encounter different maternal products.

Once the nuclei have spaced themselves evenly along the surface of the blastoderm, membranes grow between them to form the **cellular blastoderm.** Embryonic folding and primary tissue development soon follow, in a process fundamentally similar to that seen in vertebrate development. Within a day of fertilization, embryogenesis creates a segmented, tubular body—which is destined to hatch out of the protective coats of the egg as a larva.

Morphogen gradients form the basic body axes in *Drosophila*

Pattern formation in the early *Drosophila* embryo requires positional information encoded in labels that can be read by cells. The unraveling of this puzzle, work that earned the 1995 Nobel Prize for researchers Christiane Nüsslein-Volhard and Eric Wieschaus, is summarized in figure 19.13. We now know that two different genetic pathways control the establishment of A/P and D/V polarity in *Drosophila.*

Anterior–posterior axis

Formation of the A/P axis begins during maturation of the oocyte and is based on opposing gradients of two different proteins: **Bicoid** and **Nanos.** These protein gradients are established by an interesting mechanism.

Nurse cells in the ovary secrete maternally produced *bicoid* and *nanos* mRNAs into the maturing oocyte where they are differentially transported along microtubules to opposite poles of the oocyte (figure 19.14*a*). This differential transport comes about due to the use of different motor proteins to move

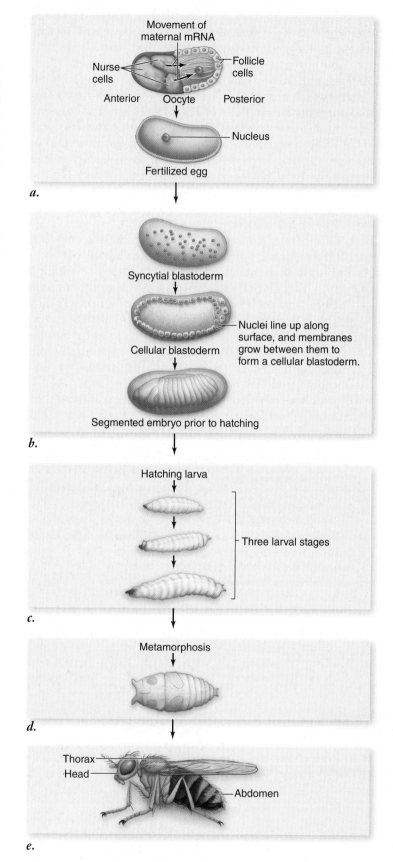

Figure 19.12 The path of fruit fly development. Major stages in the development of *Drosophila melanogaster* include formation of the (*a*) egg, (*b*) syncytial and cellular blastoderm, (*c*) larval instars, (*d*) pupa and metamorphosis into a (*e*) sexually mature adult.

Establishing the Polarity of the Embryo

Fertilization of the egg triggers the production of Bicoid protein from maternal RNA in the egg. The Bicoid protein diffuses through the egg, forming a gradient. This gradient determines the polarity of the embryo, with the head and thorax developing in the zone of high concentration (*green* fluorescent dye in antibodies that bind bicoid protein allows visualization of the gradient).

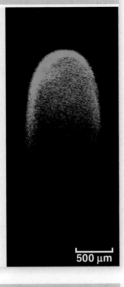

500 μm

Setting the Stage for Segmentation

About 2½ hours after fertilization, Bicoid protein turns on a series of brief signals from so-called gap genes. The gap proteins act to divide the embryo into large blocks. In this photo, fluorescent dyes in antibodies that bind to the gap proteins Krüppel (*orange*) and Hunchback (*green*) make the blocks visible; the region of overlap is yellow.

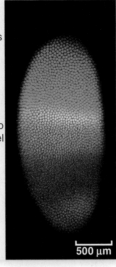

500 μm

Figure 19.13 Body organization in an early *Drosophila* embryo. In these fluorescent microscope images by 1995 Nobel laureate Christiane Nüsslein-Volhard and Sean Carroll, we watch a *Drosophila* egg pass through the early stages of development, in which the basic segmentation pattern of the embryo is established. The proteins in the photographs were made visible by binding fluorescent antibodies to each specific protein.

Laying Down the Fundamental Regions

About 0.5 hr later, the gap genes switch on the "pair-rule" genes, which are each expressed in seven stripes. This is shown for the pair-rule gene *hairy*. Some pair-rule genes are only required for even-numbered segments while others are only required for odd numbered segments.

500 μm

Forming the Segments

The final stage of segmentation occurs when a "segment-polarity" gene called *engrailed* divides each of the seven regions into anterior and posterior compartments of the future segments. This occurs a little after the formation of the cellular blastoderm (see figure 19.12). The curved appearance of the embryo at this stage is because of a phenomenon called germ band extension that causes the embryo to fold over itself.

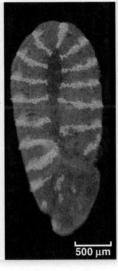

500 μm

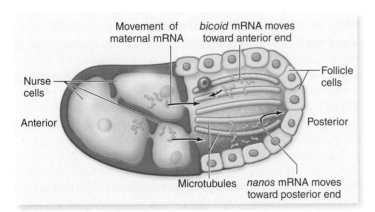

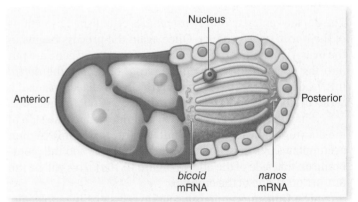

a. *b.*

Figure 19.14 Specifying the A/P axis in *Drosophila* embryos I. *a.* In the ovary, nurse cells secrete maternal mRNAs into the cytoplasm of the oocyte. Clusters of microtubules direct oocyte growth and maturation. Motor proteins travel along the microtubules transporting molecules in two directions. *Bicoid* mRNAs are transported toward the anterior pole of the oocyte, *nanos* mRNA is transported toward the posterior pole of the oocyte. *b.* A mature oocyte, showing localization of *bicoid* mRNAs to the anterior pole and *nanos* mRNAs to the posterior pole.

the two mRNAs. The *bicoid* mRNA then becomes anchored in the cytoplasm at the end of the oocyte closest to the nurse cells, and this end will develop into the anterior end of the embryo. *Nanos* mRNA becomes anchored to the opposite end of the oocyte, which will become the posterior end of the embryo. Thus, by the end of oogenesis, the *bicoid* and *nanos* mRNAs are already set to function as cytoplasmic determinants in the fertilized egg (figure 19.14*b*).

Following fertilization, translation of the anchored mRNA and diffusion of the proteins away from their respective sites of synthesis create opposing gradients of each protein: Highest levels of Bicoid protein are at the anterior pole of the embryo (figure 19.15*a*), and highest levels of the Nanos protein are at the posterior pole. Concentration gradients of soluble molecules can specify different cell fates along an axis, and proteins that act in this way, like Bicoid and Nanos, are called **morphogens.** The importance of these morphogens can be seen by the effects of loss-of-function mutants: loss of Bicoid produces an embryo with only posterior sides, and loss of Nanos protein produces an embryo with only anterior sides.

The Bicoid and Nanos proteins control the translation of two other maternal messages, *hunchback* and *caudal*, that encode transcription factors. **Hunchback** activates genes required for the formation of anterior structures, and **Caudal** activates genes required for the development of posterior (abdominal) structures. The *hunchback* and *caudal* mRNAs are evenly distributed across the egg (figure 19.15*b*), so how is it that proteins translated from these mRNAs become localized?

The answer is that Bicoid protein binds to and inhibits translation of *caudal* mRNA. Therefore, *caudal* is only translated in the posterior regions of the egg where Bicoid is absent. Similarly, Nanos protein binds to and prevents translation of the *hunchback* mRNA. As a result, *hunchback* is only translated in the anterior regions of the egg (figure 19.15*c*). Thus, shortly after fertilization, four protein gradients exist in the embryo: anterior–posterior gradients of Bicoid and Hunchback proteins, and posterior–anterior gradients of Nanos and Caudal proteins (figure 19.15*c*).

Dorsal–ventral axis

The dorsal–ventral axis in *Drosophila* is established by actions of the *dorsal* gene product. Once again the process begins in the ovary, when maternal transcripts of the *dorsal* gene are put into the oocyte. However, unlike *bicoid* or *nanos,* the *dorsal* mRNA does not become asymmetrically localized. Instead, a series of steps are required for Dorsal to carry out its function.

First, the oocyte nucleus, which is located to one side of the oocyte, synthesizes *gurken* mRNA. The *gurken* mRNA then accumulates in a crescent between the nucleus and the membrane on that side of the oocyte (figure 19.16*a*). This will be the future dorsal side of the embryo.

The Gurken protein is a soluble cell-signaling molecule, and when it is translated and released from the oocyte, it binds to receptors in the membranes of the overlying follicle cells (figure 19.16*b*). These cells then differentiate into a dorsal morphology. Meanwhile, no Gurken signal is released from the other side of the oocyte, and the follicle cells on that side of the oocyte adopt a ventral fate.

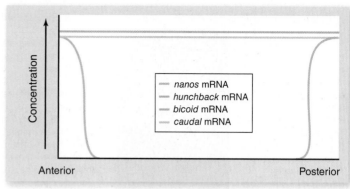

a. Oocyte mRNAs

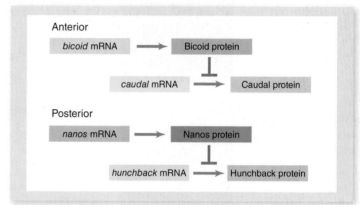

b. After fertilization

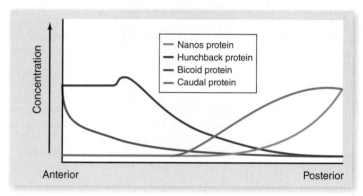

c. Early cleavage embryo proteins

Figure 19.15 Specifying the A/P axis in *Drosophila* embryos II. *a.* Unlike *bicoid* and *nanos, hunchback* and *caudal* mRNAs are evenly distributed throughout the cytoplasm of the oocyte. *b.* Following fertilization, *bicoid* and *nanos* mRNAs are translated into protein, making opposing gradients of each protein. Bicoid binds to and represses translation of *caudal* mRNAs (in anterior regions of the egg). Nanos binds to and represses translation of *hunchback* mRNAs (in posterior regions of the egg). *c.* Translation of *hunchback* mRNAs in anterior regions of the egg will create a Hunchback gradient that mirrors the Bicoid gradient. Translation of *caudal* mRNAs in posterior regions of the embryo will create a Caudal gradient that mirrors the Nanos gradient.

Following fertilization, a signaling molecule is differentially activated on the ventral surface of the embryo in a complex sequence of steps. This signaling molecule then binds to a

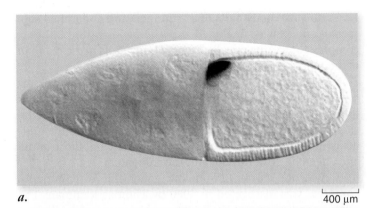

a.

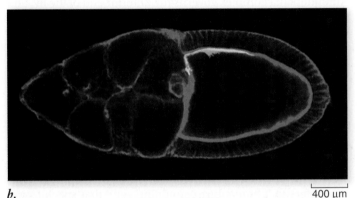

b.

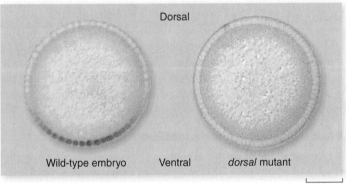

Dorsal

Wild-type embryo   Ventral   *dorsal* mutant

c.

Figure 19.16 Specifying the D/V axis in *Drosophila* embryos. *a.* The *gurken* mRNA *(dark stain)* is concentrated between the oocyte nucleus (not visible) and the dorsal, anterior surface of the oocyte. *b.* In a more mature oocyte, Gurken protein *(yellow stain)* is secreted from the dorsal anterior surface of the oocyte, forming a gradient along the dorsal surface of the egg. Gurken then binds to membrane receptors in the overlying follicle cells. Double staining for actin *(red)* shows the cell boundaries of the oocyte, nurse cells, and follicle cells. *c.* For these images, cellular blastoderm stage embryos were cut in cross section to visualize the nuclei of cells around the perimeter of the embryos. Dorsal protein *(dark stain)* is localized in nuclei on the ventral surface of the blastoderm in a wild-type embryo *(left).* The *dorsal* mutant on the right will not form ventral structures, and Dorsal is not present in ventral nuclei of this embryo.

membrane receptor in the ventral cells of the embryo and activates a signal transduction pathway in those cells. Activation of this pathway results in the selected transport of the Dorsal

protein (which is everywhere) into ventral nuclei, forming a gradient along the D/V axis. The Dorsal protein levels are highest in the nuclei of ventral cells (figure 19.16*c*).

(Note that many *Drosophila* genes are named for the mutant phenotype that results from a loss of function in that gene. A lack of *dorsal* function produces dorsalized embryos with no ventral structures.)

The Dorsal protein is a transcription factor, and once it is transported into nuclei, it activates genes required for the proper development of ventral structures, simultaneously repressing genes that specify dorsal structures. Hence, the product of the *dorsal* gene ultimately directs the development of ventral structures.

Although profoundly different mechanisms are involved, the unifying factor controlling the establishment of both A/P and D/V polarity in *Drosophila* is that *bicoid, nanos, gurken,* and *dorsal* are all maternally expressed genes. The polarity of the future embryo in both instances is therefore laid down in the oocyte using information coming from the maternal genome.

The preceding discussion simplifies events, but the outline is clear: Polarity is established by the creation of morphogen gradients in the embryo based on maternal information in the egg. These gradients then drive the expression of the zygotic genes that will actually pattern the embryo. This reliance on a hierarchy of regulatory genes is a unifying theme for all of development.

The body plan is produced by sequential activation of genes

Let us now return to the process of pattern formation in *Drosophila* along the A/P axis. Determination of structures is accomplished by the sequential activation of three classes of **segmentation genes.** These genes create the hallmark segmented body plan of a fly, which consists of three fused head segments, three thoracic segments, and eight abdominal segments (see figure 19.12*e*).

To begin, Bicoid protein exerts its profound effect on the organization of the embryo by activating the translation and transcription of *hunchback* mRNA (which is the first mRNA to be transcribed after fertilization). *Hunchback* is a member of a group of nine genes called the **gap genes.** These genes map out the initial subdivision of the embryo along the A/P axis (see figure 19.13).

All of the gap genes encode transcription factors, which, in turn, regulate the expression of eight or more **pair-rule genes.** Each of the pair-rule genes, such as *hairy,* produces seven distinct bands of protein, which appear as stripes when visualized with fluorescent reagents (see figure 19.13). These bands subdivide the broad gap regions and establish boundaries that divide the embryo into seven zones. When mutated, each of the pair-rule genes alters every other body segment.

All of the pair-rule genes also encode transcription factors, and they, in turn, regulate the expression of each other and of a group of nine or more **segment polarity genes.** The segment polarity genes are each expressed in 14 distinct bands of cells, which subdivide each of the seven zones specified by the pair-rule genes (see figure 19.13). The *engrailed* gene, for example, divides each of the seven zones established by *hairy* into anterior and posterior compartments. The segment polarity genes encode proteins that function in cell–cell signaling pathways. Thus, they function in inductive events—which occur *after* the syncytial blastoderm is divided into cells—to fix the anterior and posterior fates of cells within each segment.

In summary, within 3 hr after fertilization, a highly orchestrated cascade of segmentation gene activity transforms the broad gradients of the early embryo into a periodic, segmented structure with A/P and D/V polarity. The activation of the segmentation genes depends on the free diffusion of maternally encoded morphogens, which is only possible within the syncytial blastoderm of the early *Drosophila* embryo.

Segment identity arises from the action of homeotic genes

With the basic body plan laid down, the next step is to give identity to the segments of the embryo. A highly interesting class of *Drosophila* mutants has provided the starting point for understanding the creation of segment identity.

In these mutants, a particular segment seems to have changed its identity—that is, it has characteristics of a different segment. In wild-type flies, a pair of legs emerges from each of the three thoracic segments, but only the second thoracic segment has wings. Mutations in the *Ultrabithorax* gene cause a fly to grow an extra pair of wings, as though it has two second thoracic segments (figure 19.17). Even more bizarre are mutations in *Antennapedia*, which cause legs to grow out of the head in place of antennae!

Thus, mutations in these genes lead to the appearance of perfectly normal body parts in inappropriate places. Such mutants are termed *homeotic mutants* because the transformed body part looks similar (homeotic) to another. The genes in which such mutants occur are therefore called **homeotic genes.**

Homeotic gene complexes

In the early 1950s, geneticist and Nobel laureate Edward Lewis discovered that several homeotic genes, including *Ultrabithorax,* map together on the third chromosome of *Drosophila* in a tight cluster called the **bithorax complex.** Mutations in these genes all affect body parts of the thoracic and abdominal segments, and Lewis concluded that the genes of the bithorax complex control the development of body parts in the rear half of the thorax and all of the abdomen.

Interestingly, the order of the genes in the bithorax complex mirrors the order of the body parts they control, as though the genes are activated serially. Genes at the beginning of the cluster switch on development of the thorax; those in the middle control the anterior part of the abdomen; and those at the end affect the posterior tip of the abdomen.

A second cluster of homeotic genes, the **Antennapedia complex,** was discovered in 1980 by Thomas Kaufman. The Antennapedia complex governs the anterior end of the fly, and the order of genes in this complex also corresponds to the order of segments they control (figure 19.18*a*).

The homeobox

An interesting relationship was discovered after the genes of the bithorax and Antennapedia complexes were cloned and sequenced. These genes all contain a conserved sequence of 180 nucleotides that codes for a 60-amino-acid, DNA-binding domain. Because this domain was found in all of the homeotic genes, it was named the *homeodomain,* and the DNA that encodes it is called the homeobox. Thus, the term ***Hox* gene** now refers to a homeobox-containing gene that specifies the identity of a body part. These genes function as transcription factors that bind DNA using their homeobox domain.

Clearly, the homeobox distinguishes portions of the genome that are devoted to pattern formation. How the *Hox* genes do this is the subject of much current research. Scientists believe that the ultimate targets of *Hox* gene function must be genes that control cell behaviors associated with organ morphogenesis.

Evolution of homeobox-containing genes

A large amount of research has been devoted to analyzing the clustered complexes of *Hox* genes in other organisms. These investigations have led to a fairly coherent view of homeotic gene evolution.

It is now clear that the *Drosophila* bithorax and Antennapedia complexes represent two parts of a single cluster of genes. In vertebrates, there are four copies of *Hox* gene clusters. As in *Drosophila,* the spatial domains of *Hox* gene expression correlate with the order of the genes on the chromosome (figure 19.18*b*). The existence of four *Hox* clusters in vertebrates is viewed by many as evidence that two duplication events of the entire genome have occurred in the vertebrate lineage.

This idea raises the issue of when the original cluster arose. To answer this question, researchers have turned to more primitive organisms, such as *Amphioxus* (now called *Branchiostoma*), a lancelet chordate (see chapter 35). The finding of only one cluster of *Hox* genes in *Amphioxus* implies that indeed there

Figure 19.17 Mutations in homeotic genes. Three separate mutations in the bithorax complex caused this fruit fly to develop an additional second thoracic segment, with accompanying wings.

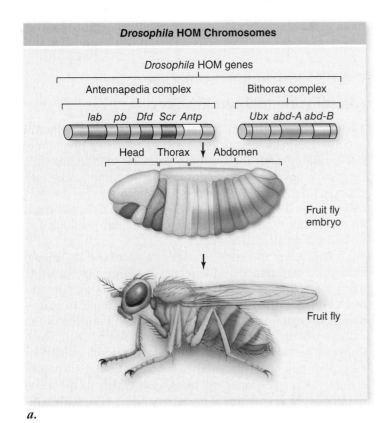

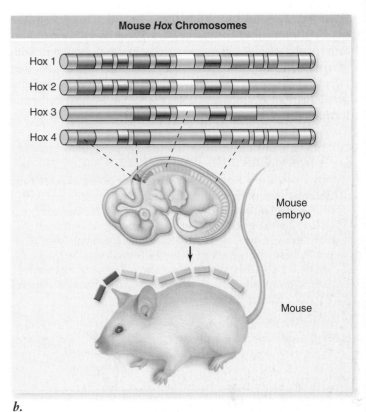

a.

b.

Figure 19.18 **A comparison of homeotic gene clusters in the fruit fly *Drosophila melanogaster* and the mouse *Mus musculus*.**
a. *Drosophila* homeotic genes. Called the homeotic gene complex, or HOM complex, the genes are grouped into two clusters: the Antennapedia complex (anterior) and the bithorax complex (posterior). *b.* The *Drosophila* HOM genes and the mouse *Hox* genes are related genes that control the regional differentiation of body parts in both animals. These genes are located on a single chromosome in the fly and on four separate chromosomes in mammals. In this illustration, the genes are color-coded to match the parts of the body along the A/P axis in which they are expressed. Note that the order of the genes along the chromosome(s) is mirrored by their pattern of expression in the embryo and in structures in the adult fly.

have been two duplications in the vertebrate lineage, at least of the *Hox* cluster. Given the single cluster in arthropods, this finding implies that the common ancestor to all animals with bilateral symmetry had a single *Hox* cluster as well.

The next logical step is to look at even more-primitive animals: the radially symmetrical cnidarians such as *Hydra* (see chapter 34). Thus far, *Hox* genes have been found in a number of cnidarian species, and recent sequence analyses suggest that cnidarian *Hox* genes are also arranged into clusters. Thus, the appearance of the ancestral *Hox* cluster likely preceded the divergence between radial and bilateral symmetries in animal evolution.

Pattern formation in plants is also under genetic control

The evolutionary split between plant and animal cell lineages occurred about 1.6 BYA, before the appearance of multicellular organisms with defined body plans. The implication is that multicellularity evolved independently in plants and animals. Because of the activity of meristems, additional modules can be added to plant bodies throughout their lifetimes. In addition, plant flowers and roots have a radial organization, in contrast to the bilateral symmetry of most animals. We may

therefore expect that the genetic control of pattern formation in plants is fundamentally different from that of animals.

Although plants have homeobox-containing genes, they are not organized into complexes of *Hox* genes similar to the ones that determine regional identity of developing structures in animals. Instead, the predominant homeotic gene family in plants appears to be the **MADS-box** genes.

MADS-box genes are a family of transcriptional regulators found in most eukaryotic organisms, including plants, animals, and fungi. The MADS-box is a conserved DNA-binding and dimerization domain, named after the first five genes to be discovered with this domain. Only a small number of *MADS*-box genes are found in animals, where their functions include the control of cell proliferation and tissue-specific gene expression in postmitotic muscle cells. They do not appear to play a role in the patterning of animal embryos.

In contrast, the number and functional diversity of *MADS*-box genes increased considerably during the evolution of land plants, and there are more than 100 *MADS*-box genes in the *Arabidopsis* genome. In flowering plants, the *MADS*-box genes dominate the control of development, regulating such processes as the transition from vegetative to reproductive growth, root development, and floral organ identity.

Although distinct from genes in the *Hox* clusters of animals, plant *Hox* genes encode transcription factors that have important developmental functions. One such example is the family of *knottedlike homeobox (knox)* genes, which are important regulators of shoot apical meristem development in both seed-bearing and nonseed-bearing plants. Mutations that affect expression of *knox* genes produce changes in leaf and petal shape, suggesting that these genes play an important role in generating leaf form.

Learning Outcomes Review 19.5

Pattern formation in animals involves the coordinated expression of a hierarchy of genes. Gradients of morphogens in *Drosophila* specify A/P and D/V axes, then lead to sequential activation of segmentation genes. Bicoid and Nanos protein gradients determine the A/P axis. The protein Dorsal determines the D/V axis, but activation requires a series of steps beginning with the oocyte's Gurken protein. The action of homeotic genes provide segment identity. These genes, which include a DNA-binding homeodomain sequence, are called *Hox* genes (for *homeobox* genes), and they are organized into clusters. Plants use a different set of developmental control genes called *MADS*-box genes.

■ **Why would you expect homeotic genes to be conserved across species evolution?**

19.6 Morphogenesis

Learning Outcomes

1. *Discuss the importance of cell shape changes and cell migration in development.*
2. *Explain how cell death can contribute to morphogenesis.*
3. *Describe the role of the extracellular matrix in cell migration.*

At the end of cleavage, the *Drosophila* embryo still has a relatively simple structure: It comprises several thousand identical-looking cells, which are present in a single layer surrounding a central yolky region. The next step in embryonic development is **morphogenesis**—the generation of ordered form and structure.

Morphogenesis is the product of changes in cell structure and cell behavior. Animals regulate the following processes to achieve morphogenesis:

■ The number, timing, and orientation of cell divisions;
■ Cell growth and expansion;
■ Changes in cell shape;
■ Cell migration; and
■ Cell death.

Plant and animal cells are fundamentally different in that animal cells have flexible surfaces and can move, but plant cells are immotile and encased within stiff cellulose walls. Each cell in a plant is fixed into position when it is created. Thus, animal cells use cell migration extensively during development while plants use the other four mechanisms but lack cell

migration. We consider the morphogenetic changes in animals here, and plant morphogenesis is detailed in chapter 41.

Cell division during development may result in unequal cytokinesis

The orientation of the mitotic spindle determines the plane of cell division in eukaryotic cells. The coordinated function of microtubules and their motor proteins determines the respective position of the mitotic spindle within a cell (see chapter 10). If the spindle is centrally located in the dividing cell, two equal-sized daughter cells will result. If the spindle is off to one side, one large daughter cell and one small daughter cell will result.

The great diversity of cleavage patterns in animal embryos is determined by differences in spindle placement. In many cases, the fate of a cell is determined by its relative placement in the embryo during cleavage. For example, in preimplantation mammalian embryos, cells on the outside of the embryo usually differentiate into trophectoderm cells, which form only extraembryonic structures later in development (for example, a part of the placenta). In contrast, the embryo proper is derived from the inner cell mass, cells which, as the name implies, are in the interior of the embryo.

Cells change shape and size as morphogenesis proceeds

In animals, cell differentiation is often accompanied by profound changes in cell size and shape. For example, the large nerve cells that connect your spinal cord to the muscles in your big toe develop long processes called *axons* that span this entire distance. The cytoplasm of an axon contains microtubules, which are used for motor-driven transport of materials along the length of the axon.

As another example, muscle cells begin as *myoblasts,* undifferentiated muscle precursor cells. They eventually undergo conversion into the large, multinucleated *muscle fibers* that make up mammalian skeletal muscles. These changes begin with the expression of the *MyoD1* gene, which encodes a transcription factor that binds to the promoters of muscle-determining genes to initiate these changes.

Programmed cell death is a necessary part of development

Not every cell produced during development is destined to survive. For example, human embryos have webbed fingers and toes at an early stage of development. The cells that make up the webbing die in the normal course of morphogenesis. As another example, vertebrate embryos produce a very large number of neurons, ensuring that enough neurons are available to make the necessary synaptic connections, but over half of these neurons never make connections and die in an orderly way as the nervous system develops.

Unlike accidental cell deaths due to injury, these cell deaths are planned—and indeed required—for proper development and morphogenesis. Cells that die due to injury typically swell and burst, releasing their contents into the extracellular fluid. This form of cell death is called necrosis. In contrast, cells programmed to die shrivel and shrink in a process called apoptosis, which means "falling away," and their remains are taken up by surrounding cells.

Genetic control of apoptosis

Apoptosis occurs when a "death program" is activated. All animal cells appear to possess such programs. In *C. elegans*, the same 131 cells always die during development in a predictable and reproducible pattern.

Work on *C. elegans* showed that three genes are central to this process. Two (*ced-3* and *ced-4*) activate the death program itself; if either is mutant, those 131 cells do not die, and go on instead to form nervous tissue and other tissue. The third gene (*ced-9*) represses the death program encoded by the other two: All 1090 cells of the *C. elegans* embryo die in *ced-9* mutants. In *ced-9/ced-3* double mutants, all 1090 cells live, which suggests that *ced-9* inhibits cell death by functioning prior to *ced-3* in the apoptotic pathway (figure 19.19*a*).

The mechanism of apoptosis appears to have been highly conserved during the course of animal evolution. In human nerve cells, the *Apaf1* gene is similar to *ced-4* of *C. elegans* and activates the cell death program, and the human *bcl-2* gene

acts similarly to *ced-9* to repress apoptosis. If a copy of the human *bcl-2* gene is transferred into a nematode with a defective *ced-9* gene, *bcl-2* suppresses the cell death program of *ced-3* and *ced-4*.

The mechanism of apoptosis

The product of the *C. elegans ced-4* gene is a protease that activates the product of the *ced-3* gene, which is also a protease. The human *Apaf1* gene is actually named for its role: *A*poptotic *p*rotease *a*ctivating *f*actor. It activates two proteases called caspases that have a role similar to the Ced-3 protease in *C. elegans* (figure 19.19*b*). When the final proteases are activated, they chew up proteins in important cellular structures such as the cytoskeleton and the nuclear lamina, leading to cell fragmentation.

The role of Ced-9/Bcl-2 is to inhibit this program. Specifically, it inhibits the activating protease, preventing the activation of the destructive proteases. The entire process is thus controlled by an inhibitor of the death program.

Both internal and external signals control the state of the Ced-9/Bcl-2 inhibitor. For example, in the human nervous system, neurons have a cytoplasmic inhibitor of Bcl-2 that allows the death program to proceed (see figure 19.19*b*). In the presence of nerve growth factor, a signal transduction pathway leads to the cytoplasmic inhibitor being inactivated, allowing Bcl-2 to inhibit apoptosis and the nerve cell to survive.

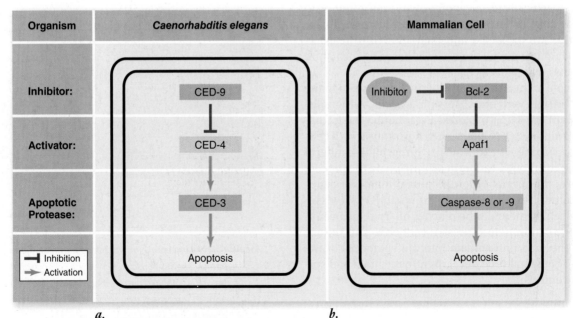

Figure 19.19 Programmed cell death pathway. Apoptosis, or programmed cell death, is necessary for the normal development of all animals. *a.* In the developing nematode, for example, two genes, *ced-3* and *ced-4,* code for proteins that cause the programmed cell death of 131 specific cells. In the other (surviving) cells of the developing nematode, the product of a third gene, *ced-9,* represses the death program encoded by *ced-3* and *ced-4*. *b.* The mammalian homologues of the apoptotic genes in *C. elegans* are *bcl-2* (*ced-9* homologue), *Apaf1* (*ced-4* homologue), and *caspase-8* or *-9* (*ced-3* homologues). In the absence of any cell survival factor, Bcl-2 is inhibited and apoptosis occurs. In the presence of nerve growth factor (NGF) and NGF receptor binding, Bcl-2 is activated, thereby inhibiting apoptosis.

Cell migration gets the right cells to the right places

The migration of cells is important during many stages of animal development. The movement of cells involves both adhesion and the loss of adhesion. Adhesion is necessary for cells to get "traction," but cells that are initially attached to others must lose this adhesion to be able to leave a site.

Cell movement also involves cell-to-substrate interactions, and the extracellular matrix may control the extent or route of cell migration. The central paradigm of morphogenetic cell movements in animals is a change in cell adhesiveness, which is mediated by changes in the composition of macromolecules in the plasma membranes of cells or in the extracellular matrix. Cell-to-cell interactions are often mediated through cadherins, but cell-to-substrate interactions often involve integrin-to-extracellular-matrix (ECM) interactions.

Cadherins

Cadherins are a large gene family, with over 80 members identified in humans. In the genomes of *Drosophila, C. elegans,* and humans, the cadherins can be sorted into several subfamilies that exist in all three genomes.

The cadherin proteins are all transmembrane proteins that share a common motif, the *cadherin domain,* a 110-amino-acid domain in the extracellular portion of the protein that mediates Ca^{2+}-dependent binding between like cadherins (homophilic binding).

Experiments in which cells are allowed to sort in vitro illustrate the function of cadherins. Cells with the same cadherins adhere specifically to one another, while not adhering to other cells with different cadherins. If cell populations with different cadherins are dispersed and then allowed to reaggregate, they sort into two populations of cells based on the nature of the cadherins on their surface.

An example of the action of cadherins can be seen in the development of the vertebrate nervous system. All surface ectoderm cells of the embryo express E-cadherin. The formation of the nervous system begins when a central strip of cells on the dorsal surface of the embryo turns off E-cadherin expression and turns on N-cadherin expression. In the process of **neurulation,** the formation of the neural tube (see chapter 53), the central strip of N-cadherin-expressing cells folds up to form the tube. The neural tube pinches off from the overlying cells, which continue to express E-cadherin. The surface cells outside the tube differentiate into the epidermis of the skin, whereas the neural tube develops into the brain and spinal cord of the embryo.

Integrins

In some tissues, such as connective tissue, much of the volume of the tissue is taken up by the spaces *between* cells. These spaces are filled with a network of molecules secreted by surrounding cells, termed a *matrix.* In connective tissue such as cartilage, long polysaccharide chains are covalently linked to proteins (proteoglycans), within which are embedded strands of fibrous protein (collagen, elastin, and fibronectin). Migrating cells traverse this matrix by binding to it with cell surface proteins called integrins.

Integrins are attached to actin filaments of the cytoskeleton and protrude out from the cell surface in pairs, like two hands. The "hands" grasp a specific component of the matrix, such as collagen or fibronectin, thus linking the cytoskeleton to the fibers of the matrix. In addition to providing an anchor, this binding can initiate changes within the cell, alter the growth of the cytoskeleton, and activate gene expression and the production of new proteins.

The process of **gastrulation** (described in detail in chapter 53), during which the hollow ball of animal embryonic cells folds in on itself to form a multilayered structure, depends on fibronectin–integrin interactions. For example, injection of antibodies against either fibronectin or integrins into salamander embryos blocks binding of cells to fibronectin in the ECM and inhibits gastrulation. The result is like a huge traffic jam following a major accident on a freeway: Cells (cars) keep coming, but they get backed up since they cannot get beyond the area of inhibition (accident site) (figure 19.20). Similarly, a

SCIENTIFIC THINKING

Hypothesis: *Fibronectin is required for cell migration during gastrulation.*

Prediction: *Blocking fibronectin with antifibronectin antibodies before gastrulation should prevent cell movement.*

Test: *Staged salamander embryos were injected either with antifibronectin antibody, or with preimmune serum as a control, prior to gastrulation. Cell movements were then monitored photographically.*

Treated with Preimmune

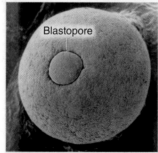

Blastopore

Cells have moved into the interior   285 μm

a.

Treated with Antifibronectin

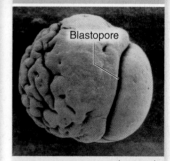

Blastopore

Cells pile up on the surface   285 μm

b.

Result: *The experimental embryos injected with antifibronectin antibody show extremely aberrant gastrulation where cells pile up and do not enter the interior of the embryo. Control embryos gastrulate normally.*

Conclusion: *Fibronectin is required for cells to migrate into the interior of the embryo during gastrulation.*

Further Experiments: *How can this same system be used to analyze the role of fibronectin in other early morphogenetic events?*

Figure 19.20 Fibronectin is necessary for cell migration during gastrulation.

targeted knockout of the fibronectin gene in mice resulted in gross defects in the migration, proliferation, and differentiation of embryonic mesoderm cells.

Thus, cell migration is largely a matter of changing patterns of cell adhesion. As a migrating cell travels, it continually extends projections that probe the nature of its environment. Tugged this way and that by different tentative attachments, the cell literally feels its way toward its ultimate target site.

Learning Outcomes Review 19.6

Morphogenesis is the generation of ordered form and structure. This process proceeds along with cell differentiation. The primary mechanisms of morphogenesis are cell shape change and cell migration. Apoptosis is programmed cell death that is a necessary part of morphogenesis. Cell migration in animals involves alternating changes in adhesion brought about by cadherins and integrins.

■ *Why is cell death important to morphogenesis?*

Chapter Review

19.1 The Process of Development

Development is the sequence of systematic, gene-directed changes throughout a life cycle. The four subprocesses of development are growth, cell differentiation, pattern formation, and morphogenesis.

19.2 Cell Division

Development begins with cell division.

In animals, cleavage stage divisions divide the fertilized egg into numerous smaller cells called blastomeres. During cleavage the G_1 and G_2 phases of the cell cycle are shortened or eliminated (figure 19.2).

Every cell division is known in the development of C. elegans.

The lineage of 959 adult somatic *Caenorhabditis elegans* cells is invariant. Knowledge of the differentiation sequence and outcome allows study of developmental mechanisms.

Plant growth occurs in specific areas called meristems.

Plant growth continues throughout the life span from meristematic stem cells that can divide and differentiate into any plant tissue.

19.3 Cell Differentiation

Cells become determined prior to differentiation.

The process of determination commits a cell to a particular developmental pathway prior to its differentiation. This is not visible but can be tracked experimentally. Determination is due to differential inheritance of cytoplasmic factors or cell-to-cell interactions.

Determination can be due to cytoplasmic determinants.

In tunicates, determination of tail muscle cells depends on the presence of mRNA for the Macho-1 transcription factor, which is deposited in the egg cytoplasm during gamete formation.

Induction can lead to cell differentiation.

Induction occurs when one cell type produces signal molecules that induce gene expression in neighboring target cells.

In frogs, cells from animal and vegetal poles do not develop into mesoderm when isolated. In tunicates, signaling by the growth factor FGF induces mesoderm development.

Stem cells can divide and produce cells that differentiate.

Stem cells replace themselves by division and produce cells that differentiate. Totipotent stem cells can give rise to any cell type including extraembryonic tissues; pluripotent cells can give rise to all cells of an organism; and multipotent stem cells can give rise to many kinds of cells.

Embryonic stem cells are pluripotent cells derived from embryos.

Embryonic stem cells are derived from the inner cell mass of the blastocyst (figure 19.8). They can differentiate into any adult tissue in a mouse.

19.4 Nuclear Reprogramming

Reversal of determination has allowed cloning.

Cells undergo no irreversible changes during development. However, transplanted nuclei from older donors are less able to direct complete development. The cloning of the sheep Dolly showed that the nucleus of an adult cell can be reprogrammed to be totipotent (figure 19.9).

Reproductive cloning has inherent problems.

Reproductive cloning has a low success rate, and clones often develop age-associated diseases.

Nuclear reprogramming has been accomplished by use of defined factors.

Adult cells can be converted into pluripotent cells by introduction of four genes for transcription factors. These induced pluripotent cells appear to be similar to ES cells.

The use of cells cloned from a patient's cells to replace damaged tissue could avoid the problem of transplant rejection.

19.5 Pattern Formation

Drosophila embryogenesis produces a segmented larva.

The maternal contribution of mRNA along with the postfertilization events of cellular blastoderm formation produce a segmented embryo.

Morphogen gradients form the basic body axes in Drosophila.

Pattern formation produces two perpendicular axes in a bilaterally symmetrical organism. Positional information leads to changes in gene activity so cells adopt a fate appropriate for their location.

Formation of the anterior/posterior (A/P) axis is based on opposing gradients of morphogens, Bicoid and Nanos, synthesized from maternal mRNA (figures 19.14, 19.15).

The dorsal/ventral (D/V) axis is established by a gradient of the Dorsal transcription factor. Successive action of transcription factors divides the embryo into segments.

The body plan is produced by sequential activation of genes.

Segment identity arises from the action of homeotic genes.

Homeotic genes, called *Hox* genes because they contain a DNA sequence called the homeobox, give identity to embryo segments.

Hox genes are found in four clusters in vertebrates.

Pattern formation in plants is also under genetic control.

Plants have *MADS*-box genes that control the transition from vegetative to reproductive growth, root development, and floral organ identity.

19.6 Morphogenesis

Cell division during development may result in unequal cytokinesis.

Cells change shape and size as morphogenesis proceeds.

Depending on the orientation of the mitotic spindle, cells of equal or different sizes can arise. Morphogenesis involves changes in cell shape and size and cell migration.

Programmed cell death is a necessary part of development.

Apoptosis, the programmed death of cells, removes structures once they are no longer needed (figure 19.19).

Cell migration gets the right cells to the right places.

The migration of cells requires both adhesion and loss of adhesion between cells and their substrate.

Cell-to-cell interactions are often mediated by cadherin proteins, whereas cell-to-substrate interactions may involve integrin-to-extracellular-matrix interactions.

Integrins bind to fibers found in the extracellular matrix. This action can alter the cytoskeleton and activate gene expression.

Review Questions

UNDERSTAND

1. During development, cells become
   a. differentiated before they become determined.
   b. determined before they become differentiated.
   c. determined by the loss of genetic material.
   d. differentiated by the loss of genetic material.

2. Determination can occur by
   a. the action of cytoplasmic determinants.
   b. induction by other cells.
   c. the loss of chromosomes during cell division.
   d. Both a and b are correct.

3. The rapid divisions that occur early in development are made possible by shortening
   a. M phase.
   b. S phase.
   c. G_1 and G_2 phases.
   d. All of the choices are correct.

4. A pluripotent cell is one that can
   a. become any cell type in an organism.
   b. produce an indefinite supply of a single cell type.
   c. produce a limited amount of a specific cell type.
   d. produce multiple cell types.

5. Plant meristems
   a. are only present during development.
   b. contain stem cells.
   c. undergo meiosis.
   d. All of the choices are correct.

6. Pattern formation involves cells determining their position in the embryo. One mechanism that can accomplish this is
   a. the loss of genetic material.
   b. alterations of chromosome structure.
   c. gradients of morphogens.
   d. changes in the cell cycle.

7. The process of nuclear reprogramming
   a. is a normal part of pattern formation.
   b. reverses the changes that occur during differentiation.
   c. requires the introduction of new DNA.
   d. is not possible with mammalian cells.

APPLY

1. What is the common theme in cell determination by induction or cytoplasmic determinants?
   a. The activation of transcription factors
   b. The activation of cell division
   c. A change in gene expression
   d. Both a and c are correct.

2. The process of reproductive cloning
   a. shows that nuclear reprogramming is possible.
   b. is very efficient in mammals.
   c. always produces adult animals that are identical to the donor.
   d. Both a and b are correct.

3. Production of anterior–posterior and dorsal–ventral axes in the fruit fly *Drosophila*
   a. both use gradients of mRNA.
   b. are conceptually similar but mechanistically different.
   c. use the exact same mechanisms.
   d. both use gradients of protein.

4. For pattern formation to occur, the cells in the developing embryo must
   a. "know" their position in the embryo.
   b. be determined during the earliest divisions.
   c. differentiate as they are "born."
   d. must all be reprogrammed after each cell division.

5. The genes that encode the morphogen gradients in *Drosophila* were all identified in mutant screens. A mutation that removes the gradient necessary for the A/P morphogen gradient would be expected to
   a. affect the larvae but not the adult.
   b. affect the adult but not the larvae.
   c. be lethal and lead to an abnormal embryo.
   d. produce replacement of one adult structure with another.

6. What would be the likely result of a mutation of the *bcl-2* gene on the level of apoptosis?
    a. No change
    b. A decrease in apoptosis
    c. An increase in apoptosis
    d. An initial decrease, followed by an increase in apoptosis
7. *MADS*-box, and *Hox* genes are
    a. found only in plants and animals, respectively.
    b. found only in animals and plants, respectively.
    c. have similar roles in development in plants and animals, respectively.
    d. have similar roles in development in animals and plants, respectively.

SYNTHESIZE

1. The fate map for *C. elegans* (refer to figure 19.3) diagrams development of a multicellular organism from a single cell. Use this fate map to determine the number of cell divisions required to establish the population of cells that will become (a) the nervous system and (b) the gonads.

2. Carefully examine the *C. elegans* fate map in figure 19.3. Notice that some of the branchpoints (daughter cells) do *not* go on to produce more cells. What is the cellular mechanism underlying this pattern?

3. You have generated a set of mutant embryonic mouse cells. Predict the developmental consequences for each of the following mutations.
    a. Knockout mutation for N-cadherin
    b. Knockout mutation for integrin
    c. Deletion of the cytoplasmic domain of integrin

4. Assume you have the factors in hand necessary to reprogram an adult cell, and the factors necessary to induce differentiation to any cell type. How could these be used to replace a specific damaged tissue in a human patient?

ONLINE RESOURCE

www.ravenbiology.com

Understand, Apply, and Synthesize—enhance your study with animations that bring concepts to life and practice tests to assess your understanding. Your instructor may also recommend the interactive eBook, individualized learning tools, and more.

Answer Key

CHAPTER 1

LEARNING OUTCOME QUESTIONS

1.1   No. The study of biology encompasses information/tools from chemistry, physics, and geology—in fact all of the "natural sciences."

1.2   A scientific theory has been tested by experimentation. A hypothesis is a starting point for explaining a body of observations. When predictions generated using the hypothesis have been tested, it gains the confidence associated with a theory. A theory still cannot be "proved," however, as new data can always force us to re-evaluate a theory.

1.3   No. Natural selection explains the patterns of living organisms we see at present and allows us to work back in time, but it is not intended to explain how life arose. This does not mean that we can never explain this, but merely that natural selection does not do this.

1.4   Viruses do not fit well into our definition of living systems. It is a matter of controversy whether viruses should be considered "alive." They lack the basic cellular machinery, but they do have genetic information. Some theories for the origin of cells view viruses as being a step from organic molecules to cell, but looking at current organisms, they do not fulfill our definition of life.

INQUIRY AND DATA ANALYSIS QUESTIONS

Page 10 Data analysis: Reducing the factor by which the geometric progression increases (lowering the value of the exponent) reduces the difference between numbers of people and amount of food production.

Page 10 Inquiry question: It can be achieved by lowering family size or delaying childbearing.

Page 11 Inquiry question: A snake would fall somewhere near the bird, as birds and snakes are closely related.

UNDERSTAND

1. b   2. c   3. a   4. b   5. d   6. b   7. c   8. c

APPLY

1. a   2. d   3. c   4. d   5. d   6. d   7. a

SYNTHESIZE

1.   For something to be considered living it would demonstrate organization, possibly including a cellular structure. The organism would gain and use energy to maintain homeostasis, respond to its environment, and grow and reproduce. These latter properties would be difficult to determine if the evidence of life from other planets comes from fossils. Similarly, the ability of an alien organism to evolve could be difficult to establish.

2.   a.   The variables that were held the same between the two experiments include the broth, the flask, and the sterilization step.
    b.   The shape of the flask influences the experiment because any cells present in the air can enter the flask with the broken neck, but they are trapped in the neck of the other flask.
    c.   If cells can arise spontaneously, then cell growth will occur in both flasks. If cells can only arise from preexisting cells (cells in the air), then only the flask with the broken neck will grow cells. Breaking the neck exposes the broth to a source of cells.
    d.   If the sterilization step did not actually remove all cells, then growth would have occurred in both flasks. This result would seem to support the hypothesis that life can arise spontaneously.

CHAPTER 2

LEARNING OUTCOME QUESTIONS

2.1   If the number of protons exceeds neutrons, there is no effect on charge; if the number of protons exceeds electrons, then the charge is (+).

2.2   Atoms are reactive when their outer electron shell is not filled with electrons. The noble gases have filled outer electron shells and are thus unreactive.

2.3   An ionic bond results when there is a transfer of electrons, resulting in positive and negative ions that are attracted to each other. A covalent bond is the result of two atoms sharing electrons. Polar covalent bonds involve unequal sharing of electrons. This produces regions of partial charge, but not ions.

2.4   C and H have about the same electronegativity, and thus form nonpolar covalent bonds. This would not result in a cohesive or adhesive fluid.

2.5   Since ice floats, a lake will freeze from the top down, not the bottom up. This means that water remains fluid on the bottom of the lake, allowing living things to overwinter.

2.6   Since pH is a log scale, this would be a change of 100-fold in [H^+].

INQUIRY AND DATA ANALYSIS QUESTION

Page 30 Data analysis: From the graph, about four volumes of base must be added to change the pH from 4 to 6.

UNDERSTAND

1. b   2. d   3. b   4. a   5. c   6. d   7. b

APPLY

1. c   2. b   3. a   4. c   5. d   6. Chemical reactions involve changes in the electronic configuration of atoms. Radioactive decay involves the actual decay of the nucleus itself, producing another atom and emitting radiation.

SYNTHESIZE

1.   A cation is an element that tends to lose an electron from its outer energy level, leaving behind a net positive charge due to the presence of the protons in the atomic nucleus. Electrons are only lost from the outer energy level if that loss is energetically favorable, that is, if it makes the atom more stable by virtue of obtaining a filled outer energy level (the octet rule). You can predict which elements are likely to function as cations by calculating which of the elements will possess one (or two) electrons in their outer energy level. Recall that each orbital surrounding an atomic nucleus can only hold two electrons. Energy level K is a single *s* orbital and can hold two electrons. Energy level L consists of another *s* orbital plus three *p* orbitals—holding a total of eight electrons. Use the atomic number of each element to predict the total number of electrons present. Examples of other cations would include hydrogen (H), lithium (Li), magnesium (Mg), and beryllium (Be).

2.   Silicon has an atomic number of 14. This means that there are four unpaired electrons in its outer energy level (comparable to carbon). Based on this fact, you can conclude that silicon, like carbon, could form four covalent bonds. Silicon also falls within the group of elements with atomic masses less than 21, a property of the elements known to participate in the formation of biologically important molecules. Interestingly, silicon is much more prevalent than carbon on Earth. Although silicon dioxide is found in the cell walls of plants and single-celled organisms called diatoms, silicon-based life has not been identified on this planet. Given the abundance of silicon on Earth you can conclude that some other aspect of the chemistry of this atom makes it incompatible with the formation of molecules that make up living organisms.

3.   Water is considered to be a critical molecule for the evolution of life on Earth. It is reasonable to assume that water on other planets could play a similar role. The key properties of water that would support its role in the evolution of life are:
    • The ability of water to act as a solvent. Molecules dissolved in water could move and interact in ways that would allow for the formation of larger, more complex molecules such as those found in living organisms.
    • The high specific heat of water. Water can modulate and maintain its temperature, thereby protecting the molecules or organisms within it from temperature extremes—an important feature on other planets.

- The difference in density between ice and liquid water. The fact that ice floats is a simple, but important feature of water environments since it allows living organisms to remain in a liquid environment protected under a surface of ice. This possibility is especially intriguing, given recent evidence of ice-covered oceans on Europa, a moon of the planet Jupiter.

CHAPTER 3

LEARNING OUTCOME QUESTIONS

3.1 Hydrolysis is the reverse reaction of dehydration. Dehydration is a synthetic reaction involving the loss of water and hydrolysis is cleavage by addition of water.

3.2 Starch and glycogen are both energy-storage molecules. Their highly branched nature allows the formation of droplets, and the similarity in the bonds holding adjacent glucose molecules together mean that the enzymes we have to break down glycogen allow us to break down starch. The same enzymes do not allow us to break down cellulose. The structure of cellulose leads to the formation of tough fibers.

3.3 The sequence of bases in an RNA would be identical to one strand and complementary to the other strand of the DNA with the exception that U would be in place of T (complementary to A).

3.4 If an unknown protein has sequence similarity to a known protein, we can infer its function is also similar. If an unknown protein has known functional domains or motifs, we can also use these to help predict function.

3.5 Phospholipids have a charged group replacing one of the fatty acids in a triglyceride. This leads to an amphipathic molecule that has both hydrophobic and hydrophilic regions. This will spontaneously form bilayer membranes in water.

UNDERSTAND

1. b   2. a   3. d   4. c   5. b   6. b   7. c   8. b

APPLY

1. c   2. d   3. b   4. d   5. b   6. b   7. d

SYNTHESIZE

1. The four biological macromolecules all have different structure and function. In comparing carbohydrates, nucleic acids, and proteins, we can think of these as being polymers with different monomers. In the case of carbohydrates, the polymers are all polymers of the simple sugar glucose. These are energy-storage molecules (with many C—H bonds) and structural molecules such as cellulose that make tough fibers.

    Nucleic acids are formed of nucleotide monomers, each of which consists of ribose, phosphate, and a nitrogenous base. These molecules are informational molecules that encode information in the sequence of bases. The bases interact in specific ways: A base-pairs with T, and G base-pairs with C. This is the basis for their informational storage.

    Proteins are formed of amino acid polymers. There are 20 different amino acids, and thus an incredible number of different proteins. These can have an almost unlimited number of functions. These functions arise from the amazing flexibility in structure of protein chains.

2. *Nucleic Acids*—Hydrogen bonds are important for complementary base-pairing between the two strands of nucleic acid that make up a molecule of DNA. Complementary base-pairing can also occur within the single nucleic acid strand of an RNA molecule.

    Proteins—Hydrogen bonds are involved in both the secondary and tertiary levels of protein structure. The α helices and β-pleated sheets of secondary structure are stabilized by hydrogen bond formation between the amino and carboxyl groups of the amino acid backbone. Hydrogen bond formation between R-groups helps stabilize the three-dimensional folding of the protein at the tertiary level of structure.

    Carbohydrates—Hydrogen bonds are less important for carbohydrates; however, these bonds are responsible for the formation of the fibers of cellulose that make up the cell walls of plants.

    Lipids—Hydrogen bonds are not involved in the structure of lipid molecules. The inability of fatty acids to form hydrogen bonds with water is key to their hydrophobic nature.

3. We have enzymes that can break down glycogen. Glycogen is formed from α-glucose subunits. Starch is also formed from α-glucose units, but cellulose is formed from β-glucose units. The enzymes that break the α-glycosidic linkages cannot break the β-glycosidic linkages. Thus we can degrade glycogen and starch but not cellulose.

CHAPTER 4

LEARNING OUTCOME QUESTIONS

4.1 The statement about all cells coming from preexisting cells might need to be modified. It would really depend on whether these Martian life-forms had a similar molecular/cellular basis as that of terrestrial life.

4.2 Bacteria and archaea both tend to be single cells that lack a membrane-bounded nucleus, and have extensive internal endomembrane systems. They both have a cell wall, although the composition is different. They do not undergo mitosis, although the proteins involved in DNA replication and cell division are not similar.

4.3 Part of what gives different organs their unique identities are the specialized cell types found in each. That does not mean that there will not be some cell types common to all (epidermal cells for example) but organs tend to have specialized cell types.

4.4 They don't!

4.5 The nuclear genes that encode organellar proteins moved from the organelle to the nucleus. There is evidence for a lot of "horizontal gene transfer" across domains; this is an example of how that can occur.

4.6 It provides structure and support for larger cells, especially in animal cells that lack a cell wall.

4.7 Microtubules and microfilaments are both involved in cell motility and in movement of substance around cells. Intermediate filaments do not have this dynamic role, but are more structural.

4.8 Cell junctions help to put together cells into higher level structures that are organized and joined in different ways. Different kinds of junctions can be used for different functional purposes.

INQUIRY AND DATA ANALYSIS QUESTIONS

Page 63 Inquiry question: Stretch, dent, convolute, fold, add more than one nucleus, anything which would increase the amount of diffusion between the cytoplasm and the external environment.

Page 75 Inquiry question: Both the cristae of mitochondria and the thylakoids of chloroplasts, where many of the reactions take place leading to the production of ATP, are highly folded. This allows for a large surface area, increasing the efficiency of the mechanisms of oxidative phosphorylation.

Page 80 Inquiry question: Ciliated cells in the trachea help to remove particulate matter from the respiratory tract so that it can be expelled or swallowed and processed in the digestive tract.

UNDERSTAND

1. d   2. d   3. c   4. a   5. c   6. d   7. b

APPLY

1. c   2. b   3. c   4. b   5. c   6. b   7. a

SYNTHESIZE

1. Your diagram should start at the SER and then move to the RER, Golgi apparatus, and finally to the plasma membrane. Small transport vesicles are the mechanism that would carry a phospholipid molecule between two membrane compartments. Transport vesicles are small "membrane bubbles" composed of a phospholipid bilayer.

2. If these organelles were free-living bacteria, they would have the features found in bacteria. Mitochondria and chloroplasts both have DNA but no nucleus, and they lack the complex organelles found in eukaryotes. At first glance, the cristae may seem to be an internal membrane system, but they are actually infoldings of the inner membrane. If endosymbiosis occurred, this would be the plasma membrane of the endosymbiont, and the outer membrane would be the plasma membrane of the engulfing cell. Another test would be to compare DNA in these organelles with current bacteria. This has actually shown similarities that make us confident of the identity of the endosymbionts.

3. The prokaryotic and eukaryotic flagella are examples of an analogous trait. Both flagella function to propel the cell through its environment by converting chemical energy into mechanical force. The key difference is in the structure of the flagella. The bacterial flagellum is composed of a single protein emerging from a basal body anchored within the cell's plasma membrane and using the potential energy of a proton gradient to cause a rotary movement. In contrast, the flagellum of the eukaryote is composed of many different proteins assembled into a complex axoneme structure that uses ATP energy to cause an undulating motion.

4. Eukaryotic cells are distinguished from prokaryotic cells by the presence of a system of internal membrane compartments and membrane-bounded organelles such as mitochondria and chloroplasts. As outlined in figure 4.19, the first step in the evolution of the eukaryotic cell was the infolding of the plasma membrane to create separate internal membranes such as the nuclear envelope and the endoplasmic reticulum. The origins of mitochondria and chloroplasts are hypothesized to be the result of a bit of cellular "indigestion" in which aerobic or photosynthetic prokaryotes were engulfed but not digested by the larger ancestor eukaryote. Given this information, there are two possible scenarios for the origin of *Giardia*. In the first scenario, the ancestor of *Giardia* split off from the eukaryotic lineage after the evolution of the nucleus but before the acquisition of mitochondria. In the second scenario, the ancestor of *Giardia* split off after the acquisition of mitochondria and subsequently lost the mitochondria. At present, neither of these two scenarios can be rejected. The first case was long thought to be the best explanation, but recently it has been challenged by evidence for the second case.

CHAPTER 5

LEARNING OUTCOME QUESTIONS

5.1 Cells would not be able to control their contents. Nonpolar molecules would be able to cross the membrane by diffusion, as would small polar molecules, but without proteins to control the passage of specific molecules, it would not function as a semipermeable membrane.

5.2 No. The nonpolar interior of the bilayer would not be soluble in the solvent. The molecules would organize with their nonpolar tails in the solvent, but the negative charge on the phosphates would repel other phosphates.

5.3 Transmembrane domains anchor protein in the membrane. They associate with the hydrophobic interior, thus they must be hydrophobic as well. If they slide out of the interior, they are repelled by water.

5.4 The concentration of the IV will be isotonic with your blood cells. If it were hypotonic, your blood cells would take on water and burst; if it were hypertonic, your blood cells would lose water and shrink.

5.5 Channel proteins are aqueous pores that allow facilitated diffusion. They cannot actively transport ions. Carrier proteins bind to their substrates and couple transport to some form of energy for active transport.

5.6 In all cases, there is recognition and specific binding of a molecule by a protein. In each case this binding is necessary for biological function.

INQUIRY AND DATA ANALYSIS QUESTIONS

Page 94 Inquiry question: As the name suggests for the fluid mosaic model, cell membranes have some degree of fluidity. The degree of fluidity varies with the composition of the membrane, but in all membranes, phospholipids are able to move about within the membrane. Also, due to the hydrophobic and hydrophilic opposite ends of phospholipid molecules, phospholipid bilayers form spontaneously. Therefore, if stressing forces happen to damage a membrane, adjacent phospholipids automatically move to fill in the opening.

Page 95 Inquiry question: Integral membrane proteins are those that are embedded within the membrane structure and provide passageways across the membrane. Because integral membrane proteins must pass through both polar and nonpolar regions of the phospholipid bilayer, the protein portion held within the nonpolar fatty acid interior of the membrane must also be nonpolar. The amino acid sequence of an integral protein would have polar amino acids at both ends, with nonpolar amino acids making up the middle portion of the protein.

UNDERSTAND

1. d   2. a   3. d   4. d   5. b   6. d   7. a

APPLY

1. c   2. b   3. d   4. c   5. d

SYNTHESIZE

1. Since the membrane proteins become intermixed in the absence of the energy molecule, ATP, one can conclude that chemical energy is not required for their movement. Since the proteins do not move and intermix when the temperature is cold, one can also conclude that the movement is temperature-sensitive. The passive diffusion of molecules also depends on temperature and does not require chemical energy; therefore, it is possible to conclude that membrane fluidity occurs as a consequence of passive diffusion.

2. The inner half of the bilayer of the various endomembranes becomes the outer half of the bilayer of the plasma membrane.

3. Lipids can be inserted into one leaflet to produce asymmetry. When lipids are synthesized in the SER, they can be assembled into asymmetric membranes. There are also enzymes that can flip lipids from one leaflet to the other.

CHAPTER 6

LEARNING OUTCOME QUESTIONS

6.1 At the bottom of the ocean, light is not an option as it does not penetrate that deep. However, there is a large source of energy in the form of reduced minerals, such as sulfur compounds, that can be oxidized. These are abundant at hydrothermal vents found at the junctions of tectonic plates. This supports whole ecosystems dependent on bacteria that oxidize reduced minerals available at the hydrothermal vents.

6.2 In a word, no. Enzymes only alter the rate of a reaction; they do not change the thermodynamics of the reaction. The action of an enzyme does not change the ΔG for the reaction.

6.3 In the text, it stated that the average person turns over approximately their body weight in ATP per day. This gives us enough information to determine approximately the amount of energy released:

$$100 \text{ kg} = 1.0 \times 10^5 \text{ g}$$
$$(1.0 \times 10^5 \text{ g})/(507.18 \text{ g/mol}) = 197.2 \text{ mol}$$
$$(197.2 \text{ mol})(7.3 \text{ kcal/mol}) = 1439 \text{ kcal}$$

6.4 This is a question that cannot be definitely answered, but we can give some reasonable conjectures. First, DNA's location is in the nucleus and not the cytoplasm, where most enzymes are found. Second, the double-stranded structure of DNA works well for information storage, but would not necessarily function well as an enzyme. Each base interacts with a base on the opposite strand, which makes for a very stable linear molecule, but does not encourage folding into the kind of complex 3-D shape found in enzymes.

6.5 Feedback inhibition is common in pathways that synthesize metabolites. In these anabolic pathways, when the end-product builds up, it feeds back to inhibit its own production. Catabolic pathways are involved in the degradation of compounds. Feedback inhibition makes less biochemical sense in a pathway that degrades compounds as these are usually involved in energy metabolism or in recycling or removal of compounds. Thus the end-product is destroyed or removed and cannot feed back.

INQUIRY AND DATA ANALYSIS QUESTION

Page 113 Data analysis: The overall ΔG would be the sum of the individual ΔGs, or 3.9 kcal/mol. This makes the overall process exergonic.

UNDERSTAND

1. b   2. a   3. b   4. a   5. d   6. b   7. d

APPLY

1. b   2. c   3. a   4. c   5. c   6. c

SYNTHESIZE

1. a. At 40°C the enzyme is at its optimum. The rate of the reaction is at its highest level.
   b. Temperature is a factor that influences enzyme function. This enzyme does not appear to function at either very cold or very hot temperatures. The shape of the enzyme is affected by temperature, and the enzyme's structure is altered enough at extreme temperatures that it no longer binds substrate. Alternatively, the enzyme may be denatured—that is a complete loss of normal three-dimensional shape at extreme temperatures. Think about frying an egg: What happens to the proteins in the egg?
   c. Everyone's body is slightly different. If the temperature optimum was very narrow, then the cells that make up a body would be vulnerable. Having a broad range of temperature optimums keeps the enzyme functioning.

2. a. The reaction rate would be slow because of the low concentration of the substrate ATP. The rate of reaction depends on substrate concentration.
   b. ATP acts like a noncompetitive, allosteric inhibitor when ATP levels are very high. If ATP binds to the allosteric site, then the reaction should slow down.
   c. When ATP levels are high, the excess ATP molecules bind to the allosteric site and inhibit the enzyme. The allosteric inhibitor functions by causing a change in the shape of the active site in the enzyme. This reaction is an

example of feedback regulation because ATP is a final product of the overall series of reactions associated with glycolysis. The cell regulates glycolysis by regulating this early step catalyzed by phosphofructokinase; the allosteric inhibitor is the "product" of glycolysis (and later stages) which is ATP.

CHAPTER 7

LEARNING OUTCOME QUESTIONS

7.1   Cells require energy for a wide variety of functions. The reactions involved in the oxidation of glucose are complex, and linking these to the different metabolic functions that require energy would be inefficient. Thus cells make and use ATP as a reusable source of energy.

7.2   The location of glycolysis does not argue for or against the endosymbiotic origin of mitochondria. It could have been located in the mitochondria previously and moved to the cytoplasm or could have always been located in the cytoplasm in eukaryotes.

7.3   For an enzyme like pyruvate decarboxylase the complex reduces the distance for the diffusion of substrates for the different stages of the reaction. Any possible unwanted side reactions are prevented. Finally the reactions occur within a single unit and thus can be controlled in a coordinated fashion. The main disadvantage is that since the enzymes are all part of a complex their evolution is more constrained than if they were independent.

7.4   At the end of the Krebs cycle, the electrons removed from glucose are all carried by soluble electron carriers. Most of these are in NADH, and a few are in $FADH_2$. All of these are all fed into the electron transport chain under aerobic conditions where they are used to produce a proton gradient.

7.5   A hole in the outer membrane would allow protons in the intermembrane space to leak out. This would destroy the proton gradient across the inner membrane, stopping the phosphorylation of ADP by ATP synthase.

7.6   Chemiosmosis means that the ATP/NADH ratio is not dependent on the number of "pumping" stations. Instead, it is dependent on the number of protons needed for one turn of the enzyme, and on the number of binding sites on the enzyme for ADP/ATP.

7.7   Glycolysis, which is the starting point for respiration from sugars, is regulated at the enzyme phosphofructokinase. This enzyme is just before the 6-C skeleton is split into two 3-C molecules. The allosteric effectors for this enzyme include ATP and citrate. Thus the "end-product" ATP, and an intermediate from the Krebs cycle, both feed back to inhibit the first part of this process.

7.8   The first obvious point is that the most likely type of ecosystem would be one where oxygen is nonexistent or limiting. This includes marine, aquatic, and soil environments. Any place where oxygen is in short supply is expected to be dominated by anaerobic organisms, and respiration produces more energy than fermentation.

7.9   The short answer is no. The reason is twofold. First the oxidation of fatty acids feeds acetyl units into the Krebs cycle. The primary output of the Krebs cycle is electrons that are fed into the electron transport chain to eventually produce ATP by chemiosmosis. The second reason is that the process of β oxidation that produces the acetyl units is oxygen dependent as well. This is because β oxidation uses FAD as a cofactor for oxidation, and the $FADH_2$ is oxidized by the electron transport chain.

7.10   The evidence for the origins of metabolism is indirect. The presence of O_2 in the atmosphere is the result of photosynthesis, so the record of when we went from a reducing to an oxidizing atmosphere chronicles the rise of oxygenic photosynthesis. Glycolysis is a universal pathway that is found in virtually all types of cells. This indicates that it is an ancient pathway that likely evolved prior to other types of energy metabolism. Nitrogen fixation probably evolved in the reducing atmosphere that preceded oxygenic photosynthesis as it is poisoned by oxygen, and aided by the reducing atmosphere.

INQUIRY AND DATA ANALYSIS QUESTION

Page 142 Data analysis: During the catabolism of fats, each round of β oxidation uses one molecule of ATP and generates one molecule each of $FADH_2$ and NADH. For a 16-carbon fatty acid, seven rounds of β oxidation would convert the fatty acid into eight molecules of acetyl-CoA. The oxidation of each acetyl-CoA in the Krebs cycle produces 10 molecules of ATP. The overall ATP yield from a 16-carbon fatty acid would be a net gain of 21 ATP from seven rounds of β oxidation [gain of 4 ATP per round – 1 per round to prime reactions] + 80 ATP from the oxidation of 8 acetyl-CoAs = 101 molecules of ATP.

UNDERSTAND

1. d   2. d   3. c   4. c   5. a   6. d   7. c

APPLY

1. b   2. b   3. c   4. c   5. c   6. b   7. b

SYNTHESIZE

1.

Molecules	Glycolysis	Cellular Respiration
Glucose	*Is the starting material for the reaction*	*Does not directly use glucose; however, does use pyruvate derived from glucose*
Pyruvate	*The end product of glycolysis*	*The starting material for cellular respiration*
Oxygen	*Not required*	*Required for aerobic respiration, but not for anaerobic respiration*
ATP	*Produced through substrate-level phosphorylation*	*Produced through oxidative phosphorylation. More produced than in glycolysis*
CO_2	*Not produced*	*Produced during pyruvate oxidation and Krebs cycle*

2.   The electron transport chain of the inner membrane of the mitochondria functions to create a hydrogen ion concentration gradient by pumping protons into the intermembrane space. In a typical mitochondrion, the protons can only diffuse back down their concentration gradient by moving through the ATP synthase and generating ATP. If protons can move through another transport protein, then the potential energy of the hydrogen ion concentration gradient would be "lost" as heat.

3.   If brown fat persists in adults, then the uncoupling mechanism to generate heat described above could result in weight loss under cold conditions. There is now some evidence to indicate that this may be the case.

CHAPTER 8

LEARNING OUTCOME QUESTIONS

8.1   Both chloroplasts and mitochondria have an outer membrane and an inner membrane. The inner membrane in both forms an elaborate structure. These inner membrane systems have electron transport chains that move protons across the membrane to allow for the synthesis of ATP by chemiosmosis. They also both have a soluble compartment in which a variety of enzymes carry out reactions.

8.2   All of the carbon in your body comes from carbon fixation by autotrophs. Thus, all of the carbon in your body was once CO_2 in the atmosphere, before it was fixed by plants.

8.3   The action spectrum for photosynthesis refers to the most effective wavelengths. The absorption spectrum for an individual pigment shows how much light is absorbed at different wavelengths.

8.4   Before the discovery of photosystems, we assumed that each chlorophyll molecule absorbed photons resulting in excited electrons.

8.5   Without a proton gradient, synthesis of ATP by chemiosmosis would be impossible. However, NADPH could still be synthesized because electron transport would still occur as long as photons were still being absorbed to begin the process.

8.6   A portion of the Calvin cycle is the reverse of glycolysis (the reduction of 3-phosphoglycerate to glyceraldehyde-3-phosphate).

8.7   Both C_4 plants and CAM plants fix carbon by incorporating CO_2 into the 4-carbon malate and then use this to produce high local levels of CO_2 for the Calvin cycle. The main difference is that in C_4 plants, this occurs in different cells, and in CAM plants this occurs at different times.

INQUIRY AND DATA ANALYSIS QUESTIONS

Page 150 Data analysis: Light energy is used in light-dependent reactions to reduce $NADP^+$ and to produce ATP. Molecules of chlorophyll absorb photons of light energy, but only within narrow energy ranges (specific wavelengths of light). When all chlorophyll molecules are in use, no additional increase in light intensity will increase the rate at which they can absorb light energy.

Page 154 Data analysis: The curves would be similar to the observed curve shown, but would plateau at a higher and lower level, respectively. Even the higher level would still be below the expected curve for all chlorophyll molecules being used.

Page 157 Data analysis: You could conclude that the two photosystems function together and not in series.

UNDERSTAND

1.c 2.a 3.a 4.b 5.c 6.c 7.a 8.b

APPLY

1.d 2.b 3.d 4.c 5.d 6.d 7.a 8.a

SYNTHESIZE

1. In C_3 plants CO_2 reacts with ribulose 1,5-bisphosphate (RuBP) to yield 2 molecules of PGA. This reaction is catalyzed by the enzyme rubisco. Rubisco also catalyzes the oxidation of RuBP. Which reaction predominates depends on the relative concentrations of reactants. The reactions of the Calvin cycle reduce the PGA to G3P, which can be used to make a variety of sugars including RuBP. In C_4 and CAM plants, an initial fixation reaction incorporates CO_2 into malate. The malate then can be decarboxylated to pyruvate and CO_2 to produce locally high levels of CO_2. The high levels of CO_2 get around the oxidation of RuBP by rubisco. In C_4 plants malate is produced in one cell, then shunted into an adjacent cell that lacks stomata to produce high levels of CO_2. CAM plants fix carbon into malate at night when their stomata are open, then use this during the day to fuel the Calvin cycle. Both are evolutionary innovations that have arisen in hot dry climates that allow plants to more efficiently fix carbon and prevent desiccation.

2. Figure 8.19 diagrams this relationship. The oxygen produced by photosynthesis is used as a final electron acceptor for electron transport in respiration. The CO_2 that results from the oxidation of glucose (or fatty acids) is incorporated into organic compounds via the Calvin cycle. Respiration also produces water, while photosynthesis consumes water.

3. Yes. Plants use their chloroplasts to convert light energy into chemical energy. During light reactions ATP and NADPH are created, but these molecules are consumed during the Calvin cycle and are not available for the cell's general use. The G3P produced by the Calvin cycle stores the chemical energy from the light reactions within its chemical bonds. Ultimately, this energy is stored in glucose and retrieved by the cell through the process of glycolysis and cellular respiration.

CHAPTER 9

LEARNING OUTCOME QUESTIONS

9.1 Ligands bind to receptors based on complementary shapes. This interaction based on molecular recognition is similar to the way enzymes interact with their ligands.

9.2 Hydrophobic molecules can cross the membrane and are thus more likely to have an internal receptor.

9.3 Intracellular receptors have direct effects on gene expression. This generally leads to effects with longer duration.

9.4 Ras protein occupies a central role in signaling pathways involving growth factors. A number of different kinds of growth factors act through Ras. So it is not surprising mutated Ras protein is a factor in a number of different cancers.

9.5 GPCRs are a very ancient and flexible receptor/signaling pathway. The genes encoding these receptors have been duplicated and then have diversified over evolutionary time, so now there are many members of this gene family.

UNDERSTAND

1.b 2.b 3.c 4.d 5.b 6.d 7.c 8.a

APPLY

1.b 2.c 3.c 4.d 5.d 6.c

SYNTHESIZE

1. All signaling events start with a ligand binding to a receptor. The receptor initiates a chain of events that ultimately leads to a change in cellular behavior. In some cases the change is immediate—for example, the opening of an ion channel. In other cases the change requires more time before it occurs, such as when the MAP kinase pathway becomes activated multiple different kinases become activated and deactivated. Some signals only affect a cell for a short time (the channel example), but other signals can permanently change the cell by changing gene expression, and therefore the number and kind of proteins found in the cell.

2. a. This system involves *both* autocrine and paracrine signaling because Netrin-1 can influence the cells within the crypt that are responsible for its production and the neighboring cells.
   b. The binding of Netrin-1 to its receptor produces the signal for cell growth. This signal would be strongest in the regions of the tissue with the greatest amount of Netrin-1—that is, in the crypts. A concentration gradient of Netrin-1 exists such that the levels of this ligand are lowest at the tips of the villi. Consequently, the greatest amount of cell death would occur at the villi tips.
   c. Tumors occur when cell growth goes on unregulated. In the absence of Netrin-1, the Netrin-1 receptor can trigger cell death—controlling the number of cells that make up the epithelial tissue. Without this mechanism for controlling cell number, tumor formation is more likely.

CHAPTER 10

LEARNING OUTCOME QUESTIONS

10.1 The concerted replication and segregation of chromosomes works well with one small chromosome, but would likely not work as well with many chromosomes.

10.2 No.

10.3 The first irreversible step is the commitment to DNA replication.

10.4 Loss of cohesins would mean that the products of DNA replication would not be kept together. This would make normal mitosis impossible, and thus lead to aneuploid cells and probably be lethal.

10.5 The segregation of chromatids that lose cohesin would be random because they could no longer be held at metaphase attached to opposite poles. This would likely lead to gain and loss of this chromosome in daughter cells due to improper partitioning.

10.6 Tumor suppressor genes are genetically recessive, but proto-oncogenes are dominant. Loss of function for a tumor suppressor gene leads to cancer, whereas inappropriate expression or gain of function lead to cancer with proto-oncogenes.

UNDERSTAND

1.d 2.b 3.b 4.b 5.a 6.c 7.b 8.d

APPLY

1.a 2.c 3.b 4.d 5.c 6.d

SYNTHESIZE

1. If Wee-1 were absent, the cell would have no way to phosphorylate Cdk. If Cdk is not phosphorylated, then it cannot be inhibited. If Cdk is not inhibited, then it will remain active. If Cdk remains active, then it will continue to signal the cell to move through the G_2/M checkpoint, but now in an unregulated manner. The cells would undergo multiple rounds of cell division without the growth associated with G_2. As a consequence, the daughter cells will become smaller and smaller with each division—hence the name of the protein!

2. Growth factor = ligand
   1. Ligand binds to receptor (the growth factor will bind to a growth factor receptor).
   2. A signal is transduced (carried) into the cytoplasm.
   3. A signal cascade is triggered. Multiple intermediate proteins or second messengers will be affected.
   4. A transcription factor will be activated to bind to a specific site on the DNA.
   5. Transcription occurs and the mRNA enters the cytoplasm.
   6. The mRNA is translated and a protein is formed.
   7. The protein functions within the cytoplasm—possibly triggering S phase.

   If you study figure 10.22 you will see a similar pathway for the formation of S phase proteins following receptor–ligand binding by a growth factor. In this diagram various proteins in the signaling pathway become phosphorylated and then dephosphorylated. Ultimately, the Rb protein that regulated the transcription factor E2F becomes phosphorylated. This releases the E2F and allows it to bind to the gene for S phase proteins and cyclins.

3. Proto-oncogenes tend to encode proteins that function in signal transduction pathways that control cell division. When the regulation of these proteins is aberrant, or they are stuck in the "on" state by mutation, it can lead to cancer.

Tumor suppressor genes, on the other hand, tend to be in genes that encode proteins that suppress instead of activate cell division. Thus loss of function for a tumor suppressor gene leads to cancer.

CHAPTER 11

LEARNING OUTCOME QUESTIONS

11.1 Stem cells divide by mitosis to produce one cell that can undergo meiosis and another stem cell.

11.2 No. Keeping sister chromatids together at the first division is key to this reductive division. Homologues segregate at the first division, reducing the number of chromosomes by half.

11.3 An improper disjunction at anaphase I would result in 4 aneuploid gametes: 2 with an extra chromosome and 2 that are missing a chromosome. Nondisjunction at anaphase II would result in 2 normal gametes and 2 aneuploid gametes: 1 with an extra chromosome and 1 missing a chromosome.

11.4 The independent alignment of homologous pairs at metaphase I and the process of crossing over. The first shuffles the genome at the level of entire chromosomes, and the second shuffles the genome at the level of individual chromosomes.

INQUIRY AND DATA ANALYSIS QUESTION

Page 217 Inquiry question: No. At the conclusion of meiosis I each cell has a single copy of each homologue. So, even if the attachment of sister chromatids were lost after a meiosis I division, the results would not be the same as mitosis.

UNDERSTAND

1. c 2. d 3. a 4. b 5. b 6. a 7. b

APPLY

1. c 2. b 3. b 4. d 5. b 6. a

SYNTHESIZE

1. Compare your figure with figure 11.8.
   a. There would be three homologous pairs of chromosomes for an organism with a diploid number of six.
   b. For each pair of homologues, you should now have a maternal and paternal pair.
   c. Many possible arrangements are possible. The key to your image is that it must show the homologues aligned pairwise—not single-file along the metaphase plate. The maternal and paternal homologues *do not* have to align on the same side of the cell. Independent assortment means that the pairs can be mixed.
   d. A diagram of metaphase II would not include the homologous pairs. The pairs have separated during anaphase of meiosis I. Your picture should diagram the haploid number of chromosomes, in this case three, aligned single-file along the metaphase plate. Remember that meiosis II is similar to mitosis.

2. The diploid chromosome number of a mule is 63. The mule receives 32 chromosomes from its horse parent (diploid 64: haploid 32) and another 31 chromosomes from its donkey parent (diploid 61: haploid 31). 32 + 31 = 63. The haploid number for the mule would be one half the diploid number 63 ÷ 2 = 31.5. Can there be a 0.5 chromosome? Even if the horse and donkey chromosomes can pair (no guarantee of that), there will be one chromosome without a partner. This will lead to aneuploid gametes that are not viable.

3. Independent assortment involves the random distribution of maternal versus paternal homologues into the daughter cells produced during meiosis I. The number of possible gametes is equal to 2^n, where n is the haploid number of chromosomes. Crossing over involves the physical exchange of genetic material between homologous chromosomes, creating new combinations of genes on a single chromosome. Crossing over is a relatively rare event that affects large blocks of genetic material, so independent assortment likely has the greatest influence on genetic diversity.

4. a. Nondisjunction occurs at the point when the chromosomes are being pulled to opposite poles. This occurs during anaphase.
   b. Use an image like figure 11.8 and illustrate nondisjunction at anaphase I versus anaphase II

Anaphase I nondisjunction:

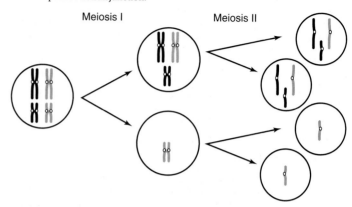

CHAPTER 12

LEARNING OUTCOME QUESTIONS

12.1 Both had an effect, but the approach is probably the most important. In theory, his approach would have worked for any plant, or even animal, he chose. In practice, the ease of both cross- and self-fertilization was helpful.

12.2 1/3 of tall F_2 plants are true-breeding.

12.3 The events of meiosis I are much more important in explaining Mendel's laws. During anaphase I homologues separate and are thus segregated, and the alignment of different homologous pairs at metaphase I is independent.

12.4 The cross is *Aa Bb × aa Bb* and the probability for (*A_ B_*) = (3/4) (1/2) =3/8.

12.5 1:1:1:1 dom-dom:dom-rec:rec-dom:rec-rec

12.6 6/16.

INQUIRY AND DATA ANALYSIS QUESTIONS

Page 223 Inquiry question: The ability to control whether the plants self-fertilized or cross-fertilized was of paramount importance in Mendel's studies. Results due to cross-fertilization would have had confounding influences on the predicted number of offspring with a particular phenotype.

Page 225 Data analysis: If the purple F_1 were backcrossed to the white parent, the phenotypic ratio would be 1 purple:1 white, and the genotypic ratio would be 1 non-true-breeding dominant (heterozygous):1 true-breeding recessive (homozygous recessive).

Page 227 Data analysis: Yes. The affected females each had one unaffected parent and thus are heterozygous. This means that the probability of affected offspring would be 50%.

Page 228 Inquiry question: Genetic defects that remain hidden or dormant as heterozygotes in the recessive state are more likely to be revealed in homozygous state among closely related individuals.

Page 231 Data analysis: The probability of being purple-flowered, round, and yellow is the same as the probability of being dominant for all three traits. The probability for the dominant phenotype from a cross of two heterozygotes is 3/4, so the probably of being dominant for all three traits in this cross would be (3/4)(3/4)(3/4) = 27/64.

Page 232 Data analysis:

TABLE 12.2	Dihybrid Testcross	
Actual Genotype	**Results of Testcross**	
	Trait A	**Trait B**
AABB	Trait A breeds true	Trait B breeds true
AaBB	———	Trait B breeds true
AABb	Trait A breeds true	———
AaBb	———	———

Page 233 Data analysis: Cuenot would have observed 2 yellow mice:1 wild type. This is because the homozygous yellow mice die, leaving 2 heterozygotes to 1 homozygous recessive.

Page 235 Inquiry question: Almost certainly, differences in major phenotypic traits of twins would be due to environmental factors such as diet.

Page 236 Data analysis: This is a case of epistasis, in which the albino gene obscures the effects of the black/brown locus. The offspring that are *B_ aa* (where the albino locus is designated by *a*) will appear the same as *bb aa* offspring. Thus the overall ratio is 9 black:3 brown:3+1 albino.

UNDERSTAND

1. b 2. c 3. c 4. c 5. c 6. d

APPLY

1. d 2. d 3. b 4. a 5. c 6. d

SYNTHESIZE

1. The approach to solving this type of problem is to identify the possible gametes. Separate the possible gamete combinations into the boxes along the top and side. Fill in the Punnett square by combining alleles from each parent.
   a. A monohybrid cross between individuals with the genotype *Aa* and *A*

	A	*a*
A	*AA*	*Aa*
a	*aA*	*aa*

   Phenotypic ratio: 3 dominant to 1 recessive

   b. A dihybrid cross between two individuals with the genotype *AaBb*

	AB	*Ab*	*aB*	*ab*
AB	*AABB*	*AABb*	*AaBB*	*AaBb*
Ab	*AAbB*	*AAbb*	*AabB*	*Aabb*
aB	*aABB*	*aABb*	*aaBB*	*aaBb*
ab	*aAbB*	*aAbb*	*aabB*	*aabb*

   Phenotypic ratio: 9 dominant dominant to 3 dominant recessive to 3 recessive dominant to 1 recessive recessive

   Using the product rule: $\text{Prob}(A_\ B_) = (3/4)(3/4) = 9/16$
   $\text{Prob}(A_\ bb) = (3/4)(3/4) = 3/16$
   $\text{Prob}(aa\ B_) = (1/4)(3/4) = 3/16$
   $\text{Prob}(aa\ bb) = (1/4)(1/4) = 1/16$

   c. A dihybrid cross between individuals with the genotype *AaBb* and *aabb*

	AB	*Ab*	*aB*	*ab*
ab	*aAbB*	*aAbb*	*aabB*	*aabb*

   Using the product rule: $\text{Prob}(A_\ B_) = (1/4)(1) = 1/16$
   $\text{Prob}(A_\ bb) = (1/4)(1) = 1/16$
   $\text{Prob}(aa\ B_) = (1/4)(1) = 1/16$
   $\text{Prob}(aa\ bb) = (1/4)(1) = 1/16$

2. The segregation of different alleles for any gene occurs due to the pairing of homologous chromosomes, and the subsequent separation of these homologues during anaphase I. The independent assortment of traits, more accurately the independent segregation of different allele pairs, is due to the independent alignment of chromosomes during metaphase I of meiosis.
3. There seems to be the loss of a genotype since there are only 3 possible outcomes (2 yellow and 1 black). A yellow gene that has a dominant effect on coat color, but also causes lethality when homozygous, could explain the observations. Therefore, a yellow mouse is heterozygous, and crossing two yellow mice yields 1 homozygous yellow (dead):2 heterozygous (appears yellow):1 black. You could test this by crossing the yellow to homozygous black. You should get 1 yellow:1 black, and all black offspring should be true-breeding, and all yellow should behave as above.
4. Two genes are involved, one of which is epistatic to the other. At one gene, there are two alleles: black and brown; at the other gene, there are two alleles: albino and colored. The albino gene is epistatic to the brown gene so that when the animal is homozygous recessive for albino, it is albino regardless of whether it is black or brown at the other locus. This leads to the 4 albino in a Mendelian kind of crossing scheme.

Chapter 13

LEARNING OUTCOME QUESTIONS

13.1 Females would be all wild type; males would be all white-eyed.

13.2 Yes, should be viable and appear female.

13.3 The mt^- DNA could be degraded by a nuclease similar to how bacteria deal with invading viruses. Alternatively, the mt^--containing mitochondria could be excluded from the zygote.

13.4 No, not by genetic crosses.

13.5 Yes. First-division nondisjunction yields four aneuploid gametes, but second-division yields only two aneuploid gametes.

INQUIRY AND DATA ANALYSIS QUESTIONS

Page 244 Inquiry question: There would probably be very little if any recombination, so the expected assortment ratios would have been skewed from the expected 9:3:3:1.

Page 247 Data analysis: Instead of equal proportions of four types of gametes, you would get 45% of each of the two parental types and only 5% of each of the recombinant types. How this would affect a dihybrid cross would depend on the original parents, but it would clearly skew the results such that the 9:3:3:1 phenotypic ratio would be completely obscured. It would have been impossible to conclude that the two loci were behaving independently, as in fact, they are not.

Page 251 Data analysis: What has changed is the mother's age. The older the woman, the higher the risk she has of nondisjunction during meiosis. Thus, she also has a much greater risk of producing a child with Down syndrome.

Page 251 Inquiry question: Nondisjunction produces an XX egg that is fertilized by a Y sperm. A normal X egg is fertilized by an XY sperm produced by nondisjunction. Note that the nondisjunction event that produces the XX egg could be either MI or MII, but the event that produces the XY sperm would have to be MI.

Page 253 Inquiry question: Advanced maternal age, a previous child with birth defects, or a family history of birth defects.

UNDERSTAND

1. c 2. d 3. d 4. a 5. c 6. c 7. c

APPLY

1. c 2. b 3. c 4. b 5. d 6. b

SYNTHESIZE

1. Theoretically, 25% of the children from this cross will be color blind. All of the color blind children will be male, and 50% of the males will be color blind.
2. Parents of heterozygous plant were green wrinkled × yellow round
   Frequency of recombinants is 36+29/1300 = 0.05
   Map distance = 5 cM
3. Male calico cats are very rare. The coloration that is associated with calico cats is the product of X inactivation. X inactivation only occurs in females as a response to dosage levels of the X-linked genes. The only way to get a male calico is to be heterozygous for the color gene and to be the equivalent of a Klinefelter's male (*XXY*).

Chapter 14

LEARNING OUTCOME QUESTIONS

14.1 The 20 different amino acid building blocks offers chemical complexity. This appears to offer informational complexity as well.

14.2 The proper tautomeric forms are necessary for proper base-pairing, which is critical to DNA structure.

14.3 Prior to replication in light N (i.e., ^{14}N) isotope there would be only one band. After one round of replication, there would be two bands with denatured DNA: one heavy and one light.

14.4 The 5′ to 3′ activity is used to remove RNA primers. The 3′ to 5′ activity is used to remove mispaired bases (proofreading).

14.5 A shortening of chromosome ends would eventually affect DNA that encodes important functions.

14.6 No. The number of DNA-damaging agents, in addition to replication errors, would cause lethal damage (this has been tested in yeast).

INQUIRY AND DATA ANALYSIS QUESTIONS

Page 262 Data analysis: The Watson–Crick helical structure fits the measurements made from Franklin's X-ray diffraction pictures. The base-pairing explains why Chargaff observed the regularities in quantities of G = C and A = T, and the base-pairing depends on the proper tautomeric forms of the bases. Taken together, the model rationalizes all of these data.

Page 264 Data analysis: If the Meselson–Stahl experiment was allowed to run for another round, the pattern of bands would be the same as the second round (light molecules and hybrid molecules), but the light, ^{14}N, band would be darker. This is because the products from the ^{14}N alone would remain ^{14}N, and the products from the hybrid molecules (^{15}N/^{14}N) would produce one hybrid molecule and one all-^{14}N molecule.

Page 265 Inquiry question: The covalent bonds create a strong backbone for the molecule, making it difficult to disrupt. Individual hydrogen bonds are more easily broken, allowing enzymes to separate the two strands without disrupting the inherent structure of the molecule.

Page 269 Inquiry question: DNA ligase is important in connecting Okazaki fragments during DNA replication. Without it, the lagging strand would not be complete.

Page 273 Inquiry question: The linear structure of chromosomes creates the end problem discussed in the text. It is impossible to finish the ends of linear chromosomes using unidirectional polymerases that require RNA primers. The size of eukaryotic genomes also means that the time necessary to replicate the genome is much greater than in prokaryotes with smaller genomes. Thus the use of multiple origins of replication.

Page 275 Inquiry question: Cells have a variety of DNA repair pathways that allow them to restore damaged DNA to its normal constitution. If DNA repair pathways are compromised, the cell will have a higher mutation rate. This can lead to higher rates of cancer in a multicellular organism such as humans.

UNDERSTAND

1. d   2. a   3. c   4. a   5. c   6. b   7. b

APPLY

1. c   2. b   3. c   4. c   5. a   6. b   7. d   8. c

SYNTHESIZE

1. a. If both bacteria are heat-killed, then the transfer of DNA will have no effect since pathogenicity requires the production of proteins encoded by the DNA. Protein synthesis will not occur in a dead cell.
    b. The nonpathogenic cells will be transformed to pathogenic cells. Loss of proteins will not alter DNA.
    c. The nonpathogenic cells remain nonpathogenic. If the DNA is digested, it will not be transferred and no transformation will occur.

2. The region could be an origin of replication. Origins of replication are adenine- and thymine-rich regions since only these nucleotides form two hydrogen bonds versus the three hydrogen bonds formed between guanine and cytosine, making it easier to separate the two strands of DNA.

    The RNA primer sequences would be 5′-ACUAUUGCUUUAUAA-3′. The sequence is antiparallel to the DNA sequence (review figure 14.16), meaning that the 5′ end of the RNA is matching up with the 3′ end of the DNA. It is also important to remember that in RNA the thymine nucleotide is replaced by uracil (U). Therefore, the adenine in DNA will form a complementary base-pair with uracil.

3. a. *DNA gyrase* functions to relieve torsional strain on the DNA. If DNA gyrase were not functioning, the DNA molecule would undergo supercoiling, causing the DNA to wind up on itself, preventing the continued binding of the polymerases necessary for replication.
    b. *DNA polymerase III* is the primary polymerase involved in the addition of new nucleotides to the growing polymer and in the formation of the phosphodiester bonds that make up the sugar–phosphate backbone. If this enzyme were not functioning, then no new DNA strand would be synthesized and there would be no replication.
    c. *DNA ligase* is involved in the formation of phosphodiester bonds between Okazaki fragments. If this enzyme were not functioning, then the fragments would remain disconnected and would be more susceptible to digestion by nucleases.
    d. *DNA polymerase I* functions to remove and replace the RNA primers that are required for DNA polymerase III function. If DNA polymerase I were not available, then the RNA primers would remain and the replicated DNA would become a mix of DNA and RNA.

CHAPTER 15

LEARNING OUTCOME QUESTIONS

15.1 There is no molecular basis for recognition between amino acids and nucleotides. The tRNA is able to interact with nucleic acid by base-pairing, and an enzyme can covalently attach amino acids to it.

15.2 There would be no specificity to the genetic code. Each codon must specify a single amino acid, although amino acids can have more than one codon.

15.3 Transcription/translation coupling cannot exist in eukaryotes where the two processes are separated in both space and time.

15.4 No. This is a result of the evolutionary history of eukaryotes but is not necessitated by genome complexity.

15.5 Alternative splicing offers flexibility in coding information. One gene can encode multiple proteins.

15.6 This tRNA would be able to "read" STOP codons. This could allow nonsense mutations to be viable, but would cause problems making longer than normal proteins. Most bacterial genes actually have more than one STOP at the end of the gene.

15.7 Attaching amino acids to tRNAs, bringing charged tRNAs to the ribosome, and ribosome translocation all require energy.

15.9 No. It depends on where the breakpoints are that created the inversion, or duplication. For duplications it also depends on the genes that are duplicated.

INQUIRY AND DATA ANALYSIS QUESTIONS

Page 280 Data analysis: This double-mutant strain would only grow on media supplemented with all of the intermediates. This is because ArgE mutants are blocked at the first step. In general, these kinds of double mutants allow you to determine which gene occurs earlier in a pathway: the double mutant will look like an organism with a mutation at the earliest point in the pathway.

Page 281 Inquiry question: One would expect higher amounts of error in transcription over DNA replication. Proofreading is important in DNA replication because errors in DNA replication will be passed on to offspring as mutations. However, RNAs have very short life spans in the cytoplasm, and therefore mistakes are not permanent.

Page 284 Inquiry question: The very strong similarity among organisms indicates a common ancestry of the code.

Page 285 Inquiry question: The promoter acts as a binding site for RNA polymerase. The structure of the promoter provides information both about where to bind and the direction of transcription. If the two sites were identical, the polymerase would need some other cue for the direction of transcription.

Page 289 Data analysis: Splicing can produce multiple transcripts from the same gene. This is shown below with the exons shown in different colors.

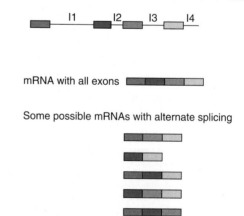

Page 297 Inquiry question: Wobble not only explains the number of tRNAs that are observed due to the increased flexibility in the 5′ position, it also accounts for the degeneracy that is observed in the genetic code. The degenerate base is the one in the wobble position.

UNDERSTAND

1. d   2. c   3. d   4. b   5. c   6. b   7. c

APPLY

1. b 2. c 3. b 4. d 5. a 6. b 7. b

SYNTHESIZE

1. The predicted sequence of the mRNA for this gene is

   5′-GCAAUGGGCUCGGCAUGCUAAUCC-3′

   The predicted amino acid sequence of the protein is

   5′-GCA AUG GGC UCG GCA UGC UAA UCC-3′

   Met-Gly-Ser-Ala-Cys-STOP

2. A frameshift essentially turns the sequence of bases into a "random" sequence. If you consider the genetic code, 3 of the 64 codons are STOP, so the probability of hitting a STOP in a random sequence is 3/64, or about 1 in every 20 codons.

3. a. mRNA = 5′-GCA AUG GGC UCG GCA UUG CUA AUC C-3′
      The amino acid sequence would then be:
      Met-Gly-Ser-Ala-Leu-Leu-Iso-.
      There is no STOP codon. This is an example of a frameshift mutation. The addition of a nucleotide alters the "reading frame," resulting in a change in the type and number of amino acids in this protein.
   b. mRNA = 5′-GCA AUG GGC UAG GCA UGC UAA UCC-3′
      The amino acid sequence would then be: Met-Gly-STOP.
      This is an example of a nonsense mutation. A single nucleotide change has resulted in the early termination of protein synthesis by altering the codon for Ser into a STOP codon.
   c. mRNA = 5′-GCA AUG GGC UCG GCA AGC UAA UCC -3′
      The amino acid sequence would then be: Met-Gly-Ser-Ala-Ser-STOP.
      This base substitution has affected the codon that would normally encode Cys (UGC) and resulted in the addition of Ser (AGC).

4. The split genes of eukaryotes offers the opportunity to control the splicing process, which does not exist in prokaryotes. This is also true for polyadenylation in eukaryotes. In prokaryotes, transcription/translation coupling offers the opportunity for the process of translation to have an effect on transcription.

CHAPTER 16
LEARNING OUTCOME QUESTIONS

16.1 The control of gene expression would be more like that in humans (fellow eukaryotes) than in *E. coli*.

16.2 The two helices both interact with DNA, so the spacing between the helices is important for both to be able to bind to DNA.

16.3 The operon would be on all of the time (constitutive expression).

16.4 The loss of a general transcription factor would likely be lethal as it would affect all transcription. The loss of a specific factor would affect only those genes controlled by the factor.

16.5 These genes are necessary for the ordinary functions of the cell. That is, the role of these genes is in ordinary housekeeping and not in any special functions.

16.6 RNA interference offers a way to specifically affect gene expression using drugs made of siRNAs.

16.7 Because there are many proteins in a cell doing a variety of functions, uncontrolled degradation of proteins would be devastating to the cell.

INQUIRY AND DATA ANALYSIS QUESTIONS

Page 308 Inquiry question: The presence of more than one gene in the operon allows for increased control over the elements of the pathway and therefore the product. A single regulatory system can regulate several adjacent genes.

Page 309 Data analysis: A mutation that prevents the repressor from binding to DNA would express the genes for lactose metabolism all the time (constitutive expression). A mutation that prevents the inducer from binding to the repressor would bind to DNA all the time, and thus never express the genes for lactose metabolism (uninducible).

Page 315 Inquiry question: Regulation occurs when various genes have the same regulatory sequences, which bind the same proteins.

Page 324 Inquiry question: Ubiquitin is added to proteins that need to be removed because they are nonfunctional or those that are degraded as part of a normal cellular cycle.

UNDERSTAND

1. c 2. d 3. a 4. c 5. b 6. c 7. b

APPLY

1. c 2. c 3. b 4. d 5. c 6. a 7. c

SYNTHESIZE

1. Mutations that affect binding sites for proteins on DNA will control the expression of genes covalently linked to them. Introducing a wild-type binding site on a plasmid will not affect this. We call this being *cis*-dominant. Mutations in proteins that bind to DNA would be recessive to a wild-type gene introduced on a plasmid.

2. Negative control of transcription occurs when the ability to initiate transcription is reduced. Positive control occurs when the ability to initiate transcription is enhanced. The *lac* operon is regulated by the presence or absence of lactose. The proteins encoded within the operon are specific to the catabolism (breakdown) of lactose. For this reason, operon expression is only required when there is lactose in the environment. Allolactose is formed when lactose is present in the cell. The allolactose binds to a repressor protein, altering its conformation and allowing RNA polymerase to bind. In addition to the role of lactose, there is also a role for the activator protein CAP in regulation of *lac*. When cAMP levels are high then CAP can bind to DNA and make it easier for RNA polymerase to bind to the promoter. The *lac* operon is an example of both positive and negative control.

   The *trp* operon encodes protein manufacture of tryptophan in a cell. This operon must be expressed when cellular levels of tryptophan are low. Conversely, when tryptophan is available in the cell, there is no need to transcribe the operon. The tryptophan repressor must bind tryptophan before it can take on the right shape to bind to the operator. This is an example of negative control.

3. Forms that control gene expression that are unique to eukaryotes include alternative splicing, control of chromatin structure, control of transport of mRNA from the nucleus to the cytoplasm, control of translation by small RNAs, and control of protein levels by ubiquitin-directed destruction. Of these, most are obviously part of the unique features of eukaryotic cells. The only mechanisms that could work in prokaryotes would be translational control by small RNAs and controlled destruction of proteins.

4. Mutation is a permanent change in the DNA. Regulation is a short-term change controlled by the cell. Like mutations, regulation can alter the number of proteins in a cell, change the size of a protein, or eliminate the protein altogether. The key difference is that gene regulation can be reversed in response to changes in the cell's environment. Mutations do not allow for this kind of rapid response.

CHAPTER 17
LEARNING OUTCOME QUESTIONS

17.1 #1 Recombinant DNA makes it possible to introduce into a different organism a single gene from the same or a very different species. Gene combinations that are impossible via conventional breeding (e.g., inserting a bacterial gene into a plant) can be created. Breeding can be more targeted and quicker.

   #2 *Eco*RI is a restriction enzyme that can be used to cut DNA at specific places. Ligase is used to "glue" together pieces of DNA that have been cut with the same restriction enzyme. The two enzymes make it possible to add foreign DNA into an *E. coli* plasmid.

17.2 A restriction digest DNA fragment is combined with a plasmid that has been cut with the same restriction enzyme. Ligase is used to insert the fragment into the plasmid, which can then be inserted into a bacterial cell, a process called transformation. The cell is cultured and divides many times. The plasmids can then be isolated, and, if desired, the many copies of the fragment can be isolated with a restriction digest and could again be separated using gel electrophoresis.

17.3 Both PCR and DNA replication result in new copies of the DNA made by separating the original strands and using a primer to initiate replication, followed by the addition of dNTPs with the help of a DNA polymerase. In DNA replication, an enzyme called helicase separates the two strands, whereas in PCR, high temperature (95°C) is used to separate the strands. DNA replication uses an RNA primer made by DNA primase, but PCR relies on synthetic DNA primers. The DNA polymerase in most organisms is heat-sensitive. In PCR, a heat-stable DNA polymerase from an archaean that is extremely heat-tolerant is used. Multiple rounds of PCR allow for an exponential increase in copies of the DNA, whereas in most cases, DNA replication results in one new copy of each chromosome before a cell divides.

17.4 A cDNA library is constructed from mRNA. Unlike the gene itself, cDNA does not include the introns or regulatory elements.

17.5 Isolate DNA from cells from you and your neighbor in separate tubes. Digest both DNA samples with the restriction endonucleases and separate the fragments using gel electrophoresis. "Blot" the gel onto nitrocellulose paper and incubate the paper with probes for the relevant RFLPs. Compare the patterns of the RFLP fragments on the two different "blots."

17.6 Your flowchart should start with the DNA sequence for an influenza coat protein, likely a restriction digest fragment. Next the DNA fragment is transformed into a plant cell, and a plant is regenerated and tested. Generations of plants can be bred from a successfully transformed plant. To finish the vaccine, a process must be established to isolate the influenza coat protein from the plant tissue.

17.7 GM plants with pest resistance are created by introducing a single gene into a plant using recombinant technologies. MAB allows traits to be linked to markers within the genome without knowing the sequence of specific genes, thus more traits can be bred into the crop plant. Furthermore, many traits are the result of multiple genes that can all be followed by markers. With MAB, a set of regions within the genome can all be followed and simultaneously bred into the crop plant.

INQUIRY AND DATA ANALYSIS QUESTIONS

Page 331 Inquiry question: A bacterial artificial chromosome or a yeast artificial chromosome would be the best way to go because only a plasmid vector can stably hold up to 10 kb.

Page 334 Data analysis: Six million clones would cover all the DNA sequences in the genome, but there would be no overlapping sequences, presenting a problem if you wanted to use the overlaps to sort out the sequence in which all the clones were found in the genome.

Page 335 Inquiry question: No, cDNA is created using mRNA as a template; therefore, intron sequences would not be expressed using the cDNA.

Page 345 Data analysis: In comparing the weights of the transgenic salmon with the wild salmon, at every day after feeding, the transgenic salmon weighed more than the wild salmon. At the end of the experiment the transgenic salmon's size was 150% of the wild salmon.

UNDERSTAND

1. b 2. b 3. d 4. d 5. c 6. b 7. d 8. a

APPLY

1. d 2. c 3. d

SYNTHESIZE

1. Genes coding for each of the subunits would need to be inserted into different plasmids that are integrated into different bacteria. The cultures would need to be grown separately, and the different protein subunits would then need to be isolated and purified. If the subunits can self-assemble in vitro, then the protein could be functional. It could be difficult to establish just the right conditions for the assembly of the multiple subunits.

2. Your proposal should explain how you will cross the nematode-resistant Chinese soybean and the otherwise robust soybean and isolate DNA from all the offspring in the seedling stage. The STRs will be amplified, and only seedlings that have the STRs associated with nematode resistance will be grown to adulthood and used in the next generation of the breeding study.

CHAPTER 18

LEARNING OUTCOME QUESTIONS

18.1 Banding sites on karyotypes depend on dyes binding to the condensed DNA that is wrapped around protein. The dyes bind to some regions, but not all, and are therefore not evenly spaced along the genome in the way that sequential base-pairs are evenly spaced.

18.2 In DNA replication both strands are copied, but in sequencing only one of the strands is copied. Both replication and sequencing require a primer to start, although in replication the primer is RNA and in sequencing a DNA primer is used. In DNA replication, an entire strand is replicated. In sequencing, the addition of another base-pair is either temporarily or permanently stopped in order to determine the sequence in which base-pairs are added. Sequencing uses labeled dNTPs, whereas DNA replication uses dNTPs without labels.

18.3 One possibility is that transposable elements can move within the genome and create new genetic variability, subject to natural selection.

18.4 The sequences may be very similar, but they could be organized in different syntenic blocks. For example, a shared length of DNA sequence could be found on two different chromosomes in Neandertals and humans.

18.5 From the transcriptome, it is possible to predict the proteins that may be translated and available for use in part of an organism at a specific time in development.

18.6 The promoter region. In the presence of the biotoxin, it would be desirable for the bioluminescent gene to be expressed. One way to regulate this is to have the biotoxin bind to the promoter and support transcription.

INQUIRY AND DATA ANALYSIS QUESTIONS

Page 350 Inquiry question: There is one copy of *bcr* (see with green probe) and one copy of *abl* (seen with red probe). The other *bcr* and *abl* genes are fused, and the yellow color is the result of red plus green fluorescence combined.

Page 351 Data analysis: Clones A and C contain the necessary information to construct the physical map. Clones A, B, and D would also work but that isn't the fewest number of clones.

Page 356 Data analysis: If there are approximately 100,000 alternative splicing events and most genes have multiple introns (only an estimate), then each gene would have about 100,000 splice events divided by 25,000 genes, or 4 splice events per gene. Keep in mind that this is an approximation, and there is likely greater variation among genes.

Page 356 Inquiry question: Count the number of open reading frames, which consist of translation start sites (ATG in the DNA) and enough base-pairs to encode a protein before a STOP codon. This might be an overestimate because not all ATG sequences are part of coding DNA sequences or may not be in the actual reading frame.

Page 358 Inquiry question: Repetitive elements are one of the main obstacles to assembling the DNA sequences in proper order because it is difficult to determine which sequences are overlapping.

Page 365 Inquiry question: Proteins exhibit posttranslational modification and the formation of protein complexes. Additionally, a single gene can code for multiple proteins using alternative splicing.

Page 366 Inquiry question: A proteome is all the proteins coded for by the genome, and the transcriptome is all the RNA present in a cell or tissue at a specific time.

Page 369 Inquiry question: You may be able to take advantage of synteny between the rice and corn genome (see figure 18.10). Let's assume that a drought-tolerance gene has already been identified and mapped in rice. Using what is known about synteny between the rice and corn genomes, you could find the region of the corn genome that corresponds to the rice drought-tolerance gene. This would narrow down the region of the corn genome that you might want to sequence to find your gene. A subsequent step might be to modify the corn gene that corresponds to the rice gene to see if you can increase drought tolerance.

UNDERSTAND

1. b 2. a 3. c 4. d 5. b 6. c 7. b 8. d

APPLY

1. b 2. a 3. d 4. b 5. c 6. d 7. d

SYNTHESIZE

1. The STSs represent unique sequences in the genome. They can be used to align the clones into one contiguous sequence of the genome based on the presence or absence of an STS in a clone. The contig, with aligned clones, would look like this:

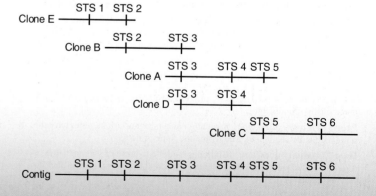

2. The anthrax genome has been sequenced. Investigators would look for differences in the genome between existing natural strains and those collected from a suspected outbreak. The genome of an infectious agent can be modified, or "weaponized," to make it more deadly. Also, single-nucleotide polymorphisms could be used to identify the source of the anthrax. In the case of the Florida anthrax outbreak it was determined that the source was a research laboratory.

CHAPTER 19

LEARNING OUTCOME QUESTIONS

19.2 The early cell divisions are very rapid and do not involve an increase in size between divisions. Interphase is greatly reduced allowing very fast cell divisions.

19.3 This requires experimentation to isolate cell from contact, which would prevent induction, or to follow a particular cell's lineage.

19.4 The nucleus must be reprogrammed. What this means exactly on the molecular level is not clear, but probably involves changes in chromatin structure and methylation patterns.

19.5 Homeotic genes seem to have arisen very early in the evolutionary history of bilaterians. These have been duplicated, and they have diversified with increasing morphological complexity.

19.6 Cell death can be a patterning mechanism. Your fingers were sculpted from a paddle-like structure by cell death.

INQUIRY AND DATA ANALYSIS QUESTIONS

Page 378 Data analysis: If you use a reagent to block FGF signaling, you would get only muscle precursor cells and nerve cord precursor cells. If you had a reagent that causes constitutive signaling, then you would get only mesenchyme precursor cells and notochord precursor cells.

Page 380 Data analysis: The difference in pigmentation pattern acts as a marker for the nuclear and cytoplasmic donors. Since the difference is genetic, the phenotype of the resulting sheep tells you which nucleus gave rise to this individual. Thus Dolly resembled the nuclear donor and not the cytoplasmic donor or the surrogate mother.

UNDERSTAND

1. b   2. d   3. c   4. d   5. b   6. c   7. b

APPLY

1. d   2. a   3. b   4. a   5. c   6. c   7. c

SYNTHESIZE

1. The horizontal lines of the fate map represent cell divisions. Starting with the egg, four cell divisions are required to establish a population of cells that will become nervous tissue. It takes another eight to nine divisions to produce the final number of cells that will make up the nervous system of the worm. It takes seven to eight rounds of cell division to generate the population of cells that will become the gonads. Once established, another seven to eight cell divisions are required to produce the actual gonad cells.

2. Not every cell in a developing embryo will survive. The process of apoptosis is responsible for eliminating cells from the embryo. In *C. elegans*, the process of apoptosis is regulated by three genes: *ced-3*, *ced-4*, and *ced-9*. Both *ced-3* and *ced-4* encode proteases, enzymes that degrade proteins. Interestingly, the *ced-3* protease functions to activate gene expression of the *ced-4* protease. Together, these proteases will destroy the cell from the inside-out. The *ced-9* gene functions to repress the activity of the protease-encoding genes, thereby preventing apoptosis.

3. a. N-cadherin plays a specific role in differentiating cells of the nervous system from ectodermal cells. Ectodermal cells express E-cadherin, but neural cells express N-cadherin. The difference in cell-surface cadherins means that the neural cells lose their contact with the surrounding ectodermal cells and establish new contacts with other neural cells. In the absence of N-cadherin, the nervous system would not form. If you assume that E-cadherin expression is also lost (as would occur normally in development), then these cells would lose all cell–cell contacts and would probably undergo apoptosis.

   b. Integrins mediate the connection between a cell and its surrounding environment, the extracellular matrix (ECM). The loss of integrins would result in the loss of cell adhesion to the ECM. These cells would not be able to move, and, therefore, gastrulation and other developmental processes would be disrupted.

   c. Integrins function by linking the cell's cytoskeleton to the ECM. This connection is critical for cell movement. The deletion of the cytoplasmic domain of the integrin would not affect the ability of integrin to attach to the ECM, but it would prevent the cytoskeleton from getting a "grip." This deletion would likely result in a disruption of development similar to the complete loss of integrin.

4. Adult cells from the patient would be cultured with factors that reprogram the nucleus into pluripotent cells. These cells would then be grown in culture with factors necessary to induce differentiation into a specific cell type that could be transplanted into the patient. This would be easiest for tissue like a liver that regenerates, but could in theory be used for a variety of cell types.

CHAPTER 20

LEARNING OUTCOME QUESTIONS

20.1 Natural selection occurs when some individuals are better suited to their environment than others. These individuals live longer and reproduce more, leaving more offspring with the traits that enabled their parents to thrive. In essence, genetic variation within a population provides the raw material on which natural selection can act thereby leading to evolution.

20.2 #1 To determine if a population is in Hardy–Weinberg equilibrium, it is first necessary to determine the actual allele frequencies, which can be calculated based on the genotype frequencies. After assigning variables p and q to the allele frequencies, we then use the Hardy–Weinberg equation, $p^2 + 2pq + q^2 = 1$ to determine the expected genotype frequencies. If the actual and expected genotype frequencies are the same (or, at least not significantly different), it is safe to say that the population is in Hardy–Weinberg equilibrium.

   #2 You would conclude that one or more of the five evolutionary agents were acting to cause the lack of equilibrium. The next step would be to design studies to test hypotheses about which assumption is not being met.

20.3 There are five mechanisms of evolution: natural selection, mutation, gene flow (migration), genetic drift, and nonrandom mating. Any of these mechanisms can alter allele frequencies within a population, although usually a change in allele frequency results from more than one mechanism working in concert (e.g., mutation can introduce a beneficial new allele into the population, and natural selection will select for that allele such that its frequency increases over the course of two or more generations). Natural selection, the first mechanism and probably the most influential in bringing about evolutionary change, is also the only one to produce adaptive change, that is, change that results in the population being better adapted to its environment. Mutation is the only way in which new alleles can be introduced—it is the ultimate source of all variation. Because it is a relatively rare event, mutation by itself is not a strong agent of allele frequency change; however, in concert with other mechanisms, especially natural selection, it can drastically change the allele frequencies in a population. Gene flow can introduce new alleles into a population from another population of the same species, thus changing the allele frequency within both the recipient and donor populations. Genetic drift is the random, chance factor of evolution—although the results of genetic drift can be negligible in a large population, small populations can undergo drastic changes in allele frequency due to this agent. Finally, nonrandom mating results in populations that vary from Hardy–Weinberg equilibrium not by changing allele frequencies but by changing genotype frequencies—nonrandom mating reduces the proportion of heterozygotes in a population.

20.4 Reproductive success relative to other individuals within an organism's population is referred to as that organism's fitness. Its fitness is determined by its longevity, mating frequency, and the number of offspring it produces for each mating. None of these factors is always the most important in determining reproductive success—instead it is the cumulative effects of all three factors that determine an individual's reproductive success. For example, an individual that has a very long life span but mates only infrequently might have lower fitness than a conspecific that lives only half as long but mates more frequently and with greater success. As seen with the water strider example in this section, traits that are favored for one component of fitness, say, for example, longevity, may be disadvantageous for other components of fitness, say, lifetime fecundity.

20.5 #1 In a population wherein heterozygotes had the lowest fitness, natural selection should favor both homozygous forms. This would result in disruptive selection and a bimodal distribution of traits within the population. Over enough time, it could lead to a speciation event.

   #2 Negative frequency-dependent selection occurs when rare alleles have a fitness advantage over common alleles. As a result, selection is maintained because once an allele becomes rare, selection operates to increase its frequency. Oscillating selection refers to the situation in which the environment changes, first favoring one allele, then another. Over the long term, negative frequency-dependent selection is more likely to preserve variation, because rare alleles are always favored. By contrast, if the environment does not change (oscillate) for an unusually long period of time, the disadvantaged allele may disappear from the population.

20.6 Directional selection occurs when one phenotype has an adaptive advantage over other phenotypes in the population, regardless of its relative frequency within the population. Frequency-dependent selection, on the other hand, results when either a common (positive frequency-dependent selection) or rare (negative frequency-dependent selection) has a selective advantage simply by virtue of its commonality or rarity. In other words, if a mutation introduces a novel allele into a population, directional selection may result in evolution because the allele is advantageous, not because it is rare.

20.7 Background color matching is a form of camouflage used by many species to avoid predation; however, this example of natural selection runs counter to sexual selection—males want to be inconspicuous to predators but attractive to potential mates. For example, to test the effects of predation on background color matching in a species of butterfly, one might raise captive populations of butterflies with a normal variation in coloration. After a few generations, add natural predators to half of the enclosures. After several generations, one would expect the butterflies in the predatory environment to have a high degree of background color matching in order to avoid predation, while the nonpredatory environment would have promoted brightly colored individuals where color would correlate with mating success.

20.8 The dynamics among the different evolutionary mechanisms are very intricate, and it is often difficult, if not impossible, to discern in which direction each process is operating within a population—it is much easier to simply see the final cumulative effects of the various agents of evolutionary change. However, in some cases more than one evolutionary process will operate in the same direction, with the resulting population changing, or evolving, more rapidly than it would have under only one evolutionary mechanism. For example, mutation may introduce a beneficial allele into a population; gene flow could then spread the new allele to other populations. Natural selection will favor this allele within each population, resulting in relatively rapid evolutionary adaptation of a novel phenotype.

20.9 Pleiotropic effects occur with many genes; in other words, a single gene has multiple effects on the phenotype of the individual. Whereas natural selection might favor a particular aspect of the pleiotropic gene, it might select against another aspect of the same gene; thus, pleiotropy often limits the degree to which a phenotype can be altered by natural selection. Epistasis occurs when the expression of one gene is controlled or altered by the existence or expression of another gene. Thus, the outcome of natural selection will depend not just on the genotype of one gene, but the other genotype as well.

INQUIRY AND DATA ANALYSIS QUESTIONS

Page 399 Data analysis: In the example of figure 20.3, the frequency of the recessive white genotype is 0.16. The remaining 84 cats (out of 100) in the population are homozygous or heterozygous black. If the 16 white cats died, they will not contribute recessive white genes to the next generation. Only heterozygous black cats will produce white kittens in a 3:1 ratio of black to white. Homozygous × homozygous black and homozygous × heterozygous black cats will have all black kittens. Since there are 36 homozygous black cats and 48 heterozygous black cats, with a new total of 84 cats, the new frequency of homozygous black cats is 36/84, or 43%, with the heterozygous black cats now comprising 57% of the population. If p^2 = 0.43, then p = 0.65 (approximately), then $1 - p = q$, and q = 0.35. The frequency of white kittens in the next generation, q^2, is 0.12, or 12%.

Page 402 Inquiry question: Rare alleles are more likely to be lost in a population bottleneck specifically because they are rare; the chance that a small population will not include an individual that has that allele is relatively high. For this reason, rare alleles are at risk of being lost. However, if by chance an individual with a rare allele is in the small population, the allele's frequency becomes much greater because of the small number of individuals in the population.

Page 405 Inquiry question: Differential predation might favor brown toads over green toads, green toads might be more susceptible to disease, or green toads might be less able to tolerate variations in climate, among other possibilities.

Page 406 Inquiry question: Since the intermediate-sized water strider has the highest level of fitness, we would expect that the intermediate size would become more prevalent in the population. If the number of eggs laid per day was not affected by body size, the small water striders would be favored because of their tendency to live longer than their larger counterparts.

Page 406 Data analysis: 12-mm striders lay about 2 eggs per day and live about 32 days, for an expected total egg number of 64; the corresponding numbers for 15-mm water striders are 6 and 18, respectively, for a total of 108.

Page 407 Data analysis: In frequency-dependent selection, the fitness of a phenotype is related to its frequency. Thus, for each color type, fitness should be related to frequency, and the color types should not exhibit consistent differences in fitness. By contrast, directional selection is not frequency-dependent; color types should differ in fitness, and those differences should not be affected by frequency.

Page 410 (figure 20.15) Inquiry question: The proportion of flies moving toward light (positive phototropism) would again begin to increase in successive generations.

Page 410 (figure 20.16) Inquiry question: The distribution of birth weights in the human population would expand somewhat to include more babies of higher and lower birth weights.

Page 410 Data analysis: Rates of infant mortality are highest at very low and very high birth weights, and lowest at intermediate birth weights. However, many more babies are born with intermediate birth weights than with extreme births. For example, there are 40 times more individuals born with a birth weight of 6.5 pounds than 2 pounds. As a result, even though the mortality rate is 8 times higher for 2-pound babies than 6.5-pound babies, the absolute number of deaths would be higher for the intermediate-weight size. Overall, the relationship between number of deaths and birth weight would show a peak at intermediate birth weights.

Page 412 Inquiry question: Guppy predators evidently locate their prey using visual cues. The more colorful the guppy, the more likely it is to be seen and thus the more likely it will become prey.

Page 413 Data analysis: On the right-hand side, the index declines with distance from the mine, which suggests that whatever process is operating, its effect is negatively related to distance from the mine. For a given distance from the mine in both directions, index values are higher on the right side, suggesting that the mechanism is stronger on that side. Dispersal of tolerance alleles driven by wind patterns can explain both results: why the allele frequency tails off with distance from the mine, and why the levels are higher on the downwind side of the mine.

Page 414 Inquiry question: Thoroughbred horse breeders have been using selective breeding for certain traits over many decades, effectively removing variation from the population of thoroughbred horses. Unless mutation produces a faster horse, it remains unlikely that winning speeds will improve.

UNDERSTAND

1. a   2. b   3. d   4. a   5. d   6. a   7. d

APPLY

1. d   2. d   3. d

SYNTHESIZE

1. The results depend on coloration of guppies increasing their conspicuousness to predators such that an individual's probability of survival is lower than if it was a drab morph. In the laboratory it may be possible to conduct trials in simulated environments; we would predict, based on the hypothesis of predation, that the predator would capture more of the colorful morph than the drab morph when given access to both. Design of the simulated environment would obviously be critical, but results from such an experiment, if successful, would be a powerful addition to the work already accomplished.

2. On the large lava flows, where the background is almost entirely black, those individuals with black coloration within a population will have a selective advantage because they will be more cryptic to predators. On the other hand, on small flows, which are disrupted by light sand and green plants, dark individuals would be at an adaptive disadvantage for the same reason. You can read more about this in chapter 21; the black peppered moths had an advantage on the trees lacking lichen, but a disadvantage on lichen-covered trees.

3. Ultimately, genetic variation is produced by the process of mutation. However, compared with the speed at which natural selection can reduce variation in traits that are closely related to fitness, mutation alone cannot account for the persistence of genetic variation in traits that are under strong selection. Other processes can account for the observation that genetic variation can persist under strong selection. They include gene flow. Populations are often distributed along environmental gradients of some type. To the extent that different environments favor slightly different variants of phenotypes that have a genetic basis, gene flow among areas in the habitat gradient can introduce new genetic variation or help maintain existing variation. Similarly, just as populations frequently encounter different

selective environments across their range (think of the guppies living above and below the waterfalls in Trinidad), a single population also encounters variation in selective environments across time (oscillating selection). Traits favored this year may not be the same as those favored next year, leading to a switching of natural selection and the maintenance of genetic variation.

CHAPTER 21

LEARNING OUTCOME QUESTIONS

21.1 No. If eating hard seeds caused individuals to develop bigger beaks, then the phenotype is a result of the environment, not the genotype. Natural selection can only act upon those traits with a genetic component. Just as a body builder develops large muscles in his or her lifetime but does not have well-muscled offspring, birds that develop large beaks in their lifetime will not necessarily have offspring with larger beaks.

21.2 An experimental design to test this hypothesis could be as simple as producing enclosures for the moths and placing equal numbers of both morphs into each enclosure and then presenting predatory birds to each enclosure. One enclosure could be used as a control. One enclosure would have a dark background, and the other would have a light background. After several generations, measuring the phenotype frequency of the moths should reveal very clear trends—the enclosure with the dark background should consist of mostly dark moths, the enclosure with the light background mostly light moths, and the neutral enclosure should have an approximately equal ratio of light to dark moths.

21.3 If the trait that is being artificially selected for is due to the environment rather than underlying genotype, then the individuals selected that have that trait will not necessarily pass it on to their offspring.

21.4 The major selective agent in most cases of natural selection is the environment; thus, climatic changes, major continental shifts, and other major geological changes would result in dramatic changes in selective pressure; during these times the rate and direction of evolutionary change would likely be affected in many, if not most, species. On the other hand, during periods of relative environmental stability, the selective pressure does not change and we would not expect to see many major evolutionary events.

21.5 The only other explanation that could be used to explain homologous characteristics and vestigial structures could be mutation. Especially in the case of vestigial structures, if one resulted from a mutation that had pleiotropic effects, and the other effects of the genetic anomaly were selected for, then the vestigial structure would also be selected for, much like a rider on a Congressional bill.

21.6 Convergence occurs when distantly related species experience similar environmental pressures and respond, through natural selection, in similar ways. For example, penguins (birds), sharks (fish), sea lions (mammals), and even the extinct ichthyosaur (reptile) all exhibit the fusiform shape. Each of these animals has similar environmental pressures in that they are all aquatic predators and need to be able to move swiftly and agilely through the water. Clearly their most recent common ancestor does not have the fusiform body shape; thus the similarities are due to convergence (environment) rather than homology (ancestry). However, similar environmental pressures will not always result in convergent evolution. Most importantly, in order for a trait to appear for the first time in a lineage, there must have been a mutation; however, mutations are rare events, and even rarer is a beneficial mutation. There may also be other species that already occupy a particular niche; in these cases it would be unlikely that natural selection would favor traits that would increase the competition between two species.

21.7 It is really neither a hypothesis nor a theory. Theories are the building blocks of scientific knowledge; they have withstood the most rigorous testing and review. Hypotheses, on the other hand, are tentative answers to a question. Unfortunately, a good hypothesis must be testable and falsifiable, and stating that humans came from Mars is not realistically testable or falsifiable; thus, it is, in the realm of biological science, a nonsense statement.

INQUIRY AND DATA ANALYSIS QUESTIONS

Page 419 Inquiry question: Assuming that the size of seeds that parents fed to offspring was unrelated to parent adult size, then no relationship would exist between parent and offspring beak depth—some offspring, by chance, would be fed more small seeds and would develop shallower beaks, whereas others would be fed larger seeds and develop deeper beaks. This result would indicate that beak depth was not a genetically determined trait. On the other hand, if parents with deeper beaks fed their offspring larger seeds, and if seed size determined beak depth, then the same relationship pictured in figure 21.2*b* would result. In this case, genes and environment would be correlated, and researchers wouldn't know which factor was responsible for beak depth. To distinguish between the two,

researchers bring nestling birds into the laboratory and feed them different-sized seeds to determine if diet determined beak depth (this would be difficult in the Galápagos, though, where Darwin's finches are strictly protected).

Page 419 Data analysis: The parents' mean beak depth would be 9 mm, so we would expect the offspring to have a beak depth of approximately 9 mm. The figure does not allow us to tell whether the sex of the parent matters; however, the fact that there is relatively little scatter around the line (i.e., most of the points lie close to the regression line) suggests that the sex of the parents (i.e., which parent is larger) doesn't have a substantial effect.

Page 421 Inquiry question: Such a parallel trend would suggest that similar processes are operating in both localities. Thus, we would conduct a study to identify similarities. In this case, both areas have experienced coincident reductions in air pollution, which most likely is the cause of the parallel evolutionary trends.

Page 422 Inquiry question: Assuming that small and large individuals would breed with each other, then middle-sized offspring would still be born (the result of matings between small and large flies). Nonetheless, there would also be many small and large individuals (the result of small × small and large × large matings). Thus, the frequency distribution of body sizes would be much broader than the distributions in the figures.

Page 426 Inquiry question: This evolutionary decrease could occur for many reasons. For example, maybe *Nannippus* adapted to forested habitats and thus selection favored smaller size, as it had in the ancestral horses before horses moved into open, grassland habitats. Another possibility is that many species of horses were present at that time, and different-sized horses ate different types of food. By evolving small size, *Nannippus* may have been able to eat a type of food not eaten by the others.

UNDERSTAND

1. d   2. b   3. b   4. a   5. b   6. b   7. b

APPLY

1. a   2. d   3. d

SYNTHESIZE

1. Briefly, they are:
   a. There must be variation among individuals within a population.
   b. Variation among individuals must be related to differences among individuals in their success in producing offspring over their lifetime.
   c. Variation related to lifetime reproductive success must have a genetic (heritable) basis.

2. Figure 21.2*a* shows in an indirect way that beak depth varies from year to year. Presumably this is a function of variation among individuals in beak size. However, the most important point of figure 21.2*a* is that it shows the result of selection. That is, if the three conditions hold, we might expect to see average beak depth change accordingly as precipitation varies from year to year. Figure 21.2*b* is more directly relevant to the conditions noted for natural selection to occur. The figure shows that beak size varies among individuals, *and* that it tends to be inherited.

3. The relationship would be given by a cloud of points with no obvious linear trend in any direction different from a zero slope. In other words, it would be a horizontal line through an approximately circular cloud of points. Such data would suggest that whether a parent(s) has a large or small beak has no bearing on the beak size of its offspring.

4. The direction of evolution would reverse, and the two populations would evolve to be more similar in bristle number, until the differences disappeared entirely. However, the rate at which evolution occurred probably would be slower than in the first part of the experiment. Because selection had initially favored low and high bristle numbers in the two populations at the expense of intermediate bristle numbers, some of the genetic variation for intermediate numbers probably would have been lost from the population. As a result, the rate at which intermediate numbers re-evolved would probably be slower because there was less appropriate genetic variation available.

5. The evolution of horses was not a linear event; instead it occurred over 55 million years and included descendants of 34 different genera. By examining the fossil record, one can see that horse evolution did not occur gradually and steadily; instead several major evolutionary events occurred in response to drastic changes in environmental pressures. The fossil record of horse evolution is remarkably detailed, and shows that although there have been trends toward certain characteristics, change has not been fluid and constant

over time, nor has it been entirely consistent across all of the horse lineages. For example, some lineages experienced rapid increases in body size over relatively short periods of geological time, but other lineages actually saw decreases in body size.

CHAPTER 22

LEARNING OUTCOME QUESTIONS

22.1 **#1** The biological species concept states that different species are capable of mating and producing viable, fertile offspring. If sympatric species are unable to do so, they will remain reproductively isolated and thus distinct species. Along the same lines, gene flow between populations of the same species allow for homogenization of the two populations such that they remain the same species.

#2 The ecological species concept states that sympatric species are adapted to use different parts of the environment, and thus hybrids between them would not be well adapted to either habitat and thus would not survive. Even if they did survive and reproduce, genes from one species that made their way into the other species' gene pool would likely be eliminated by natural selection. The concept would explain the connection of geographic populations of a species. As a result, these populations occupy similar parts of the environment and thus experience similar selective pressures.

22.2 In order for reinforcement to occur and complete the process of speciation, two populations must have some reproductive barriers in place prior to sympatry. In the absence of this initial reproductive isolation we would expect rapid exchange of genes and thus homogenization resulting from gene flow. On the other hand, if two populations are already somewhat reproductively isolated (due to hybrid infertility or a prezygotic barrier such as behavioral isolation), then we would expect natural selection to continue improving the fitness of the nonhybrid offspring, eventually resulting in speciation.

22.3 Reproductive isolation that occurs due to different environments is a factor of natural selection; the environmental pressure favors individuals best suited for that environment. As isolated populations continue to develop, they accumulate differences due to natural selection that eventually result in two populations so different that they are reproductively isolated. Reinforcement, on the other hand, is a process that specifically relates to reproductive isolation. It occurs when natural selection favors nonhybrids because of hybrid infertility or are simply less fit than their parents. In this way, populations that may have been only partly reproductively isolated become completely reproductively isolated.

22.4 Polyploidy occurs instantaneously; in a single generation, the offspring of two different parental species may be reproductively isolated; however, if it is capable of self-fertilization, then it is, according to the biological species concept, a new species. Disruptive selection, on the other hand, requires many generations as reproductive barriers between the two populations must evolve and be reinforced before the two would be considered separate species.

22.5 In the archipelago model, adaptive radiation occurs as each individual island population adapts to its different environmental pressures. On the other hand, in sympatric speciation resulting from disruptive selection, the traits selected are not necessarily best suited for a novel environment but are best able to reduce competition with other individuals. It is in the latter scenario wherein adaptive radiation due to a key innovation is most likely to occur.

22.6 It depends on what species concept you are using to define a given species. Certainly evolutionary change can be punctuated, but in times of changing environmental pressures we would expect adaptation to occur. The adaptations, however, do not necessarily have to lead to the splitting of a species—instead one species could simply adapt in accordance with the environmental changes to which it is subjected. This would be an example of nonbranching, as opposed to branching, evolution; but again, whether the end-result organism is a different species from its ancestral organism that preceded the punctuated event is subject to interpretation.

INQUIRY AND DATA ANALYSIS QUESTIONS

Page 448 Inquiry question: Speciation can occur under allopatric conditions because isolated populations are more likely to diverge over time due to drift or selection. Adaptive radiation tends to occur in places inhabited by only a few other species or where many resources in a habitat are unused. Different environmental conditions typical of adaptive radiation tend to favor certain traits within a population. Allopatric conditions would then generally favor adaptive radiation.

In character displacement, natural selection in each species favors individuals able to use resources not used by the other species. Two species might have evolved from two populations of the same species located in the same environment (sympatric species). Individuals at the extremes of each population are able to use resources not used by the other group. Competition for a resource would

be reduced for these individuals, possibly favoring their survival and leading to selection for the tendency to use the new resource. Character displacement tends to compliment sympatric speciation.

Page 452 Inquiry question: If one area experiences an unfavorable change in climate, a mobile species can move to another area where the climate was like it was before the change. With little environmental change to drive natural selection within that species, stasis would be favored.

UNDERSTAND

1. a   2. c   3. a   4. b   5. a   6. d   7. d   8. b   9. b   10. a

APPLY

1. a   2. d   3. b   4. b

SYNTHESIZE

1. If hybrids between two species have reduced viability or fertility, then natural selection will favor any trait that prevents hybrid matings. This way individuals don't waste time, energy, or resources on such matings and will have greater fitness if they instead spend the time, energy, and resources on mating with members of their own species. For this reason, natural selection will favor any trait that decreases the probability of hybridization. By contrast, once hybridization has occurred, the time, energy, and resources have already been expended. Thus, there is no reason that less fit hybrids would be favored over more fit ones. The only exception is for species that invest considerable time and energy in incubating eggs and rearing the young; for those species, selection may favor reduced viability of hybrids because parents of such individuals will not waste further time and energy on them.

2. The biological species concept, despite its limitations, reveals the continuum of biological processes and the complexity and dynamics of organic evolution. At the very least, the biological species concept provides a mechanism for biologists to communicate about taxa and know that they are talking about the same thing! Perhaps even more significantly, discussion and debate about the meaning of "species" fuels a deeper understanding about biology and evolution in general. It is unlikely that we will ever have a single unifying concept of species, given the vast diversity of life, both extinct and extant.

3. The principle is the same as in character displacement. In sympatry, individuals of the two species that look alike may mate with each other. If the species are not completely interfertile, then individuals hybridizing will be at a selective disadvantage. If a trait appears in one species that allows that species to more easily recognize members of its own species and thus avoid hybridization, then individuals bearing that trait will have higher fitness and that trait will spread through the population.

4. The two species would be expected to have more similar morphology when they are found alone (allopatry) than when they are found together (sympatry), assuming that food resources were the same from one island to the next. This would be the result of character displacement expected under a hypothesis of competition for food when the two species occur in sympatry. A species pair that is more distantly related might not be expected to show the pattern of character displacement since they show greater differences in morphology (and presumably in ecology and behavior as well), which should reduce the potential for competition to drive character divergence.

CHAPTER 23

LEARNING OUTCOME QUESTIONS

23.1 Because of convergent evolution; two distantly related species subjected to the same environmental pressures may be more phenotypically similar than two species with different environmental pressures but a more recent common ancestor. Other reasons for the possible dissimilarity between closely related species include oscillating selection and rapid adaptive radiations in which species rapidly adapt to a new available niche.

23.2 **#1** In some cases wherein characters diverge rapidly relative to the frequency of speciation, it can be difficult to construct a phylogeny using cladistics because the most parsimonious phylogeny may not be the most accurate. In most cases, however, cladistics is a very useful tool for inferring phylogenetic relationships among groups of organisms.

#2 Only shared derived characters indicate that two or more taxa are descended from an ancestor that was not an ancestor of taxa that do not possess the character state in question. Thus, taxa possessing the state are more closely related to each other than they are to taxa without the trait. As the text discusses, this assumption is usually correct, but not when rates of homoplasy are high.

23.3 Yes, in some instances this is possible. For example, assume two populations of a species become geographically isolated from one another in similar environments, and each population diverges and speciation occurs, with one group retaining its ancestral traits and the other deriving new traits. The ancestral group in each population may be part of the same biological species but would be considered polyphyletic because to include their common ancestor would also necessitate including the other, more-derived species (which may have diverged enough to be reproductively isolated).

23.4 Not necessarily; it is possible that the character changed since the common ancestor and is present in each group due to convergence. Although the most recent common ancestor possessing the character is the most parsimonious, and thus the most likely, explanation, it is possible, especially for small clades, that similar environmental pressures resulted in the emergence of the same character state repeatedly during the course of the clade's evolution.

23.5 Hypothetically it is possible; however, the viral analyses and phylogenetic analyses have provided strong evidence that HIV emergence was the other way around; it began as a simian disease and mutated to a human form, and this has occurred several times.

INQUIRY AND DATA ANALYSIS QUESTIONS

Page 459 Data analysis: The data matrix would be similar to this one:

Organisms	Traits		
	Hair	Amniotic membrane	Tail
Salamander	0	0	1
Frog	0	0	0
Lizard	0	1	1
Tiger	1	1	1
Gorilla	1	1	0
Human	1	1	0

Page 460 Inquiry question: In parsimony analyses of phylogenies, the least complex explanation is favored. High rates of evolutionary change and few character states complicate matters. High rates of evolutionary change, such as occur when mutations arise in noncoding portions of DNA, can be misleading when constructing phylogenies. Mutations arising in noncoding DNA are not eliminated by natural selection in the same manner as mutations in coding (functional) DNA. Also, evolution of new character states can be very high in nonfunctional DNA, which can lead to genetic drift. Since DNA has only four nucleotides (four character states), it is highly likely that two species could evolve the same derived character at a particular base position. This leads to a violation of the assumptions of parsimony—that the fewest evolutionary events lead to the best hypothesis of phylogenetic relationships—and resulting phylogenies are inaccurate.

Page 461 Inquiry question: The only other hypothesis is that the most recent common ancestor of birds and bats was also winged. Of course, this scenario is much less parsimonious (and thus much more unlikely) than the convergence hypothesis, especially given the vast number of reptiles and mammals without wings. Most phylogenies are constructed based on the rule of parsimony; in the absence of fossil evidence of other winged animals and molecular data supporting a closer relationship between birds and bats than previously thought, there is no way to test the hypothesis that bird and bat wings are homologous rather than analogous.

Page 467 Inquiry question: One possibility would be to closely examine the patterns of development in different species. In part *a*, all of the species in the blue box with direct development would have inherited that character state from a common ancestor. Consequently, we might expect that the developmental patterns would be similar. By contrast, in part *b* direct development evolved many different times in those species. In the latter case, it is possible that direct development could have evolved in many different ways. Thus, if you compared how development occurs in these species and found that there were different patterns of development in different species, then the hypothesis in part *b* might seem more likely. However, even if all the species inherited direct development from their common ancestor (part *a*), species could diverge evolutionarily, so it is always possible that differences you found might have arisen after divergence from a common ancestor. For this reason, definitive conclusions are always difficult in situations such as this.

Page 470 Inquiry question: If the victim had contracted HIV from a source other than the patient, the most recent common ancestor of the two strains would be much more distant. As it is, the phylogeny shows that the victim and patient strains share a relatively recent ancestor, and that the victim's strain is derived from the patient's strain.

UNDERSTAND

1. d 2. b 3. a 4. b 5. a 6. d 7. d 8. b 9. c

APPLY

1. c 2. d 3. a

SYNTHESIZE

1. Naming of groups can vary; names provided here are just examples. Jaws—shark, salamander, lizard, tiger, gorilla, human (jawed vertebrates); lungs—salamander, lizard, tiger, gorilla, human (terrestrial tetrapods); amniotic membrane—lizard, tiger, gorilla, human (amniote tetrapods); hair—tiger, gorilla, human (mammals); no tail—gorilla, human (humanoid primate); bipedal—human (human).

2. It would seem to be somewhat of a conundrum, or potentially circular chase; choosing a closely related species as an outgroup when we do not even know the relationships of the species of interest. One way of guarding against a poor choice for an outgroup is to choose several species as outgroups and examine how the phylogenetic hypothesis for the group of interest changes as a consequence of using different outgroups. If the choice of outgroup makes little difference, then that might increase one's confidence in the phylogenetic hypotheses for the species of interest. On the other hand, if the choice makes a big difference (different phylogenetic hypotheses result when choosing different outgroups), that might at least lead to the conclusion that we cannot be confident in inferring a robust phylogenetic hypothesis for the group of interest without collecting more data.

3. Recognizing that birds are reptiles potentially provides insight to the biology of both birds and reptiles. For example, some characteristics of birds are clearly of reptilian origin, such as feathers (modified scales), nasal salt-secreting glands, and strategies of osmoregulation/excretion (excreting nitrogenous waste products as uric acid) representing ancestral traits that continue to serve birds well in their environments. On the other hand, some differences from other reptiles (again, feathers) seem to have such profound significance biologically, that they overwhelm similarities visible in shared ancestral characteristics. For example, no extant nonavian reptiles can fly or are endothermic, and these two traits have created a fundamental distinction in the minds of many biologists. Indeed, many vertebrate biologists prefer to continue to distinguish birds from reptiles rather than emphasize their similarities even though they recognize the power of cladistic analysis in helping to shape classification. Ultimately, it may be nothing much more substantial than habit which drives the preference of some biologists to traditional classification schemes.

4. In fact, such evolutionary transitions (the loss of the larval mode, and the re-evolution of a larval mode from direct development) are treated with equal weight under the simplest form of parsimony. However, if it is known from independent methods (e.g., developmental biology) that one kind of change is less likely than another (loss vs. a reversal), these should and can be taken into account in various ways. The simplest way might be to assign weights based on likelihoods; two transitions from larval development to direct development is equal to one reversal from direct development back to a larval mode. In fact, such methods exist, and they are similar in spirit to the statistical approaches used to build specific models of evolutionary change rather than rely on simple parsimony.

5. The structures are both homologous, as forelimbs, and convergent, as wings. In other words, the most recent common ancestor of birds, pterosaurs, and bats had a forelimb similar in morphology to that which these organisms possess—it has similar bones and articulations. Thus, the forelimb itself among these organisms is homologous. The wing, however, is clearly convergent; the most recent common ancestor surely did not have wings (or all other mammals and reptiles would have had to have lost the wing, which violates the rule of parsimony). The wing of flying insects is purely convergent with the vertebrate wing, as the forelimb of the insect is not homologous with the vertebrate forelimb.

6. The biological species concept focuses on processes, in particular those that result in the evolution of a population to the degree that it becomes reproductively isolated from its ancestral population. The process of speciation as utilized by the biological species concept occurs through the interrelatedness of evolutionary mechanisms such as natural selection,

mutation, and genetic drift. On the other hand, the phylogenetic species concept focuses not on process but on history, on the evolutionary patterns that led to the divergence between populations. Neither species concept is more right or more wrong; species concepts are, by their very nature, subjective and potentially controversial.

CHAPTER 24

LEARNING OUTCOME QUESTIONS

24.1 There should be a high degree of similarity between the two genomes because they are relatively closely related. There could be differences in the relative amounts of noncoding DNA. Genes that are necessary for bony skeletal development might be found in the bony fish. The cartilaginous fish might lack those genes or have substantial sequences in the genes needed for skeletal development in bony fish.

24.2 The additional DNA would likely be noncoding DNA that might represent large expanses of retrotransposon DNA that duplicated and transposed multiple times.

24.3 Compare the sequence of the pseudogene with other species. If, for example, it is a pseudogene of an olfactory gene that is found in mice or chimps, the sequences will be much more similar than in a more distantly related species. If horizontal gene transfer explains the origins of the gene, there may not be a very similar gene in closely related species. You might use the BLAST algorithm discussed in chapter 18 to identify similar sequences and then construct a phylogenetic tree to compare the relationships among the different species.

24.4 A SNP can change a single amino acid in the coded peptide. If the new R group is very different, the protein may fold in a different way and not function effectively. SNPs in the *FOXP2* gene may, in part, explain why humans have speech and chimps do not.

Other examples that you may remember from earlier in the text include cystic fibrosis and sickle cell anemia.

24.5 An effective drug might bind only to the region of the pathogen protein that is distinct from the human protein. The drug could render the pathogen protein ineffective without making the human ill. If the seven amino acids that differ are scattered throughout the genome, they might have a minimal effect on the protein, and it would be difficult to develop a drug that could detect small differences. It's possible that the drug could inadvertently affect other areas of the protein as well.

INQUIRY AND DATA ANALYSIS QUESTIONS

Page 476 Data analysis: Rice has 43,000 genes in 430 Mb of DNA (100 genes/Mb), whereas humans have 22,698 genes in 2500 Mb (9 genes/Mb). Rice has over 10 times as many genes as humans per Mb. The organisms closest to humans in terms of number of genes/Mb would be the duck-billed platypus with 8.4 genes/Mb and next would be the domestic cow with 7.6 genes/Mb.

Page 478 Inquiry question: Meiosis in a 3*n* cell would be impossible because three sets of chromosomes cannot be divided equally between two cells. In a 3n cell, all three homologous chromosomes would pair in prophase I, then align during anaphase I. As the homologous chromosomes separate, two of a triplet might go to one cell and the third chromosome would go to the other cell. The same would be true for each set of homologues. Daughter cells would have an unpredictable number of chromosomes.

Page 479 Inquiry question: Polyploidization seems to induce the elimination of duplicated genes. Duplicate genes code for the same gene product. It is reasonable that duplicate genes would be eliminated to decrease the redundancy arising from the translation of several copies of the same gene.

Page 485 Inquiry question: Ape and human genomes show very different patterns of gene transcription activity, even though genes encoding proteins are over 99% similar between chimps and humans. Different genes would be transcribed when comparing apes with humans, and the levels of transcription would vary widely.

UNDERSTAND

1. c   2. d   3. d   4. b   5. b   6. a

APPLY

1. a   2. d   3. d   4. a

SYNTHESIZE

1. The two amino acid difference between the FOXP2 protein in humans and closely related primates must alter the way the protein functions in the brain.

The protein affects motor function in the brain, allowing coordination of larynx, mouth and brain for speech in humans. For example, if the protein affects transcription, there could be differences in the genes that are regulated by FOXP2 in humans and chimps.

2. Human and chimp DNA is close to 99% similar, yet our phenotypes are conspicuously different in many ways. This suggests that a catalog of genes is just the first step to identifying the mechanisms underlying genetically influenced diseases like cancer or cystic fibrosis. Clearly, gene expression, which might involve the actions of multiple noncoding segments of the DNA and other potentially complex regulatory mechanics, are important sources of how phenotypes are formed, and it is likely that many genetically determined diseases result from such complex underlying mechanisms, making the gene identification of genomics just the first step; a necessary but not nearly sufficient strategy. What complete genomes do offer is a starting point to correlating sequence differences among humans with genetic disease, as well as the opportunity to examine how multiple genes and regulatory sequences interact to cause disease.

3. Phylogenetic analysis usually assumes that most genetic and phenotypic variation arises from descent with modification (vertical inheritance). If genetic and phenotypic characteristics can be passed horizontally (i.e., not vertically through genetic lineages), then using patterns of shared character variation to infer genealogical relationships will be subject to potentially significant error. We might expect that organisms with higher rates of HGT will have phylogenetic hypotheses that are less reliable or at least are not resolved as a neatly branching tree.

CHAPTER 25

LEARNING OUTCOME QUESTIONS

25.1 A change in the promoter of a gene necessary for wing development might lead to the repression of wing development in a second segment of a fly in a species that has double wings.

25.2 Yes, although this is not the only explanation. The coding regions could be identical, but the promoter or other regulatory regions could have been altered by mutation, leading to altered patterns of gene expression. To test this hypothesis, the *Eda* gene should be sequenced in both fish and compared.

25.3 The pectoral fins are homoplastic because sharks and whales are only distantly related and pectoral fins are not found in whales' more recent ancestors.

25.4 There is no need for eyes in the dark. Perhaps the fish expend less energy when eyes are not produced and that offered a selective advantage in cavefish. In a habitat with light, a mutation that resulted in a functional *Pax6* would likely be selected for, and over time more of the fish would have eyes. Keep in mind that the probability of a mutation restoring *Pax6* function is very low, but real.

INQUIRY AND DATA ANALYSIS QUESTIONS

Page 495 Inquiry question: Because there is a stop codon located in the middle of the *CAL* (cauliflower) gene-coding sequence, the wild-type function of *CAL* must be concerned with producing flowers. Unlike the ancestral *Brassica oleracea*, cauliflower and broccoli keep branching instead of producing a flower. One interpretation is that a meristem lacking CAL protein is delayed in producing flower parts and instead keeps producing branches, resulting in the broccoli and cauliflower heads. Cauliflower and broccoli heads differ in terms of how advanced floral development is (only meristems in cauliflower and early floral buds in broccoli). This difference could be the result of a later evolutionary event. Additional evolutionary events possibly include large flower heads, unusual head coloration, protective leaves covering flower heads, or head size variants, among other possibilities.

Page 499 Inquiry question: Functional analysis involves the use of a variety of experiments designed to test the function of a specific gene in different species. By mixing and matching parts of the *AP3* and *PI* genes and introducing them into *ap3* mutant plants, it was found that the C terminus sequence of the AP3 protein is essential for specifying petal function. Without the 3 region of the *AP3* gene, the *Arabidopsis* plant cannot make petals.

UNDERSTAND

1. c   2. b   3. a   4. a   5. b   6. d   7. a   8. c   9. c   10. d

APPLY

1. c   2. a   3. d   4. b

SYNTHESIZE

1. Your supervisor might still be correct. The mutation could be in the regulatory region and the *pitx1* gene could be transcribed in cells in different tissues in the two species. You could test this by testing whether or not you are able to obtain the RNA from hindlimbs and the pelvis of both species at different times in development.

2. Development is a highly conserved and constrained process; small perturbations can have drastic consequences, and most of these are negative. Given the thousands or hundreds of thousands of variables that can change in even a simple developmental pathway, most perturbations lead to negative outcomes. Over millions of years, some of these changes will arise under the right circumstances to produce a benefit. In this way, developmental perturbations are not different from what we know about mutations in general. Beneficial mutations are rare, but with enough time they will emerge and spread under specific circumstances.

    Not all mutations provide a selective advantage. For example, reduced body armor increases the fitness of fish in fresh water, but it was not selected for in a marine environment where the armor was important for protection from predators. The new trait can persist at low levels for a very long time until a change in environmental conditions results in an increase in fitness for individuals exhibiting the trait.

3. The latter view represents our current understanding. There are many examples of small gene families (e.g., *Hox*, *MADS*) whose apparent role in generating phenotypic diversity among major groupings of organisms is in altering the expression of other genes. Alterations in timing (heterochrony) or spatial pattern of expression (homeosis) can lead to shifts in developmental events, giving rise to new phenotypes. Many examples are presented in the chapter, such as the developmental variants of two species of sea urchins, one with a normal larval phase, and another with direct development. In this case the two species do not have different sets of developmental genes; rather the expression of those genes differ. Another example that makes the same point is the evolution of an image-forming eye. Recent studies suggest, in contrast to the view that eyes across the animal kingdom evolved independently multiple times, that image-forming eyes from very distantly related taxa (e.g., insects and vertebrates) may trace back to the common origin of the *Pax6* gene. If that view is correct, then genes controlling major developmental patterns would seem to be highly conserved across long periods of time, with expression being the major form of variation.

4. Unless the *Pax6* gene was derived multiple times, it is difficult to hypothesize multiple origins of eyes. Pax6 initiates eye development in many species. The variation in eyes among animals is a result of which genes are expressed and when after Pax6 initiates eye development.

5. Maize relies on *paleoAP3* and *PI* for flower development, whereas tomato has three genes because of a duplication of *paleoAP3*. This duplication event in the ancestor of tomato, but not maize, is correlated with independent petal origin.

6. The direct developing sea urchin has an ancestor that had one or more mutations in genes that were needed to regulate the expression of other genes needed for larval stage development. When those genes were not expressed, there was no larval development and the genes necessary for adult development were expressed.

CHAPTER 26

LEARNING OUTCOME QUESTIONS

26.1 The Phanerozoic eon includes the greatest diversity of life and would be the most informative in terms of fossil record reflecting diverse life-forms. Earlier eons have a more limited fossil record, with primarily unicellular organisms.

26.2 Amino acids, including glycine and alanine, nitrogenous bases like adenine that are found in DNA and RNA, lipids, and simple carbon compounds like CH_2O might be found. If the early life was based on RNA, then ribonucleotides rather than deoxyribonucleotides would be found. Early RNA sequences would have had both enzymatic and information functions. Once the machinery was in place for RNA to encode proteins, amino acid sequences would become less random and gain functions in catalyzing metabolism as well as structural roles and regulating nucleic acid replication, transcription, and translation. Lipids would form early cell membranes, and metabolic pathways would continue to evolve within the confines of the cell membrane. Nucleic acid replication and cell division would evolve early on also.

26.3 Electron microscopy revealing organic walls and vesicles would provide good evidence, combined with spectroscopic analysis indicating the presence of complex carbon molecules.

26.4 Weathering is proposed as a key event associated with both glaciations. Weathering in the late Proterozoic was caused by warm, moist air and by shifts in plate tectonics that increased surface area for weathering. In the Ordovician period, land was being colonized for the first time. Weathering of rocks because of atmospheric changes is not sufficient to explain the CO_2 shift leading to glaciation. Rather, early land plants secreted an organic acid that weathered rocks, releasing phosphorous that ran into the oceans. In the oceans, phosphorous triggered algal blooms that pulled down CO_2 from the atmosphere, triggering a rapid drop in temperature.

26.5 Major pre-Cambrian evolutionary innovations that set the stage for rapid radiation included the evolution of eukaryotic cells with chloroplasts and mitochondria, and meiosis that allowed for sexual reproduction. The new gene combinations created by meiosis provided a set of phenotypes for natural selection to act upon.

INQUIRY AND DATA ANALYSIS QUESTION

Page 510 Data analysis: The graph would look like figure 26.4 because a plot of radioactive decay is the same, regardless of the parent isotope. It will take 7 half-lives. You can calculate this by dividing by 2 for each half-life (1/2, 1/4, 1/8, 1/6, 1/32, 1/64, 1/128). After you get past 1/100, which is 1%, you have the correct half-life. You will come very close to 0%, but there will always be a tiny, although immeasurable, amount of parent isotope since you keep halving the amount, not eliminating it.

UNDERSTAND

1. b 2. d 3. c The correct statement would read, "Brown algae gained chloroplasts by engulfing red algae (endosymbiosis)." 4. c 5. b

APPLY

1. b 2. c 3. d 4. c 5. c

SYNTHESIZE

1. Early land plants lacked roots and had substantially less biomass than the later vascular plants. Alone they could not have sequestered sufficient CO_2 to trigger glaciation. However, just like the vascular plants, they secreted organic acid that enhanced weathering of rocks, leading to the release of phosphorous. The excess phosphorous washed into the oceans. As an essential plant nutrient, the excess phosphorous triggered extensive algal blooms, which did sequester sufficient CO_2, coupled with the land plants, to trigger a glaciation.

2. The collision of tectonic plates could have multiple effects on evolution of life. When the plates collide, less surface area is exposed to water, which could reduce weathering. Reduced weathering would pull less CO_2 out of the atmosphere, which could affect climate. When plates collide, organisms that were previously separated come together. This potentially affects interbreeding and also changes selective pressures affecting evolution.

3. The evolution of meiosis provided a much greater range of genetic diversity for natural selection to act upon. The evolution of multicellularity immediately preceded the Cambrian explosion and was likely a contributing factor to the rapid diversification when ancestors of almost every group of animals evolved. The climate must also have been more hospitable to life during the Cambrian, a period following a global ice age.

CHAPTER 27

LEARNING OUTCOME QUESTIONS

27.1 Viruses use cellular machinery for replication. They do not make all of the proteins necessary for complete replication.

27.2 A prophage carrying such a mutation could not be induced to undergo the lytic cycle.

27.3 This therapy, at present, does not remove all detectable viruses, so it cannot be considered a true cure.

27.4 In addition to a high mutation rate, the influenza genome consists of multiple RNA segments that can recombine during infection. This causes the main antigens for the immune system to shift rapidly.

27.5 Prions carry information in their three-dimensional structure. This 3-D information is different from the essentially one-dimensional genetic information in DNA.

UNDERSTAND

1. c 2. b 3. c 4. d 5. b 6. d 7. b

APPLY

1. c 2. b 3. c 4. d 5. b 6. c 7. c 8. a

SYNTHESIZE

1. A set of genes that are involved in the response to DNA damage are normally induced by the same system. The protein involved destroys a repressor that keeps DNA repair genes unexpressed. Lambda has evolved to use this system to its advantage.

2. Since viruses require the replication machinery of a host cell to replicate, it is unlikely that they existed before the origin of the first cells.

3. This is a complex situation. The relevant factors include the high mutation rate of the virus and the fact that the virus targets the very cells that mount an immune response. The influenza virus also requires a new vaccine every year due to rapid changes in the virus. The smallpox virus was a DNA virus that had antigenic determinants that did not change rapidly, thus making a vaccine possible.

4. Emerging viruses are those that jump species and thus are new to humans. Recent examples include SARS and Ebola.

5. If excision of the λ prophage is imprecise, then the phage produced will carry *E. coli* genes adjacent to the integration site.

CHAPTER 28

LEARNING OUTCOME QUESTIONS

28.1 Archaea have ether-linked instead of ester-linked phospholipids; their cell wall is made of unique material.

28.2 Compare their DNA. The many metabolic tests we have used for years have been supplanted by DNA analysis.

28.3 Transfer of genetic information in bacteria is directional: from donor to recipient and does not involve fusion of gametes.

28.4 Prokaryotes do not have a lot of morphological features, but do have diverse metabolic functions.

28.5 Pathogens tend to evolve to be less virulent. If they are too good at killing, their lifestyle becomes an evolutionary dead end.

28.6 Rotating a crop that has a symbiotic association with nitrogen-fixing bacteria will return nitrogen to the soil depleted by other plants.

INQUIRY AND DATA ANALYSIS QUESTIONS

Page 549 Data analysis: An imprecise excision of the F plasmid produces a so-called F′ plasmid that carries *E. coli* DNA in addition to the normal plasmid DNA. If this is introduced into a new F⁻ cell, it will then produce a new cell that is "diploid" for the region carried on the F′ plasmid. These so-called partial diploids have many genetic uses.

Page 556 Inquiry question: The simplest explanation is that the two STDs are occurring in different populations, and one population has rising levels of sexual activity, while the other has falling levels. However, the rise in incidence of an STD can reflect many parameters other than level of sexual activity. The virulence or infectivity of one or both disease agents may be changing, for example, or some aspect of exposed people may be changing in such a way as to alter susceptibility. Only a thorough public health study can sort this out.

UNDERSTAND

1. b 2. a 3. c 4. c 5. d 6. a 7. b

APPLY

1. c 2. b 3. b 4. c 5. d 6. b 7. a

SYNTHESIZE

1. The study of carbon signatures in rocks using isotopic data assumes that ancient carbon fixation involves one of two pathways that each show a bias toward incorporation of carbon-12. If this bias were not present, it is not possible to infer early carbon fixation by this pathway. This pathway could have arisen even earlier and we would have no way to detect it.

2. The heat killing of the virulent S strain of *Streptococcus* released the genome of the virulent smooth strain into the environment. These strains of *Streptococcus* bacteria are capable of natural transformation. At least some of the rough-strain cells took up smooth-strain genes that encoded the polysaccharide coat from the environment. These genes entered into the rough-strain genome by recombination, and then were expressed. These transformed cells were now smooth bacteria.

3. Use of multiple antibiotics is not a bad idea if all of the bacteria are killed. In the case of some persistent infections, this is an effective strategy. However, it does provide very strong selective pressure for rare genetic events that produce multiple resistances in a single bacterial species. For this reason, it is not a good idea for it to be the normal practice. The more bacteria that undergo this selection for multiple resistance, the more likely it will arise. This is helped by patients not taking their entire course of antibiotic because bacteria may survive by chance and proliferate, with each generation providing the opportunity for new mutations. This is also complicated by the horizontal transfer of resistance via resistance plasmids, and by the existence of transposable genetic elements that can move genes from one piece of DNA to another.

4. Most species on the planet are incapable of fixing nitrogen without the assistance of bacteria. Without nitrogen, amino acids and other compounds cannot be synthesized. Thus a loss of the nitrogen-fixing bacteria due to increased UV radiation levels would reduce the ability of plants to grow, severely limiting the food sources of the animals.

CHAPTER 29

LEARNING OUTCOME QUESTIONS

29.1 Mitochondria and chloroplasts contain their own DNA. Mitochondrial genes are transcribed within the mitochondrion, using mitochondrial ribosomes that are smaller than those of eukaryotic cells and quite similar to bacterial ribosomes. Antibiotics that inhibit protein translation in bacteria also inhibit protein translation in mitochondria. Also, both chloroplasts and mitochondria divide using binary fission like bacteria.

29.2 Meiosis makes sexual reproduction possible. Each generation, new combinations of alleles provide much greater genetic diversity for evolution to act on than is available with asexual reproduction. Different gene combinations were advantageous in different settings, and species began to diverge as natural selection acted on the genetic diversity.

29.3 #1 Undulating membranes would be effective on surfaces with curvature that may not always be smooth, such as intestinal walls.
　　#2 Contractile vacuoles collect and remove excess water from within the *Euglena*.

29.4 #1 The *Plasmodium* often becomes resistant to new poisons and drugs. And, because the *Plasmodium* has multiple hosts, a drug for humans wouldn't eradicate the *Plasmodium* in other stages of its life cycle in the mosquito.
　　#2 Just based on outward appearances, the sporophyte of brown algae forms a larger bladelike structure, whereas the gametophyte is a small filamentous structure.

29.5 #1 Both the red and green algae obtained their chloroplasts through endosymbiosis, possibly of the same lineage of photosynthetic bacteria. The red and green algae had diverged before the endosymbiotic events, and the history recorded in their nuclear DNA is a different evolutionary history than that recorded in the plastids derived through endosymbiosis.
　　#2 The lack of water is the major barrier for sperm that move through water to reach the egg. It is more difficult for sperm to reach the egg on land.

29.6 Construct phylogenies with other traits, including DNA sequences. Then map the presence of amoeboid locomotion with pseudopods on to the other phylogenies. If the pseudopod trait is not clustered, it is likely that it evolved independently multiple times and is thus not a good trait to use in reconstructing protist phylogenies.

29.7 It is unlikely that cellular and plasmodial slime molds are closely related. They both appear in the last section of this chapter because they have yet to be assigned to clades. The substantial differences in their cell biology are inconsistent with a close phylogenetic relationship.

29.8 Comparative genomic studies of choanoflagellates and sponges would be helpful. Considering the similarities among a broader range of genes than just the conserved tyrosine kinase receptor would provide additional evidence.

INQUIRY AND DATA ANALYSIS QUESTIONS

Page 564 Inquiry question: Red and green algae obtained chloroplasts by engulfing photosynthetic bacteria by primary endosymbiosis; chloroplasts in these cells have two membranes. Brown algae obtained chloroplasts by engulfing cells of red algae through secondary endosymbiosis; chloroplasts in cells of brown algae have four membranes. Counting the number of cell membranes of chloroplasts indicates primary or secondary endosymbiosis.

Page 576 Data analysis: Your phylogeny should show a common ancestor for all three algae. The brown alga should branch from a common ancestor of the red and green algae. (See the phylogeny on p. 575 of your text and trace the three algae).

Page 577 Inquiry question: No, they are formed by mitosis. Meiosis produces haploid spores, which divide mitotically to produce multicellular gametophytes. Gametes are produced from haploid gametophyte cells by mitosis.

UNDERSTAND

1. b 2. a 3. b 4. c 5. d 6. b 7. a 8. c 9. b, c 10. a, d 11. d 12. a

APPLY

1. d 2. a 3. a

SYNTHESIZE

1. Cellular and plasmodial slime molds both exhibit group behavior and can produce mobile slime mold masses. However, these two groups are very distantly related phylogenetically.

2. The development of a vaccine, though challenging, will be the most promising in the long run. It is difficult to eradicate all the mosquito vectors, and many eradication methods can be harmful to the environment. Treatments to kill the parasites are also difficult because the parasite is likely to become resistant to each new poison or drug. A vaccine would provide long-term protection without the need to use harmful pesticides or drugs for which drug resistance is a real possibility.

3. For the first experiment, plate the cellular slime molds on a plate that has no bacteria. Spot cyclic AMP and designated places on the plate and determine if the bacteria aggregate around the cAMP.

   For the second experiment, repeat the first experiment using plates that have a uniform coating of bacteria as well as plates with no bacteria. If the cellular slime molds aggregate on both plates, resource scarcity is not an issue. If the cells aggregate only in the absence of bacteria, you can conclude that the attraction to cAMP occurs only under starvation conditions.

CHAPTER 30

LEARNING OUTCOME QUESTIONS

30.1 **#1** Make sections and examine them under the microscope to look for tracheids. Only the tracheophytes will have tracheids.

#2 Gametes in plants are produced by mitosis. Human gametes are produced directly by meiosis.

30.2 Mosses are extremely desiccation-tolerant and can withstand the lack of water. Also, freezing temperatures at the poles are less damaging when mosses have a lower water content.

30.3 The sporophyte generation has evolved to be the larger generation, and therefore an effective means of transporting water and nutrients over greater distances would be advantageous.

30.4 Substantial climate change occurred during that time period. Glaciers had spread, then melted and retreated. The resulting drier climates could have contributed to the extinction of large club mosses. Refer to chapter 26 for more information on changes in Earth's climate over geological time.

30.5 The silica can increase the strength of the hollow-tubed stems and would also deter herbivores.

INQUIRY AND DATA ANALYSIS QUESTIONS

Page 591 Inquiry question: Tracheophytes developed vascular tissue, enabling them to have efficient water- and food-conducting systems. Vascular tissue allowed tracheophytes to grow larger, possibly then enabling them to outcompete smaller, nonvascular land plants. A protective cuticle and stomata that can close during dry conditions also conferred a selective advantage.

Page 592 Data analysis: Tracheophytes first appeared 40 million years after land plants first began diverging. Another 40 million years passed before true leaves appeared.

UNDERSTAND

1. d 2. d 3. c 4. c 5. a 6. d

APPLY

1. d 2. b 3. c 4. d 5. d 6. b

SYNTHESIZE

1. Moss has a dominant gametophyte generation, whereas lycophytes have a dominant sporophyte generation. Perhaps a comparison of the two genomes would provide insight into the genomic differences associated with the evolutionary shift from dominant gametophyte to dominant sporophyte.

2. Because the sporophyte generation of the fern is much larger than the sporophyte generation of the moss, it is expected that the fern sporophyte would have more mitotic divisions in order for the plant to be larger.

3. Moss would face the greater challenge. Without vascular tissue, it would be difficult to move water and nutrients efficiently over 10 m of height. Although the fern gametophyte would be small and on the ground where water would be available for sperm to travel a short distance to fertilize eggs, getting egg and sperm together at the tops of two different moss gametophytes would be challenging at a height of 10 m.

CHAPTER 31

LEARNING OUTCOME QUESTIONS

31.1 The pollen tube grows toward the egg, carrying the sperm within the pollen tube; therefore water is not needed for fertilization.

31.2 The ovule rests, exposed on the scale (a modified leaf), which allows easier access to the ovule through wind pollination.

31.3 Any number of vectors that could acquire the moss gene and also affect the flowering plant could account for horizontal gene transfer. Pathogens including viruses and bacteria, as well as herbivores could potentially facilitate horizontal gene transfer.

31.4 We'd expect a dormancy that required a period of chilling to be broken and/or time in the ground for the seed coat to be weakened by microbes in the soil over the winter so the seedling can force its way out of the seed.

31.5 Fleshy fruits are more likely to encourage animals to eat them. Different colors will attract different animals. For example, birds are attracted to red berries.

INQUIRY AND DATA ANALYSIS QUESTIONS

Page 606 Inquiry question: Comparisons of a single gene could result in an inaccurate phylogenetic tree because it fails to take into account the effects of horizontal gene transfer. For example, the clade of *Amborella trichopoda* is a sister clade to all other flowering plants, but roughly 2/3 of its mitochondrial genes are present due to horizontal gene transfer from other land plants, including more distantly related mosses.

Page 608 Inquiry question: To determine if a moss gene had a function you would employ functional analysis, using a variety of experiments, to test for possible functions of the moss gene in *Amborella*. For example, you could create a mutation in the moss gene and see if there were any phenotypic differences in *Amborella* plants homozygous for the mutant gene. You could place the moss gene promoter in front of a reporter gene and visualize where, if any place, in the plant the gene was expressed.

Page 611 Inquiry question: Endosperm provides nutrients for the developing embryo in most flowering plants. The embryo cannot derive nutrition from soil prior to root development; therefore, without endosperm, the embryo is unlikely to survive, and fitness would be zero.

Page 611 Data analysis: $(640 \ \mu m - 80 \ \mu m)/(8 \ hr - 1 \ hr) = 80 \ \mu m/hr$. This matches the value in the data table. Differences could be the result of reading the graph incorrectly or of rounding in doing the calculation.

Page 612 Inquiry question: The prior sporophyte generation (tan) should be labeled $2n$. The degenerating gametophyte generation (purple) should be labeled $1n$. The next sporophyte generation (blue) should be labeled $2n$.

UNDERSTAND

1. a 2. c 3. b 4. d 5. a 6. d 7. d 8. b 9. a

APPLY

1. c 2. a 3. b 4. a 5. a 6. d

SYNTHESIZE

1. Answers to this question may vary. However, gymnosperms are defined as "naked" seed plants. Therefore, an ovule that is not completely protected by sporophyte tissue would be characteristic of a gymnosperm. To be classified as an angiosperm, evidence of flower structures and double fertilization are

key characteristics, although double fertilization has been observed in some gnetophytes.

2. The purpose of pollination is to bring together the male and female gametes for sexual reproduction. Sexual reproduction is designed to increase the genetic variability of a species. If a plant allows self-pollination, then the amount of genetic diversity will be reduced, but this is a better alternative than not reproducing at all. This would be especially useful in species in which the individuals are widely dispersed.

3. The benefit is that by developing a relationship with a specific pollinator, the plant species increases the chance that its pollen will be brought to another member of its species for pollination. If the pollinator is a generalist, then the pollinator might not travel to another member of the same species, and pollination would not occur. The drawback is that if something happens to the pollinator (extinction or drop in population size), then the plant species would be left with either a reduced or nonexistent means of pollination.

4. The seeds may need to be chilled before they can germinate. You can store them in the refrigerator for several weeks or months and try again. The surface of the seed may need to be scarified (damaged) before it can germinate. Usually this would happen from the effects of weather or if the seed goes through the digestive track of an animal where the seed coat is weakened by acid in the gut of the animal. You could substitute for natural scarification by rubbing your seeds on sandpaper before germinating them. It is possible that your seed needs to be exposed to light or received insufficient water when you first planted it. You may need to soak your seed in water for a bit to imbibe it. Exposing the imbibed seed to sunlight might also increase the chances of germination.

CHAPTER 32

LEARNING OUTCOME QUESTIONS

32.1 #1 In fungi, mitosis results in duplicated nuclei, but the nuclei remain within a single cell. This lack of cell division following mitosis is very unusual in animals.

#2 Hyphae are protected by chitin, which is not digested by fungal enzymes.

32.2 Microsporidians lack mitochondria, which are found in *Plasmodium*.

32.3 Blastocladiomycetes are free-living and have mitochondria. Microsporidians are obligate parasites and lack mitochondria.

32.4 Zygospores are more likely to be produced when environmental conditions are not favorable. Sexual reproduction increases the chances of offspring with new combinations of genes that will have an advantage in a changing environment. Also, the zygospore can stay dormant until conditions improve.

32.5 Glomeromycetes depend on the host plant for carbohydrates.

32.6 A dikaryotic cell has two nuclei, each with a single set of chromosomes. A diploid cell has a single nucleus with two sets of chromosomes.

32.7 Preventing the spread of the fungal infection using fungicides and good cultivation practices could help. If farmworkers must tend to infected fields, masks that filter out the spores could protect the workers.

32.8 The fungi that ants consumed may have originally been growing on leaves. Over evolutionary time, mutations that altered ant behavior so the ants would bring leaves to a stash of fungi would have been favored, and the tripartite symbiosis evolved.

32.9 Wind can spread spores over large distances, resulting in the spread of fungal disease.

INQUIRY AND DATA ANALYSIS QUESTION

Page 62 Data analysis: The first fungus had 1.31×10^8 spores/1.1 cm^2 = 1.2×10^8 spores/cm^2 versus the second with 6.87×10^9 spores/8.37 cm^2 = 8.2×10^8 spores/cm^2. The second fungus produced a little over 6 times as many spores per cm^2 as the first fungus.

UNDERSTAND

1. c   2. d   3. a   4. d   5. b   6. d   7. d

APPLY

1. d   2. b   3. a   4. c   5. d

SYNTHESIZE

1. Fungi possess cell walls. Although the composition of these cell walls differs from that of the plants, cell walls are completely absent in animals. Fungi are also immobile (except for chytrids), and mobility is a key characteristic of the animals.

2. The mycorrhizal relationships between the fungi and plants allow plants to make use of nutrient-poor soil. Without the colonization of land by plants, it is unlikely that animals would have diversified to the level they have achieved today. Lichens are important organisms in the colonization of land. Early landmasses would have been composed primarily of barren rock, with little or no soil for plant colonization. As lichens colonize an area they begin the process of soil formation, which allows other plants to grow.

3. Antibiotics are designed to combat prokaryotic organisms, and fungi are eukaryotic. In addition, fungi possess a cell wall that has a different chemical constitution (chitin) from that of prokaryotes.

4. The fungicide will increase the germination success of your seeds by preventing fungi from harming the seed and emerging seedling. However, because of the close phylogenetic relationship between fungi and animals, a compound that is lethal to fungi may also be harmful to humans. You would not want to get the fungicide on your hands.

CHAPTER 33

LEARNING OUTCOME QUESTIONS

33.1 The rules of parsimony state that the simplest phylogeny is most likely the true phylogeny. As there are living organisms that are both multicellular and unicellular, it stands to reason that the first organisms were unicellular, and multicellularity followed. Animals are also all heterotrophs; if they were the first type of life to have evolved, there would not have been any autotrophs on which they could feed.

33.2 Cephalization, the concentration of nervous tissue in a distinct head region, is intrinsically connected to the onset of bilateral symmetry. Bilateral symmetry promotes the development of a central nerve center, which in turn favors the nervous tissue concentration in the head. In addition, the onset of both cephalization and bilateral symmetry allows for the marriage of directional movement (bilateral symmetry) and the presence of sensory organs facing the direction in which the animal is moving (cephalization).

33.3 This allows systematists to classify animals based solely on derived characteristics. Using features that have only evolved once implies that the species that have that characteristic are more closely related to each other than they are to species that do not have the characteristic.

33.4 The cells of a truly colonial organism, such as a colonial protist, are all structurally and functionally identical; however, sponge cells are differentiated and these cells coordinate to perform functions required by the whole organism. Unlike all other animals, however, sponges do appear much like colonial organisms in that they are not composed of true tissues, and the cells are capable of differentiating from one type to another.

33.5 Two key morphological characters are the number of body layers, making an animal diploblastic or triploblastic, and the type of symmetry. Ctenophores were traditionally thought to be diploblastic, which is the ancestral condition. However, recent studies have suggested that they are, in fact, triploblastic, which is a synapomorphy of bilaterians. In addition, ctenophores exhibit a modified type of radial symmetry, which suggests that this character may not link them with Cnidaria.

33.6 Yes, the coelom has been lost in several clades of protostomes.

INQUIRY AND DATA ANALYSIS QUESTION

Page 646 Inquiry question: None of these characters is a completely reliable indicator of phylogenetic relationships. The coelom only evolved once and is a synapomorphy for the clade comprising protostomes and deuterostomes. Thus, all species with a coelom belong to this clade, but, a number of members of this clade have evolved a pseudocoelom or have become aceolomic. As a result, some species with a coelom are more closely related to species with a pseudocoelom or no coelom than they are to other species with a coelom. A pseudocoelom has evolved convergently in several clades. Thus, the possession of a pseudocoelom is not an indicator of phylogenetic relationships among major animal clades. The acoelomic condition is ancestral for animals, but also re-evolved within Bilateria, so this character state is also not a reliable phylogenetic trait.

UNDERSTAND

1. c   2. b   3. a   4. d   5. a   6. b   7. d   8. a   9. a   10. d   11. a
12. b   13. d

APPLY

1. d 2. b 3. Determinate development indicates that it is a protostome and the fact that it molts places it within the Ecdysozoa. The presence of jointed appendages makes it an arthropod. 4. d

SYNTHESIZE

1. The tree should contain Platyhelminthes and Nemetera on one branch, a second branch should contain nematodes, and a third branch should contain the annelids and the hemichordates. This does not coincide with the information in figure 33.5. Therefore, some of the different types of body cavities have evolved multiple times, and the body cavities are not good characteristics from which to infer phylogenetic relationships.

2. Answers may vary depending on the classification used. Many students will place the Echinoderms near the Cnidaria due to radial symmetry; others will place them closer to the annelids.

CHAPTER 34

LEARNING OUTCOME QUESTIONS

34.1 Molting is a synapomorphy of ecdysozoans, and spiral cleavage of spiralians.

34.2 Tapeworms are parasitic platyhelminthes that live in the digestive system of their host. Tapeworms have a scolex, or head, with hooks for attaching to the wall of their host's digestive system. Another way in which the anatomy of a tapeworm relates to its way of life is its dorsoventrally flattened body and corresponding lack of a digestive system. Tapeworms live in their food; as such they absorb their nutrients directly through the body wall, and their flat bodies facilitate this form of nutrient delivery.

34.3 The cilia both sweep food into the rotifer's mouth and provide the propulsion for locomotion.

34.4 In most invertebrates with a coelom, an important function is internal support by hydrostatic pressure; however, this is unnecessary in most mollusks because the shell serves this purpose.

34.5 With a flow-through digestive tract, food moves in only one direction. This allows for specialization within the tract; sections may be specialized for mechanical and chemical digestion, some for storage, and yet others for absorption. Overall, the specialization yields greater efficiency than does a gastrovascular cavity.

34.6 The main advantage is coordination. A nervous system that serves the entire body allows for coordinated movement and coordinated physiological activities such as reproduction and excretion, even if those systems themselves are segmented. Likewise, a body-wide circulatory system enables efficient oxygen delivery to all of the body cells regardless of the nature of the organism's individual segments.

34.7 Lophophorates are sessile suspension-feeding animals. Much of their body also remains submerged in the ocean floor. Thus, a traditional tubular digestive system would require either the mouth or the anus to be inaccessible to the water column—meaning the animal either could not feed or would have to excrete waste into a closed environment. The U-shaped gut allows them to both acquire nutrients from and excrete waste into their environment.

34.8 *Ascaris lumbricoides,* the intestinal roundworm, infects humans when the human swallows food or water contaminated with roundworm eggs. The most effective ways of preventing the spread of intestinal roundworms is to increase sanitation (especially in food handling), to promote education about the infection process, and to cease using human feces as fertilizer. Not surprisingly, infection by these parasites is most common in areas without modern plumbing.

34.9 One of the defining features of the arthropods is the presence of a chitinous exoskeleton. As arthropods increase in size, the exoskeleton must increase in thickness disproportionately, in order to bear the pull of the animal's muscles. This puts a limit on the size a terrestrial arthropod can reach because the increased bulk of the exoskeleton would prohibit the animal's ability to move. Water is denser than air and thus provides more support; for this reason aquatic arthropods are able to be larger than terrestrial arthropods.

UNDERSTAND

1. d 2. c 3. b 4. a 5. d 6. d 7. d 8. b 9. c 10. d 11. d

APPLY

1. d 2. b Lobsters, centipedes, and nematods are all ecdysozoans, but centipedes and lobsters have segmented bodies with appendages, which makes them more closely related. 3. a

SYNTHESIZE

1. Clams and scallops are bivalves, which are filter feeders that siphon large amounts of water through their bodies to obtain food. They act as natural pollution-control systems for bays and estuaries. A loss of bivalves (from overfishing, predation, or toxic chemicals) would upset the aquatic ecosystem and allow pollution levels to rise.

2. Chitin is an example of convergent evolution since these organisms do not share a common chitin-equipped ancestor. Chitin is often used in structures that need to withstand the rigors of stress (chaetae, exoskeletons, zoecium, etc.).

3. Since the population size of a parasitic species may be very small (just a few individuals), possessing both male and female reproductive structures would allow the benefits of sexual reproduction.

4. Answers may vary. However, it is known that the tapeworm is not the ancestral form of platyhelminthes; instead it has lost its digestive tract due to its role as an intestinal parasite. As an intestinal parasite, the tapeworm relies on the digestive system of its host to break down nutrients into their building blocks for absorption.

CHAPTER 35

LEARNING OUTCOME QUESTIONS

35.1 Echinoderms are members of the Bilateria, a clade that also includes chordates and protostomes (see figure 33.4). A synapomorphy of the Bilateria is the evolution of bilateral symmetry. Because all bilaterians are bilaterally symmetrical, the evolution of pentaradial symmetry must have occurred at the base of the Echinodermata from a bilaterally symmetrical ancestor.

35.2 Chordates have a truly internal skeleton (an endoskeleton), as opposed to the endoskeleton on echinoderms, which is functionally similar to the exoskeleton of arthropods. Whereas an echinoderm uses tube feet attached to an internal water-vascular system for locomotion, a chordate has muscular attachments to its endoskeleton. Finally, chordates have a suite of four characteristics that are unique to the phylum: a nerve chord, a notochord, pharyngeal slits, and a postanal tail.

35.3 Although mature and immature lancelets are similar in form, the tadpole-like tunicate larvae are markedly different from the sessile, vaselike adult form. Both tunicates and lancelets are chordates, but they differ from vertebrates in that they do not have vertebrae or internal bony skeletons.

35.4 The functions of an exoskeleton include protection and locomotion—arthropod exoskeletons, for example, provide a fulcrum to which the animals' muscles attach. In order to resist the pull of increasingly large muscles, the exoskeleton must dramatically increase in thickness as the animal grows larger. There is thus a limit on the size of an organism with an exoskeleton—if it gets too large it will be unable to move due to the weight and heft of its exoskeleton.

35.5 Lobe-finned fish are able to move their fins independently, whereas ray-finned fish must move their fins simultaneously. This ability to "walk" with their fins indicates that lobe-finned fish are most certainly the ancestors of amphibians.

35.6 #1 The challenges of moving onto land were plentiful for the amphibians. First, amphibians needed to be able to support their body weight and locomote on land; this challenge was overcome by the evolution of legs. Second, amphibians needed to be able to exchange oxygen with the atmosphere; this was accomplished by the evolution of more efficient lungs than their lungfish ancestors as well as cutaneous respiration. Third, since movement on land requires more energy than movement in the water, amphibians needed a more efficient oxygen delivery system to supply their larger muscles; this was accomplished by the evolution of double-loop circulation and a partially divided heart. Finally, the first amphibians needed to develop a way of staying hydrated in a nonaquatic environment, and these early amphibians developed leathery skin that helped prevent desiccation.

#2 Extant amphibian orders are monophyletic. However, reptiles evolved from a type of amphibian, now extinct. So, if one includes all amphibians, extinct and extant, then amphibians are paraphyletic. But because those amphibian groups more closely related to reptiles have gone extinct, extant amphibians are monophyletic.

35.7 Amphibians remain tied to the water for their reproduction; their eggs are jelly-like and if laid on the land will quickly desiccate. Reptile eggs, on the other hand, are amniotic eggs—they are watertight and contain a yolk, which nourishes the developing embryo, and a series of four protective and nutritive membranes.

35.8 Two primary traits are shared between birds and reptiles. First, both lay amniotic eggs. Second, they both possess scales (which cover the entire reptile body but solely the legs and feet of birds). Birds also share characteristics (e.g., a four-chambered heart) only with one group of reptiles—the crocodilians.

35.9 The most striking convergence between birds and mammals is endothermy, the ability to regulate body temperature internally. Less striking is flight; found in most birds and only one mammal, the ability to fly is another example of convergent evolution.

35.10 Only the hominids constitute a monophyletic group. Prosimians, monkeys, and apes are all paraphyletic—they include the common ancestor but not all descendants: the clade that prosimians share with the common prosimian ancestor excludes all anthropoids, the clade that monkeys share with the common monkey ancestor excludes hominoids, and the clade that apes share with the common ape ancestor excludes hominids.

INQUIRY AND DATA ANALYSIS QUESTIONS

Page 698 Inquiry question: Fish are paraphyletic because the clade comprising all other vertebrates arose from within fishes and is the sister taxon to Sarcopterygii. Reptiles are paraphyletic because birds arose from within and are sister taxon to—among living reptiles—crocodilians. If one considers extinct amphibians, then Amphibia also is paraphyletic, because some extinct amphibian taxa are more closely related to amniotes (the clade comprising reptiles, birds, and mammals) than they are to other amphibians.

Page 717 Inquiry question: The placenta is very similar to reptile and bird eggs, sharing a number of features: chorion, amnion, and yolk sac, and the umbilical cord is derived from the allantois. The reason is that the placenta is the structure that evolved in placental mammals from the egg of their egg-laying ancestors.

UNDERSTAND

1. a   2. c   3. c   4. a   5. c   6. a   7. d   8. a   9. d

APPLY

1. c   2. c   3. b

SYNTHESIZE

1. Increased insulation would have allowed birds to become endothermic and thus to be active at times that ectothermic species could not be active. High body temperature may also allow flight muscles to function more efficiently.

2. Birds evolved from one type of dinosaurs. Thus, in phylogenetic terms, birds are a type of dinosaur.

3. Like the evolution of modern-day horses, the evolution of hominids was not a straight and steady progression to today's *Homo sapiens*. Hominid evolution started with an initial radiation of numerous species. From this group, the evolutionary trend was toward increasing size, similar to what is seen in the evolution of horses. However, like in horse evolution, there are examples of evolutionary decreases in body size as seen in *Homo floresiensis*. Hominid evolution also reveals the coexistence of related species, as seen with *Homo neaderthalensis* and *Homo sapiens*. Hominid evolution, like horse evolution, was not a straight and steady progression to the animal that exists today.

CHAPTER 36

LEARNING OUTCOME QUESTIONS

36.1 Primary growth contributes to the increase in plant height, as well as branching, with shoot and root apical meristems as the source of the growth. Secondary growth makes substantial contributions to the increase in girth of the plant, allowing for a much larger sporophyte generation, with lateral meristems contributing to secondary growth.

36.2 Vessels transport water and are part of the xylem. The cells are dead and only the walls remain. Cylinders of stacked vessels move water from the roots to the leaves of plants. Sieve-tube members are part of the phloem and transport nutrients. Sieve-tube members are living cells, but they lack a nucleus. They rely on neighboring companion cells to carry out some metabolic functions. Like vessels, sieve-tube members are stacked to form a cylinder.

36.3 If abundant water were available, a mutant plant with decreased numbers of root hairs could survive.

36.4 The axillary buds in the axils of the leaves would grow in the absence of the shoot tip. These shoots would eventually flower and reproduce.

36.5 Unlike eudicot leaves, the mesophyll of monocot leaves is not divided into palisade and spongy layers. Instead, cells surrounding the vascular tissues are specialized for carbon fixation. This anatomical variation allows carbon fixation to occur in a part of the leaf where the oxygen concentration is lower, increasing the efficiency of photosynthesis.

INQUIRY AND DATA ANALYSIS QUESTIONS

Page 736 Inquiry question: Three dermal tissue traits that are adaptive for a terrestrial lifestyle include guard cells, trichomes, and root hairs. Guard cells flank an epidermal opening called a stoma and regulate its opening and closing. Stomata are closed when water is scarce, thus conserving water. Trichomes are hairlike outgrowths of the epidermis of stems, leaves, and reproductive organs. Trichomes help to cool leaf surfaces and reduce evaporation from stomata. Root hairs are epidermal extensions of certain cells in young roots and greatly increase the surface area for absorption.

Page 741 Inquiry question: Each time a meristem cell divides, one daughter cell contributes to new tissue and the other continues as a meristem cell. Each cell would have to divide 10 times for every 100 root cap cells that need to be replaced.

UNDERSTAND

1. d   2. d   3. c   4. b   5. b   6. c   7. a   8. b   9. b   10. b   11. d

APPLY

1. b   2. c   3. d   4. c   5. d   6. d   7. c   8. a   9. b   10. a

SYNTHESIZE

1. Roots lack leaves with axillary buds at nodes, although there may be lateral roots that originated from deep within the root. The vascular tissue would have a different pattern in roots and stems. If there is a vascular stele at the core with a pericycle surrounded by a Casparian strip, you are looking at a root.

2. Lenticels increase gas exchange. In wet soil, the opportunity for gas exchange decreases. Lenticels could compensate for decreased gas exchange, which would be adaptive.

3. There are many ways to answer this question. Root modifications could result in increased surface area for absorption under dry conditions, leaf modifications could better balance the loss of water through stomata by optimizing the level of CO_2 relative to O_2 in the leaf. A shoot modification could lead to increased nutrient storage.

4. Whenever water is scarce, the corn plant will wilt. Without the large cross-section vessels, there are insufficient conduits for water in the plant.

5. The plant would grow quickly, use minimal water, have leaf anatomy and physiology with optimized photosynthesis, and have a modified root or shoot that can be used as a food source for humans.

CHAPTER 37

LEARNING OUTCOME QUESTIONS

37.1 Physical pressures include gravity and transpiration, as well as turgor pressure as an expanding cell presses against its cell wall. Increased turgor pressure and other physical pressures are associated with increases in water potential. Solute concentration determines whether water enters or leaves a cell via osmosis. The smallest amount of pressure on the side of the cell membrane with the greater solute concentration that is necessary to stop osmosis is the solute potential. Water potential is the sum of the pressure from physical forces and from the solute potential.

37.2 The apoplastic route. The Casparian strip blocks water movement through the cell walls of the endodermal cells.

37.3 The driving force for transpiration is the gradient between 100% humidity inside the leaf and the external humidity. When the external humidity is low, the rate of transpiration is high, limited primarily by the amount of water available for uptake through the root system. Guttation occurs when transpiration is low, but ions continue to move into the root because of water potential differences. In turn, more water enters the root and can push the liquid up. This push is in contrast to the pull of transpiration.

37.4 Blue light triggers proton transport, creating a proton gradient that drives the opening of the K^+ channels. This leads to an influx of water, an increase in turgor in the guard cells, and the opening of the stomata. Increasing temperatures could inhibit the opening of the stomata as well as dry conditions.

37.5 Drought tolerance: Deeply embedded stomata decrease water loss through transpiration because water tension is altered in the crypts.

   Flooding tolerance: Pneumatophores are modified roots that grow above flood waters, allowing for oxygen exchange, which is limited for roots under water.

   Salt tolerance: Production of high levels of organic molecules in the roots results in uptake of water, even in saline soil, by changing the water potential inside the root.

37.6 Phloem transport can be bidirectional, whereas xylem transport is always from the base to the tip of the plant. Xylem transport depends on transpiration to move the water and dissolved minerals upwards. Phloem transport relies on active transport for loading and unloading at the source and sink, respectively.

INQUIRY AND DATA ANALYSIS QUESTIONS

Page 759 Data analysis: Before equilibrium, the solute potential of the solution is –0.5 MPa, and that of the cell is –0.2 MPa. Since the solution contains more solute than does the cell, water will leave the cell to the point that the cell is plasmolyzed. Initial turgor pressure (Ψ_p) of the cell = 0.05 MPa, and that of the solution is 0 MPa. At equilibrium, both the solution and the cell will have the same Ψ_w. Ψ_{cell} = –0.2 MPa + 0.5 MPa = 0.3 MPa before equilibrium is reached. At equilibrium, $\Psi_{cell} = \Psi_{solution}$ = –0.5MPa, thus $\Psi_{w\,cell}$ = –0.5 MPa. At equilibrium, the plasmolyzed cell Ψ_p = 0 MPa. Finally, using the relationship $\Psi_{W(cell)} = \Psi_p + \Psi_s$ and $\Psi_{W(cell)}$ = –0.5 MPa, $\Psi_{P(cell)}$ = 0 MPa, then $\Psi_{s(cell)}$ = –0.5 MPa.

Page 761 Inquiry question: The fastest route for water movement through cells has the least hindrance, and thus is the symplast route. The route that exerts the most control over what substances enter and leave the cell is the transmembrane route, which is then the best route for moving nutrients into the plant.

Page 763 Data analysis: **#1** The volume that can move through a vessel or tracheid is proportional to r^4. If a mutation increases the radius, r, of a xylem vessel threefold, then the movement of water through the vessel would increase 81-fold ($r^4 = 3^4 = 81$). A plant with larger-diameter vessels can move much more water up its stems.

#2 The volume that can move through a vessel or tracheid is proportional to r^4. $500^4/80^4$ = 1525 times faster. In the context of a plant, temperature, humidity, and whether or not the guard cells are open affects the rate of transpiration. Structural considerations, including cavitation, can also affect the rate of transpiration.

Page 769 Data analysis: Substances in phloem can move at a rate of 50 to 100 cm/hr. Sucrose could move 25 cm in 15 to 30 min. 25 cm/(50 cm/h) = 0.5 hr = 30 min. 25 cm/(100 cm/hr) = 0.25 hr = 15 min.

UNDERSTAND

1. a   2. c   3. d   4. a   5. c   6. d   7. b   8. a   9. d   10. b

APPLY

1. b   2. d   3. b   4. a   5. b

SYNTHESIZE

1. The solute concentration outside the root cells is greater than inside the cells. Thus the solute potential is more negative outside the cell, and water moves out of the root cells and into the soil. Without access to water, your plant wilts.

2. Look for wilty plants since the rate of water movement across the membrane would decrease in the aquaporin mutants.

3. At the level of membrane transport, plants and animals are very similar. Plant cell walls allow plant cells to take up more water than most animal cells, which rupture without the supportive walls. At the level of epidermal cells there is substantial variation among animals. Amphibians exchange water across the skin. Plants have waterproof epidermal tissue but lose water through stomata. Humans sweat, but dogs do not. Some animals have adaptations for living in aquatic or high-saline environment, as do plants. Vascular plants move vast amounts of water through the plant body via the xylem, using evaporation to fuel the transport. Animals with closed circulatory systems can move water throughout the organism and also excrete excess water through the urinary system, which is responsible for osmoregulation.

4. The rate of transpiration is greater during the day than the night. Since water loss first occurs in the upper part of the tree where more leaves with stomata are located, the decrease in water volume in the xylem would first be observed in the upper portion, followed by the lower portion of the tree.

5. Spring year 1—The new carrot seedling undergoes photosynthesis in developing leaves and the sucrose moves toward the growing tip.

    Summer year 1—The developing leaves are sources of carbohydrate, which now moves to the developing root and also the growing young tip.

    Fall year 1—The carrot root is now the sink for all carbohydrates produced by the shoot.

Spring year 2—Stored carbohydrate in the root begins to move upward into the shoot.

    Summer year 2—The shoot is flowering, and the developing flowers are the primary sink for carbohydrates from the root and also from photosynthesis in the leaves.

    Fall year 2—Seeds are developing and they are the primary sink. The root reserves have been utilized, and any remaining carbohydrates from photosynthesis are transported to developing seeds.

CHAPTER 38

LEARNING OUTCOME QUESTIONS

38.1 The water potential around the root decreases, and water no longer moves into the root. Transpiration stops, and the plant has insufficient water to maintain life functions.

38.2 Magnesium is found in the center of the chlorophyll molecule. Without sufficient magnesium, chlorophyll deficiencies will result in decreased photosynthesis and decreased yield per acre.

38.3 *Rhizobium* and legume roots have a symbiotic relationship in which the bacteria enter the root through an infection thread, differentiate, and produce NH_3 for the plant in exchange for carbohydrates. Although nitrogen-fixing bacteria are generally limited to the legumes, more than 90% of vascular plants have a symbiotic relationship with mycorrhizal fungi that extend the surface area of the roots and enhance phosphate transfer. Mycorrhizal symbiosis existed first, and some of the signaling pathways in this symbiosis are also found in *Rhizobium* and legume symbioses.

38.4 **#1** As the amount of nitrogen, relative to carbon, decreased in an organism, less protein is made. For example, a plant may be the same size under high- and low-CO_2 atmospheres, but the relative amount of protein is lower under the high-CO_2 conditions. For herbivores, including humans, more plant material would need to be consumed to obtain the same amount of protein under higher versus lower concentrations of CO_2.

    #2 Increasing the amount of available nitrogen in the soil is one strategy. This can be accomplished by using chemically produced ammonia for fertilizing, intercropping with nitrogen-fixing legumes, or using organic matter rich in nitrogen for enriching the soil. Efforts to reduce the relative amounts of atmospheric CO_2 would also be helpful.

38.5 Large poplar trees that are not palatable to animals offer a partial solution. Fencing in areas that are undergoing phytoremediation is another possibility, but it would be difficult to isolate all animals, especially birds. Plants that naturally deter herbivores with secondary compounds, including some mustard species (*Brassica* species) could be effective for phytoremediation.

INQUIRY AND DATA ANALYSIS QUESTIONS

Page 778 Inquiry question: CO_2 from the atmosphere and H_2O from the soil are incorporated into carbohydrates during photosynthesis to create much of the mass of the tree. The largest percentage of the mass comes from atmospheric CO_2.

Page 784 Inquiry question: At low and high temperature extremes, enzymes involved in plant respiration are denatured. Plants tend to acclimate to slower long-term changes in temperature, and rates of respiration are able to adjust. Short-term, more dramatic, changes might slow or halt respiration, especially if a temperature change is large enough to cause enzymes to denature.

UNDERSTAND

1. b   2. a   3. c   4. d   5. a   6. b   7. c   8. a

APPLY

1. c   2. a   3. a   4. d

5. a. For the micronutrient problems you would also use the estimate of 1000 kg of potatoes. The conversion you need to use is that 1 ppm is the same as 1 mg/kg. 4 ppm of copper is the same as 4 mg/kg. Multiply this by 1000 kg of potato, and you have 4000 mg or 4 grams of copper up to 30,000 mg or 33 grams.

   b. 15 ppm of zinc is the same as 15 mg/kg. Multiply this by 1000 kg of potato = 15,000 mg or 15 grams up to 100,000 mg or 100 grams.

   c. For potassium, you calculate 0.5% of 1000, which is 5 kg. You would do the same type of calculation for 6%, which is 60 kg.

   d. 25 ppm of iron is the same as 25 mg/kg. Multiply by 1000 kg of potato = 25,000 mg or 25 grams up to 300 grams.

SYNTHESIZE

1. Bacteria that are important for nitrogen fixation could be destroyed. Other microorganisms that make nutrients available to plants could also be destroyed.

2. Grow the tomatoes hydroponically in a complete nutrient solution minus boron and complete nutrient solution with varying concentrations of boron. Compare the coloration of the leaves, the rate of growth (number of new leaves per unit time), and number and size of fruits produced on plants in each treatment group. It would also be helpful to compare the dry weights of plants from each treatment group at the end of the study.

3. Other inputs include both the macronutrients and micronutrients. Nitrogen, potassium, and phosphorous are common macronutrients in fertilizers, and their levels in the circulating water, along with micronutrients, need to be monitored. CO_2 levels in the air also could be monitored.

CHAPTER 39

LEARNING OUTCOME QUESTIONS

39.1 The lipid-based compounds help to create a water-impermeable layer on the leaves.

39.2 A drug prepared from a whole plant or plant tissue would contain a number of different compounds, in addition to the active ingredient. Chemically synthesized or purified substances contain one or more known substances in known quantities.

39.3 It is unlikely that wasps will kill all the caterpillars. When attacked by a caterpillar, the plant releases a volatile substance that attracts the wasp. But, the wasp has to be within the vicinity of the signal when the plant releases the signal. As a result, some caterpillars will escape detection by wasps.

39.4 The local death of cells creates a barrier between the pathogen and the rest of the plant.

INQUIRY AND DATA ANALYSIS QUESTION

Page 795 Inquiry question: Ricin functions as a ribosome-binding protein that limits translation. A very small quantity of ricin was injected into Markov's thigh from the modified tip of his assassin's umbrella. Without translation of proteins in cells, enzymes and other gene products are no longer produced, causing the victim's metabolism to shut down and leading to death.

UNDERSTAND

1. d 2. b 3. b 4. d 5. c 6. a 7. c 8. a 9. d

APPLY

1. c 2. d 3. d 4. b 5. c 6. a

SYNTHESIZE

1. Humans learn quickly, so plants with toxins that made people ill would not become a dietary mainstay. If there was variation in the levels of toxin in the same species in different areas, humans would likely have continued to harvest plants from the area where plants had reduced toxin levels. As domestication continued, seeds would be collected from the plants with reduced toxin levels and grown the following year.

2. For parasitoid wasps to effectively control caterpillars, sufficiently large populations of wasps would need to be maintained in the area where the infestation occurred. As wasps migrate away from the area, new wasps would need to be introduced. The density of wasps is critical because the wasp has to be in the vicinity of the plant being attacked by the caterpillar when the plant releases its volatile chemical signal. Maintaining sufficient density is a major barrier to success.

3. If a plant is flowering or has fruits developing, the systemin will move toward the fruit or flowers, providing protection for the developing seed. If the plant is a biennial, such as a carrot plant, in its first year of growth, systemin will likely be diverted to the root or other storage organ that will reserve food stores for the plant for the following year.

CHAPTER 40

LEARNING OUTCOME QUESTIONS

40.1 Chlorophyll is essential for photosynthesis. Phytochromes regulate plant growth and development using light as a signal. Phytochrome-mediated responses align the plant with the light environment so photosynthesis is maximized, which is advantageous for the plant.

40.2 The plant would not have normal gravitropic responses. Other environmental signals, including light, would determine the direction of plant growth.

40.3 Folding leaves can startle an herbivore that lands on the plant. The herbivore departs, and the plant is protected.

40.4 During the winter months the leaves would cease photosynthesis except on a few warm days. If the weather warmed briefly, water would move into the leaves and photosynthesis would begin. Unfortunately, the minute the temperature dropped, the leaves would freeze and be permanently damaged. Come the spring, the leaves would not be able to function, and the tree would die. It is to the tree's advantage to shed its leaves and grow new, viable leaves in the spring when the danger of freezing is past.

40.5 Gibberellins and brassinosteroids are likely candidates. Applying brassinosteroids or gibberellins to mutant plants grown under low light intensity would be a good initial experiment. If the plants became taller than the wild-type plants, then you would have a candidate hormone. No response does not indicate that neither hormone pathway is altered. It could be that the mutation is in the receptor for the hormone. One way to determine which hormone receptor could be mutated would be to make the mutant transgenic with a wild-type receptor for either gibberellins or brassinosteroids.

INQUIRY AND DATA ANALYSIS QUESTIONS

Page 804 Inquiry question: A number of red-light–mediated responses are linked to phytochrome action alone, including seed germination, shoot elongation, and plant spacing. Only some of the red-light–mediated responses leading to gene expression depend on the action of protein kinases. When phytochrome converts to the Pfr form, a protein kinase triggers phosphorylation that, in turn, initiates a signaling cascade that triggers the translation of certain light-regulated genes. Not all red-light–mediated responses are disrupted in a plant with a mutation in the protein kinase domain of phytochrome.

Page 805 Data analysis: Red light is absorbed by the leaves at a greater rate than far-red light as the sunlight passes through the canopy. Plant-signaling pathways integrate information about the relative amounts of red and far-red light via phytochrome to regulate plant growth and development. For example, seed germination is inhibited as the relative amount of far-red light increases. Thus, below the shady canopy, seed germination would be less likely to occur. With reduced sunlight, the seedlings would have had less chance of survival because of reduced photosynthesis. Alternatively, the information about reduced sunlight could signal rapid stem elongation to get the plant closer to sufficient sunlight for photosynthesis.

Page 807 Inquiry question: Auxin is involved in the phototropic growth responses of plants, including the bending of stems and leaves toward light. Auxin increases the plasticity of plant cells and signals their elongation. The highest concentration of auxin would most likely occur at the tips of stems where sun exposure is maximal.

Page 815 Inquiry question: A chemical substance, such as the hormone auxin, could trigger the elongation of cells on the shaded side of a stem, causing the stem to bend toward the light.

Page 816 Data analysis: A protractor would be a simple tool for determining the angle of the bend relative to either a vertical or horizontal axis.

UNDERSTAND

1. c 2. a 3. d 4. d 5. b 6. d

APPLY

1. b 2. a 3. b 4. c 5. c 6. b 7. d

SYNTHESIZE

1. You are observing etiolation. Etiolation is an energy conservation strategy to help plants growing in the dark to reach the light before they die. They don't green up until light becomes available, and they divert energy to internode elongation. This strategy is useful for potato shoots. The sprouts will be long so they can get to the surface more quickly. They will remain white until exposed to sunlight which will signal the production of chlorophyll.

2. Tropism refers to the growth of an organism in response to an environmental signal such as light. Taxis refers to the movement of an organism in response to an environmental signal. Since plants cannot move, they will not exhibit taxis, but they do exhibit tropisms.

3. Auxin accumulates on the lower side of a stem in a gravitropism, resulting in elongation of cells on the lower side. If auxin or vesicles containing auxin responded to a gravitational field, it would be possible to have a gravitropic response without amyloplasts.

4. Farmers are causing a thigmotropic response. In response to touch, the internodes of the seedlings will increase in diameter. The larger stems will be more resistant to wind and rain once they are moved to the field. The seedlings will be less likely to snap once they are moved to the more challenging environment.

CHAPTER 41

LEARNING OUTCOME QUESTIONS

41.1 Without flowering in angiosperms, sexual reproduction is impossible and the fitness of a plant drops to zero.

41.2 Set up an experiment in a controlled growth chamber with a day–night light regimen that promotes flowering. Then interrupt the night length with a brief exposure to light. If day length is the determining factor, the brief flash of light will not affect flowering. If night length is the determining factor, the light flash may affect the outcome. For example, if the plant requires a long night, interrupting the night will prevent flowering. If the plant flowers whether or not you interrupt the night with light, it may be a short-night plant. In that case, you would want to set up a second experiment where you lengthen the night length. That should prevent the plant from flowering.

41.3 Flowers can attract pollinators, enhancing the probability of reproduction.

41.4 No, because the gametes are formed by meiosis, which allows for new combinations of alleles to combine. You may want to review Mendel's law of independent assortment.

41.5 In gymnosperms, the megagametophyte is the nutritional source for the embryo, in contrast with the double-fertilization event in angiosperms that produces the endosperm and the embryo.

41.6 Retaining the seed in the ground might provide greater stability for the seedling until its root system is established.

41.7 When conditions are uniform and the plant is well adapted to those constant conditions, genetic variation would not be advantageous. Rather, vegetative reproduction would ensure that the genotypes that are well adapted to the current conditions are maintained.

41.8 A biennial life cycle allows an organism to store up substantial reserves to be used to support reproduction during the second season. The downside to this strategy is that the plant might not survive the winter between the two growing seasons, and its fitness would therefore be reduced to zero.

INQUIRY AND DATA ANALYSIS QUESTIONS

Page 833 Inquiry question: Strict levels of *CONSTANS (CO)* gene protein are maintained according to the circadian clock. Phytochrome, the pigment that perceives photoperiod, regulates the transcription of *CO*. By examining posttranslational regulation of *CO,* it might be possible to determine whether protein levels are modulated by means other than transcription. An additional level of control might be needed to ensure that the activation of floral meristem genes coincides with the activation of genes that code for individual flower organs.

Page 834 Inquiry question: Flower production employs up to four genetically regulated pathways. These pathways ensure that the plant flowers when it has reached adult size, when temperature and light levels are optimal, and when nutrition is sufficient to support flowering. All of these factors combine to ensure the success of flowering and the subsequent survival of the plant species.

Page 835 Inquiry question: Once vernalization occurred and nutrition was optimal, flowering could occur in the absence of flower-repressing genes, even if the plant had not achieved adult size. Thus flowering might occur earlier than normal.

Page 849 Data analysis: Seven cell divisions. One cell divides to produce 2 cells, which divide to produce 4, which divide to produce 8, which proceed through four more divisions to produce a total of 128.

Page 849 Inquiry question: #1 Because it is mutant for monopteros, it does not make a functional MONOPTEROS protein, which is a transcription factor needed for transcribing genes required for root development.

#2 If MONOPTEROS could not be repressed, root development would occur whenever there was auxin available. Roots might develop in unexpected places on the plant.

UNDERSTAND

1. a   2. c   3. a   4. d   5. d   6. c   7. d   8. c   9. a   10. d   11. a   12. c   13. c   14. a   15. b   16. c   17. a

APPLY

1. b   2. c   3. b   4. a   5. b   6. c   7. c   8. b   9. c

SYNTHESIZE

1. Poinsettias are short-day plants. The lights from the cars on the new highway interrupt the long night and prevent flowering.

2. Spinach is a long-day plant, and you want to harvest the vegetative, not the reproductive, parts of the plant. Spinach will flower during the summer as the days get longer, but only leaves will be produced during the spring. If you grow and harvest your spinach in the early spring, you will be able to harvest the leaves before the plant flowers and begins to senesce.

3. Cross-pollination increases the genetic diversity of the next generation. However, self-pollination is better than no pollination. The floral morphology of columbine favors cross-pollination, but self-pollination is a backup option. Should this backup option be utilized, there is still one more opportunity for cross-pollination to override self-pollination because the pollen tube from the other plant can still grow through the style more rapidly than the pollen tube from the same plant.

4. Potatoes grown from true seed take longer to produce new potatoes than potatoes grown from tubers. Seeds are easier to store between growing seasons and require much less storage space than whole potatoes. The seed-grown potatoes will have greater genetic diversity than the asexually propagated potato tubers. If environmental conditions vary from year to year, the seed-grown potatoes may have a better yield because different plants will have an advantage under different environmental conditions. The tuber-grown potatoes will be identical. If conditions are optimal for that genotype, the tuber-grown potatoes will outperform the more-variable seed-grown potatoes. But, if conditions are not optimal for the asexually propagated potatoes, the seed-grown potatoes may have the higher yield.

5. Place *Fucus* zygotes on a screen and shine a light from the bottom. If light is more important, the rhizoid will form toward the light, even though that is the opposite direction gravity would dictate. If gravity is more important, the rhizoid will form away from the direction of the light.

CHAPTER 42

LEARNING OUTCOME QUESTIONS

42.1 Organs may be made of multiple tissue types. For example, the heart contains muscle, connective tissue, and epithelial tissue.

42.2 The epithelium in glandular tissue produces secretions, the epithelium has microvilli on the apical surface that increase surface area for absorption.

42.3 Blood is a form of connective tissue because it contains abundant extracellular material: the plasma.

42.4 The function of heart cell requires their being electrically connected. The gap junctions allow the flow of ions between cells.

42.5 Neurons may be a meter long, but this is a very thin projection that still can allow diffusion of materials along its length. They do require specialized transport along microtubules to move proteins from the cell body to the synapse.

42.6 The organ systems may overlap. Consider the respiratory and circulatory systems. These systems are interdependent.

42.7 Yes.

42.8 The distinction should be between the ability to generate metabolic heat to modulate temperature, and the lack of that ability. Thus ectotherms and endotherms have replaced cold-blooded and warm-blooded.

INQUIRY AND DATA ANALYSIS QUESTIONS

Page 879 Inquiry question: After 2 min of shivering, the thoracic muscles have warmed up enough to engage in full contractions. The muscle contractions that allow the full range of motion of the wings utilize kinetic energy in the movement of the wings, rather than releasing the energy as heat, which occurred in the shivering response.

Page 881 Data analysis: Small mammals, with a proportionately larger surface area, dissipate heat readily, which is helpful in a warm environment, but detrimental in a cold environment. In cold conditions, small mammals must seek shelter or have adaptations, such as insulating hair, to maintain body temperature. Because of a greater volume and proportionately less surface area, large mammals are better adapted to cold environments since it takes much longer for them to lose body heat. Hot environments pose a greater challenge for them for the same reason.

Page 882 Data analysis: Pyrogens target the integrating center in the hypothalamus. They act by increasing the "set point," thus leading to a consistently higher body temperature.

UNDERSTAND

1. a   2. c   3. c   4. d   5. a   6. d   7. b   8. b   9. b

APPLY

1. b   2. c   3. c   4. d   5. a   6. c

SYNTHESIZE

1. Yes, both the gut and the skin include epithelial tissue. A disease that affects epithelial cells could affect both the digestive system and the skin. For example, cystic fibrosis affects the ion transport system in epithelial membranes. It is manifested in the lungs, gut, and sweat glands.

2. The nervous system and endocrine system are involved in regulation and maintenance. They function in sensing the internal and external environments and cause changes in the body to respond to changes to maintain homeostasis. The digestive, circulatory, and respiratory systems are also involved in regulation and maintenance. They are grouped together because they all provide necessary nutrients for the body. The digestive system is responsible for the acquisition of nutrients from food; the respiratory system provides oxygen and removes waste (carbon monoxide). The circulatory system transports nutrients to the cells of the body and removes metabolic wastes.

3. Hunger is a negative feedback stimulus. Hunger stimulates an individual to eat, which in turn causes a feeling of fullness that removes hunger. Hunger is the stimulus; eating is the response that removes the stimulus.

4. The internal environment is constantly changing. As you move through your day, muscle activity raises your body temperature, but when you sit down to eat or rest, your temperature cools. The body must constantly adjust to changes in activity or the environment.

CHAPTER 43

LEARNING OUTCOME QUESTIONS

43.1   The somatic nervous system is under conscious control.

43.2   A positive current inward (influx of Na^+) depolarizes the membrane, and a positive current outward (efflux of K^+) repolarizes the membrane.

43.3   Tobacco contains the compound nicotine, which can bind some acetylcholine receptors. This leads to the classic symptoms of addiction due to underlying habituation involving changes to receptor numbers and responses.

43.4   Reflex arcs allow you to respond to a stimulus that is damaging before the information actually arrives at your brain.

43.5   These two systems work in opposition. This may seem counterintuitive, but it is the basis for much of homeostasis.

INQUIRY AND DATA ANALYSIS QUESTIONS

Page 892 Data analysis: The sum of all three is shown in the picture. The other possible pairwise sums of potentials are shown in the following graphs.

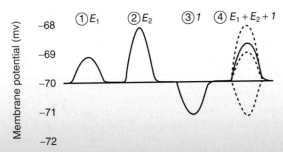

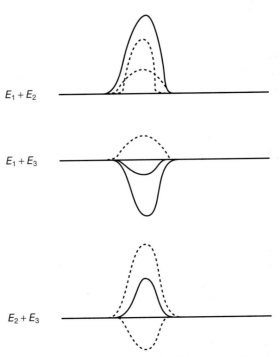

Page 897 Data analysis   The excitatory and inhibitory potentials shown in the figure would sum to a membrane potential close to, or at, the resting potential.

UNDERSTAND

1. a   2. c   3. a   4. a   5. d   6. d   7. a

APPLY

1. d   2. b   3. c   4. a   5. a   6. c   7. d

SYNTHESIZE

1. TEA blocks K^+ channels so that they will not permit the passage of K^+ out of the cell, thereby preventing the cell from returning to the resting potential. Voltage-gated Na^+ channels would still be functional and Na^+ would still flow into the cell, but there would be no repolarization. Na^+ would continue to flow into the cell until an electrochemical equilibrium was reached for Na^+, which is +60 mV. After the membrane potential reached +60 mV, there would be no net movement of Na^+, but the membrane would also not be able to repolarize back to the resting membrane potential. The neuron would no longer be able to function.

   The effects on the postsynaptic cell would be somewhat similar if TEA were applied to the presynaptic cell. The presynaptic cell would depolarize and would continue to release neurotransmitter until it had exhausted its store of synaptic vesicles. As a result, the postsynaptic cell would be bombarded with neurotransmitters and would be stimulated continuously until the stores of presynaptic neurotransmitter were depleted. The postsynaptic cell would, however, recover, being able to repolarize its membrane, and would return to the resting membrane potential.

2. Rising: Na^+ gates open, K^+ closed

   Falling: Na^+ inactivation gate closed, K^+ open

   Undershoot: Na^+ activation gate closed, inactivation gate open, K^+ gate closing.

3. Action potential arrives at the end of the axon.

   Ca^{2+} channels open.

   Ca^{2+} causes synaptic vesicles to fuse with the axon membrane at the synapse.

   Synaptic vesicles release their neurotransmitter.

   Neurotransmitter molecules diffuse across synaptic cleft.

   Postsynaptic receptor proteins bind neurotransmitter.

   Postsynaptic membrane depolarizes.

   If this were an inhibitory synapse, the binding of receptor protein and neurotransmitter would cause the postsynaptic membrane to hyperpolarize.

4. Cells exposed to a stimulus repeatedly may lose their ability to respond. This is known as habituation. Karen's postsynaptic cells may have decreased the number of receptor proteins they produce because the stimulatory signal is so abundant. The result is that it now takes more stimuli to achieve the same result.

Chapter 44

LEARNING OUTCOME QUESTIONS

44.1 When the log values of the intensity of the stimulus and the frequency of the resulting action potentials are plotted against each other, a straight line results; this is referred to as a logarithmic relationship.

44.2 Proprioceptors detect the stretching of muscles and subsequently relay information about the relative position and movement of different parts of the organism's body to the central nervous system. This knowledge is critical for the central nervous system; it must be able to respond to these data by signaling the appropriate muscular responses, allowing for balance, coordinated locomotion, and reflexive responses.

44.3 The lateral line system supplements the sense of hearing in fish and amphibian larvae by allowing the organism to detect minute changes in the pressure and vibrations of its environment. This is facilitated by the density of water; without an aquatic environment, the adult, terrestrial amphibian will no longer be able to make use of this system. On land, sound waves are more easily detectable by the sense of hearing than are vibratory or pressure waves by the similar structures of a lateral line.

44.4 Many insects, such as the housefly, have chemoreceptors on their feet with which they can detect the presence of edible materials as they move through their environment. These insects can thus "taste" what they are walking on, and when they encounter an edible substrate they can then descend their proboscis and consume the food.

44.5 Individuals with complete red-green color blindness (those who have no red cones or no green cones, as opposed to those who lack only some red or green cones) would be highly unlikely to be able to learn to distinguish these colors. In order for an individual to perceive the colors in the red-green area of the spectrum, both red and green cones are required; without both cones there is no reference point by which individuals could compare the signals between the retina and the brain. If there are other cues available, such as color saturation or object shape and size, individuals with a less severe form of color blindness may be able to learn to distinguish these colors. In the absence of other references, however, it would be very difficult for individuals with even partial red-green color blindness to distinguish these colors.

44.6 The body temperature of an ectothermic organism is not necessarily the same as the ambient temperature; for example, other reptiles may bask in the sun, wherein on a chilly day the sun may warm the animal's body temperature above the ambient temperature. In this situation, the heat-sensing organs of, for example, a pit viper would still be effective in hunting because it would be able to distinguish the differences between the environment and its ectothermic prey.

INQUIRY AND DATA ANALYSIS QUESTIONS

Page 919 Inquiry question: As the injured fish thrashed around, it would produce vibrations—rapid changes in the pressure of the water. The lateral line system in fish consists of canals filled with sensory cells that send a signal to the brain in response to the changes in water pressure.

Page 926 Inquiry question: Both taste and smell utilize chemoreceptors as sensory receptors, wherein the binding of specific proteins to the receptor induces an action potential, which is sent as a sensory signal to the brain. The chemicals detected by both systems must first be dissolved in extracellular fluid before they can be detected. One major difference between the two systems is that the olfactory system does not route a signal through the thalamus; instead, action potentials are routed directly to the olfactory cortex. Another difference is that olfactory receptors occur in larger numbers—tens of millions, as opposed to tens or hundreds of thousands for taste receptors.

Page 930 Inquiry question: Additional kinds of cones can enhance color vision in two ways. First, they may be sensitive to regions of the color spectrum not covered by other cones, such as those that detect ultraviolet light in some animals. In addition, they may allow enhanced discrimination of color even in regions to which other cones are sensitive. Consider figure 45.19 and the color yellow. Humans have three cones, each of which is sensitive to a varying extent to spectra with a wavelength of approximately 520 nm. The human brain integrates the response of the three cones and interprets the color as yellow. Imagine, however, if we had a fourth cone whose peak sensitivity was in the region of 520 nm. Output

from that cone would provide additional discrimination not possible based on the other three cones, and thus would allow an individual to identify shades of color not distinguishable by individuals lacking that cone.

Page 931 Data analysis: Ultraviolet light has shorter wavelengths than the blue light in figure 44.19, and so the peak absorption would fall to the left of the blue cone's peak absorption of 420 nm. According to figure 8.4, the UV portion of the electromagnetic spectrum is between 10 nm and 400 nm, which is the end of the visual spectrum. The peak would fall in that range, probably closer to the 400 nm to be considered "near-ultraviolet."

UNDERSTAND

1. d   2. b   3. d   4. b   5. a   6. c   7. b   8. d   9. a

APPLY

1. c   2. a   3. c   4. b

SYNTHESIZE

1. When blood pH becomes acidic, chemoreceptors in the circulatory and the nervous systems notify the brain and the body responds by increasing the breathing rate. This causes an increase in the release of carbon dioxide through the lungs. Decreased carbon dioxide levels in the blood cause a decrease in carbonic acid, which, in turn, causes the pH to rise.

2. In order to reach the retina and generate action potentials on the optic nerve, light must first pass through the ganglion and bipolar cells to reach the rods and cones that synapse with the bipolar cells. The bipolar cells then synapse with ganglion cells. These in turn send action potentials to the brain. Because the retina comprises three layers, with the rods and cones located farthest from the pupil, light must travel to the deepest level to set off reactions that move up through the more superficial levels and result in optic signals.

3. Without gravity to force the otoliths down toward the hair cells, the otolith organ will not function properly. The otolith membrane would not rest on the hair cells and would not move in response to movement of the body parallel or perpendicular to the pull of gravity. Consequently, the hair cell would not bend and so would not produce receptor potentials. Because the astronauts can see, they would have an impression of motion—they can see themselves move in relation to objects around them—but with their eyes closed, they would not know if they were moving in relation to their surroundings. Because their proprioceptors would still function, they would be able to sense when they moved their arms or legs, but they would not have the sensation of their enter body moving through space.

   The semicircular canals would not function equally well in zero-gravity conditions. Although the fluid in the semicircular canals is still able to move around, some sensation of angular movement would most likely occur, but the full function of the semicircular canals requires the force of gravity to aid in the directional movement of the fluid in the canals.

Chapter 45

LEARNING OUTCOME QUESTIONS

45.1 Neurotransmitters are released at a synapse and act on the postsynaptic membrane. Hormones enter the circulatory system and are thus delivered to the entire body.

45.2 The response of a particular tissue depends first on the receptors on its surface, and second on the response pathways active in a cell. Different receptor subtypes can bind the same hormone, and the same receptor can stimulate different response pathways.

45.3 This might lower the amount of GH in circulation. As a treatment, it may have unwanted side effects.

45.4 With two hormones that have antagonistic effects, the body can maintain a fine-tuned level of blood sugar.

45.5 Reducing blood volume should also reduce blood pressure.

INQUIRY AND DATA ANALYSIS QUESTIONS

Page 952 Data analysis: If hypophysectomy is performed on a very early tadpole, the entire signaling axis is disrupted and metamorphosis is blocked. If the surgery is performed later, TSH signaling has already begun, so metamorphosis is not prevented because the pituitary hormones are no longer needed.

Page 956 Data analysis: The use of juvenile hormone as an insecticide is not lethal, but it does prevent metamorphosis and thus prevents reaching sexual maturity, effectively sterilizing the insect. For an insect whose larval form does damage, preventing the next generation will not stop damage from the present generation and, in fact, may increase it.

UNDERSTAND

1. b 2. d 3. c 4. b 5. d 6. b 7. a

APPLY

1. a 2. c 3. c 4. b 5. b 6. b 7. b

SYNTHESIZE

1. If the target cell for a common hormone or paracrine regulator becomes cancerous, it may become hypersensitive to the messenger. This may in turn cause overproduction of cells, which would result in tumor formation. By blocking the production of the hormone specific to that tissue (for example, sex steroids in breast or prostate tissue), it would be possible to slow the growth rate and decrease the size of the tumor.

2. The same hormone can affect two different organs in different ways because the second messengers triggered by the hormone have different targets inside the cell, owing to the cell's different functions. Epinephrine affects the cells of the heart by increasing metabolism so that their contractions are faster and stronger. However, liver cells do not contract and so the second messenger in liver cells triggers the conversion of glycogen into glucose. That is why hormones are so valuable but also economical to the body. One hormone can be produced, one receptor can be made, and one second-messenger system can be used, but there can be two different targets inside the cell.

3. With hormones such as thyroxine, whose effects are slower and have a broader range of activity, a negative feedback system using one hormone adequately controls the system. However, for certain parameters that have a very narrow range and change constantly within that range, a regulatory system that uses up-and-down regulation is desirable. Too much or too little Ca^{2+} or glucose in the blood can have devastating effects on the body, and so those levels must be controlled within a very narrow range. Relying on negative feedback loops would restrict the quick "on" and "off" responses needed to keep the parameters within a very narrow range.

CHAPTER 46

LEARNING OUTCOME QUESTIONS

46.1 Terrestrial invertebrates experience three limitations due to an exoskeleton. First, animals with an exoskeleton can only grow by shedding, or molting, the exoskeleton, leaving them vulnerable to predation. Second, muscles that act on the exoskeleton cannot strengthen and grow because they are confined within a defined space. Finally, the exoskeleton, in concert with the respiratory system of many terrestrial invertebrates, limits the size to which these animals can grow. In order for the exoskeleton of a terrestrial animal to be strong, it has to have a sufficient surface area, and thus it has to increase in thickness as the animal gets larger. The weight of a thicker exoskeleton would impose debilitating constraints on the animal's ability to move.

46.2 Vitamin D is important for the absorption of dietary calcium as well as the deposition of calcium phosphate in bone. Children undergo a great deal of skeletal growth and development; without sufficient calcium deposition, their bones can become soft and pliable, leading to a condition known as rickets, which causes a bending or bowing of the lower limbs. In the elderly, bone remodeling without adequate mineralization of the bony tissue can lead to brittle bones, a condition known as osteoporosis.

46.3 First, unlike the chitinous exoskeleton, a bony endoskeleton is made of living tissue; thus, the endoskeleton can grow along with the organism. Second, because the muscles that act on the bony endoskeleton are not confined within a rigid structure, they are able to strengthen and grow with increased use. Finally, the size limitations imposed by a heavy exoskeleton that covers the entire organism are overcome by the internal bony skeleton, which can support a greater size and weight without itself becoming too cumbersome.

46.4 Slow-twitch fibers are found primarily in muscles adapted for endurance rather than strength and power. Myoglobin provides oxygen to the muscles for the aerobic respiration of glucose, thus providing a higher ATP yield than anaerobic respiration. Increased mitochondria also increases the ATP productivity of the muscle by increasing availability of cellular respiration and thus allows for sustained aerobic activity.

46.5 Locomotion via alternation of legs requires a greater degree of nervous system coordination and balance; the animal needs to constantly monitor its center of gravity in order to maintain stability. In addition, a series of leaps will cover more ground per unit time and energy expenditure than will movement by alternation of legs.

INQUIRY AND DATA ANALYSIS QUESTIONS

Page 969 Inquiry question: The idea is very similar; both quadrupeds and insects such as grasshoppers have flexors and extensors that exert antagonistic control over many of their muscles. The main difference is in structure rather than function—in a grasshopper, the muscles are covered by the skeletal elements, whereas in organisms with an endoskeleton, the muscles overlie the bony skeleton.

Page 974 (figure 46.18) Inquiry question: Increasing the frequency of stimulation to a maximum rate will yield the maximum amplitude of a summated muscle contraction. The strength of a contraction increases because little or no relaxation time occurs between successive twitches.

Page 974 (figure 46.19) Inquiry question: A rough estimate of the composition of the calf muscle could be obtained by measuring the amount of time the calf muscle takes to reach maximum tension and compare that amount with the contraction speed of muscles of known fiber composition. Alternatively, a small sample of muscle could be extracted and examined for histological differences in fiber composition.

UNDERSTAND

1. d 2. b 3. d 4. a 5. c 6. a 7. b 8. a

APPLY

1. c 2. b 3. d 4. b 5. b 6. b

SYNTHESIZE

1. Although a hydrostatic skeleton might have advantages in terms of ease of transport and flexibility of movement, the exoskeleton would probably do a better job at protecting the delicate instruments within. This agrees with our observations of these support systems on Earth. Worms and marine invertebrates use hydrostatic skeletons, although arthropods ("hard bodies") use an exoskeleton. Worms are very flexible, but easily crushed.

2. The first 90 seconds of muscle activity are anaerobic in which the cells utilize quick sources of energy (creatine phosphate, lactic acid fermentation) to generate ATP. After that, the respiratory and circulatory systems will catch up and begin delivering more oxygen to the muscles, which allows them to use aerobic respiration, a much more efficient method of generating ATP from glucose.

3. If acetylcholinesterase is inhibited, acetylcholine will continue to stimulate muscles to contract. As a result, muscle twitching, and eventually paralysis, will occur. In March 1995, canisters of Sarin were released into a subway system in Tokyo. Twelve people were killed and hundreds injured.

4. Natural selection is not goal-oriented. In other words, evolution does not anticipate environmental pressures, and the structures that result from evolution by natural selection are those most well suited to the previous generations' environment. Since vertebral wing development occurred several times during evolution, it is probable that the animals in question—birds, pterosaurs, and bats—all encountered different evolutionary pressures during wing evolution.

CHAPTER 47

LEARNING OUTCOME QUESTIONS

47.1 The cells and tissues of a one-way digestive system are specialized such that ingestion, digestion, and elimination can happen concurrently, making food processing and energy utilization more efficient. With a gastrovascular cavity, however, all of the cells are exposed to all aspects of digestion.

47.2 Herbivores and omnivores chew their food, using the flat surfaces of their molars to break it into small components and to introduce saliva, which begins the digestive process. Carnivores tear off their food with their sharp teeth (canines and carnasial premolars) and swallow whole chunks of flesh, providing little time or opportunity for digestion to occur in the mouth.

47.3 A chicken sandwich includes carbohydrate (bread), protein (chicken), and fat (mayonnaise). The breakdown of carbohydrates begins with salivary amylase in the mouth. The breakdown of proteins begins in the stomach with pepsinogen, and the emulsification of fats begins in the duodenum with the introduction of bile. Therefore, the chicken begins its breakdown in the stomach.

47.4 Fats are broken down, by emulsification, into fatty acids and monoglycerides, both of which are nonpolar molecules. Nonpolar molecules are able to enter the epithelial cells by simple diffusion.

47.5 The success of any mutation depends on the selective pressures to which that species is subjected. Thus, if two different species are subjected to similar environmental conditions and undergo the same mutation, then, yes, the mutation should be similarly successful. If two species undergo the same mutation but are under different selective pressures, then the mutation may not be successful in both species.

47.6 The sight, taste, and, yes, smell of food are the triggers the digestive system needs to release digestive enzymes and hormones. The saliva and gastric secretions that are required for proper digestion and are triggered by the sense of smell would be affected by anosmia.

47.7 Any ingested compounds that might be dangerous are metabolized first by the liver, thus reducing the risk to the rest of the body.

47.8 Even with normal leptin levels, individuals with reduced sensitivity in the brain to the signaling molecule may still become obese.

INQUIRY AND DATA ANALYSIS QUESTIONS

Page 984 Inquiry question: Recall the old expression: a jack of all trades is master of none. Omnivores are proficient at eating many different types of food, but they're not specialized for any particular type, and thus are less efficient. However, herbivores, with teeth specialized for cutting and grinding, are more effective at eating plant material, and carnivores, with teeth specialized for slicing and tearing, are more efficient at eating muscle tissue. Thus, if a species' diet is solely one type, it is better off having teeth specialized for that purpose.

Page 985 Inquiry question: If the epiglottis does not properly seal off the larynx and trachea, food can accidentally become lodged in the airway, causing choking.

Page 986 Inquiry question: The digestive system secretes a mucus layer that helps to protect the delicate tissues of the alimentary canal from the acidic secretions of the stomach.

Page 988 Data analysis: One meter equals 3.28 feet. The area of a square is length squared. Consider a square with sides 1 meter long. The area is $1 \times 1 = 1$ square meter (1 m^2). But because a meter is 3.28 feet, the area of this square in feet is $3.28 \times 3.28 = 10.76$. Hence, 1 m^2 = 10.76 feet^2. Therefore the exact area of the small intestine that is 300 m^2 = 3228 feet^2.

Page 992 Data analysis: The amino acid sequences for lysozyme evolved convergently among ruminants and langur monkeys. Thus, if a phylogeny was constructed using solely the lysozyme molecular data, these species—ruminants and langur monkeys—would be adjacent to each other on the phylogenetic tree.

Page 997 Inquiry question: GIP and CCK send inhibitory signals to the hypothalamus when food is ingested. If the hypothalamus sensors did not work properly, leptin levels would increase; increased leptin levels would result in a loss of appetite.

UNDERSTAND

1. b   2. c   3. c   4. b   5. d   6. a   7. c

APPLY

1. d   2. b   3. c   4. c

SYNTHESIZE

1. Birds feed their young with food they acquire from the environment. The adult bird consumes the food but stores it in her crop. When she returns to the nest, she regurgitates the food into the mouths of the fledglings. Mammals on the other hand feed their young with milk that is produced in the mother's mammary glands. Their young feed by latching onto the mother's nipples and sucking the milk. Mammals have no need for a crop in their digestive system because they feed their young a liquid, which does not require the grinding provided by the crop in birds.

2. Leptin is produced by the adipose cells and serves as a signal for feeding behavior. Since low blood leptin levels signal the brain to initiate feeding, a treatment for obesity would need to raise leptin levels, thereby decreasing appetite.

3. The liver plays many important roles in maintaining homeostasis. Two of those roles are detoxifying drugs and chemicals and producing plasma proteins. A drop in plasma protein levels is indicative of liver disease, which in turn could be caused by abuse of alcohol or other drugs.

4. The selective pressures that guide the adaptation of mutated alleles within a population were the same in these two groups of organisms. Both ruminants and langur monkeys eat tough, fibrous plant materials, which are broken down by intestinal bacteria. The ruminants and langurs then absorb the nutrients from the cellulose by digesting those bacteria; this is accomplished through the use of these adapted lysozymes. Normal lysozymes, found in saliva and other secretions, work in a relatively neutral pH environment. These intestinal lysozymes, however, needed to adapt to an acidic environment, which explains the level of convergence.

5. Whereas mammalian dentition is adapted to processing different food types, birds are able to process different types of food by breaking up food particles in the gizzard. Bird diets are comparably diverse to mammalian diets; some birds are carnivores, others are insectivores or frugivores, still others omnivores.

CHAPTER 48

LEARNING OUTCOME QUESTIONS

48.1 Fick's Law states that the rate of diffusion *(R)* can be increased by increasing the surface area of a respiratory surface, increasing the concentration difference between respiratory gases, and decreasing the distance the gases must diffuse: $R = \frac{DA \, \Delta p}{d}$. Continually beating cilia increase the concentration difference (Δp).

48.2 Countercurrent flow systems maximize the oxygenation of the blood by increasing Δp; therefore, maintaining a higher oxygen concentration in the water than in the blood throughout the entire diffusion pathway is required. This process is enhanced by allowing water to flow in only one direction, counter to the blood flow. The lamellae, found within a fish's gill filaments, achieves this.

48.3 Birds have a more efficient respiratory system than other terrestrial vertebrates. Birds that live or fly at high altitudes are subjected to lower oxygen partial pressure and thus have evolved a respiratory system that is capable of maximizing the diffusion and retention of oxygen in the lungs. In addition, efficient oxygen exchange is crucial during flight; flying is more energetically taxing than most forms of locomotion, and without efficient oxygen exchange birds would be unable to fly even short distances safely.

48.4 There are both structural and functional differences in bird and mammalian respiration. Both mammals and birds have lungs, but only birds also have air sacs, which they use to move air in and out of the respiratory system, whereas only mammals have a muscular diaphragm used to move air in and out of the lungs. Mammalian lungs are pliable, and gas exchange occurs within small closed-ended sacs called alveoli in the mammalian lung. In contrast, bird lungs are rigid, and gas exchange occurs in the unidirectional parabronchi. In addition, because air flow in mammals is bidirectional, oxygenated and deoxygenated air are mixed, but the unidirectional air flow in birds increases the purity of the oxygen entering the capillaries. Mammalian respiration is less efficient than avian respiration; birds transfer more oxygen with each breath than do mammals. Finally, mammals only have one respiratory cycle, whereas birds have two complete cycles.

48.5 Most oxygen is transported in the blood bound to hemoglobin (forming oxyhemoglobin), whereas only a small percentage is dissolved in the plasma. Carbon dioxide, on the other hand, is predominantly transported as bicarbonate (having first been combined with water to form carbonic acid and then dissociated into bicarbonate and hydrogen ions). Carbon dioxide is also transported dissolved in the plasma and bound to hemoglobin.

INQUIRY AND DATA ANALYSIS QUESTIONS

Page 1002 Data analysis: The rate is a function of area *(A)* multiplied by differences in pressure (Δp). Thus, increases in either directly increase the rate, so whichever increases to a greater extent would have a greater effect on increasing the rate of diffusion.

Page 1005 Data analysis: Exchange is greatest when the difference in O$_2$ concentration is greatest. So, for the countercurrent exchange example, the difference is about the same throughout, so exchange would be about the same along the length of the capillaries, although the greatest difference occurs at the top, where the difference is 15% (100% – 85%). In concurrent exchange, the greatest difference is at the bottom, where it is 80% (90% – 10%).

Page 1012 Inquiry question: Fick's Law of Diffusion states that for a dissolved gas, the rate of diffusion is directly proportional to the pressure difference between the two sides of the membrane and to the area over which the diffusion occurs.

In emphysema, alveolar walls break down and alveoli increase in size, effectively reducing the surface area for gas exchange. Emphysema thus reduces the diffusion of gases.

Page 1013 Data analysis: The difference in oxygen content between arteries and veins during rest and exercise shows how much oxygen was unloaded to the tissues.

Page 1014 Data analysis: Not really. A healthy individual still has a substantial oxygen reserve in the blood even after intense exercise.

Page 1014 (figure 48.16) Data analysis: Oxyhemoglobin saturation decreases with increasing temperature, and so for any given P_{O_2}, oxygen will unload at higher temperatures, resulting in lower percent saturation and will remain bound at lower temperatures, resulting in higher percent saturation.

Page 1014 Inquiry question: It increases it. At any pH or temperature, the percentage of O_2 saturation falls (e.g., more O_2 is delivered to tissues) as pressure increases.

UNDERSTAND

1. c 2. d 3. d 4. d 5. b 6. a 7. d 8. c

APPLY

1. d 2. c 3. a 4. c 5. a 6. c

SYNTHESIZE

1. Fish gills have not only a large respiratory surface area but also a countercurrent flow system, which maintains an oxygen concentration gradient throughout the entire exchange pathway, thus providing the most efficient system for the oxygenation of blood. Amphibian respiratory systems are not very efficient. They practice positive-pressure breathing. Bird lungs are quite effective, in that they have a large surface area and one-way air flow; mammals, on the other hand, have only a large surface area but no mechanism to ensure the maintenance of a strong concentration gradient.

2. During exercise, cellular respiration increases the amount of carbon dioxide released, thus decreasing the pH of the blood. In addition, the increased cellular respiration increases temperature, as heat is released during glucose metabolism. Decreased pH and increased temperature both facilitate an approximately 20% increase in oxygen unloading in the peripheral tissues.

3. Unicellular prokaryotic organisms, protists, and many invertebrates are small enough that gas exchange can occur over the body surface directly from the environment. Only larger organisms, for which most cells are not in direct contact with the environment with which gases must be exchanged, require specialized structures for gas exchange.

CHAPTER 49

LEARNING OUTCOME QUESTIONS

49.1 Following an injury to a vessel, vasoconstriction is followed by the accumulation of platelets at the site of injury and the subsequent formation of a platelet plug. This triggers a positive feedback enzyme cascade, attracting more platelets, clotting factors, and other chemicals, each of which continually attracts additional clotting molecules until the clot is formed. The enzyme cascade also causes fibrinogen to come out of solution as fibrin, forming a fibrin clot that will eventually replace the platelet plug.

49.2 When the insect heart contracts, it forces hemolymph out through the vessels and into the body cavities. When it relaxes, the resulting negative pressure gradient, combined with muscular contractions in the body, draws the blood back to the heart.

49.3 The primary advantage of having two ventricles rather than one is that oxygenated blood is separated from deoxygenated blood. In fish and amphibians, oxygenated and deoxygenated blood mix, leading to less oxygen being delivered to the body's cells.

49.4 The delay following auricular contraction allows the atrioventricular valves to close prior to ventricular contraction. Without that delay, the contraction of the ventricles would force blood back up through the valves into the atria.

49.5 During systemic gas exchange, only about 90% of the fluid that diffuses out of the capillaries returns to the blood vessels; the rest moves into the lymphatic vessels, which then return the fluid to the circulatory system via the left and right subclavian veins.

49.6 Breathing rate is regulated to ensure ample oxygen is available to the body. However, the heart rate must be regulated to ensure efficient delivery of the available oxygen to the body cells and tissues. For example, during exertion, respiratory rates will increase in order to increase oxygenation and allow for increased aerobic cellular respiration. But simply increasing the oxygen availability is not enough—the heart rate must also increase so that the additional oxygen can be quickly delivered to the muscles undergoing cellular respiration.

INQUIRY DATA ANALYSIS QUESTIONS

Page 1020 Inquiry question: It depends what organisms you are studying. In mammals, the nucleus is ejected during maturation of the erythrocyte, and thus nuclear DNA cannot be obtained. In other vertebrates, this is not true, and thus nuclear DNA is present in mature red blood cells.

Page 1021 Inquiry question: Erythropoietin is a hormone that stimulates the production of erythrocytes from the myeloid stem cells. If more erythrocytes are produced, the oxygen-carrying capacity of the blood is increased. This could potentially enhance athletic performance and is why erythropoietin is banned from use during the Olympics and other sporting events.

Page 1030 Data analysis: The difference between the two is 15-fold (60/4). Because resistance increases to the fourth power in inverse proportion, the difference in resistance would be 15 to the fourth power, or 15^4, which equals 50,625.

Page 1034 Data analysis: Output equals the number of beats per minute multiplied by volume per beat (output = beats × volume). At rest, output is 5 L/min, so to increase it to 25 L/min requires a fivefold increase. In theory, this could be accomplished by increasing the number of heartbeats fivefold, to 360/min, while keeping volume the same, but this is not physically possible. Similarly, one could keep the number of beats constant but increase the volume fivefold, to 350 mL/beat, but this is also impossible. In reality, both heartbeat number and volume must increase by amounts that, when multiplied together, equal 5. So, for example, if heartbeat doubled to 144 beats/min and volume increased by 2.5-fold to 175 mL/beat, then the total increase (beat × volume) would be a fivefold increase.

UNDERSTAND

1. a 2. b 3. c 4. a 5. c 6. d 7. c 8. a

APPLY

1. a 2. b 3. c 4. a

SYNTHESIZE

1. Antidiuretic hormone (ADH) is secreted by the posterior pituitary but its target cells are in the kidney. In response to the presence of ADH, the kidneys increase the amount of water reabsorbed. This water eventually returns to the plasma where it causes an increase in volume and subsequent increase in blood pressure. Another hormone, aldosterone, also causes an increase in blood pressure by causing the kidney to retain Na^+, which sets up a concentration gradient that also pulls water back into the blood.

2. Blood includes plasma (composed primarily of water with dissolved proteins) and formed elements (red blood cells, white blood cells, and platelets). Lymph is composed of interstitial fluid and is found only within the lymphatic vessels and organs. Both blood and lymph are found in organisms with closed circulatory systems. Hemolymph is both the circulating fluid and the interstitial fluid found in organisms with open circulatory systems.

3. Many argue that the evolution of endothermy was less an adaptation to maintain a constant internal temperature and more an adaptation to function in environments low in oxygen. If this is the case, then yes, it makes sense that the evolution of the four-chambered heart, an adaptation that increases the availability of oxygen in the body tissues and which would be highly beneficial in an oxygen-poor environment, and the evolution of endothermy were related. These two adaptations can also be looked at as related in that the more efficient heart would be able to provide the oxygen necessary for the increased metabolic activity that accompanies endothermy.

4. The SA node acts as a natural pacemaker. If it is malfunctioning, one would expect a slow or irregular heartbeat or irregular electrical activity between the atria and the ventricles.

CHAPTER 50

LEARNING OUTCOME QUESTIONS

50.1 Water moves toward regions of higher osmolarity.

50.2 Nitrogenous waste results from the degradation of old proteins and it is a problem because it is toxic in the body.

50.3 They are both involved in water conservation.

50.4 This may have arisen independently in both the mammalian and avian lineages or have been lost from the reptilian lineage.

50.5 This would increase the osmolarity within the tubule system and thus should decrease the reabsorption of water, leading to water loss.

50.6 Blocking aquaporin channels would prevent reabsorption of water from the collecting duct.

INQUIRY AND DATA ANALYSIS QUESTION

Page 1043 Data analysis: An increase of any solute in the blood will reduce the amount of water that is reabsorbed.

UNDERSTAND

1. d 2. a 3. c 4. c 5. d 6. d 7. d

APPLY

1. d 2. c 3. b 4. b 5. c 6. b

SYNTHESIZE

1. a. Antidiuretic hormone (ADH) is produced in the hypothalamus and is secreted by the posterior pituitary. ADH targets the collecting duct of the nephron and stimulates the reabsorption of water from the urine by increasing the permeability of water in the walls of the duct. The primary stimulus for ADH secretion is an increase in the osmolarity of blood.

   b. Aldosterone is produced and secreted by the adrenal cortex in response to a drop in blood Na^+ concentration. Aldosterone stimulates the distal convoluted tubules to reabsorb Na^+, thus decreasing the excretion of Na^+ in the urine. The reabsorption of Na^+ is followed by the reabsorption of both Cl^- and water, and so aldosterone has the net effect of retaining both salt and water. Aldosterone secretion, however, is not stimulated by a decrease in blood osmolarity, but rather by a decrease in blood volume. A group of cells located at the base of the glomerulus, called the juxtaglomerular apparatus, detects drops in blood volume that then stimulates the renin–angiotensin–aldosterone system.

   c. Atrial natriuretic hormone (ANH) is produced and secreted by the right atrium of the heart, in response to an increase in blood volume. The secretion of ANH results in the reduction of aldosterone secretion. With the secretion of ANH, the distal convoluted tubules reduce the amount of Na^+ that is reabsorbed, and likewise reduce the amount of Cl^- and water that is reabsorbed. The final result is a reduction in blood volume.

   John's normal renal blood flow rate would be 21% of cardiac output, or 7.2 L/min × 0.21 = 1.5 L/min. If John's kidneys are not affected by his circulatory condition, his renal blood flow rate should be about 1.5 L/min.

CHAPTER 51

LEARNING OUTCOME QUESTIONS

51.1 No, innate immunity shows some specificity for classes of molecules common to pathogens.

51.2 Hematopoietic stem cells.

51.3 T-cell receptors are rearranged to generate a large number of different receptors with specific binding abilities. Toll-like receptors are not rearranged and recognize specific classes of molecules, not specific molecules.

51.4 Ig receptors are rearranged to generate many different specificities. TLR innate receptors are not rearranged and bind to specific classes of molecules.

51.5 Allergies are a case of the immune system overreacting, whereas autoimmune disorders involve the immune system being compromised.

51.6 Diagnostic kits use monoclonal antibodies because they are developed against a single specific epitope of an antigen. They are also more efficient to produce because they use cells that can be grown in culture and do not require a more complex process of immunizing animals, bleeding them, and then isolating the antibodies from their sera.

51.7 The main difference between polio and influenza is the rate at which the viruses can change. The poliovirus is a RNA virus with a genome that consists of a single RNA. The viral surface proteins do not change rapidly, allowing immunity via a vaccine. Influenza is an RNA virus with a high mutation rate, which means that surface proteins change rapidly. Influenza has a genome that consists of multiple RNAs, which allows recombination of the different viral RNAs during infection with different strains.

INQUIRY AND DATA ANALYSIS QUESTIONS

Page 1059 Inquiry question: The viruses would be liberated into the body where they could infect numerous additional cells.

Page 1063 Inquiry question: The antigenic properties of the two viruses must be similar enough that immunity to cowpox also enables protection against smallpox.

Page 1074 Inquiry question: The common structure and mechanism of formation of B-cell immunoglobulins (Igs) and T-cell receptors (TCRs) suggests a common ancestral form of adaptive immunity gave rise to the two cell lines existing today.

Page 1078 Data analysis: A high level of hCG in a urine sample will block the binding of the antibody to hCG-coated particles, thus preventing any agglutination.

Page 1079 Inquiry question: Influenza frequently alters its surface antigens, making it impossible to produce a vaccine with a long-term effect. Smallpox virus has a considerably more stable structure.

UNDERSTAND

1. b 2. a 3. b 4. c 5. c 6. b 7. c

APPLY

1. d 2. c 3. c 4. b, a, d, c 5. c 6. b 7. a

SYNTHESIZE

1. It would be difficult to advertise this lotion as immune enhancing. The skin serves as a barrier to infection because it is oily and acidic. Applying a lotion that is watery and alkaline will dilute the protective effects of the skin secretions, thereby inhibiting the immune functions. Perhaps it is time to look for another job.

2. The scratch has caused an inflammatory response. Although it is very likely that some pathogens entered her body through the broken skin, the response is actually generated by the injury to her tissue. The redness is a result of the increased dilation of blood vessels caused by the release of histamine. This also increases the temperature of the skin by bringing warm blood closer to the surface. Leakage of fluid from the vessels causes swelling in the area of the injury, which can cause pressure on the pain sensors in the skin. All of these serve to draw defensive cells and molecules to the injury site, thereby helping to defend her against infection.

3. This could be done a number of ways. However, one method would be to show that viral genetic material never appears within the cells of those who claim immunity. Another method would involve testing for the presence of interferon, which is released by cells in response to viral infection.

4. These data imply that innate immunity is a very ancient defense mechanism. The presence of these proteins in cnidarians indicates that they arose soon after multicellularity.

CHAPTER 52

LEARNING OUTCOME QUESTIONS

52.1 Genetic sex determination essentially guarantees equal sex ratios; when sex ratios are not equal, the predominant sex is selected against because those individuals have more competition for mates. Temperature-dependent sex determination can result in skewed sex ratios in which one sex or the other is selected against. Genetic sex determination, on the other hand, can provide much greater stability within the population, and consequently the genetic characteristics that provide that stability are selected for.

52.2 Estrous cycles occur in most mammals, and most mammalian species have relatively complex social organizations and mating behaviors. The cycling of sexual receptivity allows for these complex mating systems. Specifically, in social groups where male infanticide is a danger, synchronized estrous among females may be selected for as it would eliminate the ability of the male to quickly impregnate the group females. Physiologically, estrous cycles result in the maturation of the egg accompanying the hormones that promote sexual receptivity.

52.3 In mating systems where males compete for mates, sperm competition, a form of sexual selection, is very common. In these social groups, multiple males may mate with a given female, and thus those individuals who produced the highest number of sperm would have a reproductive advantage—a higher likelihood of siring the offspring.

52.4 The answer varies depending on the circumstances. In a species that is very *r*-selected, in other words, one that reproduces early in life and often but does not invest much in the form of parental care, multiple offspring per pregnancy would definitely be favored by natural selection. In *K*-selected species where parental care is very high, on the other hand, single births might be favored because the likelihood of offspring survival is greater if the parental resources are not divided among the offspring.

52.5 The birth control pill works by hormonally controlling the ovulation cycle in women. By releasing progesterone continuously the pill prevents ovulation. Ovulation is a cyclical event and under hormonal control, thus it is relatively easy for the process to be controlled artificially. In addition, the female birth control pill only has to halt the release of a single ovum. An analogous male birth control pill, on the other hand, would have to completely cease sperm production (and men produce millions of sperm each day), and such hormonal upheaval in the male could lead to infertility or other intolerable side effects.

INQUIRY AND DATA ANALYSIS QUESTIONS

Page 1085 Inquiry question: The ultimate goal of any organism is to maximize its relative fitness. Small females are able to reproduce but once they become very large they would be better able to maximize their reproductive success by becoming male, especially in groups where only a few males mate with all of the females. Protandry might evolve in species where the supply of mates is limited and there is relatively little space; a male of such a species in close proximity to another male would have higher reproductive success by becoming female and mating with the available male than by waiting for a female (and then having to compete for her with the other male).

Page 1088 Inquiry question: The evolutionary progression from oviparity to viviparity is a complex process; requiring the development of a placenta or comparable structure. Once a complex structure evolves, it is rare for an evolutionary reversal to occur. Perhaps more importantly, viviparity has several advantages over oviparity, especially in cold environments where eggs are vulnerable to mortality due to cold weather (and predation). In aquatic reptiles such as sea snakes, viviparity allows the female to remain at sea and avoid coming ashore, where both she and her eggs would be exposed to predators.

Page 1094 Inquiry question: Under normal circumstances, the testes produce hormones, testosterone and inhibin, which exert negative feedback inhibition on the hormones produced and secreted by the anterior pituitary (luteinizing hormone and follicle-stimulating hormone). Following castration, testosterone and inhibin are no longer produced, and thus the brain will overproduce LH and FSH. For this reason, hormone therapy is usually prescribed following castration.

Page 1095 Data analysis: In the menstrual cycle FSH exceeds the levels of LH for only a short period at the end of one cycle and continuing to the beginning of the next (approx. days 27–28 and 1–2, respectively).

UNDERSTAND

1. c 2. d 3. d 4. d 5. c 6. c 7. a 8. c 9. a

APPLY

1. a 2. b 3. d 4. a

SYNTHESIZE

1. A mutation that makes *SRY* nonfunctional would mean that the embryo would lack the signal to form male structures during development. Therefore, the embryo would have female genitalia at birth.

2. Amphibians and fish that rely on external fertilization also have access to water. Lizards, birds, and mammals have adaptations that allow them to reproduce away from a watery environment. These adaptations include eggs that have protective shells or internal development, or both.

3. FSH and LH are produced by the anterior pituitary in both males and females. In both cases they play roles in the production of sex hormones and gametogenesis. However, FSH stimulates spermatogenesis in males and oogenesis in females, whereas LH promotes the production of testosterone in males and estradiol in females.

4. It could indeed work. The hormone hCG is produced by the zygote to prevent menstruation, which would in turn prevent implantation in the uterine lining. Blocking the hormone receptors would prevent implantation and therefore pregnancy.

5. Parthenogenic species reproduce from gametes that remain diploid. Sperm are haploid, whereas eggs do not complete meiosis (becoming haploid) until

after fertilization. Therefore, only eggs could develop without DNA from an outside source. In addition, only eggs have the cellular structures needed for development. Therefore only females can undergo parthenogenesis.

CHAPTER 53

LEARNING OUTCOME QUESTIONS

53.1 Ca^{2+} ions act as second messengers and bring about changes in protein activity that result in blocking polyspermy and increasing the rate of protein synthesis within the egg.

53.2 In a mammal, the cells at the four-cell stage are still uncommitted, so separating them will still allow for normal development. In frogs, on the other hand, yolk distribution results in displaced cleavage; thus, at the four-cell stage the cells do not each contain a nucleus, which contains the genetic information required for normal development.

53.3 The cellular behaviors necessary for gastrulation differ across organisms; however, some processes are necessary for any gastrulation to occur. Specifically, cells must rearrange and migrate throughout the developing embryo.

53.4 No—neural crest cell fate is determined by its migratory pathway.

53.5 Marginal zone cells in both the ventral and dorsal regions express bone morphogenetic protein 4 (BMP4). The fate of these cells is determined by the number of receptors on the cell membrane to bind to BMP4; greater BMP4 binding will induce a ventral mesodermal fate. The organizer cells, which previously were thought to activate dorsal development, have been found to actually inhibit ventral development by secreting one of many proteins that block the BMP4 receptors on the dorsal cells.

53.6 Most of the differentiation of the embryo, in which the initial structure formation occurs, happens during the first trimester; the second and third trimesters are primarily times of growth and organ maturation, rather than the actual development and differentiation of structures. Thus, teratogens are most potent during this time of rapid organogenesis.

INQUIRY AND DATA ANALYSIS QUESTIONS

Page 1120 Data analysis: Since both mutants cause a loss of pigment cells, and one is a signaling molecule, the other is likely to be the receptor for the signaling molecule. In the mouse system, the signaling molecule is called Steel and the receptor is called c-Kit (an RTK, see chapter 9 for details).

Page 1127 Inquiry question: High levels of estradiol and progesterone in the absence of pregnancy would still affect the body in the same way. High levels of both hormones would inhibit the release of FSH and LH, thereby preventing ovulation. This is how birth control pills work. The pills contain synthetic forms of either both estradiol and progesterone or just progesterone. The high levels of these hormones in the pill trick the body into thinking that it is pregnant and so the body does not ovulate.

UNDERSTAND

1. d 2. b 3. d 4. c 5. d 6. b 7. a

APPLY

1. c 2. b 3. a 4. d 5. b 6. c

SYNTHESIZE

1. By starting with a series of embryos at various stages, you could try removing cells at each stage. Embryos that failed to compensate for the removal (evidenced by missing structures at maturity) would be those that lost cells after they had become committed; that is, when their fate has been determined.

2. Homeoboxes are sequences of conserved genes that play crucial roles in development of both mammals (Fifi) and *Drosophila* (the fruit fly). In fact, we know that they are more similar than dissimilar; research has demonstrated that both groups use the same transcription factors during organogenesis. The major difference between them is in the genes that are transcribed. Homeoboxes in mammals turn on genes that cause the development of mammalian structures, and those in insects would generate insect structures.

3. After fertilization, the zygote produces hCG, which inhibits menstruation and maintains the corpus luteum. At 10 weeks' gestation, the placenta stops releasing hCG, but it continues to release estradiol and progesterone, which maintain the uterine lining and inhibit the pituitary production of FSH and LH. Without FSH and LH, no ovulation and no menstruation occur.

4. Spemann and Mangold removed cells from the dorsal lip of one amphibian embryo and transplanted them to a different location on a second embryo. The transplanted cells caused cells that would normally form skin and belly to instead form somites and the structures associated with the dorsal area. Because of this and because the secondary dorsal structures contained both host and transplanted cells, Spemann and Mangold concluded that the transplanted cells acted as organizers for dorsal development.

CHAPTER 54

LEARNING OUTCOME QUESTIONS

54.1 Just as with morphological characteristics that enhance an individual's fitness, behavioral characteristics can also affect an individual's survivability and reproductive success. Understanding the evolutionary origins of many behaviors allows biologists insights into animal behavior, including that of humans.

54.2 A male songbird injected with testosterone prior to the usual mating season would likely begin singing prior to the usual mating season. However, since female mating behavior is largely controlled by hormones (estrogen) as well, most likely that male will not have increased fitness (and may actually have decreased fitness, if the singing stops before the females are ready to mate, or if the energetic expenditure from singing for two additional weeks is compensated by reduced sperm production).

54.3 The genetic control over pair-bonding in prairie voles has been fairly well established. The fact that males sometimes seek extra-pair copulations indicates that the formation of pair-bonds is under not only genetic control but also behavioral control.

54.4 In species in which males travel farther from the nest (and thus have larger range sizes), there should be significant sex differences in spatial memory. However, in species without sexual differences in range sizes, males and females should not express sex differences in spatial memory. To test the hypothesis you could perform maze tests on males and females of species with sex differences in range size as well as those species without range size differences between the sexes. (NOTE: Such experiments have been performed and do support the hypothesis that there is a significant correlation between range size and spatial memory, so in species with sex differences in range size there are indeed sex differences in spatial memory. See C.M. Jones, V.A. Braithwaite, S.D. Healy SD. The Evolution of Sex Differences in Spatial Ability. *Behav Neurosci* 2003;117(3): 403–411.

54.5 Although there may be a link between IQ and genes in humans, there is most certainly also an environmental component to IQ. The danger of assigning a genetic correlation to IQ lies in the prospect of selective "breeding" and the emergence of "designer babies."

54.6 One experiment that has been implemented in testing counting ability among different primate and bird species is to present the animal with a number and have him match the target number to one of several arrays containing that number of objects. In another experiment, the animal may be asked to select the appropriate number of individual items within an array of items that equals the target number.

54.7 Butterflies and birds have extremely different anatomy and physiology and thus most likely use very different navigation systems. Birds generally migrate bidirectionally; moving south during the cold months and back north during the warmer months in the northern hemisphere. Usually, then, migrations are multigenerational events and it could be argued that younger birds can learn migratory routes from older generations. Butterflies, on the other hand, fly south to breed and die. Their offspring must then fly north having never been there before.

54.8 In addition to chemical reproductive barriers, many species also employ behavioral and morphological reproductive barriers, such that even if a female moth is attracted by the pheromones of a male of another species, the two may be behaviorally or anatomically incompatible.

54.9 The benefits of territorial behavior must outweigh the potential costs, which may include physical danger due to conflict, energy expenditure, and the loss of foraging or mating time. In a flower that is infrequently encountered, the honeycreeper would lose more energy defending the resource than it could gain by utilizing it. On the other hand, there is usually low competitive pressure for highly abundant resources, thus the bird would expend unnecessary energy defending a resource to which its access is not limited.

54.10 The males should exhibit mate choice because they are the sex with the greater parental investment and energy expenditure; thus, like females of most species, they should be the "choosier" sex.

54.11 Generally, reciprocal behaviors are low-cost, whereas behaviors due to kin selection may be low- or high-cost. Protecting infants from a predator is definitely a high-risk/potentially high-cost behavior; thus it would seem that the behavior is due to kin selection. The only way to truly test this hypothesis, however, is to conduct genetic tests or, in a particularly well-studied population, consult a pedigree.

54.12 **#1** Living in a group is associated with both costs and benefits. The primary cost is increased competition for resources, and the primary benefit is protection from predation.

 #2 Altruism toward kin is considered selfish because helping individuals closely related to you will directly affect your inclusive fitness.

 #3 Most armies more closely resemble insect societies than vertebrate societies. Insect societies consist of multitudes of individuals congregated for the purpose of supporting and defending a select few individuals. One could think of these few protected and revered individuals as the society the army is charged with protecting. These insect societies, like human armies, are composed of individuals each "assigned" to a particular task. Most vertebrate societies, on the other hand, are less altruistic and express increased competition and aggression between group members. In short, vertebrate societies are composed of individuals whose primary concern is usually their own fitness, whereas insect societies are composed of individuals whose primary concern is the colony itself.

INQUIRY AND DATA ANALYSIS QUESTIONS

Page 1135 Inquiry question: Selection for learning ability would cease, and thus change from one generation to the next in maze-learning ability; would only result from random genetic drift.

Page 1135 Data analysis: In populations with a symmetrical distribution with a peak in the middle (a "bell curve" also called a "normal" curve is an example), the mean value usually corresponds to the peak of the curve. In somewhat skewed distributions, such as those in the seventh generation, the mean usually lies a little bit away from the peak, toward the side of the long tail. In this case, the mean of the parental population is about 64, and that of the fast rat population in generation 7 is around 39, so the difference would be approximately 25. This is an example of directional selection (see chapter 21).

Page 1136 Inquiry question: Normal *fosB* alleles produce a protein that in turn affects enzymes that affect the brain. Ultimately, these enzymes trigger maternal behavior. In the absence of the enzymes, normal maternal behavior does not occur.

Page 1137 Data analysis: This experiment tests the effect on rodent pair-bonding behavior of injecting them with the neuropeptide vasopressin. In the control (normal) treatment, vasopressin is not injected (sometimes scientists inject saline (= salt water) solutions, which have no physiological effect but control for the effect of giving an injection). In the control treatment (red bars), wild-type mice exhibit the highest level of pair-bonding behavior, and montane voles exhibit the lowest.

Page 1140 Inquiry question: Peter Marler's experiments addressed this question and determined that both instinct and learning are instrumental in song development in birds.

Page 1148 Inquiry question: Many factors affect the behavior of an animal other than its attempts to maximize energy intake. For example, avoiding predation is also important. Thus, it may be that larger prey require more time to subdue and ingest, thus making the crabs more vulnerable to predators. Hence, the crabs may trade off decreased energy gain for decreased vulnerability for predators. Many other similar explanations are possible.

Page 1148 Data analysis: Assuming that it takes no time to subdue or eat the prey, the raccoon can get 20 J/hr eating frogs (one every 30 min) and 10 J/hr eating crickets (5 crickets/hr—one every 12 minutes—multiplied by 2 J/cricket). The raccoon should search in the stream for frogs.

Follow-up Question: In this scenario, it takes 45 min to find and eat a frog, which means that, on average, a raccoon can eat 1 1/3 frogs/hr. Multiplied by 10 J/frog, results in an average of 13.33 J/hr. By contrast, it takes 15 min to find and devour a cricket, so four can be eaten per hour, leading to a rate of 8 J/hr. Frogs are still favored, but less so.

Page 1150 Inquiry question: This question is the subject of much current research. Ideas include the possibility that males with longer tails (and therefore more spots) are in better condition (because males in poor condition couldn't survive the disadvantage imposed by the tail). The advantage to a female mating with a male in better condition might be either that the male is less likely to be parasitized and thus less likely to pass that parasite on to the female, or the male may have better genes, which in turn would be passed on to the offspring. Another possibility is the visual system for some reason is better able to detect males with long tails, and thus long-tailed males are preferred by females simply because the longer tails are more easily detected and responded to.

Page 1150 Data analysis: To get the predicted number of mates, find 155 on the x-axis and then see the corresponding y-axis value where the regression line hits 155 on the x-axis. You can visualize this by drawing a vertical line from 155 on the x-axis, and then drawing a horizontal line from the intersection of the vertical line and the regression line. Where the horizontal line crosses the y-axis is the predicted value, which is approximately 4.

Regression lines are calculated by determining the line that best fits the data. The "best fit" line is the one that minimizes the squared vertical distance of each point from the line. To test this, measure the vertical distance from each point to the regression line, square it, and then add them all together. Then draw a different line and do the same thing. The sum of the squared distances in the new line will be greater.

Note, however, that most points don't fall on the line. That means there is variation in the population, and all of that variation is not accounted for by the regression line. As a result, the regression line can only give a predicted value for a male with a particular number of spots, but in reality, most males will deviate from that line by some unpredictable amount. As a result, you wouldn't expect multiple males with the same number of eyespots to have the same number of mates.

Page 1151 Inquiry question: Yes, the larger the male, the larger the prenuptial gift, which provides energy that the female converts into egg production.

Page 1155 Data analysis: Your aunt is the sister of one of your parents. Siblings share 1/2 of their genes, so your aunt is 1/2 genetically related to your mother or father. You also are 1/2 related to your mother or father. Thus, of the 1/2 of your parent's genes that your aunt has, you are likely to have 1/2 of them. 1/2 of 1/2 = 1/4.

Page 1156 Data analysis: Males get all of their genes from their mother. Because the mother has two copies of each gene, on average, two brothers would be related by 1/2. Because males are haploid, however, their offspring get all of their genes. As a result, cousins that are daughters of brothers would also be related by 1/2 in the genes they get from their father. Because their mothers are unrelated, they would share no genes from their mother, and thus would be related by 1/4. Alternatively, if the cousins were daughters of sisters, the two sisters would share 3/4 of their genes, so the two cousins would share 3/8 of their genes. Because the males were unrelated, the cousins would be 3/16 related.

UNDERSTAND

1. b   2. a   3. a   4. c   5. a   6. c   7. d   8. a   9. b   10. a   11. c   12. d

APPLY

1. Presumably, the model is basic, taking into account only size and energetic value of mussels. However, it may be that larger mussels are in places where shore crabs would be exposed to higher levels of predation or greater physiological stress. Similarly, it could be that the model underestimated time costs or energy returns as a function of mussel size. In the case of large mussels being in a place where shore crabs are exposed to costs not considered by the model, one could test the hypothesis in several ways. First, how are the sizes of mussels distributed in space? If they are completely interspersed that would tend to reject the hypothesis. Alternatively, if the mussels were differentially distributed such that the hypothesis was reasonable, mussels could be experimentally relocated (change their distribution in space) and the diets would be expected to shift to match more closely the situation predicted by the model.

2. The four new pairs may have been living in surrounding habitat that was of lower quality, or they may have been individuals that could not compete for a limited number of suitable territories for breeding. Often, the best territories are won by the most aggressive or largest or otherwise best competitors, meaning that the new territory holders would likely have been less fierce competitors. If new residents were weaker competitors (due to aggression or body size), then the birds not removed would have been able to expand their territories to acquire even more critical resources.

3. The key here is that if the tail feathers are a handicap, then by reducing the handicap in these males should enhance their survival compared with males with naturally shorter tail feathers. The logic is simple. If the male with long tail feathers is superior such that it can survive the negative effect of the long tail feathers, then that superior phenotype should be "exposed" with the removal or reduction of the tail feathers. Various aspects of performance could be measured since it is thought that the tail feathers hinder flying. Can males with shorter tails fly faster? Can males with shorter tails turn better? Ultimately, whether males with shorter tails survive better than males with unmanipulated tails can be measured.

4. Both reciprocity and kin selection explain the evolution of altruistic acts by examining the hidden benefits of the behavior. In both cases, altruism actually *benefits* the individual performing the act in terms of its fitness effects. If it didn't, it would be very hard to explain how such behavior could be maintained because actions that reduce the fitness of an individual should be selected against. Definition of the behavior reflects the apparent paradox of the behavior because it focuses on the cost and not the benefit that also accrues to the actor.

SYNTHESIZE

1. The best experiment for determining whether predatory avoidance of certain coloration patterns would involve rearing a predator without an opportunity to learn avoidance and subsequently presenting the predator with prey with different patterns. If the predator avoids the black and yellow coloration more frequently than expected, the avoidance is most likely innate. If the predator does not express any preference but after injury from a prey with the specific coloration does begin to express a preference, then the avoidance is most likely learned. In this case, the learning is operant conditioning; the predator has learned to associate the coloration with pain and thus subsequently avoids prey with that coloration. To measure the adaptive significance of black and yellow coloration, both poisonous (or stinging) and harmless prey species with the coloration and without the coloration pattern could be presented to predators; if predators avoid both the harmful and the harmless prey, the coloration is evolutionary significant.

2. In many cases the organisms in question are unavailable for or unrealistic to study in a laboratory setting. Model organisms allow behavioral geneticists to overcome this obstacle by determining general patterns and then applying these patterns and findings to other, similar organisms. The primary disadvantage of the model system is, of course, the vast differences that are usually found between groups of taxa; however, when applying general principles, in particular those of genetic behavioral regulation, the benefits of using a model outweigh the costs. Phylogenetic analysis is the best way to determine the scale of applicability when using model organisms.

3. Extra-pair copulations and mating with males that are outside a female's territory are, by and large, more beneficial than costly to the female. By mating with males outside her territory, she reduces the likelihood that a male challenging the owner of her territory would target her offspring; males of many species are infanticidal but would not likely attack infants that could be their own. Historical data have actually shown that in many cases, females are more attracted to infanticidal males if those males win territory prior to their infanticidal behavior.

CHAPTER 55

LEARNING OUTCOME QUESTIONS

55.1 It depends on the type of species in question. Conformers are able to adapt to their environment by adjusting their body temperature and making other physiological adjustments. Over a longer period of time, individuals within a nonconforming species might not adjust to the changing environment, but we would expect the population as a whole to adapt due to natural selection.

55.2 If the populations in question comprised source-sink metapopulations, then the lack of immigration into the sink populations would, most likely, eventually result in the extinction of those populations. The source populations would likely then increase their geographic ranges.

55.3 It depends on the initial sizes of the populations in question; a small population with a high survivorship rate will not necessarily grow faster than a large population with a lower survivorship rate.

55.4 A species with high levels of predation would likely exhibit an earlier age at first reproduction and shorter interbirth intervals in order to maximize its fitness under the selective pressure of the predation. On the other hand, species with few predators have the luxury of waiting until they are more mature before reproducing and can increase the interbirth interval (and thus invest more in each offspring) because their risk of early mortality is decreased.

55.5 Many different factors might affect the carrying capacity of a population. For example, climate changes, even on a relatively small scale, could have large effects on carrying capacity by altering the available water and vegetation, as well as the phenology and distribution of the vegetation. Regardless of the type of change in the environment, however, most populations will move toward carrying capacity; thus, if the carrying capacity is lowered, the population should decrease, and if the carrying capacity is raised, the population should increase.

55.6 A given population can experience both positive and negative density-dependent effects, but not at the same time. Negative density-dependent effects, such as low food availability or high predation pressure, would decrease the population size. On the other hand, positive density-dependent effects, such as is seen with the Allee effect, results in a rapid increase in population size. Since a population cannot both increase and decrease at the same time, the two cannot occur concurrently. However, the selective pressures on a population are on a positive–negative continuum, and the forces shaping population size can not only vary in intensity but can also change direction from negative to positive or positive to negative.

55.7 The two are closely tied together, and both are extremely important if the human population is not to exceed the Earth's carrying capacity. As population growth increases, the human population approaches the planet's carrying capacity; as consumption increases, the carrying capacity is lowered—thus, both trends must be reversed.

INQUIRY AND DATA ANALYSIS QUESTIONS

Page 1164 Inquiry question: Very possibly. How fast a lizard runs is a function of its body temperature. Researchers have shown that lizards in shaded habitats have lower temperatures and thus lower maximal running speeds. In such circumstances, lizards often adopt alternative escape tactics that rely less on rapidly running away from potential predators.

Page 1164 Data analysis: Yes. A large value for the slope (at the extreme, 1.0) indicates that as air temperature increases, body temperature also increases. This indicates that the lizard is conforming to environmental conditions; as the air gets hotter (or colder), so does the lizard. In contrast, a low slope (at the extreme, 0.0) indicates that the lizard's body temperature is not affected by air temperature. This could result if the lizard is extremely effective at regulating its body temperature by moving into and out of the shade.

Page 1169 Inquiry question: Because of their shorter generation times, smaller species tend to reproduce more quickly, and thus would be able to respond more quickly to increased resources in the environment.

Page 1169 Data analysis: In general terms, you could make a reasonable prediction: the bigger the animal, the longer the life span. But it's important to realize that a lot of variation still exists, independent of body size. Notice that the axes of this graph are not arithmetic; each interval covers a larger span than the one before it (e.g., the time in the intervals jumps from one day to one week to one month to one year). If you look carefully at the data, you will see that some species are very similar in body size, but differ greatly in life span. Compare, for example, the mouse and the newt, which are about the same size, but the mouse lives for months and the newt for years.

Page 1170 Data analysis: No. The age classes that produce the most seeds are the two oldest, but so few individuals survive to that age that they make a very minor contribution to the overall reproduction of the population. Instead, you might focus on the Age 2 cohort, as their combination of survivors multiplied by seeds per survivor made the greatest contribution to reproduction. One circumstance in which your answer might be different is if the oldest individuals produced a huge number of seeds per individual. In that case, even though there would only be a few old individuals, they still might make the most important contribution to the population. Such a phenomenon occurs in some fish and other organisms, in which the oldest individuals are also the largest, and the number of eggs produced increases exponentially with body size.

Page 1170 Inquiry question: Based on the survivorship curve of meadow grass, the older the plant, the less likely it is to survive. It would be best to choose a plant that is very young to ensure the longest survival as a house plant. A survivorship curve that is shaped like a type I curve, in which most individuals survive to an old age and then die would also lead you to select a younger plant. A type III survivorship curve, in which only a few individuals manage to survive to an older age, would suggest the selection of a middle-aged plant that had survived the early stages of life since it would also be more likely to survive to old age.

Page 1171 Data analysis: The effect seems to be about equal. Adding two eggs reduces clutch size the following year approximately 0.8; taking away two eggs increases clutch size by almost exactly the same amount! Note that the one outlying point in the figure is what happens when one egg is added. Most likely, this is a random fluctuation, the sort of noise that one encounters in any study of natural populations. Perhaps, for example, just by chance those nests that had an egg added were situated in trees that were especially near food sources, so that the effect of adding an egg was not as great as it might have been otherwise. This sort of natural variation can complicate research on natural populations.

Page 1172 Data analysis: Many factors could affect the amount of energy required, but one obvious one is the total amount of offspring mass produced; two

chicks 3/4 the size of one larger chick probably require more food than the singleton. In this example, you can see that although the average nestling size decreases with increasing clutch size, the amount of the increase is relatively slight. Each nestling in the clutch of 13 still weights about 90% of the weight of the singleton. Hence, parents raising 13 such birds must have put in a lot more effort than the parents of the lone chick in the smallest clutch.

Page 1172 Inquiry question: It depends on the situation. If only large individuals are likely to reproduce (as is the case in some territorial species, in which only large males can hold a territory), then a few large offspring would be favored; alternatively, if body size does not affect survival or reproduction, then producing as many offspring as possible would maximize the representation of an individual's genes in subsequent generations. In many cases, intermediate values are favored by natural selection.

Page 1173 Data analysis: The first population would double in population each generation (2 adults producing 4 offspring), whereas the second population would increase by 2.5 each generation. After one generation, the second species would be 25% greater in population size (2.5/2). After two generations, the second species would have a population of 12.5 (don't ask what half a mouse looks like) and the first species, 8, a difference of 1.56. After 10 generations, the second species would have a population of 19,073, the first species, 1024, a difference of 1863%! In exponential growth, small differences in rate, compounded yearly, can add up to major differences in total numbers.

Page 1174 Inquiry question: Because when the population is below carrying capacity, the population increases in size. As it approaches the carrying capacity, growth rate slows down either from increased death rates, or decreased birth rates, or both, becoming zero as the population hits the carrying capacity. Similarly, populations well above the carrying capacity will experience large decreases in growth rate, resulting either from low birth rates or high death rates, that also approach zero as the population hits the carrying capacity.

Page 1175 (figure 55.19) Inquiry question: There are many possible reasons. Perhaps resources become limited, so that females are not able to produce as many offspring. Another possibility is that space is limited so that, at higher populations, individuals spend more time in interactions with other individuals and squander energy that otherwise could be invested in producing and raising more young.

Page 1175 (figure 55.20) Inquiry question: The answer depends on whether food is the factor regulating population size. If it is, then the number of young produced at a given population size would increase and the juvenile mortality rate would decrease. However, if other factors, such as the availability of water or predators, regulated population size, then food supplementation might have no effect.

Page 1177 Inquiry question: If hare population levels were kept high, then we would expect lynx populations to stay high as well because lynx populations respond to food availability. If lynx populations were maintained at a high level, we would expect hare populations to remain low because increased reproduction of hares would lead to increased food for the lynxes.

Page 1178 Inquiry question: If human populations are regulated by density-dependent factors, then as the population approaches the carrying capacity, either birth rates will decrease or death rates will increase, or both. If populations are regulated by density-independent factors, and if environmental conditions change, then either both rates will decline, death rates will increase, or both.

Page 1179 Inquiry question: The answer depends on whether age-specific birth and death rates stay unchanged. If they do, then the Swedish distribution would remain about the same. By contrast, because birth rates are far outstripping death rates, the Kenyan distribution will become increasingly unbalanced as the bulge of young individuals enter their reproductive years and start producing even more offspring.

Page 1181 Inquiry question: Both are important causes, and the relative importance of the two depends on which resource we are discussing. One thing is clear: The world cannot support its current population size if everyone lived at the level of resource consumption of people in the United States.

UNDERSTAND

1. b 2. c 3. a 4. b 5. d 6. b 7. c

APPLY

1. d 2. c 3. b 4. c

SYNTHESIZE

1. The genetic makeup of isolated populations will change over time based on the basic mechanisms of evolutionary change; that is, natural selection,

mutation, assortative mating, and drift. These same processes affect the genetic makeup of populations in a metapopulation, but the outcomes are likely to be much more complicated. For example, if immigration between a source and a sink population is very high, then local selection in a sink population may be swamped by the regular flow of individuals carrying alleles of lower fitness from a source population where natural selection may not be acting against those alleles; divergence might be slowed or even stopped under some circumstances. On the other hand, if sinks go through repeated population declines such that they often are made up of a very small number of individuals, then they may lose considerable genetic diversity due to drift. If immigration from source populations is greater than zero but not large, these small populations might begin to diverge substantially from other populations in the metapopulation due to drift. The difference is that in the metapopulation, such populations might actually be able to persist and diverge, rather than just going extinct due to small numbers of individuals and no ability to be rescued by neighboring sources.

2. The probability that an animal lives to the next year should decline with age (note that in figure 55.11, all the curves decrease with age), so the cost of reproduction for an old animal would, all else being equal, be lower than for a young animal. The reason is that the cost of reproduction is measured by changes in fitness. Imagine a very old animal that has almost no chance in surviving to another reproductive event; it should spend all its effort on a current reproductive effort since its future success is likely to be zero anyway.

3. If offspring size does not affect offspring quality, then it is in the parent's interest to produce absolutely as many small offspring as possible. In doing so, it would be maximizing its fitness by increasing the number of related individuals in the next generation. This would shift the curve to the right side of the x-axis with larger clutch sizes.

4. By increasing the mean generation time (increasing the age at which an individual can begin reproducing; age at first reproduction), keeping all else equal, one would expect that the population growth rate would be reduced. That comes simply from the fact of reducing the number of individuals that are producing offspring in the adult age classes; lower population birth rates would lead to a reduced population growth rate. As to which would have a larger influence, that is hard to say. If the change in generation time (increased age at first reproduction) had an overall larger effect on the total number of offspring an individual female had than a reduced fecundity at any age, then population growth rate would probably be more sensitive to the change in generation time. Under different scenarios, the comparison of these two effects could become more complicated, however. Suffice it to say that population growth control can come from more than one source: fecundity and age at first reproduction.

Chapter 56

LEARNING OUTCOME QUESTIONS

56.1 The answer depends on the habitat of the community in question. Some habitats are more hospitable to animals, and others to plants. The abundance of plants and animals in most habitats is also closely tied; thus the variation in abundance of one would affect the variation in abundance of the other.

56.2 It depends on whether we are talking about fundamental niche or realized niche. Two species can certainly have identical fundamental niches and coexist indefinitely, because they could develop different realized niches within the fundamental niche. In order for two species with identical realized niches to coexist indefinitely, the resources within the niche must not be limited.

56.3 This is an example of Batesian mimicry, in which a nonpoisonous species evolves coloration similar to that of a poisonous species.

56.4 In an ecosystem with limited resources and multiple prey species, one prey species could outcompete another to extinction in the absence of a predator. In the presence of the predator, however, the prey species that would have otherwise been driven to extinction by competitive exclusion is able to persist in the community. The predators that lower the likelihood of competitive exclusion are known as keystone predators.

56.5 Selective harvesting of individual trees would be preferable from a community point of view. According to the intermediate disturbance hypothesis, moderate degrees of disturbance, as occur in selective harvesting, increase species richness and biodiversity more than severe disturbances, such as from clear-cutting.

INQUIRY AND DATA ANALYSIS QUESTIONS

Page 1187 (figure 56.2) Inquiry question: The different soil types require very different adaptations, and thus different species are adapted to each soil type.

Page 1187 Data analysis: The ecotone, the area that separates the normal soil from the serpentine soil, is approximately 7–8 m, so the normal and serpentine soils are approximately 7–8 m apart.

Page 1187 (figure 56.3) Inquiry question: The sharp transition between the communities occurs because two different habitats are in close contact with each other.

Page 1189 Inquiry question: Yes. Both species reach higher population densities when they are by themselves than when they are in the presence of each other. The most likely explanation—although there are others—is that they compete for resources, limiting the carrying capacity each species experiences in the presence of the others.

Page 1191 (figure 56.7) Inquiry question: Presumably the resource distribution is the same on the two islands, thus favoring the same intermediate beak size when there is only one species on an island

Page 1191 (figure 56.8) Inquiry question: The kangaroo rats competed with all the other rodent species for resources, keeping the size of other rodent populations smaller. In the absence of competition when the kangaroo rats were removed, more resources were available, which allowed the other rodent populations to increase in size.

Page 1192 Inquiry question: This could be accomplished in a variety of ways. One option would be to provide refuges to give some *Paramecium* a way of escaping the predators. Another option would be to include predators of the *Didinium*, which would limit their populations (see chapter 57).

Page 1201 Data analysis: When rodents are removed, more seeds are available to the ants, so the number of ant colonies initially increases. However, through time, the greater number of large seeds leads to an increase in plants that produce large seeds. The increase in these plants leads to a decrease in the number of plants that produce small seeds, which are more useful to ants. As the number of small seeds declines, the number of ant colonies declines.

Page 1201 Inquiry question: By removing the kangaroo rats from the experimental enclosures and measuring the effects on both plants and ants. At first, the number of small seeds available to ants increases due to the absence of rodents. However, over time, plants that produce large seeds outcompete plants that produce small seeds, and thus fewer small seeds are produced and available to ants; hence, ant populations decline.

UNDERSTAND

1. b   2. a   3. d   4. a   5. b   6. d   7. c   8. c

APPLY

1. d   2. b   3. d   4. d   5. d

SYNTHESIZE

1. Experiments are useful means to test hypotheses about ecological limitations, but they are generally limited to rapidly reproducing species that occur in relatively small areas. Alternative means of studying species' interactions include detailed studies of the mechanisms by which species might interact; sometimes, for long-lived species, instead of monitoring changes in population size, which may take a very long time, other indices can be measured, such as growth or reproductive rate. Another means of assessing interspecific interactions is to study one species in different areas, in only some of which a second species occurs. Such studies must be interpreted cautiously, however, because there may be many important differences between the areas in addition to the difference in the presence or absence of the second species.

2. Adding differentially preferred prey species might have the same effect as putting in a refuge for prey in the single-species system. One way to think about it is that if a highly preferred species becomes rare due to removal by the predator, then a predator might switch to a less desirable species, even if it doesn't taste as good or is harder to catch, simply because it is still provides a better return than chasing after a very rare preferred species. Although the predator has switched, there might be enough time for the preferred species to rebound. All of these dynamics depend on the time it takes a predator to reduce the population size of its prey relative to the time it takes for those prey populations to rebound once the predator pressure is removed.

3. Although the mechanism might be known in this system, hidden interactions might affect interpretations in many ways because ecological systems are complex. For example, what if some other activity of the rodents besides their reduction of large seeds leading to an increase in the number of small seeds was responsible for the positive effect of rodents on ants? One way to test the

specific mechanism would be to increase the abundance of small seeds experimentally independent of any manipulation of rodents. Under the current hypothesis, an increase in ant population size would be expected and should be sustained, unlike the initial increase followed by a decrease seen when rodents are removed.

4. By itself, the pattern shown in figure 56.7 suggests character displacement, but alternative hypotheses are possible. For example, what if the distribution of seeds available on the two islands where the species are found alone is different from that seen where they are found in sympatry? If there were no large and small seeds seen on Los Hermanos or Daphne, just medium-sized ones, then it would be hard to conclude that the bill size on San Cristóbal has diverged relative to that on the other islands just due to competition. This is a general criticism of inferring the process of character displacement with just comparing the size distributions in allopatry and sympatry. In this case, however, the Galápagos system has been very well studied. It has been established that the size distribution of seeds available is not measurably different. Furthermore, natural selection–induced changes seen in the bill size of birds on a single island, in response to drought-induced changes in seed size lend further support to the role of competition in establishing and maintaining these patterns.

5. It is possible, because the definition of an ecosystem depends on scale. In some ecosystems, there may be other, smaller ecosystems operating within it. For example, within a rainforest ecosystem, there are small aquatic ecosystems, ecosystems within the soil, ecosystems on an individual tree. Research seems to indicate that most species behave individualistically, but in some instances groups of species do depend on one another and do function holistically. We would expect this kind of dual-community structure especially in areas of overlap between distinct ecosystems, where ecotones exist.

CHAPTER 57

LEARNING OUTCOME QUESTIONS

57.1   Yes, fertilization with natural materials such as manure is less disruptive to the ecosystem than is chemical fertilization. Many chemical fertilizers, for example, contain higher levels of phosphates than does manure, and thus chemical fertilization has disrupted the natural global phosphorus cycle.

57.2   Both matter and energy flow through ecosystems by changing form, but neither can be created or destroyed. Both matter and energy also flow through the trophic levels within an ecosystem. The flow of matter such as carbon atoms is more complex and multileveled than is energy flow, largely because it is truly a cycle. The atoms in the carbon cycle truly cycle through the ecosystem, with no clear beginning or end. The carbon is changed during the process of cycling from a solid to a gaseous state and back again. On the other hand, energy flow is unidirectional. The ultimate source of the energy in an ecosystem is the Sun. The solar energy is captured by the primary producers at the first trophic level and is changed in form from solar to chemical energy. The chemical energy is transferred from one trophic level to another, until only heat, low-quality energy, remains.

57.3   Yes, there are certainly situations in ecosystems in which the top predators in one trophic chain affect the lower trophic levels, and within the same ecosystem the primary producers affect the higher trophic levels within another trophic chain.

57.4   It depends on whether the amount of sunlight captured by the primary producers was affected. Currently, only approximately 1% of the solar energy in Earth's atmosphere is captured by primary producers for photosynthesis. If less sunlight reached Earth's surface, but a correlating increase in energy capture accompanied the decrease in sunlight, then the primary productivity should not be affected.

57.5   The equilibrium model of island biogeography describes the relationship between species richness and not only island size but also distance from the mainland. A small island closer to the mainland would be expected to have more species than would a larger island that is farther from the mainland.

INQUIRY AND DATA ANALYSIS QUESTIONS

Page 1213 Data analysis: The nitrogen concentration in the runoff from the undisturbed area was between 1 and 2 mg/L, whereas the nitrogen concentration in the runoff in the deforested area varied between about 35 and 80 mg/L. This was at least a 17-fold increase (from 2 to 35) and even more if you consider the maximal values after deforestation. Note that the figure doesn't seem to reflect such a large change, but notice the break in the y-axis from 4 to 40 mg/L. This reflects a change in the scale of the y-axis and is sometimes done in scientific figures to save space when two sets of data vary by a large amount. It is understood that the data within that area continued the progression trend shown.

Page 1217 Data analysis: No. The two highest habitats for world NPP are habitats that differ greatly in NPP per unit area (tropical rainforest, high; open ocean, low). Overall, you can see that the habitats are arranged by NPP per unit area, with highest at the top, but when you look at world NPP, there is no general trend from top to bottom.

Page 1218 Inquiry question: At each link in the food chain, only a small fraction of the energy at one level is converted into mass of organisms at the next level. Much energy is dissipated as heat or excreted.

Page 1219 Inquiry question: In the inverted pyramid, the primary producers reproduce quickly and are eaten quickly, so that at any given time, a small population of primary producers exist relative to the heterotroph population.

Page 1220 (figure 57.14) Inquiry question: Because the trout eat the invertebrates, which graze the algae. With fewer grazers, there is more algae.

Page 1220 (figure 57.15) Inquiry question: The food chain has four levels in this experiment and only three in the previous one. The snakes might reduce the number of fish, which would allow an increase in damselflies, which would reduce the number of chironomids and increase the algae. In other words, lower levels of the food chain would be identical for the "snake and fish" and "no fish and no snake" treatments. Both would differ from the enclosures with only fish.

Page 1222 (figure 57.17) Inquiry question: Herbivores consume much of the algal biomass even as primary productivity increases. Increases in primary productivity can lead to increased herbivore populations. The additional herbivores crop the biomass of the algae even while primary productivity increases.

Page 1222 Data analysis: The angle of the line is called the slope. It indicates how the two variables are positively related. A large slope (greater angle) indicates that as the x-variable increases, so does the y-variable, as in the top and bottom diagrams. A low angle (as in the middle diagram) indicates no relationship: as the x-variable increases, the y-variable changes little. Of course, a negative slope, not indicated here, would indicate a negative relationship, as x increases, y decreases.

Page 1222 (figure 57.18) Inquiry question: Secondary carnivores would keep the primary carnivore biomass at a relatively constant, low level, which would allow herbivore biomass to increase with increasing light level, which would keep primary producer biomass at a low and constant level. In other words, the increased productivity at higher light levels would flow up the food chain. This situation is an extension of figure 57.17 to the addition of a fourth food chain level.

Page 1223 Data analysis: As figure 57.19b illustrates, there is a general declining relationship between number of species in a plot and number of invading species (what scientists called a "statistically significant" relationship). Nonetheless, as the figure illustrates, there is quite a lot of scatter in the data. For example, when there are 24 species in a plot, the number of invaders in different plots ranged from 1 to a very large number. So, in answer to the question, there is an overall relationship, but the ability to make an accurate prediction for any given plot is relatively low because there is so much variation. One would be correct to expect that in general, plots with more species would have invaders, but it is very possible that if one randomly chose one plot with many species and one with few, the opposite outcome might occur.

Page 1224 Inquiry question: (a) Perhaps because an intermediate number of predators is enough to keep numbers of superior competitors down. (b) Perhaps because more habitats are available and thus more different ways of surviving in the environment. (c) Hard to say. Possibly more-stable environments permit greater specialization, thus permitting coexistence of more species.

UNDERSTAND

1. d   2. d   3. b   4. d   5. a   6. a   7. b   8. a   9. a   10. c

APPLY

1. a   2. d   3. d

SYNTHESIZE

1. Because the length of food chains appears to be ultimately limited by the amount of energy entering a system, and the characteristic loss of usable energy (about 90%) as energy is transferred to each higher level, it would be reasonable to expect that the ectotherm-dominated food chains would be longer than the endotherm-dominated chains. In fact, there is some indirect evidence for this from real food chains, and it is also predicted by some advanced ecological models. However, it is difficult to determine whether, in reality, this is the case because all of the complex factors that determine food chain length and structure. Moreover, many practical difficulties are associated with measuring actual food chain length in natural systems.

2. It is critical to distinguish, as this chapter points out, between energy and mass transfer in trophic dynamics of ecosystems. The standing biomass of phytoplankton is not necessarily a reliable measure of the energy contained in the trophic level. If phytoplankton are eaten as quickly as they are produced, they may contribute a tremendous amount of energy, which can never be directly measured by a static biomass sample. The standing crop, therefore, is an incomplete measure of the productivity of the trophic level.

3. As figure 57.17 suggests, trophic structure and dynamics are interrelated and are primary determinants of ecosystem characteristics and behavior. For example, if a particularly abundant herbivore is threatened, energy that is abundant at the level of primary productivity in an ecosystem may be relatively unavailable to higher trophic levels (e.g., carnivores). That is, the herbivores are an important link in transducing energy through an ecosystem. Cascading effects, whether they are driven from the bottom up or from the top down are a characteristic of energy transfer in ecosystems, and that translates into the reality that effects on any particular species are unlikely to be limited to that species itself.

4. There are many ways to answer this question, but the obvious place to start is to think about the many ways plant structural diversity potentially affects animals that are not eating the plants directly. For example, plants may provide shelter, refuges, food for prey, substrate for nesting, among other things. Therefore, increasing complexity might increase the ability of lizards to partition the habitat in more ways, allow more species to escape their predators or seek refuge from harsh physical factors (e.g., cold or hot temperatures), provide a greater substrate for potential prey in terms of food resources, for instance. If we want to know the exact mechanisms for the relationship, we would need to conduct experiments to test specific hypotheses. For example, if we hypothesize that some species require greater structural complexity in order to persist in a particular habitat, we could modify the habitat (reduce plant structure) and test whether species originally present were reduced in numbers or became unable to persist.

CHAPTER 58

LEARNING OUTCOME QUESTIONS

58.1 If the Earth rotated in the opposite direction, the Coriolis effect would be reversed. In other words, winds descending between 30° north or 30° south and the equator would still be moving more slowly than the underlying surface so it would be deflected; however, they would be deflected to the left in the northern hemisphere and to the right in the southern hemisphere. The pattern would be reversed between 30° and 60° because the winds would be moving more rapidly than the underlying surface and would thus be deflected again in the opposite directions from normal—to the left in the northern hemisphere and to the right in the southern hemisphere. All of this would result in Trade Winds that blew from west to east and "Westerlies" that were actually "Easterlies," blowing east to west.

58.2 As with elevation, latitude is a primary determinant of climate and precipitation, which together largely determine the vegetational structure of a particular area, which in turn defines biomes.

58.3 The spring and fall turnovers that occur in freshwater lakes found in temperate climates result in the oxygen-poor water near the bottom of the lake getting remixed with the oxygen-rich water near the top of the lake, essentially eliminating, at least temporarily, the thermocline layer. In the tropics, there is less temperature fluctuation; thus the thermocline layer is more permanent and the oxygen depletion (and resulting paucity of animal life) is sustained.

58.4 Regions affected by the ENSO, or El Niño Southern Oscillation events, experience cyclical warming events in the waters around the coastline. The warmed water lowers the primary productivity, which stresses and subsequently decreases the populations of fish, seabirds, and sea mammals.

58.5 CFCs, or chlorofluorocarbons, are an example of point-source pollution. CFCs and other types of point-source pollutants are, in general, easier to combat because their sources are more easily identified and thus the pollutants more easily eliminated.

58.6 Global climate change and ozone depletion may be interconnected. However, although climate change and ozone depletion are both global environmental concerns due to the impact each has on human health, the environment, economics, and politics, there are some different approaches to combating and understanding each dilemma. Ozone depletion results in an increase in the ultraviolet radiation reaching the Earth's surface. Global climate change, on the other hand, results in long-term changes in sea level, ice flow, and storm activity.

INQUIRY AND DATA ANALYSIS QUESTIONS

Page 1231 Data analysis: Seasonal variation is positively related to the distance from the equator because the farther north (or south), the stronger the Sun's rays are in the winter and the weaker they are in the summer. The effect is much stronger in the northern hemisphere for complicated reasons related to the differing amounts of landmass in the two hemispheres and other factors.

Page 1232 Inquiry question: Because of the tilt of the Earth's axis and the spherical shape of the planet, the light (and heat) from the Sun hits the equator and nearby latitudes more directly than it does at the poles.

Page 1236 Inquiry question: Increased precipitation and temperature allows for the sustainability of a larger variety and biomass of vegetation, and primary productivity is a measure of the rate at which plants convert solar energy into chemical energy.

Page 1236 Data analysis: Figure 58.8 indicates that biomes with approximately 125 cm of precipitation/year vary tremendously in mean annual temperature, from hot savannas to cold taigas. Figure 58.9b indicates that productivity is a function of temperature. Hence the variation in figure 58.9a results from the different temperatures of ecoystems with intermediate amounts of precipitation.

UNDERSTAND

1. d   2. b   3. a   4. c   5. c   6. c   7. a   8. c

APPLY

1. d   2. b   3. c   4. b

SYNTHESIZE

1. The Earth is tilted on its axis such that regions away from the equator receive less incident solar radiation per unit surface area (because the angle of incidence is oblique). The northern and southern hemispheres alternate between angling toward versus away from the Sun on the Earth's annual orbit. These two facts mean that the annual mean temperature declines as you move away from the equator, and that variation in the mean temperatures of the northern and southern hemispheres is complementary to each other; when one is hot, the other is cold.

2. Energy absorbed by the Earth is maximized at the equator because of the angle of incidence. Because there are large expanses of ocean at the equator, warmed air picks up moisture and rises. As it rises, equatorial air, now saturated with moisture, cools and releases rain, the air falling back to Earth's surface displaced north and south to approximately 30°. The air, warming as it descends, absorbs moisture from the land and vegetation below, resulting in desiccation in the latitudes around 30°.

3. Even though global climate changes have occurred in the past, conservation biologists are concerned about the current warming trend for two reasons. First, the warming rate is rapid, thus the selective pressures on the most vulnerable organisms may be too strong for the species to adapt. Second, the natural areas that covered most of the globe during past climatic changes are now in much more limited, restricted areas, thus greatly impeding the ability of organisms to migrate to more suitable habitats.

CHAPTER 59

LEARNING OUTCOME QUESTIONS

59.1 Unfortunately, most of the Earth's biodiversity hotspots are also areas of the greatest human population growth; human population growth is accompanied by increased resource utilization and exploitation.

59.2 I would tell the shrimp farmers that if they were to shut down the shrimp farm and remediate the natural mangrove swamp on which their property sits, other, more economically lucrative businesses could be developed, such as timber, charcoal production, and offshore fishing.

59.3 Absolutely. The hope of conservation biologists is that even if a species is endangered to the brink of extinction due to habitat degradation, the habitat may someday be restored. The endangered species can be bred in captivity (which also allows for the maintenance of genetic diversity within the species) and either reintroduced to a restored habitat or even introduced to another suitable habitat.

59.4 It depends on the reason for the degradation of the habitat in the first place, but yes, in some cases, habitat restoration can approach a pristine state. For example, the Nashau River in New England was heavily polluted, but habitat restoration efforts returned it to a relatively pristine state. However, because habitat degradation affects so many species within the ecosystem, and the depth and complexity of the trophic relationships within the ecosystem are difficult if not impossible to fully understand, restoration is rarely if ever truly pristine.

INQUIRY AND DATA ANALYSIS QUESTIONS

Page 1260 Inquiry question: Many factors affect human population trends, including resource availability, governmental support for settlement in new areas or for protecting natural areas, and the extent to which governments attempt to manage population growth.

Page 1260 Data analysis: Some hotspots that don't have particularly high population densities today, but are growing quickly are the Chocó, tropical Andes, Madagascar, and Indian Ocean Islands. The Brazilian Cerrado has a very high population growth rate, but because densities there are currently very low, this area is of less immediate concern.

Page 1262 Data analysis: The mangroves provide many economic services. For example, without them, fisheries become less productive and storm damage increases. However, because the people who benefit from these services do not own the mangroves, governmental action is needed to ensure that the value of what economists call "common goods" is protected.

Page 1266 Data analysis: Examination of the figure indicates that for every 90% reduction in area, extinction rate approximately doubles. For example, at an area of 100 (10^2) km^2, extinction rate is approximately 0.08, but at 10 km^2, it increases to approximately 0.15, and at 1 km^2, it drops to about 0.23.

Page 1268 Data analysis: Reproductive success would decline through time, perhaps with the same slope, but negative instead of positive, as shown in the figure.

Page 1269 Inquiry question: As discussed in this chapter, populations that are small face many problems that can reinforce one another and eventually cause extinction.

Pate 1269 Data analysis: Yes. Additional species were hunted when the number of the "catch" in the number of whales already being hunted started to decline. Thus, the number of sperm and sei whales increases markedly at the same time that the number of fin whales decreases (and note that the number of fin whales caught soared when blue whales declined). Then, when sei and sperm whale numbers begin to decline, minke whaling accelerated.

Page 1274 Inquiry question: As we discussed in chapter 21, allele frequencies change randomly in a process called genetic drift. The smaller the population size, the greater these random fluctuations will be. Thus, small populations are particularly prone to one allele being lost from a population due to these random changes.

UNDERSTAND

1. a   2. c   3. d   4. d   5. b   6. c

APPLY

1. d   2. d   3. a   4. d

SYNTHESIZE

1. Although it is true that extinction is a natural part of the existence of a species, several pieces of evidence suggest that current rates of extinction are considerably elevated over the natural background level and the disappearance is associated with human activities (which many of the most pronounced extinction events in the history of the Earth were not). It is important to appreciate the length of time over which the estimate of 99% is made. The history of life on Earth extends back billions of years. Certainly, clear patterns of the emergence and extinction of species in the fossil record extend back many hundreds of millions of years. Since the average time of species' existence is short relative to the great expanse of time over which we can estimate the percentage of species that have disappeared, the perception might be that extinction rates have always been high, when in fact the high number is driven by the great expanse of time of measurement. We have very good evidence that modern extinction rates (over human history) are considerably elevated above background levels. Furthermore, the circumstances of the extinctions may be very different because they are also associated with habitat and resource removal; thus potentially limiting the natural processes that replace extinct species.

2. The problem is not unique and not new. It represents a classic conflict that is the basic source of societal laws and regulations, especially in the management of resources. For example, whether or not to place air pollution scrubbers on the smoke stacks of coal-fired power plants is precisely the same issue. In this case, it is not ecosystem conversion, per se, but the fact that the businesses that run the power plants benefit from their operation, but the public "owns" and relies on the atmosphere is a conflict between public and private interests. Some of the ways to navigate the dilemma is for society to create regulations to protect the public interest. The problem is difficult and clearly does not depend solely on economic valuation of the costs and benefits because there can be considerable debate about those estimates. One only has to look at the global climate change problem to suggest how hard it will be to make progress in an expedient manner.

3. This is not a trivial undertaking, which is why, since the first concerns were raised in the late 1980s, it has taken nearly 15 years to collect evidence showing a decline is likely. Although progress has been made on identifying potential causes, much work remains to be done. Many amphibians are secretive, relatively long-lived, and subject to extreme population fluctuations. Given those facts about their biology, documenting population fluctuations (conducting censuses of the number of individuals in populations) for long periods of time is the only way to ultimately establish the likely fate of populations, and that process is time-consuming and costly.

4. Within an ecosystem, every species is dependent on and depended on by any number of other species. Even the smallest organisms, bacteria, are often specific about the species they feed on, live within, parasitize, and so on. So, the extinction of a single species anywhere in the ecosystem will affect not only the organisms it directly feeds on and that directly feed on it, but also those related more distantly. In the simplest terms, if, for example, a species of rodent goes extinct, the insects and vegetation on which it feeds would no longer be under the same predation pressure and thus could grow out of control, outcompeting other species and leading to their demise. In addition, the predators of the rodent would have to find other prey, which would result in competition with those species' predators. And so on, and so on. The effects could be catastrophic to the entire ecosystem. By looking at the trophic chains in which a particular organism is involved, you could predict the effects its extinction would have on other species.

5. Population size is not necessarily a direct cause of extinction, but it certainly is an indirect cause. Smaller populations have a number of problems that themselves can lead directly to extinction, such as loss of diversity (and thus increased susceptibility to pathogens) and greater vulnerability to natural catastrophes.

Glossary

A

ABO blood group A set of four phenotypes produced by different combinations of three alleles at a single locus; blood types are A, B, AB, and O, depending on which alleles are expressed as antigens on the red blood cell surface.

abscission In vascular plants, the dropping of leaves, flowers, fruits, or stems at the end of the growing season, as the result of the formation of a layer of specialized cells (the abscission zone) and the action of a hormone (ethylene).

absorption spectrum The relationship of absorbance vs. wavelength for a pigment molecule. This indicates which wavelengths are absorbed maximally by a pigment. For example, chlorophyll *a* absorbs most strongly in the violet-blue and red regions of the visible light spectrum.

acceptor stem The 3′ end of a tRNA molecule; the portion that amino acids become attached to during the tRNA charging reaction.

accessory pigment A secondary light-absorbing pigment used in photosynthesis, including chlorophyll *b* and the carotenoids, that complement the absorption spectrum of chlorophyll *a*.

aceolomate An animal, such as a flatworm, having a body plan that has no body cavity; the space between mesoderm and endoderm is filled with cells and organic materials.

acetyl-CoA The product of the transition reaction between glycolysis and the Krebs cycle. Pyruvate is oxidized to acetyl-CoA by NAD⁺, also producing CO_2, and NADH.

achiasmate segregation The lining up and subsequent separation of homologues during meiosis I without the formation of chiasmata between homologues; found in *Drosophila* males and some other species.

acid Any substance that dissociates in water to increase the hydrogen ion (H⁺) concentration and thus lower the pH.

actin One of the two major proteins that make up vertebrate muscle; the other is myosin.

action potential A transient, all-or-none reversal of the electric potential across a membrane; in neurons, an action potential initiates transmission of a nerve impulse.

action spectrum A measure of the efficiency of different wavelengths of light for photosynthesis. In plants it corresponds to the absorption spectrum of chlorophylls.

activation energy The energy that must be processed by a molecule in order for it to undergo a specific chemical reaction.

active site The region of an enzyme surface to which a specific set of substrates binds, lowering the activation energy required for a particular chemical reaction and so facilitating it.

active transport The pumping of individual ions or other molecules across a cellular membrane from a region of lower concentration to one of higher concentration (i.e., against a concentration gradient); this transport process requires energy, which is typically supplied by the expenditure of ATP.

adaptation A peculiarity of structure, physiology, or behavior that promotes the likelihood of an organism's survival and reproduction in a particular environment.

adapter protein Any of a class of proteins that acts as a link between a receptor and other proteins to initiate signal transduction.

adaptive radiation The evolution of several divergent forms from a primitive and unspecialized ancestor.

adenosine triphosphate (ATP) A nucleotide consisting of adenine, ribose sugar, and three phosphate groups; ATP is the energy currency of cellular metabolism in all organisms.

adherins junction An anchoring junction that connects the actin filaments of one cell with those of adjacent cells or with the extracellular matrix.

ATP synthase The enzyme responsible for producing ATP in oxidative phosphorylation; it uses the energy from a proton gradient to catalyze the reaction $ADP + P_i \longrightarrow ATP$.

adenylyl cyclase An enzyme that produces large amounts of cAMP from ATP; the cAMP acts as a second messenger in a target cell.

adhesion The tendency of water to cling to other polar compounds due to hydrogen bonding.

adipose cells Fat cells, found in loose connective tissue, usually in large groups that form adipose tissue. Each adipose cell can store a droplet of fat (triacylglyceride).

adventitious Referring to a structure arising from an unusual place, such as stems from roots or roots from stems.

aerenchyma In plants, loose parenchymal tissue with large air spaces in it; often found in plants that grow in water.

aerobic Requiring free oxygen; any biological process that can occur in the presence of gaseous oxygen.

aerobic respiration The process that results in the complete oxidation of glucose using oxygen as the final electron acceptor. Oxygen acts as the final electron acceptor for an electron transport chain that produces a proton gradient for the chemiosmotic synthesis of ATP.

aleurone In plants, the outer layer of the endosperm in a seed; on germination, the aleurone produces α-amylase that breaks down the carbohydrates of the endosperm to nourish the embryo.

alga, pl. algae A unicellular or simple multicellular photosynthetic organism lacking multicellular sex organs.

allantois A membrane of the amniotic egg that functions in respiration and excretion in birds and reptiles and plays an important role in the development of the placenta in most mammals.

allele One of two or more alternative states of a gene.

allele frequency A measure of the occurrence of an allele in a population, expressed as proportion of the entire population, for example, an occurrence of 0.84 (84%).

allometric growth A pattern of growth in which different components grow at different rates.

allelopathy The release of a substance from the roots of one plant that block the germination of nearby seeds or inhibits the growth of a neighboring plant.

allopatric speciation The differentiation of geographically isolated populations into distinct species.

allopolyploid A polyploid organism that contains the genomes of two or more different species.

allosteric activator A substance that binds to an enzyme's allosteric site and keeps the enzyme in its active configuration.

allosteric inhibitor A noncompetitive inhibitor that binds to an enzyme's allosteric site and prevents the enzyme from changing to its active configuration.

allosteric site A part of an enzyme, away from its active site, that serves as an on/off switch for the function of the enzyme.

alpha (α) helix A form of secondary structure in proteins where the polypeptide chain is wound into a spiral due to interactions between amino and carboxyl groups in the peptide backbone.

alternation of generations A reproductive cycle in which a haploid (*n*) phase (the gametophyte), gives rise to gametes, which, after fusion to form a zygote, germinate to produce a diploid (2*n*) phase (the sporophyte). Spores produced by meiotic division from the sporophyte give rise to new gametophytes, completing the cycle.

alternative splicing In eukaryotes, the production of different mRNAs from a single primary transcript by including different sets of exons.

altruism Self-sacrifice for the benefit of others; in formal terms, the behavior that increases the fitness of the recipient while reducing the fitness of the altruistic individual.

alveolus, pl. alveoli One of many small, thin-walled air sacs within the lungs in which the bronchioles terminate.

amino acid The subunit structure from which proteins are produced, consisting of a central carbon atom with a carboxyl group (—COOH), an amino group (—NH$_2$), a hydrogen, and a side group (R group); only the side group differs from one amino acid to another.

aminoacyl-tRNA synthetase Any of a group of enzymes that attach specific amino acids to the correct tRNA during the tRNA-charging reaction. Each of the 20 amino acids has a corresponding enzyme.

amniocentesis Indirect examination of a fetus by tests on cell cultures grown from fetal cells obtained from a sample of the amniotic fluid or tests on the fluid itself.

amnion The innermost of the extraembryonic membranes; the amnion forms a fluid-filled sac around the embryo in amniotic eggs.

amniote A vertebrate that produces an egg surrounded by four membranes, one of which is the amnion; amniote groups are the reptiles, birds, and mammals.

amniotic egg An egg that is isolated and protected from the environment by a more or less impervious shell during the period of its development and that is completely self-sufficient, requiring only oxygen.

ampulla In echinoderms, a muscular sac at the base of a tube foot that contracts to extend the tube foot.

amyloplast A plant organelle called a plastid that specializes in storing starch.

anabolism The biosynthetic or constructive part of metabolism; those chemical reactions involved in biosynthesis.

anaerobic Any process that can occur without oxygen, such as anaerobic fermentation or H$_2$S photosynthesis.

anaerobic respiration The use of electron transport to generate a proton gradient for chemiosmotic synthesis of ATP using a final electron acceptor other than oxygen.

analogous Structures that are similar in function but different in evolutionary origin, such as the wing of a bat and the wing of a butterfly.

anaphase In mitosis and meiosis II, the stage initiated by the separation of sister chromatids, during which the daughter chromosomes move to opposite poles of the cell; in meiosis I, marked by separation of replicated homologous chromosomes.

anaphase-promoting complex (APC) A protein complex that triggers anaphase; it initiates a series of reactions that ultimately degrades cohesin, the protein complex that holds the sister chromatids together. The sister chromatids are then released and move toward opposite poles in the cell.

anchoring junction A type of cell junction that mechanically attaches the cytoskeleton of a cell to the cytoskeletons of adjacent cells or to the extracellular matrix.

androecium The floral whorl that comprises the stamens.

aneuploidy The condition in an organism whose cells have lost or gained a chromosome; Down syndrome, which results from an extra copy of human chromosome 21, is an example of aneuploidy in humans.

angiosperms The flowering plants, one of five phyla of seed plants. In angiosperms, the ovules at the time of pollination are completely enclosed by tissues.

animal pole In fish and other aquatic vertebrates with asymmetrical yolk distribution in their eggs, the hemisphere of the blastula comprising cells relatively poor in yolk.

anion A negatively charged ion.

annotation In genomics, the process of identifying and making note of "landmarks" in a DNA sequence to assist with recognition of coding and transcribed regions.

anonymous markers Genetic markers in a genome that do not cause a detectable phenotype, but that can be detected using molecular techniques.

antenna complex A complex of hundreds of pigment molecules in a photosystem that collects photons and feeds the light energy to a reaction center.

anther In angiosperm flowers, the pollen-bearing portion of a stamen.

antheridium, pl. antheridia A sperm-producing organ.

anthropoid Any member of the mammalian group consisting of monkeys, apes, and humans.

antibody A protein called immunoglobulin that is produced by lymphocytes in response to a foreign substance (antigen) and released into the bloodstream.

anticodon The three-nucleotide sequence at the end of a transfer RNA molecule that is complementary to, and base-pairs with, an amino-acid–specifying codon in messenger RNA.

antigen A foreign substance, usually a protein or polysaccharide, that stimulates an immune response.

antiporter A carrier protein in a cell's membrane that transports two molecules in opposite directions across the membrane.

anus The terminal opening of the gut; the solid residues of digestion are eliminated through the anus.

aorta (Gr. *aeirein,* to lift) The major artery of vertebrate systemic blood circulation; in mammals, carries oxygenated blood away from the heart to all regions of the body except the lungs.

apical meristem In vascular plants, the growing point at the tip of the root or stem.

apoplast route In plant roots, the pathway for movement of water and minerals that leads through cell walls and between cells.

apoptosis A process of programmed cell death, in which dying cells shrivel and shrink; used in all animal cell development to produce planned and orderly elimination of cells not destined to be present in the final tissue.

aposematic coloration An ecological strategy of some organisms that "advertise" their poisonous nature by the use of bright colors.

aquaporin A membrane channel that allows water to cross the membrane more easily than by diffusion through the membrane.

aquifers Permeable, saturated, underground layers of rock, sand, and gravel, which serve as reservoirs for groundwater.

archegonium, pl. archegonia The multicellular egg-producing organ in bryophytes and some vascular plants.

archenteron The principal cavity of a vertebrate embryo in the gastrula stage; lined with endoderm, it opens up to the outside and represents the future digestive cavity.

arteriole A smaller artery, leading from the arteries to the capillaries.

artificial selection Change in the genetic structure of populations due to selective breeding by humans. Many domestic animal breeds and crop varieties have been produced through artificial selection.

ascomycetes A large group comprising part of the "true fungi." They are characterized by separate hyphae, asexually produced conidiospores, and sexually produced ascospores within asci.

ascus, pl. asci A specialized cell, characteristic of the ascomycetes, in which two haploid nuclei fuse to produce a zygote that divides immediately by meiosis; at maturity, an ascus contains ascospores.

asexual reproduction The process by which an individual inherits all of its chromosomes from a single parent, thus being genetically identical to that parent; cell division is by mitosis only.

A site In a ribosome, the aminoacyl site, which binds to the tRNA carrying the next amino acid to be added to a polypeptide chain.

assembly The phase of a virus's reproductive cycle during which the newly made components are assembled into viral particles.

assortative mating A type of nonrandom mating in which phenotypically similar individuals mate more frequently.

aster In animal cell mitosis, a radial array of microtubules extending from the centrioles toward the plasma membrane, possibly serving to brace the centrioles for retraction of the spindle.

atom The smallest unit of an element that contains all the characteristics of that element. Atoms are the building blocks of matter.

atrial peptide Any of a group of small polypeptide hormones that may be useful in treatment of high blood pressure and kidney failure; produced by cells in the atria of the heart.

atrioventricular (AV) node A slender connection of cardiac muscle cells that receives the heartbeat impulses from the sinoatrial node and conducts them by way of the bundle of His.

atrium An antechamber; in the heart, a thin-walled chamber that receives venous blood and passes it on to the thick-walled ventricle; in the ear, the tympanic cavity.

autonomic nervous system The involuntary neurons and ganglia of the peripheral nervous system of vertebrates; regulates the heart, glands, visceral organs, and smooth muscle.

autopolyploid A polyploid organism that contains a duplicated genome of the same species; may result from a meiotic error.

autosome Any eukaryotic chromosome that is not a sex chromosome; autosomes are present in the same number and kind in both males and females of the species.

autotroph An organism able to build all the complex organic molecules that it requires as its own food source, using only simple inorganic compounds.

auxin (Gr. *auxein*, to increase) A plant hormone that controls cell elongation, among other effects.

auxotroph A mutation, or the organism that carries it, that affects a biochemical pathway causing a nutritional requirement.

avirulent pathogen Any type of normally pathogenic organism or virus that utilizes host resources but does not cause extensive damage or death.

axil In plants, the angle between a leaf's petiole and the stem to which it is attached.

axillary bud In plants, a bud found in the axil of a stem and leaf; an axillary bud may develop into a new shoot or may become a flower.

axon A process extending out from a neuron that conducts impulses away from the cell body.

B

b6–f **complex** *See* cytochrome *b6–f* complex.

bacteriophage A virus that infects bacterial cells; also called a *phage*.

Barr body A deeply staining structure, seen in the interphase nucleus of a cell of an individual with more than one X chromosome, that is a condensed and inactivated X. Only one X remains active in each cell after early embryogenesis.

basal body A self-reproducing, cylindrical, cytoplasmic organelle composed of nine triplets of microtubules from which the flagella or cilia arise.

base Any substance that dissociates in water to absorb and therefore decrease the hydrogen ion (H^+) concentration and thus raise the pH.

base-pair A complementary pair of nucleotide bases, consisting of a purine and a pyrimidine.

basidium, pl. **basidia** A specialized reproductive cell of the basidiomycetes, often club-shaped, in which nuclear fusion and meiosis occur.

basophil A leukocyte containing granules that rupture and release chemicals that enhance the inflammatory response. Important in causing allergic responses.

Batesian mimicry A survival strategy in which a palatable or nontoxic organism resembles another kind of organism that is distasteful or toxic. Both species exhibit warning coloration.

B cell A type of lymphocyte that, when confronted with a suitable antigen, is capable of secreting a specific antibody protein.

behavioral ecology The study of how natural selection shapes behavior.

biennial A plant that normally requires two growing seasons to complete its life cycle. Biennials flower in the second year of their lives.

bilateral symmetry A single plane divides an organism into two structural halves that are mirror images of each other.

bile salts A solution of organic salts that is secreted by the vertebrate liver and temporarily stored in the gallbladder; emulsifies fats in the small intestine.

binary fission Asexual reproduction by division of one cell or body into two equal or nearly equal parts.

binomial distribution The distribution of phenotypes seen among the progeny of a cross in which there are only two alternative alleles.

binomial name The scientific name of a species that consists of two parts, the genus name and the specific species name, for example, *Apis mellifera*.

biochemical pathway A sequence of chemical reactions in which the product of one reaction becomes the substrate of the next reaction. The Krebs cycle is a biochemical pathway.

biodiversity The number of species and their range of behavioral, ecological, physiological, and other adaptations, in an area.

bioenergetics The analysis of how energy powers the activities of living systems.

biofilm A complex bacterial community comprising different species; plaque on teeth is a biofilm.

biogeography The study of the geographic distribution of species.

biological community All the populations of different species living together in one place; for example, all populations that inhabit a mountain meadow.

biological species concept (BSC) The concept that defines species as groups of populations that have the potential to interbreed and that are reproductively isolated from other groups.

biomass The total mass of all the living organisms in a given population, area, or other unit being measured.

biome One of the major terrestrial ecosystems, characterized by climatic and soil conditions; the largest ecological unit.

bipolar cell A specialized type of neuron connecting cone cells to ganglion cells in the visual system. Bipolar cells receive a hyperpolarized stimulus from the cone cell and then transmit a depolarization stimulus to the ganglion cell.

biramous Two-branched; describes the appendages of crustaceans.

blade The broad, expanded part of a leaf; also called the lamina.

blastocoel The central cavity of the blastula stage of vertebrate embryos.

blastodisc In the development of birds, a disclike area on the surface of a large, yolky egg that undergoes cleavage and gives rise to the embryo.

blastomere One of the cells of a blastula.

blastopore In vertebrate development, the opening that connects the archenteron cavity of a gastrula stage embryo with the outside.

blastula In vertebrates, an early embryonic stage consisting of a hollow, fluid-filled ball of cells one layer thick; a vertebrate embryo after cleavage and before gastrulation.

Bohr effect The release of oxygen by hemoglobin molecules in response to elevated ambient levels of CO_2.

bottleneck effect A loss of genetic variability that occurs when a population is reduced drastically in size.

Bowman's capsule In the vertebrate kidney, the bulbous unit of the nephron, which surrounds the glomerulus.

β-oxidation The oxygen-dependent reactions where 2-carbon units of fatty acids are cleaved and combined with CoA to produce acetyl-CoA, which then enters the Krebs cycle. This occurs cyclically until the entire fatty acid is oxidized.

β sheet A form of secondary structure in proteins where the polypeptide folds back on itself one or more times to form a planar structure stabilized by hydrogen bonding between amino and carboxyl groups in the peptide backbone. Also known as a β-pleated sheet.

book lung In some spiders, a unique respiratory system consisting of leaflike plates within a chamber over which gas exchange occurs.

bronchus, pl. **bronchi** One of a pair of respiratory tubes branching from the lower end of the trachea (windpipe) into either lung.

bud An asexually produced outgrowth that develops into a new individual. In plants, an embryonic shoot, often protected by young leaves; buds may give rise to branch shoots.

buffer A substance that resists changes in pH. It releases hydrogen ions (H^+) when a base is added and absorbs H^+ when an acid is added.

C

C_3 photosynthesis The main cycle of the dark reactions of photosynthesis, in which CO_2 binds to ribulose 1,5-bisphosphate (RuBP) to form two 3-carbon phosphoglycerate (PGA) molecules.

C_4 photosynthesis A process of CO_2 fixation in photosynthesis by which the first product is the 4-carbon oxaloacetate molecule.

cadherin One of a large group of transmembrane proteins that contain a Ca^{2+}-mediated binding between cells; these proteins are responsible for cell-to-cell adhesion between cells of the same type.

callus Undifferentiated tissue; a term used in tissue culture, grafting, and wound healing.

Calvin cycle The dark reactions of C_3 photosynthesis; also called the Calvin–Benson cycle.

calyx The sepals collectively; the outermost flower whorl.

CAM plant Plants that use C_4 carbon fixation at night, then use the stored malate to generate CO_2 during the day to minimize dessication.

Cambrian explosion The huge increase in animal diversity that occurred at the beginning of the Cambrian period.

cAMP response protein (CRP) *See* catabolite activator protein (CAP)

cancer The unrestrained growth and division of cells; it results from a failure of cell division control.

capillary The smallest of the blood vessels; the very thin walls of capillaries are permeable to many molecules, and exchanges between blood and the tissues occur across them; the vessels that connect arteries with veins.

capsid The outermost protein covering of a virus.

capsule In bacteria, a gelatinous layer surrounding the cell wall.

carapace (Fr. from Sp. *carapacho*, shell) Shieldlike plate covering the cephalothorax of decapod crustaceans; the dorsal part of the shell of a turtle.

carbohydrate An organic compound consisting of a chain or ring of carbon atoms to which hydrogen and oxygen atoms are attached in a ratio of approximately 2:1; having the generalized formula $(CH_2O)_n$; carbohydrates include sugars, starch, glycogen, and cellulose.

carbon fixation The conversion of CO_2 into organic compounds during photosynthesis; the first stage of the dark reactions of photosynthesis, in which carbon dioxide from the air is combined with ribulose 1,5-bisphosphate.

carotenoid Any of a group of accessory pigments found in plants; in addition to absorbing light energy, these pigments act as antioxidants, scavenging potentially damaging free radicals.

carpel A leaflike organ in angiosperms that encloses one or more ovules.

carrier protein A membrane protein that binds to a specific molecule that cannot cross the membrane and allows passage through the membrane.

carrying capacity The maximum population size that a habitat can support.

cartilage A connective tissue in skeletons of vertebrates. Cartilage forms much of the skeleton of embryos, very young vertebrates, and some adult vertebrates, such as sharks and their relatives.

Casparian strip In plants, a band that encircles the cell wall of root endodermal cells. Adjacent cells' strips connect, forming a layer through which water cannot pass; therefore, all water entering roots must pass through cell membranes and cytoplasm.

catabolism In a cell, those metabolic reactions that result in the breakdown of complex molecules into simpler compounds, often with the release of energy.

catabolite activator protein (CAP) A protein that, when bound to cAMP, can bind to DNA and activate transcription. The level of cAMP is inversely related to the level of glucose, and CAP/cAMP in *E. coli* activates the *lac* (lactose) operon. Also called *cAMP response protein* (*CRP*).

catalysis The process by which chemical subunits of larger organic molecules are held and positioned by enzymes that stress their chemical bonds, leading to the disassembly of the larger molecule into its subunits, often with the release of energy.

cation A positively charged ion.

cavitation In plants and animals, the blockage of a vessel by an air bubble that breaks the cohesion of the solution in the vessel; in animals more often called embolism.

CD4$^+$ cell A subtype of helper T cell that is identified by the presence of the CD4 protein on its surface. This cell type is targeted by the HIV virus that causes AIDS.

cecum In vertebrates, a blind pouch at the beginning of the large intestine.

cell cycle The repeating sequence of growth and division through which cells pass each generation.

cell determination The molecular "decision" process by which a cell becomes destined for a particular developmental pathway. This occurs before overt differentiation and can be a stepwise process.

cell-mediated immunity Arm of the adaptive immune system mediated by T cells, which includes cytotoxic cells and cells that assist the rest of the immune system.

cell plate The structure that forms at the equator of the spindle during early telophase in the dividing cells of plants and a few green algae.

cell-surface marker A glycoprotein or glycolipid on the outer surface of a cell's membrane that acts as an identifier; different cell types carry different markers.

cell-surface receptor A cell surface protein that binds a signal molecule and converts the extracellular signal into an intracellular one.

cellular blastoderm In insect embryonic development, the stage during which the nuclei of the syncitial blastoderm become separate cells through membrane formation.

cellular respiration The metabolic harvesting of energy by oxidation, ultimately dependent on molecular oxygen; carried out by the Krebs cycle and oxidative phosphorylation.

cellulose The chief constituent of the cell wall in all green plants, some algae, and a few other organisms; an insoluble complex carbohydrate formed of microfibrils of glucose molecules.

cell wall The rigid, outermost layer of the cells of plants, some protists, and most bacteria; the cell wall surrounds the plasma membrane.

central nervous system (CNS) That portion of the nervous system where most association occurs; in vertebrates, it is composed of the brain and spinal cord; in invertebrates, it usually consists of one or more cords of nervous tissue, together with their associated ganglia.

central vacuole A large, membrane-bounded sac found in plant cells that stores proteins, pigments, and waste materials, and is involved in water balance.

centriole A cytoplasmic organelle located outside the nuclear membrane, identical in structure to a basal body; found in animal cells and in the flagellated cells of other groups; divides and organizes spindle fibers during mitosis and meiosis.

centromere A visible point of constriction on a chromosome that contains repeated DNA sequences that bind specific proteins. These proteins make up the kinetochore to which microtubules attach during cell division.

cephalization The evolution of a head and brain area in the anterior end of animals; thought to be a consequence of bilateral symmetry.

cerebellum The hindbrain region of the vertebrate brain that lies above the medulla (brainstem) and behind the forebrain; it integrates information about body position and motion, coordinates muscular activities, and maintains equilibrium.

cerebral cortex The thin surface layer of neurons and glial cells covering the cerebrum; well developed only in mammals, and particularly prominent in humans. The cerebral cortex is the seat of conscious sensations and voluntary muscular activity.

cerebrum The portion of the vertebrate brain (the forebrain) that occupies the upper part of the skull, consisting of two cerebral hemispheres united by the corpus callosum. It is the primary association center of the brain. It coordinates and processes sensory input and coordinates motor responses.

chaetae Bristles of chitin on each body segment that help anchor annelid worms during locomotion.

channel protein (ion channel) A transmembrane protein with a hydrophilic interior that provides an aqueous channel allowing diffusion of species that cannot cross the membrane. Usually allows passage of specific ions such as K^+, Na^+, or Ca^{2+} across the membrane.

chaperone protein A class of enzymes that help proteins fold into the correct configuration and can refold proteins that have been misfolded or denatured.

character displacement A process in which natural selection favors individuals in a species that use resources not used by other species. This results in evolutionary change leading to species dissimilar in resource use.

character state In cladistics, one of two or more distinguishable forms of a character, such as the presence or absence of teeth in amniote vertebrates.

charging reaction The reaction by which an aminoacyl-tRNA synthetase attaches a specific amino acid to the correct tRNA using energy from ATP.

chelicera, pl. **chelicerae** The first pair of appendages in horseshoe crabs, sea spiders, and arachnids—the chelicerates, a group of arthropods. Chelicerae usually take the form of pincers or fangs.

chemical synapse A close association that allows chemical communication between neurons. A chemical signal (neurotransmitter) released by the first neuron binds to receptors in the membrane of the second neurons.

chemiosmosis The mechanism by which ATP is generated in mitochondria and chloroplasts; energetic electrons excited by light (in chloroplasts) or extracted by oxidation in the Krebs cycle (in mitochondria) are used to drive proton pumps, creating a proton concentration gradient; when protons subsequently flow back across the membrane, they pass through channels that couple their movement to the synthesis of ATP.

chiasma An X-shaped figure that can be seen in the light microscope during meiosis; evidence of crossing over, where two chromatids have exchanged parts; chiasmata move to the ends of the chromosome arms as the homologues separate.

chitin A tough, resistant, nitrogen-containing polysaccharide that forms the cell walls of certain fungi, the exoskeleton of arthropods, and the epidermal cuticle of other surface structures of certain other invertebrates.

chlorophyll The primary type of light-absorbing pigment in photosynthesis. Chlorophyll *a* absorbs light in the violet-blue and the red ranges of the visible light spectrum; chlorophyll *b* is an accessory pigment to chlorophyll *a,* absorbing light in the blue and red-orange ranges. Neither pigment absorbs light in the green range, 500–600 nm.

chloroplast A cell-like organelle present in algae and plants that contains chlorophyll (and usually other pigments) and carries out photosynthesis.

choanocyte A specialized flagellated cell found in sponges; choanocytes line the body interior.

chorion The outer member of the double membrane that surrounds the embryo of reptiles, birds, and mammals; in placental mammals, it contributes to the structure of the placenta.

chorionic villi sampling A technique in which fetal cells are sampled from the chorion of the placenta rather than from the amniotic fluid; this less invasive technique can be used earlier in pregnancy than amniocentesis.

chromatid One of the two daughter strands of a duplicated chromosome that is joined by a single centromere.

chromatin The complex of DNA and proteins of which eukaryotic chromosomes are composed; chromatin is highly uncoiled and diffuse in interphase nuclei, condensing to form the visible chromosomes in prophase.

chromatin-remodeling complex A large protein complex that has been found to modify histones and DNA and that can change the structure of chromatin, moving or transferring nucleosomes.

chromosomal mutation Any mutation that affects chromosome structure.

chromosome The vehicle by which hereditary information is physically transmitted from one generation to the next; in a bacterium, the chromosome consists of a single naked circle of DNA; in eukaryotes, each chromosome consists of a single linear DNA molecule and associated proteins.

chromosomal theory of inheritance The theory stating that hereditary traits are carried on chromosomes.

cilium A short cellular projection from the surface of a eukaryotic cell, having the same internal structure of microtubules in a 9 + 2 arrangement as seen in a flagellum.

circadian rhythm An endogenous cyclical rhythm that oscillates on a daily (24-hour) basis.

circulatory system A network of vessels in coelomate animals that carries fluids to and from different areas of the body.

cisterna A small collecting vessel that pinches off from the end of a Golgi body to form a transport vesicle that moves materials through the cytoplasm.

cisternal space The inner region of a membrane-bounded structure. Usually used to describe the interior of the endoplasmic reticulum; also called the *lumen.*

clade A taxonomic group composed of an ancestor and all its descendents.

cladistics A taxonomic technique used for creating hierarchies of organisms that represent true phylogenetic relationship and descent.

class A taxonomic category between phyla and orders. A class contains one or more orders, and belongs to a particular phylum.

classical conditioning The repeated presentation of a stimulus in association with a response that causes the brain to form an association between the stimulus and the response, even if they have never been associated before.

clathrin A protein located just inside the plasma membrane in eukaryotic cells, in indentations called clathrin-coated pits.

cleavage In vertebrates, a rapid series of successive cell divisions of a fertilized egg, forming a hollow sphere of cells, the blastula.

cleavage furrow The constriction that forms during cytokinesis in animal cells that is

responsible for dividing the cell into two daughter cells.

climax vegetation Vegetation encountered in a self-perpetuating community of plants that has proceeded through all the stages of succession and stabilized.

cloaca In some animals, the common exit chamber from the digestive, reproductive, and urinary system; in others, the cloaca may also serve as a respiratory duct.

clone-by-clone sequencing A method of genome sequencing in which a physical map is constructed first, followed by sequencing of fragments and identifying overlap regions.

clonal selection Amplification of a clone of immune cells initiated by antigen recognition.

cloning Producing a cell line or culture all of whose members contain identical copies of a particular nucleotide sequence; an essential element in genetic engineering.

closed circulatory system A circulatory system in which the blood is physically separated from other body fluids.

coacervate A spherical aggregation of lipid molecules in water, held together by hydrophobic forces.

coactivator A protein that functions to link transcriptional activators to the transcription complex consisting of RNA polymerase II and general transcription factors.

cochlea In terrestrial vertebrates, a tubular cavity of the inner ear containing the essential organs for hearing.

coding strand The strand of a DNA duplex that is the same as the RNA encoded by a gene. This strand is not used as a template in transcription, it is complementary to the template.

codominance Describes a case in which two or more alleles of a gene are each dominant to other alleles but not to each other. The phenotype of a heterozygote for codominant alleles exhibit characteristics of each of the homozygous forms. For example, in human blood types, a cross between an AA individual and a BB individual yields AB individuals.

codon The basic unit of the genetic code; a sequence of three adjacent nucleotides in DNA or mRNA that codes for one amino acid.

coelom In animals, a fluid-filled body cavity that develops entirely within the mesoderm.

coenzyme A nonprotein organic molecule such as NAD that plays an accessory role in enzyme-catalyzed processes, often by acting as a donor or acceptor of electrons.

coevolution The simultaneous development of adaptations in two or more populations, species, or other categories that interact so closely that each is a strong selective force on the other.

cofactor One or more nonprotein components required by enzymes in order to function; many cofactors are metal ions, others are organic coenzymes.

cohesin A protein complex that holds sister chromatids together during cell division. The loss of cohesins at the centromere allows the anaphase movement of chromosomes.

collenchyma cell In plants, the cells that form a supporting tissue called collenchyma; often found in regions of primary growth in stems and in some leaves.

colloblast A specialized type of cell found in members of the animal phylum Ctenophora (comb jellies) that bursts on contact with zooplankton, releasing an adhesive substance to help capture this prey.

colonial flagellate hypothesis The proposal first put forth by Haeckel that metazoans descended from colonial protists; supported by the similarity of sponges to choanoflagellate protists.

commensalism A relationship in which one individual lives close to or on another and benefits, and the host is unaffected; a kind of symbiosis.

community All of the species inhabiting a common environment and interacting with one another.

companion cell A specialized parenchyma cell that is associated with each sieve-tube member in the phloem of a plant.

competitive exclusion The hypothesis that two species with identical ecological requirements cannot exist in the same locality indefinitely, and that the more efficient of the two in utilizing the available scarce resources will exclude the other; also known as Gause's principle.

competitive inhibitor An inhibitor that binds to the same active site as an enzyme's substrate, thereby competing with the substrate.

complementary Describes genetic information in which each nucleotide base has a complementary partner with which it forms a base-pair.

complementary DNA (cDNA) A DNA copy of an mRNA transcript; produced by the action of the enzyme reverse transcriptase.

complement system The chemical defense of a vertebrate body that consists of a battery of proteins that become activated by the walls of bacteria and fungi.

complete digestive system A digestive system that has both a mouth and an anus, allowing unidirectional flow of ingested food.

compound eye An organ of sight in many arthropods composed of many independent visual units called ommatidia.

concentration gradient A difference in concentration of a substance from one location to another, often across a membrane.

condensin A protein complex involved in condensation of chromosomes during mitosis and meiosis.

cone (1) In plants, the reproductive structure of a conifer. (2) In vertebrates, a type of light-sensitive neuron in the retina concerned with the perception of color and with the most acute discrimination of detail.

conidia An asexually produced fungal spore.

conjugation Temporary union of two unicellular organisms, during which genetic material is transferred from one cell to the other; occurs in bacteria, protists, and certain algae and fungi.

consensus sequence In genome sequencing, the overall sequence that is consistent with the sequences of individual fragments; computer programs are used to compare sequences and generate a consensus sequence.

conservation of synteny The preservation over evolutionary time of arrangements of DNA segments in related species.

contig A contiguous segment of DNA assembled by analyzing sequence overlaps from smaller fragments.

continuous variation Variation in a trait that occurs along a continuum, such as the trait of height in human beings; often occurs when a trait is determined by more than one gene.

contractile vacuole In protists and some animals, a clear fluid-filled vacuole that takes up water from within the cell and then contracts, releasing it to the outside through a pore in a cyclical manner; functions primarily in osmoregulation and excretion.

conus arteriosus The anteriormost chamber of the embryonic heart in vertebrate animals.

convergent evolution The independent development of similar structures in organisms that are not directly related; often found in organisms living in similar environments.

cork cambium The lateral meristem that forms the periderm, producing cork (phellem) toward the surface (outside) of the plant and phelloderm toward the inside.

cornea The transparent outer layer of the vertebrate eye.

corolla The petals, collectively; usually the conspicuously colored flower whorl.

corpus callosum The band of nerve fibers that connects the two hemispheres of the cerebrum in humans and other primates.

corpus luteum A structure that develops from a ruptured follicle in the ovary after ovulation.

cortex The outer layer of a structure; in animals, the outer, as opposed to the inner, part of an organ; in vascular plants, the primary ground tissue of a stem or root.

cotyledon A seed leaf that generally stores food in dicots or absorbs it in monocots, providing nourishment used during seed germination.

crassulacean acid metabolism (CAM) A mode of carbon dioxide fixation by which CO_2 enters open leaf stomata at night and is used in photosynthesis during the day, when stomata are closed to prevent water loss.

crista A folded extension of the inner membrane of a mitochondrion. Mitochondria contain numerous cristae.

cross-current flow In bird lungs, the latticework of capillaries arranged across the air flow, at a 90° angle.

crossing over In meiosis, the exchange of corresponding chromatid segments between homologous chromosomes; responsible for genetic recombination between homologous chromosomes.

ctenidia Respiratory gills of mollusks; they consist of a system of filamentous projections of the mantle that are rich in blood vessels.

cuticle A waxy or fatty, noncellular layer (formed of a substance called cutin) on the outer wall of epidermal cells.

cutin In plants, a fatty layer produced by the epidermis that forms the cuticle on the outside surface.

cyanobacteria A group of photosynthetic bacteria, sometimes called the "blue-green algae," that contain the chlorophyll pigments most abundant in plants and algae, as well as other pigments.

cyclic AMP (cAMP) A form of adenosine monophosphate (AMP) in which the atoms of the phosphate group form a ring; found in almost all organisms, cAMP functions as an intracellular second messenger that regulates a diverse array of metabolic activities.

cyclic photophosphorylation Reactions that begin with the absorption of light by reaction center chlorophyll that excites an electron. The excited electron returns to the photosystem, generating ATP by chemiosmosis in the process. This is found in the single bacterial photosystem, and can occur in plants in photosystem I.

cyclin Any of a number of proteins that are produced in synchrony with the cell cycle and combine with certain protein kinases, the cyclin-dependent kinases, at certain points during cell division.

cyclin-dependent kinase (Cdk) Any of a group of protein kinase enzymes that control progress through the cell cycle. These enzymes are only active when complexed with cyclin. The cdc2 protein, produced by the *cdc2* gene, was the first Cdk enzyme discovered.

cytochrome Any of several iron-containing protein pigments that serve as electron carriers in transport chains of photosynthesis and cellular respiration.

cytochrome *b6–f* complex A proton pump found in the thylakoid membrane. This complex uses energy from excited electrons to pump protons from the stroma into the thylakoid compartment.

cytokinesis Division of the cytoplasm of a cell after nuclear division.

cytokine Signaling molecules secreted by immune cells that affect other immune cells.

cytoplasm The material within a cell, excluding the nucleus; the protoplasm.

cytoskeleton A network of protein microfilaments and microtubules within the cytoplasm of a eukaryotic cell that maintains the shape of the cell, anchors its organelles, and is involved in animal cell motility.

cytosol The fluid portion of the cytoplasm; it contains dissolved organic molecules and ions.

cytotoxic T cell A special T cell activated during cell-mediated immune response that recognizes and destroys infected body cells.

D

deamination The removal of an amino group; part of the degradation of proteins into compounds that can enter the Krebs cycle.

deductive reasoning The logical application of general principles to predict a specific result. In science, deductive reasoning is used to test the validity of general ideas.

dehydration reaction A type of chemical reaction in which two molecules join to form one larger molecule, simultaneously splitting out a molecule of water; one molecule is stripped of a hydrogen atom, and another is stripped of a hydroxyl group (—OH), resulting in the joining of the two molecules, while the H and —OH released may combine to form a water molecule.

dehydrogenation Chemical reaction involving the loss of a hydrogen atom. This is an oxidation that combines loss of an electron with loss of a proton.

deletion A mutation in which a portion of a chromosome is lost; if too much information is lost, the deletion can be fatal.

demography The properties of the rate of growth and the age structure of populations.

denaturation The loss of the native configuration of a protein or nucleic acid as a result of excessive heat, extremes of pH, chemical modification, or changes in solvent ionic strength or polarity that disrupt hydrophobic interactions; usually accompanied by loss of biological activity.

dendrite A process extending from the cell body of a neuron, typically branched, that conducts impulses toward the cell body.

deoxyribonucleic acid (DNA) The genetic material of all organisms; composed of two complementary chains of nucleotides wound in a double helix.

dephosphorylation The removal of a phosphate group, usually by a phosphatase enzyme. Many proteins can be activated or inactivated by dephosphorylation.

depolarization The movement of ions across a plasma membrane that locally wipes out an electrical potential difference.

derived character A characteristic used in taxonomic analysis representing a departure from the primitive form.

dermal tissue In multicellular organisms, a type of tissue that forms the outer layer of the body and is in contact with the environment; it has a protective function.

desmosome A type of anchoring junction that links adjacent cells by connecting their cytoskeletons with cadherin proteins.

derepression Seen in anabolic operons where the operon that encodes the enzymes for a biochemical pathway is repressed in the presence of the end product of the pathway and derepressed in the absence of the end product. This allows production of the enzymes only when they are necessary.

determinate development A type of development in animals in which each embryonic cell has a predetermined fate in terms of what kind of tissue it will form in the adult.

deuterostome Any member of a grouping of bilaterally symmetrical animals in which the anus develops first and the mouth second; echinoderms and vertebrates are deuterostome animals.

diacylglycerol (DAG) A second messenger that is released, along with inositol-1,4,5-trisphosphate (IP_3), when phospholipase C cleaves PIP_2. DAG can have a variety of cellular effects through activation of protein kinases.

diaphragm (1) In mammals, a sheet of muscle tissue that separates the abdominal and thoracic cavities and functions in breathing. (2) A contraceptive device used to block the entrance to the uterus temporarily and thus prevent sperm from entering during sexual intercourse.

diapsid Any of a group of reptiles that have two pairs of temporal openings in the skull, one lateral and one more dorsal; one lineage of this group gave rise to dinosaurs, modern reptiles, and birds.

diastolic pressure In the measurement of human blood pressure, the minimum pressure between heartbeats (repolarization of the ventricles). *Compare with* systolic pressure.

dicer An enzyme that generates small RNA molecules in a cell by chopping up double-stranded RNAs; dicer produces miRNAs and siRNAs.

dicot Short for dicotyledon; a class of flowering plants generally characterized as having two cotyledons, net-veined leaves, and flower parts usually in fours or fives.

dideoxynucleotide A nucleotide lacking — OH groups at both the 2′ and 3′ positions; used as a chain terminator in the enzymatic sequencing of DNA.

differentiation A developmental process by which a relatively unspecialized cell undergoes a progressive change to a more specialized form or function.

diffusion The net movement of dissolved molecules or other particles from a region where they are more concentrated to a region where they are less concentrated.

dihybrid An individual heterozygous at two different loci; for example *A/a B/b.*

dihybrid cross A single genetic cross involving two different traits, such as flower color and plant height.

dikaryotic In fungi, having pairs of nuclei within each cell.

dioecious Having the male and female elements on different individuals.

diploid Having two sets of chromosomes ($2n$); in animals, twice the number characteristic of gametes; in plants, the chromosome number characteristic of the sporophyte generation; in contrast to haploid (n).

directional selection A form of selection in which selection acts to eliminate one extreme from an array of phenotypes.

disaccharide A carbohydrate formed of two simple sugar molecules bonded covalently.

disruptive selection A form of selection in which selection acts to eliminate rather than favor the intermediate type.

dissociation In proteins, the reversible separation of protein subunits from a quaternary structure without altering their tertiary structure. Also refers to the dissolving of ionic compounds in water.

disassortative mating A type of nonrandom mating in which phenotypically different individuals mate more frequently.

diurnal Active during the day.

DNA-binding motif A region found in a regulatory protein that is capable of binding to a specific base sequence in DNA; a critical part of the protein's DNA-binding domain.

DNA fingerprinting An identification technique that makes use of a variety of molecular techniques to identify differences in the DNA of individuals.

DNA gyrase A topoisomerase involved in DNA replication; it relieves the torsional strain caused by unwinding the DNA strands.

DNA library A collection of DNAs in a vector (a plasmid, phage, or artificial chromosome) that taken together represent a complex mixture of DNAs, such as the entire genome, or the cDNAs made from all of the mRNA in a specific cell type.

DNA ligase The enzyme responsible for formation of phosphodiester bonds between adjacent nucleotides in DNA.

DNA microarray An array of DNA fragments on a microscope slide or silicon chip, used in hybridization experiments with labeled mRNA or DNA to identify active and inactive genes, or the presence or absence of particular sequences.

DNA polymerase A class of enzymes that all synthesize DNA from a preexisting template. All synthesize only in the 5′-to-3′ direction, and require a primer to extend.

DNA vaccine A type of vaccine that uses DNA from a virus or bacterium that stimulates the cellular immune response.

domain (1) A distinct modular region of a protein that serves a particular function in the action of the protein, such as a regulatory domain or a DNA-binding domain. (2) In taxonomy, the level higher than kingdom. The three domains currently recognized are Bacteria, Archaea, and Eukarya.

Domain Archaea In the three-domain system of taxonomy, the group that contains only the Archaea, a highly diverse group of unicellular prokaryotes.

Domain Bacteria In the three-domain system of taxonomy, the group that contains only the Bacteria, a vast group of unicellular prokaryotes.

Domain Eukarya In the three-domain system of taxonomy, the group that contains eukaryotic organisms including protists, fungi, plants, and animals.

dominant An allele that is expressed when present in either the heterozygous or the homozygous condition.

dosage compensation A phenomenon by which the expression of genes carried on sex chromosomes is kept the same in males and females, despite a different number of sex chromosomes. In mammals, inactivation of one of the X chromosomes in female cells accomplishes dosage compensation.

double fertilization The fusion of the egg and sperm (resulting in a $2n$ fertilized egg, the zygote) and the simultaneous fusion of the second male gamete with the polar nuclei (resulting in a primary endosperm nucleus, which is often triploid, $3n$); a unique characteristic of all angiosperms.

double helix The structure of DNA, in which two complementary polynucleotide strands coil around a common helical axis.

duodenum In vertebrates, the upper portion of the small intestine.

duplication A mutation in which a portion of a chromosome is duplicated; if the duplicated region does not lie within a gene, the duplication may have no effect.

E

ecdysis Shedding of outer, cuticular layer; molting, as in insects or crustaceans.

ecdysone Molting hormone of arthropods, which triggers when ecdysis occurs.

ecology The study of interactions of organisms with one another and with their physical environment.

ecosystem A major interacting system that includes organisms and their nonliving environment.

ecotype A locally adapted variant of an organism; differing genetically from other ecotypes.

ectoderm One of the three embryonic germ layers of early vertebrate embryos; ectoderm gives rise to the outer epithelium of the body (skin, hair, nails) and to the nerve tissue, including the sense organs, brain, and spinal cord.

ectomycorrhizae Externally developing mycorrhizae that do not penetrate the cells they surround.

ectotherms Animals such as reptiles, fish, or amphibians, whose body temperature is regulated by their behavior or by their surroundings.

electronegativity A property of atomic nuclei that refers to the affinity of the nuclei for valence electrons; a nucleus that is more electronegative has a greater pull on electrons than one that is less electronegative.

electron transport chain The passage of energetic electrons through a series of membrane-associated electron-carrier molecules to proton pumps embedded within mitochondrial or chloroplast membranes. *See* chemiosmosis.

elongation factor (Ef-Tu) In protein synthesis in *E. coli,* a factor that binds to GTP and to a charged tRNA to accomplish binding of the charged tRNA to the A site of the ribosome, so that elongation of the polypeptide chain can occur.

embryo A multicellular developmental stage that follows cell division of the zygote.

embryonic stem cell (ES cell) A stem cell derived from an early embryo that can develop into different adult tissues and give rise to an adult organism when injected into a blastocyst.

emergent properties Novel properties arising from the way in which components interact. Emergent properties often cannot be deduced solely from knowledge of the individual components.

emerging virus Any virus that originates in one organism but then passes to another; usually refers to transmission to humans.

endergonic Describes a chemical reaction in which the products contain more energy than the reactants, so that free energy must be put into the reaction from an outside source to allow it to proceed.

endocrine gland Ductless gland that secretes hormones into the extracellular spaces, from which they diffuse into the circulatory system.

endocytosis The uptake of material into cells by inclusion within an invagination of the plasma membrane; the uptake of solid material is phagocytosis, and that of dissolved material is pinocytosis.

endoderm One of the three embryonic germ layers of early vertebrate embryos, destined to give rise to the epithelium that lines internal structures and most of the digestive and respiratory tracts.

endodermis In vascular plants, a layer of cells forming the innermost layer of the cortex in roots and some stems.

endomembrane system A system of connected membranous compartments found in eukaryotic cells.

endometrium The lining of the uterus in mammals; thickens in response to secretion of estrogens and progesterone and is sloughed off in menstruation.

endomycorrhizae Mycorrhizae that develop within cells.

endonuclease An enzyme capable of cleaving phosphodiester bonds between nucleotides located internally in a DNA strand.

endoplasmic reticulum (ER) Internal membrane system that forms a netlike array of channels and interconnections within the cytoplasm of eukaryotic cells. The ER is divided into rough (RER) and smooth (SER) compartments.

endorphin One of a group of small neuropeptides produced by the vertebrate brain; like morphine, endorphins modulate pain perception.

endosperm A storage tissue characteristic of the seeds of angiosperms, which develops from the union of a male nucleus and the polar nuclei of the embryo sac. The endosperm is digested by the growing sporophyte either before maturation of the seed or during its germination.

endospore A highly resistant, thick-walled bacterial spore that can survive harsh environmental stress, such as heat or dessication, and then germinate when conditions become favorable.

endosymbiosis Theory that proposes that eukaryotic cells evolved from a symbiosis between different species of prokaryotes.

endotherm An animal capable of maintaining a constant body temperature. *See* homeotherm.

energy level A discrete level, or quantum, of energy that an electron in an atom possesses. To change energy levels, an electron must absorb or release energy.

enhancer A site of regulatory protein binding on the DNA molecule distant from the promoter and start site for a gene's transcription.

enthalpy In a chemical reaction, the energy contained in the chemical bonds of the molecule, symbolized as H; in a cellular reaction, the free energy is equal to the enthalpy of the reactant molecules in the reaction.

entropy A measure of the randomness or disorder of a system; a measure of how much energy in a system has become so dispersed (usually as evenly distributed heat) that it is no longer available to do work.

enzyme A protein that is capable of speeding up specific chemical reactions by lowering the required activation energy.

enzyme–substrate complex The complex formed when an enzyme binds with its substrate. This complex often has an altered configuration compared with the nonbound enzyme.

epicotyl The region just above where the cotyledons are attached.

epidermal cell In plants, a cell that collectively forms the outermost layer of the primary plant body; includes specialized cells such as trichomes and guard cells.

epidermis The outermost layers of cells; in plants, the exterior primary tissue of leaves, young stems, and roots; in vertebrates, the nonvascular external layer of skin, of ectodermal origin; in invertebrates, a single layer of ectodermal epithelium.

epididymis A sperm storage vessel; a coiled part of the sperm duct that lies near the testis.

epistasis Interaction between two nonallelic genes in which one of them modifies the phenotypic expression of the other.

epithelium In animals, a type of tissue that covers an exposed surface or lines a tube or cavity.

equilibrium A stable condition; the point at which a chemical reaction proceeds as rapidly in the reverse direction as it does in the forward direction, so that there is no further net change in the concentrations of products or reactants. In ecology, a stable condition that resists change and fairly quickly returns to its original state if disturbed by humans or natural events.

erythrocyte Red blood cell, the carrier of hemoglobin.

erythropoiesis The manufacture of blood cells in the bone marrow.

E site In a ribosome, the exit site that binds to the tRNA that carried the previous amino acid added to the polypeptide chain.

estrus The period of maximum female sexual receptivity, associated with ovulation of the egg.

ethology The study of patterns of animal behavior in nature.

euchromatin That portion of a eukaryotic chromosome that is transcribed into mRNA; contains active genes that are not tightly condensed during interphase.

eukaryote A cell characterized by membrane-bounded organelles, most notably the nucleus, and one that possesses chromosomes whose DNA is associated with proteins; an organism composed of such cells.

eutherian A placental mammal.

eutrophic Refers to a lake in which an abundant supply of minerals and organic matter exists.

evolution Genetic change in a population of organisms; in general, evolution leads to progressive change from simple to complex.

excision repair A nonspecific mechanism to repair damage to DNA during synthesis. The damaged or mismatched region is excised, and DNA polymerase replaces the region removed.

exergonic Describes a chemical reaction in which the products contain less free energy than the reactants, so that free energy is released in the reaction.

exhalant siphon In bivalve mollusks, the siphon through which outgoing water leaves the body.

exocrine gland A type of gland that releases its secretion through a duct, such as a digestive gland or a sweat gland.

exocytosis A type of bulk transport out of cells in which a vacuole fuses with the plasma membrane, discharging the vacuole's contents to the outside.

exon A segment of DNA that is both transcribed into RNA and translated into protein. *See* intron.

exonuclease An enzyme capable of cutting phosphodiester bonds between nucleotides located at an end of a DNA strand. This allows sequential removal of nucleotides from the end of DNA.

exoskeleton An external skeleton, as in arthropods.

experiment A test of one or more hypotheses. Hypotheses make contrasting predictions that can be tested experimentally in control and test experiments where a single variable is altered.

expressed sequence tag (EST) A short sequence of a cDNA that unambiguously identifies the cDNA.

expression vector A type of vector (plasmid or phage) that contains the sequences necessary to drive expression of inserted DNA in a specific cell type.

exteroceptor A receptor that is excited by stimuli from the external world.

extremophile An archaean organism that lives in extreme environments; different archaean species may live in hot springs (thermophiles), highly saline environments (halophiles), highly acidic or basic environments, or under high pressure at the bottom of oceans.

F

5′ cap In eukaryotes, a structure added to the 5′ end of an mRNA consisting of methylated GTP attached by a 5′ to 5′ bond. The cap protects this end from degradation and is involved in the initiation of translation.

facilitated diffusion Carrier-assisted diffusion of molecules across a cellular membrane through specific channels from a region of higher concentration to one of lower concentration; the process is driven by the concentration gradient and does not require cellular energy from ATP.

family A taxonomic grouping of similar species above the level of genus.

fat A molecule composed of glycerol and three fatty acid molecules.

feedback inhibition Control mechanism whereby an increase in the concentration of some molecules inhibits the synthesis of that molecule.

fermentation The enzyme-catalyzed extraction of energy from organic compounds without the involvement of oxygen.

fertilization The fusion of two haploid gamete nuclei to form a diploid zygote nucleus.

fibroblast A flat, irregularly branching cell of connective tissue that secretes structurally strong proteins into the matrix between the cells.

first filial (F_1) generation The offspring resulting from a cross between a parental generation (P); in experimental crosses, these parents usually have different phenotypes.

First Law of Thermodynamics Energy cannot be created or destroyed, but can only undergo conversion from one form to another; thus, the amount of energy in the universe is unchangeable.

fitness The genetic contribution of an individual to succeeding generations. Relative fitness refers to the fitness of an individual relative to other individuals in a population.

fixed action pattern A stereotyped animal behavior response, thought by ethologists to be based on programmed neural circuits.

flagellin The protein composing bacterial flagella, which allow a cell to move through an aqueous environment.

flagellum A long, threadlike structure protruding from the surface of a cell and used in locomotion.

flame cell A specialized cell found in the network of tubules inside flatworms that assists in water regulation and some waste excretion.

flavin adenine dinucleotide (FAD, FADH$_2$) A cofactor that acts as a soluble (not membrane-bound) electron carrier (can be reversibly oxidized and reduced).

fluorescent in situ hybridization (FISH) A cytological method used to find specific DNA sequences on chromosomes with a specific fluorescently labeled probe.

food security Having access to sufficient, safe food to avoid malnutrition and starvation; a global human issue.

foraging behavior A collective term for the many complex, evolved behaviors that influence what an animal eats and how the food is obtained.

founder effect The effect by which rare alleles and combinations of alleles may be enhanced in new populations.

fovea A small depression in the center of the retina with a high concentration of cones; the area of sharpest vision.

frameshift mutation A mutation in which a base is added or deleted from the DNA sequence. These changes alter the reading frame downstream of the mutation.

free energy Energy available to do work.

free radical An ionized atom with one or more unpaired electrons, resulting from electrons that have been energized by ionizing radiation being ejected from the atom; free radicals react violently with other molecules, such as DNA, causing damage by mutation.

frequency-dependent selection A type of selection that depends on how frequently or infrequently a phenotype occurs in a population.

fruit In angiosperms, a mature, ripened ovary (or group of ovaries), containing the seeds.

functional genomics The study of the function of genes and their products, beyond simply ascertaining gene sequences.

functional group A molecular group attached to a hydrocarbon that confers chemical properties or reactivities. Examples include hydroxyl (—OH), carboxylic acid (—COOH) and amino groups (—NH$_2$).

fundamental niche Also referred to as the hypothetical niche, this is the entire niche an organism could fill if there were no other interacting factors (such as competition or predation).

G

G$_0$ phase The stage of the cell cycle occupied by cells that are not actively dividing.

G$_1$ phase The phase of the cell cycle after cytokinesis and before DNA replication called the first "gap" phase. This phase is the primary growth phase of a cell.

G$_1$/S checkpoint The primary control point at which a cell "decides" whether or not to divide. Also called START and the restriction point.

G$_2$ phase The phase of the cell cycle between DNA replication and mitosis called the second "gap" phase. During this phase, the cell prepares for mitosis.

G$_2$/M checkpoint The second cell-division control point, at which division can be delayed if DNA has not been properly replicated or is damaged.

gametangium, pl. **gametangia** A cell or organ in which gametes are formed.

gamete A haploid reproductive cell.

gametocytes Cells in the malarial sporozoite life cycle capable of giving rise to gametes when in the correct host.

gametophyte In plants, the haploid (*n*), gamete-producing generation, which alternates with the diploid (2*n*) sporophyte.

ganglion, pl. **ganglia** An aggregation of nerve cell bodies; in invertebrates, ganglia are the integrative centers; in vertebrates, the term is restricted to aggregations of nerve cell bodies located outside the central nervous system.

gap gene Any of certain genes in *Drosophila* development that divide the embryo into large blocks in the process of segmentation; *hunchback* is a gap gene.

gap junction A junction between adjacent animal cells that allows the passage of materials between the cells.

gastrodermis In eumetazoan animals, the layer of digestive tissue that develops from the endoderm.

gastrula In vertebrates, the embryonic stage in which the blastula with its single layer of cells turns into a three-layered embryo made up of ectoderm, mesoderm, and endoderm.

gastrulation Developmental process that converts blastula into embryo with three embryonic germ layers: endoderm, mesoderm, and ectoderm. Involves massive cell migration to convert the hollow structure into a three-layered structure.

gene The basic unit of heredity; a sequence of DNA nucleotides on a chromosome that encodes a protein, tRNA, or rRNA molecule, or regulates the transcription of such a sequence.

gene conversion Alteration of one homologous chromosome by the cell's error-detection and repair system to make it resemble the sequence on the other homologue.

gene expression The conversion of the genotype into the phenotype; the process by which DNA is transcribed into RNA, which is then translated into a protein product.

gene pool All the alleles present in a species.

gene-for-gene hypothesis A plant defense mechanism in which a specific protein encoded by a viral, bacterial, or fungal pathogen binds to a protein encoded by a plant gene and triggers a defense response in the plant.

general transcription factor Any of a group of transcription factors that are required for formation of an initiation complex by RNA polymerase II at a promoter. This allows a basal level that can be increased by the action of specific factors.

generalized transduction A form of gene transfer in prokaryotes in which any gene can be transferred between cells. This uses a lytic bacteriophage as a carrier where the virion is accidentally packaged with host DNA.

genetic counseling The process of evaluating the risk of genetic defects occurring in offspring, testing for these defects in unborn children, and providing the parents with information about these risks and conditions.

genetic drift Random fluctuation in allele frequencies over time by chance.

genetic map An abstract map that places the relative location of genes on a chromosome based on recombination frequency.

genome The entire DNA sequence of an organism.

genomic imprinting Describes an exception to Mendelian genetics in some mammals in which the phenotype caused by an allele is exhibited when the allele comes from one parent, but not from the other.

genomic library A DNA library that contains a representation of the entire genome of an organism.

genomics The study of genomes as opposed to individual genes.

genotype The genetic constitution underlying a single trait or set of traits.

genotype frequency A measure of the occurrence of a genotype in a population, expressed as a proportion of the entire population, for example, an occurrence of 0.25 (25%) for a homozygous recessive genotype.

genus, pl. **genera** A taxonomic group that ranks below a family and above a species.

germination The resumption of growth and development by a spore or seed.

germ layers The three cell layers formed at gastrulation of the embryo that foreshadow the future organization of tissues; the layers, from the outside inward, are the ectoderm, the mesoderm, and the endoderm.

germ-line cells During zygote development, cells that are set aside from the somatic cells and that will eventually undergo meiosis to produce gametes.

gill (1) In aquatic animals, a respiratory organ, usually a thin-walled projection from some part of the external body surface, endowed with a rich capillary bed and having a large surface area. (2) In basidiomycete fungi, the plates on the underside of the cap.

globular protein Proteins with a compact tertiary structure with hydrophobic amino acids mainly in the interior.

glomerular filtrate The fluid that passes out of the capillaries of each glomerulus.

glomerulus A cluster of capillaries enclosed by Bowman's capsule.

glucagon A vertebrate hormone produced in the pancreas that acts to initiate the breakdown of glycogen to glucose subunits.

gluconeogenesis The synthesis of glucose from noncarbohydrates (such as proteins or fats).

glucose A common six-carbon sugar (C$_6$H$_{12}$O$_6$); the most common monosaccharide in most organisms.

glucose repression In *E. coli*, the preferential use of glucose even when other sugars are present; transcription of mRNA encoding the enzymes for utilizing the other sugars does not occur.

glycocalyx A "sugar coating" on the surface of a cell resulting from the presence of polysaccharides on glycolipids and glycoproteins embedded in the outer layer of the plasma membrane.

glycogen Animal starch; a complex branched polysaccharide that serves as a food reserve in animals, bacteria, and fungi.

glycolipid Lipid molecule modified within the Golgi complex by having a short sugar chain (polysaccharide) attached.

glycolysis The anaerobic breakdown of glucose; this enzyme-catalyzed process yields two molecules of pyruvate with a net of two molecules of ATP.

glycoprotein Protein molecule modified within the Golgi complex by having a short sugar chain (polysaccharide) attached.

glyoxysome A small cellular organelle or microbody containing enzymes necessary for conversion of fats into carbohydrates.

glyphosate A biodegradable herbicide that works by inhibiting EPSP synthetase, a plant enzyme that makes aromatic amino acids; genetic engineering has allowed crop species to be created that are resistant to glyphosate.

Golgi apparatus (Golgi body) A collection of flattened stacks of membranes in the cytoplasm of eukaryotic cells; functions in collection, packaging, and distribution of molecules synthesized in the cell.

G protein A protein that binds guanosine triphosphate (GTP) and assists in the function of cell-surface receptors. When the receptor binds its signal molecule, the G protein binds GTP and is activated to start a chain of events within the cell.

G protein-coupled receptor (GPCR) A receptor that acts through a heterotrimeric (three component) G protein to activate effector proteins. The effector proteins then function as enzymes to produce second messengers such as cAMP or IP_3.

gradualism The view that species change very slowly in ways that may be imperceptible from one generation to the next but that accumulate and lead to major changes over thousands or millions of years.

Gram stain Staining technique that divides bacteria into gram-negative or gram-positive based on retention of a violet dye. Differences in staining are due to cell wall construction.

granum (pl. grana) A stacked column of flattened, interconnected disks (thylakoids) that are part of the thylakoid membrane system in chloroplasts.

gravitropism Growth response to gravity in plants; formerly called geotropism.

ground meristem The primary meristem, or meristematic tissue, that gives rise to the plant body (except for the epidermis and vascular tissues).

ground tissue In plants, a type of tissue that performs many functions, including support, storage, secretion, and photosynthesis; may consist of many cell types.

growth factor Any of a number of proteins that bind to membrane receptors and initiate intracellular signaling systems that result in cell growth and division.

guard cell In plants, one of a pair of sausage-shaped cells flanking a stoma; the guard cells open and close the stomata.

guttation The exudation of liquid water from leaves due to root pressure.

gymnosperm A seed plant with seeds not enclosed in an ovary; conifers are gymnosperms.

gynoecium The aggregate of carpels in the flower of a seed plant.

H

habitat The environment of an organism; the place where it is usually found.

habituation A form of learning; a diminishing response to a repeated stimulus.

halophyte A plant that is salt-tolerant.

haplodiploidy A phenomenon occurring in certain organisms such as wasps, wherein both haploid (male) and diploid (female) individuals are encountered.

haploid Having only one set of chromosomes (n), in contrast to diploid ($2n$).

haplotype A region of a chromosome that is usually inherited intact, that is, it does not undergo recombination. These are identified based on analysis of SNPs.

Hardy-Weinberg equilibrium A mathematical description of the fact that allele and genotype frequencies remain constant in a random-mating population in the absence of inbreeding, selection, or other evolutionary forces; usually stated: if the frequency of allele a is p and the frequency of allele b is q, then the genotype frequencies after one generation of random mating will always be $p_2 + 2pq + q_2 = 1$.

Haversian canal Narrow channels that run parallel to the length of a bone and contain blood vessels and nerve cells.

heat A measure of the random motion of molecules; the greater the heat, the greater the motion. Heat is one form of kinetic energy.

heat of vaporization The amount of energy required to change 1 g of a substance from a liquid to a gas.

heavy metal Any of the metallic elements with high atomic numbers, such as arsenic, cadmium, lead, etc. Many heavy metals are toxic to animals even in small amounts.

helicase Any of a group of enzymes that unwind the two DNA strands in the double helix to facilitate DNA replication.

helix-turn-helix motif A common DNA-binding motif found in regulatory proteins; it consists of two α-helices linked by a nonhelical segment (the "turn").

helper T cell A class of white blood cells that initiates both the cell-mediated immune response and the humoral immune response; helper T cells are the targets of the AIDS virus (HIV).

hemoglobin A globular protein in vertebrate red blood cells and in the plasma of many invertebrates that carries oxygen and carbon dioxide.

hemopoietic stem cell The cells in bone marrow where blood cells are formed.

hermaphroditism Condition in which an organism has both male and female functional reproductive organs.

heterochromatin The portion of a eukaryotic chromosome that is not transcribed into RNA; remains condensed in interphase and stains intensely in histological preparations.

heterochrony An alteration in the timing of developmental events due to a genetic change; for example, a mutation that delays flowering in plants.

heterokaryotic In fungi, having two or more genetically distinct types of nuclei within the same mycelium.

heterosporous In vascular plants, having spores of two kinds, namely, microspores and megaspores.

heterotroph An organism that cannot derive energy from photosynthesis or inorganic chemicals, and so must feed on other plants and animals, obtaining chemical energy by degrading their organic molecules.

heterozygote advantage The situation in which individuals heterozygous for a trait have a selective advantage over those who are homozygous; an example is sickle cell anemia.

heterozygous Having two different alleles of the same gene; the term is usually applied to one or more specific loci, as in "heterozygous with respect to the W locus" (that is, the genotype is W/w).

Hfr cell An E. coli cell that has a high frequency of recombination due to integration of an F plasmid into its genome.

histone One of a group of relatively small, very basic polypeptides, rich in arginine and lysine, forming the core of nucleosomes around which DNA is wrapped in the first stage of chromosome condensation.

histone protein Any of eight proteins with an overall positive charge that associate in a complex. The DNA duplex coils around a core of eight histone proteins, held by its negatively charged phosphate groups, forming a nucleosome.

holoblastic cleavage Process in vertebrate embryos in which the cleavage divisions all occur at the same rate, yielding a uniform cell size in the blastula.

homeobox A sequence of 180 nucleotides located in homeotic genes that produces a 60-amino-acid peptide sequence (the homeodomain) active in transcription factors.

homeodomain motif A special class of helix-turn-helix motifs found in regulatory proteins that control development in eukaryotes.

homeosis A change in the normal spatial pattern of gene expression that can result in homeotic mutants where a wild-type structure develops in the wrong place in or on the organism.

homeostasis The maintenance of a relatively stable internal physiological environment in an organism; usually involves some form of feedback self-regulation.

homeotherm An organism, such as a bird or mammal, capable of maintaining a stable body temperature independent of the environmental temperature. *See* endotherm.

homeotic gene One of a series of "master switch" genes that determine the form of segments developing in the embryo.

hominid Any primate in the human family, Hominidae. *Homo sapiens* is the only living representative.

hominoid Collectively, hominids and apes; the monkeys and hominoids constitute the anthropoid primates.

homokaryotic In fungi, having nuclei with the same genetic makeup within a mycelium.

homologue One of a pair of chromosomes of the same kind located in a diploid cell; one copy of each pair of homologues comes from each gamete that formed the zygote.

homologous (1) Refers to similar structures that have the same evolutionary origin. (2) Refers to a pair of the same kind of chromosome in a diploid cell.

homoplasy In cladistics, a shared character state that has not been inherited from a common ancestor exhibiting that state; may result from convergent evolution or evolutionary reversal. The wings of birds and of bats, which are convergent structures, are examples.

homosporous In some plants, production of only one type of spore rather than differentiated types. *Compare with* heterosporous.

homozygous Being a homozygote, having two identical alleles of the same gene; the term is usually applied to one or more specific loci, as in "homozygous with respect to the *W* locus" (i.e., the genotype is *W/W* or *w/w*).

horizontal gene transfer (HGT) The passing of genes laterally between species; more prevalent very early in the history of life.

hormone A molecule, usually a peptide or steroid, that is produced in one part of an organism and triggers a specific cellular reaction in target tissues and organs some distance away.

host range The range of organisms that can be infected by a particular virus.

Hox **gene** A group of homeobox-containing genes that control developmental events, usually found organized into clusters of genes. These genes have been conserved in many different multicellular animals, both invertebrates and vertebrates, although the number of clusters changes in lineages, leading to four clusters in vertebrates.

humoral immunity Arm of the adaptive immune system involving B cells that produce soluble antibodies specific for foreign antigens.

humus Partly decayed organic material found in topsoil.

hybridization The mating of unlike parents.

hydration shell A "cloud" of water molecules surrounding a dissolved substance, such as sucrose or Na⁺ and Cl⁻ ions.

hydrogen bond A weak association formed with hydrogen in polar covalent bonds. The partially positive hydrogen is attracted to partially negative atoms in polar covalent bonds. In water, oxygen and hydrogen in different water molecules form hydrogen bonds.

hydrolysis reaction A reaction that breaks a bond by the addition of water. This is the reverse of dehydration, a reaction that joins molecules with the loss of water.

hydrophilic Literally translates as "water-loving" and describes substances that are soluble in water. These must be either polar or charged (ions).

hydrophobic Literally translates as "water-fearing" and describes nonpolar substances that are not soluble in water. Nonpolar molecules in water associate with each other and form droplets.

hydrophobic exclusion The tendency of nonpolar molecules to aggregate together when placed in water. Exclusion refers to the action of water in forcing these molecules together.

hydrostatic skeleton The skeleton of most soft-bodied invertebrates that have neither an internal nor an external skeleton. They use the relative incompressibility of the water within their bodies as a kind of skeleton.

hyperosmotic The condition in which a (hyperosmotic) solution has a higher osmotic concentration than that of a second solution. *Compare with* hypoosmotic.

hyperpolarization Above-normal negativity of a cell membrane during its resting potential.

hypersensitive response Plants respond to pathogens by selectively killing plant cells to block the spread of the pathogen.

hypertonic A solution with a higher concentration of solutes than the cell. A cell in a hypertonic solution tends to lose water by osmosis.

hypha, pl. hyphae A filament of a fungus or oomycete; collectively, the hyphae constitute the mycelium.

hypocotyl The region immediately below where the cotyledons are attached.

hypoosmotic The condition in which a (hypoosmotic) solution has a lower osmotic concentration than that of a second solution. *Compare with* hyperosmotic.

hypothalamus A region of the vertebrate brain just below the cerebral hemispheres, under the thalamus; a center of the autonomic nervous system, responsible for the integration and correlation of many neural and endocrine functions.

hypotonic A solution with a lower concentration of solutes than the cell. A cell in a hypotonic solution tends to take in water by osmosis.

I

icosahedron A structure consisting of 20 equilateral triangular facets; this is commonly seen in viruses and forms one kind of viral capsid.

imaginal disk One of about a dozen groups of cells set aside in the abdomen of a larval insect and committed to forming key parts of the adult insect's body.

immune response In vertebrates, a defensive reaction of the body to invasion by a foreign substance or organism. *See* antibody and B cell.

immunoglobulin An antibody molecule.

immunological tolerance Process where immune system learns to not react to self-antigens.

in vitro mutagenesis The ability to create mutations at any site in a cloned gene to examine the mutations' effects on function.

inbreeding The breeding of genetically related plants or animals; inbreeding tends to increase homozygosity.

inclusive fitness Describes the sum of the number of genes directly passed on in an individual's offspring and those genes passed on indirectly by kin (other than offspring) whose existence results from the benefit of the individual's altruism.

incomplete dominance Describes a case in which two or more alleles of a gene do not display clear dominance. The phenotype of a heterozygote is intermediate between the homozygous forms. For example, crossing red-flowered with white-flowered four o'clocks yields pink heterozygotes.

independent assortment In a dihybrid cross, describes the random assortment of alleles for each of the genes. For genes on different chromosomes this results from the random orientations of different homologous pairs during metaphase I of meiosis. For genes on the same chromosome, this occurs when the two loci are far enough apart for roughly equal numbers of odd- and even-numbered multiple crossover events.

indeterminate development A type of development in animals in which the first few embryonic cells are identical daughter cells, any one of which could develop separately into a complete organism; their fate is indeterminate.

inducer exclusion Part of the mechanism of glucose repression in *E. coli* in which the presence of glucose prevents the entry of lactose such that the *lac* operon cannot be induced.

induction (1) Production of enzymes in response to a substrate; a mechanism by which binding of an inducer to a repressor allows transcription of an operon. This is seen in catabolic operons and results in production of enzymes to degrade a compound only when it is available. (2) In embryonic development, the process by which the development of a cell is influenced by interaction with an adjacent cell.

inductive reasoning The logical application of specific observations to make a generalization. In science, inductive reasoning is used to formulate testable hypotheses.

industrial melanism Phrase used to describe the evolutionary process in which initially light-colored organisms become dark as a result of natural selection.

inflammatory response A generalized nonspecific response to infection that acts to clear an infected area of infecting microbes and dead tissue cells so that tissue repair can begin.

inhalant siphon In bivalve mollusks, the siphon through which incoming water enters the body.

inheritance of acquired characteristics Also known as Lamarckism; the theory, now discounted, that individuals genetically pass on to their offspring physical and behavioral changes developed during the individuals' own lifetime.

inhibitor A substance that binds to an enzyme and decreases its activity.

initiation factor One of several proteins involved in the formation of an initiation complex in prokaryote polypeptide synthesis.

initiator tRNA A tRNA molecule involved in the beginning of translation. In prokaryotes, the initiator tRNA is charged with *N*-formylmethionine (tRNA^{fMet}); in eukaryotes, the tRNA is charged simply with methionine.

inorganic phosphate A phosphate molecule that is not a part of an organic molecule; inorganic phosphate groups are added and removed in the formation and breakdown of ATP and in many other cellular reactions.

inositol-1,4,5-trisphosphate (IP₃) Second messenger produced by the cleavage of phosphatidylinositol-4,5-bisphosphate.

insertional inactivation Destruction of a gene's function by the insertion of a transposon.

instar A larval developmental stage in insects.

integrin Any of a group of cell-surface proteins involved in adhesion of cells to substrates.

Critical to migrating cells moving through the cell matrix in tissues such as connective tissue.

intercalary meristem A type of meristem that arises in stem internodes in some plants, such as corn and horsetails; responsible for elongation of the internodes.

interferon In vertebrates, a protein produced in virus-infected cells that inhibits viral multiplication.

intermembrane space The outer compartment of a mitochondrion that lies between the two membranes.

interneuron (association neuron) A nerve cell found only in the middle of the spinal cord that acts as a functional link between sensory neurons and motor neurons.

internode In plants, the region of a stem between two successive nodes.

interoceptor A receptor that senses information related to the body itself, its internal condition, and its position.

interphase The period between two mitotic or meiotic divisions in which a cell grows and its DNA replicates; includes G_1, S, and G_2 phases.

intracellular receptor A signal receptor that binds a ligand inside a cell, such as the receptors for NO, steroid hormones, vitamin D, and thyroid hormones.

intron Portion of mRNA as transcribed from eukaryotic DNA that is removed by enzymes before the mature mRNA is translated into protein. *See* exon.

inversion A reversal in order of a segment of a chromosome; also, to turn inside out, as in embryogenesis of sponges or discharge of a nematocyst.

ionizing radiation High-energy radiation that is highly mutagenic, producing free radicals that react with DNA; includes X-rays and γ-rays.

isomer One of a group of molecules identical in atomic composition but differing in structural arrangement; for example, glucose and fructose.

isosmotic The condition in which the osmotic concentrations of two solutions are equal, so that no net water movement occurs between them by osmosis.

isotonic A solution having the same concentration of solutes as the cell. A cell in an isotonic solution takes in and loses the same amount of water.

isotope Different forms of the same element with the same number of protons but different numbers of neutrons.

J

jasmonic acid An organic molecule that is part of a plant's wound response; it signals the production of a proteinase inhibitor.

K

karyotype The morphology of the chromosomes of an organism as viewed with a light microscope.

keratin A tough, fibrous protein formed in epidermal tissues and modified into skin, feathers, hair, and hard structures such as horns and nails.

key innovation A newly evolved trait in a species that allows members to use resources or

other aspects of the environment that were previously inaccessible.

kidney In vertebrates, the organ that filters the blood to remove nitrogenous wastes and regulates the balance of water and solutes in blood plasma.

kilocalorie Unit describing the amount of heat required to raise the temperature of a kilogram of water by 1°C; sometimes called a Calorie, equivalent to 1000 calories.

kinase cascade A series of protein kinases that phosphorylate each other in succession; a kinase cascade can amplify signals during the signal transduction process.

kinesis Changes in activity level in an animal that are dependent on stimulus intensity. *See* kinetic energy.

kinetic energy The energy of motion.

kinetochore Disk-shaped protein structure within the centromere to which the spindle fibers attach during mitosis or meiosis. *See* centromere.

kingdom The second highest commonly used taxonomic category.

kin selection Selection favoring relatives; an increase in the frequency of related individuals (kin) in a population, leading to an increase in the relative frequency in the population of those alleles shared by members of the kin group.

knockout mice Mice in which a known gene is inactivated ("knocked out") using recombinant DNA and ES cells.

Krebs cycle Another name for the citric acid cycle; also called the tricarboxylic acid (TCA) cycle.

L

labrum The upper lip of insects and crustaceans situated above or in front of the mandibles.

***lac* operon** In *E. coli*, the operon containing genes that encode the enzymes to metabolize lactose.

lagging strand The DNA strand that must be synthesized discontinuously because of the 5′-to-3′ directionality of DNA polymerase during replication, and the antiparallel nature of DNA. Compare *leading strand*.

larva A developmental stage that is unlike the adult found in organisms that undergo metamorphosis. Embryos develop into larvae that produce the adult form by metamorphosis.

larynx The voice box; a cartilaginous organ that lies between the pharynx and trachea and is responsible for sound production in vertebrates.

lateral line system A sensory system encountered in fish, through which mechanoreceptors in a line down the side of the fish are sensitive to motion.

lateral meristems In vascular plants, the meristems that give rise to secondary tissue; the vascular cambium and cork cambium.

Law of Independent Assortment Mendel's second law of heredity, stating that genes located on nonhomologous chromosomes assort independently of one another.

Law of Segregation Mendel's first law of heredity, stating that alternative alleles for the same gene segregate from each other in production of gametes.

leading strand The DNA strand that can be synthesized continuously from the origin of replication. Compare *lagging strand*.

leaf primordium, pl. primordia A lateral outgrowth from the apical meristem that will eventually become a leaf.

lenticels Spongy areas in the cork surfaces of stem, roots, and other plant parts that allow interchange of gases between internal tissues and the atmosphere through the periderm.

leucine zipper motif A motif in regulatory proteins in which two different protein subunits associate to form a single DNA-binding site; the proteins are connected by an association between hydrophobic regions containing leucines (the "zipper").

leucoplast In plant cells, a colorless plastid in which starch grains are stored; usually found in cells not exposed to light.

leukocyte A white blood cell; a diverse array of nonhemoglobin-containing blood cells, including phagocytic macrophages and antibody-producing lymphocytes.

lichen Symbiotic association between a fungus and a photosynthetic organism such as a green alga or cyanobacterium.

ligand A signaling molecule that binds to a specific receptor protein, initiating signal transduction in cells.

light-dependent reactions In photosynthesis, the reactions in which light energy is captured and used in production of ATP and NADPH. In plants this involves the action of two linked photosystems.

light-independent reactions In photosynthesis, the reactions of the Calvin cycle in which ATP and NADPH from the light-dependent reactions are used to reduce CO_2 and produce organic compounds such as glucose. This involves the process of carbon fixation, or the conversion of inorganic carbon (CO_2) to organic carbon (ultimately carbohydrates).

lignin A highly branched polymer that makes plant cell walls more rigid; an important component of wood.

limbic system The hypothalamus, together with the network of neurons that link the hypothalamus to some areas of the cerebral cortex. Responsible for many of the most deep-seated drives and emotions of vertebrates, including pain, anger, sex, hunger, thirst, and pleasure.

linked genes Genes that are physically close together and therefore tend to segregate together; recombination occurring between linked genes can be used to produce a map of genetic distance for a chromosome.

linkage disequilibrium Association of alleles for 2 or more loci in a population that is higher than expected by chance.

lipase An enzyme that catalyzes the hydrolysis of fats.

lipid A nonpolar hydrophobic organic molecule that is insoluble in water (which is polar) but dissolves readily in nonpolar organic solvents; includes fats, oils, waxes, steroids, phospholipids, and carotenoids.

lipid bilayer The structure of a cellular membrane, in which two layers of phospholipids spontaneously align so that the hydrophilic head groups are exposed to water, while the hydrophobic fatty acid tails are pointed toward the center of the membrane.

lipopolysaccharide A lipid with a polysaccharide molecule attached; found in the outer membrane layer of gram-negative bacteria; the outer membrane layer protects the cell wall from antibiotic attack.

locus The position on a chromosome where a gene is located.

long interspersed element (LINE) Any of a type of large transposable element found in humans and other primates that contains all the biochemical machinery needed for transposition.

long terminal repeat (LTR) A particular type of retrotransposon that has repeated elements at its ends. These elements make up 8% of the human genome.

loop of Henle In the kidney of birds and mammals, a hairpin-shaped portion of the renal tubule in which water and salt are reabsorbed from the glomerular filtrate by diffusion.

lophophore A horseshoe-shaped crown of ciliated tentacles that surrounds the mouth of certain spiralian animals; seen in the phyla Brachiopoda and Bryozoa.

lumen A term for any bounded opening; for example, the cisternal space of the endoplasmic reticulum of eukaryotic cells, the passage through which blood flows inside a blood vessel, and the passage through which material moves inside the intestine during digestion.

luteal phase The second phase of the female reproductive cycle, during which the mature eggs are released into the fallopian tubes, a process called ovulation.

lymph In animals, a colorless fluid derived from blood by filtration through capillary walls in the tissues.

lymphatic system In animals, an open vascular system that reclaims water that has entered interstitial regions from the bloodstream (lymph); includes the lymph nodes, spleen, thymus, and tonsils.

lymphocyte A type of white blood cell. Lymphocytes are responsible for the immune response; there are two principal classes: B cells and T cells.

lymphokine A regulatory molecule that is secreted by lymphocytes. In the immune response, lymphokines secreted by helper T cells unleash the cell-mediated immune response.

lysis Disintegration of a cell by rupture of its plasma membrane.

lysogenic cycle A viral cycle in which the viral DNA becomes integrated into the host chromosome and is replicated during cell reproduction. Results in vertical rather than horizontal transmission.

lysosome A membrane-bounded vesicle containing digestive enzymes that is produced by the Golgi apparatus in eukaryotic cells.

lytic cycle A viral cycle in which the host cell is killed (lysed) by the virus after viral duplication to release viral particles.

M

macroevolution The creation of new species and the extinction of old ones.

macromolecule An extremely large biological molecule; refers specifically to proteins, nucleic acids, polysaccharides, lipids, and complexes of these.

macronutrients Inorganic chemical elements required in large amounts for plant growth, such as nitrogen, potassium, calcium, phosphorus, magnesium, and sulfur.

macrophage A large phagocytic cell that is able to engulf and digest cellular debris and invading bacteria.

madreporite A sievelike plate on the surface of echinoderms through which water enters the water–vascular system.

***MADS* box gene** Any of a family of genes identified by possessing shared motifs that are the predominant homeotic genes of plants; a small number of *MADS* box genes are also found in animals.

major groove The larger of the two grooves in a DNA helix, where the paired nucleotides' hydrogen bonds are accessible; regulatory proteins can recognize and bind to regions in the major groove.

major histocompatibility complex (MHC) A set of protein cell-surface markers anchored in the plasma membrane, which the immune system uses to identify "self." All the cells of a given individual have the same "self" marker, called an MHC protein.

Malpighian tubules Blind tubules opening into the hindgut of terrestrial arthropods; they function as excretory organs.

mandibles In crustaceans, insects, and myriapods, the appendages immediately posterior to the antennae; used to seize, hold, bite, or chew food.

mantle The soft, outermost layer of the body wall in mollusks; the mantle secretes the shell.

map unit Each 1% of recombination frequency between two genetic loci; the unit is termed a centimorgan (cM) or simply a map unit (m.u.).

marsupial A mammal in which the young are born early in their development, sometimes as soon as eight days after fertilization, and are retained in a pouch.

mass extinction A relatively sudden, sharp decline in the number of species; for example, the extinction at the end of the Cretaceous period in which the dinosaurs and a variety of other organisms disappeared.

mass flow hypothesis The overall process by which materials move in the phloem of plants.

mast cells Leukocytes with granules containing molecules that initiate inflammation.

maternal inheritance A mode of uniparental inheritance from the female parent; for example, in humans mitochondria and their genomes are inherited from the mother.

matrix In mitochondria, the solution in the interior space surrounded by the cristae that contains the enzymes and other molecules involved in oxidative respiration; more generally, that part of a tissue within which an organ or process is embedded.

medusa A free-floating, often umbrella-shaped body form found in cnidarian animals, such as jellyfish.

megapascal (MPa) A unit of measure used for pressure in water potential.

megaphyll In plants, a leaf that has several to many veins connecting it to the vascular cylinder of the stem; most plants have megaphylls.

mesoglea A layer of gelatinous material found between the epidermis and gastrodermis of eumetazoans; it contains the muscles in most of these animals.

mesohyl A gelatinous, protein-rich matrix found between the choanocyte layer and the epithelial layer of the body of a sponge; various types of amoeboid cells may occur in the mesohyl.

metacercaria An encysted form of a larval liver fluke, found in muscle tissue of an infected animal; if the muscle is eaten, cysts dissolve in the digestive tract, releasing the flukes into the body of the new host.

methylation The addition of a methyl group to bases (primarily cytosine) in DNA. Cytosine methylation is correlated with DNA that is not expressed.

meiosis I The first round of cell division in meiosis; it is referred to as a "reduction division" because homologous chromosomes separate, and the daughter cells have only the haploid number of chromosomes.

meiosis II The second round of division in meiosis, during which the two haploid cells from meiosis I undergo a mitosis-like division without DNA replication to produce four haploid daughter cells.

membrane receptor A signal receptor present as an integral protein in the cell membrane, such as GPCRs, chemically gated ion channels in neurons, and RTKs.

Mendelian ratio The characteristic dominant-to-recessive phenotypic ratios that Mendel observed in his genetics experiments. For example, the F_2 generation in a monohybrid cross shows a ratio of 3:1; the F_2 generation in a dihybrid cross shows a ratio of 9:3:3:1.

menstruation Periodic sloughing off of the blood-enriched lining of the uterus when pregnancy does not occur.

meristem Undifferentiated plant tissue from which new cells arise.

meroblastic cleavage A type of cleavage in the eggs of reptiles, birds, and some fish. Occurs only on the blastodisc.

mesoderm One of the three embryonic germ layers that form in the gastrula; gives rise to muscle, bone and other connective tissue, the peritoneum, the circulatory system, and most of the excretory and reproductive systems.

mesophyll The photosynthetic parenchyma of a leaf, located within the epidermis.

messenger RNA (mRNA) The RNA transcribed from structural genes; RNA molecules complementary to a portion of one strand of DNA, which are translated by the ribosomes to form protein.

metabolism The sum of all chemical processes occurring within a living cell or organism.

metamorphosis Process in which a marked change in form takes place during postembryonic development as, for example, from tadpole to frog.

metaphase The stage of mitosis or meiosis during which microtubules become organized into a spindle and the chromosomes come to lie in the spindle's equatorial plane.

metastasis The process by which cancer cells move from their point of origin to other locations in the body; also, a population of cancer cells in a secondary location, the result of movement from the primary tumor.

methanogens Obligate, anaerobic archaebacteria that produce methane.

microarray DNA sequences are placed on a microscope slide or chip with a robot. The microarray can then be probed with RNA from specific tissues to identify expressed DNA.

microbody A cellular organelle bounded by a single membrane and containing a variety of enzymes; generally derived from endoplasmic reticulum; includes peroxisomes and glyoxysomes.

microevolution Refers to the evolutionary process itself. Evolution within a species. Also called adaptation.

micronutrient A mineral required in only minute amounts for plant growth, such as iron, chlorine, copper, manganese, zinc, molybdenum, and boron.

microphyll In plants, a leaf that has only one vein connecting it to the vascular cylinder of the stem; the club mosses in particular have microphylls.

micropyle In the ovules of seed plants, an opening in the integuments through which the pollen tube usually enters.

micro-RNA (miRNA) A class of RNAs that are very short and only recently could be detected. *See also* small interfering RNAs (siRNAs).

microtubule In eukaryotic cells, a long, hollow protein cylinder, composed of the protein tubulin; these influence cell shape, move the chromosomes in cell division, and provide the functional internal structure of cilia and flagella.

microvillus Cytoplasmic projection from epithelial cells; microvilli greatly increase the surface area of the small intestine.

middle lamella The layer of intercellular material, rich in pectic compounds, that cements together the primary walls of adjacent plant cells.

mimicry The resemblance in form, color, or behavior of certain organisms (mimics) to other more powerful or more protected ones (models).

miracidium The ciliated first-stage larva inside the egg of the liver fluke; eggs are passed in feces, and if they reach water they may be eaten by a host snail in which they continue their life cycle.

missense mutation A base substitution mutation that results in the alteration of a single amino acid.

mitochondrion The organelle called the powerhouse of the cell. Consists of an outer membrane, an elaborate inner membrane that supports electron transport and chemiosmotic synthesis of ATP, and a soluble matrix containing Krebs cycle enzymes.

mitogen-activated protein (MAP) kinase Any of a class of protein kinases that activate transcription factors to alter gene expression. A mitogen is any molecule that stimulates cell division. MAP kinases are activated by kinase cascades.

mitosis Somatic cell division; nuclear division in which the duplicated chromosomes separate to form two genetically identical daughter nuclei.

molar concentration Concentration expressed as moles of a substance in 1 L of pure water.

mole The weight of a substance in grams that corresponds to the atomic masses of all the component atoms in a molecule of that substance. One mole of a compound always contains 6.023×10^{23} molecules.

molecular clock method In evolutionary theory, the method in which the rate of evolution of a molecule is constant through time.

molecular cloning The isolation and amplification of a specific sequence of DNA.

monocot Short for monocotyledon; flowering plant in which the embryos have only one cotyledon, the floral parts are generally in threes, and the leaves typically are parallel-veined.

monocyte A type of leukocyte that becomes a phagocytic cell (macrophage) after moving into tissues.

monoecious A plant in which the staminate and pistillate flowers are separate, but borne on the same individual.

monomer The smallest chemical subunit of a polymer. The monosaccharide α-glucose is the monomer found in plant starch, a polysaccharide.

monophyletic In phylogenetic classification, a group that includes the most recent common ancestor of the group and all its descendants. A clade is a monophyletic group.

monosaccharide A simple sugar that cannot be decomposed into smaller sugar molecules.

monosomic Describes the condition in which a chromosome has been lost due to nondisjunction during meiosis, producing a diploid embryo with only one of these autosomes.

monotreme An egg-laying mammal.

morphogen A signal molecule produced by an embryonic organizer region that informs surrounding cells of their distance from the organizer, thus determining relative positions of cells during development.

morphogenesis The development of an organism's body form, namely its organs and anatomical features; it may involve apoptosis as well as cell division, differentiation, and changes in cell shape.

morphology The form and structure of an organism.

morula Solid ball of cells in the early stage of embryonic development.

mosaic development A pattern of embryonic development in which initial cells produced by cleavage divisions contain different developmental signals (determinants) from the egg, setting the individual cells on different developmental paths.

motif A substructure in proteins that confers function and can be found in multiple proteins. One example is the helix-turn-helix motif found in a number of proteins that is used to bind to DNA.

motor (efferent) neuron Neuron that transmits nerve impulses from the central nervous system to an effector, which is typically a muscle or gland.

M phase The phase of cell division during which chromosomes are separated. The spindle assembles, binds to the chromosomes, and moves the sister chromatids apart.

M phase-promoting factor (MPF) A Cdk enzyme active at the G_2/M checkpoint.

Müllerian mimicry A phenomenon in which two or more unrelated but protected species resemble one another, thus achieving a kind of group defense.

multidrug-resistant (MDR) strain Any bacterial strain that has become resistant to more than one antibiotic drug; MDR *Staphylococcus* strains, for example, are responsible for many infection deaths.

multienzyme complex An assembly consisting of several enzymes catalyzing different steps in a sequence of reactions. Close proximity of these related enzymes speeds the overall process, making it more efficient.

multigene family A collection of related genes on a single chromosome or on different chromosomes.

muscle fiber A long, cylindrical, multinucleated cell containing numerous myofibrils, which is capable of contraction when stimulated.

mutagen An agent that induces changes in DNA (mutations); includes physical agents that damage DNA and chemicals that alter DNA bases.

mutation A permanent change in a cell's DNA; includes changes in nucleotide sequence, alteration of gene position, gene loss or duplication, and insertion of foreign sequences.

mutualism A symbiotic association in which two (or more) organisms live together, and both members benefit.

mycelium, pl. mycelia In fungi, a mass of hyphae.

mycorrhiza, pl. mycorrhizae A symbiotic association between fungi and the roots of a plant.

myelin sheath A fatty layer surrounding the long axons of motor neurons in the peripheral nervous system of vertebrates.

myofilament A contractile microfilament, composed largely of actin and myosin, within muscle.

myosin One of the two protein components of microfilaments (the other is actin); a principal component of vertebrate muscle.

N

natural killer cell A cell that does not kill invading microbes, but rather, the cells infected by them.

natural selection The differential reproduction of genotypes; caused by factors in the environment; leads to evolutionary change.

nauplius A larval form characteristic of crustaceans.

negative control A type of control at the level of DNA transcription initiation in which the frequency of initiation is decreased; repressor proteins mediate negative control.

negative feedback A homeostatic control mechanism whereby an increase in some substance or activity inhibits the process leading to the increase; also known as feedback inhibition.

nematocyst A harpoonlike structure found in the cnidocytes of animals in the phylum Cnidaria, which includes the jellyfish among other groups; the nematocyst, when released, stings and helps capture prey.

nephridium, pl. **nephridia** In invertebrates, a tubular excretory structure.

nephrid organ A filtration system of many freshwater invertebrates in which water and waste pass from the body across the membrane into a collecting organ, from which they are expelled to the outside through a pore.

nephron Functional unit of the vertebrate kidney; one of numerous tubules involved in filtration and selective reabsorption of blood; each nephron consists of a Bowman's capsule, an enclosed glomerulus, and a long attached tubule; in humans, called a renal tubule.

nephrostome The funnel-shaped opening that leads to the nephridium, which is the excretory organ of mollusks.

nerve A group or bundle of nerve fibers (axons) with accompanying neurological cells, held together by connective tissue; located in the peripheral nervous system.

nerve cord One of the distinguishing features of chordates, running lengthwise just beneath the embryo's dorsal surface; in vertebrates, differentiates into the brain and spinal cord.

neural crest A special strip of cells that develops just before the neural groove closes over to form the neural tube in embryonic development.

neural groove The long groove formed along the long axis of the embryo by a layer of ectodermal cells.

neural tube The dorsal tube, formed from the neural plate, that differentiates into the brain and spinal cord.

neuroglia Nonconducting nerve cells that are intimately associated with neurons and appear to provide nutritional support.

neuromuscular junction The structure formed when the tips of axons contact (innervate) a muscle fiber.

neuron A nerve cell specialized for signal transmission; includes cell body, dendrites, and axon.

neurotransmitter A chemical released at the axon terminal of a neuron that travels across the synaptic cleft, binds a specific receptor on the far side, and depending on the nature of the receptor, depolarizes or hyperpolarizes a second neuron or a muscle or gland cell.

neurulation A process in early embryonic development by which a dorsal band of ectoderm thickens and rolls into the neural tube.

neutrophil An abundant type of granulocyte capable of engulfing microorganisms and other foreign particles; neutrophils comprise about 50–70% of the total number of white blood cells.

niche The role played by a particular species in its environment.

nicotinamide adenine dinucleotide (NAD) A molecule that becomes reduced (to NADH) as it carries high-energy electrons from oxidized molecules and delivers them to ATP-producing pathways in the cell.

NADH dehydrogenase An enzyme located on the inner mitochondrial membrane that catalyzes the oxidation by NAD^+ of pyruvate to acetyl-CoA. This reaction links glycolysis and the Krebs cycle.

nitrification The oxidization of ammonia or nitrite to produce nitrate, the form of nitrogen taken up by plants; some bacteria are capable of nitrification.

nociceptor A naked dendrite that acts as a receptor in response to a pain stimulus.

nocturnal Active primarily at night.

node The part of a plant stem where one or more leaves are attached. *See* internode.

node of Ranvier A gap formed at the point where two Schwann cells meet and where the axon is in direct contact with the surrounding intercellular fluid.

nodule In plants, a specialized tissue that surrounds and houses beneficial bacteria, such as root nodules of legumes that contain nitrogen-fixing bacteria.

nonassociative learning A learned behavior that does not require an animal to form an association between two stimuli, or between a stimulus and a response.

noncompetitive inhibitor An inhibitor that binds to a location other than the active site of an enzyme, changing the enzyme's shape so that it cannot bind the substrate.

noncyclic photophosphorylation The set of light-dependent reactions of the two plant photosystems, in which excited electrons are shuttled between the two photosystems, producing a proton gradient that is used for the chemiosmotic synthesis of ATP. The electrons are used to reduce NADP to NADPH. Lost electrons are replaced by the oxidation of water producing O_2.

nondisjunction The failure of homologues or sister chromatids to separate during mitosis or meiosis, resulting in an aneuploid cell or gamete.

nonextreme archaea Archaean groups that are not extremophiles, living in more moderate environments on Earth today.

nonpolar Said of a covalent bond that involves equal sharing of electrons. Can also refer to a compound held together by nonpolar covalent bonds.

nonsense codon One of three codons (UAA, UAG, and UGA) that are not recognized by tRNAs, thus serving as "stop" signals in the mRNA message and terminating translation.

nonsense mutation A base substitution in which a codon is changed into a stop codon. The protein is truncated because of premature termination.

Northern blot A blotting technique used to identify a specific mRNA sequence in a complex mixture. *See* Southern blot.

notochord In chordates, a dorsal rod of cartilage that runs the length of the body and forms the primitive axial skeleton in the embryos of all chordates.

nucellus Tissue composing the chief pair of young ovules, in which the embryo sac develops; equivalent to a megasporangium.

nuclear envelope The bounding structure of the eukaryotic nucleus. Composed of two phospholipid bilayers with the outer one connected to the endoplasmic reticulum.

nuclear pore One of a multitude of tiny but complex openings in the nuclear envelope that allow selective passage of proteins and nucleic acids into and out of the nucleus.

nuclear receptor Intracellular receptors are found in both the cytoplasm and the nucleus. The site of action of the hormone–receptor complex is in the nucleus where they modify gene expression.

nucleic acid A nucleotide polymer; chief types are deoxyribonucleic acid (DNA), which is double-stranded, and ribonucleic acid (RNA), which is typically single-stranded.

nucleoid The area of a prokaryotic cell, usually near the center, that contains the genome in the form of DNA compacted with protein.

nucleolus In eukaryotes, the site of rRNA synthesis; a spherical body composed chiefly of rRNA in the process of being transcribed from multiple copies of rRNA genes.

nucleosome A complex consisting of a DNA duplex wound around a core of eight histone proteins.

nucleotide A single unit of nucleic acid, composed of a phosphate, a five-carbon sugar (either ribose or deoxyribose), and a purine or a pyrimidine.

nucleus In atoms, the central core, containing positively charged protons and (in all but hydrogen) electrically neutral neutrons; in eukaryotic cells, the membranous organelle that houses the chromosomal DNA; in the central nervous system, a cluster of nerve cell bodies.

nutritional mutation A mutation affecting a synthetic pathway for a vital compound, such as an amino acid or vitamin; microorganisms with a nutritional mutation must be grown on medium that supplies the missing nutrient.

O

ocellus, pl. **ocelli** A simple light receptor common among invertebrates.

octet rule Rule to describe patterns of chemical bonding in main group elements that require a total of eight electrons to complete their outer electron shell.

Okazaki fragment A short segment of DNA produced by discontinuous replication elongating in the 5′-to-3′ direction away from the replication.

olfaction The function of smelling.

ommatidium, pl. **ommatidia** The visual unit in the compound eye of arthropods; contains light-sensitive cells and a lens able to form an image.

oncogene A mutant form of a growth-regulating gene that is inappropriately "on," causing unrestrained cell growth and division.

oocyst The zygote in a sporozoan life cycle. It is surrounded by a tough cyst to prevent dehydration or other damage.

open circulatory system A circulatory system in which the blood flows into sinuses in which it mixes with body fluid and then reenters the vessels in another location.

open reading frame (ORF) A region of DNA that encodes a sequence of amino acids with no stop codons in the reading frame.

operant conditioning A learning mechanism in which the reward follows only after the correct behavioral response.

operator A regulatory site on DNA to which a repressor can bind to prevent or decrease initiation of transcription.

operculum A flat, bony, external protective covering over the gill chamber in fish.

operon A cluster of adjacent structural genes transcribed as a unit into a single mRNA molecule.

opisthosoma The posterior portion of the body of an arachnid.

oral surface The surface on which the mouth is found; used as a reference when describing the body structure of echinoderms because of their adult radial symmetry.

orbital A region around the nucleus of an atom with a high probability of containing an electron. The position of electrons can only be described by these probability distributions.

order A category of classification above the level of family and below that of class.

organ A body structure composed of several different tissues grouped in a structural and functional unit.

organelle Specialized part of a cell; literally, a small cytoplasmic organ.

orthologues Genes that reflect the conservation of a single gene found in an ancestor.

oscillating selection The situation in which selection alternately favors one phenotype at one time, and a different phenotype at a another time, for example, during drought conditions versus during wet conditions.

osculum A specialized, larger pore in sponges through which filtered water is forced to the outside of the body.

osmoconformer An animal that maintains the osmotic concentration of its body fluids at about the same level as that of the medium in which it is living.

osmosis The diffusion of water across a selectively permeable membrane (a membrane that permits the free passage of water but prevents or retards the passage of a solute); in the absence of differences in pressure or volume, the net movement of water is from the side containing a lower concentration of solute to the side containing a higher concentration.

osmotic concentration The property of a solution that takes into account all dissolved solutes in the solution; if two solutions with different osmotic concentrations are separated by a water-permeable membrane, water will move from the solution with lower osmotic concentration to the solution with higher osmotic concentration.

osmotic pressure The potential pressure developed by a solution separated from pure water by a differentially permeable membrane. The higher the solute concentration, the greater the osmotic potential of the solution; also called *osmotic potential.*

ossicle Any of a number of movable or fixed calcium-rich plates that collectively make up the endoskeleton of echinoderms.

osteoblast A bone-forming cell.

osteocyte A mature osteoblast.

outcrossing Breeding with individuals other than oneself or one's close relatives.

ovary (1) In animals, the organ in which eggs are produced. (2) In flowering plants, the enlarged basal portion of a carpel that contains the ovule(s); the ovary matures to become the fruit.

oviduct In vertebrates, the passageway through which ova (eggs) travel from the ovary to the uterus.

oviparity Refers to a type of reproduction in which the eggs are developed after leaving the body of the mother, as in reptiles.

ovoviviparity Refers to a type of reproduction in which young hatch from eggs that are retained in the mother's uterus.

ovulation In animals, the release of an egg or eggs from the ovary.

ovum, pl. **ova** The egg cell; female gamete.

oxidation Loss of an electron by an atom or molecule; in metabolism, often associated with a gain of oxygen or a loss of hydrogen.

oxidation–reduction reaction A type of paired reaction in living systems in which electrons lost from one atom (oxidation) are gained by another atom (reduction). Termed a *redox reaction* for short.

oxidative phosphorylation Synthesis of ATP by ATP synthase using energy from a proton gradient. The proton gradient is generated by electron transport, which requires oxygen.

oxygen debt The amount of oxygen required to convert the lactic acid generated in the muscles during exercise back into glucose.

oxytocin A hormone of the posterior pituitary gland that affects uterine contractions during childbirth and stimulates lactation.

ozone O_3, a stratospheric layer of the Earth's atmosphere responsible for filtering out ultraviolet radiation supplied by the Sun.

P

***p53* gene** The gene that produces the p53 protein that monitors DNA integrity and halts cell division if DNA damage is detected. Many types of cancer are associated with a damaged or absent *p53* gene.

pacemaker A patch of excitatory tissue in the vertebrate heart that initiates the heartbeat.

pair-rule gene Any of certain genes in *Drosophila* development controlled by the gap genes that are expressed in stripes that subdivide the embryo in the process of segmentation.

paleopolyploid An ancient polyploid organism used in analysis of polyploidy events in the study of a species' genome evolution.

palisade parenchyma In plant leaves, the columnar, chloroplast-containing parenchyma cells of the mesophyll. Also called *palisade cells.*

panspermia The hypothesis that meteors or cosmic dust may have brought significant amounts of complex organic molecules to Earth, kicking off the evolution of life.

papilla A small projection of tissue.

paracrine A type of chemical signaling between cells in which the effects are local and short-lived.

paralogues Two genes within an organism that arose from the duplication of one gene in an ancestor.

paraphyletic In phylogenetic classification, a group that includes the most recent common ancestor of the group, but not all its descendants.

parapodia One of the paired lateral processes on each side of most segments in polychaete annelids.

parasexuality In certain fungi, the fusion and segregation of heterokaryotic haploid nuclei to produce recombinant nuclei.

parasitism A living arrangement in which an organism lives on or in an organism of a different species and derives nutrients from it.

parenchyma cell The most common type of plant cell; characterized by large vacuoles, thin walls, and functional nuclei.

parthenogenesis The development of an egg without fertilization, as in aphids, bees, ants, and some lizards.

partial diploid (merodiploid) Describes an *E. coli* cell that carries an F′ plasmid with host genes. This makes the cell diploid for the genes carried by the F′ plasmid.

partial pressure The components of each individual gas—such as nitrogen, oxygen, and carbon dioxide—that together constitute the total air pressure.

passive transport The movement of substances across a cell's membrane without the expenditure of energy.

pedigree A consistent graphic representation of matings and offspring over multiple generations for a particular genetic trait, such as albinism or hemophilia.

pedipalps A pair of specialized appendages found in arachnids; in male spiders, these are specialized as copulatory organs, whereas in scorpions they are large pincers.

pelagic Free-swimming, usually in open water.

pellicle A tough, flexible covering in ciliates and euglenoids.

pentaradial symmetry The five-part radial symmetry characteristic of adult echinoderms.

peptide bond The type of bond that links amino acids together in proteins through a dehydration reaction.

peptidoglycan A component of the cell wall of bacteria, consisting of carbohydrate polymers linked by protein cross-bridges.

peptidyl transferase In translation, the enzyme responsible for catalyzing the formation of a peptide bond between each new amino acid and the previous amino acid in a growing polypeptide chain.

perianth In flowering plants, the petals and sepals taken together.

pericycle In vascular plants, one or more cell layers surrounding the vascular tissues of the root, bounded externally by the endodermis and internally by the phloem.

periderm Outer protective tissue in vascular plants that is produced by the cork cambium and functionally replaces epidermis when it is destroyed during secondary growth; the periderm includes the cork, cork cambium, and phelloderm.

peristalsis In animals, a series of alternating contracting and relaxing muscle movements along the length of a tube such as the oviduct or alimentary canal that tend to force material such as an egg cell or food through the tube.

peroxisome A microbody that plays an important role in the breakdown of highly oxidative hydrogen peroxide by catalase.

petal A flower part, usually conspicuously colored; one of the units of the corolla.

petiole The stalk of a leaf.

phage conversion The phenomenon by which DNA from a virus, incorporated into a host cell's genome, alters the host cell's function in a significant way; for example, the conversion of *Vibrio cholerae* bacteria into a pathogenic form that releases cholera toxin.

phage lambda (λ) A well-known bacteriophage that has been widely used in genetic studies and is often a vector for DNA libraries.

phagocyte Any cell that engulfs and devours microorganisms or other particles.

phagocytosis Endocytosis of a solid particle; the plasma membrane folds inward around the particle (which may be another cell) and engulfs it to form a vacuole.

pharyngeal pouches In chordates, embryonic regions that become pharyngeal slits in aquatic and marine chordates and vertebrates, but do not develop openings to the outside in terrestrial vertebrates.

pharyngeal slits One of the distinguishing features of chordates; a group of openings on each side of the anterior region that form a passageway from the pharynx and esophagus to the external environment.

pharynx A muscular structure lying posterior to the mouth in many animals; aids in propelling food into the digestive tract.

phenotype The realized expression of the genotype; the physical appearance or functional expression of a trait.

pheromone Chemical substance released by one organism that influences the behavior or physiological processes of another organism of the same species. Pheromones serve as sex attractants, as trail markers, and as alarm signals.

phloem In vascular plants, a food-conducting tissue basically composed of sieve elements, various kinds of parenchyma cells, fibers, and sclereids.

phoronid Any of a group of lophophorate invertebrates, now classified in the phylum Brachiopoda, that burrows into soft underwater substrates and secretes a chitinous tube in which it lives out its life; it extends its lophophore tentacles to feed on drifting food particles.

phosphatase Any of a number of enzymes that removes a phosphate group from a protein, reversing the action of a kinase.

phosphodiester bond The linkage between two sugars in the backbone of a nucleic acid molecule; the phosphate group connects the pentose sugars through a pair of ester bonds.

phospholipid Similar in structure to a fat, but having only two fatty acids attached to the glycerol backbone, with the third space linked to a phosphorylated molecule; contains a polar hydrophilic "head" end (phosphate group) and a nonpolar hydrophobic "tail" end (fatty acids).

phospholipid bilayer The main component of cell membranes; phospholipids naturally associate in a bilayer with hydrophobic fatty acids oriented to the inside and hydrophilic phosphate groups facing outward on both sides.

phosphorylation Chemical reaction resulting in the addition of a phosphate group to an organic molecule. Phosphorylation of ADP yields ATP. Many proteins are also activated or inactivated by phosphorylation.

photic zone The area in an aquatic habitat that receives sufficient light for photosynthesis to occur and net primary productivity to be positive.

photoelectric effect The ability of a beam of light to excite electrons, creating an electrical current.

photon A particle of light having a discrete amount of energy. The wave concept of light explains the different colors of the spectrum, whereas the particle concept of light explains the energy transfers during photosynthesis.

photoperiodism The tendency of biological reactions to respond to the duration and timing of day and night; a mechanism for measuring seasonal time.

photoreceptor A light-sensitive sensory cell.

photorespiration Action of the enzyme rubisco, which catalyzes the oxidization of RuBP, releasing CO_2; this reverses carbon fixation and can reduce the yield of photosynthesis.

photosystem An organized complex of chlorophyll, other pigments, and proteins that traps light energy as excited electrons. Plants have two linked photosystems in the thylakoid membrane of chloroplasts. Photosystem II passes an excited electron through an electron transport chain to photosystem I to replace an excited electron passed to NADPH. The electron lost from photosystem II is replaced by the oxidation of water.

phototropism In plants, a growth response to a light stimulus.

pH scale A scale used to measure acidity and basicity. Defined as the negative log of H^+ concentration. Ranges from 0 to 14. A value of 7 is neutral; below 7 is acidic and above 7 is basic.

phycobiliprotein A type of accessory pigment found in cyanobacteria and some algae. Complexes of phycobiliprotein are able to absorb light energy in the green range.

phycologist A scientist who studies algae.

phyllotaxy In plants, a spiral pattern of leaf arrangement on a stem in which sequential leaves are at a 137.5° angle to one another, an angle related to the golden mean.

phylogenetic species concept (PSC) The concept that defines species on the basis of their phylogenetic relationships.

phylogenetic tree A pattern of descent generated by analysis of similarities and differences among organisms. Modern gene-sequencing techniques have produced phylogenetic trees showing the evolutionary history of individual genes.

phylogeny The evolutionary history of an organism, including which species are closely related and in what order related species evolved; often represented in the form of an evolutionary tree.

phylum, pl. phyla A major category, between kingdom and class, of taxonomic classifications.

physical map A map of the DNA sequence of a chromosome or genome based on actual landmarks within the DNA.

phytochrome A plant pigment that is associated with the absorption of light; photoreceptor for red to far-red light.

phytoestrogen One of a number of secondary metabolites in some plants that are structurally and functionally similar to the animal hormone estrogen.

phytoremediation The process that uses plants to remove contamination from soil or water.

pigment A molecule that absorbs light.

pilus, pl. pili Extensions of a bacterial cell enabling it to transfer genetic materials from one individual to another or to adhere to substrates.

pinocytosis The process of fluid uptake by endocytosis in a cell.

pistil Central organ of flowers, typically consisting of ovary, style, and stigma; a pistil may consist of one or more fused carpels and is more technically and better known as the gynoecium.

pith The ground tissue occupying the center of the stem or root within the vascular cylinder.

pituitary gland Endocrine gland at the base of the hypothalamus composed of anterior and posterior lobes. Pituitary hormones affect a wide variety of processes in vertebrates.

placenta, pl. placentae (1) In flowering plants, the part of the ovary wall to which the ovules or seeds are attached. (2) In mammals, a tissue formed in part from the inner lining of the uterus and in part from other membranes, through which the embryo (later the fetus) is nourished while in the uterus and through which wastes are carried away.

plankton Free-floating, mostly microscopic, aquatic organisms.

plant receptor kinase Any of a group of plant membrane receptors that, when activated by binding ligand, have kinase enzymatic activity. These receptors phosphorylate serine or threonine, unlike RTKs in animals that phosphorylate tyrosine.

planula A ciliated, free-swimming larva produced by the medusae of cnidarian animals.

plasma The fluid of vertebrate blood; contains dissolved salts, metabolic wastes, hormones, and a variety of proteins, including antibodies and albumin; blood minus the blood cells.

plasma cell An antibody-producing cell resulting from the multiplication and differentiation of a B lymphocyte that has interacted with an antigen.

plasma membrane The membrane surrounding the cytoplasm of a cell; consists of a single phospholipid bilayer with embedded proteins.

plasmid A small fragment of extrachromosomal DNA, usually circular, that replicates independently of the main chromosome, although it may have been derived from it.

plasmodesmata In plants, cytoplasmic connections between adjacent cells.

plasmodium Stage in the life cycle of myxomycetes (plasmodial slime molds); a multinucleate mass of protoplasm surrounded by a membrane.

plasmolysis The shrinking of a plant cell in a hypertonic solution such that it pulls away from the cell wall.

plastid An organelle in the cells of photosynthetic eukaryotes that is the site of photosynthesis and, in plants and green algae, of starch storage.

platelet In mammals, a fragment of a white blood cell that circulates in the blood and functions in the formation of blood clots at sites of injury.

pleiotropy Condition in which an individual allele has more than one effect on production of the phenotype.

plesiomorphy In cladistics, another term for an ancestral character state.

plumule The epicotyl of a plant with its two young leaves.

point mutation An alteration of one nucleotide in a chromosomal DNA molecule.

polar body Minute, nonfunctioning cell produced during the meiotic divisions leading to gamete formation in vertebrates.

polar covalent bond A covalent bond in which electrons are shared unequally due to differences in electronegativity of the atoms involved. One atom has a partial negative charge and the other a partial positive charge, even though the molecule is electrically neutral overall.

polarity (1) Refers to unequal charge distribution in a molecule such as water, which has a positive region and a negative region although it is neutral overall. (2) Refers to axial differences in a developing embryo that result in anterior–posterior and dorsal–ventral axes in a bilaterally symmetrical animal.

polarize In cladistics, to determine whether character states are ancestral or derived.

pollen tube A tube formed after germination of the pollen grain; carries the male gametes into the ovule.

pollination The transfer of pollen from an anther to a stigma.

polyandry The condition in which a female mates with more than one male.

polyclonal antibody An antibody response in which an antigen elicits many different antibodies, each fitting a different portion of the antigen surface.

polygenic inheritance Describes a mode of inheritance in which more than one gene affects a trait, such as height in human beings; polygenic inheritance may produce a continuous range of phenotypic values, rather than discrete either-or values.

polygyny A mating choice in which a male mates with more than one female.

polymer A molecule composed of many similar or identical molecular subunits; starch is a polymer of glucose.

polymerase chain reaction (PCR) A process by which DNA polymerase is used to copy a sequence of interest repeatedly, making millions of copies of the same DNA.

polymorphism The presence in a population of more than one allele of a gene at a frequency greater than that of newly arising mutations.

polyp A typically sessile, cylindrical body form found in cnidarian animals, such as hydras.

polypeptide A molecule consisting of many joined amino acids; not usually as complex as a protein.

polyphyletic In phylogenetic classification, a group that does not include the most recent common ancestor of all members of the group.

polyploidy Condition in which one or more entire sets of chromosomes is added to the diploid genome.

polysaccharide A carbohydrate composed of many monosaccharide sugar subunits linked together in a long chain; examples are glycogen, starch, and cellulose.

polyunsaturated fat A fat molecule having at least two double bonds between adjacent carbons in one or more of the fatty acid chains.

population Any group of individuals, usually of a single species, occupying a given area at the same time.

population genetics The study of the properties of genes in populations.

positive control A type of control at the level of DNA transcription initiation in which the frequency of initiation is increased; activator proteins mediate positive control.

posttranscriptional control A mechanism of control over gene expression that operates after the transcription of mRNA is complete.

postzygotic isolating mechanism A type of reproductive isolation in which zygotes are produced but are unable to develop into reproducing adults; these mechanisms may range from inviability of zygotes or embryos to adults that are sterile.

potential energy Energy that is not being used, but could be; energy in a potentially usable form; often called "energy of position."

precapillary sphincter A ring of muscle that guards each capillary loop and that, when closed, blocks flow through the capillary.

pre-mRNA splicing In eukaryotes, the process by which introns are removed from the primary transcript to produce mature mRNA; pre-mRNA splicing occurs in the nucleus.

pressure potential In plants, the turgor pressure resulting from pressure against the cell wall.

prezygotic isolating mechanism A type of reproductive isolation in which the formation of a zygote is prevented; these mechanisms may range from physical separation in different habitats to gametic in which gametes are incapable of fusing.

primary endosperm nucleus In flowering plants, the result of the fusion of a sperm nucleus and the (usually) two polar nuclei.

primary growth In vascular plants, growth originating in the apical meristems of shoots and roots; results in an increase in length.

primary immune response The first response of an immune system to a foreign antigen.

If the system is challenged again with the same antigen, the memory cells created during the primary response will respond more quickly.

primary induction Inductions between the three primary tissue types: mesoderm and endoderm.

primary meristem Any of the three meristems produced by the apical meristem; primary meristems give rise to the dermal, vascular, and ground tissues.

primary nondisjunction Failure of chromosomes to separate properly at meiosis I.

primary phloem The cells involved in food conduction in plants.

primary plant body The part of a plant consisting of young, soft shoots and roots derived from apical meristem tissues.

primary productivity The amount of energy produced by photosynthetic organisms in a community.

primary structure The specific amino acid sequence of a protein.

primary tissues Tissues that make up the primary plant body.

primary transcript The initial mRNA molecule copied from a gene by RNA polymerase, containing a faithful copy of the entire gene, including introns as well as exons.

primary wall In plants, the wall layer deposited during the period of cell expansion.

primase The enzyme that synthesizes the RNA primers required by DNA polymerases.

primate Monkeys and apes (including humans).

primitive streak In the early embryos of birds, reptiles, and mammals, a dorsal, longitudinal strip of ectoderm and mesoderm that is equivalent to the blastopore in other forms.

primordium In plants, a bulge on the young shoot produced by the apical meristem; primordia can differentiate into leaves, other shoots, or flowers.

principle of parsimony Principle stating that scientists should favor the hypothesis that requires the fewest assumptions.

prions Infectious proteinaceous particles.

procambium In vascular plants, a primary meristematic tissue that gives rise to primary vascular tissues.

product rule *See* rule of multiplication.

proglottid A repeated body segment in tapeworms that contains both male and female reproductive organs; proglottids eventually form eggs and embryos, which leave the host's body in feces.

prokaryote A bacterium; a cell lacking a membrane-bounded nucleus or membrane-bounded organelles.

prometaphase The transitional phase between prophase and metaphase during which the spindle attaches to the kinetochores of sister chromatids.

promoter A DNA sequence that provides a recognition and attachment site for RNA polymerase to begin the process of gene transcription; it is located upstream from the transcription start site.

prophase The phase of cell division that begins when the condensed chromosomes become visible and ends when the nuclear envelope breaks down. The assembly of the spindle takes place during prophase.

proprioceptor In vertebrates, a sensory receptor that senses the body's position and movements.

prosimian Any member of the mammalian group that is a sister group to the anthropoids; prosimian means "before monkeys." Members include the lemurs, lorises, and tarsiers.

prosoma The anterior portion of the body of an arachnid, which bears all the appendages.

prostaglandins A group of modified fatty acids that function as chemical messengers.

prostate gland In male mammals, a mass of glandular tissue at the base of the urethra that secretes an alkaline fluid that has a stimulating effect on the sperm as they are released.

protease An enzyme that degrades proteins by breaking peptide bonds; in cells, proteases are often compartmentalized into vesicles such as lysosomes.

proteasome A large, cylindrical cellular organelle that degrades proteins marked with ubiquitin.

protein A chain of amino acids joined by peptide bonds.

protein kinase An enzyme that adds phosphate groups to proteins, changing their activity.

protein microarray An array of proteins on a microscope slide or silicon chip. The array may be used with a variety of probes, including antibodies, to analyze the presence or absence of specific proteins in a complex mixture.

proteome All the proteins coded for by a particular genome.

proteomics The study of the proteomes of organisms. This is related to functional genomics as the proteome is responsible for much of the function encoded by a genome.

protoderm The primary meristem that gives rise to the dermal tissue.

proton pump A protein channel in a membrane of the cell that expends energy to transport protons against a concentration gradient; involved in the chemiosmotic generation of ATP.

proto-oncogene A normal cellular gene that can act as an oncogene when mutated.

protostome Any member of a grouping of bilaterally symmetrical animals in which the mouth develops first and the anus second; flatworms, nematodes, mollusks, annelids, and arthropods are protostomes.

pseudocoel A body cavity located between the endoderm and mesoderm.

pseudogene A copy of a gene that is not transcribed.

pseudomurien A component of the cell wall of archaea; it is similar to peptidoglycan in structure and function but contains different components.

pseudopod A nonpermanent cytoplasmic extension of the cell body.

P site In a ribosome, the peptidyl site that binds to the tRNA attached to the growing polypeptide chain.

punctuated equilibrium A hypothesis about the mechanism of evolutionary change proposing that long periods of little or no change are punctuated by periods of rapid evolution.

Punnett square A diagrammatic way of showing the possible genotypes and phenotypes of genetic crosses.

pupa A developmental stage of some insects in which the organism is nonfeeding, immotile, and sometimes encapsulated or in a cocoon; the pupal stage occurs between the larval and adult phases.

purine The larger of the two general kinds of nucleotide base found in DNA and RNA; a nitrogenous base with a double-ring structure, such as adenine or guanine.

pyrimidine The smaller of two general kinds of nucleotide base found in DNA and RNA; a nitrogenous base with a single-ring structure, such as cytosine, thymine, or uracil.

pyruvate A three-carbon molecule that is the end product of glycolysis; each glucose molecule yields two pyruvate molecules.

Q

quantitative trait A trait that is determined by the effects of more than one gene; such a trait usually exhibits continuous variation rather than discrete either–or values.

quaternary structure The structural level of a protein composed of more than one polypeptide chain, each of which has its own tertiary structure; the individual chains are called subunits.

R

radial canal Any of five canals that connect to the ring canal of an echinoderm's water–vascular system.

radial cleavage The embryonic cleavage pattern of deuterostome animals in which cells divide parallel to and at right angles to the polar axis of the embryo.

radial symmetry A type of structural symmetry with a circular plan, such that dividing the body or structure through the midpoint in any direction yields two identical sections.

radicle The part of the plant embryo that develops into the root.

radioactive isotope An isotope that is unstable and undergoes radioactive decay, releasing energy.

radioactivity The emission of nuclear particles and rays by unstable atoms as they decay into more stable forms.

radula Rasping tongue found in most mollusks.

reaction center A transmembrane protein complex in a photosystem that receives energy from the antenna complex exciting an electron that is passed to an acceptor molecule.

reading frame The correct succession of nucleotides in triplet codons that specify amino acids on translation. The reading frame is established by the first codon in the sequence as there are no spaces in the genetic code.

realized niche The actual niche occupied by an organism when all biotic and abiotic interactions are taken into account.

receptor-mediated endocytosis Process by which specific macromolecules are transported into eukaryotic cells at clathrin-coated pits, after binding to specific cell-surface receptors.

receptor protein A highly specific cell-surface receptor embedded in a cell membrane that responds only to a specific messenger molecule.

receptor tyrosine kinase (RTK) A diverse group of membrane receptors that when activated have kinase enzymatic activity. Specifically, they phosphorylate proteins on tyrosine. Their activation can lead to diverse cellular responses.

recessive An allele that is only expressed when present in the homozygous condition, but being "hidden" by the expression of a dominant allele in the heterozygous condition.

redia A secondary, nonciliated larva produced in the sporocysts of liver flukes.

regulatory protein Any of a group of proteins that modulates the ability of RNA polymerase to bind to a promoter and begin DNA transcription.

replicon An origin of DNA replication and the DNA whose replication is controlled by this origin. In prokaryotic replication, the chromosome plus the origin consist of a single replicon; eukaryotic chromosomes consist of multiple replicons.

replisome The macromolecular assembly of enzymes involved in DNA replication; analogous to the ribosome in protein synthesis.

reciprocal altruism Performance of an altruistic act with the expectation that the favor will be returned. A key and very controversial assumption of many theories dealing with the evolution of social behavior. *See* altruism.

reciprocal cross A genetic cross involving a single trait in which the sex of the parents is reversed; for example, if pollen from a white-flowered plant is used to fertilize a purple-flowered plant, the reciprocal cross would be pollen from a purple-flowered plant used to fertilize a white-flowered plant.

reciprocal recombination A mechanism of genetic recombination that occurs only in eukaryotic organisms, in which two chromosomes trade segments; can occur between nonhomologous chromosomes as well as the more usual exchange between homologous chromosomes in meiosis.

recombinant DNA Fragments of DNA from two different species, such as a bacterium and a mammal, spliced together in the laboratory into a single molecule.

recombination frequency The value obtained by dividing the number of recombinant progeny by the total progeny in a genetic cross. This value is converted into a percentage, and each 1% is termed a map unit.

reduction The gain of an electron by an atom, often with an associated proton.

reflex In the nervous system, a motor response subject to little associative modification; a reflex is among the simplest neural pathways, involving only a sensory neuron, sometimes (but not always) an interneuron, and one or more motor neurons.

reflex arc The nerve path in the body that leads from stimulus to reflex action.

refractory period The recovery period after membrane depolarization during which the membrane is unable to respond to additional stimulation.

reinforcement In speciation, the process by which partial reproductive isolation between populations is increased by selection against mating between members of the two populations, eventually resulting in complete reproductive isolation.

replica plating A method of transferring bacterial colonies from one plate to another to make a copy of the original plate; an impression of colonies growing on a Petri plate is made on a velvet surface, which is then used to transfer the colonies to plates containing different media, such that auxotrophs can be identified.

replication fork The Y-shaped end of a growing replication bubble in a DNA molecule undergoing replication.

repolarization Return of the ions in a nerve to their resting potential distribution following depolarization.

repression In general, control of gene expression by preventing transcription. Specifically, in bacteria such as *E. coli* this is mediated by repressor proteins. In anabolic operons, repressors bind DNA in the absence of corepressors to repress an operon.

repressor A protein that regulates DNA transcription by preventing RNA polymerase from attaching to the promoter and transcribing the structural gene. *See* operator.

reproductive isolating mechanism Any barrier that prevents genetic exchange between species.

residual volume The amount of air remaining in the lungs after the maximum amount of air has been exhaled.

resting membrane potential The charge difference (difference in electric potential) that exists across a neuron at rest (about 70 mV).

restriction endonuclease An enzyme that cleaves a DNA duplex molecule at a particular base sequence, usually within or near a palindromic sequence; also called a restriction enzyme.

restriction fragment length polymorphism (RFLP) Restriction enzymes recognize very specific DNA sequences. Alleles of the same gene or surrounding sequences may have base-pair differences, so that DNA near one allele is cut into a different-length fragment than DNA near the other allele. These different fragments separate based on size on electrophoresis gels.

retina The photosensitive layer of the vertebrate eye; contains several layers of neurons and light receptors (rods and cones); receives the image formed by the lens and transmits it to the brain via the optic nerve.

retinoblastoma susceptibility gene (*Rb*) A gene that, when mutated, predisposes individuals to a rare form of cancer of the retina; one of the first tumor-suppressor genes discovered.

retrovirus An RNA virus. When a retrovirus enters a cell, a viral enzyme (reverse transcriptase) transcribes viral RNA into duplex DNA, which the cell's machinery then replicates and transcribes as if it were its own.

reverse genetics An approach by which a researcher uses a cloned gene of unknown function, creates a mutation, and introduces the mutant gene back into the organism to assess the effect of the mutation.

reverse transcriptase A viral enzyme found in retroviruses that is capable of converting their RNA genome into a DNA copy.

Rh blood group A set of cell-surface markers (antigens) on the surface of red blood cells in humans and rhesus monkeys (for which it is named); although there are several alleles, they are grouped into two main types: Rh-positive and Rh-negative.

rhizome In vascular plants, a more or less horizontal underground stem; may be enlarged for storage or may function in vegetative reproduction.

rhynchocoel A true coelomic cavity in ribbonworms that serves as a hydraulic power source for extending the proboscis.

ribonucleic acid (RNA) A class of nucleic acids characterized by the presence of the sugar ribose and the pyrimidine uracil; includes mRNA, tRNA, and rRNA.

ribosomal RNA (rRNA) A class of RNA molecules found, together with characteristic proteins, in ribosomes; transcribed from the DNA of the nucleolus.

ribosome The molecular machine that carries out protein synthesis; the most complicated aggregation of proteins in a cell, also containing three different rRNA molecules.

ribosome-binding sequence (RBS) In prokaryotes, a conserved sequence at the 5′ end of mRNA that is complementary to the 3′ end of a small subunit rRNA and helps to position the ribosome during initiation.

ribozyme An RNA molecule that can behave as an enzyme, sometimes catalyzing its own assembly; rRNA also acts as a ribozyme in the polymerization of amino acids to form protein.

ribulose 1,5-bisphosphate (RuBP) In the Calvin cycle, the five-carbon sugar to which CO_2 is attached, accomplishing carbon fixation. This reaction is catalyzed by the enzyme rubisco.

ribulose bisphosphate carboxylase/oxygenase (rubisco) The four-subunit enzyme in the chloroplast that catalyzes the carbon fixation reaction joining CO_2 to RuBP.

RNA interference A type of gene silencing in which the mRNA transcript is prevented from being translated; small interfering RNAs (siRNAs) have been found to bind to mRNA and target its degradation prior to its translation.

RNA polymerase An enzyme that catalyzes the assembly of an mRNA molecule, the sequence of which is complementary to a DNA molecule used as a template. *See* transcription.

RNA primer In DNA replication, a sequence of about 10 RNA nucleotides complementary to unwound DNA that attaches at a replication fork; the DNA polymerase uses the RNA primer as a starting point for addition of DNA nucleotides to form the new DNA strand; the RNA primer is later removed and replaced by DNA nucleotides.

RNA splicing A nuclear process by which intron sequences of a primary mRNA transcript are cut out and the exon sequences spliced together to give the correct linkages of genetic information that will be used in protein construction.

rod Light-sensitive nerve cell found in the vertebrate retina; sensitive to very dim light; responsible for "night vision."

root The usually descending axis of a plant, normally below ground, which anchors the plant and serves as the major point of entry for water and minerals.

root cap In plants, a tissue structure at the growing tips of roots that protects the root apical meristem as the root pushes through the soil; cells of the root cap are continually lost and replaced.

root hair In plants, a tubular extension from an epidermal cell located just behind the root tip; root hairs greatly increase the surface area for absorption.

root pressure In plants, pressure exerted by water in the roots in response to a solute potential in the absence of transpiration; often occurs at night. Root pressure can result in guttation, excretion of water from cells of leaves as dew.

root system In plants, the portion of the plant body that anchors the plant and absorbs ions and water.

R plasmid A resistance plasmid; a conjugative plasmid that picks up antibiotic resistance genes and can therefore transfer resistance from one bacterium to another.

rule of addition The rule stating that for two independent events, the probability of either event occurring is the sum of the individual probabilities.

rule of multiplication The rule stating that for two independent events, the probability of both events occurring is the product of the individual probabilities.

rumen An "extra stomach" in cows and related mammals wherein digestion of cellulose occurs and from which partially digested material can be ejected back into the mouth.

S

salicylic acid In plants, an organic molecule that is a long-distance signal in systemic acquired resistance.

saltatory conduction A very fast form of nerve impulse conduction in which the impulses leap from node to node over insulated portions.

saprobes Heterotrophic organisms that digest their food externally (e.g., most fungi).

sarcolemma The specialized cell membrane in a muscle cell.

sarcomere Fundamental unit of contraction in skeletal muscle; repeating bands of actin and myosin that appear between two Z lines.

sarcoplasmic reticulum The endoplasmic reticulum of a muscle cell. A sleeve of membrane that wraps around each myofilament.

satellite DNA A nontranscribed region of the chromosome with a distinctive base composition; a short nucleotide sequence repeated tandemly many thousands of times.

saturated fat A fat composed of fatty acids in which all the internal carbon atoms contain the maximum possible number of hydrogen atoms.

Schwann cells The supporting cells associated with projecting axons, along with all the other nerve cells that make up the peripheral nervous system.

sclereid In vascular plants, a sclerenchyma cell with a thick, lignified, secondary wall having many pits; not elongate like a fiber.

sclerenchyma cell Tough, thick-walled cells that strengthen plant tissues.

scolex The attachment organ at the anterior end of a tapeworm.

scrotum The pouch that contains the testes in most mammals.

scutellum The modified cotyledon in cereal grains.

second filial (F_2) generation The offspring resulting from a cross between members of the first filial (F_1) generation.

secondary cell wall In plants, the innermost layer of the cell wall. Secondary walls have a highly organized microfibrillar structure and are often impregnated with lignin.

secondary growth In vascular plants, an increase in stem and root diameter made possible by cell division of the lateral meristems.

secondary immune response The swifter response of the body the second time it is invaded by the same pathogen because of the presence of memory cells, which quickly become antibody-producing plasma cells.

secondary induction An induction between tissues that have already differentiated.

secondary metabolite A molecule not directly involved in growth, development, or reproduction of an organism; in plants these molecules, which include nicotine, caffeine, tannins, and menthols, can discourage herbivores.

secondary plant body The part of a plant consisting of secondary tissues from lateral meristem tissues; the older trunk, branches, and roots of woody plants.

secondary structure In a protein, hydrogen-bonding interactions between — CO and — NH groups of the primary structure.

secondary tissue Any tissue formed from lateral meristems in trees and shrubs.

Second Law of Thermodynamics A statement concerning the transformation of potential energy into heat; it says that disorder (entropy) is continually increasing in the universe as energy changes occur, so disorder is more likely than order.

second messenger A small molecule or ion that carries the message from a receptor on the target cell surface into the cytoplasm.

seed bank Ungerminated seeds in the soil of an area. Regeneration of plants after events such as fire often depends on the presence of a seed bank.

seed coat In plants, the outer layers of the ovule, which become a relatively impermeable barrier to protect the dormant embryo and stored food.

segment polarity gene Any of certain genes in *Drosophila* development that are expressed in stripes that subdivide the stripes created by the pair-rule genes in the process of segmentation.

segmentation The division of the developing animal body into repeated units; segmentation allows for redundant systems and more efficient locomotion.

segmentation gene Any of the three classes of genes that control development of the segmented body plan of insects; includes the gap genes, pair-rule genes, and segment polarity genes.

segregation The process by which alternative forms of traits are expressed in offspring rather than blending each trait of the parents in the offspring.

selection The process by which some organisms leave more offspring than competing ones, and their genetic traits tend to appear in greater proportions among members of succeeding generations than the traits of those individuals that leave fewer offspring.

selectively permeable Condition in which a membrane is permeable to some substances but not to others.

self-fertilization The union of egg and sperm produced by a single hermaphroditic organism.

semen In reptiles and mammals, sperm-bearing fluid expelled from the penis during male orgasm.

semicircular canal Any of three fluid-filled canals in the inner ear that help to maintain balance.

semiconservative replication DNA replication in which each strand of the original duplex serves as the template for construction of a totally new complementary strand, so the original duplex is partially conserved in each of the two new DNA molecules.

senescent Aged, or in the process of aging.

sensory (afferent) neuron A neuron that transmits nerve impulses from a sensory receptor to the central nervous system or central ganglion.

sensory setae In insects, bristles attached to the nervous system that are sensitive mechanical and chemical stimulation; most abundant on antennae and legs.

sepal A member of the outermost floral whorl of a flowering plant.

septation In prokaryotic cell division, the formation of a septum where new cell membrane and cell wall is formed to separate the two daughter cells.

septum, pl. septa A wall between two cavities.

sequence-tagged site (STS) A small stretch of DNA that is unique in a genome, that is, it occurs only once; useful as a physical marker on genomic maps.

seta, pl. setae (L., bristle) In an annelid, bristles of chitin that help anchor the worm during locomotion or when it is in its burrow.

severe acute respiratory syndrome (SARS) A respiratory infection with an 8% mortality rate that is caused by a coronavirus.

sex chromosome A chromosome that is related to sex; in humans, the sex chromosomes are the X and Y chromosomes.

sex-linked A trait determined by a gene carried on the X chromosome and absent on the Y chromosome.

Sexual dimorphism Morphological differences between the sexes of a species.

sexual reproduction The process of producing offspring through an alternation of fertilization (producing diploid cells) and meiotic reduction in chromosome number (producing haploid cells).

sexual selection A type of differential reproduction that results from variable success in obtaining mates.

shared derived character In cladistics, character states that are shared by species and that are different from the ancestral character state.

shoot In vascular plants, the aboveground portions, such as the stem and leaves.

short interspersed element (SINE) Any of a type of retrotransposon found in humans and other primates that does not contain the biochemical machinery needed for transposition; half a million copies of a SINE element called Alu is nested in the LINEs of the human genome.

shotgun sequencing The method of DNA sequencing in which the DNA is randomly cut into small fragments, and the fragments cloned and sequenced. A computer is then used to assemble a final sequence.

sieve cell In the phloem of vascular plants, a long, slender element with relatively unspecialized sieve areas and with tapering end walls that lack sieve plates.

signal recognition particle (SRP) In eukaryotes, a cytoplasmic complex of proteins that recognizes and binds to the signal sequence of a polypeptide, and then docks with a receptor that forms a channel in the ER membrane. In this way the polypeptide is released into the lumen of the ER.

signal transduction The events that occur within a cell on receipt of a signal, ligand binding to a receptor protein. Signal transduction pathways produce the cellular response to a signaling molecule.

simple sequence repeat (SSR) A one- to three-nucleotide sequence such as CA or CCG that is repeated thousands of times.

single-nucleotide polymorphism (SNP) A site present in at least 1% of the population at which individuals differ by a single nucleotide. These can be used as genetic markers to map unknown genes or traits.

sinus A cavity or space in tissues or in bone.

sister chromatid One of two identical copies of each chromosome, still linked at the centromere, produced as the chromosomes duplicate for mitotic division; similarly, one of two identical copies of each homologous chromosome present in a tetrad at meiosis.

small interfering RNAs (siRNAs) A class of micro-RNAs that appear to be involved in control of gene transcription and that play a role in protecting cells from viral attack.

small nuclear ribonucleoprotein particles (snRNP) In eukaryotes, a complex composed of snRNA and protein that clusters together with other snRNPs to form the spliceosome, which removes introns from the primary transcript.

small nuclear RNA (snRNA) In eukaryotes, a small RNA sequence that, as part of a small nuclear ribonucleoprotein complex, facilitates recognition and excision of introns by base-pairing with the 5′ end of an intron or at a branch site of the same intron.

sodium–potassium pump Transmembrane channels engaged in the active (ATP-driven) transport of Na^+, exchanging them for K^+, where both ions are being moved against their respective concentration gradients; maintains the resting membrane potential of neurons and other cells.

solute A molecule dissolved in some solution; as a general rule, solutes dissolve only in solutions of similar polarity; for example, glucose (polar) dissolves in (forms hydrogen bonds with) water (also polar), but not in vegetable oil (nonpolar).

solute potential The amount of osmotic pressure arising from the presence of a solute or solutes in water; measure by counterbalancing the pressure until osmosis stops.

solvent The medium in which one or more solutes is dissolved.

somatic cell Any of the cells of a multicellular organism except those that are destined to form gametes (germ-line cells).

somatic cell nuclear transfer (SCNT) The transfer of the nucleus of a somatic cell into an enucleated egg cell that then undergoes development. Can be used to make ES cells and to create cloned animals.

somatic mutation A change in genetic information (mutation) occurring in one of the somatic cells of a multicellular organism, not passed from one generation to the next.

somatic nervous system In vertebrates, the neurons of the peripheral nervous system that control skeletal muscle.

somite One of the blocks, or segments, of tissue into which the mesoderm is divided during differentiation of the vertebrate embryo.

Southern blot A technique in which DNA fragments are separated by gel electrophoresis, denatured into single-stranded DNA, and then "blotted" onto a sheet of filter paper; the filter is then incubated with a labeled probe to locate DNA sequences of interest.

S phase The phase of the cell cycle during which DNA replication occurs.

specialized transduction The transfer of only a few specific genes into a bacterium, using a lysogenic bacteriophage as a carrier.

speciation The process by which new species arise, either by transformation of one species into another, or by the splitting of one ancestral species into two descendant species.

species, pl. species A kind of organism; species are designated by binomial names written in italics.

specific heat The amount of heat that must be absorbed or lost by 1 g of a substance to raise or lower its temperature 1°C.

specific transcription factor Any of a great number of transcription factors that act in a time- or tissue-dependent manner to increase DNA transcription above the basal level.

spectrin A scaffold of proteins that links plasma membrane proteins to actin filaments in the cytoplasm of red blood cells, producing their characteristic biconcave shape.

spermatid In animals, each of four haploid (n) cells that result from the meiotic divisions of a spermatocyte; each spermatid differentiates into a sperm cell.

spermatozoa The male gamete, usually smaller than the female gamete, and usually motile.

sphincter In vertebrate animals, a ring-shaped muscle capable of closing a tubular opening by constriction (e.g., between stomach and small intestine or between anus and exterior).

spicule Any of a number of minute needles of silica or calcium carbonate made in the mesohyl by some kinds of sponges as a structural component.

spindle The structure composed of microtubules radiating from the poles of the dividing cell that will ultimately guide the sister chromatids to the two poles.

spindle apparatus The assembly that carries out the separation of chromosomes during cell division; composed of microtubules (spindle fibers) and assembled during prophase at the equator of the dividing cell.

spindle checkpoint The third cell-division checkpoint, at which all chromosomes must be attached to the spindle. Passage through this checkpoint commits the cell to anaphase.

spinnerets Organs at the posterior end of a spider's abdomen that secrete a fluid protein that becomes silk.

spiracle External opening of a trachea in arthropods.

spiral cleavage The embryonic cleavage pattern of some protostome animals in which cells divide at an angle oblique to the polar axis of the embryo; a line drawn through the sequence of dividing cells forms a spiral.

spiralian A member of a group of invertebrate animals; many groups exhibit spiral cleavage. Mollusks, annelids, and flatworms are examples of spiralians.

spliceosome In eukaryotes, a complex composed of multiple snRNPs and other associated proteins that is responsible for excision of introns and joining of exons to convert the primary transcript into the mature mRNA.

spongin A tough protein made by many kinds of sponges as a structural component within the mesohyl.

spongy parenchyma A leaf tissue composed of loosely arranged, chloroplast-bearing cells. *See* palisade parenchyma.

sporangium, pl. sporangia A structure in which spores are produced.

spore A haploid reproductive cell, usually unicellular, capable of developing into an adult without fusion with another cell.

sporophyte The spore-producing, diploid ($2n$) phase in the life cycle of a plant having alternation of generations.

stabilizing selection A form of selection in which selection acts to eliminate both extremes from a range of phenotypes.

stamen The organ of a flower that produces the pollen; usually consists of anther and filament; collectively, the stamens make up the androecium.

starch An insoluble polymer of glucose; the chief food storage substance of plants.

start codon The AUG triplet, which indicates the site of the beginning of mRNA translation; this codon also codes for the amino acid methionine.

stasis A period of time during which little evolutionary change occurs.

statocyst Sensory receptor sensitive to gravity and motion.

stele The central vascular cylinder of stems and roots.

stem cell A relatively undifferentiated cell in animal tissue that can divide to produce more differentiated tissue cells.

stereoscopic vision Ability to perceive a single, three-dimensional image from the simultaneous but slightly divergent two-dimensional images delivered to the brain by each eye.

stigma (1) In angiosperm flowers, the region of a carpel that serves as a receptive surface for pollen grains. (2) Light-sensitive eyespot of some algae.

stipules Leaflike appendages that occur at the base of some flowering plant leaves or stems.

stolon A stem that grows horizontally along the ground surface and may form adventitious roots, such as runners of the strawberry plant.

stoma, pl. stomata In plants, a minute opening bordered by guard cells in the epidermis of leaves and stems; water passes out of a plant mainly through the stomata.

stop codon Any of the three codons UAA, UAG, and UGA, that indicate the point at which mRNA translation is to be terminated.

stratify To hold plant seeds at a cold temperature for a certain period of time; seeds of many plants will not germinate without exposure to cold and subsequent warming.

stratum corneum The outer layer of the epidermis of the skin of the vertebrate body.

striated muscle Skeletal voluntary muscle and cardiac muscle.

stroma In chloroplasts, the semiliquid substance that surrounds the thylakoid system and that contains the enzymes needed to assemble organic molecules from CO_2.

stromatolite A fossilized mat of ancient bacteria formed as long as 2 BYA, in which the bacterial remains individually resemble some modern-day bacteria.

style In flowers, the slender column of tissue that arises from the top of the ovary and through which the pollen tube grows.

stylet A piercing organ, usually a mouthpart, in some species of invertebrates.

suberin In plants, a fatty acid chain that forms the impermeable barrier in the Casparian strip of root endoderm.

subspecies A geographically defined population or group of populations within a single species that has distinctive characteristics.

substrate (1) The foundation to which an organism is attached. (2) A molecule on which an enzyme acts.

subunit vaccine A type of vaccine created by using a subunit of a viral protein coat to elicit an immune response; may be useful in preventing viral diseases such as hepatitis B.

succession In ecology, the slow, orderly progression of changes in community composition that takes place through time.

summation Repetitive activation of the motor neuron resulting in maximum sustained contraction of a muscle.

supercoiling The coiling in space of double-stranded DNA molecules due to torsional strain, such as occurs when the helix is unwound.

surface tension A tautness of the surface of a liquid, caused by the cohesion of the molecules of liquid. Water has an extremely high surface tension.

surface area-to-volume ratio Relationship of the surface area of a structure, such as a cell, to the volume it contains.

suspensor In gymnosperms and angiosperms, the suspensor develops from one of the first two cells of a dividing zygote; the suspensor of an angiosperm is a nutrient conduit from maternal tissue to the embryo. In gymnosperms the suspensor positions the embryo closer to stored food reserves.

swim bladder An organ encountered only in the bony fish that helps the fish regulate its buoyancy by increasing or decreasing the amount of gas in the bladder via the esophagus or a specialized network of capillaries.

swimmerets In lobsters and crayfish, appendages that occur in lines along the ventral surface of the abdomen and are used in swimming and reproduction.

symbiosis The condition in which two or more dissimilar organisms live together in close association; includes parasitism (harmful to one of the organisms), commensalism (beneficial to one, of no significance to the other), and mutualism (advantageous to both).

sympatric speciation The differentiation of populations within a common geographic area into species.

symplast route In plant roots, the pathway for movement of water and minerals within the cell cytoplasm that leads through plasmodesmata that connect cells.

symplesiomorphy In cladistics, another term for a shared ancestral character state.

symporter A carrier protein in a cell's membrane that transports two molecules or ions in the same direction across the membrane.

synapomorphy In systematics, a derived character that is shared by clade members.

synapse A junction between a neuron and another neuron or muscle cell; the two cells do not touch, the gap being bridged by neurotransmitter molecules.

synapsid Any of an early group of reptiles that had a pair of temporal openings in the skull behind the eye sockets; jaw muscles attached to these openings. Early ancestors of mammals belonged to this group.

synapsis The point-by-point alignment (pairing) of homologous chromosomes that occurs before the first meiotic division; crossing over takes place during synapsis.

synaptic cleft The space between two adjacent neurons.

synaptic vesicle A vesicle of a neurotransmitter produced by the axon terminal of a nerve. The filled vesicle migrates to the presynaptic membrane, fuses with it, and releases the neurotransmitter into the synaptic cleft.

synaptonemal complex A protein lattice that forms between two homologous chromosomes in prophase I of meiosis, holding the replicated chromosomes in precise register with each other so that base-pairs can form between nonsister chromatids for crossing over that is usually exact within a gene sequence.

syncytial blastoderm A structure composed of a single large cytoplasm containing about 4000

nuclei in embryonic development of insects such as *Drosophila*.

syngamy The process by which two haploid cells (gametes) fuse to form a diploid zygote; fertilization.

synthetic polyploidy A polyploidy organism created by crossing organisms most closely related to an ancestral species and then manipulating the offspring.

systematics The reconstruction and study of evolutionary relationships.

systemic acquired resistance (SAR) In plants, a longer-term response to a pathogen or pest attack that can last days to weeks and allow the plant to respond quickly to later attacks by a range of pathogens.

systemin In plants, an 18-amino-acid peptide that is produced by damaged or injured leaves that leads to the wound response.

systolic pressure A measurement of how hard the heart is contracting. When measured during a blood pressure reading, ventricular systole (contraction) is what is being monitored.

T

3′ poly-A tail In eukaryotes, a series of 1–200 adenine residues added to the 3′ end of an mRNA; the tail appears to enhance the stability of the mRNA by protecting it from degradation.

T box A transcription factor protein domain that has been conserved, although with differing developmental effects, in invertebrates and chordates.

tagma, pl. **tagmata** A compound body section of an arthropod resulting from embryonic fusion of two or more segments; for example, head, thorax, abdomen.

Taq polymerase A DNA polymerase isolated from the thermophilic bacterium *Thermus aquaticus* (Taq); this polymerase is functional at higher temperatures, and is used in PCR amplification of DNA.

TATA box In eukaryotes, a sequence located upstream of the transcription start site. The TATA box is one element of eukaryotic core promoters for RNA polymerase II.

taxis, pl. **taxes** An orientation movement by a (usually) simple organism in response to an environmental stimulus.

taxonomy The science of classifying living things. By agreement among taxonomists, no two organisms can have the same name, and all names are expressed in Latin.

T cell A type of lymphocyte involved in cell-mediated immunity and interactions with B cells; the "T" refers to the fact that T cells are produced in the thymus.

telencephalon The most anterior portion of the brain, including the cerebrum and associated structures.

telomerase An enzyme that synthesizes telomeres on eukaryotic chromosomes using an internal RNA template.

telomere A specialized nontranscribed structure that caps each end of a chromosome.

telophase The phase of cell division during which the spindle breaks down, the nuclear envelope of each daughter cell forms, and the chromosomes uncoil and become diffuse.

telson The tail spine of lobsters and crayfish.

temperate (lysogenic) phage A virus that is capable of incorporating its DNA into the host cell's DNA, where it remains for an indeterminate length of time and is replicated as the cell's DNA replicates.

template strand The DNA strand that is used as a template in transcription. This strand is copied to produce a complementary mRNA transcript.

tendon (Gr. *tendon*, stretch) A strap of cartilage that attaches muscle to bone.

tensile strength A measure of the cohesiveness of a substance; its resistance to being broken apart. Water in narrow plant vessels has tensile strength that helps keep the water column continuous.

tertiary structure The folded shape of a protein, produced by hydrophobic interactions with water, ionic and covalent bonding between side chains of different amino acids, and van der Waal's forces; may be changed by denaturation so that the protein becomes inactive.

testcross A mating between a phenotypically dominant individual of unknown genotype and a homozygous "tester," done to determine whether the phenotypically dominant individual is homozygous or heterozygous for the relevant gene.

testis, pl. **testes** In mammals, the sperm-producing organ.

tetanus Sustained forceful muscle contraction with no relaxation.

thalamus That part of the vertebrate forebrain just posterior to the cerebrum; governs the flow of information from all other parts of the nervous system to the cerebrum.

therapeutic cloning The use of somatic cell nuclear transfer to create stem cells from a single individual that may be reimplanted in that individual to replace damaged cells, such as in a skin graft.

thermodynamics The study of transformations of energy, using heat as the most convenient form of measurement of energy.

thermogenesis Generation of internal heat by endothermic animals to modulate temperature.

thigmotropism In plants, unequal growth in some structure that comes about as a result of physical contact with an object.

threshold The minimum amount of stimulus required for a nerve to fire (depolarize).

thylakoid In chloroplasts, a complex, organized internal membrane composed of flattened disks, which contain the photosystems involved in the light-dependent reactions of photosynthesis.

Ti (tumor-inducing) plasmid A plasmid found in the plant bacterium *Agrobacterium tumefaciens* that has been extensively used to introduce recombinant DNA into broadleaf plants. Recent modifications have allowed its use with cereal grains as well.

tight junction Region of actual fusion of plasma membranes between two adjacent animal cells that prevents materials from leaking through the tissue.

tissue A group of similar cells organized into a structural and functional unit.

tissue plasminogen activator (TPA) A human protein that causes blood clots to dissolve; if used within 3 hours of an ischemic stroke, TPA may prevent disability.

tissue-specific stem cell A stem cell that is capable of developing into the cells of a certain tissue, such as muscle or epithelium; these cells persist even in adults.

tissue system In plants, any of the three types of tissue; called a system because the tissue extends throughout the roots and shoots.

tissue tropism The affinity of a virus for certain cells within a multicellular host; for example, hepatitis B virus targets liver cells.

tonoplast The membrane surrounding the central vacuole in plant cells that contains water channels; helps maintain the cell's osmotic balance.

topoisomerase Any of a class of enzymes that can change the topological state of DNA to relieve torsion caused by unwinding.

torsion The process in embryonic development of gastropods by which the mantle cavity and anus move from a posterior location to the front of the body, closer to the location of the mouth.

totipotent A cell that possesses the full genetic potential of the organism.

trachea, pl. tracheae A tube for breathing; in terrestrial vertebrates, the windpipe that carries air between the larynx and bronchi (which leads to the lungs); in insects and some other terrestrial arthropods, a system of chitin-lined air ducts.

tracheids In plant xylem, dead cells that taper at the ends and overlap one another.

tracheole The smallest branches of the respiratory system of terrestrial arthropods; tracheoles convey air from the tracheae, which connect to the outside of the body at spiracles.

trait In genetics, a characteristic that has alternative forms, such as purple or white flower color in pea plants or different blood type in humans.

transcription The enzyme-catalyzed assembly of an RNA molecule complementary to a strand of DNA.

transcription complex The complex of RNA polymerase II plus necessary activators, coactivators, transcription factors, and other factors that are engaged in actively transcribing DNA.

transcription factor One of a set of proteins required for RNA polymerase to bind to a eukaryotic promoter region, become stabilized, and begin the transcription process.

transcription bubble The region containing the RNA polymerase, the DNA template, and the RNA transcript, so called because of the locally unwound "bubble" of DNA.

transcription unit The region of DNA between a promoter and a terminator.

transcriptome All the RNA present in a cell or tissue at a given time.

transfection The transformation of eukaryotic cells in culture.

transfer RNA (tRNA) A class of small RNAs (about 80 nucleotides) with two functional sites; at one site, an "activating enzyme" adds a specific amino acid, while the other site carries the nucleotide triplet (anticodon) specific for that amino acid.

transformation The uptake of DNA directly from the environment; a natural process in some bacterial species.

transgenic organism An organism into which a gene has been introduced without conventional breeding, that is, through genetic engineering techniques.

translation The assembly of a protein on the ribosomes, using mRNA to specify the order of amino acids.

translation repressor protein One of a number of proteins that prevents translation of mRNA by binding to the beginning of the transcript and preventing its attachment to a ribosome.

translocation (1) In plants, the long-distance transport of soluble food molecules (mostly sucrose), which occurs primarily in the sieve tubes of phloem tissue. (2) In genetics, the interchange of chromosome segments between nonhomologous chromosomes.

transmembrane domain Hydrophobic region of a transmembrane protein that anchors it in the membrane. Often composed of α-helices, but sometimes utilizing β-pleated sheets to form a barrel-shaped pore.

transmembrane route In plant roots, the pathway for movement of water and minerals that crosses the cell membrane and also the membrane of vacuoles inside the cell.

transpiration The loss of water vapor by plant parts; most transpiration occurs through the stomata.

transposable elements Segments of DNA that are able to move from one location on a chromosome to another. Also termed *transposons* or *mobile genetic elements*.

transposition Type of genetic recombination in which transposable elements (transposons) move from one site in the DNA sequence to another, apparently randomly.

transposon DNA sequence capable of transposition.

trichome In plants, a hairlike outgrowth from an epidermal cell; glandular trichomes secrete oils or other substances that deter insects.

triglyceride (triacylglycerol) An individual fat molecule, composed of a glycerol and three fatty acids.

triploid Possessing three sets of chromosomes.

trisomic Describes the condition in which an additional chromosome has been gained due to nondisjunction during meiosis, and the diploid embryo therefore has three of these autosomes. In humans, trisomic individuals may survive if the autosome is small; Down syndrome individuals are trisomic for chromosome 21.

trochophore A specialized type of free-living larva found in lophotrochozoans.

trophic level A step in the movement of energy through an ecosystem.

trophoblast In vertebrate embryos, the outer ectodermal layer of the blastodermic vesicle; in mammals, it is part of the chorion and attaches to the uterine wall.

tropism Response to an external stimulus.

tropomyosin Low-molecular-weight protein surrounding the actin filaments of striated muscle.

troponin Complex of globular proteins positioned at intervals along the actin filament of skeletal muscle; thought to serve as a calcium-dependent "switch" in muscle contraction.

***trp* operon** In *E. coli*, the operon containing genes that code for enzymes that synthesize tryptophan.

true-breeding Said of a breed or variety of organism in which offspring are uniform and consistent from one generation to the next. This is due to the genotypes that determine relevant traits being homozygous.

tube foot In echinoderms, a flexible, external extension of the water–vascular system that is capable of attaching to a surface through suction.

tubulin Globular protein subunit forming the hollow cylinder of microtubules.

tumor-suppressor gene A gene that normally functions to inhibit cell division; mutated forms can lead to the unrestrained cell division of cancer, but only when both copies of the gene are mutant.

turgor pressure The internal pressure inside a plant cell, resulting from osmotic intake of water, that presses its cell membrane tightly against the cell wall, making the cell rigid. Also known as *hydrostatic pressure*.

tympanum In some groups of insects, a thin membrane associated with the tracheal air sacs that functions as a sound receptor; paired on each side of the abdomen.

U

ubiquitin A 76-amino-acid protein that virtually all eukaryotic cells attach as a marker to proteins that are to be degraded.

unequal crossing over A process by which a crossover in a small region of misalignment at synapsis causes two homologous chromosomes to exchange segments of unequal length.

uniporter A carrier protein in a cell's membrane that transports only a single type of molecule or ion.

uniramous Single-branched; describes the appendages of insects.

unsaturated fat A fat molecule in which one or more of the fatty acids contain fewer than the maximum number of hydrogens attached to their carbons.

urea An organic molecule formed in the vertebrate liver; the principal form of disposal of nitrogenous wastes by mammals.

urethra The tube carrying urine from the bladder to the exterior of mammals.

uric acid Insoluble nitrogenous waste products produced largely by reptiles, birds, and insects.

urine The liquid waste filtered from the blood by the kidney and stored in the bladder pending elimination through the urethra.

uropod One of a group of flattened appendages at the end of the abdomen of lobsters and crayfish that collectively act as a tail for a rapid burst of speed.

uterus In mammals, a chamber in which the developing embryo is contained and nurtured during pregnancy.

V

vacuole A membrane-bounded sac in the cytoplasm of some cells, used for storage or digestion purposes in different kinds of cells; plant cells often contain a large central vacuole that stores water, proteins, and waste materials.

valence electron An electron in the outermost energy level of an atom.

variable A factor that influences a process, outcome, or observation. In experiments, scientists attempt to isolate variables to test hypotheses.

vascular cambium In vascular plants, a cylindrical sheath of meristematic cells, the division of which produces secondary phloem outwardly and secondary xylem inwardly; the activity of the vascular cambium increases stem or root diameter.

vascular tissue Containing or concerning vessels that conduct fluid.

vas deferens In mammals, the tube carrying sperm from the testes to the urethra.

vasopressin A posterior pituitary hormone that regulates the kidney's retention of water.

vector In molecular biology, a plasmid, phage or artificial chromosome that allows propagation of recombinant DNA in a host cell into which it is introduced.

vegetal pole The hemisphere of the zygote comprising cells rich in yolk.

vein (1) In plants, a vascular bundle forming a part of the framework of the conducting and supporting tissue of a stem or leaf. (2) In animals, a blood vessel carrying blood from the tissues to the heart.

veliger The second larval stage of mollusks following the trochophore stage, during which the beginning of a foot, shell, and mantle can be seen.

ventricle A muscular chamber of the heart that receives blood from an atrium and pumps blood out to either the lungs or the body tissues.

vertebrate A chordate with a spinal column; in vertebrates, the notochord develops into the vertebral column composed of a series of vertebrae that enclose and protect the dorsal nerve cord.

vertical gene transfer (VGT) The passing of genes from one generation to the next within a species.

vesicle A small intracellular, membrane-bounded sac in which various substances are transported or stored.

vessel element In vascular plants, a typically elongated cell, dead at maturity, which conducts water and solutes in the xylem.

vestibular apparatus The complicated sensory apparatus of the inner ear that provides for balance and orientation of the head in vertebrates.

vestigial structure A morphological feature that has no apparent current function and is thought to be an evolutionary relic; for example, the vestigial hip bones of boa constrictors.

villus, pl. **villi** In vertebrates, one of the minute, fingerlike projections lining the small intestine that serve to increase the absorptive surface area of the intestine.

virion A single virus particle.

viroid Any of a group of small, naked RNA molecules that are capable of causing plant diseases, presumably by disrupting chromosome integrity.

virus Any of a group of complex biochemical entities consisting of genetic material wrapped in protein; viruses can reproduce only within living host cells and are thus not considered organisms.

visceral mass Internal organs in the body cavity of an animal.

vitamin An organic substance that cannot be synthesized by a particular organism but is required in small amounts for normal metabolic function.

viviparity Refers to reproduction in which eggs develop within the mother's body and young are born free-living.

voltage-gated ion channel A transmembrane pathway for an ion that is opened or closed by a change in the voltage, or charge difference, across the plasma membrane.

W

water potential The potential energy of water molecules. Regardless of the reason (e.g., gravity, pressure, concentration of solute particles) for the water potential, water moves from a region where water potential is greater to a region where water potential is lower.

water–vascular system A fluid-filled hydraulic system found only in echinoderms that provides body support and a unique type of locomotion via extensions called tube feet.

Western blot A blotting technique used to identify specific protein sequences in a complex mixture. *See* Southern blot.

wild type In genetics, the phenotype or genotype that is characteristic of the majority of individuals of a species in a natural environment.

wobble pairing Refers to flexibility in the pairing between the base at the 5′ end of a tRNA anticodon and the base at the 3′ end of an mRNA codon. This flexibility allows a single tRNA to read more than one mRNA codon.

wound response In plants, a signaling pathway initiated by leaf damage, such as being chewed by a herbivore, and lead to the production of proteinase inhibitors that give herbivores indigestion.

X

X chromosome One of two sex chromosomes; in mammals and in *Drosophila*, female individuals have two X chromosomes.

xylem In vascular plants, a specialized tissue, composed primarily of elongate, thick-walled conducting cells, which transports water and solutes through the plant body.

Y

Y chromosome One of two sex chromosomes; in mammals and in *Drosophila*, male individuals have a Y chromosome and an X chromosome; the Y determines maleness.

yolk plug A plug occurring in the blastopore of amphibians during formation of the archenteron in embryological development.

yolk sac The membrane that surrounds the yolk of an egg and connects the yolk, a rich food supply, to the embryo via blood vessels.

Z

zinc finger motif A type of DNA-binding motif in regulatory proteins that incorporates zinc atoms in its structure.

zona pellucida An outer membrane that encases a mammalian egg.

zone of cell division In plants, the part of the young root that includes the root apical meristem and the cells just posterior to it; cells in this zone divide every 12–36 hr.

zone of elongation In plants, the part of the young root that lies just posterior to the zone of cell division; cells in this zone elongate, causing the root to lengthen.

zone of maturation In plants, the part of the root that lies posterior to the zone of elongation; cells in this zone differentiate into specific cell types.

zoospore A motile spore.

zooxanthellae Symbiotic photosynthetic protists in the tissues of corals.

zygomycetes A type of fungus whose chief characteristic is the production of sexual structures called zygosporangia, which result from the fusion of two of its simple reproductive organs.

zygote The diploid (2*n*) cell resulting from the fusion of male and female gametes (fertilization).

Photo Credits

Chapter 1

Opener: © Soames Summerhays/Natural Visions; 1.1(organelle): © Dr. Donald Fawcett & Porter/Visuals Unlimited; 1.1(cell): © Steve Gschmeissner/Getty Images; 1.1(tissue): © Ed Reschke; 1.1(organism): © Russell Illig/Getty Images RF; 1.1(population): © George Ostertag/agefotostock; 1.1(species): © PhotoDisc/Volume 44 RF; 1.1(community): © Ryan McGinnis/Alamy; 1.1(ecosystem): © Robert and Jean Pollock; 1.1(biosphere): NASA; 1.5: © Huntington Library/SuperStock; 1.11a: © Dennis Kunkel/Phototake; 1.11b: © Karl E. Deckart/Phototake; 1.12(plantae left): © Alan L. Detrick/Photo Researchers, Inc.; 1.12(plantae middle): © David M. Dennis/Animals Animals; 1.12(plantae right): © Corbis/Volume 46 RF; 1.12(fungi left): © Royalty-Free/Corbis; 1.12(fungi middle): © Mediscan/Corbis; 1.12(fungi right): © PhotoDisc BS/Volume 15 RF; 1.12(animalia left): © Royalty-Free/Corbis; 1.12(animalia middle): © Tom Brakefield/Corbis; 1.12(animalia right): © PhotoDisc/Volume 44 RF; 1.12(protista left): © Corbis/Volume 64 RF; 1.12(protista middle): © Tom Adams/Visuals Unlimited; 1.12(protista right): © Douglas P. Wilson/Frank Lane Picture Agency/Corbis; 1.12(archaea left): © Ralph Robinson/Visuals Unlimited; 1.12(archaea right): © Kari Lounatman/Photo Researchers, Inc.; 1.12(bacteria left): © Dwight R. Kuhn; 1.12(bacteria right): © Alfred Pasieka/SPL/Photo Researchers, Inc.; pp.15-16: © Soames Summerhays/Natural Visions.

Chapter 2

Opener: Courtesy of IBM Zurich Research Laboratory. Unauthorized use not permitted; 2.2: Image Courtesy of Bruker Corporation; 2.10a: © Glen Allison/Getty Images RF; 2.10b: © PhotoLink/Getty Images RF; 2.10c: © Jeff Vanuga/Corbis; 2.13: © Hermann Eisenbeiss/National Audubon Society Collection/Photo Researchers, Inc.; pp. 31-32: Courtesy of IBM Zurich Research Laboratory. Unauthorized use not permitted.

Chapter 3

Opener: © Deco/Alamy; 3.10b: © Asa Thoresen/Photo Researchers, Inc.; 3.10c: © J. Carson/Custom Medical Stock Photo; 3.11b: © Science VU/Visuals Unlimited; 3.12: © Scott Johnson/Animals Animals; 3.13a: © Driscoll, Youngquist & Baldeschwieler, Caltech/SPL/Photo Researchers, Inc.; 3.13b: © M. Freeman/PhotoLink/Getty Images RF; pp. 56-57: © Deco/Alamy.

Chapter 4

Opener: © Dr. Gopal Murti/Photo Researchers, Inc.; p. 62(bright-field microscope): © David M. Phillips/Visuals Unlimited; p. 62(dark-field microscope): © Mike Abbey/Visuals Unlimited; p. 62(phase-contrast microscope): © David M. Phillips/Visuals Unlimited; p. 62(differential-interference-contrast microscope): © Mike Abbey/Visuals Unlimited; p. 62(fluorescence microscope): © Dr. Torsten Wittmann/Photo Researchers, Inc.; p. 62(confocal microscope): © Med. Mic. Sciences, Cardiff Uni./Wellcome Images; p. 62(transmission electron microscope): © Microworks/Phototake; p. 62 (scanning electron microscope): © Stanley Flegler/Visuals Unlimited; p. 62(bottom right): © Dr. Donald Fawcett/Visuals Unlimited; 4.3: © Phototake; 4.4: Courtesy of E.H. Newcomb & T.D. Pugh, University of Wisconsin; 4.5a: © Eye of Science/Photo Researchers, Inc.; 4.8b: © Dr. Richard Kessel & Dr. Gene Shih/Visuals Unlimited; 4.8c: © John T. Hansen, Ph.D./Phototake; 4.8d: © Dr. Ueli Aebi; 4.10(inset): © Dr. Donald Fawcett & R. Bolender/Visuals Unlimited; 4.11(inset): © Dennis Kunkel/Phototake; 4.14(inset): From S.E. Frederick and E.H. Newcomb, "Microbody-like organelles in leaf cells," *Science*, 163:1353-5. © 21 March 1969. Reprinted with permission from AAAS; 4.15(inset): © Henry Aldrich/Visuals Unlimited; 4.16(inset): © Dr. Donald Fawcett & Dr. Porter/Visuals Unlimited; 4.17(inset): © Dr. Jeremy Burgess/Photo Researchers, Inc.; 4.23(top & bottom insets): © William Dentler, University of Kansas; 4.24a-b: © SPL/Photo Researchers, Inc.; 4.25: © Biophoto Associates/Photo Researchers, Inc.; 4.28a: Courtesy of Daniel Goodenough; 4.28b: © Dr. Donald Fawcett/Visuals Unlimited; 4.28c: © Dr. Donald Fawcett/D. Albertini/Visuals Unlimited; pp. 85-86: © Dr. Gopal Murti/Photo Researchers, Inc.

Chapter 5

Opener: © Dr. Gopal Murti/SPL/Photo Researchers, Inc.; 5.2b: © Whitney L. Stutts, University of Florida; p. 91: © Dr. Donald Fawcett/Photo Researchers, Inc.; 5.4 (4): © Dr. Donald Fawcett/Visuals Unlimited; 5.12: © David M. Phillips/Visuals Unlimited; 5.15a: CDC/Dr. Edwin P. Ewing, Jr.; 5.15b: © BCC Microimaging, Inc. Reproduced with permission; 5.15c (top-bottom): Reproduced with permission from M.M. Perry and A.B. Gilbert, "Yolk transport in the ovarian follicle of the hen (*Gallus domesticus*): lipoprotein-like particles at the periphery of the oocyte in the rapid growth phase," *Journal of Cell Science*, 39:257-72, October 1979. © The Company of Biologists; 5.16b: © Dr. Brigit Satir; pp. 105-106: © Dr. Gopal Murti/SPL/Photo Researchers, Inc.

Chapter 6

Opener: © Robert Caputo/Aurora Photos; 6.3: © Jill Braaten; 6.11b: © Professor Emeritus Lester J. Reed, University of Texas at Austin; pp. 119-120: © Robert Caputo/Aurora Photos.

Chapter 7

Opener: © Creatas/PunchStock RF; 7.18a: © Wolfgang Baumeister/Photo Researchers, Inc.; 7.18b: NPS Photo; pp. 144-145: © Creatas/PunchStock RF.

Chapter 8

Opener: © Royalty-Free/Corbis; 8.1(middle right): Courtesy Dr. Kenneth Miller, Brown University; 8.8: © Eric Soder/pixsource.com; 8.20: © Dr. Jeremy Burgess/Photo Researchers, Inc.; 8.22a: © John Shaw/Photo Researchers, Inc.; 8.22b: © Joseph Nettis/National Audubon Society Collection/Photo Researchers, Inc.; 8.24(inset): © 2011 Jessica Solomatenko/Getty Images RF; pp. 166-167: © Royalty-Free/Corbis.

Chapter 9

Opener & pp. 183-184: © RMF/Scientifica/Visuals Unlimited.

Chapter 10

Opener: © Stem Jems/Photo Researchers, Inc.; 10.2: Courtesy of William Margolin; 10.4: © Biophoto Associates/Photo Researchers, Inc.; 10.6: © CNRI/Photo Researchers, Inc.; 10.10: Image courtesy of S. Hauf and J-M. Peters, IMP, Vienna, Austria; 10.11-10.12: © Andrew S. Bajer, University of Oregon; 10.13: © Dr. Jeremy Pickett-Heaps; 10.14a: © David M. Phillips/Visuals Unlimited; 10.14b: © Guenter Albrecht-Buehler, Northwestern University, Chicago; 10.15(top): © E.H. Newcomb & W.P. Wergin/Biological Photo Service; pp. 205-206: © Stem Jems/Photo Researchers, Inc.

Chapter 11

Opener: © Science VU/L. Maziarski/Visuals Unlimited; 11.3b: Reprinted with permission from the *Annual Review of Genetics*, Volume 6 © 1972 by Annual Reviews, www.annualreviews.org; 11.6: © Clare A. Hasenkampf/Biological Photo Service; pp. 218-219: © Science VU/L. Maziarski/Visuals Unlimited.

Chapter 12

Opener: © Corbis RF; 12.1: © Norbert Schaefer/Corbis; 12.2: © David Sieren/Visuals Unlimited; 12.3: © Leslie Holzer/Photo Researchers, Inc.; 12.11(top): From Albert F. Blakeslee, "CORN AND MEN: The Interacting Influence of Heredity and Environment—Movements for Betterment of Men, or Corn, or Any Other Living Thing, One-sided Unless They Take Both Factors into Account," *Journal of Heredity*, 1914, 5:511-8, by permission of Oxford University Press; 12.14: © DK Limited/Corbis; pp. 237-238: © Corbis RF.

Chapter 13

Opener: © Adrian T. Sumner/Photo Researchers, Inc.; 13.1: © Cabisco/Phototake; p.

Images RF; 34.17: © Stringer/New Zealand/ X01244/Reuters/Corbis; 34.18: © Jeff Rotman/ Photo Researchers, Inc.; 34.19: © Kjell Sandved/ Butterfly Alphabet; 34.20: © Ken Lucas/Visuals Unlimited; 34.22: © Ronald L. Shimek; 34.23: Photo by Fred Grassle © Woods Hole Oceanographic Institution; 34.24: © David M. Dennis/Animals Animals; 34.25: © Pascal Goetgheluck/Photo Researchers, Inc.; 34.26b: © Robert Brons/ Biological Photo Service; 34.27b: © Fred Bavendam/Minden Pictures; 34.29: © Gary D. Gaugler/Photo Researchers, Inc.; 34.30: © Educational Images Ltd., Elmira, NY, USA. Used by Permission; 34.36: © Andrew J. Martinez/Photo Researchers, Inc.; 34.37a: © National Geographic/ Getty Images; 34.37b: © S. Camazine/K. Visscher/ Photo Researchers, Inc.; 34.38: © Tom Adams/ Visuals Unlimited; 34.41: © David Liebman/Pink Guppy; 34.42: © Kjell Sandved/Butterfly Alphabet; 34.43a: © Cleveland P. Hickman; 34.43b: © Valorie Hodgson/Visuals Unlimited; 34.43c: © Gyorgy Csoka, Hungary Forest Research Institute, Bugwood.org; 34.43d: © Kjell Sandved/Butterfly Alphabet; 34.43e: © Greg Johnston/Lonely Planet Images/Getty Images; 34.43f: © Nature's Images/ Photo Researchers, Inc.; 34.45: © Dwight R. Kuhn; 34.46: © Kjell Sandved/Butterfly Alphabet; 34.47a: © Alex Kerstitch/Visuals Unlimited; 34.47b: © Edward S. Ross; pp. 688-689: © James H. Robinson/Animals Animals.

Chapter 35

Opener: © Ingram Publishing/SuperStock RF; 35.1b: © Frederic Pacorel/Getty Images; 35.2: © Wim van Egmond/Visuals Unlimited; 35.3a: © Alex Kerstitch/Visuals Unlimited; 35.3b: © Randy Morse/GoldenStateImages.com; 35.3c: © Daniel W. Gotshall/Visuals Unlimited; 35.3d: © Reinhard Dirscherl/Visuals Unlimited; 35.3e: © Jeff Rotman/ Photo Researchers, Inc.; 35.5: © Eric N. Olson, Ph.D./The University of Texas MD Anderson Cancer Center; 35.7a: © Rick Harbo; 35.8: © Heather Angel/Natural Visions; 35.12a: © agefotostock/SuperStock; 35.12b: © Royalty-Free/Corbis; 35.12c: © Jeff Rotman/Getty Images; 35.14: © Corbis/Volume 33 RF; 35.16a: © Federico Cabello/SuperStock; 35.16b: © Raymond Tercafs/ Bruce Coleman Inc./Photoshot; 35.19a: © Digital Vision/Getty Images RF; 35.19b: © Suzanne L. Collins & Joseph T. Collins/Photo Researchers, Inc.; 35.19c: © Jany Sauvanet/Photo Researchers, Inc.; 35.25: © Didier Dutheil/Sygma/Corbis; 35.27a(left): © William Weber/Visuals Unlimited; 35.27a(right): © Frans Lemmens/Getty Images; 35.27b, c(left): © Jonathan Losos; 35.27c(right): © Rod Planck; 35.27d(left): © Corbis/Volume 6 RF; 35.27d(right): © Zigmund Leszczynski/Animals Animals; 35.31: © Layne Kennedy/Corbis; 35.32a: © Corbis RF; 35.32b: © Tom Vezo/Minden Pictures; 35.32c: © David Boyle/Animals Animals; 35.32d: © John Cancalosi/Alamy; 35.35: © Stephen Dalton/ National Audubon Society Collection/Photo Researchers, Inc.; 35.36a(left): © B.J. Alcock/ Visuals Unlimited; 35.36a(right): © Dave Watts/ Alamy; 35.36b(left): © Corbis/Volume 6 RF; 35.36b(right): © W. Perry Conway/Corbis; 35.36c(left): © Image Source/Getty Images RF; 35.36c(right): © Juergen & Christine Sohns/ Animals Animals; 35.37: © Alan G. Nelson/Animals Animals; 35.38a: © J & C Sohns/agefotostock;

35.38b: © PhotoDisc/Getty Images RF; 35.38c(left): © Dynamic Graphics Group/IT Stock Free/Alamy RF; 35.38c(right): © Joe McDonald/Visuals Unlimited; 35.42: © AP Photo; pp. 727-728: © Ingram Publishing/SuperStock RF.

Chapter 36

Opener: © Susan Singer; 36.4: © Biodisc/Visuals Unlimited; 36.6a: © Brian Sullivan/Visuals Unlimited; 36.6b: © Dr. Jeremy Burgess/SPL/Photo Researchers, Inc.; 36.6c: © EM Unit, Royal Holloway, University of London, Egham, Surrey; 36.7: © Jessica Lucas & Fred Sack; 36.8: © Andrew Syred/SPL/Photo Researchers, Inc.; 36.9a-b: Courtesy of Allan Lloyd; 36.10: © Dennis Drenner/Visuals Unlimited; 36.11a: © Lee W. Wilcox; 36.11b: © George Wilder/Visuals Unlimited; 36.11c: © Lee W. Wilcox; 36.12(top): © NC Brown Center for Ultrastucture Studies, SUNY, College of Environmental Science and Forestry, Syracuse, NY; 36.12(bottom): USDA Forest Service, Forest Products Laboratory, Madison, WI; 36.13b: © Dr. Richard Kessel & Dr. Gene Shih/Visuals Unlimited; 36.14: © Biodisc/ Visuals Unlimited; 36.15b: Reprinted from Myeong Min Lee & John Schiefelbein, "WEREWOLF, a MYB-related protein in *Arabidopsis*, is a position-dependent regulator of epidermal cell patterning," *Cell*, 99(5):473-83, © 24 November 1999, with permission from Elsevier; 36.16b: Courtesy of Dr. Philip Benfey, from Wysocka-Diller, J.W., Helariutta,Y, Fukaki, H., Malamy, J.E. and Benfey, P.N., (2000), "Molecular analysis of SCARECROW function reveals a radial patterning mechanism common to root and shoot development," *Cell*, 127:595-603; 36.17(top left): © Carolina Biological Supply Company/Phototake; 36.17(top right): Photo by George S. Ellmore; 36.17(bottom left): © Lee W. Wilcox; 36.17(bottom right): Photo by George S. Ellmore; 36.19a: © E.R. Degginger/Photo Researchers, Inc.; 36.19b: © Richard Carlton/ Visuals Unlimited; 36.19c: © FLPA/Mark Newman/ agefotostock; 36.19d: © Gerald & Buff Corsi/ Visuals Unlimited; 36.19e: © Kingsley Stern; 36.20: Courtesy of J.H. Troughton and L. Donaldson/ Industrial Research Ltd.; 36.23, 36.26-36.27a: © Ed Reschke; 36.27b: © Biodisc/Visuals Unlimited; 36.28a: © Jerome Wexler/Visuals Unlimited; 36.28b: © Lee W. Wilcox; 36.28c: © Andrew McRobb/Dorling Kindersley/Getty Images; 36.28d: © Chase Studio Inc./Photo Researchers, Inc.; 36.28e: © Charles D. Winters/Photo Researchers, Inc.; 36.28f: © Lee W. Wilcox; 36.29: © Scott Poethig, University of Pennsylvania; 36.30a: © Kjell Sandved/Butterfly Alphabet; 36.30b: © Pat Anderson/Visuals Unlimited; 36.31a: © Gusto/ Photo Researchers, Inc.; 36.31b: © Peter Chadwick/ Dorling Kindersley/Getty Images; 36.32: Reprinted from Julie Hofer, Lynda Turner, Roger Hellens, Mike Ambrose, Peter Matthews, Anthony Michael, Noel Ellis, "*UNIFOLIATA* regulates leaf and flower morphogenesis in pea," *Current Biology*, 7(8):581-7, © 1 August 1997, with permission from Elsevier. 36.34: © Ed Reschke; pp. 752-753: © Susan Singer.

Chapter 37

Opener: © Richard Rowan's Collection Inc./Photo Researchers, Inc.; 37.5: © David Cook/ blueshiftstudios, photographer/Alamy RF; 37.7: © Ken Wagner/Phototake; 37.11: © Dr. Ryder/Jason

Borns/Phototake; 37.14: Anita Roth-Nebelsick, Foteini Hassiotou, Erik J. Veneklaas, "Stomatal crypts have small effects on transpiration: a numerical model analysis," *Plant Physiology*, 151(4):2018-27, Fig. 4C. © 2009 American Society of Plant Biologists. Reprinted with permission; 37.15a: © Ed Reschke; 37.15b: © Jon Bertsch/ Visuals Unlimited; 37.16: © Mark Boulton/Photo Researchers, Inc.; 37.18a: © Andrew Syred/Photo Researchers, Inc.; 37.18b: © Bruce Iverson Photomicrography; pp. 770-771: © Richard Rowan's Collection Inc./Photo Researchers, Inc.

Chapter 38

Opener: © PhotoDisc/Getty Images RF; 38.4a: © Hulton Archive/Getty Images; 38.4b: © Karim Sahib/AFP/Getty Images; 38.6a: © McPHOTO/ SHU/agefotostock; 38.6b: © Nigel Cattlin/Visuals Unlimited; 38.6c: © Dave Bevan/agefotostock; 38.6d: © Allen Barker; 38.8: © George Bernard/ Animals Animals; 38.9: © Ken Wagner/Phototake; 38.9(inset): © Bruce Iverson Photomicrography; 38.11a: © Kjell Sandved/Butterfly Alphabet; 38.11b: © Steven P. Lynch; 38.11c: © Perennov Nuridsany/ Photo Researchers, Inc.; 38.11d: © Barry Rice; 38.13: © Don Albert; 38.15(1): © Ed Reschke/Getty Images; 38.15(2): © Herve Conge/ISM/Phototake; 38.16a-b: Courtesy of Nicholas School of the Environment and Earth Sciences, Duke University. Photo by Will Owens; 38.18: Greg Harvey USAF; 38.19a: © Daniel Beltra/epa/Corbis; 38.19b: © Marcelo del Pozo/Reuters; 39.19c: © AP Photo; pp. 788-789: © PhotoDisc/Getty Images RF.

Chapter 39

Opener: © Emily Keegin/fstop/Getty Images RF; 39.1: © David Cappaert/agefotostock; 39.2a: Photo by William Wergin and Richard Sayre/USDA/ARS; 39.2b: Photo by Scott Bauer/USDA/ARS; 39.5: © Clarence Styron/agefotostock; Table 39.1(1-3): © Inga Spence/Visuals Unlimited; Table 39.1(4): © Heather Angel/Natural Visions; Table 39.1(5): © Pallava Bagla/Corbis; 39.6: © Adam Jones/Photo Researchers, Inc.; 39.7 (left): © Gilbert S. Grant/ Photo Researchers, Inc.; 39.7(inset): © Lee W. Wilcox; 39.8: © Martin Shields/Photo Researchers, Inc.; 39.12: Courtesy R.X. Latin. Reprinted with permission from *Compendium of Cucurbit Diseases*, 1996, American Phytopathological Society, St. Paul, MN; pp. 800-801: © Emily Keegin/ fstop/Getty Images RF.

Chapter 40

Opener: © Alan G. Nelson/Animals Animals; 40.5a-d: © Niko Geldner, UNIL; 40.8: © Ray F. Evert; 40.10a: © Jee Jung and Philip Benfey; 40.11: © Lee W. Wilcox; 40.13: © Frank Krahmer/Corbis; 40.16: © Don Johnston/agefotostock; 40.26a-c: © Prof. Malcolm B. Wilkins, Botany Dept., Glasgow University; 40.28: © Robert Calentine/Visuals Unlimited; 40.30: © Science Source/Photo Researchers, Inc.; 40.31: © Amnon Lichter, The Volcani Center; 40.36a: © John Sohlden/Visuals Unlimited; 40.36b: From D. R. McCarty, C. B. Carson, P. S. Stinard, and D. S. Robertson, "Molecular analysis of viviparous-1: an abscisic acid-insensitive mutant of maize," *The Plant Cell*, 1(5):523-32 © 1989 American Society of Plant Biologists; 40.36c: © ISM/Phototake; pp. 827-828: © Alan G. Nelson/Animals Animals.

Chapter 41

Opener: © Heather Angel/Natural Visions; 41.3a: © Imagebrokers/Photoshot; 41.3b: © Pat Breen, Oregon State University; 41.4: Courtesy of Lingjing Chen & Renee Sung; 41.5a: © Mack Henley/Visuals Unlimited; 41.5a(inset): © Michael Gadomski/Animals Animals; 41.5b: © Ove Nilsson and Detlef Weigel, Umeå Plant Science Centre/Max Planck Institute; 41.5b(inset): © Ove Nilsson and Detlef Weigel, Salk Institute/Max Planck Institute; 41.7: © Design Pics/Don Hammond RF; 41.9(1-4): Courtesy of John L. Bowman; 41.12: © John Bishop/Visuals Unlimited; 41.13: © Paul Gier/Visuals Unlimited; 41.14a-b: Courtesy of Enrico Coen; 41.16a-b: © L. DeVos/Free University of Brussels; 41.17: © Kingsley Stern; 41.18: © David Cappaert, Bugwood.org; 41.20: © Michael Fogden/Animals Animals; 41.21a-b: © Thomas Eisner, Cornell University; 41.22: © Science VU/Visuals Unlimited; 41.23: © Edward S. Ross; 41.24a: © David Sieren/Visuals Unlimited; 41.24b: © Barbara Gerlach/Visuals Unlimited; 41.29: © Edward Yeung, University of Calgary and David Meinke, Oklahoma State University; 41.30a-d: Kindly provided by Prof. Chun-Ming Liu, Institute of Botany, Chinese Academy of Sciences; 41.31: © Jan Lohmann, Max Planck Institute for Developmental Biology; 41.32c: © Ben Scheres, University of Utrecht; 41.32d-e: Courtesy of George Stamatiou and Thomas Berleth; 41.34: © A. P. Mähönen; 41.35 (top right): © S. Kirchner/photocuisine/Corbis; 41.35(bottom right): © Metta image/Alamy RF; 41.37a: © Nigel Cattlin/Alamy; 41.37b: © Martin Shields/Alamy; 41.39: © Jerome Wexler/Photo Researchers, Inc.; 41.40a: © Sinclair Stammers/Photo Researchers, Inc.; 41.40b-d: From N. Kuchuk, R. G. Herrmann and H.-U. Koop, "Plant regeneration from leaf protoplasts of evening primrose (*Oenothera hookeri*)," *Plant Cell Reports*, 17(8):601-4, Fig. 2 © 5 May 1998 Springer; 41.41a: © Anthony Arendt/Alamy; 41.41b: © David Lazenby/Animals Animals; pp. 858-859: © Heather Angel/Natural Visions.

Chapter 42

Opener: © Dr. Roger C. Wagner, Professor Emeritus of Biological Sciences, University of Delaware; Table 42.1(1): © Ed Reschke; Table 42.1(2): © Arthur Siegelman/Visuals Unlimited; Table 42.1(3): © Ed Reschke; Table 42.1(4): © Gladden Willis, M.D./Visuals Unlimited; Table 42.1(5): © Ed Reschke; 42.3: © J. Gross, Biozentrum/Photo Researchers, Inc.; 42.4: © Biophoto Associates/Photo Researchers, Inc.; Table 42.2(1): © Ed Reschke; Table 42.2(2): © Dr. John D. Cunningham/Visuals Unlimited ; Table 42.2(3): © Chuck Brown/Photo Researchers, Inc.; Table 42.2(4): © Ed Reschke; Table 42.2(5): © Kenneth Eward/Photo Researchers, Inc.; Table 42.3(1-3): © Ed Reschke; pp. 883-884: © Dr. Roger C. Wagner, Professor Emeritus of Biological Sciences, University of Delaware.

Chapter 43

Opener: Courtesy of David I. Vaney, University of Queensland Australia; 43.3: © Enrico Mugnaini/Visuals Unlimited; 43.13: © John Heuser, Washington University School of Medicine, St. Louis, MO; 43.15: © Ed Reschke; 43.17b: © Science VU/Lewis-Everhart-Zeevi/Visuals Unlimited; 43.25: © Dr. Marcus E. Raichle, Washington University, McDonnell Center for High Brain Function; 43.27: © Lennart Nilsson/Scanpix; 43.30: © E.R. Lewis/Biological Photo Service; pp. 911-912: Courtesy of David I. Vaney, University of Queensland Australia.

Chapter 44

Opener: © Omikron/Photo Researchers, Inc.; 44.11d: © Dr. John D. Cunningham/Visuals Unlimited; 44.21: © A. T. D. Bennett; 44.24: © Leonard Lee Rue III; pp. 934-935: © Omikron/Photo Researchers, Inc.

Chapter 45

Opener: © Nature's Images/Photo Researchers, Inc.; 45.10: © Mike Goldwater/Alamy; 45.11: © Bettmann/Corbis; pp. 958-959: © Nature's Images/Photo Researchers, Inc.

Chapter 46

Opener: © Stockbyte RF; 46.3(1): © Ed Reschke; 46.3(2): © David M. Phillips/Photo Researchers, Inc.; 46.3(3): © Biophoto Associates/Photo Researchers, Inc.; 46.3(4): © CNRI/Photo Reserachers, Inc.; 46.3(5): © Dr. Richard Kessel & Dr. Randy Kardon/*Tissues & Organs*/Visuals Unlimited; 46.3(6): © Ed Reschke/Getty Images; 46.3(7): © Ed Reschke; 46.3(8): © Ed Reschke/Getty Images; 46.10: © Dr. H.E. Huxley; 46.21: © Treat Davidson/Photo Researchers, Inc.; pp. 978-979: © Stockbyte RF.

Chapter 47

Opener: © Datacraft/UIG/agefotostock; 47.10: © Ron Boardman/Stone/Getty Images; 47.19: © The Rockefeller University/AP Photo; pp. 999-1000: © Datacraft/UIG/agefotostock.

Chapter 48

Opener: © PhotoDisc/Alamy RF; 48.1: © Bruce Watkins/Animals Animals; 48.3: © Juniors Bildarchiv/Alamy; 48.13a: © Clark Overton/Phototake; 48.13b: © Martin Rotker/Phototake; 48.14: © Kenneth Eward/BioGrafx/Photo Researchers, Inc.: pp. 1016-1017: © PhotoDisc/Alamy RF.

Chapter 49

Opener: © Biophoto Associates/Photo Researchers, Inc.; 49.16a-b: © Ed Reschke; 49.16c: © Dr. Gladden Willis/Visuals Unlimited; pp. 1036-1037: © Biophoto Associates/Photo Researchers, Inc.

Chapter 50

Opener & pp. 1053-1054: © Rick & Nora Bowers/Alamy.

Chapter 51

Opener: © National Museum of Health and Medicine, Armed Forces Institute of Pathology/AP Photo; 51.3: © KAGE-Mikrofotografie; 51.6: © Wellcome Library, London; 51.12a-b: © Dr. Andrejs Liepins/Photo Researchers, Inc.; 51.22: © CDC/Science Source/Photo Researchers, Inc.; pp. 1081-1082: © National Museum of Health and Medicine, Armed Forces Institute of Pathology/AP Photo.

Chapter 52

Opener: © Geordie Torr/Alamy; 52.1: © Dennis Kunkel Microscopy, Inc.; 52.2: © Fred McConnaughey/The National Audubon Society Collection/Photo Researchers, Inc.; 52.4: © Doug Perrine/SeaPics.com; 52.6: © Derek Middleton/FLPA/Minden Pictures/Corbis; 52.7a: © Jonathan Losos; 52.7b: © Photoshot/SuperStock; 52.7c-d: © Michael Fogden/OSF/Animals Animals; 52.8: © 2009 Frans Lanting/www.lanting.com; 52.9a: © Jean Phllippe Varin/Jacana/Photo Researchers, Inc.; 52.9b: © Tom McHugh/The National Audubon Society Collection/Photo Researchers, Inc.; 52.9c: © Corbis/Volume 86 RF; 52.12a: © David M. Phillips/Photo Researchers, Inc.; 52.17: © Ed Reschke; 52.21a: © Jonathan A. Meyers/Photo Researchers, Inc.; 52.21b: © The McGraw-Hill Companies, Inc. Jill Braaten, photographer; 52.21c: © The McGraw-Hill Companies, Inc. Bob Coyle, photographer; 52.21d: © Kumar Sriskandan/Alamy; pp. 1102-1103: © Geordie Torr/Alamy.

Chapter 53

Opener: © Neil Bromhall/Photo Researchers, Inc.; 53.1c-d: © David M. Phillips/Visuals Unlimited; 53.3a-d: Dr. Mathias Hafner, Mannheim University of Applied Sciences, Institute for Molecular Biology, Mannheim, Germany, and Dr. Gerald Schatten, Pittsburgh Development Centre Deputy Director, Magee-Woman's Research Institute, Professor and Vice-Chair of Obstetrics, Gynecology & Reproductive Sciences and Professor of Cell Biology & Physiology, Director, Division of Developmental and Regnerative Medicine, University of Pittsburgh School of Medicine Pittsburgh, PA 15213; 53.7: © David M. Phillips/Visuals Unlimited; 53.8a: © Cabisco/Phototake; 53.9: © David M. Phillips/Visuals Unlimited; 53.11a-c: From, "An Atlas of the Development of the Sea Urchin *Lytechinus variegatus*." Provided by Dr. John B. Morrill (left to right) Plate 20, p. 62, #I/Plate 33, p. 93, #C/Plate 38, p. 105, #G; 53.17: Courtesy of Manfred Frasch; 53.20c: © Roger Fleischman, University of Kentucky; 53.26b: © Scott Camazine/Phototake; 53.27a: © Omikron Omikron/Photo Researchers, Inc.; 53.27b: © doc-stock/Visuals Unlimited; 53.27c: © Brand X Pictures/PunchStock RF; 53.27d: © Nestle/Petit Format/Photo Researchers, Inc.; pp. 1129-1130: © Neil Bromhall/Photo Researchers, Inc.

Chapter 54

Opener: © K. Ammann/Bruce Coleman Inc./Photoshot; 54.2: © Dr. Nicolette Siep; 54.4a-b: Reprinted from Jennifer R. Brown, Hong Ye, Roderick T. Bronson, Pieter Dikkes and Michael E. Greenberg, "A defect in nurturing in mice lacking the immediate early gene fosB," *Cell*, 86(2):297-309, © 26 July 1996, with permission from Elsevier; 54.5a-b: From Hemanth P. Nair, Larry J. Young, "Vasopressin and pair-bond formation: genes to brain to behavior," *Physiology*, 21(2):146-52, © 2006. Reprinted by permission from The American Physiological Society; 54.6a-c: © Boltin Picture Library/The Bridgeman Art Library; 54.7: © William Grenfell/Visuals Unlimited; 54.8: © Thomas McAvoy, Life Magazine/Time, Inc./Getty Images; 54.9: © Harlow Primate Laboratory, University of Wisconsin-Madison USA; 54.11: © Roger Wilmhurst/The National Audubon Society

Boldface page numbers correspond with **boldface terms** in the text. Page numbers followed by an "f" indicate figures; page numbers followed by a "t" indicate tabular material.

of plants, 856f, 857
    reproductive, **381**
    of sheep, 380f-381f, 381
    therapeutic, **383**, 383f
Cloning vector, **330**
    plasmids, 330-331, 331f
Clonorchis sinensis, 661, 662f
Closed circulatory system, **640**, 1022f, 1023
Clostridium botulinum, 544f, 555t
Clover, 832f
Club moss, 592f, 592t
Clutch size, in birds, 414, 1171, 1172f
Cnidaria (phylum), 638, 639f, 640, 643t, 646f, 649-654, 650f-654f
    body plan of, 650-651, 650f
    body structure of, 650-651, 650f
    circulatory system of, 1022, 1022f
    classes of, 651-654
    digestive cavity of, 982, 982f
    eye development of, 503, 503f
    life cycle of, 650f, 651
    nervous system of, 900-901, 900f
    reproduction in, 1085, 1085f
Coactivator, **174**, 314-315, 315f
Coal, 1246
Coastal ecosystem, destruction of, 1248
Cocaine, 899, 899f
Coccidioides posadasii, 628
Coccus, 546
Cochlea, **920**, 920f, 922, 922f
Cocklebur, 832f
Cockles, 669
Coding strand, **281**, 285f, 286f
Codominance, 233t, **234**, 234f
Codon, **282**, 283t, 296f
    spaced or unspaced, 282-283
    start, **283**
    stop (nonsense), **283**, 296f, 297
Coelom, **640**, 640f, 642, 645, 646f
    formation of, 641f, 642
Coelomate, 640f
Coenzyme, **117**
Coevolution, **1193**
    mutualism and, 1197-1198
    of plants and animals, 796, 1193, 1193f, 1196
    predation and, 1193
Cofactor, **117**
Cognition, animal, 1141, 1141f-1142f
Cognitive behavior, **1141**
Cohesin, **191**, 191f, 193, 193f, 201
Cohesion, 26, 27f, 27t
Coleoptera (order), 684f, 685t
Coleoptile, 853, 854f
Coleorhiza, 853, 854f
Collagen, 45t, 80, 81f, 392, 867, 867f, 869
Collar cell. *See* Choanocyte
Collared flycatcher, 442, 442f
Collecting duct, 1047f, **1048**
Collenchyma cells, **737-738**, 737f
Collins, Francis, 355
Colloblast, **654**
Colon, **990**. *See also* Large intestine
Colon cancer, 990
Colonization, human influence on, 1270-1271
Color blindness, 227t, 242, **932**

Color vision, 929-930, 930f
Coloration, warning, 1194, 1195f
Colorectal cancer. *See* Colon cancer
Columella root cap, 740, 740f
Columnar epithelium, 865, 866t
    pseudostratified, 866t
    simple, 865, 866t
Comb jelly, 644t, 653-654, 654f
Combination joint, **967**, 968f
Combined DNA Index System (CODIS), 337
Commensalism, 558, **629**, 1198-1199, 1198f-1199f
Communicating junction, 83-84, 84f
Communication, animal, 1144-1147, 1144f-1147f
Community, 3f, **4**, **1186**, 1186f-1187f
    across space and time, 1186, 1187f
    concepts of, 1186
    fossil records of, 1186
Community ecology, 1185-1204
Compact bone, 965f, **966**
Compaction, 1112
Companion cells, 739, 739f
Comparative anatomy, 11, 11f
Comparative biology, 463-468, 464f-468f
Comparative genomics, 360, 361f, 473-476, 474f, 493
    medical applications of, 486-488, 487f
Comparator, **875**
Compartmentalization
    in eukaryotes, 517, 518, 542
    in prokaryotes, 542
Competition
    among barnacle species, 1188, 1188f
    direct and indirect effects of, 1200-1201, 1201f
    effect of parasitism on, 1200
    experimental studies of, 1190-1191, 1191f
    exploitative, **1187**
    interference, **1187**
    interspecific, **1187**, 1191, 1191f
    reduction by predation, 1199-1200, 1200f
    resource, 1190-1191, 1190f
    sperm, **1151**
Competitive exclusion, **1189**-1190, 1189f
Competitive inhibitor, **117**, 117f
Complement system, **1059-1060**
Complementary base-pairing, **43**, 43f, 262, 262f, 265, 265f
    base-pairs, **262**, 262f
Complementary DNA (cDNA), **334**, 335f, 366
Complete flower, 837, 837f
Complexity, as characteristic of life, 3
Compound, 22-23
Compound eye, 414, 414f, **680**, 681f
Compound leaf, **750**, 750f
Compound microscope, 61
Compsognathus, 714
Concentration gradient, 96, 100
Concurrent flow, 1005, 1005f
Condensation, 37
Condensin, 193, 201

Conditioning
    classical (Pavlovian), **1137**
    operant, **1138**
Condom, 1099f, 1099t, 1100
Conduction (heat transfer), 879
Cone (eye), **929**, 929f
Confocal microscope, 62t
Confuciornis, 715f
Conidia, **627**, 627f
Conifer, **602**, 602f, 602t, 607f
Coniferophyta (phylum), 602t
Conjugation, **548**
    in bacteria, 548-550, 549f
        gene transfer by, 549-550, 550f
    in ciliates, 572-573, 573f
Conjugation bridge, 549, 549f
Connective tissue, **863**, 867, 867f, 868t, 869
    dense, **867**, 868t
    dense irregular, 867
    dense regular, 867
    loose, **867**, 868t
    special, **867**, 869
Connell, Joseph, 1188
Connexons, 84
Consensus sequence, **354**
Conservation biology, 1256-1278
Conservation of synteny, **482**, 483f
Conservative replication, 263-265, 263f
CONSTANS gene, of *Arabidopsis*, 833
Constitutive heterochromatin, 357
Consumer, **1215**, 1215f
Consumption, of resources, 1181
Contig, **349**, 354
Continental drift, 432
Continental shelf, 1241f, 1242-1243
Continuous variation, **232**, 233f
Contraception, 1098-1101, 1099f, 1099t, 1101f
Contractile root, 744, 744f
Contractile vacuole, 73, 99, 103
Control experiment, **6**
Controlling elements, 480
Conus arteriosus, **1023**, 1023f
Convection (heat transfer), 879
Convergent evolution, 430-432, **430**, 431f, 457, 464, 499-500, 500f, 502, 638
Cooksonia, 591, 591f
COPD, **1012**
Coprophagy, 992
Copy number variation, 250
Copy numbers, 481
Coral, 638, 643t, 651
Coral reef, 652, **1243**, 1243f, 1252
Coriolis effect, **1232**-1233, 1232f
Cork, 747f
Cork cambium, **733**, 734f, 746, 747f
Cork cells, 746
Corm, 748
Corn (*Zea mays*), 368f, 744f, 826f, 854f
    artificial selection in, 422, 423f
    chromosome number in, 189t
    endosperm of, 852, 852f
    epistasis in, 236, 236f
    genome of, 361f, 474f, 475, 478f, 480
    grain color in, 233t, 236, 236f, 245-246, 245f

oil content of kernels, 422
    recombination in, 245, 245f
    root structure of, 740f
    transgenic, 343
Cornea, **928**, 928f
Corolla, **837**, 837f
Coronary artery, **1029**
Corpus callosum, 901t, **902**, 903f
Corpus luteum, **1097**, 1097f
Correns, Carl, 240, 244
Cortex (plant), 742f, **743**, 746
Cortical granule, **1108**
Cortical nephron, **1047**
Corticosteroid, 954
Corticotropin, 948
Corticotropin-releasing hormone (CRH), 949
Cortisol, 943f, 954
Corynebacterium diphtheriae, 529
Cost of reproduction, **1171**
Costa Rica, biosphere reserves in, 1277, 1277f
Cotransduction frequency, 551
Cotton
    genome of, 478f
    transgenic, 343
Cotyledon, **850**
Countercurrent flow, **1005**, 1005f
Countercurrent heat exchange, 880, 880f
Countertransport, 102
Coupled transport, 101-102, 101f, 104t
Courtship behavior/signaling, 439, 439f, 443, 443f, 1144f, 1145, 1152, 1152f
    of *Anolis* lizards, 443, 443f
    of blue-footed boobies, 439, 439f
    of lacewings, 439, 439f
Covalent bond, 23t, 24-25, 24f
Cowper's gland, 1091f, 1092
Cowpox, 1061
COX. *See* Cyclooxygenase
COX-2 inhibitor, 943
Crab, 643t, 682, 683, 683f
Cranial neural crest cells, 1120
Crassulacean acid metabolism, **164**
Crassulacean acid pathway, 165
Craton, 513
Crawling, cellular, 79
Crayfish, 683
Creighton, Harriet, 245-246, 245f
Cretinism, 952
Creutzfeldt-Jakob disease, 536
CRH. *See* Corticotropin-releasing hormone
Cri-du-chat syndrome, 300
Crick, Francis, 259-263, 261f, 280, 282, 283, 299
Crinoidea (class), 693, 693f
Cristae, **74**
Cro-Magnons, 725, 725f
Crocodile, 461, 697f, 699f, 707t, 711-712, 711f, 1025
    parental care in, 463-464, 463f
Crocodylia (order), 699f, 707t, 710f, 711-712, 711f
Crop plant
    artificial selection in, 422, 423f
    transgenic, 342-345
Cross-fertilization, 223, 223f